THE SOURCES OF SCIENCE

Editor-in-Chief: HARRY WOOLF

WILLIS K. SHEPARD PROFESSOR OF THE HISTORY OF SCIENCE
THE JOHNS HOPKINS UNIVERSITY

AGASSIZ. *Bibliographia Zoologiae et Geologiae.* 4 vols. 1968. (No. 20)

ASHMOLE. *Theatrum Chemicum Britannicum.* With a new Introduction by Allen G. Debus. 1967. (No. 39)

BERGMAN. *Dissertation on Elective Attractions.* Translated and with a new Introduction by J. A. Schufle. 1968. (No. 43)

BIRCH. *History of the Royal Society of London.* 4 vols. With a new introduction by A. Rupert Hall and a Bibliographical Note by Marie Boas Hall. 1968. (No. 44)

BOYLE. *Experiments and Considerations Touching Colours.* With a new Introduction by Marie Boas Hall. 1964. (No. 2)

BREWSTER. *Memoirs of the Life, Writings, and Discoveries of Sir Isaac Newton.* With a new Introduction by Richard S. Westfall. 1966. (No. 14)

Bullettino di Bibliografia e di Storia delle Scienze Matematische e Fisiche. 20 vols. Edited by B. Boncompagni. 1964. (No. 10)

Catalogus Bibliothecae Historico-Naturalis Josephi Banks. 5 vols. Compiled by Jonas Dryander. 1966. (No. 22)

CHARLETON. *Physiologia Epicuro-Gassendo-Charltoniana.* With Indexes and a new Introduction by Robert Hugh Kargon. 1966. (No. 31)

CHINCHILLA. *Anales históricos de la Medicina en general y biográfico-biográficos de la Española en particular. Historia de la Medicina Española.* 4 vols. With a new Introduction by Francisco Guerra, M.D. 1967. (No. 8)

CORNUT. *Canadensium Plantarum.* With a new Introduction by Jerry Stannard. 1966. (No. 37)

DARMSTAEDTER. *Naturforscher und Erfinder.* 1965. (No. 26)

DELAMBRE. *Histoire de l'Astronomie Ancienne.* 2 vols. With a new Preface by Otto Neugebauer. 1966. (No. 23)

DELAMBRE. *Histoire de l'Astronomie du Moyen Age.* 1966. (No. 24)

DELAMBRE. *Histoire de l'Astronomie Moderne.* With a new Introduction by I. Bernard Cohen. 1968. (No. 25)

Essayes of Natural Experiments made in the Academie del Cimento. Translated by Richard Waller. With a new Introduction by A. Rupert Hall. 1964. (No. 1)

FARADAY. *The Achievements of Michael Faraday.* Edited and with a new Introduction by L. Pearce Williams. 1968. (No. 6)

FUSS. *Correspondance Mathématique et Physique de quelques célèbres Géomètres du XVIIIème Siècle.* 2 vols. 1968. (No. 35)

GRANT. *History of Physical Astronomy.* With a new Introduction by Harry Woolf. 1966. (No. 38)

GREW. *The Anatomy of Plants.* With a new Introduction by Conway Zirkle. 1965. (No. 11)

HALLER. *First Lines of Physiology.* 2 vols. in 1. With a new Introduction by Lester S. King, M.D. 1966. (No. 32)

HALLIWELL. *A Collection of Letters Illustrative of the Progress of Science in England from the Reign of Queen Elizabeth to that of Charles II.* With a new Introduction by Carl B. Boyer. 1968. (No. 12)

HARRIS. *Lexicon Technicum; Or an Universal Dictionary of Arts and Sciences Explaining not only the Terms of Art, but the Arts Themselves.* 2 vols. 1966. (No. 28)

HARVEY. *The Works of William Harvey.* Translated from the Latin with a Life of the Author by Robert Willis. 1965. (No. 13)

HERNANDEZ MOREJÓN. *Historia bibliográfica de la Medicina Española*. 7 vols. With a new Introduction by Francisco Guerra, M.D. 1967. (No. 9)

HERSCHEL. *A Preliminary Discourse on the Study of Natural Philosophy*. With a new Introduction by Michael Partridge. 1967. (No. 17)

HOOKE. *The Posthumous Works of Robert Hooke*. With a new Introduction by Richard S. Westfall. 1968. (No. 73)

The Interpretation of Animal Form. Essays by Jeffries Wyman, Carl Gegenbaur, E. Ray Lankester, Henri Lacaze Duthiers, Wilhelm His and H. Newell Martin. With Translations and an Introduction by William Coleman. 1967. (No. 15)

KEPLER. *Kepler's Conversation with Galileo's Sidereal Messenger*. Translated and with an Introduction by Edward Rosen. 1965. (No. 5)

LIEBIG. *Animal Chemistry*. With a new Introduction by Frederic L. Holmes. 1964. (No. 4)

MACLAURIN. *An Account of Sir Isaac Newton's Philosophical Discoveries*. With a new Introduction by L. L. Laudan. 1968. (No. 74)

MAUPERTUIS. *The Earthly Venus*. Translated by Simone Brangier Boas; and with an Introduction by George Boas. 1966. (No. 29).

METCHNIKOFF. *Immunity in Infective Diseases*. Translated by F. G. Binnie. With a new Introduction by Gert Brieger. 1968. (No. 61)

NEWTON. *The Mathematical Works of Isaac Newton*. 2 vols. Assembled with an Introduction by Derek T. Whiteside. 1967. (No. 3)

POWER. *Experimental Philosophy*. With a new Introduction by Marie Boas Hall. 1966. (No. 21)

PRIESTLEY. *The History and Present State of Electricity*. 2 vols. With a new Introduction by Robert E. Schofield. 1966. (No. 18)

SCHLEIDEN. *Principles of Scientific Botany*. Translated by Edwin Lankester. With a new Introduction by Jacob Lorch. 1968. (No. 40)

SEMMELWEIS. *Die Aetiologie, der Begriff und die Prophylaxis des Kindbett-fiebers*. With a new Introduction by Alan F. Guttmacher, M.D. 1966. (No. 19)

Société d'Arcueil: Mémoires de Physique et de Chimie. 3 vols. With a new Introduction by Maurice Crosland. 1967. (No. 36)

STOKES. *Mathematical and Physical Papers*. 5 vols. With a new Preface by C. Truesdell. 1967. (No. 33)

TAYLOR. *Scientific Memoirs*. Selected from the Transactions of Foreign Academies of Science and Learned Societies, and from Foreign Journals. 7 vols. With a new Preface by Harry Woolf. 1966. (No. 7)

TYNDALL. *Essays on the Floating-Matter of the Air in Relation to Putrefaction and Infection*. With a new Introduction by Raymond N. Doetsch. 1966. (No. 16)

WARD. *The Lives of the Professors of Gresham College*. 1968. (No. 71)

WHEWELL. *The Philosophy of the Inductive Sciences*. 2 vols. With a new Introduction by John Herivel. 1967. (No. 41)

WILSON. *The Cell in Development and Inheritance*. With a new Introduction by Hermann J. Muller. 1966. (No. 30)

WOOD. *Athenae Oxonienses*. 4 vols. Edited by Philip Bliss. 1967. (No. 55)

Zeitschrift für wissenschaftliche Botanik. Vol. 1. Edited by M. J. Schleiden and Carl Nägeli. 1966. (No. 27)

The Posthumous Works of Robert Hooke

The Posthumous
WORKS
of
ROBERT HOOKE

With a New Introduction by
RICHARD S. WESTFALL
PROFESSOR OF THE HISTORY OF SCIENCE
INDIANA UNIVERSITY

The Sources of Science, No. 73

JOHNSON REPRINT CORPORATION
New York and London
1969

This edition reproduces the original
publication of London, 1705

Library of Congress Catalog Card Number: 68-26912

Printed in the United States of America

INTRODUCTION

There will be few so churlish as to demand that a republication of Robert Hooke's *Posthumous Works* be defended and justified. The chances are good that anyone who has picked up the volume and is reading these lines is a partisan of Hooke, and he will be less inclined to question why the work is being reprinted than to ask why it was not done sooner. For Hooke is a man who evokes enthusiasm and generates partisans, and the steadfast champion of Hooke is a well-established phenomenon in the historiography of 17th century science. I can speak of the phenomenon from personal experience. Some five years ago in London, I had occasion to read a paper on the critics of Newton's theory of colors. Inevitably Hooke's name was used—though not in vain, or at least not intentionally so—with the result that I found myself after the talk face to face with a steadfast champion. Hooke, he informed me without further preliminary, was the greatest genius ever produced by the English people and not improbably by the human race. The statement might sound belligerent, especially when flung in the face of a Newtonian scholar. Quite the contrary, it was uttered in the matter of fact tone one reserves for the obvious and unexceptionable—a thing must either be or not be; two plus two equals four; Hooke was the greatest genius ever produced by the English people. Even to have raised an eyebrow, it was evident, would have entailed explanations and arguments stretching on through the evening. I opted for dinner instead, and now, five years later and willingly abetted by the Johnson Reprint Corporation, I offer to my unnamed informant and to steadfast champions everywhere the one major work by Hooke not readily available. Numerous editions of the *Micrographia* exist. Gunther reprinted the *Cutlerian Lectures* in his *Early Science in Oxford,* a collection found on the shelves even of most secondary libraries. Only the *Posthumous Works,* published but once at the beginning of the 18th century, has not been easy to obtain. As I said above, a justification of its republication is not required.

An introduction may be. Enthusiasm is not necessarily equivalent to understanding. Neither is lack of enthusiasm for that matter, and if Hooke has generated enthusiasts, the enthusiasts in turn have generated debunkers. The problem in reading Hooke is to seek understanding despite the extremes of partisanship and denial. The problem in writing an introduction is identical. Is it possible to achieve a dispassionate appraisal of Hooke's role in the history of science? Above all, is it possible for a Newtonian scholar? I can only say that if I am unable seriously to consider the extreme position of the gentleman mentioned above, neither do I find it necessary to condone Newton's behavior toward Hooke or to share in his rancor. Newton, of course, and not Hooke, was the greatest scientist of the 17th century—a thing must either be or not be; two plus two equals four; Newton was the greatest scientist of the 17th century! To say as much, however, is not to deny that his sometime critic Robert Hooke also contributed to the growth of modern science.

Before I turn to the *Posthumous Works,* let me examine what it is about Hooke that forever arouses excitement. Since the original editor of the *Posthumous Works,* Richard Waller, included a biographical essay, I shall forego the temptation to write another, but I cannot avoid a summary sketch of the range of Hooke's activities. Mechanical genius was perhaps his outstanding trait; as Curator of Experiments for the Royal Society he found ample scope for its exercise. Whatever the Royal Society wanted to investigate, Hooke was able to devise an instrument for the purpose. When observation of the weather was the topic, Hooke invented a wheel barometer and a wind gauge and a weather clock with a rotating cylinder on which were recorded the pressure, temperature, and moisture of the air, the direction and velocity of the wind, and the rainfall. Once interested, he went on to compose a *Method for Making a History of the Weather,* and he has been hailed as the first meteorologist. In Restoration England, the ocean was bound to be a matter of discussion; Hooke invented devices to measure its depth and to retrieve samples of water from the bottom for chemical analysis (to be sure, an invention of limited use before the invention of chemical analysis). For astronomers he invented the clock-driven telescope. Before his appointment to the Royal Society, when he was Robert Boyle's assistant, Hooke had improved on von Guericke's crude machine and invented the modern air pump; more than a mere mechanic, he had participated prominently in the investigation utilizing the pump that concluded in the formulation of Boyle's Law. Clocks could not fail to interest one with Hooke's natural gifts; unresolvable charges surround his work in this area, but at least he claimed to have invented both the anchor escapement and the spring driven watch. Whatever the truth of those claims, no one questions his right to two inventions that still remain in daily use, the iris diaphragm, which is now applied to cameras though it was made originally for telescopes, and the universal joint, which has a thousand uses.

Clearly Hooke was an ingenious man, and part of the interest he excites is connected with his ingenuity and with the tendency to mistake ingenuity for scientific genius. In the same way, Thomas Edison is often presented in the United States as a leading scientist. It would be grossly unfair to Hooke, however, to limit an account of his abilities to ingenuity. As already suggested, he knew how to employ his instruments himself. Thus the air pump led to investigations of air pressure. It led also to experimentation which established the analogy of combustion and respiration and placed Hooke among the small circle engaged in this investigation who foreshadowed, very imperfectly to be sure, the discovery of oxygen. Similarly the compound microscope, another of his inventions, led to pioneering work in microscopy and to his imperishable monument, the *Micrographia.* The *Micrographia* in turn included more than its title suggests. By observing the structure of cork, he made himself the pioneer from which the science of cytology has grown. It was Hooke who borrowed a word from the monastic tradition to describe the structure of cork and thus coined the biological application of the word "cell." The microscope led to the study of light as well, and the passages devoted to optics in the *Micrographia* have ensured Hooke's position in the history of that science. He both observed the colors of thin films and suggested their periodicity. Optics, as embodied in the "Lectures of Light," is one of the major topics of the *Posthumous Works,* and I shall return to the subject later. The *Micrographia* also contained observations of fossils and petrified wood, a topic of life-long interest to Hooke and one which led to his pioneering role in yet another science, geology. The "Lectures and Discourses of Earthquakes" comprise the largest unit of the *Posthumous Works,* and to them I shall also return.

As everyone knows, there is another science with which Hooke's name is connected, celestial mechanics. There can be no doubt, I believe, that a good part of the attraction of Hooke derives from sympathy for a victim of apparent injustice. Not only was he a genius, but he was a genius wronged. By his own account, which a considerable number have undertaken to substantiate, he first announced the basic ideas of the law of universal gravitation only to see Newton appropriate his work and reap his reward. In her recent biography, Mrs. 'Espinasse contends that Hooke's "reputation suffered this extraordinary eclipse chiefly because he incurred the enmity of Newton."[1] The *Posthumous Works* touches significantly on celestial mechanics, both in the "Discourse of Comets" and in the "Lectures concerning Navigation and Astronomy." Because of the immensity of the achievement that the law of universal gravitation represents, a judgment of Hooke's contribution to it must figure prominently in any estimate of his place in the history of science; I shall discuss it at some length in a moment.

Meanwhile one other area of Hooke's activity should be mentioned to complete the picture. Hooke had artistic talents as well. Aubrey reports that he was apprenticed to Sir Peter Lely for a time during his youth, and the draftsmanship displayed in the *Micrographia* does not belie the report. When the fire of London created an unparalleled opportunity for architecture, Hooke's artistic talents found a new outlet. As surveyor for the city of London, he worked closely with Sir Christopher Wren, and some of the buildings that have added luster to Wren's name are known now to have been Hooke's work. The Monument is the only one that still survives, but he also designed the building of the Royal College of Physicians and Bedlam Hospital, as well as several private homes.

The record is one of considerable activity—and of considerable achievement. Small wonder that the man to whom it belongs arouses enthusiasm. Small wonder, in view of his accomplishments, that scholars have been willing to explore his claim to the law of universal gravitation. There is a touch of the *uomo universale* in each of us, a hankering after manifold achievement of which we privately enjoy imagining ourselves to be capable. Hooke strikes a responsive chord, and such is the third and perhaps the most important element of his attraction.

And despite it all I am unable to avoid the judgment that Hooke was not a scientist of the first rank. The question is one of degree. It should be obvious that he played a role in the history of science, and indeed a significant one. Can he be placed, as some of his partisans would have him placed, on the same plane with Newton or Galileo or Huygens? To me at least, it is equally obvious that he cannot. The nature of his contribution was radically different from theirs. Hooke was the natural philosopher distilled to his purest essence. Whatever the topic under discussion, whatever the phenomenon to be understood, Hooke was prepared to discourse on it, applying a profound comprehension of the current mechanical philosophy to the whole realm of nature, spraying out a shower of provocative ideas wherever the flint of his mind touched. To describe him thus is not to contend that his work was superficial. Many of his ideas were extraordinarily penetrating, often pointing uncannily in the direction that scientific progress was to take. With Hooke, however, they remained for the most part ideas only; others advanced them to the level of scientific conclusions. Observing the colors of thin films, Hooke ventured the opinion that the colors are periodic. That suggestion became the cornerstone of Book II of Newton's *Opticks;* Newton, not Hooke, contrived to measure the films and through measurement to establish periodicity as a fact. Contemplating the mechanics of orbital motion, Hooke correctly defined its basic elements. Again it was Newton,

---

[1] Margaret 'Espinasse, *Robert Hooke* (Berkeley and Los Angeles, 1956), p. 1. Quoted by permission of the University of California Press.

following his own independent insight in this case, who carried out a precise quantitative analysis, correlated his calculations with the observed phenomena, and demonstrated the law of universal gravitation. The corpus of scientific knowledge has been built from the work, not of the Hookes, but of the Newtons. However provocative Hooke's insights may have been, however correct some of them may have been proved, with Hooke they mostly remained insights rather than conclusions. To become conclusions they had first to be demonstrated. Ample evidence confirms the judgment that peculiarity of temperament, and in many cases deficiency in ability, barred Hooke's advance from insight to demonstration.

In reading the *Posthumous Works,* then, one is ill advised to search for further evidence of the neglected genius unjustly deprived of recognition. To be sure, the steadfast champion of Hooke may well find cause to confirm his faith. Here, as elsewhere in Hooke's writings, he will find brilliant insights foreshadowing the future course of science. He would do well, however, to ask himself how many other "insights" have proved to be, not brilliantly foresighted, but wildly mistaken. He would do well to examine carefully the exact meaning the words held for Hooke and the body of information on which the ideas rested. Above all, he would do well to learn what the rest of the scientific community in Hooke's day had to say on the matter at hand before he reaches any conclusions about Hooke's originality and pre-eminence. I would even argue that one can most profitably read the *Posthumous Works* as a reflection of the questions and problems to which science in the late 17th century was addressing itself—the questions, not the answers. Since Hooke was, in my opinion, just one of a large body of competent practitioners and not their leader, his works serve more as a mirror of his own age than as a beacon toward the next.

Although celestial mechanics is not the major topic of the *Posthumous Works,* it does figure in two of the five sections; and since it plays the leading role in every estimate of Hooke's contribution to science, I propose to discuss it first. My assessment of Hooke cannot be valid in general if it is not valid on this particular issue. Two questions lie at the core of Hooke's claim to the law of universal gravitation—on the one hand the very concept of universal gravitation, and on the other the inverse square relation. Both are involved in what is perhaps the best statement of a generally accepted estimate of Hooke's contribution—that Hooke first sketched out the program of the *Principia* although Newton alone was able to write it.[2] Even though the judgment does not appear to be at variance with my appraisal of Hooke's career, I cannot withhold my opinion that it attributes to Hooke more than he deserves.

The danger exists that Hooke's discussions of gravity may be interpreted in the light of Newton's *Principia,* which appeared later, unless we exercise care to understand them in the total context of Hooke's thought. Especially important is a concept around which he built a pamphlet on capillary action, his first publication.[3] Both the successful explanation of the barometer, still a recent event in 1661, and Hooke's association with the air pump led him to see capillary action as a phenomenon of pressure. Inside of narrow glass pipes the pressure

[2] Lohne quotes the judgment with approval from Vavilov's biography of Newton; Johs. Lohne, "Hooke *versus* Newton," *Centaurus,* **7** (1960), 42.

[3] *An Attempt for the Explication of the Phaenomena, Observable in the Experiment Published by the Honourable Robert Boyle, Esq; in the XXXV. Experiment of his Epistolical Discourse Touching the Aire* (London, 1661). R. T. Gunther, *Early Science in Oxford,* 14 vols. (Oxford, 1923–45), includes a facsimile reproduction of the pamphlet in vol. 10, pp. 1–50, and its contents are more readily available, with only minor alterations, in the *Micrographia* (London, 1665), pp. 11–31.

of the air decreases because of what Hooke called the "inconformity or incongruity" of air to glass. He defined conformity or congruity as a "property of a fluid Body, whereby any part of it is readily united or intermingled with any other part, either of it self or of any other Homogeneal or Similar, fluid, or firm and solid body; And unconformity or incongruity . . . [as] a property of a fluid, by which it is kept off and hindered from uniting or mingling with any heterogeneous or dissimilar, fluid or solid Body."[4] Hooke could point to many phenomena in confirmation of such a principle, especially the fact that many fluids are immiscible one in another. When shaken together, they remain separated, taking the form of spherical drops. In the context of the 17th century's mechanical philosophy, the concepts of congruity and incongruity presented difficulties, and it is not surprising that Hooke sometimes attempted to give them a mechanical interpretation in terms of harmonious and inharmonious vibrations. More generally, he referred to them unabashedly as attractions and repulsions, even as sympathies and antipathies. If the latter terms appeared to violate both the fundamental tenets of the mechanical philosophy and the fundamental sensibilities of the mechanical philosophers, the concepts of congruity and incongruity also called into question another basic premise of 17th century thought, the uniformity of matter. Congruous bodies were similar bodies, and incongrous ones dissimilar. The concepts tended in the direction, not of universal gravity, but of particular gravities whereby similar bodies attracted each other. By Hooke's day the idea of particular gravities had a venerable tradition. Kepler had defined gravity as "a mutual corporeal affection to unity or conjunction among cognate bodies. . . ."[5] Hooke's contemporary, Roberval, spoke of terrestrial, lunar, solar, and jovial gravities.[6] Such an idea could stand in the way of a concept of universal gravitation.

The principles of congruity and incongruity did not disappear from Hooke's thought; they formed the primary content of a lecture delivered before the Royal Society in 1684, which Waller mistakenly included among the lectures on earthquakes.[7] They provided one of Hooke's working concepts throughout the period when his most famous pronouncements on gravity were made, and we must keep them constantly in mind as we seek to understand his meaning. Consider for example the concluding paragraph in his *Attempt to Prove the Motion of the Earth* (1674), in which he referred to his system of the world based on the principles of mechanics.

> This depends upon three Suppositions. First, That all Coelestial Bodies whatsoever, have an attraction or gravitating power towards their own Centers, whereby they attract not only their own parts, and keep them from flying from them, as we may observe the Earth to do, but that they do also attract all the other Coelestial Bodies that are within the sphere of their activity; and consequently that not only the Sun and Moon have an influence upon the body and motion of the Earth, and the Earth upon them, but that ☿ also ♀, ♂, ♄, and ♃ by their attractive powers, have a considerable influence upon its motion as in the same manner the corresponding attractive power of the Earth hath a considerable influence upon every one of their motions also. The second supposition is this, That all bodies whatsoever that are put into a direct and simple motion, will so continue

[4] Gunther, *Early Science in Oxford*, 10, 7–8.

[5] Johannes Kepler, *Gesammelte Werke*, 18 vols., ed. Walther von Dyck & Max Caspar (München, 1937–63), 3, 25.

[6] Roberval's memoire on the cause of gravity, read before the *Académie des sciences*, 7 August 1669; Christiaan Huygens, *Oeuvres complètes*, 22 vols. (La Haye, 1888–1950), 19, 628.

[7] *Posthumous Works*, pp. 365–370.

to move forward in a streight line, till they are by some other effectual powers deflected and bent into a Motion, describing a Circle, Ellipsis, or some other more compounded Curve Line. The third supposition is, That these attractive powers are so much the more powerful in operating, by how much the nearer the body wrought upon is to their own Centers. Now what these several degrees are I have not yet experimentally verified; but it is a notion, which if fully prosecuted as it ought to be, will mightily assist the Astronomer to reduce all the Coelestial Motions to a certain rule, which I doubt will never be done true without it. He that understands the nature of the Circular Pendulum and Circular Motion, will easily understand the whole ground of this Principle, and will know where to find direction in Nature for the true stating thereof.[8]

The passage testifies to Hooke's clear grasp of the mechanical elements of orbital motion. When we read it hastily in the light of Newton's *Principia,* it appears to state the concept of universal gravitation as well. When we read it more carefully in the light of Hooke's own thought, we may wonder about some of the phrases. Celestial bodies attract "their own parts" toward "their own Centers"; on other bodies "within the sphere of their activity" they exert "a considerable influence." Such phrases might spring from the principle of congruity and express the concept of particular gravities.

If we had only the passage above on which to base a conclusion, I might be charged with trifling when I question whether Hooke's was a concept of universal gravitation. Fortunately, a number of other passages exist. In *Cometa,* which apepared four years after the work quoted above, he considered how the tails of comets are formed. Perhaps the ether through which comets pass agitates and mixes their parts so as to make them act upon and dissolve each other. "That this internal agitation may confound the gravitating principle, and so leave the parts in a greater freedom to be dissolved by the encompassing AEther. . . ." [sic] The parts dissolved, with their gravitating principle confounded, would recede from the center of the comet, and when the comet was attracted by another body, they would tend to be left behind.

I suppose the gravitating power of the Sun in the center of this part of the Heaven in which we are, hath an attractive power upon all the bodies of the Planets, and of the Earth that move about it, and that each of those again have a respect answerable, whereby they may be said to attract the Sun in the same manner as the Load-stone hath to Iron, and the Iron hath to the Load-stone. I conceive also that this attractive virtue may act likewise upon several bodies that come within the center of its sphere of activity, though 'tis not improbable also but that as on some bodies it may have no effect at all, no more than the Load-stone which acts on Iron, hath upon a bar of Tin, Lead, Glass, Wood, &c. so on other bodies, it may have a clean contrary effect, that is, of protrusion, thrusting off, driving away, as we find one Pole of the Magnet doth the end of a Needle touched on the opposite part; whence it is, I conceive, that the parts of the body of this Comet (being confounded or jumbled, as 'twere together, and so the gravitating principle destroyed) become of other natures than they were before, and so that body may cease to maintain its place in the Universe, where first it was placed.[9]

Similarly many passages in the *Posthumous Works* express the concept, not of universal gravity, but of particular gravities.

By Gravity then I understand such a Power, as causes Bodies of a similar or homogeneous nature to be moved one towards the other, till they are united. . . .[10]

[8] *Lectiones Cutlerianae;* facsimile reproduction in Gunther, *Early Science in Oxford,* **8,** 27–28. Cf. *Posthumous Works,* pp. 46 and 202.
[9] Gunther, *Early Science in Oxford,* **8,** 228–229.
[10] *Posthumous Works,* p. 176.

Other passages suggest, not so much several matters completely incongruous to each other, but a scale of congruity which would determine the degree of one body's attraction for another. Thus bodies differ in their receptivity to gravity in Hooke's opinion. Quantity of matter alone does not determine a body's weight, which depends instead on the modification of its matter. Those bodies the particles of which are greatest in bulk and closest in texture are most subject to its action.[11] A series of headings on a paper dating apparently from the early 1680's expresses the idea most succinctly.

> Similars work most powerfully on each other.
> Similar Bodies join together more easily.[12]

After the passages above, it is of great interest to find another statement from a lecture of 25 May 1687, after Hooke had publicly claimed priority over Newton and scarcely a month before the *Principia* appeared. In considering possible irregularities in the earth's diurnal rotation, Hooke raised the following question: "whether there may not be in the Body of the Earth some parts which, tho' as to the gravitating powers of the Earth, may be duly situated and poised for its equal Revolution upon its Axis, yet with respect to the gravitating Power of the Sun or Moon may not be counterpois'd, but be over ballanc'd on one side of its Axis."

> I know that if the gravitating Power in the Sun and Moon be exactly the same with that of the Earth, the Query I propounded can have no ground; but tho' they may in most particulars be consonant, as I shall prove in my Theory of Gravity, yet there may be a cause (and there seems to be some assignable) why there may be something Specifick in each of them, of that kind which I now propose, as may be possibly conceiv'd from the Moons Libration, or its turning or keeping pretty near the same side of its Body to the Surface of the Earth. For tho' the supposing it to turn upon its Axis in respect of the Sun, so as to make a Revolution Isocrone to its Synodick Revolution about the Earth, be an ingenious Hypothesis; yet the Physical Reason of such an equality seems pretty difficult to be conceiv'd, unless we suppose some cause from the Constitution of the Body of the Moon itself, which makes one part of it gravitate more toward the Center of the Earth than another in such a Revolution.[13]

Hooke showed that if one side of the earth had a greater gravitation toward the sun than the other, the earth's rotation would be first accelerated and then retarded in every circuit. He wondered if a similar phenomenon might be found in respect to the moon, "between which and the Earth there seems to be a much nearer kindred and affinity than between that of the Earth and of the Sun; and possibly somewhat of the Phaenomena of the change of the Sea by Tides and Currents, and of the Air by Winds or Motions thereof may be found to be influenc'd by such a Discovery."[14] In May 1687, Hooke was face to face with the concept of universal gravitation, but even then the concept of particular gravities based on the congruity or incongruity of different forms of matter rendered him unable to grasp it.

Like Kepler and Roberval, Hooke was prepared to consider gravity as an attraction. This break with the prevailing mode of mechanical philosophizing was vitally necessary for the conceptualization of universal gravity, and Hooke may well have influenced Newton to make the same break. In at least two respects, Hooke's concept shows a distinct advance over those of Kepler and of Roberval. He extended the sphere of gravity's action to immensely greater

---

[11] *Posthumous Works,* p. 182.
[12] *Posthumous Works,* p. 191.
[13] *Posthumous Works,* p. 546.
[14] *Posthumous Works,* p. 547.

distances, though perhaps not to infinity, and he admitted the influence of one celestial body on another. Nevertheless he never succeeded in breaking free of the confines of particular gravities. There is irony in the fact that Newton, who did succeed in breaking free, was greatly influenced by Hooke's principles of congruity and incongruity. Under the names of "sociability" and "unsociability," they appeared in his speculations on nature throughout his life. Newton greatly expanded their application to chemistry, and the final product of his chemical speculations, the 31st Query in the *Opticks,* lent the primary impetus to the study of chemical affinities in the 18th century. The very word "affinity" recalls the idea of different varieties of matter, the idea which emerged continually from Hooke's principle to thwart the movement of his thought toward universal gravitation. If Newton was influenced by the same tendency in some areas of his speculation, he overcame it in the case of gravity. As far as gravitational attraction is concerned, he concluded that all matter is uniform and that weight is exactly proportional to mass. Such is the concept of universal gravitation, and to it Hooke has no legitimate claim.

To Hooke, however, the concept of universal gravitation was never the central issue. What he claimed was the inverse square law.[15] The claim moves the discussion from the realm of concepts to the realm of mathematical mechanics since the inverse square law can demand acceptance only as the conclusion of a rigorous demonstration. In Newton's case, it emerged initially from the application of his analysis of centrifugal force to Kepler's third law. Unfortunately for Hooke's claim, mathematical mechanics appears almost to have been invented in order to reveal his deficiencies. There can be no doubt that Hooke announced the inverse square relation well before the publication of the *Principia*—though not before it appeared in Newton's private papers. When we examine the argument on which he based his conclusion, however, and compare it with Newton's demonstration in the *Principia,* we cannot fail to be impressed by the distance separating the two men. With its vastly superior grasp and precision, Newton's analysis simply occupies a different plane. Hooke's indeed was no demonstration at all.

The issue turns on the difference between Hooke's intuition and his power of demonstration. In 1666, for example, Hooke set out to treat planetary motion as a simple mechanical problem. Starting with the principle of inertia, he stated that some cause must operate to deflect a body's motion into a curve. Variations in the density of the medium could have that effect or, in the case of the planets, an attraction from the sun. Hooke's paper of 1666 stands as the first published statement which correctly defined the mechanical elements of orbital motion. At first blush, he appears to have been equally happy in seizing on the conical pendulum as an illustration of it. A close examination of his discussion of the conical pendulum, however, reveals the severe limitations of intuition alone. Hooke stated that in one respect the conical pendulum gives an inexact representation of planetary motion. In the case of planets, gravity must decrease with distance from the center, but in the conical pendulum "the degrees of conatus at several distances from the perpendicular" are proportional to the angle between the string and the perpendicular. Hence "the conatus of returning to the centre in a pendulum is greater and greater, according as it is farther and farther removed from the centre, which seems to be otherwise in the attrac-

---

[15] *Cf.* A. R. Hall,, "Two Unpublished Lectures of Robert Hooke," *Isis,* **42** (1951), 224–225. The same emphasis on the inverse square law is found in the well-known letter of 15 September 1689 to Anthony à Wood; *The Correspondence of Isaac Newton,* ed. H. W. Turnbull, 3 vols. continuing (Cambridge, 1959 continuing), **3,** 40–42.

tion of the sun. . . ."[16] In fact, the whole conception of centripetal force was lost in Hooke's demonstration as he allowed the role of gravity, to which the centripetal force of the conical pendulum was being compared, to confuse him. Hooke treated the different elevations of a conical pendulum as different positions along the arc of a simple pendulum, and the final ratio of *conatus* toward the center at which he arrived compared the components of gravity along the tangents at those points. When we compare the confusion and crudity in Hooke's analysis to the finesse displayed at much the same time by Huygens and Newton in their analyses of conical pendulums, our confidence in Hooke's power as a student of analytic mechanics is not likely to survive.

Mechanics as such is not a topic which occupies much space in the *Posthumous Works*. There is one lecture from 1690 on the handling of sails which gets into questions of theoretical mechanics. By 1690, Hooke was publicly charging Newton with plagiarizing the inverse square law, and in the lecture, he complained bitterly about his mistreatment. Yet the discussion of mechanics in the lecture shows all too clearly limitations which render his complaints groundless. Bodies in motion, Hooke argued, impress motions proportional to their gravities and to their velocities on other bodies. The specific gravity of air is to that of water about as 1 to 800 or 900.

> It follows therefore, that the motion of this fluid Body must, according to the quantity of its Gravity, impress upon another Body that it is mov'd against, such a quantity of motion in the same manner as the like quantity of another fluid Body, as Water, and if the motion be the same the motion communicated will be as 1 to 800. If the Motions be reciprocal to the Gravities of the striking Bodies, the motions or powers communicated will be equal; for if there be by the Velocity 28,3 times as much Air in bulk mov'd against the Recipient Body as there is of the bulk of Water in the same time, and that the Velocity be 28,3 swifter than that of the Water, then 28,3 × 28,3 will produce an equality of Motion with the eight hundred Gravitating parts in the Water mov'd with one degree of Velocity. . . .

Hooke proceeded to apply his analyses to a specific problem. Consider a sail *ab* set perpendicular to the wind and let the wind move a distance *da* in a given time, so that a total volume of wind *abcd* moves against the sail. (It is all too typical that Hooke treated a plane figure as a volume; of course he assumed a second dimension for the sail, but he never mentioned it.) Now let *abon* represent a prism of water on the same base *ab* (again the height of the sail was assumed) such that *na*, the length of the prism of water, equals 1/30 *da*, the length of the prism of air. The water was assumed to move (against the sail!) in a direction opposite to the motion of the air and in this case the ratio of specific gravities was set at 1 to 900.

> I say, the Sail shall not be mov'd either way, but remain in an aequilibrium: For as the Velocity of the motion of the Water an, 1 is to the Velocity of the Air ad 30; so the Gravity of the Prism of the Air abcd 30, to the Gravity of the Prism of Water abon 900. Now because the same power is imprest on the Sail, whether the Cylinder of Water be mov'd against the Sail from no to ab, or the Sail be mov'd against the Water from ab to no; if the said Cylinder of Air be made one degree swifter, it must drive the same Sail from ab, to no.[17]

One might wander forever down this path without stumbling upon clarity.

---

[16] Thomas Birch, *The History of the Royal Society of London,* 4 vols. (London, 1756–57), 2, 91–92.
[17] *Posthumous Works,* pp. 565–566.

One basic relation emerged from Hooke's ventures into mechanics—force is proportional to velocity squared. We may look upon the fomula as a rendering in terms of dynamics of Galileo's kinematic conclusion, that the square of the velocity of a body falling from rest is proportional to the distance transversed. Force in this case would correspond to the action of gravity through the fall. Hooke employed the relation in various forms. In 1669, for example, he sought to demonstrate by experiment that the "strength" of a body in motion is proportional to the square of its velocity.[18] A week later, another experiment showed that one must quadruple the depth of a fluid to double the rate at which it flows from a vessel.[19] He repeated the proposition on fluids in his Cutlerian lecture, *Lampas.*

> Now this is exactly according to the General Rule of Mechanicks. Which is, that the proportion of the strength or power of moving any Body is always in duplicate proportion of the Velocity it receives from it; [sic] that is, if any Body whatsoever be moved with one degree of Velocity, by a determinate quantity of strength, that body will require four times that strength to be moved twice as fast, and nine times that strength to be moved thrice as fast, and sixteen times the strength to be moved four times as fast, and so forwards.[20]

He asserted further that the rule holds good in the motion of bullets and of arrows, of stones thrown by hand or by sling, of pendulums, of musical strings, of springs, and of all vibrating bodies in general, of wheels turned by weights or springs, of falling bodies—which is to say, he considered it to be a general formula of dynamics.

Obviously the formula embodied a great deal of confusion. Confusion appears in the imprecision of Hooke's terminology. Thus he employed interchangeably "strength," "quantity of strength," "force," "force of a moving body," "pressure," "power," and once he referred to "force, pressure, indeavour, impetus, strength, gravity, power, motion, or whatever else you will call it."[21] Behind the confusion of terms was a more disabling confusion of concepts. Sometimes his concept of force was identical to Newton's (and hence to ours), but more frequently we can only render it by our term "work." In no area more than in mechanics does the judgment of Hooke's work require the perspective offered by the work of his contemporaries. We are dealing here with basic concepts which we meet today in the very first stage of our study of physics, and we can easily underestimate the difficulty of formulating them for the first time, as the 17th century had to do. When Hooke's writings on mechanics are compared with those of Borelli or Pardies, who were able men and recognized as such, Hooke's appear in no way inferior. To say that he was confused on basic concepts is not to charge him with incompetence by any means. Competence is not the issue, however, and the comparison with Borelli and Pardies will not do. We are assessing Hooke's derivation of the inverse square law of gravitational attraction, and we are forced to measure Hooke with a stick cut to Newton's size. It is impossible, I believe, to avoid the judgment that Hooke lacked the capacity to carry out a rigorous demonstration of the inverse square law.

Indeed Hooke did not attempt a formal demonstration of the law, but we can piece together what appears to be his closest approach to one. Starting with the proportionality of force to the square of velocity, he applied the formula to Kepler's "law" of planetary velocities—that the velocity of a given planet

[18] Birch, *History,* **2,** 337.
[19] Birch, *History,* **2,** 338–339.
[20] Gunther, *Early Science in Oxford,* **8,** 186–187.
[21] Gunther, *Early Science in Oxford,* **8,** 184.

varies inversely as its radius vector. In the mid 1670's, the period following the publication of his statement of the mechanical elements of planetary motion, Hooke made several entries relevant to Kepler's law of velocities in his diary. "Tuesday, August 22nd [1676].—Invented planetary Line on hyperbolicall consect the velocity about one asymptote and planet in the other."[22] Apparently Hooke referred to the rectangular hyperbole $vr = k$. Although he soon noted that the curve was not satisfactory, he continued to examine the inverse relation of distance and velocity. On 20 September 1677 he wrote: "he [Sir Christopher Wren] affirmed that if the motion were reciprocall to the Distance the Degree of velocity should always be as the areas, the curve whatever it will."[23] In the letter of 1679 announcing to Newton the inverse square relation, the letter on which he based his charge of plagiary, Hooke combined his dynamic equation of force with Kepler's law of velocities. The passage was his closest approach to a derivation of the inverse square law.

> Your Calculation of the Curve by a body attracted by an aequall power at all Distances from the center such as that of a ball Rouling in a inverted Concave Cone is right and the two Auges will not unite by about a third of a Revolution. But my supposition is that the Attraction always is in a duplicate proportion to the Distance from the Center Reciprocall, and Consequently that the Velocity will be in a subduplicate proportion to the Attraction and Consequently as Kepler Supposes Reciprocall to the Distance.[24]

Would anyone seriously support Hooke's claim to the inverse square law with a derivation such as that?

Instead of the word "derivation," I should probably use "justification," since Hooke's efforts give every appearance of an attempt to justify by mathematics a conviction resting on other grounds. He considered gravity and light to be the basic motions or phenomena of nature, and sometimes he traced them both to a vibratory motion through the ether. A simple relation deriving from the geometry of the sphere governs the intensity of light, and several passages in the *Posthumous Works* suggest that he arrived at the inverse square law of gravity initially by considering the analogy of gravity to light.[25] Once again, Hooke brings me back to my original contention. His physical intuition was superb. Unfortunately for him, intuition unbacked by demonstration had no more rights in the 17th century than it has in the 20th.

Much of what Hooke had to say on celestial mechanics in the *Posthumous Works* is found in the "Discourse of the Nature of Comets." Before I leave the subject, a brief word on Hooke's contribution to cometary theory is in order. Neither in quantity nor in technical detail was his contribution large, but in his conceptualization of the problem—here again Hooke's peculiar strength is manifest—he registered an advance over most of his age. Until Newton reduced cometary motion to the general principles of orbital motion, opinion on comets varied widely with a considerable majority agreed that any objects so unusual, so irregular, and so ephemeral could not be closely related to other celestial bodies or governed by the same laws. To some extent Hooke agreed; he looked upon comets as a sort of intermediary between lucid and opaque bodies, shining

[22] *The Diary of Robert Hooke, M.A., M.D., F.R.S. 1672–1680,* ed. Henry W. Robinson and Walter Adams (London, 1935), p. 246. This quotation together with the following one was called to my attention by Lohne, "Hooke *versus* Newton," p. 14.

[23] *The Diary of Robert Hooke,* p. 314. We must assume that in writing hastily Hooke inadvertently put down "Degree of velocity" where he meant to say that time is proportional to area.

[24] Hooke to Newton, 6 January 1679–80; *Correspondence of Newton,* 2, 309.

[25] *Posthumous Works,* pp. 93, 114, 178, 185.

partly by their own light and partly by reflection. When he rejected absolutely the tendency to see them as extraordinary creations, however, and insisted "that in many Proprieties they may be consonant and agreeable to the other Celestial Bodies,"[26] and when his discussion of comets led on to a discussion of gravity, he was beginning to transcend traditional ideas and to move toward the conclusion that the *Principia* later embodied.

Hooke clashed with Newton, and raised the cry of plagiary, not only on the theory of gravitation, but also—and earlier—on the study of light. Since his "Lectures of Light" constitute one of the major divisions of the *Posthumous Works,* let us turn to examine his achievement here. It was not inconsiderable. Hooke was the first man to suggest the periodicity of light. Describing color phenomena in thin films, he went on in the *Micrographia* to develop a theory explaining them which treated light as a periodic motion. What is more, we know beyond any reasonable doubt that Newton was profoundly influenced by this passage in the *Micrographia.* He devised a means to measure the thickness of films by observing the colored rings in the film of air between a lens of known curvature and a flat sheet of glass; and through the resulting investigation, he substantiated quantitatively Hooke's suggestion of periodicity. It is true that Newton's periodicity was not exactly Hooke's. Hooke held that the pulses which constitute light are periodic. Newton demonstrated that the colored rings in his experiment are periodic, reappearing with equal increments of thickness. As an adherent to the corpuscular view of light, he could not ascribe periodicity to it, and he devised a theory in which a vibrating ether supplied the periodic element—and the basis for Hooke's charge of plagiary. Whatever the theory, the original experimental foundation on which the periodic nature of light was ultimately established was Newton's investigation, finally embodied in Book II of the *Opticks;* and through Newton, periodicity justly traces its history back to Hooke.

I argued earlier that Hooke's role in optics is typical of his general role in the history of science. Hooke suggested periodicity. Newton demonstrated periodicity. It is typical as well, I believe, that in the "Lectures of Light," delivered more than fifteen years after the *Micrographia* and published in the *Posthumous Works,* the periodic nature of light was not mentioned, unless we wish to find it implied in his discussion of pulses. Certainly the colors of thin films were not mentioned. I mean to infer that Hooke himself did not recognize the importance of his suggestion. It was after all only one of a number of ideas thrown out in the *Micrographia,* and it remained for later history to select that one as significant. The "Lectures of Light" indicate that it never held great significance for Hooke.

What was significant to Hooke was the mechanical nature of light. His purpose, he said, was "to make the manner of its Operations mechanically and sensibly intelligible. . . ."[27] No phrase could better reflect the basic concerns of 17th century optics. Committed to the mechanical philosophy of nature, science in the 17th century faced the necessity of showing how the most nonmechanical of appearances might in fact derive from particles of matter in motion. From Descartes to Huygens, optics concentrated on this basic problem, and when Hooke asserted that light is the action of a body "subjected to the Laws that other corporeal Actions or Motions are subjected to, and consequently is a Subject that falls under the Laws of Quantity . . ."[28] he was voicing the common judgment of his age.

[26] *Posthumous Works,* p. 165.
[27] *Posthumous Works,* p. 135.
[28] *Posthumous Works,* p. 79.

The problem, then, was to decide the exact nature of the mechanical phenomenon we call light. Within the terms allowed, only two alternatives presented themselves—light was either some sort of matter in motion, or it was some sort of motion propagated through matter. To the first alternative, which is best known in its corpuscular form, Hooke had serious objections. If light is material, how can it spread instantaneously throughout the vast sphere in which a fire is visible, let alone the immeasureably vaster sphere in which a star is visible? Not only must it spread instantaneously (Hooke had serious doubts about the accuracy of Roemer's measurement), but it must renew itself with every instant, and this without visibly wasting such lucid bodies as the sun or stars. We know, moreover, that rays of light cross each other without interference, which would be impossible if light were material.[29] Hence the only other alternative must necessarily be so.

> Light is the in-working of the Transparent Body or Medium; that is, the internal Action of the Pellucid or Transparent Body, is that which is the Light of which we are sensible, or that Light which moves the Eye. And this *energeia* is nothing but Motion, and this Motion is impressed by the Motion of the Lucid Body, and that Body is Lucid that has such a Motion in it.[30]

Hooke's argument, and the exposition he gave of light as motion, suffice to place him among the progenitors of the wave theory of light.

To say that Hooke held a wave theory of light is not entirely correct, however. His was more a theory of pulses—discrete pulses of motion propagated through a medium. It was based, not on the study of light itself, but on the prior convictions that light is a mechanical phenomenon and that it cannot be material. In one of the "Lectures of Light," Hooke listed the various sources of light—fires, bodies that glow with heat, phosphorus, bodies such as the Bononian stone that continue to shine for a while after having been exposed to light, bodies that give off light when struck. "Light then is nothing else but a peculiar Motion of the parts of the Luminous Body, which does affect a fluid Body that incompasses the Luminous Body. . . ."[31] The conclusion emerged from the consideration of luminous bodies, not from the consideration of the properties of light. Newton was almost unique in the 17th century in his approach to optics. He too was committed to the view that light is a mechanical phenomenon, but his *Opticks* is devoted to an experimental investigation of its properties, an investigation from which two hitherto unsuspected properties emerged, the composition of white light and the periodicity of some optical phenomena. In contrast, most of the treatises on light in the 17th century started from the assumption that the properties of light were known, and that the problem was merely to explain their mechanism. For the most part, Hooke's work in optics fell into that category. His early investigations of thin films, it is true, did not; and neither did the lecture, published in this volume, on diffraction, a phenomenon discovered by Grimaldi and possibly rediscovered independently by Hooke.[32] Except for these two cases, his work in optics followed a well-established pattern, accurately reflecting basic concerns of the mechanical philosophy of nature but not illuminating new paths into the future.

By far the largest section of the *Posthumous Works* is devoted to the "Lectures and Discourses of Earthquakes, and Subterraneous Eruptions." The title barely hints at the contents—the lectures on earthquakes comprise a general

[29] *Posthumous Works*, pp. 73–74.
[30] *Posthumous Works*, p. 76.
[31] *Posthumous Works*, p. 113.
[32] *Posthumous Works*, pp. 186–190.

treatise on geology. Although Hooke's contribution to geology is not unknown, it does not figure prominently in popular accounts of his work. It should, and most prominently of all. Not only was the subject one of life-long interest, so that the lectures spanned a period of nearly thirty years, but it was a topic on which Hooke's peculiar genius could work to best advantage. In a field that was almost untouched, there was no huge body of data to be systematically mastered, and here his agile mind could roam unrestrained by the limitations of mathematical demonstration. The result was a remarkable display of Hooke's power to cut himself free from the shackles of received opinion and to look at evidence with a fresh eye.

The evidence consisted primarily of fossils. In an age when *Genesis* still cast a long shadow, accumulating knowledge of fossils posed a problem. Fossils remarkably similar in form to shell fish—and in some cases disturbingly dissimilar to known species—were found in deposits far removed from the sea and high above its level. Even a naturalist on the order of John Ray could find the questions raised by fossils insoluble. As a student of biology, he could not avoid the conclusion that they were the remains of organic creatures. As a Christian, he could not avoid rejecting a conclusion which called the Biblical account of creation into doubt. The outstanding feature of Hooke's discussions was his absolute refusal even to consider that fossils were not organic remains. If they were not organic remains, what were they? One theory designed to save the Bible argued that they were *lusus naturae*, sports of nature produced to no purpose by a plastic virtue in the earth which molded matter into their shapes. Hooke annihilated the theory with a classic piece of scientific argumentation. Whereas nature adapts substance to form, he argued first, he had seen fossils similar in shape formed from clay, chalk. spar, marble, flint, marcasites, and other materials, and even some fossils composed of more than one substance. In fossils, only the outer figure is formed but never the internal organs. Some fossils are of broken shells and not of entire figures. In some cases, he had found the shell still attached to the figure it shaped, and sometimes in the same deposit shells filled with loose sand that had not been bonded together into stone. Finally, among the so-called serpentine stones, which were shaped like the shell of the nautilus, he had discovered some in which single cavities between the diaphragms or partitions were empty while other cavities were filled with differing substances.[33]

> I confess it seemed to me a little hard, because I could not give the Pedigree of the Fish, therefore I should not be allowed to believe it a Fish, when I saw all the sensible marks of a Fish; and that, because I could not tell who it was, or upon what occasion that caused the Stones on Salisbury Plain to be dispersed in that irregular Regularity, that therefore I must allow them to be a *Lusus Naturae*, or placed there by Merlin or, some such unknown way, and not by the Hands, Labour, or Workmanship of some such Men as are now living.[34]

For Hooke, then, no doubt existed—fossils were the petrified remains of once living creatures, many of them the remains of shell fish, but also some of them the remains of parts of animals, such as teeth and bones, and in some cases the remains of parts of plants. The fossils of shell fish were the most prominent. If they were in fact the remains of sea life, how had they been placed in deposits so far from the sea? The question had only to be raised for the Biblical deluge to suggest itself; Hooke again demonstrated his independence

[33] *Posthumous Works*, pp. 291–293.
[34] *Posthumous Works*, p. 404.

of mind by refusing seriously to consider the argument. At most the deluge could have covered the land some two hundred days; he had seen deposits which could not possibly have been laid down in that short period. Rejecting the deluge, Hooke advanced the startling opinion that "a great part of the Surface of the Earth hath been since the Creation transformed and made of another Nature; namely, many Parts which have been Sea are now Land, and diverse other Parts are now Sea which were once a firm Land; Mountains have been turned into Plains, and Plains into Mountains, and the like."[35] Indeed, since deposits of fossils were found nearly everywhere, the entire surface of land on the globe may well have been under water in earlier times. With his conception of changes in the earth's surface, the earthquakes mentioned in the title enter the picture. In Hooke's view, earthquakes and volcanoes were identical—he spoke of "the Eruption of some kind of subterraneous Fires, or Earthquakes. . . ."[36]—and they were the agents which thrust up areas formerly under the seas, bearing incidentally the beds of fossils.

Not content with calling the stability of the earth's surface into question, Hooke proceeded to call into question the stability of its creatures as well. Since some of the fossils differed from species known to exist, the theory seemed to demand such a conclusion. Hooke did not hesitate to pronounce it.

> That there have been many other Species of Creatures in former Ages, of which we can find none at present; and that 'tis not unlikely also but that there may be divers new kinds now, which have not been from the beginning.[37]

We must not leap to read more into Hooke's words than they will bear. Fuller expositions of his ideas imply a limited variation of species under the pressure of environmental change.[38] The 17th century was not equipped to produce the concept of organic evolution, and Hooke was not its ultimate forebear.

Among the obstacles that stood between Hooke and the concept of evolution was the limited extent he allowed to time. For all the boldness of his approach to fossils, he could not shake off the conviction that time had been, from our point of view, short. In this case, he did not even recognize the tradition that bound him. Thus in one discussion of changes in the earth's surface, he suggested that islands had been thrust up, not all at once, but in different ages by different earthquakes and that continents were probably more ancient than islands. How startling to the reader of the 20th century to read on and learn that no evidence proves that continents existed in the Western Hemisphere by the time of the deluge.[39] The shortness of time emphasized the role of earthquakes. Hooke had to be a catastrophist; he may have been the first catastrophist in the history of geological theory. With only a limited span of time at his disposal, he had to call upon cataclysmic changes, and he devoted long passages to combing ancient literature for evidence of such. Perhaps Hooke's example, with his total lack of theological bias, may teach us to understand better the difficulty men had in accepting an unlimited extent of time and the natural attraction catastrophism must have exerted. Hooke's treatment of time should instruct us also not to read excessive modernity into his views. Even so, we cannot avoid the conclusion that his opinions constituted a striking advance over those of his contemporaries, and he was not far wrong when he remarked

[35] *Posthumous Works*, p. 290.
[36] *Posthumous Works*, p. 291.
[37] *Posthumous Works*, p. 291.
[38] *Posthumous Works*, p. 327.
[39] *Posthumous Works*, p. 422.

that some might think he had "turned the World upside down for the sake of a Shell. . . ."[40]

More pregnant with the future than his specific opinions was Hooke's approach to the study of geology, and in particular to the study of fossils. He regarded the surface of the earth as the record of past changes wrought upon it. Fossils he referred to as "petrify'd Monuments" and "curious Medals of former Ages"[41]—the remains, that is to say, from which the history of the earth could be reconstructed.

> The Doctrine aimed at, is, the Cause and Reason of the present Figure, Shape and Constitution of the Surface of this Body of the Earth, whether Sea or Land, as we now find it presented unto us under various and very irregular Forms and Fashions and constituted of very differing Substances.
>
> Now, because when we look into Natural Histories of past Times, we find very few, if any, Footsteps of what alterations or transactions of this Nature have been performed, we must be fain to make use of other helps than what Natural Historians will furnish us with, to make out an account of the History thereof: Nor are there any Monuments or Medals with Literal, Graphical, or Hieroglyphical Inscriptions that will help us out in this our Inquiry, by which the Writers of Civil Histories have of late Years been much assisted from the great curiosity of modern Travellers and Collectors of such Curiosities.
>
> The great transactions of the Alterations, Formations, or Dispositions of the Superficial Parts of the Earth into that Constitution and Shape which we now find them to have, preceded the Invention of Writing, and what was preserved till the times of that Invention were more dark and confused, that they seem to be altogether Romantick, Fabulous, and Fictitious, and cannot be much relied on or heeded, and at best will only afford us occasions of Conjecture. . . .
>
> If in digging a Mine, or the like, an artificial Coin or Urne, or the like Substance be found, no one scruples to affirm it to be of this or that Metal or Earth he finds them by trial to be of: Nor that they are Roman, Saxon, Norman, or the like, according to the Relievo, Impression, Characters, or Form they find them of. Now these Shells and other Bodies are the Medals, Urnes, or Monuments of Nature, whose Relievoes, Impressions, Characters, Forms, Substances, &c. are much more plain and discoverable to any unbiassed Person, and therefore he has no reason to scruple his assent: nor to desist from making his Observations to correct his natural Chronology, and to conjecture how, and when, and upon what occasion they came to be placed in those Repositories. These are the greatest and most lasting Monuments of Antiquity, which, in all probability, will far antidate all the most ancient Monuments of the World, even the very Pyramids, Obelisks, Mummys, Hieroglyphicks, and Coins, and will afford more information in Natural History, than those other put altogether will in Civil. Nor will there be wanting Media or Criteria of Chronology, which may give us some account even of the time when, as I shall afterward mention.[42]

Hooke's words read like a prospectus for the future science of geology. His partisans have done him a disservice in concentrating on his work in areas where other men outshone him. Geology was the field of Hooke's greatest scientific achievement. In geology he yielded preeminence to no man in the 17th century.

The *Posthumous Works* consists of five major divisions. It remains to discuss the one which Waller chose to place first and which Hooke entitled "A General Scheme, or Idea of the Present State of Natural Philosophy, and How its Defects may be Remedied by a Methodical Proceeding in the making Experiments and

[40] *Posthumous Works*, p. 411.
[41] *Posthumous Works*, p. 372.
[42] *Posthumous Works*, pp. 334–335.

Collecting Observations. Whereby to Compile a Natural History, as the Solid Basis for the Superstructure of True Philosophy." Questions of method were frequently and happily probed in scientific circles of the 17th century. The "General Scheme" was Hooke's contribution to the discussion. Let me say right out that in my opinion the contribution was negligible. Revealing himself here as the disciple of Bacon, he spoke much about a "philosophical algebra" which would do for natural enquiry what algebra had done for geometry by laying out a procedure of investigation which could be followed and fulfilled by persistence alone. Method was to replace genius. Like Bacon before him, Hooke succeeded primarily in convincing the reader that a method which replaces genius does not exist.

The mark of Bacon cannot be missed in Hooke's "General Scheme." With Bacon he began by examining the present state of natural philosophy, and with Bacon he found it lamentable. With Bacon he passed on to analyze the nature and shortcomings of the human mind, although he showed the good sense, I might remark, not to discover four idols. Too much had happened since Bacon's day for Hooke to discuss simple natures, but he listed no less than twenty-nine ways of "discovering Nature." Above all, the "General Scheme" reminds us of Bacon in its constant insistence that the primary desideratum was a general natural history—"a sufficient Store of sound and good Materials. . . ."[43] Although Hooke predicted hopefully that the natural history complete would comprise less volume than the works of some single men, he compiled a list of headings for it running to four large pages, thereby suggesting that the single men he had in mind were built on the heroic scale of Alexandrian scholars. Empirical fact, the fundamental role of empirical fact—such is the theme that pervades the "General Scheme."

> But as to the Inquiry into Natural Operations, what are the Kinds of secret and subtile Actors, and what the abstruse and hidden Instruments and Engines there made use of, may be; It [logic] seems not, to me, as yet at all adapted and wholly deficient. For 'tis not to be expected from the Accomplishments the Creator has endowed Man withal, that he should be able to leap, from a few particular Informations of his Senses, and those very superficial at best, and for the most part fallacious, to the general Knowledge of Universals or abstracted Natures, and then be able, as out of an inexhaustable Fountain, to draw out a perfect Knowledge of all Particulars, to deduce the Causes of all Effects and Actions from this or that Axiome or Sentence, and as it were intuitively, to know what Nature does or is capable of effecting: And after what manner and Method she works; and yet that Method [logic again] supposes little less.[44]

If the pervasive tone of the essay is empirical, recurring use of the word "engine" suggests quite a different insight as its basic animation. The "Intellect is not to be suffer'd to act without its Helps, but is continually to be assisted by some Method or Engine. . . ."[45] When we recall the role of the simple machines in 17th century mechanics, the treatises devoted to their analysis, the fascination in their multiplication of force, we may see the thrust of Hooke's figure. The mind was to be equipped as the hand had been; like physical force, mental force also was to be multiplied. The history of science may perhaps reveal in the development of systematic procedure an enhancement of intellectual effort. It is difficult, however, to discover anything at all similar to the mental levers and winches that Hooke seems to have envisaged.

[43] *Posthumous Works*, p. 21.
[44] *Posthumous Works*, p. 6.
[45] *Posthumous Works*, p. 6.

How are we to understand this method of Hooke's? Can it have been in some unconscious way Hooke's judgment on himself? Certainly it is hard to imagine anything further removed from his actual practice than his vigorous admonitions on orderly procedure and systematic coverage. There is irony, to be sure, in his determination to render superfluous his strongest trait, what I have called intuition. To insist on orderly procedure and systematic coverage, however, was to examine his own shortcomings with some insight and to stress the virtues which would have allowed him to exploit his own intuitions instead of leaving them to others. Ironically again, and symbolically as well, Hooke did not complete the essay on method stressing orderly procedure and systematic coverage.

We can pick many similar instances from his career. A passage from his diary is dated 10 April 1697.

> I began this Day to write the History of my own Life, wherein I will comprize as many remarkable Passages, as I can now remember or collect out of such Memorials as I have kept in Writing, or are in the Registers of the Royal Society; together with all my Inventions, Experiments, Discoveries, Discourses, &c. which I have made, the time when, the manner how, and means by which, with the success and effect of them together with the state of my Health, my employments and Studies, my good or bad Fortune, my Friends and Enemies, &c. all which shall be the truth of Matter of Fact, so far as I can be inform'd by my Memorials or my own Memory, which Rule I resolve not to transgress.[46]

He failed to complete the account; all that remained was the intention, first published by Waller in this volume, which was dedicated to Isaac Newton. Waller also records that Hooke intended to leave his estate to build a laboratory for the Royal Society and to found a series of lectures on natural philosophy. "But tho' he was often solicited by his Friends to put his Designs down in Writing, and make his Will as to the disposal of his Estate to his own liking in the time of his Health; and after when himself, and all thought, his End drew near, yet he could never be prevail'd with to perfect it, still procrastinating it, till at last this great Design prov'd an airy Phantom and vanish'd into nothing. Thus he dy'd at last without any Will and Testament that could be found."[47]

More than one of Hooke's projects ended up as airy phantoms. At least in terms of his own achievement they were airy phantoms, but after 1687 he was increasingly prepared to recognize his ghosts in the work of others. We cannot mistake the pervasive bitterness in those parts of the *Posthumous Works* which date from his final years.

> A Man may rationally enough distrust his own Thoughts and Reasons, nay, and even his Senses too, if he finds those he converses with to be of another Opinion, tho' acquainted with the Arguments that prevail'd with him, at least 'till he finds, that it was done for some Sinister Designs to defraud him of his Discovery. . . . the generallity of Men are not much concern'd for the first Discoverer, and . . . they usually take him for such, who first acquainted them with it; and for one Reader that can disprove them, or detect them of Plagiary, there are a thousand that can not, and for those that can, they find ways to evade and by Confidence carry the point, and even with a general Approbation and Advantage.[48]

Hooke was mistaken. He did not understand the lesson of his "General Scheme" after all, and he vastly overestimated the significance of naked intuition un-

---

[46] *Posthumous Works*, p. *i*.
[47] *Posthumous Works*, p. *xxvii*.
[48] *Posthumous Works*, p. **446**.

clothed in the raiment of demonstration. Hooke was mistaken. Others had not stolen the fruit he had gathered. If he had on occasion caught sight of it on the bough, he had lacked the persistence and the ability to pluck it himself. Whatever his judgment of himself, he was not a Newton unrecognized.

To deny that he was a Newton, however, is not to deny his importance. As an inventor of practical instruments, he was unrivaled in his age. In the infant field of geology, he stood at the head of his contemporaries. In mechanics and optics, in the whole area of natural philosophy, he reflected faithfully the problems of his age. If the history of science requires first of all, not that we discover the first announcement of opinions we still hold, but that we understand the questions scientists asked and the problems they attacked, then Hooke's *Posthumous Works* provides one of the indispensable sources for the study of the late 17th century.

Richard S. Westfall

The Poſthumous
WORKS
OF
ROBERT HOOKE, *M. D. S. R. S.*
Geom. Prof. Greſh. *&c.*

Containing his

Cutlerian Lectures,
AND OTHER
DISCOURSES,

Read at the MEETINGS of the Illuſtrious

ROYAL SOCIETY.
IN WHICH

I. The preſent Deficiency of NATURAL PHILOSOPHY is diſcourſed of, with the Methods of rendering it more certain and beneficial.

II. The Nature, Motion and Effects of LIGHT are treated of, particularly that of the *Sun* and *Comets.*

III. An Hypothetical Explication of MEMORY; how the Organs made uſe of by the Mind in its Operation may be Mechanically underſtood.

IV. An Hypotheſis and Explication of the cauſe of GRAVITY, or GRAVITATION, MAGNETISM, *&c.*

V. Diſcourſes of EARTHQUAKES, their *Cauſes* and *Effects*, and Hiſtories of ſeveral; to which are annext, *Phyſical Explications* of ſeveral of the Fables in *Ovid*'s *Metamorphoſes*, very different from other Mythologick Interpreters.

VI. Lectures for improving NAVIGATION and ASTRONOMY, with the Deſcriptions of ſeveral new and uſeful *Inſtruments* and *Contrivances*; the whole full of curious Diſquiſitions and Experiments.

Illuſtrated with SCULPTURES.

To theſe DISCOURSES is prefixt the AUTHOR'S LIFE, giving an Account of his Studies and Employments, with an Enumeration of the many Experiments, Inſtruments, Contrivances and Inventions, by him made and produc'd as Curator of Experiments to the *Royal Society.*

PUBLISH'D
By *RICHARD WALLER*, R. S. Secr.

LONDON:
Printed by SAM. SMITH and BENJ. WALFORD, (Printers to the Royal Society) at the *Princes Arms* in St. *Paul*'s Church-yard. 1705.

TO
Sir *ISAAC NEWTON*, Kt.
PRESIDENT,

And to the

Council and Fellows

OF THE

ROYAL SOCIETY

OF

LONDON,

FOR THE

Advancement of *Natural Knowledge.*

THESE

POSTHUMOUS WORKS

OF

Dr. Robert Hooke

Are humbly Dedicated

By *Richard Waller*, S. R. Secr.

THE
PUBLISHER
TO THE
READER.

CUstom having made a Preface or Epistle to the Reader almost necessary, I shall so far comply as to give some short Account of the following Treatises. The Reputation of the Author is so well establish'd, that I shall wave all that might be said upon that Head, and only desire the Reader to observe, that soon after his Decease, his Papers were, by his Relations, committed to my care to Publish what I thought might prove acceptable to the Learned, which I have endeavour'd in this Volume.

The Tracts here Publish'd are for the most part Lectures, made and read by him at several distant times upon different Subjects, which the Reader is here presented with as the Author left them; for I was unwilling to Model or Methodize them a new, by reducing the Subjects and Discourses of many Lectures into one continu'd Discourse, as his method has been in the Treatises formerly Publish'd by him in Quarto; much less have I ventur'd upon any Epitome, Abridgments too often distorting and curtailing the Author's true Sense, and disguising it so, that his own Sentiments are hard to be distinguish'd and always dubious, which Errors I have desir'd as much as possible to shun. I am sensible, by publishing his Discourses thus at large, some Recapitulations have been unavoidable, especially in Discourses of this Nature, which it is possible may disgust some nice Criticks; nevertheless I hope the Canded Reader will not find these Repetitions so many or large, as to be dissatisfy'd thereat, most, if not all of them, containing some new Matter added to what was said before.

The Subjects here handl'd are some of the most difficult in Natural Philosophy, and the Discourses were all well accepted and approv'd of when read before competent Judges of the ROYAL SOCIETY, at their usual Meetings.

The first contains a general Scheme or Draught of a method of advancing and promoting Natural Philosophy, shewing its present deficiency, with the several Queries to be made, and how they may be answer'd to render it more instructive and beneficial. It must be granted the last and chief Part of this Physical Algebra, or New Organ, viz. The method of ranging the Experiments and Observations in order, so as to frame and raise Axioms from them is wanting (which I believe was never wrote by the Author) however I make no doubt but what is here offer'd will prove acceptable for the many curious Informations and Experiments therein contain'd.

What follows is a Collection of several Lectures concerning the Nature of Light, in which its Cause, Motion, Action, Velocity and Properties are largely treated of, with many new, useful and entertaining Subjects, either more copiously handled or hinted in Transitu. Tho' the Author has not in these Discourses treated of the several alterations and affections of the Rays of Light from Reflection, Inflection, and Refraction, &c.

as his intention was to do (which is evident from several Passages in his Writings) yet the Learned will here meet with several no less difficult than curious Matters explain'd, among the rest that great Problem of Memory, which is here at least intelligibly explicated with the Organs, necessary to perform that action of the Mind, or Reflection, which Organs possibly are not immaterial or incorporeal

From this Contemplation he comes to treat of Time and Duration, shewing whence we gain the Notion of it, which he supposes from the formation of, and impressions upon sensible and corporeal Ideas, or Images stored up in the Repository of the Brain, tho' he positively asserts the recipient and directing Power or Soul to be a self-moving immaterial Being.

Next to this is a Physical Treatise of Comets, *proving from many Observations, that they are actually burning Bodies, with an account of the unconceivable Velocity of the motion of the Flashes or Accension of the Steames in the Blaze or Taile far surpassing those of Light'ning : To this is join'd the Author's* Hypothesis *of the cause of* Gravity, *a Subject that has hitherto puzzl'd, as well as exercis'd the most ingenious Heads. This Hypothesis is deduc'd from Mechanick Principles, and back'd with Experiments ; to which is added a short Account of his Hypothesis of* Magnetism.

After these are many Lectures concerning the external Shell or Superfices of the Earth, *of the Cause and Original of Mountains, Vallies and Lakes. Of Fossile Shells, and other marine Remains found on the highest Hills over most part of the known World, with Historical Accounts of* Earthquakes, *fiery Eruptions, Deluges, &c. and a Physical Interpretation of the most antient* Mythologick Representations *of Natural History. In these Lectures the figure of the Terraqueous Globe and encompassing Air is prov'd from the diurnal Motion and Gravitation.*

Lastly, I have added some Lectures relating to the Improvement of Astronomy *and* Navigation, *wherein, tho' I cannot promise the Reader the Invention of the* Longitude, *or the like great Matters, yet I hope they will prove agreeable for the several new and useful Suggestions and Instruments therein mention'd and describ'd, with some new methods of making Observations at Land and Sea, to determine the true Meridian Latitude of the Place, &c.*

In all these Discourses I have fairly and truly given the Author's own Opinions and Reasonings in his own words, with the several times when they were read before the Royal Society, *when I could any way discover them.*

I could wish the Author had himself fitted these Papers for the Press in his Life time, or at least stich'd the several agreeing Subjects together, which would have prevented some Errors that possibly have happen'd in the Order and Disposition of them, for which I desire the Reader to accept this Excuse, that several of his Papers came to my Sight and Hands, when others that might better have follow'd them, were Printed off.

R. W.

T H E

THE
LIFE
OF
Dr. Robert Hooke.

Understanding that it would be acceptable to several Learned and Ingenious Persons to have some publick Account given of the Life, Studies and Employments of so knowing and diligent an Inquirer into Nature, as Dr. *Robert Hooke* is generally allow'd to have been, and who was one of the greatest Promoters of Experimental Natural Knowledge, as well as Ornaments of the last Century (so fruitful of great *Genii*) I could not well refuse that Task, which (knowing my own insufficiency for such an Attempt) I could hardly undertake, being conscious it requir'd a Person much better qualify'd with natural and acquir'd Abilities to perform it with Satisfaction ; especially in so judicious and nice an Age, more ready to find Faults than pardon Mistakes : Besides my desire has always been not to expose my self to Censure, when I might live quietly, *Studiis ignobilis otii.* But the following Papers of Dr. *Hooke* having been put into my Hands to be Publish'd, I was, in some manner, oblig'd to appear in Print. What Mistakes the Candid Reader may observe, in the following Relation of his Life, I hope he will obligingly pardon. In which I profess the utmost Sincerity, the greatest part of my Vouchers being either taken out his own Memorials, or from the Journals of the Royal Society.

Had Dr. *Hooke* prosecuted a Design which I find he once proposed to himself, my present Undertaking had been as vain as needless, for in a small Pocket-Diary of his I found these Words written.

‘ *Saturday April* the 10th 1697. I began this Day to write the
‘ History of my own Life, wherein I will comprize as many re-
‘ markable Passages, as I can now remember or collect out of such
‘ Memorials as I have kept in Writing, or are in the Registers of
‘ the ROYAL SOCIETY; together with all my Inventions, Ex-
‘ periments, Discoveries, Discourses, &c. which I have made, the
‘ time when, the manner how, and means by which, with the suc-
‘ cess and effect of them, together with the state of my Health,
‘ my Employments and Studies, my good or bad Fortune , my
‘ Friends and Enemies, &c. all which shall be the truth of Matter
‘ of Fact, so far as I can be inform'd by my Memorials or my own
‘ Memory, which Rule I resolve not to transgress.

Accordingly

Accordingly I found a beginning of his Life, which tho' it affords but little satisfaction, being only concerning his Childhood, yet I have here given an Abstract of what is contained in it.

Dr. *Robert Hooke* was Born at *Freshwater*, a Peninsula on the West side of the Isle of *Wight*, on the eighteenth of *July*, being *Saturday*, 1635, at twelve a Clock at Noon, and Christened the twenty sixth following by his own Father Minister of that Parish.

He was very infirm and weakly, and therefore Nurst at Home, tho' his Brothers and Sisters were Nurst Abroad; and for at least seven Years his Parents had very little hopes of his Life, being often sick; all which time his chief Food was Milk, or things made thereof, and Fruits, no Flesh in the least agreeing with his weak Constitution.

For his Age he was very sprightly and active in Running, Leaping, &c. tho' very weak as to any robust Exercise: Was very apt to learn any thing, and after his English soon learnt his Grammar by Heart; but, as he says, with but little understanding, till his Father designing him for the Ministry, took some pains to instruct him. But he still being often subject to the Head-ach which hindered his Learning, his Father laid aside all Thoughts of breeding him a Scholar, and finding himself also grow very infirm through Age and Sickness, wholly neglected his farther Education, who being thus left to himself spent his time in making little mechanical ' Toys, (as he says) in which he was very intent, and for the Tools ' he had successful; so that there was nothing he saw done by any ' Mechanick, but he endeavoured to imitate, and in some parti- ' culars could exceed (which are his own words.) His Father observing by these Indications, his great inclination to Mechanicks, thought to put him Apprentice to some easy Trade (as a Watchmakers or Limners) he shewing most inclinations to those or the like curious Mechanical Performances; for making use of such Tools as he could procure, ' seeing an old Brass Clock taken to pieces, ' he attemted to imitate it, and made a wooden one that would go: ' Much about the same time he made a small Ship about a Yard ' long, fitly shaping it, adding its Rigging of Ropes, Pullies, Masts, ' &c. with a contrivance to make it fire off some small Guns, as it ' was Sailing cross a Haven of a pretty breadth: He had also a ' great fancy for drawing, having much about the same Age Cop- ' pied several Prints with a Pen, that Mr. *Hoskins* (Son to the fa- ' mous *Hoskins Cowpers* Master) much admired one not instructed ' could so well imitate them.

These Indications of a Mechanick Genius appeared in him when very young; for by the same Paper I find that his Father died in *October* 1648, having for three or four Years before his Death been much afflicted with a Cough, a Palsy, Jaundice and Dropsy.

This is the sum of what he has left of his own Writing, by which we find him at the time of his Fathers Death, to be thirteen Years and about three Months Old.

This early Propensity of his to Mechanicks was a sign of his future Excellency in such Contrivances, and admirable Facility he afterwards manifested in applying Mechanical Principles to the explication of the most difficult *Phænomena* of Nature, and I remember it has been often observed by several Persons, that whatever *apparatus* he contrived for the exhibiting any Experiment before the

ROYAL

ROYAL SOCIETY, it was performed with the leaft Embarraff-ment clearly and evidently, to explain the prefent Subject, which was a fufficient proof of his true knowledge of the Mechanical Powers, and of a method of applying them to the Explication of Nature.

How he fpent the next fix or feven Years of his Life I have not been particularly informed; but I underftand he was for fome time with Sir *Peter Lely*, how long I am not certain: I fuppofe but a fhort time; for I have heard that the fmell of the Oil Colours did not agree with his Conftitution, increafing his Head-ach, to which he was ever too much fubject.

It was after this that he lived with Dr. *Busby*, the late famous Mafter of *Weftminfter-School*, as a Scholar in his own Houfe, where with more diligence he apply'd himfelf to *Latin* and *Greek*, in which he made a fufficient proficiency for the time, and had a competent Knowledge, and at the fame time got fome infight into the *Hebrew* and fome other Oriental Languages. While he liv'd with Dr. *Busby*, he fell ferioufly upon the ftudy of the Mathematicks, the Dr. encouraging him therein, and allowing him particular times for that purpofe. In this he took the moft regular Method, and firft made himfelf Mafter of *Euclide*'s Elements, and thence proceeded orderly from that fure Bafis to the other parts of the Mathematicks, and after to the application thereof to Mechanicks, his firft and laft Miftrefs.

From *Weftminfter-School* he went to the Univerfity of *Oxford*, in 1653. but as 'tis often the Fate of Perfons great in Learning to be fmall in other Circumftances, his were but mean. I find that he was a Student of *Chrift-Church*, tho' not of the Foundation, but was, as I have heard, a Servitor to one Mr. *Goodman*, and took his Degree of *Mafter of Arts* feveral Years after, about 1662, or 1663.

About the Year 1655, he began to fhew himfelf to the World, and that he had not fpent his Juvenile Years in vain; for there be-ing a Concourfe at that time of extraordinary Perfons at *Oxford*, each of which afterwards were particularly diftinguifh'd for the great Light they gave the Learned World by their juftly admired Labours; he was foon taken notice of, and for his Facility in Me-chanick Inventions much priz'd by them.

For the proof of his being at this time brought into the acquain-tance of thefe great Men, I fhall tranfcribe fome Paffages which I met with among his Manufcripts; and firft fpeaking of their Phi-lofophical Meetings at *Oxford*, he fays,

' At thefe Meetings, which were about the Year 1655 (before
' which time I knew little of them) divers Experiments were fug-
' gefted, difcours'd and try'd with various fuccefles, tho' no other
' account was taken of them but what particular Perfons perhaps
' did for the help of their own Memories; fo that many excellent
' things have been loft, fome few only by the kindnefs of the Au-
' thors have been fince made publick; among thefe may be reckon'd
' the Honourable Mr. *Boyle*'s *Pneumatick Engine* and Experiments,
' firft Printed in the Year 1660. for in 1658, or 9, I contriv'd and
' perfected the Air-pump for Mr *Boyle*, having firft feen a Contri-
' vance for that purpofe made for the fame honourable Perfon by
' Mr. *Gratorix*, which was too grofs to perform any great matter.

The Draught of this Air-pump and all its parts, as it was after Publiſh'd by Mr. *Boyle*, I have now by me deſign'd by Mr. *Hooke*, and I have heard him ſay, he was then ſent to *London* by Mr. *Boyle* to get the Barrel and other parts for that Engine which could not be made at *Oxford*.   But to return to ſome other Notes.

' The ſame Year I contriv'd and made many trials about the Art ' of flying in the Air, and moving very ſwift on the Land and Wa- ' ter, of which I ſhew'd ſeveral Deſigns to Dr. *Wilkins* then *War-* ' *den* of *Wadham College*, and at the ſame time made a Module, ' which, by the help of Springs and Wings, rais'd and ſuſtain'd it ' ſelf in the Air; but finding by my own trials, and afterwards by ' Calculation, that the Muſcles of a Mans Body were not ſuffici- ' ent to do any thing conſiderable of that kind, I apply'd my Mind ' to contrive a way to make artificial Muſcles; divers deſigns where- ' of I ſhew'd alſo at the ſame time to Dr. *Wilkins*, but was in ma- ' ny of my Trials fruſtrated of my expectations.

What is mention'd here of his attempts about flying, is con- firm'd by ſeveral Draughts and Schemes upon Paper, of the Me- thods that might be attempted for that purpoſe, and of ſome con- trivances for faſtening ſuccedaneous Wings, not unlike thoſe of Bats, to the Arms and Legs of a Man, as likewiſe of a Contri- vance to raiſe him up by means of Horizontal Vanes plac'd a little aſlope to the Wind, which being blown round, turn'd an endleſs Screw in the Center, which help'd to move the Wings, to be ma- nag'd by the Perſon by this means rais'd aloft: Theſe Schemes I have now by me, with ſome few Fragments relating thereto, but ſo imperfect, that I do not judge them fit for the Publick.   But to return to his own Notes.

' About this time having an opportunity of acquainting my ſelf ' with Aſtronomy by the kindneſs of Dr. *Ward*, I apply'd my ſelf ' to the improving of the *Pendulum* for ſuch Obſervations, and in the ' Year 1656, or 57, I contriv'd a way to continue the motion of *Tom. 1. Lib. 2.* ' the *Pendulum*, ſo much commended by *Ricciolus* in his *Almageſtum*, *Cap. 20. & 21.* ' which Dr. *Ward* had recommended to me to peruſe; I made ſome ' trials for this end, which I found to ſucceed to my wiſh.

' The ſucceſs of theſe made me farther think of improving it for **I never could* ' finding the Longitude, and * *the Method I had made for my ſelf for* *meet with* ' *Mechanick Inventions*, quickly led me to the uſe of Springs inſtead *what is menti-* ' of Gravity for the making a Body vibrate in any Poſture, where- *oned here, and* ' upon I did firſt in great, and afterwards in ſmaller Modules, ſatiſ- *in ſeveral o-* ' fy my ſelf of the Practicableneſs of ſuch an Invention, and hop- *ther places of* ' ing to have made great advantage thereby, I acquainted divers *his Tracts al-* ' of my Friends, and particularly Mr. *Boyle*, that I was poſſeſt of *ready Printed,* ' ſuch an Invention, and crav'd their Aſſiſtance for improving the *and of thoſe* ' uſe of it to my advantage. *contained in* *this Volume, of* *a method for* *Mechanick* *Inventions,* *which he ſomewhere calls a* Mechanick Algebra *for ſolving any Probleme in Mechanicks, as eaſily and cer- tainly as any Geometrick by Algebra, and ſays, that by this his method he could readily determine whether any ſuch Probleme was poſſible, and if ſo, which was the neareſt and eaſieſt way of ſolving it.*

' Immediately after his *Majeſty's* Reſtoration, Mr. *Boyle* was plea- ' ſed to acquaint the Lord *Brouncher* and Sir *Robert Moray* with it, ' who adviſ'd me to get a Patent for the Invention, and propoun- ' ded very probable ways of making conſiderable advantage by it. ' To induce them to a belief of my performance, I ſhew'd a Pocket- ' watch,

' watch, accommodated with a Spring, apply'd to the Arbor of
' the Ballance to regulate the motion thereof; concealing the way
' I had for finding the Longitude; this was fo well approv'd of,
' that Sir *Robert Moray* drew me up the form of a Patent, the prin-
' cipal part whereof, *viz.* the defcription of the Watch, fo regulat-
' ed, is his own hand Writing, which I have yet by me, the dif-
' couragement I met with in the management of this Affair, made
' me defift for that time.

So far this Paper. In confirmation of what is abovefaid, I met
with a Draught of an Agreement between the Lord *Brouncher*, Mr.
Boyle, and Sir *Robert Moray*, with *Robert Hooke* Mafter of Arts to
this purpofe, that *Robert Hooke* fhould difcover to them the whole
of his Invention to meafure the parts of Time at Sea as exactly and
truly as they are at Land by the *Pendulum* Clocks invented by Monfieur *Huygens*; That of the Profits to be made thereby not exceeding 6000 *l. Robert Hooke* was to have ¾ of whatever was made more
of it, not exceeding 4000 *l. Robert Hooke* was to have ⅔ of the reft,
if more could be made of it, he was to have the ½, and *Robert Hooke*
to be publickly owned the Author and Inventor thereof. This is
the fum of one Draught; there are indeed fome others which differ
only in the divifion of the Profits, which it is needlefs here to trouble the Reader with. In purfuance of this Defign there were feveral Papers drawn up, *viz.* The Draught of an Act of Parliament to
oblige all Mafters of Ships to pay fo much *per* Tun for the ufe of
this Invention, as alfo of a Warrant to be granted by the *King* to
Robert Hooke, *M. A.* &c. for a Patent for the fole ufe of the faid Invention for fourteen Years, and fign'd by His Majefty's Command,
William Morrice. I have fome other Papers which are unneceffary to
be here mention'd.

Thus far the Matter then proceeded, and how it came to ftop
here may be juftly wondred; but to give the Reader the beft fatif-
faction I can in this matter, I fhall tranfcribe a Paragraph out of
the Poftcript to *Hooke*'s Treatife of *Heliofcopes* Printed 1676.   Pag. 27.

' This Treaty with me had been finally concluded for feveral
' Thoufand Pounds, had not the inferting of one Claufe broke it
' off, which was, *That if after I had difcover'd my Invention about*
' *the finding the Longitude by Watches (tho' in themfelves fufficient) they,*
' *or any other Perfon fhould find a way of improving my Principles, he or*
' *they fhould have the benefit thereof during the term of the Patent, and*
' *not I.* To which Claufe I could no ways agree, knowing 'twas
' eafy to vary my Principles an hundred ways; and 'twas not im-
' probable, but there might be fome addition of conveniency to
' what I fhould at firft difcover, it being *facile inventis addere*; and
' judging it unreafonable to be depriv'd of the benefit of my In-
' ventions, in themfelves fufficient, becaufe others might vary
' them, or any other ways improve them, of which it was very
' probable they would have no thought if they had not the advan-
' tage of being inftructed by my Difcovery, it having been hid
' fome Thoufands of Years already; as indeed the effect hath made
' evident and certain, there having been nothing done by any Bo-
' dy elfe upon that matter ever fince.

There is more in the fame place worth the perufal, which, for
brevity, I omit.

Dr.

Dr. *Hooke* suffering this Invention to lie undiscover'd to the last, gave some Persons cause to question whether he was ever Possessor of it, and to doubt whether what in Theory seem'd very promising, wou'd answer when put to the Test of Practice; others indeed more severely judged, that it was only a kind of boasting in him, to assert he knew that which had not yet been perform'd, tho' attempted by many. However the matter is, it is certain he persisted in the affirmation to the last, and not many Weeks before his Death, told me and other Persons, that he knew a certain and infallible method to descover the true place of a Vessel at Sea, as to its East and West distance from the Port departed from : Whether by Watches, or other Time-keepers, or by any other ways, I know not, tho' indeed by what is before mention'd, it should seem to be by Watches, for the improvement of which he made many Trials, and read several Discourses.

However this matter produc'd the discovery of that most useful and practicable method of regulating Pocket-watches by a spiral Spring, apply'd to the Arbor of the Ballance as they are now made without any considerable addition since; the History of which, as I have heard it from himself and find publish'd, is thus.

In Discourse once he told me, that about the Year 1660. he having shewn a Movement so regulated to the Lord *Brouncher*, &c. as is above related, Monsieur *Huygens* having for some time apply'd himself to invent several ways to regulate Time-keepers by the correspondence he held with Mr. *Oldenburgh*, among other matters had notice of this, for which there was afterwards an application made to procure a Patent. This indeed is possible, but whether it were so or not I cannot determine. That Mr. *Hooke* had many Years before *(Huygens* mention'd it) discover'd the Invention is certain, by what is related in the History of the R o y a l S o c i e t y among several new Inventions, in these words, *There have been invented several*

Pag. 247. *kinds of Pendulum Watches for the Pocket, wherein the motion is regulated by Springs,* &c.

Now tho' this does not mention the Springs being spiral or fastened to the Arbor of the Ballance, yet it appears it was so by what is related above, and a Passage I have seen in a Leter from Sir *Robert Moray* to Mr. *Oldenburgh,* dated *Oxon Sept.* 30. 1665. clears it, in which are these words. ' You (meaning *Oldenburgh*) will be
' the first that knows when his (that is *Hugyens*'s) Watches will be
' ready, and I will therefore expect from you an account of them,
' and if he imparts to you what he does, let me know it; to that
' purpose you may ask him if he doth not *apply a Spring to the Arbor*
' *of the Ballance,* and that will give him occasion to say somewhat
' to you; if it be that, you may tell him what *Hooke has done in*
' *that matter, and what he intends more.* Altho' I cannot be assur'd what *Oldenburgh* wrote to Monsieur *Huygens,* yet it is probable their intimacy procur'd what he knew; and it is evident that *Huygens*'s discovery of this was first publish'd in the *Journal des Scavans,* and from thence in the Philos. Transact. for *March* 25th. 1675, about ten Years after that Letter of Sir *Robert Morays,* and near fifteen after *Hooke*'s first discovery of it.

To this I shall add what Mr. *Oldenburgh* has Printed, *Philos. Transact.* N°. 118. ' 'Tis certain the describer of Helioscopes (mean-
' ing *Hooke*) some Years ago caus'd to be actually made some
        ' Watches

' Watches of this kind; which (indeed he there says) were unsuccessful. Which whether so or not, I cannot learn, so many Years after, tho' I am inclin'd to think that Expression proceeded from Passion, the Invention and Principle of *Hooke*'s and *Huygens*'s being both the very same as are now us'd.

To this of Mr. *Oldenburgh*, Mr. *Hooke* made his Reply in a Postscript to his *Lampas*: In rejoinder to which *Oldenburg* Printed a *Philos. Transf.* Declaration of the Council of the R O Y A L S O C I E T Y, to testify *N°. 129. p.* his faithfulness in managing the Correspondence of the Society ; *749.* but it is observable that in this place there is no contradiction to *Hooke*'s being the first in that Invention.

It cannot be deny'd but that Mr. *Hooke* was frequently desir'd to perfect his Inventions about Watches and Time-keepers, which, when urg'd, he as often promis'd, and when any new Contrivance was by any Person produc'd, he then shew'd something of his own, either the same, or excelling it, a Proof he had try'd the same before. ' Particularly when on the *9th* of *August* 1666. Mr. *Mer-* ' *cator* shew'd to the Society a Watch of his Invention, represent- ' ing the Æquation of Time to the approbation of the Company. ' Mr. *Hooke* at the same time produc'd a new piece of Watch- ' work of his own Contrivance to measure Time exactly both at *Journal R. Soc.* ' Sea and Land, of which he was desir'd to bring in the Descrip- ' tion, which, tho' promis'd, was, as I think, never done.

It must be confess'd that very many of his Inventions were never brought to the perfection they were capable of, nor put in practice till some other Person either Foreigner or of our own Nation cultivated the Invention, which, when *Hooke* found, it put him upon the finishing that which otherwise possibly might have lain 'till this time in its first Defects : Whether this mistake arose from the multiplicity of his Business which did not allow him a sufficient time, or from the fertility of his Invention which hurry'd him on, in the quest of new Entertainments, neglecting the former Discoveries when he was once satisfied of the feazableness and certainty of them, tho' there wanted some small matter to render their use more practicable and general, I know not, and whether this was the Case in the present Subject : But this I suppose may be an undoubted Truth, the spiral Springs were not apply'd generally to regulate Watches, 'till after this Dispute with *Huygens*.

I have been the more particular in this matter, that I Might, as far as I was able, assert the Invention to the true Author, and suppose I have wrong'd no Person. They that require more of this Subject may consult the Philosophical Transactions, and *Hooke*'s Tracts in the places before quoted : I have in this brought all that relates to this Question together, that the Reader may the better understand the whole matter, tho' thereby I have disorder'd the series of his Life, and order of Time.

But to return (from this Digression, which, to make it more plain, I have enlarg'd upon) to *Oxford*, I find that 1655, or 6 there were many curious Experiments, Observations and Inquiries made, and Instruments for those purposes contriv'd, as particularly the *Barometer*, of which he says, the first occasion of the Invention was a Suggestion of Sir *Ch. Wren* in order to find whether the Hypothesis of *Des Cartes* for giving the Reason of the Tides from the pressure of

the

the Moon upon the Air in its paſſage by the Meridian, were true or not.   At this time I have heard Mr. *Hooke* ſay, it was firſt obſerv'd, that the height of the *Mercury* in the *Barometer* did not conform itſelf to the Moon's motion, but to that of the different Gravitation of the Air, as has been ſince ſufficiently verified.   Yet in a *French* Treatiſe Printed at *Paris*, ſeveral Years after this Obſervation at *Oxford*, the diſcovery of the Gravitation of the Air is attributed to Monſieur *Paſcal* deduced from ſeveral Experiments, made about the Year 1650. at *Clermont* in *Auvergne* by Monſieur *Perier*, at *Paris* by others : And at *Stockholm* by Meſſeures *Des Cartes* and *Chanute* ; which if it be, as is there related, and the Inferences from that Experiment ſuch as are in the ſame Tract mentioned, 'tis ſtrange they ſhould not have been apply'd to the uſe of ſo beneficial an Inſtrument ſooner, which I do not find it was till after this Obſervation at *Oxford*.

*Traitez de l'
Equilibre de-
liqueurs,* &c.
1664.

By the perſuaſion of Dr. *Seth Ward*, afterwards Biſhop of *Salisbury*, about 1656, he apply'd himſelf more particularly to the Study of Aſtronomy, and about 58, or 59, he ſays thus, ' I contriv'd ſe-
' veral Aſtronomical Inſtruments for making Obſervations both at
' Sea and Land, which I afterwards produc'd before the R o y a l
' S o c i e t y.

Vide p. 500.
&c. *infra.*

Some of theſe, I ſuppoſe, are the Inſtruments hereafter mention'd in his Aſtronomical Lectures, where I have endeavour'd to retrieve as many as I could, partly from ſome rough Draughts, partly from old Modules, and ſome from the verbal Deſcriptions where both thoſe helps were wanting ; in which how I have ſucceeded, is left to the candid Readers Judgment.

' Much about this time (as he ſays) he contriv'd the *Circular Pen-*
' *dulum*, and the uſe of it for continuing the motion of another *Pen-*
dulum, which he afterwards ſhew'd to the R o y a l S o c i e t y in 1663 ; about which time, and afterwards, there are ſeveral particulars relating to the *Circular Pendulum* enter'd in the Journals as his : A Movement to this purpoſe ; is deſcrib'd in his *Animadverſions* on *Machina Cæleſtis*, pag. 68. Printed 1674.

In the Year 1660. the moſt Illuſtrious R o y a l S o c i e t y was founded, for a full account of which, and its Inſtitution, the Reader is referred to the Right Reverend and Learned, Dr. *Sprat*'s Hiſtory thereof, Publiſh'd 1667.   I ſhall only obſerve the Occaſion and Time when Mr. *Hooke* was introduc'd into their Service as *Curator*.   Soon after the beginning of the R o y a l S o c i e t y, *viz.* about *April* 1661. a Debate aroſe in the Society, occaſion'd by a ſmall Tract Printed in 1660. about the cauſe of the riſing of Water in ſlender Glaſs Pipes, higher than in larger, and that in a certain proportion to their Bores ; this Diſcourſe was wrote and Publiſh'd by *Hooke* ; the Explication of which difficult *Phænomenon* made him the more regarded.   The ſum of his Reaſonings upon this Subject he Publiſh'd afterward, *Micrography Obſerv*. the 6th. in which there are ſeveral very curious and then new Remarks and Hints ; as to the Nature of Fluidity and Gravity, which laſt is farther proſecuted in his Treatiſe of Springs, with other excellent Subjects, to which the Inquiſitive are referr'd for a more ample ſatisfaction.

This,

This, together with his former Performances, made him much respected by the *R. Society*, and on the fifth of *November* 1662.ʻ Sir ʻ *Robert Moray* propos'd a Person that was willing to be entertain'd ʻ as a *Curator* by the *Society*, offering to furnish them every day ʻ when they met, with three or four considerable Experiments; ʻ which Proposition was unanimously receiv'd, Mr. *Hooke* being ʻ nam'd to be the Person; and accordingly the next Day of their ʻ meeting on the twelfth of *November* he was unanimously accep- ʻ ted and taken as *Curator*, with the Thanks of the *Society* order'd ʻ to Mr. *Boyle* for dispensing with him for their use, and order'd ʻ that Mr. *Hooke* should come and sit among them, and both bring ʻ in every Day three or four of his own Experiments, and take care ʻ of such others as should be recommended to him by the *So-* ʻ *ciety*.

From this time the *Societies* Journals gave sufficient Testimonials of his Performances, all which would be too many to particularize here, therefore I shall only touch upon some of the chief, as the Experiment of breaking Glass-Bubbles inward, the Air contain'd in them being rarify'd by heat in their blowing, and so hermetically sealing them whilst hot; which Bubbles were observ'd at a certain degree of Tension, both in the distending them whilst blowing, and in their contracting as they cool'd, to yield a smart sound, several of these in cooling would break inwards with a brisk noise, tho' others broak without any noise, upon which the Experimenter made several Remarks.

Many Experiments were made to explicate the Nature and Quality of the Air, *viz.* as to its Gravitation, its different Effects when Rarify'd, Condens'd and Natural, with its use as to the Life of Animals, and maintaining a lucid Flame, or cause the Dissolution of Bodies by Fire, a live Animal and Lamp being inclosed together in a Receiver, shew'd the *Pabulum vitæ* and *flammæ* to be much the same: At which time also he try'd how long the same Air would serve for breathing. This leads me to remember that noble Experiment made by him of keeping a Dog alive, his *Thorax* being laid open, by blowing fresh Air into his Lungs, of which a particular Account is given in the History of the ROYAL SOCIETY, pag. 232. which plainly shews the use of the Air, and difference between venal and arterial Blood.

He shew'd what addition of weight is given to Fluids, by ascending and descending Bodies in them. The different Specifick weight of Hot and Cold Water, with the uses to be made thereof in heating large quantities of Water. Of the difference of Ice and Water, with the Refraction of other Fluids, by an Instrument describ'd in the Preface to his Micrography.

Experiments and a Contrivance to shew the Force and Velocity of Bodies falling from several heights, weighing Bodies at several heights. *Pendulums* of two hundred Foot long. The difference of the *Barometer* at several heights. Experiments to improve Land Carriage. Methods of conveying secret and quick Intelligence.

Instruments to measure time exactly. To observe a second Minute by the Sun or Stars. To try the strength of Gun-power, and several others, particularly an Engine to cut down the Teeth of Watch Wheels more exactly than can be done by the most expert Hand, an Invention now of constant use.

About

About this time he fix'd the Standard for the *Thermometer* from the Point of Freezing ; and contriv'd a way to make the motions of the *Barometer* more fenfible, which is fince with farther Improvements, Publifh'd in the *Philofoph. Tranfact.* N°. 185. p. 241.

In *Feb.* 166¾. he contriv'd a way to fupply frefh Air to the Urinator under the Diving Bell by a Chain of Buckets and a Leaden Box for his Head, when he went out of the Bell to be fupply'd with frefh Air from the Bell, &c.

At this time he fhew'd Experiments of the dilating of Glafs and other Bodies by Heat.

In *July* 1664. he produc'd an Experement to fhew the number of Vibrations of an extended String, made in a determinate time, requifite to give a certain Tone or Note, by which it was found that a Wire making two hundred feventy two vibrations in one Second of Time, founded *G Sol Re Vt* in the Scale of all Mufick. Other Experiments were made of the divifion of a Monochord, which I omit.

Philof. Tranf. N°. 9. p. 147. & N°. 24. p. 439.
About this time many Experiments were made of the Velocity of Bodies finking and rifing in Water, in order to afcertain that Contrivance, which was after made publick, of founding the Seas depth with the founding Ball, which is too well known to infift on it.

At feveral Meetings of the *Society* in 1663, and 4. he produc'd his Microfcopial Obfervations, and read the Explications and Difcourfes made upon them, which were after publifh'd in his *Micrographia,* at the beginning of the Year 1665. In which Book, I fuppofe, it will hardly be deny'd, that there are more excellent Philofophical Difcoveries and Hints, that in moft extant of its bulk: The Book itfelf being well known, I fhall only obferve that there are defcrib'd in it feveral forts of Microfcopes, with the ways of ufing them. The Barofcope, Hygrofcope, an Inftrument to graduate Thermometers, an Engine to grind Optick-glaffes, an Inftrument to meafure the Refraction of Liquors, &c. I remember Mr. *Marfhal* when he defir'd the *Societies* Approbation of his new Method of grinding Spectacles and other Optick-glaffes, own'd he had the firft intimation of it from a hint of Mr. *Hooke*'s in this Book about the Polifhing many very fmall Microfcope Object-glaffes at once.

A more particular Account of this Book is extant in the *Philofoph. Tranfact.* N° 2. p. 29. and to fhew the Efteem Foreigners had of it, I fhall refer the Reader to the account given of it in the *Journal des Scavans* for the Month of *December* 1666. In this the Journalift fpeaks with great Refpect of the Author, and Efteem for the Work itfelf, obferving the vaft number of curious Remarks made therein concerning the improvement of the other Senfes, as well as that of feeing : Obfervations of Colours and Light, the Moon, Stars, Reflexion, Inflection, &c. concluding after (having mention'd feveral) that the Book contains more than can be taken notice of in an Extract.

In the beginning of *June* 1664. Sir *John Cutler* having intimated his Defign to fome Members of the *Society* of founding a Mechanick Lecture, with a Yearly Gratuity of fifty Pounds, on the twenty fecond of the fame Month feveral Members met to confer about the manner of fetling that Lecture, and on the ninth of *November* following, it is enter'd in the Journals to this purpofe ; ' Sir

' *John*

' *John Cutler* having founded a Lecture, and settl'd an Annual Sti-
' pend upon *Robert Hooke*, M. A. of fifty Pounds during Life (en-
' trusting the President, Council and Fellows of the said *Society* to
' direct and appoint the said Mr. *Hooke* as to the Subject and Number
' of his Lectures) the *Society* order'd several of their Members to
' wait upon Sir *John Cutler*, with their Thanks for his particular
' Favour to a worthy Member, and for that Respect and Confidence
' he hath hereby exprest towards their whole Body, *&c.*

' On the twenty seventh of *June* 1664. it was voted that at the
' first Opportunity Mr. *Hooke* should be put to the Scrutiny for
' the *Curators* place by Office; on the twenty third of *November*
' following he was propos'd as a *Setled Curator* of Experiments;
' and on the eleventh of *Jan.* 1664. elected and made *Curator by Of-*
' *fice* for Life, with an additional Salary to Sir *John Cutler*'s Annu-
' ity.

At this time he read several Astronomical Lectures, some of
which are publish'd in this Volume, and invented many Instruments, particularly his Quadrant with a Roler on the Limb; an
Instrument to measure the Velocity of the Wind, and repeated
the Experiment of the Vibrations of a Pendule two hundred
Foot long. The first proposal for the Weather-Clock was then offer'd upon the Description of one made by Sir *Christopher Wren.*
The Experiment was made and account given of the suspension of
the Mercury to seventy five Inches in the Tube, which, with some
additions, is Printed in this Volume. From this time he brought
in almost at every Meeting Experiments, Observations, Schemes
of new Instruments and Inventions, or something considerable to
the advancement of Knowledge, and very frequently read his *Cut-*
lerian Lectures, of many whereof he publish'd, the most material
parts in his Tracts Printed at different times, in Quarto, call'd
Lectures and Collections, &c. comprizing compendiously in one continu'd Discourse, the chief Matters and Subjects handled in several
Lectures.

Thus the generous Ardor with which the ROYAL SOCIETY
was inspir'd, continu'd 'till the Year 1665. when, by reason of the
great Mortaity then reigning, they were oblig'd to desist and break
up their Weekly Meetings till the fourteenth of *March* 166⅚. when,
upon Summons, they met again. In this Interim the Members
retir'd to several Places in the Country, and Mr. *Hooke* attended Dr. *Wilkins*, and some other ingenious Gentlemen into *Sur-*
ry, near *Banstead Downs*, where several Experiments were made
during this Recess, an account of which was after brought into
the *Society.*

At some of the first Meetings, after they came together again,
' Mr. *Hooke* produc'd a very small Quadrant for observing accu-
' rately to Minutes and Seconds, it had an Arm moving on it by
' means of a Screw lying on the Limb of the Quadrant; this is
all the account I find of it. Possibly this was the first ever made
after that manner, tho' it is now sufficiently known and practis'd:
A large one of this sort, and of all its parts, with the rest of the
apparatus and manner of using it, is at large publish'd by the Inventor, *Anno* 1674. in his Animadversions on *Hevelius*'s *Machina*
Cælestis, pag. 54. in which Book also several other ingenious Contrivances, Instruments and Inventions are mention'd.

' May

Journal R. S.

' *May* 23d. 1666. There was read a Paper of Mr. *Hooke's* ex-
' plicating the Inflexion of a direct motion into a Curve, by a fu-
' pervening, attractive Principle, which was order'd to be Regi-
' ster'd. The Difcourfe contain'd therein is an Introduction to an
' Experiment to fhew that Circular Motion, is compounded of an
' indeavour by a direct motion by the Tangent, and of another in-
' deavour tending to the Center: To which purpofe there was a
' *Pendulum* faftened to the Roof of the Room with a large wooden
' Ball of *Lignum Vitæ* on the end of it; and it was found, that if
' the *Impetus* of the indeavour by the Tangent, at the firft fetting
' out, was ftronger than the indeavour to the Center, there was
' generated fuch an Elliptical Motion, whofe longeft Diameter was
' parallel to the direct indeavour of the Body at the firft Impulfe:
' But if that *Impetus* were weaker than that indeavour to the Cen-
' ter, there was generated fuch an Elliptical Motion, whofe fhor-
' ter Diameter was parallel to the direct indeavour of the Body in
' the firft point of the Impulfe; if both were equal there was made
' a perfect Circular Motion. There was alfo made another Expe-
' riment, by faftening another Pendulous Body by a fhort String
' on the lower part of the Wire, by which the greater weight was
' fufpended, that it might freely make a Circular or Elliptical Mo-
' tion round the bigger, whilft the bigger mov'd Circularly or El-
' liptically about the firft Center. The intention whereof was to
' explicate the manner of the Moons motion about the Earth, it
' appearing evidently thereby, that neither the bigger Ball, which
' reprefented the Earth, nor the lefs which reprefented the Moon,
' were mov'd in fo perfect a Circle or Ellipfis, as otherwife they
' would have been, if either of them had been fufpended and
' mov'd fingly: But that a certain Point which feem'd to be the
' Center of Gravity of the two Bodies (howfoever pofited and
' confider'd as one) feem'd to be regularly mov'd, in fuch a Circle
' or Ellipfis, the two Balls having other perculiar motions in fmall
' Epicicles about the faid Point.

' *Aug.* 1ft. 1666. he read his Obfervations of the Comet in 1664.
' after Printed among his Tracts, and call'd *Cometa*. The fame
' produc'd a certain Contrivance to fhew that the Circular Pendu-
' lum was made of two ftrait Lines croffing each other, *&c.* and
about the fame time his Inftrument to take the diftance of the
Stars from the Moon, the one Object feen direct, the other by
Reflexion, this is publifh'd in his Book, pag. 503.

The dreadful Conflagration of a great part of the City of *London* happening in the beginning of *September* 1666. brought another great hindrance to the *Societies* Proceedings; fo that they
were oblig'd to remove their ufual place of Meeting from *Grefham
College* to *Arundel* Houfe in the *Strand*, where, by the favour of the
then Duke of *Norfolk*, they profecuted their former Inquiries, their
firft Meeting at *Arundel* Houfe being on the ninth of *Jan.* 1665.

' On the nineteenth of *Sep.* 1666. he produc'd a Module he had
' defign'd for the Rebuilding of the City, with which the *Society*
' were very well pleas'd, and Sir *John Laurence* the then late *Lord*
' *Major*, addrefs'd himfelf to the *Society*, expreffing the prefent *Lord*
' *Majors and Aldermens* liking thereof, as alfo their defire that it might
' be fhewn to his *Majefty*, they preferring it far before the Model
' drawn up by the City Surveyor.

What

What this Model was, I cannot so well determine, but I have heard that it was defign'd in it to have all the chief Streets as from *Leaden-Hall* corner to *Newgate*, and the like, to lie in an exact strait Line, and all the other cross Streets turning out of them at right Angles, all the Churches, publick Buildings, Market-places, and the like, in proper and convenient places, which, no doubt, would have added much to the Beauty and Symmetry of the whole. How this came not to be accepted of I know not, but it is probable this might contribute not a little to his being taken notice off by the Magiftrates of the City, and foon after made Surveyor.

The Rebuilding of the City, according to the Act of Parliament, requiring an able Perfon to fet out the Ground to the feveral Proprietors, Mr. *Hooke* was pitch'd upon, and appointed *City-Surveyor* for that difficult Work, which being very great, took up a large proportion of his Time, to the no fmall hindrance of his Philofophical Difquifitions.

In this Employment he got the moft part of that Eftate he died poffeffed of, as was evident by a large Iron Cheft of Money found after his Death, which had been lock'd down with the Key in it, with a date of the Time, by which it appear'd to have been fo fhut up for above thirty Years : In this was contain'd the greateft part of what he left behind him, which was to the value of many thoufands in Gold and Silver. That he might by this place juftly acquire a confiderable Eftate, I think cannot be deny'd, every particular Perfon after the Fire being in hafte to have his concerns expedited; fo that as I have been inform'd he had no Reft early and late from Perfons foliciting to have their Grounds fet out, which, without any Fraud or Injuftice, deferv'd a due recompence in fo fatiguing an Employ.

Oct. 31. 1666. He fhew'd his inclineing *Pendulum*, with the ufes thereof, to regulate the motions of a Clock as exactly as a long one.

On the 9th of *Jan.* 166⅚. he was order'd to profecute his Obfervations of the Earth's *Paralax* formerly by him propos'd : A large Account of the Refult of his Obfervations therein were after Printed in his *Attempt to prove the motion of the Earth* 1674, being the firft of his *Cutlerian* Lectures Publifh'd.

On the 6th of *Feb.* following, he produc'd his new *Lamp* contriv'd fo as to fupply the Oil in equal quantity as it waftes, that it may never rife too much or too little, the farther Defcription and Explication of which, with many curious Remarks, were Publifh d 1677. and intitl'd *Lampas*, or *Defcriptions of fome Improvements of Lamps and Water-poifes*, &c.

Feb. the 28th. He firft produc'd his *Reflecting Telefcope*, which is defcrib'd with the Reafon of the Principle, with fome other Inftruments in his Treatife of *Helioscopes*, Printed 1676.

On the 17th of *June* 1667. and afterwards he read large Difcourfes of the Caufes, Powers and Effects of *Earthquakes*, affirming the great Hills and Mountains in the World to have been raifed by them, of which Subject he at feveral times afterwards made very many Difcourfes and Lectures, the moft part of which are collected together in this Volume, beginning at Page 279.

In *July* 1667. he try'd several Experiments upon himself in an *exhausted Receiver*, big enough to contain a Man, I think the only Experiment of that kind ever try'd.

At this time he contriv'd a *Micrometer* of less Charge and Difficulty than that invented by Mr. *Gascoin* with Screws; this, I suppose, is Publish'd in this Volume, Page 498.

Dec. 26. 1667. He brought in a farther Description of a *Sea Barometer*.

Jan. the 16th 166⅞. he produc'd 'his new Contrivance of promoting the Vibrations of Pendules, so as to prevent all Checks, which 'he affirmed had not been provided against by any Contrivance to 'that time.

Apr. 9. 1668. He produc'd two Instruments to promote the sense of Hearing.

May the 14th He shew'd an Experiment of the penetration of Liquors in Oil of Vitriol and fair Water.

About this time he produc'd many other Experiments and Inventions, which I omit, and shall only observe, that there being several Discourses about the measuring a of Degree of the Earth, he propos'd divers Methods of performing it, and invented several Instruments; and as is enter'd in the Journal, *Oct.* 28. 1669. Mr. *Hooke* was of Opinion, *That one of the exactest ways of measuring, was by making accurate Observations of the Heavens to a second, by a Perpendicular Tube, and then to take exact distances by Angles to a second also*, which I take to be the Method observ'd by the *French* not long after, as may be seen by a particular Treatise of it Publish'd by Monsieur *Picart*, as likewise by what *Duhamel* says in his History of that Society, p. 98. to which the curious are refer'd. I find also by some Notices and loose Papers of our Curator, that he invented a sort of travelling Calesh for this purpose, which should describe upon a Paper, not only the Mensuration of the way gone over, but the several Ascents and Descents, together with the turnings and windings of the Calesh, or the Points of the Compass upon which the Person travell'd with other Contrivances, which I know not by what misfortune, were never put in practise. There were also other Methods for measuring a Degree propos'd to be made in St. *James*'s Park on the Canal, which also had the like fate of not being prosecuted.

In *Jan* 166⁹⁄₀. He first propos'd a drop of Mercury for an universal Standard, which is more at large describ'd, Page 472. of the following Volume. And in *April* shew'd an Experiment with a solution of Copper to represent the appearance of Clouds and other aerial Meteors, by dropping into it several Salts, *&c.* and at the same time shew'd the use of introducing the Species into a dark Room for Painting, and contriv'd a Box for that purpose, which is here Printed.

In *March* 1671. 'he shew'd several Experiments to explain the 'Nature and Cause of *Gravity:* Particularly on the 9th an Ex- 'periment was made, in which some Flower put into a void shal- 'low Glass with a large sloping brim, and a pretty tall Foot was 'made to rise and run over like a fluid, by the knocking on the 'edge of the Glass, and also by the forceably moving of ones Fin- 'ger round the edge of the same. Leaden Bullets also being put 'into this Glass, did, by knocking, move it like a fluid.----This 'was

' was propos'd to confider what might be the caufe of Gravity,
' and fuggeft an Hypothefis to explicate the motion of Gravity
' by, &c.

Thefe, and feveral other Experiments, he fhew'd to explain Natural Bodies and Actions, in fome of which I have been the more particular out of a hope thefe hints may excite fome inquifitive Perfon to proceed farther in fuch Inquiries.

This fame Year feveral Difcourfes and Papers paft between the Learned Mr. *Newton* and Mr. *Hooke* concerning a new Theory of Light and Colours, which being now fo generally known, I fhall not farther infift on.

About this time he made a Propofition for perfecting all forts of Optick-glaffes, the fecret of which was deliver'd in an Anagram to the Prefident my Lord *Brouncher*.

Not long after this time began that unhappy Difpute between Monfieur *Hevelius* and *Hooke* concerning the preference of Plain and Telefcopical Sights for Aftronomical Inftruments, which, as I can collect, was thus occafion'd. Mr. *Hooke*, by means of Mr. *Oldenburgh*, had recommended to Monfieur *Hevelius* the Application of Telefcopick Sights to his exquifitely contriv'd and elobrated Inftruments, affirming that by them an Angle might be taken to a much greater nicenefs than with plain Sights, and gave them a fhort, but as he thought a fufficient information of the manner of applying them to the Inftrument, and intimated that if any thing requir'd a farther Explication, he was ready to give it. Neverthelefs *Hevelius* could not be prevail'd with to make ufe of them, whether he thought himfelf too experienc'd to be inform'd by a young Aftronomer, as he reckon'd *Hooke*, or whether having made fo many Obfervations with plain Sights, he was unwilling to alter his Method leaft he might bring their exactnefs into Queftion, or whether being by long practice accuftom'd to the ufe of them, and not thoroughly apprehending the ufe of the other, nor well underftanding the difference, as Mr. *Molineux* has obferv'd in his Opticks, is indeed uncertain. *The Difpute with Hevelius.*

Not long after came out his curious and pompous Book of the firft part of his *Machina Cæleftis*; and *Hooke* took occafion in his *Cutlerian Lectures*, to read feveral Difcourfes upon that Book, and the Inftruments therein defcrib'd, which were Printed *Anno* 1674. under the Title of *Animadverfions upon Hevelius's Machina Cæleftis*.

In which Treatife vindicating fomewhat warmly the benefit of Telefcopick Sights and their preference, he chanc'd to let flip fome Expreffions, which, tho' poffibly ftrictly true, could yet never be digefted by *Hevelius*.

Several Years after *Hevelius* Publifh'd his *Annus Climactericus*, which again reviv'd the Difpute, and caus'd feveral Learned Men to intereft themfelves in the Controverfy. This, I think, is the true Hiftory of the Matter. I fhall here fubjoin what *Hooke* wrote himfelf in Anfwer to what fome Perfons thought fit to write upon this Subject, as I found them drawn up by himfelf in a Paper or two among his Manufcripts; for the better underftanding of which, I fhall obferve, Firft, That *Hevelius* having fent his *Annus Climactericus* to the R O Y A L S O C I E T Y, Dr. *Wallis* was defir'd to give an account of it, which is Printed in the *Philofophical Tranfactions* N°. 175. p. 1162. in which the Dr. having ufed fome Expreffions which

Hooke

Hooke thought reflected too feverely upon him; and Mr. *Molineux* not long after fending a Letter to the fame purpofe, he wrote his own Vindication almoft verbatim, as I have here Printed it, at leaft nothing material is omitted or added.

' There having been lately read in a Meeting of this Honour-
' able *Society* a Letter from Mr. *Molineux* containing feveral Re-
' flections that concern'd me, which, without fome fatisfactory an-
' fwer, muft needs make me fuffer in the Opinion of thofe who
' have not truly underftood the Matter in Controverfy, and the
' high Efteem I have of the Juftice and Judgment of this Illuftri-
' ous Company, perfuades me the rather to make my Defence
' here.

' The Objections in the Letter were thefe.

' That if it be true which has been afferted, not only by fome
' celebrated Aftronomers, but chiefly by Mr. *Hooke* in his *Animad-*
' *verfions*, &c. the Indeavours of *Hevelius* will be fruftrated and his
' vaft Charges to no more purpofe than *Ticho*'s and all his fplendid
' *apparatus* but meer Lumber; for upon this Queftion as to plain
' Sights, the price of his Aftronomical Labours of his whole Life
' depends; but furely this were an Event highly deplorable, not
' only to the party himfelf immediately concern'd, but the whole
' *Refpublica Literaria.*

Secondly, Mention is made of the flightnefs and fmallnefs of
' what I had publifh'd, which was only a Pamphlet, that afferted,
' that notwithftanding all this, yet meerly for want of Telefcopick
' Sights and fome new kind of invented Divifions on Mr. *Hevelius*'s
' Inftruments, I went fo far as to doubt whether his Obfervations
' could be true, and always the fame to two or three Minutes, and
' that the whole import of it befides this, was nothing but the De-
' fcription of an Inftrument which he never heard was put in
' practice.

' The Third Objection againft me is that, tho' Monfieur *Heve-*
' *lius* had earneftly requefted from me, or any one elfe that had Te-
' lefcopick Inftruments, to fend him fome diftances of fixt Stars
' obferv'd by them, yet he could never be fo happy as to obtain a-
' ny from me, tho' afterwards he did from fome others, *&c.*

' Thefe, and fome other Difcourfes, fpread abroad tacitely infi-
' nuate, that the Publifhing thofe *Animadverfions* was a very ill
' Action, and that the Learned in general have receiv'd a great pre-
' judice thereby, it concerns me therefore to clear my felf of this
' Imputation: For Anfwer then I fay,

' Firft, If what I have Publifh'd in thofe *Animadverfions* be true
' and certain, then I defire to know whether it were better for the
' *Refpublica Literaria* to be acquainted with it, or to remain poffeft
' with the belief of fome Affertions of Monfieur *Hevelius*, which
' are really Miftakes (not to fay worfe) tho' poffibly till that time,
' wherein I publifh'd them, they were generally believ'd to be Truths,
' as he has taken a great deal of pains to induce a belief of, in the firft
' part of his *Machina Cæleftis*, from Page 293, to Page 300, which I
' the

' the rather mention, becaufe fome Perfons have thought and af-
' ferted, that I was the firft Aggreffor in Print, the contrary of
' which thofe fix Pages evince.

Secondly, ' Whether thofe deplorable Events of leffening the
' price of Monfieur *Hevelius*'s Works, if that were true, when
' put into the Ballance, will out-weigh the detecting a Miftake, or
' difcovery of a Truth in a matter of fo great Moment in Natu-
' ral Philofophy, as concerns the moft confiderable parts of Know-
' ledge in the Theory of the Univerfe, efpecially of Celeftial Bo-
' dies ; for if Truth be that which is moft prevalent with all Phi-
' lofophical Spirits againft any particular Intereft, then I hope I fhall
' prove I have not offended in that particular in my publication of
' thofe *Animadverfions*. And *Hevelius* himfelf was of the fame
' Mind, when at the fixty firft Page of his Preface he writes
' (fpeaking of his difparaging fome things of *Ticho Brahe*) *in hoc ne-*
' *gotio femper in cujufuis animo hærere debet. Amicus Plato, Amicus*
' *Ariftoteles, fed magis tamen amica veritas.* Nor do I find him fo
' fhy in proclaiming the Miftakes of *Ticho*'s Obfervations, when it
' made for his own Reputation ; for in the thirty fourth Page of his
' Preface he fays, that the greateft part of *Ticho*'s Obfervations dif-
' fer'd from his own four, five, fix, and even ten Min. At the
' thirty ninth Page he fays, That of 780 in *Ticho*'s Catalogue there
' are but 260 which differ, not lefs than two Minutes ; but all the
' reft differ 3'. 5'. 10'. 20'. 30'. 40'. 45'. 50'. nay a whole Degree from
' the truth, and that fifteen differ above a Degree, and fome many
' more, even to eight Degrees in Longitude, and in Latitude to
' thirteen whole Degrees, fometimes in defect, fometimes in ex-
' cefs, yet for all this *Hevelius* would be thought highly to value
' *Ticho Brahe*, and not to have made any Reflections upon him.
' Nor has the detecting Miftakes even in Perfons of as great
' Fame been look'd upon fo ill a thing, but rather a meritorious
' Action, as might be inftanc'd in Dr. *Pell*'s fhort Anfwer in a ¼ of
' a Sheet of Paper to *Longomontanus* his Work, which had been the
' bufinefs of thirty Years. Another inftance may be of *Phocilides*
' upon *Lansbergius*, the learned *Savilian Aftronomick Profeffor* againft
' *Bulialdus*, &c. all which Authors were well efteem'd for their de-
' tecting Miftakes, and difcovering Truth. And as for any difre-
' fpectful or undervaluing Sentiments I had of *Hevelius* or his Per-
' formances, I hope what I have printed in my *Admadverfions* will
' prevail with the unprejudiced to believe the contrary ; where I P. 43. & 44.
' fay, *That I would not be underftood by thefe Animadverfions to under-*
' *value the Works and Performances of a Perfon fo highly meriting the*
' *Thanks of the Learned World for his great Expence and vaft Pains, in*
' *performing a Work fo highly ufeful to Aftronomy and Navigation, that*
' *I did not in the leaft doubt but that it would be a Work of perpetual*
' *Efteem, and much preferrable to any thing of the like kind yet done in the*
' *World ; and that he had gone as far as was poffible for humane Induftry*
' *to go with Inftruments of that kind, which were as compleat and exact*
' *as Inftruments with plain Sights could be made ; and that he had calcu-*
' *lated with all imaginable care and skill, and deliver'd them with the like*
' *Candor and Integrity : But yet that it was my Opinion, that this ought*
' *not to difcourage others from making ufe of Telefcope-fights, and to make*
' *better Obfervations with Inftruments by that means more exact.*

f   ' This

‘ This I hope may Apologize for my writing those *Animadverfions.*

‘ But in the next place I muft make fome defence for what is
‘ faid in them. This Gentleman fays I went fo far as to doubt
‘ whether *Hevelius*'s Obfervations could be made true and always
‘ the fame to two or three Minutes, I wifh the place had been quo-
‘ ted where I faid fo, fince I only faid that I believ'd it impoffible
‘ for any one to diftinguifh with common Sights any diftance in
‘ the Heavens to lefs than half a Minute, and very few to a Mi-
‘ nute, and I am apt to believe there may be fome inftances even
‘ in *Hevelius*'s Catalogue that will verify this Affertion.

*Animadverfi-
ons, Pag.* 7.

‘ And for any other Affertion, which is *really mine* in that Trea-
‘ tife, I do not doubt of fatisfying any unprejudiced Perfon by ex-
‘ periment, if defir'd, which I fay, is *really my Affertion* ; for by
‘ miftake or otherwife, fome things have been fathered upon me
‘ I never faid, *viz.* that I fhould affert, *That an Inftrument of a fpan*
‘ *Radius might be made, that fhould perform Obfervations fixty times more*
‘ *accurate than could be done with his beft Inftruments :* Which Affer-
‘ tion is none of mine, and whoever have fpread thefe Falfities,
‘ might have found better Employment. I fay indeed, that a very
‘ fmall Inftrument, curioufly made, exactly divided and inftructed
‘ with Telefcope-Sights will perform much better in all Obferva-
‘ tions (except of the Sun) than the largeft Inftrument without
‘ fuch Sights, for the reafon before alledged from the defect in our
‘ Eyes which cannot diftinguifh an Angle lefs than half a Minute,
‘ nor is this a defect in my own Eyes only (as *Hevelius* fomewhere feems
‘ to hint) for the Experiment may eafily be try'd with the beft Eyes.

‘ Nor is it any difparagement to *Hevelius*'s Obfervations to com-
‘ pare them with *Ticho Brahe*'s, tho' I fhould have fuppos'd them
‘ but of equal value, fince the mere repeating of his Obfervations
‘ would be of great ufe in Aftronomy, thefe being almoft one hun-
‘ dred Years after his; for we muft by fuch comparifons judge
‘ of many confiderable inquiries concerning Celeftial Bodies, which
‘ cannot by other means be fo well detected, for which I refer to
‘ the feventy fixth Page of my *Animadverfions*, viz. to know whe-
‘ ther thofe Celeftial Bodies which are fuppos'd fo fixt, do not vary
‘ their Pofitions to each other, and alfo their Magnitudes, which I
‘ had good grounds to believe.

‘ As to the Objection that my Pamphlet contain'd *little befides the*
‘ *Defcription of an Inftrument never put in practice.* I conceive there
‘ may be feveral Miftakes; for I am of Opinion, upon perufal there
‘ will be fomewhat elfe in that Treatife worth confideration. Next
‘ that there has been Inftruments made, perfected and ufed after
‘ that way, by Sir *Jonas More*, by Mr. *Gregory* in *Scotland*, by Mr.
‘ *Halley*, and many others, and I believe very few Aftronomical In-
‘ ftruments fince have been made with plain Sights; and if the
‘ multitude of Authorities were neceffary, I could produce *Auzout*,
‘ *Picart, Mariot, Romer, De la Hire, Montanari, Gotignies*, and o-
‘ thers, not to name thofe of our own Nation.

‘ As to my not returning the Obfervations of certain diftances
‘ of Stars, which *Hevelius* defir'd, 'tis fufficiently known what in-
‘ conveniences we lay under in this place after the Fire of *London*,
‘ and had I found conveniences, yet the unkind Reception thofe
‘ things found, which I fent him, was enough to deter me from
‘ fuch a Compliance ; tho' he was fenfible how I had often been rea-

‘ dy

' dy to gratify his Curiofity in many other particulars.   But when
' his *Machina Cælestis* was publifh'd, I was oblig'd to write thofe *A-*
' *nimadverfions*, in which I hope all unprejudic'd Readers will juftify
' my proceedure, at leaft I am ready to prove any thing I have
' therein afferted.

I have been the larger in the Account of this Controverfy that
the intelligent Reader may make the better judgment thereof, it
being the moft confiderable he ever had with any Perfon, and fhall
wave the giving my Opinion of it.

In 1674. he fhew'd an Engine or Inftrument to perform any A-
rithmetical Operation, but the more particular account of this and
other Inftruments not defcrib'd in this Volume, I fhall referve for
another opportunity.

About the latter end of the fame Year the ROYAL SOCIETY
kept their Weekly Meeting at *Grefham College* again, and on the fifteenth of *Jan.* following he fhew'd a way to determine how fmall
an Angle the unaffifted Eye is able to difcern, by which it was found,
that none of the Perfons Eyes prefent could obferve a much lefs Angle than of a Minute; for a more ample account of which the Reader is referr'd to the eighth Page of his *Animadverfions*.

From this time many Magnetical Experiments were made by
him, and on the nineteenth of *March* he propos'd a Theory of the
variation, the fubftance of which was this, ' That the Magnet
' hath its peculiar Poles diftant ten Degrees from the Poles of the
' Earth, about which they move fo as to make a Revolution in
' three hundred and feventy Years, whence the variation hath al-
' tered of late about ten or eleven Minutes every Year, and will
' probably continue fo to do for fome time, till it begins to grow
' flower and flower, and will at length be Stationary and Retro-
' grade, and in probability may return; but whether it will be fo or
' not Time muft fhew.   At the fame time he propos'd the making
' of a very eafy and nice Inftrument to obferve the variation of the
' variations of the Needle in different parts of the World.

What this Inftrument was is not eafy now to be determin'd, but
the Reader will find the Figure of an Inftrument fomething to this
purpofe at Page 486.

On the 4th of *Feb.* 167⅘. feveral Obfervations and Difcourfes
having been made about the Structure of the Mufcles of Animals,
Mr. *Hooke* faid, ' That his Obfervation was, that the flefhy part of
' a Mufcle confifted of an infinite number of exceeding fmall round
' Pipes, extended between the two tendons of the Mufcles, and
' feem'd to end in them.   Which Tendons, in the Mufcles of Beef
' boyl'd would be eafily ftript off from thofe Pipes, and fo leave the
' round ends of thofe Pipes very diftinct and vifible :   He faid that
' the reafon of the moving of a Mufcle might be from the filling
' or emptying of thofe Pipes, whofe fides feem'd to be flexible like
' thofe of a Gut.   He intimated alfo, that he knew a way of mak-
' ing fuccedaneous Mufcles for a Man to fupply the defect of his
' Mufcles for flying, and give one Man the ftrength of ten or
' twenty, if required.

' *March* the 18th 167⅘. he made an Experiment of a new proper-
' ty of Light, having before read fome Difcourfes upon that Sub-
' ject.   This Experiment is to be feen Page 186 of this Book, to
which the Reader is referr'd for a more full account.

                                                                    Mr.

Mr. *Oldenburgh*, the then Secretary, dying in the time of the Societies Recefs, 1677. Mr. *Hooke* was defir'd to take his place, and take the Minutes of what confiderable Matters paft, which he did on the twenty fifth of *October* 1677. and the fame day produc'd his Water-poife and fhew'd the nicety thereof. The Defcription of this is in the *Philof. Tranfact.* N°. 197. p. 623. There were afterwards fome other Hydroftatical Inftruments produc'd, as likewife many Improvements of the double and fingle Microfcopes, with the ufe of fmall glafs Canes and other Contrivances, by which he verify'd Monfieur *Leuenhook*'s Obfervations; thefe, with feveral others, I omit, they not being fo intelligible without Schemes.

From that time he officiated in that Place, as well as his Curatorfhip, fhewing feveral Experiments and Inftruments in order to explain the Gravitation and Alterations in the Air by Vapours, &c. Contriving an Air-poife to fhew the different fpecifick Gravity of the Air by a large thin ball of Glafs counter-poifed.

In *Feb.* 167⅞. upon an account of Monfieur *Gallet*'s Obfervation of the Oval Figure of *Mercury* in the Sun, he gave feveral reafons for the prolated Oval Figure of the Planets, fome of which are Printed in this Volume, Page 355. with a Demonftration thereof, ' and faid, ' That all Fluids on the Surface would run into that ' Shape, and that 'twas not improbable but that the Water here ' about the Earth might do fo by the influence of the diurnal Mo- ' tion of the Earth, which compounded with that of the Moon, he ' conceiv'd was the caufe of the Tides.

From this time he made Microfcopal Obfervations on *Animalcules* in Peper-water, and other Seeds fteeped in Water, confirming Monfieur *Leuenhook*'s Affertions, and propos'd fome Improvements of Microfcopes.

Some propofals were made by him of Inftruments more accurate than thofe formerly invented for founding the Seas depth, bringing up Water, or other Subftances from the bottom, or any affigned depth which were fome Years after more perfected.

Apr. 25. 1678. he fhew'd an Experiment farther to explain the action of a Mufcle, ' which was by a Chain of fmall Bladders fa- ' ftened together, fo as by blowing into one Pipe, the whole might ' be fuccefively fill'd, and by that means contracted, fuppofing the ' Fibres of the Mufcles which feem'd like a Necklace of Pearl in ' the Microfcope, might be fill'd with a very agill Matter, which ' he thought moft likely to be Air, which being included in fo thin ' Skins, was eafily wrought upon by Heat, Cold, or the acting ' Properties of the Liquors that pafs between them, and fo perform ' the lengthening and contracting of the Mufcles.

Aug. 1678. he read feveral Difcourfes, and fhew'd Experiments in order to confirm his Theory of Springs and fpringy Bodies, which are publifh'd in his Treatife *de Potentia reftitutiva* the fame Year, the fum of which Hypothefis is comprized in a Cypher at the end of his Defcription of Heliofcopes, being the third of a Decimate of Inventions which he there mentions he was Mafter of, fome of which he difcover'd himfelf, affirming he had a Centry of the like ufeful Inventions: Others of them I have had the luck to find out, which I fhall take this opportunity of mentioning. I fhall firft tranfcribe what he fays of them, and then add the deciphering of them.

The

Pag. 31.

The second Invention, which is the first Cypher, is thus worded.

' The true Mathematical and Mechanical Form of all manner of
' Arches for building with the true butment neceſſary to each of
' them, a Problem which no Architectonick Writer hath ever yet
' attempted, much leſs perform'd. ab, ccc, dd, eeeee, f, gg, iiiiiiii, ll,
' mmmm, nnnnn, oo, p, rr, sss, tttttt, uuuuuuuu, x, which deci-
' phered is theſe words, *Ut pendet continuum flexile, ſic ſtabit conti-*
' *guum rigidum inverſum,* which is the *Linea Catenaria.*

The third is his Theory of Springineſs in theſe Letters, ce, iii, no,
sss, tt, uu, which is *Ut Tenſio ſic vis* ; this is the principle of his Theory of Springs.

' The ninth, which is the next Cypher, is concerning a new
' ſort of Philoſophical Scales of great uſe in Experimental Philo-
' ſophy, cde, ii, nn, oo, p, sss, tt, uu, *Ut Pondus ſic Tenſio.*

The laſt is mention'd as a very extraordinary invention in Mechanicks above the Chimeras of perpetual motions for ſeveral uſes,
aa, æ, b, cc, dd, eeeeee, g, iii, l, mmm, nn, oo, pp, q, rrrr, s, ttt, uuuuu.
Pondere premit aer vacuum quod ab igne relictum eſt. This is one of
the Principles upon which Mr. *Savery*'s late invented Engine for
raiſing Water is founded. See *Lexicon Technicum* under Engine.

On the 29th of *Aug.* 1678. his Grace the Duke of *Norfolke* having
given the *Arundelian* Library to the ROYAL SOCIETY, Mr.
Hooke was order'd to be Aſſiſtant in making a Catalogue thereof, and
removing it to *Greſham College.*

In the beginning of the Year 1679. and afterwards, ſeveral Experiments were repeated to examine the uſe of the Air in Reſpiration by including Animals in common rarify'd and condenſed Air,
as likewiſe concerning the neceſſity of the Air to maintain Fire, to
illuſtrate his Theory of Fire farther, *viz.* ' That Air is a *Menſtruum*
' that diſſolves all Sulphureous Bodies by burning, and that without
' Air no ſuch diſſolution will follow, tho' the heat apply'd be ne-
' ver ſo great, which was try'd particularly by a Charcoal encloſ-
' ed in an Iron Caſe with a Screw-ſtopper, which tho' violently
' heated yet the Cole was not burnt nor waſted when taken out.

Some Experiments were made to explain the different Gravitation of the Air, and to ſhew that Vapours preſs only according to
their own Gravity, and not according to the ſpace they take up in
the Atmoſphere.

Some Contrivances were ſhewn by him to be added to the Weather-Clock, as a Hygroſcope, a contrivance to meaſure the quantity of Rain, Snow, or Hail fallen in a certain time ; which Engine was ſoon after perfected in all its parts, and ſet up in the Repoſitory.

In *July* 1679. he read a Diſcourſe concerning a way to help ſhor-
ted Sighted Perſons, which he call'd *Myopibus Invamen* ; this is Printed in his third Collection, p. 59. ' At the ſame time he gave his
' Thoughts of the reaſon of the different apparent Magnitude of
' the Sun and Moon in the Meridian and near the Horizon, which
' he ſuppos'd to be a deception of the Eye as judging them when near
' the Horizon, to be farther off than when nearer the Zenith, for
' that he ſaid the Diameters meaſur'd were really the ſame in both
' places, or rather ſomething leſs in the Horizon than in the Zenith,
' being remov'd a Semidiameter of the Earth farther off.

Experiments

Experiments were made by him of the mixtures of Metals, particularly of Copper and Tin, in which there was obſerv'd a real Penetration, the *Compoſitum* being ſpecifically heavier than either of the Metals before mixture; for whereas Copper is to Water as 8 ½ to 1. and Tin to Water as 7 $\frac{17}{10}$ to 1. the compoſitum was to Water as 8 ¾ to 1.

'In *December*, the ſame Year, an Experiment being ſuggeſted to
'try whether the Earth mov'd with a diurnal motion or not, by the
'fall of a Body from a conſiderable height, alledging it would fall to
'the Eaſt of true Perpendicular: Mr. *Hooke* read a Diſcourſe up-
'on that Subject, wherein he explain'd what the Line deſcrib'd by
'a falling Body muſt be, ſuppos'd to be mov'd circularly by the di-
'urnal motion of the Earth, and perpendicularly by the power of
'Gravity, and ſhew'd it would not be a Spiral Line, but an Ex-
'centrical-Elliptoeid, ſuppoſing no reſiſtance in the *medium*, but ſup-
'poſing a Reſiſtance, it would be an Excentric-Ellipti-Spiral,
'which after many Revolutions, would reſt in the Center at laſt;
'that the fall of the Body would not be directly Eaſt, but to the
'South-Eaſt, and more to the South than the Eaſt. This was try'd,
'in which the Ball was ſtill found to fall to the South-Eaſt.

The remainder of this Year was ſpent in making Experiments of the mixture of ſeveral Metals, among the reſt Mr. *Hooke* took notice in the mixture of Copper and Tin of ſeveral particulars, as Firſt, 'That the colour of the Copper was quite deſtroy'd, it ap-
'pearing much of the colour of Iron Poliſh'd. Secondly, That
'the Compoſition, tho' made of two very malleable Metals, was
'yet very brittle and friable. Thirdly, That it bore a pretty good
'Poliſh and Reflection. Fourthly, That tho' Copper is exceeding
'hard to be melted, yet the mixture melted very eaſily. Fifthly,
'That viewing the Poliſh'd Surface with a Microſcope, he found
'it very full of very ſmall holes or blebs in the Metal.

In *April* 1680. he produc'd a new invented Level.

In *May* he read a Paper of Obſervations upon an unuſual ſort of Hail-ſtones that fell on the 18th. the ſum of which was to this pur-poſe. About ten a Clock in the Morning it grew very dark and Thundered much, and near to the S. E. when ſoon after the Hail fell from the ſize of Piſtol-Bullets to the bigneſs of Pullets Eggs, the ſmaller were white like Chalk, and pretty round, the larger Conical or Oval, upon breaking them they were found to be made of ſeveral Orbs, encompaſſing one another; ſeveral had a white Center or Nucleus in the middle, which in others was more toward one ſide; they that exceeded in bigneſs were made by an additional accretion of tranſparent Icecles, radiating from the white Ball in the middle; ſome of theſe ſtood in diſtinct tranſpa-rent Rays, in others the Interſtices were fill'd up between the Rays with a white opaque Concretion: The lower part of theſe Stones were more flat and like a Turnip, the radiations appearing more towards the upper ſide; the ſides and top were more rough, and the ends of the Stiriæ were prominent. Before they fell a great noiſe was heard in the Sky: From the manner of their Figure Mr. *Hooke* conceiv'd their accretion was made by a congelation of Wa-ter as they fell; that the Globe in the middle about the bigneſs of a Pea, was the firſt drop that concreted into Hail, the Coats being added to it as it paſt through the watry Clouds, of which ſome

were

were white, some pellucid, according to the different coldness of the Regions they past through.

July 8th 1680. upon a Debate concerning the Experiment of my Lord *Bacon*'s of the internal motion of Bodies, Mr. *Hooke* related, ' That he had observ'd that the motion of the Glass, fill'd with ' Water, was observ'd to be vibrative, perpendicular to the Sur- ' face of the Glass, and that the Circular Figure chang'd into an ' Oval one way, and that the Reciprocation presently changed it ' into an Oval the other way, which he discover'd by the motion ' of the Undulation or rising of the Water in the Glass, which was ' observ'd to be in four places of the Surface in a square posture, ' the same Glass being struck on the edge with a Viol-bow, this ' square Undulation was very plain, and there was also discover'd ' another Undulation, by which the Water was observ'd to rise in ' six places like an Hexagon, and upon farther trials also in eight ' places like an Octagon; each of these gave their particular and ' distinct Sounds or Notes, the 4 and 8 were Octaves, and the 6 and ' 4 were Fifths, *&c.*

In *November* 1680. he read some Observations he had made of a *Comet* then appearing, which, with other Observations and Dis- courses of other Comets are publish'd in this Volume under that Title, beginning at Page 194.

And about this time Mr. *Hooke* shew'd a Contrivance by a *Statera* to examine the attractive power of the Magnet at several distances, and made many Experiments therewith.

In *April* 1681. and afterwards, he read his Lectures of *Light* and *Luminous* Bodies, which are here collected together, and begin at Page 71.

In *July* the same Year he shew'd a way of making *Musical and o- ther Sounds*, by the striking of the Teeth of several Brass Wheels, proportionally cut as to their numbers, and turned very fast round, in which it was observable, that the equal or proportional stroaks of the Teeth, that is, 2 to 1, 4 to 3, *&c.* made the Musical Notes, but the unequal stroaks of the Teeth more answer'd the sound of the Voice in speaking.

November following he mention'd a new Sea-Quadrant for mak- ing Observations more accurate than could be done by any Instru- ment yet known; this is what the Reader will find towards the end of this Volume: At the same time he first mention'd his new Compasses for describing all sorts of Spirals, as likewise of the Rumb-lines, which Instrument I also have indeavour'd to retrieve from being lost.

Soon after this he shew'd and demonstrated a very expeditious way of drawing the Rumb-lines exactly true upon a Globe, by an Instrument grounded upon the same Principle with the other. He shew'd also a very easy way of finding all the possible *foci* of Rays refracted by a *Plano-Spherical Lens*, whereof the Convex side was turn'd toward the *focus*, as also the quantity of Rays that would pass thro' such a Glass, whose Convexity was of the full bigness of a Hemisphere.

' In *Jan.* 168$\frac{1}{2}$. he shew'd an Instrument to describe all sorts of ' *Helixes* upon a Cone, by which he affirm'd to be able to divide any ' given length, tho' very short, into almost any assignable number ' of given parts, as suppose an Inch into 100000 equal parts; this

' he

' he conceiv'd very useful for perfecting Aftronomical and Geogra-
' phical Inftruments. And at the next Meeting he produc'd ano-
' ther Inftrument, by which he defcrib'd a certain Curve Line,
' which may be call'd an *Invented Parabola,* or *Parabolical-Hyperbo-*
' *la,* having thefe Proprieties, that it is infinite both ways, and
' hath two *Afymptotes* as an *Hyperbola,* &c. A third Inftrument
' was alfo fhew'd for exactly defcribing the *Spiral* of *Archimedes* by
' a new Propriety thereof, and that as eafily and truly as a Circle,
' whereby not only any given Arch might be divided into any
' number of equal parts, but a ftrait Line given equal to the Cir-
' cumference of a Circle.

' *March* the firft, he fhew'd a way, by the fame Inftrument, of
' defcribing all varieties of Ellipfes.

In the fame Year he read the remainder of his Difcourfes of *Light,*
which are in the following Volume Printed, and particularly that
Lecture explicating the Memory, and how we come by the notion
of Time.

From this time, or rather fomething before, he began to be more
referv'd than he had been fo.merly, fo that altho' he often made
Experiments, and fhew'd new Inftruments and Inventions, and
read his *Cutlerian* Lectures, yet he feldom left any full Account of
them to be enter'd, defigning, as he faid, to fit them himfelf for
the Prefs, and then make them publick, which he never perform'd.
This is the reafon that I am oblig'd to be the fhorter in the remaining part of his Life; and fhall only touch upon fome few of his Performances, fince the bare nameing of them, or mentioning their
Titles, will but create an uneafy Curiofity in the Reader without
any fatisfaction.

Several of thefe Lectures and Difcourfes I have indeavour'd to
preferve from being loft, by Publifhing them in this Book, and fome
Inftruments are there defcrib'd.

In the beginning of the Year 1687. his Brothers Daughter, Mrs.
Grace Hooke dy'd, who had liv'd with him feveral Years, the concern for whofe Death he hardly ever wore off, being obferv'd from
that time to grow lefs active, more Melancholly and Cynical.

On the fifth of *May* he read a Lecture of the unequal *diurnal* motion of the Earth, which the Reader may find in this Book

In *July* he fhew'd an Experiment of the communication of Motion by a Packthread extended a very confiderable length, and, after running over a Pulley, brought back to the place, near to which
the other end was faftened, and it was found that any addition of
Weight or Motion given to the one end, would be immediately
fenfible at the other end of the String, tho' it muft pafs in going and
returning fo great a length; there were other ways fhewn of communicating motion, as by a long Cane fufpended by Strings, or by
Wires diftended a great length; in which it was obfervable, that
the found was propagated inftantaneoufly, even as quick as the motion of Light, the found convey'd by the Air coming a confiderable
time after that by the Wire.

A great part of the next Year he was very weak and ill, being
often troubl'd with Head-achs, Giddinefs and Fainting, and with a
general decay all over, which hinder'd his Philofophical Studies,
yet ftill he read fome Lectures whenever he was able. At the fame
time a Chancery-Suit, which he was forc'd to have with Sir *John*
                                                              Cutler

Cutler for his yearly Salary, made him very uneafy, the trouble of which increas'd his Illnefs.

But on the 20th of *June* he read a farther Defcription concerning feveral ways of making a portable *Sea-Barometer*, with the great ufes thereof in foretelling changes of the Weather and Storms.

From this time, for fome Years, I find but little done by him, except his reading the Lectures founded by Sir *John Cutler*, feveral of which are here Printed, to which the curious are referr'd : Of thefe he read in *Dec.* 1691. feveral relating to improvements of founding Inftruments which he call'd *Nuntii inanimati ad fundum Abyffi emiffarii*. Having receiv'd a warrant from Dr. *Tillotfon* the Arch-bifhop of *Canterbury*, for a *Degree of Dr. of Phyfick*, he went on the 7th of *Dec.* the fame Year, and took the Oaths before Sir *Charles Hedges* in *Doctors Commons*.

About this time he was employ'd about the contriving and furveying the Hofpital ftanding near *Hoxton*, given by the Will of Alderman *Ask*, a Building that few will judge any difreputation to the Contriver, for the due proportion of its Parts, and Beauty of the whole. I have heard indeed that Dr. *Hooke* has been blam'd for exceeding the Sum at firft propos'd to be expended thereon ; and once difcourfing with him upon that Subject, he own'd to me that it had far exceeded the firft Eftimate he had given in of the Charges, but not by this Fault or Miftake, but partly by new additions and alterations of the firft Defign, and chiefly by his not procuring and agreeing with the Workmen himfelf, which if he had done, as he faid, he would have ingag'd it fhould have come to little or no more than his firft propos'd Sum. He alfo propos'd that there might be inftituted in that place, a *Mathematical*-School for Boys to be inftructed in the Principles of *Aftronomy* and *Navigation*, which at firft was well approv'd of by the Perfons concern'd in the Management of that Affair.

On *Thurfday* the 8th of *Sep.* 1692. he fets down an Earthquake to be obferv'd by himfelf exactly 55 Min. paft one a Clock p. m. he notes that there was no Wind but Rain all Day. It was remarkable that this Earthquake was felt at the fame time not only in moft parts of *England*, but alfo in feveral parts of *Germany*.

This Year he read a curious Difcourfe defcribing the Tower of *Babel* or *Belus*. The Year following he read feveral Lectures about Earthquakes, and an Explication of *Ovid's Metamorphofis*, of which it is needlefs to mention the Contents, or the Times, the Dates of moft of them being affixt to them in the following Book, they begin at Page

On the 18th of *July* 1696. being his Birth Day, his Chancery-Suit for Sir *John Cutler*'s Salary, was determin'd for him, to his great fatisfaction, which had made him very uneafy for feveral Years. In his Diary he fhews his fenfe of it in thefe Terms DOMSHLGISS: A. which I read thus *Deo Opt. Max. fummus Honor, Gloria in fecula fecularum, Amen. I was Born on this Day of* July 1635. *and* GOD *has given me a new Birth, may I never forget his Mercies to me ; whilft he gives me Breath may I praife him.*

March the 5th 169⅞. he read a Lecture about the prolated Spheroedical Figure of the Sun, and other *Phænomena* thereof, of the *Maculæ* and *Faculæ*, &c. of making a Heliofcope by four reflex Planes in a twenty four Foot Tube, or a Telefcope for Planets and

fix'd Stars, by two Reflexions in a Tube of forty Foot with Monfieur *Huygens* 120 Foot Glafs, which was well lik'd of.

June 27. 1698. he read a Lecture upon *Huygen's Cofmotheoros*, and
fhew'd a Module of *Saturn* and his Ring.

Thus I have mention'd fome of his Performances, in the latter of
which I have been the more fuccinct, having exceeded the bounds I
at firft intended in the Accounts of the former. It muft be confef-
fed that the later part of his Life was nothing near fo fruitful of
Inventions as the former; tho' it is certain he had a defign to repeat
the moft part of his Experiments, and finifh the Accounts, Obfervations and Deductions from them, and had an Order for the Societies bearing the Charge thereof, in *June* 1696. when he propos'd
likewife to perfect the Description of all the Inftruments he had at
any time contriv'd; but by reafon of his increafing Weaknefs and
a general Decay, he was abfolutely unable to perform it, had he
defir'd it never fo much.

He had for feveral Years been often taken with a giddinefs in his
Head, and fometimes great Pain, little Appetite, and great faintnefs, that he was foon very much tir'd with walking, or any Exercife. About *July* 1697. he began to complain of the fwelling and
forenefs of his Legs, and was much over-run with the Scurvy, and
about the fame time being taken with a giddinefs he fell down Stairs
and cut his Head, bruis'd his Shoulder, and hurt his Ribbs, of
which he complain'd often to the laft. About *September* he thought
himfelf (as indeed all others did that faw him) that he could not laft
out a Month. About which time his Legs fwell'd more and more,
and not long after broke, and for want of due care Mortify'd a little before his Death. From this time he grew blinder and blinder,
that at laft he could neither fee to Read nor Write. Some of the
laft he wrote, I believe was on the 17th of *Dec.* 1702. when he fets
down a Memorandum about an Inftrument to take the Horizontal
Diameter of the Sun to the tenth of a fecond Minute, but difcovers not the way.

Thus he liv'd a dying Life for a confiderable time, being more
than a Year very infirm, and fuch as might be call'd Bed-rid for
the greateft part, tho' indeed he feldom all the time went to Bed
but kept in his Cloaths, and when over tir'd, lay down upon his
Bed in them, which doubtlefs brought feveral Inconveniences upon
him, fo that at laft his Diftempers of fhortnefs of Breath, Swelling,
partly of his Body, but moftly of his Legs, increafing, and at laft
Mortifying, as was obferv'd after his Death by their looking very
black, being emaciated to the utmoft, his Strength wholly worn
out, he dy'd on the third of *March* 170⅔. being 67 Years, 7 Months,
and 13 Days Old.

His Corps was decently and handfomely interr'd in the Church
of St. *Hellen* in *London*, all the Members of the ROYAL SOCIETY
then in Town attending his Body to the Grave, paying the Refpect
due to his extraordinary Merit.

His Character.   As to his Perfon he was but defpicable, being very crooked, tho' I
have heard from himfelf, and others, that he was ftrait till about 16
Years of Age when he firft grew awry, by frequent practicing,
turning with a Turn-Lath, and the like incurvating Exercifes, being
but of a thin weak habit of Body, which increas'd as he grew older,
fo as to be very remarkable at laft: This made him but low of Stature,

ture, tho' by his Limbs he fhou'd have been moderately tall. He was always very pale and lean, and laterly nothing but Skin and Bone, with a meagre Afpect, his Eyes grey and full, with a fharp ingenious Look whilft younger; his Nofe but thin, of a moderate height and length; his Mouth meanly wide, and upper Lip thin; his Chin fharp, and Forehead large; his Head of a middle fize. He wore his own Hair of a dark Brown colour, very long and hanging neglected over his Face uncut and lank, which about three Year before his Death he cut off, and wore a Periwig. He went ftooping and very faft (till his weaknefs a few Years before his Death hindred him) having but a light Body to carry, and a great deal of Spirits and Activity, efpecially in his Youth.

He was of an active, reftlefs, indefatigable Genius even almoft to the laft, and always flept little to his Death, feldom going to Sleep till two three, or four a Clock in the Morning, and feldomer to Bed, oftener continuing his Studies all Night, and taking a fhort Nap in the Day. His Temper was Melancholy, Miftruftful and Jealous, which more increas'd upon him with his Years. He was in the beginning of his being made known to the Learned, very communicative of his Philofophical Difcoveries and Inventions, till fome Accidents made him to a Crime clofe and referv'd. He laid the caufe upon fome Perfons, challenging his Difcoveries for their own, taking occafion from his Hints to perfect what he had not; which made him fay he would fuggeft nothing till he' had time to perfect it himfelf, which has been the Reafon that many things are loft, which he affirm'd he knew. He had a piercing Judgment into the Difpofitions of others, and would fometimes give fhrewd Gueffes and fmart Characters.

From his Youth he had been us'd to a Collegiate, or rather Monaftick Life, which might be fome reafon of his continuing to live fo like an Hermit or Cynick too penurioufly, when his Circumftances, as to Eftate, were very confiderable, fcarcely affording himfelf Neceffaries.

I indeed, as well as others, have heard him declare fometimes that he had a great Project in his Head as to the difpofal of the moft part of his Eftate for the advancement of Natural Knowledge, and to promote the Ends and Defigns for which the ROYAL SOCIETY was inftituted: To build an handfome Fabrick for the *Societies* ufe, with a Library, Refpofitary, Laboratory, and other Conveniencies for making Experiments, and to found and endow a perpetual *Phyfico-Mechanick Lecture* of the Nature of what himfelf read. But tho' he was often folicited by his Friends to put his Defigns down in Writing, and make his Will as to the difpofal of his Eftate to his own liking in the time of his Health; and after when himfelf, and all thought, his End drew near, yet he could never be prevail'd with to perfect it, ftill procraftinating it, till at laft this great Defign prov'd an airy Phantom and vanifh'd into nothing. Thus he dy'd at laft without any Will and Teftament that could be found. It is indeed but a melancholy Reflexion, that while fo many rich and great Men leave confiderable Sums for founding Hofpitals, and the the like pious Ufes, few fince Sir *Thomas Grefham* fhould do any thing of this kind for the promoting of Learning, which no doubt would be as much for the Good of the Nation, and Glory of God, as the other of releiving the Poor.

He

He always expreſt a great Veneration for the eternal and immenſe Cauſe of all Beings, as may be ſeen in very many Paſſages in
his Writings, and ſeldom receiv'd any remarkable Benefit from
God without thankfully ackowledging the Mercy ; never made a-
ny conſiderable diſcovery in Nature, invented any uſeful Contrivance, or found out any difficult Problem, without ſetting down
hisAcknowledgement to the Omnipotent Providence,as many places
in his Diary teſtify, frequently in theſe or the like words, abbreviated thus, D O M G M. and was a frequent ſtudier of the Holy Scripture in the Originals : If he was particular in ſome Matters, let
us leave him to the ſearcher of Hearts.

To conclude, all his Errors and Blemiſhes were more than made
amends for, by the Greatneſs and Extent of his natural and acquired Parts, and more than common, if not wonderful Sagacity, in
diving into the moſt hidden Secrets of Nature, and in contriving
proper Methods of forcing her to confeſs the Truth, by driving
and purſuing the *Proteus* thro' all her Changes, to her laſt and utmoſt Receſſes ; ſo that what *Ovid* ſaid of *Pythagoras* may not unfitly be apply'd to him.

Mente Deos adiit, & quæ Natura negavit
Viſibus humanis, oculis ea Pectoris hauſit.

Metamorph.
Lib, 15.

There needs no other Proof for this than the great number of
Experiments he made, with the Contrivances for them, amounting
to ſome hundreds ; his new and uſeful Inſtruments and Inventions,
which were numerous, his admirable Facility and Clearneſs, in explaining the Phænomena of Nature, and demonſtrating his Aſſertions ; his happy Talent in adapting Theories to the Phænomena obſerv'd, and contriving eaſy and plain, not pompous and amuſing
Experiments to back and prove thoſe Theories ; proceeding from Obſervations to Theories, and from Theories to farther trials, which
he often aſſerted to be the moſt proper method to ſucceed in the interpretation of Nature. For theſe, his happy Qualifications, he
was much reſpected by the moſt learned Philoſophers both at home
and abroad : And as with all his Failures, he may be reckon'd a-
mong the great Men of the laſt Age, ſo had he been free from
them, poſſibly, he might have ſtood in the Front. But *humanum eſt*
errare.

A

General Scheme, or Idea

Of the PRESENT STATE of

Natural Philoſophy,

AND

How its DEFECTS may be Remedied

By a Methodical Proceeding in the making

EXPERIMENTS

AND COLLECTING

OBSERVATIONS.

WHEREBY

To Compile a NATURAL HISTORY, as
the Solid Baſis for the Superſtructure of True

PHILOSOPHY.

B   *This*

THIS Treatise of Dr. Hook's tho' it was never brought to its designed Perfection, yet I thought best to present the Learned with in the first place, since it treats of the Method he proposed to himself in his Inquiries into Nature; and which he has very much observed, I have here publisht it as he left it, not presuming to alter any thing in his Writings, lest it might be doubted what were his Genuine Thoughts. I have only added the Marginal Contents, believing they would not be unacceptable. The Discourse contains Two Principal Parts, or Generals. The First Treats of the State of Philosophy, as delivered to us by the Ancients, with its Defects. The Second, How these Defects may be Remedied, for the building up a solid Philosophical Structure.

R. Waller.

FIRST GENERAL.

The Present State of Natural Philosophy, and wherein it is deficient.

THE Bufinefs of Philofophy is to find out a perfect Knowledge of the Nature and Proprieties of Bodies, and of the Caufes of Natural Productions, and this Knowledge is not barely acquir'd for it felf, but in order to the inabling a Man to underftand how by the joyning of fit Agents to Patients according to the Orders, Laws, Times and Methods of Nature, he may be able to produce and bring to pafs fuch Effects, as may very much conduce to his well being in this World, both for *fatisfying his Defires*, and the relieving of his *Neceffities* : And for advancing his State above the common Condition of Men, and make him able to excel them as much, almoft, as they do Brutes or Ideots.

Now though there have been many Men, in divers Ages of the World, which *The Prefent* feem to have had fome confus'd and imperfect Conception of this Idea of the *State of Na-* Bufinefs of Philofophy, and accordingly feem to have had fome Aims and De- *tural Philofo-* figns towards the attaining of their propos'd end; yet having not a right Un- *phy.* derftanding of the chief end, and failing much more in the Knowledge of the Means, or the manner of making ufe of them, they have generally left Philofophical Knowledge almoft in the Condition they found it: Without making any confiderable Increafe or Addition to it. Whence this kind of Knowledge has been very little promoted ever fince the very firft times we have had any Hiftory of it. And though it has always made a fair fhew of flourifhing; yet upon Examination, it has been found to yield Leaves inftead of folid Fruit, to be a Knowledge very confus'd and imperfect, and very infignificant as to the inabling a Man to practife or operate by it.

This feems to have proceeded from divers Caufes, as

Firft, from the Unskilfulnefs of the Inventors and Founders of it, who feem to have many ways contributed thereto.

1. Firft in that they had not a true Idea of the Defign and thing it felf, their *The Reafons of* Aims were low and mean, and reacht but at fmall things, fuch as the giving the *the Deficiency* Explication of things in hard words, which might ferve to amufe their Auditors, *of Natural Phi-* and to raife fome Efteem of themfelves amongft them, fcarce ever thinking, *lofophy.* much lefs indeavouring to find out the true Nature and Proprieties of Bodies ; *I. From the* what the inward Texture and Conftitution of them is, and what the Internal *firft Inventors* Motions, Powers and Energies are, and how they may be made ufe of for produ- *& Ways.* cing fuch Changes and Transformations of Bodies from one thing to another as is defired.

2. Next in that they were as ignorant of the true *means* of attaining it, as they were of the Knowledge of the End. Some efteem indeed we find them to have had of *Natural Hiftory*, and fome Imagination they had that it was conducive to Natural Knowledge, but what Hiftory was requifite, they neither had, or indeed fo much as knew, for what we find in *Ariftotle, Pliny*, and others called by that Name is fo uncertain and fuperficial, taking notice only of fome flight and obvious things, and thofe fo unaccurately, as makes them fignify but little ; but as for the more fubtile Examinations of Natural Bodies, by Diffections, Experiments, or Mechanical Tryals, we find them not to mention them as needful, much lefs to have practifed them. Nor can I perceive that they had any Affection or Induftry for Experiments, much lefs for fuch as ought to be vigoroufly profecuted with Care and Judgment: Nor do they feem to have had that Strictnefs and Accuratenefs as is requifite in fetting down or regiftring thofe things which their Writings contain, but good and indifferent

and

and ſtark naught are without Diſtinction mixt together, true and probable and falſe are all alike dignified, nor are they ſo accurate in their Deſcriptions, even of not common things that they help us with; but a great part of them we find to be a needleſs inſiſting upon the outward Shape and Figure, or Beauty, and the like, or elſe of ſome Magical and Superſtitious Effects Producible by it ſeeming to aim at creating Pleaſure, and Divertiſement or Admiration and Wonder, and not of ſuch a Knowledge of Bodies as might tend to Practice.

3. _Thirdly,_ In that, as they knew not the means, ſo neither did they the _manner_ of making uſe of them, in which Particular we may find them to be much more to ſeek than in knowing what Materials were requiſite. Their Method herein indeed was moſt prepoſterous and very pernicious, for firſt we find them much inclin'd to a Belief of implanted Notions, at leaſt in their Practice, though ſome of them affirm, _Nihil eſſe in intellectu quod non fuit prius in ſenſu,_ yet upon the whole, we may find that in their manner of proceeding they did quite otherwiſe. From a very few uncertain Hiſtories they uſually rais'd the moſt general Deductions, and from them though never ſo imperfect, would needs preſcribe Laws to the Univerſe and Nature it ſelf. In this they were very ſupercilious, and very angry to be contradicted, and maintained their Opinions more becauſe they had aſſerted them, than becauſe they were true, they ſtudied more to gain Applauſe and make themſelves admired, or the Head of ſome Sect, or the Author of ſome ſtrange Opinion, or the Oppoſer of ſome one already famous Doctrine, or the like, than to perfect their Knowledge, or to diſcern the Secrets of Nature, or advance the active Power of Man over the Creatures. Nor was this all; but we may find them even to wreſt thoſe few Experiments and Obſervations they had read, or collected, and to endeavour rather to adapt them to their Hypotheſis, than to regulate their Thoughts by them, eſteeming their own Underſtandings to be the Mine of all Science, and that by pertinacious ruminating, they could thence produce the true Image and Picture of the Univerſe.

II. From the Sectators from ſeveral Cauſes. Nor was this the only ill Fortune of true Science, but there is ſomewhat more behind. A Second Reaſon therefore why Philoſophy has not increaſed is to be aſcribed to the Sectators of theſe Theories, who at beſt have not improv'd it to a nearer Approach to Truth, but have rather made it worſe than better, and more obſcure by Interpretation. The Reaſon of which ſeems to be from theſe Particulars.

1. From their manner of Inſtitution, being bred up with a Prejudice againſt the ſearch of Truth elſewhere, than in Books thereby chained up by the imbib'd Principles and Dictates of their Teachers, and their Minds habituated to a loathing of any thing that offered it ſelf as a Novelty or new Diſcovery, and upon that account whether true or falſe rejected. This proceeded partly in the 2d. Place.

2. From an Imagination they have that Arts are already come to their higheſt pitch of Perfection, and that therefore 'tis in vain to endeavour to find out that by the moſt difficult way, which might be obtained more eaſily and fully out of Books.

This Averſion alſo to Inquiries and New Diſcoveries proceeded partly alſo in the 3d. Place.

3. From a too great Reverence and Eſteem for the Writings of the Ancients, as ſuppoſing thoſe to be the greateſt Men for Wiſdom and Knowledge, and thoſe Ages wherein they liv'd to be the elder Times of the World; and therefore they accounted it a great piece of Folly, and a kind of Impiety to contradict, or endeavour to be wiſer than their Fore-fathers.

Hence proceeded a _Fourth_ Impediment, namely,

4. From their following the ſame Way and Method in illuſtrating or endeavouring to underſtand their Writings, that the Authors themſelves did in compoſing them: And therefore 'tis not to be expected that Water ſhould riſe higher than the Fountain Head from whence it came; or that greater and more notable Effects ſhould be produced by any other than an extraordinary Method. For the Logick or way of Ratiocination they have made uſe of, hath been rather an Hindrance than a Furtherance. For neither is the way of _Syllogiſing_ as it ought

nor

nor are their first *Notions* stated aright, and consequently their Axioms and Conclusions cannot be better than the Grounds and Principles from which they were rais'd ; so that it does not only not promote real Knowledge, but is injurious to it, by begetting an Opinion of Science where there is no such thing.

5*ly*, From their mistaken Aim or Scope, which is an indeavour by Nice Distinctions to wrest over all the Observations they chance to stumble upon, and make them correspondent with their already believ'd Theory ; instead of an indeavour to rectify and regulate those so receiv'd Theories by those Intimations, which careful and accurate Observations would afford.

6*ly*, Such as have a little varied from the receiv'd Opinions, the Alteration has been rather for the bringing in some one New Hypothesis or Opinion of their own instead of the Old, and not for the renewing or Amending the whole.

7*ly*, And some that have indeavoured to make use of Arguments rais'd from the Experiments, and Observations, have been so confounded with them, for want of a Method of proceeding ; that it has been to little purpose, save the putting of Men upon new Tryals, whereby perhaps some useful Experiment has been light on, and thereby some latent Error in the former Theories detected. For neither having a true Idea of making Observations and Experiments, nor a convenient way of ordering, nor a right Method of using them, the greater number of them they have, the more are they confounded ; for 'tis not the Multitude of Experiments nor the Excellency of them, nor is it indeed the subtile and curious Ratiocinations of an accomplisht Mind, nor the Endeavours of a Multitude of such joyned together, that will be able to do any great matter in this Design ; for such Endeavours do at best but raise new Probabilities, and consequently augment Disputes on the one hand, and new Tryals on the other, and all to as little purpose as 'twould be to attempt to find some extreamly difficult Geometrical Problem by the Ruler and Compass, without the Knowledge or Help of Geometrical Algebra.

For where the Examination and Comparison of so great a Number of Particulars is requisite, and where the Process is long, and the Informations but thinly scatter'd, and those also in the Dark, 'tis not to be expected from the most subtile Wit, that the whole Operation should be only performed by the Strength of its Memory, and the Activity of its Ratiocination, though each of them in the greatest pitch of Perfection ; much less can it be hoped from Endeavours, that want either of these Accomplishments. And how usual 'tis for one of these to be defective where the other prevails, may be sufficiently evident from the almost Proverbial Saying, that good Wits have ill Memories. Some things indeed have been by lucky Inquirers light on by chance, but those so few and seldom, that 'twas not absurd in *Pythagoras* to offer up a *Hecatomb* for a single Invention in Geometry. I do not here with the Scepticks affirm, that nothing is or can be known, my Design is quite another thing ; their end only in denying any thing to be knowable, seems to be Dispute, and tends to Ignorance and Laziness, mine on the other side supposes all things as possible to be known, and accordingly studies and considers of the Means that seem to tend to that end, and rouses up the deceiv'd Faculties to seek a Means of recovering themselves out of their Thraldom, and of improving, rectifying and inlarging their Powers. They affirm positively nothing can be known any way, I only that many more things may be discover'd by this Method I here propound, than are already known.

Nor is the State of Philosophy as yet very much improved by our Modern Writers, who have endeavour'd to illustrate or piece up the old, by adding some Placits of their own : There are yet many Impediments to be removed, and many Helps to be supplied before any very great Increase in Knowledge is to be expected. It may be questioned whether piecing or mending will serve the turn, or whether there must not be a new Foundation laid on the Informations of our Senses, and more strictly examined and surveyed by accurate and judicious Experiments and Observations. That which hath had the Cultivation of many Hundreds of Years, and by divers very acute Men in all Ages, and yet as to the Inquiry after the Causes of Natural Efficients, has made so little, if any Progress at all, cannot with any Probability be imagined to afford a Method sufficient for this Inquiry. I do not here altogether reject *Logick*, or the

III. *Philosophy hitherto not much improved by the Moderns, and the Reasons why.*

C　way

way of Ratiocination already known; as a thing of no use. It has its peculiar Excellencies and Uses, in ordinary Discourse and Conversation: And affords some Helps to some kinds of Invention, especially of Arguments, as well as to the Memory, by its Method: It affords copious Matter for Disputes as well for, as against the Truth, and teaches how to solve, as well as how to make a fallacious Assertion. It shews how the Modes of speaking and arguing may be reduced to certain Rules, and how each compleat Sentence may be trisected into its constituent Parts, and how those may be various ways shuffl'd and chang'd, and likewise on occasion also how each of these bigger may be divided into three less. But as to the Inquiry into Natural Operations, what are the Kinds of secret and subtile Actors, and what the abstruse and hidden Instruments and Engines there made use of, may be; It seems not, to me, as yet at all adapted and wholly deficient. For 'tis not to be expected from the Accomplishments the Creator has endowed Man withal, that he should be able to leap, from a few particular Informations of his Senses, and those very superficial at best, and for the most part fallacious, to the general Knowledge of Universals or abstracted Natures, and thence be able, as out of an inexhaustible Fountain, to draw out a perfect Knowledge of all Particulars, to deduce the Causes of all Effects and Actions from this or that Axiome or Sentence, and as it were intuitively, to know what Nature does or is capable of effecting: And after what manner and Method she works; and yet that Method supposes little less: Man's Memory seems very shallow and infirm, and so is very prone to forget many Circumstances, besides it cannot so well propound all it does remember, to be examin'd at once by the Judgment; but prefers some things first in order, before others, and some things with more Vehemence and greater concern, and accordingly the Understanding is more apt to be sway'd to this or that hand, according as it is more affected or prest by this or that Instance, and is very liable to oversee some considerable Passages, or to neglect them; and thence very apt to be seduc'd, in pronouncing positively for this or that Opinion, especially being very prone to run into the affirmative way of judging, and wanting Patience to follow and prosecute the negative way of Inquiry, by Rejection of Disagreeing Natures.

Farther, a great Cause why Philosophy has not formerly or of late increased, is because the greatest part of Learned Men have applied themselves to other Studies, Divinity, Law, Physick, &c. as being those standing Professions whereby Men of the most liberal and ingenuous Education and Spirit might provide for themselves, and promote their Fortune in the World: Taking only a transient View of Natural Philosophy, in their Passage to other things, thinking it sufficient to be able to talk of it in the Phrase of the School. Nor is it only so now, but it has been so almost in all Ages, so that for about two Thousand Years, of which we have some account in History, there is not above one quarter of that space wherein Men have been Philosophically given, and among such as have been so, several of them have been so far disjoined by Time, Language, and Climate, by manner of Education, Manners, Opinions, and divers other Prejudices, that it could not be expected it should make any considerable Progress: For either because it seemed to promise little, Men for the most part have neglected it, or in those short spaces of time in which it was somewhat more minded and look'd after, what from the want of Dowry belonging to other liberal Professions, what from the Contests of several Theorists, and the Defect of applying of it to such things as might be useful to Humane Life; Men have been either discouraged from the Study, or tired out in it.

Some other Course therefore must be taken to promote the Search of Knowledge. Some other kind of Art for Inquiry than what hath been hitherto made use of, must be discovered; the Intellect is not to be suffer'd to act without its Helps, but is continually to be assisted by some Method or Engine, which shall be as a Guide to regulate its Actions, so as that it shall not be able to act amiss: Of this Engine, no Man except the incomparable *Verulam*, hath had any Thoughts, and he indeed hath promoted it to a very good pitch; but there is yet somewhat more to be added, which he seem'd to want time to compleat. By this, as by that Art of *Algebra* in Geometry, 'twill be very easy to proceed in any Natural Inquiry, regularly and certainly: And indeed it may not

improperly

improperly be call'd a Philosophical Algebra, or an Art of directing the Mind in the search after Philosophical Truths, for as 'tis very hard for the most acute Wit to find out any difficult Problem in Geometry, without the help of *Algebra* to direct and regulate the Acts of the Reason in the Process from the Question to the *quæsitum*, and altogether as easy for the meanest Capacity acting by that Method to compleat and perfect it, so will it be in the Inquiry after Natural Knowledge.

The greatest and most accomplisht Wits for these many Ages have labour'd and sweat in these Inquiries, and yet they have not been able to bring forth any greater Effects than Probabilities: Whereas I cannot doubt but that if this Art be well prosecuted and made use of, an ordinary Capacity with Industry, will be able to do very much more than has yet been done, and to shew that even Physical and Natural Enquiries as well as Mathematical and Geometrical, will be capable also of Demonstration; so that henceforward the business of Invention will not be so much the Effect of acute Wit, as of a serious and industrious Prosecution : And therefore, I hope as I shall not seem to detract from the Parts and Excellency of the Ancients, but rather to admire and magnify their Wit and Industry that they were able to proceed so far as they did, without the Help of this Method, so I hope I shall not be look'd on as vain or boasting, or extolling of the present Abilities of this Age, if by the Prosecution of this Method I expect and assert a much greater Proficiency.   And this Art we owe first and chiefly to that excellent Person I now mention'd, who was able to overcome all the Difficulties of Prejudice, with which Mens Minds are usually beset, and to consider and weigh the Nature of things so far, as not only to discover the Impediments of Learning, but to contrive a Method how to free the Mind from them ; and likewise to fortify and inrich it with such a Method, as shall be a constant Guide and Assistant to regulate all its Motions, so that by the use of it, it may be able to go through with its Undertaking, and as with an Engine to perform incomparably much more than 'tis possible to do without that Assistance.

SECOND GENERAL.

Of the True Method of Building a Solid Philosophy, or of a Philosophical Algebra.

THIS Method of a Philosophical Algebra, I shall divide into two main Branches. *Philosophical Algebra consists of two Parts.*

The First shall contain the manner of Preparing the Mind, and Furnishing it with fit Materials to work on.

The Second shall contain the Rules and Methods of proceeding or operating with this so collected and qualify'd Supellex.

Of the former only I shall speak at present, reserving the Explication of the later to some other Opportunity. *This I think Dr.* Hook *never wrote ; for I have not found any Tract of that kind amongst his Papers.* R. W.

The former therefore has these Three Parts considerable in it, which shall be treated of in three distinct Sections. *The former has three Parts.*

1st. An Examination of the Constitution and Powers of the Soul, or an Attempt of Disclosing the Soul to its self, being an Endeavour of Discovering the Perfections and Imperfections of Humane Nature, and finding out ways and means for the attaining of the one, and of helping the other.

2dly, A Method of making use of, or employing these Means and Assistances of Humane Nature for collecting the Phenomena of Nature, and for compiling of a Philosophical History. Consisting of an exact Description of all sorts of
Natural

Natural and Artificial Operations, or a Method of making Experiments and Obfervations for the Profecution and Examination of any Philofophical Inquiry.

3*dly*, A Method of defcribing, regiftring and ranging thefe Particulars fo collected, as that they may become the moft adapted Materials for the raifing of Axioms and the Perfecting of Natural Philofophy.

Of the Powers the Soul. Part I.] There are two things confiderable, the Imperfections of our Natures and the Perfections as to the firft, the Imperfections: The Mind of Man fuffers under various Prejudices, which do either darken or clog its Faculties, fo as that it cannot exert and make ufe of them, and thefe we are fubject to.

§ I. Of the Imperfections thereof, and how they may be helped. Firft, From our own Nature and Conftitution, as we are Men, and indued with fuch Organs as are capable of taking Information of the Operations of Nature, only by fome few peculiar ways of Senfation : Man is not indued with an intuitive Faculty, to fee farther into the Nature of things at firft, than the Superficies and out-fides, and fo muft go a long way about before he can be able to behold the Internal Nature of things, and in this Progrefs there is very *1ft. Caufe of Prejudice from our own Nature.* great Danger of his mifcarrying ; for endeavouring to make ufe of the Informations of Senfe, for that end, there are fo many ways of miftaking, that moft have fallen into them : Some have fallen prefently upon abftracted Notions, and flown immediately from a very few particular Senfations to the moft General and Univerfal Conclufions and Theories, others on the other fide have been fo amazed and confounded with Particulars, that they have only proceeded, groping on after other Particulars, thinking at laft they may by chance light upon fomething that may afford them Information in what they look after : Some others have endeavoured to intermix both thefe together, but with fo very ill Succefs, that they have left but little Fruit of their Endeavours.

The chief Defign of the Senfes. The greateft Defign indeed of the Organs of Senfe, feems to have been for fome other Ufe than for the acquiring of this kind of Knowledge, and to have a very great Affinity with the Senfes of other Animals ; which feem to have been made purpofely for the peculiar Ufe of each feveral Species : The Sight for difcovering Conveniences and Inconveniences at a greater Diftance as well as near at hand : The Ear, for receiving Warning or Information from Sound, where the Eye could not affift : The Nofe, for diftinguifhing by the Effluvia of Bodies, of wholfome or unwholfome Nourifhment : The Tafte for the fame purpofe, by the Diffolution of them in the Mouth, and for the determining of the Quantity requifite to be taken at a time : The Feeling, for the Senfation of External Textures or Motions. But yet the greater Perfection of Ratiocination in Man, may make them capable of other kind of Informations : Though indeed of themfelves they afford little as to what we are looking after. The Apprehenfion alfo or common Senfe is not of the Nature of the things fo fenfated, but only with fome peculiar Reference to our own Structure. Thus fome Taftes are fweet or fowre to us, which I make a great doubt whether they are fo to the Senfes of other Creatures : And thofe things feem pleafant in the Smell to other Creatures Senfes, which to our Senfes feem quite otherwife.

Our Apprehenfions appropriated to our Species. So that our Apprehenfions of things feem to be appropriated to our Species : And that if there were another Species of Intelligent Creatures in the World, they might have quite another kind of Apprehenfion of the fame thing, and neither perhaps fuch as they ought to be, and each of them adapted to the peculiar Structure of that Animal Body in which the Senfation is made. Thus we, by having our Organ of Hearing moved by a certain Motion of the Air, caufed by a quick Vibration of fome folid Body, have a peculiar Conception of Sound ; not to be expreft to a deaf Man, or one that has not the fame kind of Organ or manner of Apprehenfion. We do not fo conceive of it as of a Notion in the Sonorous Body, but as of a Quality which we know not how to exprefs our Conception of, but as of fomething that does pleafingly affect our Hearing, and we call that Conception we have of it Sound. But if we obferve that Propriety in the founding Body by the Eye, we have there quite another Idea of it impreft on our Phantcy, and nothing at all of the Imagination of Sound, but only of a

Body

Body in a Vibrative Motion. And if we fenfate that Propriety in the Vibrating Body by our Feeling, we have quite a differing Idea of the fame Propriety, and there we have an Imagination of it, which we call tingling or tickling, or Heat: From which it feems evident, that thofe Imaginations we have of things, are not according to the Nature of the things themfelves; but only appropriated to the peculiar Organs, by which they are made fenfible to the Underftanding: So that had we other kinds of Organs, we fhould have other kinds of Conceptions of thofe Effects. And thofe perhaps we have may be quite differing from what other Creatures have of the fame thing. Thus that Conftitution of Air, which we call dark, is not fo to Cats and Owls, and the like; nor is it fo indeed to a Man if his Eyes are affifted by fome peculiar kind of Inftruments, as I have divers times found by Experiment, wherein I have been able to fee to read the Letters and Words diftinct in fuch a Light, wherein, without that help, I have hardly been able to fee the Lines. Thus Heat and Cold are only Relative to our Conftitution, as is evident by the Weather Glafs, which feels many Degrees of Heat before it be fenfible to us.

The beft Remedy therefore that feems to be againft this Prejudice is, to compare the feveral Informations we receive of the fame thing, from the feveral Impreffions it makes on the feveral Organs of Senfe and (by a Rejection of what is not confonant) by degrees to find out its Nature, and thereby to inform the Intellect with a Notion of the thing; which is not according to this or that Idea, rais'd from the Impreffion of this or that Senfe, but by a comparative Act of the Underftanding from all the various Informations 'tis capable of receiving, more immediately by any of the Senfes, or more mediately by various other Obfervations or Experiments. *Remedy for thefe Prejudices from the Senfes.*

We ought to conceive of things as they are part of, and Actors or Patients in the Univerfe, and not only as they have this or that peculiar Relation or Influence on our own Senfes or felves. And for this caufe we ought to be very careful in what Senfe we underftand Philofophical Words already in ufe, for thefe having been for the moft part made by fuch as had thofe Prejudices remaining on them, and we alfo having firft received in or imbibed the Senfes of thofe words, whilft under the like Prejudices: It cannot be expected but that the Notions muft be very confufed and inconfiftent with the things themfelves.

Another Caufe of Prejudice is from every Man's own peculiar Structure: Every Man has born with him, or contracted by fome way or other, a Conftitution of Body and Mind, that does more or lefs difpofe him to this or that kind of Imagination or Phant'fy of things, and every one has fome kind of Accident or other, that does more or lefs difpofe him for this Opinion or that Operation of the Mind as well as of the Body. Thus fome kind of Conftitutions of Body does more incline a Man to Contemplation, and Speculation, another to Operation, Examination, and making Experiments, and look what way the Conftitution of a Man, or fome other Accident has inclin'd him to, that way almoft are bent all his other Faculties and Powers. Thus one is for fpeaking, and another for Writing, and all things are look'd on, or difregarded by fuch, as they are fubfervient to fuch an end: And not only many things, not very inftructive, are let pafs; but fometimes alfo many things that have no fuch Indication in them, are brought in as 'twere by the Head and Shoulders, and wrefted, to be made compliable to this or that Opinion. Juft as a Man that is troubled with the Jaundice, fuppofes all things to be Yellow, and all things he eats, till otherwife prevented, ferve to augment his Choler, by being chang'd into it: Or a melancholy Perfon, that thinks he meets with nothing but frightful Apparitions, does convert all things he either fees or hears into dreadful Reprefentations, and makes ufe of them to ftrengthen his Phant'fy, and fill it fuller of fuch uneafy Apprehenfious, fo is it in Conftitutions of Mind as to Philofophy. Thus *Ariftotle's* Phyfick is very much influenced by his Logick: *Des Cartes* Philofophy favours much of his Opticks: *Van Helmonts*, and the reft of the Chymifts of their Chimical Operations: *Gilberts* of the Loadftone: *Pythagoras's* and *Jordanus Brunus's*, *Kepler's*, &c. of Arithmetick and the Harmony of Numbers. The Philofophy, of fome Divines, is intermingled with Divinity; of others with Spirits and immaterial Agents: Aftrologers endeavour to bring *2d. Caufe of Prejudice from the peculiar Structure of every Man, or particular bent of his Studies.*

all things under the Power and Influence of Cæleftial Bodies, and would have them the chief Efficients of the World, and indeed every one according to the things he moft fancies naturally, or has accidentally ftudied, and is moft converfant in, endeavours to make all things he meets with, agreeable or fubfervient thereto. And he is much the more inclin'd to maintain and defend this or that Opinion, if he has once any way publickly owned it, whether in Writing or Difcourfe, fo far too perhaps fometimes, that though at firft he defended it when he thought otherwife, yet by continuing to do fo for the maintaining of an Argument, or of his Credit, he at laft comes to believe it, and the Fallacy, which he endeavoured to put upon others, impofes moft of all upon himfelf.

The Remedies againft this. The beft Remedy againft this Inconvenience, is the finding out of what Conftitution ones felf is, and to what one is either naturally or accidentally moft inclin'd to believe, and accordingly by reafoning and comparing things together to confider what the things themfelves hint, and what Intimation proceeds from ones own Conftitution.

Next, to accuftom ones felf as much as can be for a while at leaft, to a quite contrary Suppofal or Practice: Or which is indeed more general, not to receive any Notion for certain, till throughly confirm'd by very Cogent Arguments and Ratiocinations, and always moft to fufpect that which feems moft confonant and pleafing to our Inclination: Thus one, that fancies Novelty fhould be moft cautious of what he admits for Truth or Demonftration that is new; left his Mind being prejudiced with a Love of Novelties, fhould otherwife impofe upon his Belief and Underftanding: Thus one that is addicted to Chymical or Mechanical Operations, fhould be very cautious of admitting of a Chymical or Mechanical Solution, and fo for the reft; for that may feem very probable and rational to one, whofe Mind is fo inclin'd; which to one of another Conftitution will feem moft unlikely and abfurd: So one, inclin'd to Speculation and abftracting, fhould bridle his Nature and not fly too foon to the moft geral Conclufions, for as a Nature fo inclin'd does willingly oftentimes impofe upon it felf, and longs to be acting, and running in its proper and moft known Road, and avoids that Method it is not acquainted with, finding it very uncouth and full of many new Difficulties. So though the reafon fhould be fatisfied, and the Phant'fy full of the Truth of this or that Opinion, another Mind otherwife qualified, may find many Flaws and Errors in it, and perceive many things to have proceeded from Prejudice.

A 3d. Caufe of Prejudice from Education and the unaccurate ufe of words. A Third Caufe of Prejudice is from Language, Education, Breeding, Converfation, Inftruction, Study, from an Efteem of Authors, Tutors, Mafters, Antiquity, Novelty, Fafhions, Cuftoms, or the like. The Philofophical words, of all Languages yet known in the World, feem to be for the moft part very improper Marks, fet on confufed and complicated Notions, together with the Learning of which Language we have imbibed thofe confus'd Notions, which are commonly underftood by the mention of thofe Words, thefe Words therefore being ufed in our Difcourfe, and thofe Notions in our Ratiocinations, muft needs very much perplex the Operations of the Mind, and much puzzle and difturb the Ratiocination. The Notions of the Mind therefore ought to be ftated aright, and the Signification of many words ought to be more defin'd, divers new Words alfo to be made and fet upon more diftinct Conceptions and Notions, and many other words ought to be wholly blotted out and rejected, as either fignifying fomething imperfectly, which is otherwife better expreft, or elfe a Phantafm, for which there is no ground in Nature: Education alfo, Breeding, Converfation and Inftruction, do all of them very much work upon the Affection, and ferve to fway it this way or that way according to the Will of the Teacher, whereby the Underftanding becomes inflaved to the Dictates of Education, and the Ratiocination bound up or fettered by the *Placits* of a Tutor, fo as not to be able to lay hold of Truth though never fo fairly offer'd: For moft of thofe things being inftilled into our Minds when young and tender, and incapacitated to diftinguifh between Affertions and Demonftrations, and between Opinions and Realities, have taken fo deep a Root, and fo poffeft the Mind with Prejudice againft many Ways and Methods of Truth, that they are not freed without very much Trouble and Circumfpection; and 'tis a kind of Soveraignty

which

which Men do most of all affect, to captivate and inslave Mens Minds to a Reverence or good Opinion of their Abilities, and Doctrines; so that we have not only a great many Enemies to Knowledge and Freedom, lodg'd within our Breasts and Fabricks, but are every way encompassed; and those which seem our greatest Friends, do in this regard prove our greatest Enemies.

And this Bond is so much the more difficult to be shaken off, if together with their Doctrines we have entertain'd an Admiration, Awe, Reverence, or Esteem of the Persons themselves that instructed us, or were the Authors of the Books or Opinions we have approv'd. Add to all these Multitudes of false Opinions, which have been impos'd upon our Belief by fallacious Demonstrations in Discourse and Conversation: For Words being ill set Marks on very confused Notions; the Reason of a Man is very easily impos'd on by Discourse, unless the Mind be extreamly attent, and watchful, not to take any thing for granted, that is not evidently prov'd, and very perspicacious in finding out the distinct Notion of the Word, in every such Sentence, wherein it is used, for the Notions signified by some words being very many and very perplex, unless that Notion there meant be (by some Periphrasis or otherwise) determin'd to be always signified when that word is pronounced; the Circumspection of the Intellect is so slow in examining over Particulars, and running over all the particular Siginifications some words may have, that it may very easily be impos'd upon by a quick and cunning Disputant, and being once impos'd on without being detected, the Admission of that Error is the occasion of bringing in Multitudes of others; Error being a kind of Ferment which tends to the turning or conforming all things to its own Nature, and like an infected Person has Influence on all things it comes near.

The best Remedy, for which Inconvenience, is not to consider so much what *The Remedy* the Person is that instructs, as how true the things are he asserts, nor of what Au- *for these.* thority those Authors are esteem'd we read; but what Arguments are by them brought for that which they assert, and if we are so over born with Love, or Reverence, to this or that Author, as to esteem of whatever he says, whether right or wrong, than to imagine what he says to be spoken by one *against* whose Person or Doctrine we have a Prejudice; for that will somewhat incline the Mind to a contrary Opinion, and thereby help to ballance the Inclination of it the better, so that it shall not reject Truth when offer'd on the one hand, nor embrace an Error when asserted by the other.

Another way is to consider with what Vehemence and Earnestness two contrary Opinions are believed and asserted on both sides, and to consider what are or have been the occasions to incline the Parties to those Opinions or Doctrines they maintain, and as near as may be to distinguish what manner of Actings there are which proceed from Reason, and what from Prejudice, and from thence to endeavour to fortify the Mind with Arguments against Dogmaticalness and Opinionativeuess upon too small Grounds, and to accustom the Mind to an Equilibrium or Indifferency, so as to be sway'd and turn'd to the embracing of Truth from whence or whomsoever brought.

A third way of remedying or rooting out Prejudices already impos'd on us, and of preventing the like Impositions for the future; is an Hypothetical Scepticism, whereby to impose upon our selves a Disbelief of every thing whatsoever, that we have already imbraced or taken in as a Truth: And in so doing, to throw out not only those things we may a little doubt of, but even all those things of which we are most confident, and those especially which our particular Constitutions seem most of all to incline us to believe, rejecting them all as Impostures and Fallacies, that have by some indirect means or other crept into our Understandings, or have been impos'd upon our Minds by some or other that either wilfully or purposely endeavoured to deceive us, which having so done by leasure and degrees, not too many at a time, by much Caution and Circumspection, not without weighing well all the Arguments and Circumstances that can be alledg'd either for or against them by many Tryals and Experiments and Siftings, to take such of them in again, distinctly and determin'd as can produce sufficient Evidence of Truth: Others, whose Truth we cannot make out, to reject them in all our Ratiocinations as uncertain and of doubtful Credit, and not to be relied on; till by farther Tryals or Experience
the

the Truth or Falſhood of them be made evident, and then accordingly to deal finally with them by a Reception of them into the number of Truths, or a final Rejection of them as Falſities and Errors.

§. II. *Of the Perfections of humane Nature, and how they may be improved.*

The Second thing to be done, is the finding out the Perfections of our Nature, and the particular Helps we have for Information, and with what means of Diſcovery we are furniſht, and how thoſe Means may be improved. Now the Faculties of the Soul are Three; Senſe, Memory and Reaſon, or Ratiocination the particular Buſineſs, of each of which is to be examined how far their Ability and Power, when in the greateſt Perfection extends, and wherein each of them are deficient, and by what means they may be aſſiſted and perfected.

Firſt, As to the Senſes their Examination, and how aſſiſted.

The firſt therefore that will be neceſſary to this end, will be the Examination of the particular Conſtitution of our Senſes, to ſee what Propriety of a Body each of them takes notice of, and how far they are capable of aſſiſting in the finding out of that Propriety, and wherein that Propriety of a Body does conſiſt, where the Help of the Senſes fails or leaves us in this Inquiry, and then what Inſtruments will farther aſſiſt the Senſes in this Inquiry, and how far alſo their Power will extend, and by what means we may be farther aſſiſted in this Search.

The differing ways of Senſation we find to be Five, which are provided with as many diſtinct Organs; the 1ſt. and moſt Spiritual is plac'd in the Eye, a 2d. in the Ear, a 3d. in the Noſe, a 4th. in the Mouth, the 5th. over the whole Body.

The Senſe of Seeing.

The Fabrick of the Eye is moſt admirably contrived for receiving in the Impreſſion of the Rays of Light, and for ſo diſpoſing and ordering of them, that thoſe Rays that proceed from the ſeveral Points of any Object that either emits or reflects Light, and fall on the Cornea of the Eye, ſhall be all of them collected into ſo many diſtinct Points at the bottom of the Eye, and that in the ſame Order, that the Points were ſcituated in reſpect of the Eye, but in a leſſer Proportion, according as the Object is farther removed in diſtance from the Eye, and in a greater Proportion as the Object is nearer; ſo that the Picture or Repreſentation of the Object in the ſenſible part, or bottom of the Eye, may according to the Poſture or Diſtance of it from the Cornea, be either leſs equal or bigger than the Object it ſelf: Whence were the Senſe of diſtinguiſhing the Parts of the Picture at the bottom of the Eye, as nice and particular as the Body has diſtinct Parts, we might very eaſily by this Senſe only find out the Texture or Schematiſm of any Body within our reach; for 'tis very eaſy by one ſingle Lens of a ſmall Sphere, or of a very Convex Figure, plac'd juſt before the Eye, to make the Object diſtinctly viſible, when much nearer to the Cornea than the Cornea is to the bottom of the Eye, and conſequently the Rays croſſing near the Cornea, the Picture or Repreſentation at the bottom muſt be bigger than the Object it ſelf; but the diſcerning Power of the Senſe is not capable of making Diſtinction of Parts when they are ſmaller than ſuch a Bulk, the Terminus of which, I find to my Eye, to be when the Repreſentation is about the Bigneſs of the ſmaller Pores of Wood: Which I find by this Expedient, by a convenient ſingle Lens I bring the Object I look on ſo near my Eye, that the croſſing of Rays in the Eye may be about the middle Space between the viſible ſide of the Object, and the bottom of my Eye; from whence it follows, that the Picture of the viſible part of the Object is as big as the thing repreſented: But the Eye being then at moſt but capable of ſeeing or diſtinguiſhing thoſe Pores; it follows, that (if the Cauſe of that Diſtinction be from the ends of the Filaments of the Optick Nerve, as *Des Cartes* ingeniouſly ſuppoſes) the Filaments cannot be ſmaller than the Microſcopical Pores of Wood, and that the Eye is uncapable of diſtinguiſhing the Parts of any Picture that are ſmaller than thoſe: So that any Object being ſo far removed from the Eye as to make the Picture of it on the Retira leſs than a Microſcopical Pore, that Object becomes inviſible, if at leaſt it be but of a dull Radiation; for if it be otherwiſe of a very bright Radiation, the whole Filament is mov'd by having one part of it powerfully acted on, and ſo we have a Senſation of the Object, the ſame as if it were much bigger, and this ſeems to be the reaſon why the Stars appear to

our

our naked Eye many Thousand times bigger in bulk than really they are, and even as big as through a long Telescope, which would not be if our Sense were sufficiently fine and nice. I could have instanc'd likewise in the other Senses, but this may suffice for an Example.

Having considered therefore the Power and Property of the Sense, we may be so much the better inabled to find out its Defects, and by what means it may be improv'd.

The Eye therefore presenting to the Sense a Picture of the Objects that are plac'd before it, is capable of Informing of the Sense of Four or Five Qualities of Bodies, first of the Radiation, or the shining or not shining Properties of Bodies, next of the Pellucidity and Opacousness of Bodies. 3*ly,* Of the Reflexiveness of Bodies. 4. Of the Figure, Magnitude and Position of Bodies. 5. Of the Motion; when therefore these Proprieties of Bodies are inquir'd after, the Information concerning the three first must be wholly fetcht from this Sense, but the Information concerning the other two may be had partly from this and partly also from some of the other Senses. In the discovering of each of these Properties, the Sense may be various ways assisted, both by Engines, Observations and Experiments.

What this Sense informs us off, and how its Defects may be helped.

As First, for the discovering of the shining Properties of many Bodies, there are these two more immediate Assistances; the first is by placing the Eye and Object in such a place where all other Radiations of Light may be wholly excluded, for by this means, many weak Degrees of Radiation will become visible to the Eye, which in a greater Light would be altogether insensible, and this proceeds from a Twofold Cause; First, because there is no stronger Impression made on the Eye from the Radiation of any other Object, which is the reason why the Stars disappear in the day time: Next the Eye thereby opens its Apperture much wider, and so admits a much greater number of Rays, whence 'tis that the Eye by a long stay in a somewhat dark Room begins to see and distinguish things almost as well as in a much lighter, because the Apperture is not opened in an instant but by degrees. Hence the Radiation of Gloworms Tails, of the Juice of the Hundred Legged Worm, of rotten Wood, of Salt Water, of Putrifying Fish, of a rubbed or warmed Diamond, and the like, becomes visible to the naked Eye in a dark Room, which disappears and vanishes in a bigger Light, but because we find that the more Rays the Eye is capable of collecting, the better is it able to discover this Propriety where it is very languid; therefore if the Eye can by any Contrivance of Glasses be made capable of collecting a much greater quantity of Rays from a Point, and making them meet on the Retina, 'tis not improbable but that a much greater number of Bodies may be discover'd Radiant than are yet suppos'd to be such, perhaps also it may discover to us the Properties of many other Motions; for it seems not improbable, but that the Motions of Corrosion in many Bodies may generate some faint Degree of Light; perhaps also, the Motion of Fermentation, and many Degrees of Heat, much less than what we now esteem requisite, may produce the like effect. And that this help of this Sense in this Inquiry, is not a Supposition without any ground from the Nature of the thing, will appear first in that Cats and Owls, and Bats, and divers other Creatures, are able to see in a much less degree of Light than is sufficient for a Man's Sight. Next from this, that making Tryal upon this very Supposition with a convenient Lens, I have divers times been able to read in the Night by the help of it, when I could hardly with my naked Eye distinguish the Lines. Now this being done with an ordinary double Convex Spherical Lens, 'tis not improbable but that much more may be done by a double Hyperbolical one, if the way of making it can be found (which seems not altogether improbable to be done with Niceness enough as to this use of collecting the Rays of Light, though in Glass it be very difficult to be done accurate enough for distinct Vision) or, by the help of an Elliptical Concave, by placing the Body to be examin'd in one of its Focuses, and the Eye with a Concave Lens before it in the other, and for this use 'tis easy enough to make a Concave sufficiently accurate of an Elliptical Figure.

1st. It informs of the Radiation of Bodies.

With some such Glasses it were very desirable that Tryal should be made with several Bodies in a perfectly dark Room, such as an unrubb'd or cold Diamond, with corroding Bodies, with fermenting Bodies, and such as are treated by various other ways.

E　　　　　　　　Further

Farther, If our Eyes fhould not be capable of being brought up to fuch a Degree of Nicenefs in Senfation as is requifite ; 'tis not impoffible but that by fome Obfervations and Tryals, one may come to the Knowledge of the Truth as to this Inquiry. 'Tis poffible perhaps to find a way to difcover whether a Cat or fome fuch other Creature can fee by fuch a Light, which I think might be many ways done, were it not much eafier and more certain to make a Difcovery with ones own Eyes, and that perhaps to as great, if not much greater Degree of Nicety than Cats can.

There may perhaps alfo be found, upon farther Inquiry into the Nature of things, fome Body that is acted on or mov'd by Light, which is much more fenfible of the Degrees thereof than the Eye, which, if found, would be a huge Affiftance to a diligent Inquirer into this Property of Body ; and for this we may have fome reafon to hope, if we confider, how lately 'tis that the Beard of an Oat was found out for the Senfation of the Moifture or Drynefs of the Air : And 'tis not yet above ――― Years fince I firft difcover'd the like, but fomewhat more nice Property in the Seeds of *Geranium Mofchatum*: *Athanafius Kircher* tells us, that the Sun-Flower follows the Light of the Sun, but whether true or not, I difpute not now : Sufficient it is to the prefent Defign (which is only to hint by what ways poffibly the Senfe may be affifted) to fhew that fuch an Help is not altogether improbable to be found. Perhaps alfo the augmenting the Bulk of fuch a Body, may make that Propriety become fenfible which might otherwife lie hid.

2dly, Of their Pellucidity. Next as to the Pellucidity, Colours, or Opacoufnefs of Bodies, the Eye may be various ways affifted in the finding out that Propriety and reducing its Degrees to a Meafure or Standard. One way is, by placing the examining Eye in a Room perfectly darkened, without any Cranny to admit Light into it, fave only one or two Holes ; againft one of which whilft the other is quite ftopt the Body to be examin'd may be plac'd, of various Thickneffes according to its diftinct Nature : The more tranfparent it be, the thicker Mafs of Body may be feen through, and the more opacous, the thinner muft the plated Body be : And by this Contrivance a great Number of Bodies will be found *aliquatenus* tranfparent, which are judg'd wholly opacous, and by the Thinnefs, requifite to admit a fenfible Degree of Light through, may the comparative Opacity of Bodies be found and determin'd.

A fecond way whereby the Eye may be affifted in this Inquiry, is by the Microfcope ; for the Body being, by beating or otherwife, reduced into fmall parts, the Microfcope does plainly diftinguifh thofe Particles *aliquatenus* tranfparent. Thus the parts of moft forts of Stones when reduc'd to Sand, appear manifeftly tranfparent, the moft Metalline and other Colours ufed by Painters, appear to confift of fomewhat tranfparent Parts, and very many of thofe Bodies which the Eye is not able to difcover fuch the other way, is by this means very eafily manifefted ; and indeed, there feems to be fcarce any Body in Nature, unlefs perhaps fome of the white Metaline that are not in fome Degree or other tranfparent, and this is fo much the more probable ; fince we find that the moft compacted, we know in the World, namely Gold, is manifeftly tranfparent, when beaten very thin and held up againft the Light.

Next, the Tranfparency, Opacity, or Colours of Bodies may be farther inquired into, by mixing and incorporating feveral of them with divers forts of appropriated Homogeneous Tranfparent Bodies ; that is, with fuch as with whom they will readily mix. Thus Cochineel, which looks like an opacous dark Body, when mixt with Water that diffolves it, yields a tranfparent Crimfon Colour. Thus Iron melted with Glafs yields a kind of Red. Thus Copper mixt or diffolv'd by fome Saline Liquors yields a Green, with others a Blew, with others a Purple. Thus many forts of Stones and Earths, which feemed before perfectly opacous, by this means fhew their Colour.

3dly, Of their Reflexivenefs. Thirdly, The reflecting Property of Bodies may be partly difcover'd and diftinguifht by the above mention'd Methods, and partly alfo by reducing the Bodies into the Shape of a Burning-Glafs of a determinate Bignefs, and fmoothing the Superficies of it very well ; for by the comparing of divers of thofe Inftruments fo made, by the Effects of burning they produce when expos'd to the Sun, 'twill not be difficult to determine the comparative Power of reflecting the Rays of Light.

Another way of judging of the comparative Reflection of Bodies, may be by viewing them in a Microfcope in feveral Lights, and with feveral Apertures, and by pitching upon fome one Body to the Strength of the Reflection of which the proportionate Reflection of all the reft may be referr'd ; for by knowing the Smalnefs of the Aperture of the Glafs requifite to make each of them difappear, we know alfo their comparative Power of Reflection.

Tryal alfo of this Property may be made with the Eye, only affifted with feveral Apertures, and only finding the Smalnefs of the Aperture requifite to make the Reflection of Light from fuch a Body to difappear.

The Ufe of which Inquiry into this Property of Bodies may be of very great Ufe, as to the Invention of the Nature and Texture of Bodies.

Fourthly, As to the Magnitude, Figure, and Pofition of Bodies, though the Eye can pretty well guefs at them in Bodies pretty near, and within its reach as 'twere, yet beyond that, and even in that too if Accuratenefs be required ; it is deficient, and does much need the Help of Inftruments and Contrivances to affift it. *4thly, Of their Magnitude, Figure, and Pofition.*

As to the Magnitude and Pofition of Bodies ; the Eye may be affifted by making Experiments with divers forts of Mathematical Inftruments, efpecially by the Ufe of fome which I fhall afterwards defcribe, by which means the Magnitude, Diftance, and Pofition of the Celeftial Bodies, that are fo far out of our reach, may be much more accurately meafur'd, than by any other fort of Inftrument yet made publick to the World.

As for the Figure and Magnitude of fome Bodies ; the Eye (being unable to diftinguifh the Pofition of Parts, when the Appearance of them is lefs than fuch an Angle) may be affifted by two forts of Inftruments, namely the Telefcope for the appearing Figure of fmall Bodies, abfent, and out of our reach ; and the Mifcrofcope for fuch minute Bodies as we have accefs to ; the Melioration of both which Inftruments would be a Matter of huge Concernment, as to the Refolution of this Inquiry. And I cannot doubt, but that the Induftry of fome of the many Ingenious Men, that are now imploy'd about it, will be fo fuccefsful as to accomplifh it.

The Figures alfo of fome, inacceffible Bodies may be judg'd by the Obfervation of divers Circumftances : Thus the ingenious Monfieur *Hygens* difcover'd the true Figure of the Body of *Saturn*, which had fo much puzled Learned Men before.

Fifthly, The Eye may be various ways affifted for the Difcovery of the Motion and Velocity of Bodies ; as by meafuring the time it has paft fuch a length or fpace by the help of a Pendulum, and whereas the Motion of fome Bodies is fo flow that their Velocity does not make a fenfible Angle to the Eye, therefore the Velocity of fuch Motions is beft gathered by Confequents, fuch as all the Motions of the Celeftial Bodies, many of which cannot be otherwife difcern'd. *5thly, Of their Motion.*

The Internal Motions alfo of Bodies may be difcover'd by various Effects, fuch as thofe of Fermentation, Heat, Corruption, Generation, Growth, Decay, Diffolution, Coagulation, and the like, from the accurate Obfervation of divers of which compared with feveral other Circumftances, may be very well collected the Degree, Nature and Manner of Internal Motions.

The Telefcope alfo and Microfcope may much affift the Eye in this Inquiry ; thus the Body of the Sun has been found to vertiginate on its Axis. I did alfo by the Help of a good Telefcope, about two Years fince, difcover the Motion of ♃ about its own Axis, by means of a fomewhat darker fpot in the Body of it ; the Moon, ♄, and ♃ have alfo been found to have a Motion of Libration, the Satellites of ♃ and Moon of *Saturn* to make their Periodick Revolution in fuch or fuch a time. The Microfcope alfo can make the Motion of the Legs of Mites, and many other fmall Creatures fenfible, as alfo the Motion of the Hand of a Watch, and perhaps alfo Mifcrofcopes may be made fo accurate as to discover the vegetating Motion of Plants (though I confess I have not yet found the Growth of any so fast as to be quickly sensible through a Microscope) and of corrosive and corroding Liquors, and the like; however in the search after every of these the Eye is not left without many Assistances, whereby it may perfectly discover what it seeks after.

Thus for the finding the Velocity and Strength of falling Bodies, I made this following Contrivance, which succeeded according to Expectation.

A Description of the Instrument for falling Bodies. Vid. the Fig.

The Instrument was thus contrived. See the 1st. Figure in which A B C is the Pedestal or Bottom to sustain the Scales and other Parts. D E a double Beam, or two Beams well fastened together by cross pieces of Steel at the Ends, or other ways, between the two Cheeks of which the Steel Ball F falls from any determinate Height upon the Steel Plate or Basin G; and if by that Fall it moves the double Beam and the Counterpoise H, lying in the Scale I K, it gives the small Spring L a free Passage to slip between the end of the double Beam and the Stay M, by which means there is given a certain Sign whether the falling Body has moved the Scale or Counterpoise so far, as to admit the very thin Edge of the Spring L, the rest of the Contrivance is obvious enough from the Scheme it self. *" That the Reader may the better understand " the Use and Performance of this Instrument, I have added some of the Experi- " ments made with it, as I find them entered in the Registers of the Royal Society, " which I thought might not be unacceptable to the Ingenious. R. W.*

The Account is as follows,

" *The Instrument being thus prepared, I. (i.e. Dr. Hook) put into the oppo-* " *site Scale I K, a 4 Ounce Weight H that is four times the Weight of the Steel* " *Ball F, and letting this Steel Ball or Bullet F fall from just the Height of an* " *Inch above the Steel Plate G (by cutting the Thread that held it) I found it* " *very sensibly to move it; I repeated the Tryal so long, till I found that letting* " *this Ball fall but $\frac{4}{21}$ of an Inch above the Plate, it would move the Beam so as* " *to admit the Spring ; but if I let it fall from a less Height it would not, then* " *I put in 8 Ounces, and by several repeated Tryals, I found $\frac{1}{3}$ of an Inch to be* " *the Height requisite for the falling Bullet to pass, before it would move 8 times* " *its own Weight, I proceeded farther, and from the Experiments collected in the* " *first Table A.*

" *Afterwards I took a small Ball of Clay that was very round, and exceeding* " *hard, in Weight near a quarter of an Ounce, and proceeding with this as I had* " *done with the Steel, I collected from the several Tryals the Second Table B.*

TABLE A.		TABLE B.	
$\frac{4}{21}$	4	$\frac{1}{4}$	4
$\frac{1}{3}$	8	$\frac{3}{4}$	8
$1\frac{3}{4}$	16	$1\frac{4}{5}$	16
$2\frac{2}{3}$	32	$5\frac{4}{5}$	32
$3\frac{1}{3}$	48	18	64
$3\frac{5}{6}$	64	36	128
5	96		
$6\frac{3}{4}$	128		

" *The first row of Numbers in both which Tables shew the perpendicular Height* " *from which the Balls were let fall, to move the several Counterpoises, which* " *are noted by the second Row of Numbers in both Tables, 4, 8, 16, &c. signifying* " *the Counterpoise to be 4, 8, 16, &c. times the Weight of the Ball.*
" *Which Tryals and Observations, though they do not absolutely answer our* " *Expectation as to the thing sought, that a Body moved with twice the Celerity* " *acquires twice the Force, yet they serve for several good Uses; for first, it shews* " *us the Difficulty of such Tryals, where though all things as to ones Sense appeared* " *the same, yet some small insensible Circumstances made the Effects so differing,* " *that we need not wonder, if oftentimes when we endeavour to repeat an Experi-*
ment

" ment delivered upon good Credit, as done by another with such or such Mate-
" rials, thus or thus us'd, though we do all things just according to Prescriptions,
" yet we miss of producing the promised Effects. And therefore I conceive it not
" less instructive to any one that may attempt to make a farther Discovery of
" this kind, to shew wherein our present Tryals were deficient, than to declare
" what they did.

" Now the first and greatest Defect in our Tryals seems to be, that there is a
" yielding in the Materials which we make use of; first, that part of the Ball which
" first touches the Plain is a little flatted by the Knock, and consequently a part
" of the Force is returned into the Ball, and so lost. Secondly, The yielding of the
" Plate; thirdly, the stretching the Ears of the Plate, every one of which yieldings
" must necessarily take off from the Force of the falling Ball, that it cannot work
" the expected Effect so accurately as it would were those remov'd.

" Next in this Contrivance, there is besides the Counterpoise of Weights, a
" great deal of a massy heavy Body, namely, the double Beam, and the Plate, and
" Scale; all which, or at least the greatest part of it, must be moved, and that
" with a very quick and sudden Motion before the Spring, though it be so very
" thin can get between the End of the Beam and Stay, to make the Effect sensible.
" Now this quick Motion it self does require a considerable Strength to effect it,
" were the Counterpoise remov'd; for such a Bulk of Body cannot be put into such
" a quick Degree of Motion, but by another Bulk of Body mov'd with a determinate
" Degree of Celerity.

" Thirdly, The Scales and Counterpoise may be all mov'd, and yet the small
" Spring, though it be so thin as not to be above $\frac{1}{45}$ or $\frac{1}{58}$ part of an Inch in Thick-
" ness, yet is that a Space, and the Beam may perhaps be moved half that way,
" and the forcible Resistance of Gravity may make it return back again before it
" have mov'd the whole Space, so that it may be moved a little, and yet not so
" much as to make it sensible by this Contrivance. Nor would the making that
" Spring thiner much mend the matter, since there are other Inconveniences: And
" that this is so, I try'd the following Experiment, when in my last Tryal I had
" found that the Ball of a quarter of an Ounce required to be let fall from the
" Height of 36 Inches, before it would move the end of the Beam so much as to
" let in the Spring, when there was 128 times its Weight of Counterpoise, that I
" might try whether the same Ball would not sensibly move the same Counterpoise,
" though it were let fall from a much smaller Height. I placed the Spring so as that
" it was between the Stay and the end of the Beam, but not so far in as it would
" spring in if it were left free; then letting fall the Ball at 4 Inches Height, I
" found that it had moved the end sufficiently to let the Spring slide in as far as
" it would, I put the Spring in Order as before, and let it fall from $3\frac{1}{2}$ Inches
" Height, and found it there likewise to move the end of the Beam.

" I repeated it again at 3 Inches Height, but though I try'd several times, I could
" not find that it had at all moved or let slip the Spring. Now as exact Tryals
" of this kind may be very useful in Mechanicks, so could they be made with Bo-
" dies perfectly solid, would they be for the Establishment of one of the chief Prin-
" ciples of Philosophy, namely, the Strength a Body moved has to move another.
" And though Des Cartes puts it as a Principle, that Si Corpus C plane qui-
" esceret essetq; paulo majus quam B, quacumq; cum celeritate B moveretur
" versus C nunquam ipsum C moveret, sed ab eo repelleretur in contrariam
" partem, and gives this Reason for it, Quia Corpus quiescens magis resistit
" magnæ celeritati quam parvæ, idq; pro ratione excessus unius supra alteram.
" Et idcirco semper màjor esset vis in C ad resistendum, quam in B ad impel-
" lendum. Yet these Experiments do rather seem to hint, that the least Body by
" any acquir'd Celerity, may be able to move the greatest, though how much of its
" Motion is imparted to the bigger Body, and how much of it is recoil'd into the
" smaller be not hereby determin'd.

But to proceed, I could thus have gone over all the other Senses, by examining their particular Construction, and what Proprieties of Bodies they each of
them take Notice of, what Information they can afford us alone, and where
they leave us, and by what Instruments and Methods they might be helpt and
assisted in the Prosecution of the Inquiry. But these being more proper to be

F

inftanced in hereafter, when I come to give Examples of this Method for the finding out of particular Inquiries, and my Bufinefs at prefent being only to give a Specimen for the Explication of my Defign, and as it is preparatory to the finding out fuch Helps for the Senfes for making Difcoveries as may affift a Natural Hiftorian in the collecting of Materials for a Philofophical Supellex, to fill up the Repofitory of the Memory withal; for the Ratiocination to work on, for finding out the Caufes, Manner, and Method of Nature's proceeding in all thofe Operations, we inquire into. I fhall now pafs on to confider of thofe other Faculties of the Soul, namely, Memory and Ratiocination. The Bufinefs of the former being nothing elfe but a faithful Prefervation of the things committed to it, and a ready recollecting them when neceffary, will be rectified and perfected by this Method of the Philofophick Algebra, and the rectifying and perfecting of the Reafon, we fhall refer to another Opportunity.

Part II. *Of collecting the Phenomena of Nature, for the compiling an Hiftory.*

The fecond thing therefore, is a Method of collecting a Philofophical Hiftory, which fhall be as the Repofitory of Materials, out of which a new and found Body of Philofophy may be raifed. This is to comprize a brief and plain Account of a great Store of choice and fignificant Natural and Artificial Operations, Actions and Effects, ranged in a convenient Order, and interwoven here and there with fome fhort Hints of Accidental Remarks or Theories, of correfponding or difagreeing received Opinions, of Doubts and Queries and the like, and indeed until this Repofitory be pretty well ftored with choice and found Materials, the Work of raifing new Axiomes or Theories is not to be attempted, left beginning without Materials, the whole Defign be given over in the middle, for out of this are to be taken the Foundation Stones, on which the whole Structure fhould be raifed, and thofe ought to be proportioned according to the reft of the Materials; for otherwife there may follow great Inconveniences, in profecuting of it, here therefore ought to be laid up the more fubftantial Parts: But as for the moft curious and precious things which may ferve for the finifhing or compleating this grand Structure, they are to be fought for as occafion fhall require and prompt. For as in any great building, none can be fo perfpicacious as to forefee every particular thing he fhall need, for the compleating of it, but leaves the Care of providing them till occafions call for them, as being then beft able to judge which of that kind of Material which is wanting will be moft fitting for his purpofe, and fo with that proceeds till other occafions call for, other Requifites and Helps: And fo from time to time furnifhes himfelf with thofe more choice things, as the Occafions require; fo there is none but before he fets upon fuch a Defign, will be fure to provide himfelf of a fufficient Store of fuch Materials as he knows altogether neceffary, nor will he neglect to lay hold on fuch things, as offering themfelves by chance, put him in mind that he fhall have occafion for them before he can finifh his Defign; and certainly much better it were, if the Architect were fo skilful as to forefee to provide all kinds of Materials before he begins; for thereby his Work would be carried on the more compleatly and uniformly, without Neceffity of pulling down, or altering, or piecing, or transforming any part, or ftaying or interrupting.

The Cafe is much the fame in providing a proper Hiftory for the perfecting of a new Body of Philofophy, the Intellect fhould firft like a skilful Architect, underftand what it defigns to do, and then confider as near as can be, what things are requifite to be provided in order to this Defign, then thofe Materials are to be carefully fought for and collected, and fafely laid up in fo convenient an Order, that they may not be far to feek when they are wanting, nor hard to be come by when they are found: In the choice of which, Care ought to be taken that they are found and good, and cleans'd and freed from all thofe things which are fuperfluous and infignificant to the great Defign; for thofe do nothing elfe but help to fill the Repofitory, and to incumber and perplex the Ufer, yet notwithftanding, Brevity is not fo much to be ftudied, as to omit many little Circumftances which may be confiderable in the ufe of it, for as in the laying up of Timber, the keeping on a branching part does make it ferviceable for many Defigns which it would be wholly unfit for, if it had been fquared off, fo it will be in the fitting and preparing the Particulars for a Philofophical Hiftory,

ftory, there muft be Judgment in the Hiftorian to difcern what will be material and ufeful in general, and what will be more efpecially adapted for the Inquiry whatever he defigns.

This Similitude therefore hints unto us the whole Method of making a Philofophical Hiftory, according to which, I fhall enumerate the feveral things neceffary to this Defign, and according to my Ability, endeavour to explain each Particular in fuch Order, and fo far forth as to me feems moft natural and confonant to my prefent Purpofe. But firft I fhall premife fome of the Accomplifhments requifite for a Natural Hiftorian.

There feem therefore thefe Requifites to accomplifh one, that intends to profecute or do any thing confiderable in this Work, without which the Collections may very much fail of the defirable Excellency in this or that Particular, though perhaps as to the kind they may contain many good things. *§ I. Of the Requifites in a Natural Hiftorian.*

The Firft is, That he ought to be very well skill'd in thofe feveral kinds of Philofophy already known, to underftand their feveral Hypothefes, Suppofitions, Collections, Obfervations, &c. their various ways of Ratiocinations and Proceedings, the feveral Failings and Defects both in their way of Raifing, and in their way of managing their feveral Theories: For by this Means the Mind will be fomewhat more ready at gueffing at the Solution of many Phenomena almoft at firft Sight, and thereby be much more prompt at making Queries, and at tracing the Subtilty of Nature, and in difcovering and fearching into the true Reafon of things; and though perhaps none of thofe Methods of Philofophy he has been accuftomed to, may any way direct him in the Contrivance of this New Fabrick, yet 'tis with the Exercifes of the Mind as with the Operations of the Body; one that has been bred up, and well skill'd in any Trade, fhall go much more readily and handily about it, and make a much better piece of Work of a quite new Defign in that Trade, than one that has not been at all us'd to fuch kind of Operations; there muft be a time to bring and fix the Mind to a Regard and Heedfulnefs of this kind of Contemplation, and a time alfo to accuftom it to Meditation and Contrivance, and a time to acquaint it with rationating from material Obfervations before it can go about fuch a Defign dexteroufly. Befides this alfo, the Mind will, by being acquainted with various Conjectures and Solutions of things, be much fooner and better freed from Prejudice; for by difcovering experimentally the Errors in this or that Hypothefis, 'twill be much eafier taken off from adhering to any, and fo enjoy a greater Freedom of perceiving and imbracing Truth from what occafion foever it be offered.

Next, As he ought to be knowing in Hypothefes, fo ought he alfo to be very well furnifhed with thofe things, which will moft affift the Mind in making, examining, and ratiocinating from Experiments. And thefe are chiefly two, Mathematicks and Mechanicks; the one fomewhat more fpeculative, the other more practical: The one qualifying the Mind with a moft exact Idea and Pattern of Ratiocination, Demonftration, Invention, and Detection: The other acquainting and inftructing it with the Proceffes of Action, and Operation. He ought firft of all, and chiefly to be very well skill'd in Geometry and Arithmetick, the more demonftrative Parts, and Algebra the more inventive Part of it: And this not only, as it furnifhes the Mind as it were with Numbers, Weights, and Meafures to inquire into, examine and prove all things; but as it alfo inftructs and accuftoms the Mind to a more ftrict way of Reafoning to a more nice and exact way of examining, and to a much more accurate way of inquiring into the Nature of things: The other more Phyfical Parts of Mathematicks are alfo very ufeful in their kind; fhewing a Way and Method of applying the former to Phyfical Ufes and Inquiries. Mechanicks alfo being partly Phyfical, and partly Mathematical, do bring the Mind more clofely to the Bufinefs it defigns, and fhews it a Pattern of Demonftration, in Phyfical Operations, manifefts the poffible Ways, how Powers may act in the moving refifting Bodies: Gives a Scheme of the Laws and Rules of Motion, and as it were enters the Mind into a Method of accurate and demonftrative Inquiry and Examination of Phyfical Operations. For though the Operations of Nature are more fecret and abftrufe;

and

and hid from our difcerning, or difcovering of them, than thofe more grofs and obvious ones of Engines, yet it feems moft probable, by the Effects and Circumftances ; that moft of them may be as capable of Demonftration and Reduction to a certain Rule, as the Operations of Mechanicks or Art. And from thofe, which are yet fomewhat more fpeculative, he ought to proceed to acquaint himfelf with others more complicated Mechanical Operations : Such as Chymical, and the Phyfical, yea even divers Mechanical Operations in many other Trades : For by thefe Ways, he will be better acquainted and enabled how to deal with Nature, for the procuring and getting more hidden Jewels and greateft Myfteries. But this is not yet enough, for the way to acquire thefe things certainly is not as yet fully difcovered, much lefs has it been practifed, he cannot have a Pilot to direct him certainly, to fhew the exact Courfe, and defcribe all the Turnings and Windings, and Shoalds, and many other Difficulties that are to be met withal, in this Attempt : Moft of thefe things muft be left to his own prudent and wary Management of his own Defigns.

And, as *Columbus* did in the Difcovery of the New World of *America*, he ought to contrive his Defign well ; then to procure what Helps and Affiftances he is able, laftly, thoroughly to profecute it, and not be difcouraged by the many Croffes and ill Succeffes he may at firft chance to meet with in the Attempt, and afterwards alfo in the Profecution thereof.

Thirdly, Therefore being thus well provided, he ought very thoroughly and ferioufly to confider of his Defign ; and this he fhould do firft by propofing to himfelf the end of his Inquiry ; then by confidering from the Nature of the Inquiry, what things feem moft likely to be conducive thereunto, and accordingly to fet down thofe things as *quæfita* or Requifites ; then further to confider well, and contrive by what means each of thefe Properties may be attain'd, *viz.* By what Experiments or Obfervations, what Engines, and Contrivances are neceffary, and how to be ufed : And for this end it is altogether neceffary, that he be able to defign and draw very well, thereby to be able both to exprefs his own Ideas the better to himfelf, to enable him to examine them and ratiocinate upon them himfelf, and alfo for the better informing and inftructing of others ; for there are many things which cannot be made as plain to the Underftanding, by a large Defcription in Words, as by the Delineation of them in a quarter of a Sheet of Paper. Drawing therefore is not only neceffary in point of Invention of Mechanick Contrivances and Demonftrations, but for the Regiftring Particulars, and compiling a defirable Hiftory. Next, Having contrived his Methods of Examination, he ought to profecute them with great Diligence and Judgment, in ordering, ufing, and deducting from them.

4thly, In the Profecution of each of which, he ought to proceed with the greateft Degree of Candor and Freedom from Prejudice, not to be byaffed by this or that Opinion in making of Deductions, nor by the Pleafantnefs or Gainfulnefs of the Experiment, or any other by Confideration that does not immediately look at the prefent Difcovery he is fearching after ; for though thofe things are not to be wholly neglected, but rather mark'd by the by, and *in tranfitu*, yet the Mind is not to dwell upon them, or look otherwife after them, than as they are conducive to the prefent Inquiry, as they manifeft a Truth or difcover an Error, left like fweet finging Syrens they feduce their Followers out of their right way to their utter Deftruction. He ought alfo to proceed with the greateft Circumfpection and Diligence to find out fuch things, as are Indications of what he feeks, and from thofe to take Incouragement to profecute his Intentions, as *Columbus* did from the decreafing Depth of the Sea, the Drift of Weeds on the Surface of the Water, and the White Clouds that appear'd near the Horizon, and the like to incourage and direct him in his Courfe.

5. He ought to get what Help he can from others to affift him in this his Undertaking ; for 'tis not to be expected from the fingle Endeavours of any one Man, though the moft accomplifht, that any great Matter fhould be done, Man's Life will be well near half fpent, before he can be fit to undertake this
Work,

Work, and 'twill be a long time afterwards, before a sufficient Supellex can be gathered by his single Endeavours: Besides, there is much of Expence requisite, which every one cannot so well bear, that may perhaps be otherwise fit for this Employment; he must therefore here also imitate *Columbus*, endeavour to be provided with Ships, and Men, and Money, and all those Assistances he finds requisite for the thorough Prosecution of this Discovery.

6. *Lastly*, He ought, as *Columbus* did, freely and impartially to discover what he finds; but yet with particular and more especial Regard to the great Promoters and Benefactors of this Design, and what Assistances he has receiv'd he ought candidly to acknowledge: And whatsoever he registers, he ought to do it in the plainest, shortest, and most significant Description, the Matter is capable of, and in such a Method as may neither cause Repetition of History, in more places than one, nor the Rejection of some others, because it fits not punctually to his Method: He ought likewise to own what Information any one has contributed toward the compiling of such a History; and to be as careful that he be not impos'd on, either by the Ignorance or Deceit of such as seem to be assisting.

The next thing to be considered is, what the Subject of his Enquiry is; which I shall endeavour to explain, by setting down the General Scheme of the whole Matter, about which a Philosophical History is to treat.

And this is not of less extent than the World, there is no Body or Operation in the Universe, at least if it can be any way brought to our Knowledge, that is not some way or other to be taken notice of in this Great Work, the most precious are here not more considerable, nor perhaps so much as the most trivial and vile: Every thing is here to be taken notice of only as it is lucriferous or conducive to the Discovery of Truth, and for a while at least the Lucriferousness of any that occurs (unless for the Cause of encouraging others in the Search) is to be omitted; lest thereby the Mind be diverted before it have gone through with its first Undertaking. Nor though the Volumes requisite to be filled with this kind of History be many, and so may seem to confound the Mind with the very thought of making use, or examining over the Particulars therein, and much more with the thought of compiling and collecting them; yet if we consider but the Volumes that are already writ on Subjects that have much less of Reality, and those perhaps by some one Man, and the Volumes he has been fain to tumble and search over for the collecting of the Matter contain'd in them, besides the Multitude of Thoughts and Perplexities of Mind in spinning out Niceties and ranging them, we may find the Labour and Perplexities of these Collections of real things, nothing comparable for Difficulty to those of Fiction, and Imagination; for I have very good Reason to believe, that the whole Mass of Natural History, may be contain'd in much fewer words than the Writings of divers single Authors: And the Method of using them will be much more easy, and the Labour of interpreting or understanding them, if done aright, will be almost as easy as to unravel a Bottom when you begin at the right end. The Method of distributing the Matter of Philosophical History, both for making Heads of Inquiry, and consequently also of registring them, need not be very nice or curious, they being in them laid up only in Heaps as it were, as in a Granary or Store-House; from thence afterwards to be transcribed, fitted, ordered and rang'd, and Tabled, as I shall afterward explain to be made fit for Use; for (as I instanced before) a sufficient Store of sound and good Materials, ought to be collected before the Work of Superstructure can be begun.

We will divide the whole Business of Philosophical History into these particular Heads of Inquiry, in which we have not so much proceeded according to the Nature of the things themselves, as according to their Appearance or Respect to us: For though the Earth, in Comparison of the Heavens, be as it were a Point, yet in Relation to its Nearness and Sensibleness to us, it becomes much more considerable, and the Consideration of it and its Parts will take up the greatest Part of this History. We will divide the Subject of Philosophical History into two Parts; to wit, into things Natural and things Artificial.

§ II. The Subject of Philosophical History in general.

G

Natural

Natural things may according to their Refpects to us, be diftinguifhed into containing or contain'd Bodies; the great containing Body we call Æther, in this may be confider'd either its Magnitude and Figure; or its Parts: Or its Motions: Or its Mixtures: Or the things contain'd by it. Thefe laft are either Comets, or Planets, or Stars, the Planets we yet know of are either Primary or Secundary; the Primary are thefe ☿, ♀, the Earth, ♂, ♃, ♄, the Secundary are the Moon, the Satellites of ♃ the Lunal of *Saturn.* All thefe, faving the Earth, being remov'd much out of reach, may be compriz'd under one only Head; but of the Earth being nearer to us, we may confider its Parts. By the Earth I underftand, all the Bodies contain'd within the Compafs of the Atmofphere: In the Atmofphere therefore being that which contains the reft, we may confider either its Figure and Extent, its Parts its Mixtures, its Motions, the things it contains: Thefe laft are either greater or lefs, the greater are the two great Maffes of Body, of which the Earth is made up, Namely, Water and Earth; the leffer are Animals. Animals are Infects, Birds, Beafts, Men: In the Water we may confider either its Figure and Extent, its Parts, its Mixtures, its Motions. The things contain'd, thefe, are either Vegetables or Animals; Vegetables fofter, and ftony Animals, Infects, Fifhes, Beafts. In the Earth we may confider its Magnitude and Figure, its Parts, its Mixtures, its Motions, the things it contains; thefe may be Metals. Plants, Mufhrooms, Moffes, Herbs, Shrubs, Trees, from which Confideration of the Matters of which Hiftory is to be written, might be collected Tables or Heads for Inquiry; but becaufe thefe might feem Dogmatical, and thereby be offenfive to fome, and might feem to favour of Prejudice, or favour to the *Copernican* Hypothefis, which I have been endeavouring to provide againft; I fhall make choice of this following Diftribution, which is made only according to the Appearance of things.

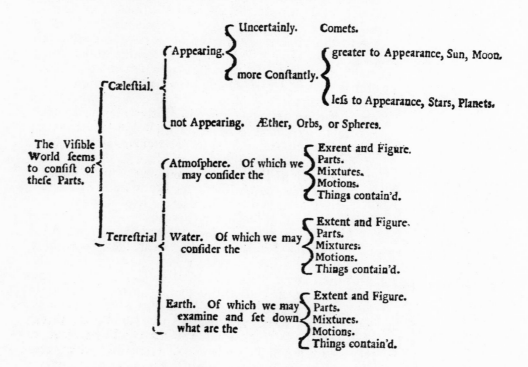

From which Diftribution of things on the firft of thefe, we may make thefe particular Heads of Inquiry, which for the Journal or firft Book of Entries, will be particular and diftinct enough.

Artic. I. *The Hiftories of Natural things.*

1. The Hiftory of Comets and Blazing Stars.
2. The Hiftory of the Sun, Moon, Stars and Planets.
3. The Hiftory of the Æther.
4. The Hiftory of the Height, Extent, Figure, &c. of the Atmofphere or Air.

5. The

5. The Hiſtory of the Variety of its Parts, or ſeveral Climates, and in ſeveral Regions or Heights.

6. The Hiſtory of the various kinds of Mixtures it ſuffers from Meteors.

7. The Hiſtory of its various Motions, Breizes, Winds, Storms, Hurricanes, &c

8. The Hiſtory of Inſects.

9. The Hiſtory of Birds.

10. The Hiſtory of Beaſts.

11. The Hiſtory of Man.
- Anatomical Hiſtory of the Internal Parts of Man, compar'd with thoſe of other Animals.
- Anat. Hiſt. of the Humors and Motions in the Bodies of Men, compar'd alſo.
- The Hiſtory of the Shapes, Cuſtoms, Diets, Ages, Diſeaſes, Cures of Men in divers Countries.
- The Hiſt. of Senſation, Motion of the Mind, Memory, Reaſon, Folly, Madneſs, Sleeping, & Dreams, &c.

12. The Hiſtory of the Figure, Extent, Bulk, &c. of the Water.

13. The Hiſtory of the Seas, Lakes, Ponds, Rivers, Fountains, Subterraneous Rivers, &c.

14. The Hiſtory of the various ſorts of Bodies that are found incorporate, or that may be diſſolv'd by it, as Salts, Slimes, Gums, &c.

15. The Hiſtory of Currents, Ebbings and Flowings, Increaſe and Decreaſe, Overflowings, Inundations, and Deſertings of ſeveral Parts, of Voragoes, Submarine Fountains, &c.

16. The Hiſtory of Sea-Inſects, compar'd with Aerial and Terreſtrial.

17. The Hiſtory of Fiſh, both of freſh Water and Salt, deſcribing their Internal Structure, and Shapes as well as Outwards.

18. The Hiſtory of Sea Beaſts, &c. Morſes, Seales, Tortoiſes, &c. Anatomiz'd and compar'd with other Creatures.

19. The Hiſtory of the Extent, Figure, Magnitude, &c. of the Earth, both in reſpect of other great Bodies in the World, as the Sun, the Moon, the Sea, &c. and in reſpect alſo of the Body of Man, or our common Meaſures.

20. The Hiſtory of its various Parts, External Mountains, Vales, Plains, Clifts, Places of Reception for the Sea, &c.

21. The Hiſtory of its Mixtures, Metals, Minerals, Stones, Clays, Earths, Sands, Oyls, Salts, &c. and the various Conſtitution of its Parts; the ſeveral Regions of it, of what kind of Shells, or Layers of Sand, Stone, Earth, Clay, &c. it conſiſts at ſeveral Depths.

22. The Hiſtory of its Motions, Diurnal, Annual, Lunar, or Tide making.

23. The Hiſtory of its Internal Motions, Earthquakes, Eruptions, &c. Tranſpoſitions and Transformations.

24. The Hiſtory of the Magnetiſm of it.

25. The Hiſtory of its Gravitating Power.

26. The Hiſtory of the Subterraneous Fires, Rivers, Caverns, Damps, &c.

27. The Hiſtory of Muſhrooms, Moſſes and Plants, Roots, &c.

28. The Hiſtory of Shrubs and Trees.

29. The Hiſtory of Ground Animals and Worms.

Beſides theſe particular Hiſtories of the ſeveral parts of the World, there ought to be ſeveral Hiſtories compos'd of the prime ſenſible Qualities, ſuch as may ſerve afterwards for the finding out of thoſe Proprieties firſt which are more ſimple, ſuch as theſe.

1. The Hiſtory of Light and Darkneſs.

2. The Hiſtory of Tranſparency and Opacouſneſs.

3. The Hiſtory of Colours, commonly diſtinguiſht into real and appearing.

4. The Hiſtory of Sounds, Muſical and Harmonious.

5. The Hiſtory of Taſtes.

6. The Hiſtory of Smells.

7. The Hiſtory of Heat and Cold.

8. The Hiſtory of Gravity and Levity.

9. The

9. The History of Density and Expansion.
10. The History of Flexibility and Stiffness.
11. The History of Malleability and Brittleness.

2dly, The Histories of Artificial and Mechanical Operations. And these Histories will be most adorn'd and compleated from the History of Mechanical Employments and Operations, and most especially by judicious and accurate Experiments, designedly tried; the true Nature of each of which Proprieties being exactly determin'd, will hugely facilitate all the other Inquiries in Philosophy. It were very desirable therefore, that though these Histories are here placed in the Second Place; yet they were primarily and chiefly to be regarded; for the Knowledge of these, will extreamly rectify the Mind both in propounding Queries, and also in making Examinations aright, for the Nature of all these Proprieties being known in a Body, the true Texture and Constitution of the Body may be much more easily found.

Thus much for the Heads of Natural Histories, next for Artificial. It will be requisite to take notice of, and enumerate all the Trades, Arts, Manufactures, and Operations, about which Men are imployed, especially such as either contain some Physical Operation, or some extraordinary Mechanical Contrivance, for such as these will very much inrich a Philosophical Treasury. And these we may distinguish into these several Heads, according to the various Materials about which they are conversant. We may refer

To Fire. 1. The History of { Chymists, either such as make Tryals on Metals, or operate on Mineral, Vegetable, or Animal Substances.

To Air. 2. The History of { the various Ways of making use of the Air for the Motion of Ships, Mills, Engines, &c.

To the Water. 3. The History of { Rowers, ways of cutting Rivers and making them Navigable, Engines for raising Water; for sinking Water, &c. for sounding the Depth, the History of Divers, Swimmers, Sailors, &c.

To the Earth. 4. The History of { Surveyors, the most expedite ways, as also the most exact.
Miners, their ways of finding the Mineral; of digging, clearing, and breaking through Rocks and Rivers in their Passage, of the various Earths they meet with, as also of their Damps, and other Exhalations.

The Histories also of such as are conversant about Mineral, Vegetable, and Animal Substances, such as these.

To Earths and Clays. 5. The History of { Potters, Tobacco-Pipe-Makers, Glass makers, Glasiers, Glass Grinders, Looking-Glass-Makers, or Foilers, Spectacle Makers, and Optick Glass-Makers, Makers of Counterfeit Pearl and precious Stones, Bugle-Makers, of Lamp-blowers, Colour Makers, Colour-Grinders, Glass-Painters, Enamellers, Varnishers, Colour-Sellers, Painters, Limners, Picture-Drawers, Makers of Baby Heads, and Bowling Stones or Marbles, Counterfeit Marble, Wax-work, Casters.
Brick-makers, Tile-makers, Lime-burners, Plasterers, Paviers, Pargiters, Furnace makers, China Potters, Crucible Makers.

To Stones. 6. The History of { Masons, Stone-cutters, Statuaries, Sculptors, Architects, &c. Crystal-cutters, Engravers in Stones, Jewellers, or Stone-Setters.

7. The History of { Making Salt, Alum, Salt-peter, Vitriol, Gunpowder, Sul phur, Bitumen Naphtha, Sal Armoniac, Sandiver, Kelp, Borax, Pot-ashes, Soap-boilers, Refiners, Colliers. *To Minerals.*

8. The History of {
Iron-Mills, and Founding in Iron, of forging it into Bars, *To Iron.* of Anchor-Smiths, &c. Plate-makers, Nail-makers.
Steel-making.
Lock-smiths, Gun-smiths, Jack-smiths, Edge-tool makers and Hardners; Grinders and Forgers, Armourers, Spur-riers, Bit makers, Needle makers, Hook-makers, Tool-makers, Wire Lettice and Cage-makers, or Latton-men, Spring-makers, File-cutters, Chirurgeons Instrument-ma-kers, Engine-makers, and Crofs-bow-makers.

9. The History of { Plumbers, Shot-making, Cerufe-making, Red Lead ma- *To Lead.* king, &c.

10. The History of { Latin-makers, and Tin-men, Type-founders, Printers, of *To Tin belong* making Soder and Putte, Glafs colours. *these Trades,* Pewterers, Pipe or Worm-founders, Organ Pipe-makers. *whose Hiftories fhould be col-lected.*

11. The History of {
Copper-fmiths and Founders. *Copper and*
Ingravers, Etchers, Emboffers, &c. *Brafs.*
Brafs-making, and Founders of Bells, Ordnance, Pots, Nails, and other fmall things.
Brafiers and Tinkers, Clafp-makers, Scale-makers and Weight makers, Thimble-makers.
Plate makers, Burnifhers, Roll-Prefs Printers.
Clock makers and Watchmakers, Mathematick Inftru-ment makers, Turners.
Wire, drawers, Tinfey-makers, Pin-makers, Taggers.
Trumpet-makers, &c.

12. The History of {
Smelters and Refiners. *Gold and Sil-*
Gold and Silver-fmiths, and Guilders, Coiners, Inlayers, *ver.*
Enamellers.
Gold-beaters, and Wire-drawers, and Throfter or Spin-ners, Lace and Stuff makers, Spangle makers.

13. The History of {
Husbandry and Gardning, Botanicks, and Sugar Planters, *Vegetables.* Tobacco Planters, Saffron, and Ginger, Liquorice Plan-ters, &c. Threfhers, Ploughmen.
Flax-makers, Dreffers, Spinners, Lace makers, Button-makers, Weavers, Calenders, Hatchelers, Whitefters, Painter Stainers, Fuftian-makers, Twine and Packthread-makers, Net-makers, Sieve-makers and Serce makers, Rope-makers, Cauckers, Sail-makers, Mat-makers, Semf-pters, Bone-lace Makers, Tape-makers, Straw-work makers.
Malters, Millers, Brewers, Bakers, Vintagers, Vintners, Diftillers, Strong-water-men, Alehoufe-keepers, and Ci-der-makers, the Makers of Coffee, Chocolate, and vari-ous other Drinks, Victuallers.
Preservers of Corn, Fruit, Hops, Wood, Indico, Spices and various other Drugs, as Meal-men, Fruiterers, Co-ftermongers, Brazil-grinders, Hop-dreffers, Wood men, Madder Planters, Rape-Oyl Makers, Seed-men.
Grocers, Drugfters, Apothecaries, Confectioners, Sugar-Bakers, Smokers, Tobacco-cutters, Huckfters, Perfumers, Garblers of Spices.

H   Paper

Paper and Paftboard making, Stationers, Bookfellers, Printers, Compofers, Scriveners, Starch-makers, &c.

Woodfellers, Barkers and Cole Charrers, Woodmongers.

Sawyers and Saw-mills, Carpenters, Shipwrights, Mill-wrights, Pump-makers, Joyners, Cabinet-makers, Screw-makers, Mufical Inftrument-makers, Organ-makers, Car-vers, Turners, Fletchers, Bowyers, Archers, Buttonmold-makers, Coopers, Gagers, Basket-makers, Box makers, Comb-makers, Laft and Heel makers, Broom and Mop-makers, Bellows makers, Hoop-makers, Lath-makers.

To Animals. — **14. The Hiftory of**

Shepherds, Grafiers, Goatherds, Swineherds, Sow-gelders, Grooms, and Horfe-Courfers, Bear and Lyon Keepers, Dog-catchers and Keepers, Rangers or Keepers of Parks, Warrens or Forefts.

Farriers, and the various ways of Curing Beafts, Mole-catchers, Rat-catchers.

Hunters, Hawkers, Fowlers, Decoyers, Fifhers, Draggers, Gunners, Fowl keepers and Lookers to Aviaries, &c.

About the Parts of Animals. — **15. The Hiftory of**

Sheep-fheerers, Fellmongers, Clothiers, worfted Combers, Spinfters, Knitters, Weavers, Cloth-dyers, Fullers, Cloth-workers, Sheerers, Hot-preffers, Taylors, Drawers, Embroiderers, Tapeftry-makers, Carpet-makers.

Felt-makers, Caftor-makers, Cap-makers, Furriers, Hair cloth-makers, and other kinds of Stuff, as Arras, Mille-ners, Pencil-makers, Brufh-makers.

Horners, Horn-turners, Comb-makers, Horn-makers, Hafters, Dice-makers.

Upholfterers, Feathermongers, Pen-makers.

Silk Trofters, Dyers, Weavers, Stocking-weavers and Knit-ters, Ribbond weavers, Gumflower makers, Mercers, Silk-men, Button-makers, Lace-makers, Embroiderers, Preffers and Waterers.

Bee-keepers, Silkworm-keepers.

Leather-dreffers, Parchment makers, Glovers, Perfumers, Tanners, Curriers, Shooe makers, Bottle-makers, Harnefs and Coller-makers, Sadlers, Coach-makers, Cafe makers, Trunk makers, Book-binders, Sheath-makers, Leather-fellers, Leather-guilders, Belt-makers.

Butchers, Cooks, Tallow-chandlers, Wax-chandlers, Cheefemongers.

Fifhmongers, Ripiers, Oyle-makers, Soap-boylers, &c.

There are other Imployments, more particu-larly about Man. — **16. The Hiftory of**

School-mafters, Writing mafters, Printers, Mufick-mafters, Stage-players, Dancing-mafters, Horfe-riders, Fencers, Vaulters, Tumblers, Wreftlers, &c.

Apothecaries, Chirurgeons, Barbers, Laundreffes, Cofme-ticks, Seamfters, Taylors, &c.

In the writing of all which Hiftories there may be two things defign'd, either a Defcription of the things themfelves, whereby Inquifitive Perfons that are ignorant of them, may come to a more perfe&t Knowledge of them ; in order to fome other Defign as for Curiofity, or Difcourfe, or Profit, and Gain, or the like : Or fuch a Defcription of them as is only in order to the Ufe of Philo-fophical Inquiry, for the Invention of Caufes, and for the finding out the ways and means Nature ufes, and the Laws by which fhe is reftrain'd in producing divers Effe&ts.

And this laft is that which is chiefly aim'd at in this Defign (though others alfo whofe Intenfions are only of the former kind, may find much to fatisfy
their

their Defires) for thefe being known and applied, not only the Reafons of the ways already made ufe of in feveral Trades might be eafily known : But each of them highly amended and improved, and by other ways performed with much more Eafe, Speed and Certainty.

In the Hiftory therefore of Trades, we are chiefly to look after the Phyfical Proprieties of each, as what is hard or foft, what flexible or ftiff, what fharp, corrofive, what odoriferous, balfamick and prefervative, what putrifactive and corruptive, &c. together with the manner of applying Agents to Patients, and to obferve the manner of Natures proceeding, where fhe is impos'd on by Art, and limited to this or that Degree, and not fuffer'd to act otherwife, by what Ways fhe may be affifted, accelerated, regarded, ftopt, and the like, in her ufual Proceedings; for thefe being known, moft of the other things will be very eafy and follow of courfe. We ought alfo, to take notice of the various forts of Mechanical Engines, which ferve to affift and direct the hand in performing many Operations together, with Eafe and Speed and certainty : which are not otherwife done without much Uncertainty, Time, and Difficulty; and of the feveral Slights and Contrivances in Operations, and the order of them, which precede and which follow, and the Efficacioufnefs of them in this or that Method.

Befides thefe Trades I have been mentioning, there are many excellent Experiments and Secrets to be found fcattered up and down in Mens Practifes, which have not come up to that Confiderablenefs in the Commonwealth as to be made a Trade, which yet contain in them divers Circumftances of very excellent Ufe and Information, thofe alfo ought to be fought out and collected and rang'd into their proper Places, if at leaft they can properly be referr'd to any of the foregoing Heads, otherwife they are to make a particular Head of themfelves: Of this kind there are a multitude almoft in all Eftates and Conditions of Men, which to this Defign will be of huge Importance, and will afford very much Information, even out of the moft vile and feemingly moft foolifh and trivial things, and of thofe which are moft common, and therefore pafs without regard, becaufe ufual, may be collected things of moft excellent Ufe; and therefore, nothing in this Defign is to be look'd on with the Eye of the Vulgar, and with Prejudice, according to the Efteem it has obtain'd in the World with the Generality of Men, who generally judge or efteem of things only for the immediate Pleafure or Profit they afford, and look no further; therefore 'tis not equal to make their Efteem who underftand them, the Standard of the value of things for this ufe. So that a diligent Naturalift can go no-where, but he may find a Subject for him to contemplate and examine, but efpecially in fuch Places as are moft or leaft frequented, for the Obvioufnefs in the one, and Difficulty in the other, has made Multitudes of confiderable Obfervations to be neglected.

Having thus curforily fumm'd up the chief Heads of thofe things that are fit to be the Subject of Natural Hiftory, I fhall next adjoyn a Specimen of what things are to be inquired after in them, that fo any other that fhall have an Opportunity, and willing to promote this Defign, may accordingly, whatever the thing be he defigns to write a Hiftory of, firft propound to himfelf the things, which upon a ferious Confideration of the Matter, he fhall judge to be moft likely to be inftructive for the difcovering of the true Nature of that which he inquires into. *§ III. The Methods of making the Enquiries.*

For it cannot be expected, that any one fhould be alike able to make Queries of thofe things in which he has not been much, if at all converfant; as one that has had an Opportunity of acquainting himfelf more particularly with the Nature of it, and has imbib'd in (though he knows not how) a great deal of imperfect Knowledge of the Proprieties of it. He ought therefore to confider with himfelf, what things there are in the Subject he would inquire into, which being told him, he fhould be able to know the true Propriety, Nature and Texture of it : And fuppofing he had met with fome one that could refolve him, what Queftions he would ask him, by the Refolution of which he fhould be able to find out what he feeks; and accordingly he ought to fet down thofe Queftions in Writing, that fo he may have a Scheme before his Eyes what are the things he looks after, what his Scope and Aim is.

And

The way of an-
swering the
Queries.

And having set down these Queries, he ought in the next place to consider what things seem requisite to attain those ends ; what means he can imagine may be conducive to the solving or answering those Questions, that is, what Observations, Examinations, or Experiments would seem conducive thereunto, and accordingly under every such Query or Question, he ought to set down the things requisite to be known for the obtaining the full Knowledge of a compleat and full Answer to it ; afterwards with Care and Diligence he ought to make Examination and Try-al of what he has propounded, one thing after another, with much Circumspection, for accordingly as these Queries are made with more or less Judgment, and as the means conducive to the Resolution of them are more judiciously pitcht on, and diligently try'd more or less considerable, so will the Particulars to be en-tred in the Diary be ; and the more or less useful for a Philosophical Treasury. In the making of which Experiments and Tryals, it were very desirable that the Inquirer would first make Tryal of them once all over, and observe diligently and enter into a Paper by themselves as many Particulars as he can discover worth noting, and then a second time to make them over again. In the doing of which, it would be very convenient to get some such Person to be present as has not been acquainted with Experiments on that Subject, though ingenious and inquisitive in other Physical Searches, because such a Person may take no-tice of many Particulars which are in themselves very observable, but were and would still have been neglected because of their being obvious, and because the Inquirer having been long accustomed to the seeing of them without thinking them any ways considerable, will be now very prone to do as formerly, slight and neglect them, and this will be instructive to him in shewing him in what things he is most likely to be overseen in, as well as shewing him the things themselves. The Tryal of these Experiments, 'tis very likely, will much further his Knowledge, and shew him perhaps the Solution of some of his Queries, as well as the Error and Insignificancy of others ; and may perhaps much better instruct him how to make his second Class of Queries, and how to proceed in the solving and answering them, they will not only facilitate the Labour of making and accustome his Mind to a greater Circumspection, but will suggest also various ways of examining and experimenting, which without this Method of inquiring would not have been thought of.

And though indeed the Multitude of Queries that may be made upon every Subject, may seem to make this Work infinite and impossible to be compleated, yet if Men would but prosecute thoroughly, according to the ways I propound in this Tract, such kind of Inquiries in order to the Discoveries of the Pro-prieties of some Bodies, or for finding out the Nature of some general Qualities. I cannot doubt but that such Endeavours would produce so considerable Disco-veries, as would not only serve for the Explication of that one Body inquir'd into, but of Multitudes of Bodies of the like Nature ; and every such Inven-tion will ease the Inquiries in most other Bodies, half in half, after the same Propriety. As to give an Instance propounding to my self to find out the Rea-

An Example of
the Method.

son of the Lightness of Cork. I set down among other ways of Tryal to exa-mine the Texture of it with a good Microscope, hoping that possibly I might thereby be able to discover its Texture, to this end I examin'd several Pieces of Cork, whose sides I had cut very smooth with a Razor, but the glaring Refle-ction from the Multitude of sides that compose its Surface made me unable, though I try'd it in several Lights to discern any kind of Pores, I bethought me therefore of shaving off a very thin Sliver of Cork, and laying it on a black Ground, I could with my Microscope then plainly perceive the Texture of its Substance, that it was as porous as a Honey-comb ; that is, all over full of small long Pores, upon and down, through the length of which were inter-spers'd many cross Diaphragms, or Valves, by which means the Air is impri-son'd in very curious close Boxes. Finding these in Cork, I proceeded to find the same in Wood, not doubting but the Lightness of that might proceed from some such Cause, I made tryal with Wood both green and dry, shav'd after the same way, but in green Wood it succeeded not at all, but I could perceive di-vers larger up and down the dry. I conceived therefore, that it might be the Juice of the Plant which had fill'd those Holes, and therefore considering that in

Charcole

Charcole all that fuperfluous Juice is wafted, and evaporated, I made tryal of viewing a Coal in a Microfcope, and even beyond my Expectation, I could difcover fuch Multitudes of them and fo fmall, that I could hardly at firft believe my own Eyes, till trying the Experiment over and over again, I found the fame Propriety was not only to be found in one or two other kinds of Wood, but was common to all forts of Vegetables that I was able to charr.

Thus the Experiment of *Saccharum Saturni*, by diffolving Lead in an acid Liquor, and evaporating away the watery part, will hint to us a way of difcovering the Taftes of all kinds of Bodies ; that is, by diffolving thofe referved and taftelefs Bodies, in fome convenient *Menstruum*, for being once diffolv'd, it becomes diffoluble alfo, by the Vehicle of that *Menstruum*, to the *Saliva* or Juice in the Mouth, or Tongue which feems to be the Organ of Tafte.

Thus the finding out the Caufe of Fluidity, Heat, Gravity, Brittlenefs, *&c.* in one Body, will much facilitate the Inquiry after the like Properties in any other Body, fo that though indeed upon every fpecifick Body to be examin'd, there may be a Multitude of Queries propounded, yet the more præceeding Bodies have been by this Method examin'd, the fewer of them will there remain to be anfwer'd.

The Queries that may be made on the firft Head, I fhall refer to a following *The 1ft Head,* Difcourfe, concerning the late Comets, and of the Nature of Comets in ge- *of Comets.* neral.

The Queftions on the Second may be fome fuch as thefe.

The Difference between Stars and Planets ? *The 2d Head,*
How many Planets, Primary, or Secundary ? *of the Stars*
And how many fixt Stars ? *and Planets.*
In what Order plac'd ?
Of what Figure ?
Of what Magnitude compar'd to the Earth ?
How far diftant from the Earth ?
In what way they are mov'd ?
With what Velocity ?
In what time they perform their Revolutions ?
What Heat, or Light they have ?
From what Caufe their Heat or Light proceeds ?
What Influence they have on each other, or on the Earth ?
Whether they are conftant or changeable in being or appearing ?
Whether conftant in Magnitude and Figure ?
Whether conftant in Motion and Diftance ?
Whether conftant in Light, and Heat, and Influence ?
What Proprieties are common to them with the Earth ?
Whether included in Orbs, or fwimming in Æther ?
Whether the Ambient Body move them, or they the Ambient ?
Whether moving together with the Ambient, or mov'd through it ?
What the Confiftence of the Ambient Body may be ?
How much it may hinder or retard their Motions ?

Divers of thefe may be referr'd to the Third Head, concerning the Solidity *The 3d Head,* or Fluidity of the Æther, the Motion of it and the Refiftence of it to Bodies *of the Æther.* mov'd through it, and of the Tranfparency and Communicativenefs of it as a Medium : There might be many other things alfo propounded on this Head, as whether it permeates all Bodies, be the Medium of Light, be the Fluid Body in which the Air is but as a Tincture ? Whether it caufe Gravity ; in the Earth, or other Cæleftial Bodies ? Whether it affifts in the Action of Fire and burning, and in the Diffolution of other Bodies by *Menstruums*; in the Fermentation of Bodies, and Multitudes of the like ; which will be difpers'd up and down in the Queries, on feveral other Subjects, and are there beft refolv'd, though they may afterwards be referr'd and tranfcribed under this Third Head.

The Queries on the Fourth Head concerning the Atmofphere, may be fome fuch as thefe.

The 4th Head, of the Atmofphere, as to its Extent,&c.

Whether the Atmofphere, or Air be defin'd, or not; by a Superficies?

Whether it be not indefinitely extended upward, and continually more and more rarified the farther 'tis diftant from a' gravitating Body, as the Earth, Moon, &c.

Of what kind of Figure the groffer or more vaporous Air near the Surface of the Earth is; that is, Whether it be not much lower near the Poles than under the Torrid Zone?

Whether the Torricellian Experiments made at feveral Altitudes from the Earth, may not determine it?

Whether the Refraction and Gravitation of the Air, examin'd in both places by Inftruments, may not clear this Query? Since 'tis demonftrable that where the Refraction is greater with an equal Degree of Preffure, the Denfity of the Air muft needs be much greater near the Surface.

With what Bodies it is mixt? Whether with Water, Wood, Earth, Animal Subftances, and Vegetable Subftances, and with all forts of Liquors and Spirits?

Whether it helps to nourifh the Fires kindled within the Bowels of the Earth?

Whether it encompaſs the Sun and Planets, and that each of them have a peculiar Atmofphere, as well as they have a gravitating Power?

Whether the Fire, in the Sun, is not maintain'd by the Air that incompaffes it?

Whether the Spots in the Sun may not be Clouds of Smoke, or Vapours, rais'd up into that Atmofphere?

Whether the Combuftion of Comets may not be afcrib'd to the Diffolution of them by the incompaffing Air, which is fomewhat more condenfed near them?

The Queries on the Fifth Head, of the Variety of the Parts of the Air, may be fome fuch as thefe.

The 5th Head, of the Variety of the parts of the Air.

Whether the Air be not a kind of Volatile or fmall ramify'd Bodies fwimming in the Æther, like a Tincture in Water or in fome fuch fluid Body? Or, Whether the parts of it are infinitely fluid, or definitely folid, and if folid, then

Of what Figure and Magnitude, how they are kept afunder, or what fills the diffeminated Spaces between them?

What is the Caufe of making them capable of fo vaft a degree of Expanfion, and yet of being able to preferve their Elaftick Power outwards.

What Condenfation it is capable of bearing by Preffure from an Engine: Or from being let down to the bottom of a very deep Sea, or from Cold or from being let down a great Depth into the Earth?

What refractive Power it then has compar'd with the ordinary Air?

How much the Air may be rarified by Heat, by Exfuction, by the Torricellian Experiment, by Engines, by Vapours and the like?

By what Degrees the Air expands it felf, being carried upwards, and from the Surface of the Earth, and whether this comparative Expanfion be the fame in divers Countries, and in differing Seafons of the Year?

What the Height of the Air is that bears the higheft Clouds, what are the Height of Thunder Showers, Hail Showers, white dry Clouds, Halo's, Maccarel Skies, and the like?

What difference between the Air in thofe very high Places of the Earth, as *Tenariff*, the *Alps*, and the *Andes* in *Peru*, aud other Places as to Healthfulnefs, or Aptitude for Burning or Refpiration, or the Flight of Birds, or the like?

From what Bodies the Air may be generated anew, or whether that Air fo made be not fuch as had been formerly imprifon'd?

By

By what Varieties of Operations it may be produced, and by what Helps?

How the Air so generated may be preserved in the Form of Air?

How any kind of Air may be made to loose the Form of Air, and to be condens'd into a solid or fluid Body?

How much the Air in the Torrid Zone differs in Heat, and Dryness, or Moisture, or Rarefaction, or Pressure, or the like, from the Air nearer the Poles?

In what Proprieties it chiefly differs from other Liquors?

To the Sixth, Of the various kinds of Mixtures the Air suffers from Meteors, these Queries may be propounded.

What is the Cause of the sudden thickning or clearing of the Air?

The 6th Head, of the various Mixtures the Air suffers.

From what Power so great a Quantity of Water as has been observed to fall in some Thunder Showers, should be collected or gathered together?

Whether the Heat of the Sun alone, or some internal Heat in the Bowels of Earth should raise up so great a Quantity of Water?

Whether there be any such Meteors, as Earthy ones, rais'd up into the Air, and if so what becomes of them? Whether Smoke and Dust and such like Fumes do not fall, as fast as the Air cools, to the Earth?

Whether there were ever any such thing as a Thunder-bolt, or other such massy Body thrown out of the Air?

How much more space is fill'd by generated Vapours, than by the Water from whence they are made?

Why all Rains and falling Water are fresh?

Whether from the Coalition of divers sorts of Vapours together, there be not ingendred a new Quantity of Air, and the rest falls down in Drops or Flakes, as in the Experiment of making *Tartarum Vitriolatum*, whether that may not be the reason of the Figure of the Flakes of Snow, &c.

What is the Reason of the Shining or Light of the Star shootings, and in what Region or Height they are generated? Whether this may not be observed easily enough by two Confederates?

Whether they have any thing of Fire in them, or whether the Light may not be an effect of their rapid Motion?

Whether the rising of certain Steams from the Earth into the Air, may not be the Cause of precipitating the Exhalations, by causing the Air to throw off its Load in the same manner as a charged *Menstruum* will relinquish its dissolv'd Body, when it is penetrated by another Liquor of a contrary Nature, since by such kind of Experiments may be very well represented in little, almost all the Phenomena of the Changes of Air in the great Ocean of the Atmosphere.

What are the Causes of the Rain-bows, and their Colours?

What are the Reasons of the Duplication, Triplication, Quadruplication, &c. of both the Rain-bows? Which are obvious enough when the Bows are very vivid.

What are the Reasons of Rings about the Sun and Moon, and of their varying Bignesses at several times.

Why the under Superficies of Clouds are smooth, and seem to lie at the same level Distance from the Earth, whereas the Tops are Mountainous and unequal?

Why there are sometimes divers of these Regions of Clouds one above another, and in what those Clouds differ?

What is the reason of the various Figure of the Clouds, undulated, hairy, crisped, coyled, confus'd, and the like?

What is the cause of the Redness, &c. of high exalted Vapours?

What is the reason of those Multitudes of small Cobwebs that cloth the whole Face of the Ground after a Fogg? And why there are divers such white Substances flying up and down in the Air after such Fogs?

What is the cause of Lightning, whence that accensible Matter is rais'd up into the Air, and how collected, and how kindled?

What Artificial Experiments, with Fumes or Spirits accensible, will help to explicate them?

Whether

Whether all theſe Phenomena may not be ſolv'd by Chymical Experiments (of which kind I may perhaps hereafter manifeſt ſome not vulgar.)

Whether Fire in general be not the effect of the Air's corroding or diſſolving a heated combuſtible Body? How it comes firſt to be begun or kindled, how preſerved and continu'd, and how deſtroy'd, why it riſes in the Air whilſt it laſts, but quickly vaniſhes?

By what other means Fires may be generated, continued, made more intenſe, and much more violent?

What is the Nature and Properties of Niter or Salt peter, as to this Particular?

What the Mixture Coal-duſt performs in Gunpowder, and Alcalys in fulminating Powders?

The 7th Head, of the Motions and Qualities of the Air. To the Seventh, to wit, What are the Motions or Qualities of the Air? Theſe Queſtions, and divers others of the like kind, may be propounded.

What the Air contributes to the Generation and Corruption of Bodies, whether Mineral, Vegetable, Animal, *&c.*

What it contributes to the Preſervation or Deſtruction of Lifeleſs Bodies, by hardning, drying, ruſting, fermenting, *&c.*?

What it contributes to the Nouriſhment of Vegetables that grow in it? Since the Air is a kind of fluid that encompaſſes all things in it, after the ſame manner as the Water in the Sea incompaſſes the Vegetables that grow in it.

What is the uſe of it in Reſpiration, whether Fiſhes, Worms, Inſects, *&c.* have any uſe of it; or whether Water be not of the ſame uſe to Fiſhes, that Air is to the Anmals that live in it? Whether the comparing of the one with the other will not much facilitate the Explication?

What is the uſe of it in Fire? Whether it does not perform that Action after the manner of a *Menſtruum?*

Whether that Property in Air which promotes burning, be not of the ſame Nature with that of Salt peter?

By what means Fires may be extinguiſhed, by dry Bodies, by wet, or fluid Bodies, by the Air, and divers other liquid Bodies?

What Flame is, the Expanſion of it compar'd to the Denſity of common Air?

Why Fire or burning Bodies produce Light, Heat, Smoke, Aſhes, Salt, *&c.*

What the Air contributes to Corroſion and Diſſolution of Bodies?

What it contributes to the Fermentation, and Concoction or changing of Bodies?

What are its Motions, conſtant, anniverſary, periodical, accidental?

What are the Reaſons of Breizes, Winds, Storms, Hurricanes, Whirlwinds?

What are the Velocities and Strengths of each of theſe, and the Concomitants?

What are the Ebbings and Flowings of the Air diſcover'd by the Barometer, to what Regularity reducible, from what Cauſe they proceed, whether from the riſing of new Vapours, or from the flowing in of the Air from other Climates, or from the Motion of the Earth, Moon, *&c.*

What are the Motions of the upper Parts of the Air, whether in the ſame way, and with the ſame Velocity with the lower part of the Atmoſphere, why the Clouds that are plac'd one higher than another in ſeveral Regions and Stations, are ſometimes obſerv'd to go various ways at the ſame time, and none of them perhaps the ſame way with the Wind below.

Whence the Air is able to bear up the Clouds that ſeem denſer Bodies, whether from the Abatement of Gravity, or from the greater Cold and Denſity of the Air, at that height than near the Earth, or whether it be not more Denſe as to Expanſion, than the Clouds though the cloudy be more denſe in reſpect of Opacouſneſs.

Hence the Air is able to carry up Smoke, Duſt, and ſeveral bulky Bodies that are manifeſtly heavier, and why moſt apt in Summer when 'tis moſt expanded, whether it be not from longer Continuance of Heat, and from the Dryneſs of the Air in the Summer, and from the ſudden cooling, and the interſper'd Moiſture of the Air in Winter.

How

How it becomes able to sustain the heavy Bodies of Birds and Insects, and the like, and by what means it may be serviceable to raise and sustain much greater Bodies?

How much the Air impedes the Velocity of Bodies mov'd through it?

What part of the Air is the Medium of Light?

What is the Transparency or Opacousness of the Air, and from what Causes they proceed?

How much better a Body may be seen just upward at a Distance, than at the like Distance in a Horizontal or level Posture?

At what Distance a Body may be distinctly seen in a Horizontal Posture?

What is the comparative Reflectiveness and Refractiveness of the Air?

By what means may the Inflection or Multiplicate Refraction of the Air be found and determin'd?

What is the reason of the Undulations of the Sun and Moon, and bigger Planets, and of the twinkling of Stars?

What are the Causes of the appearing Blewness, Yellowness, Redness, &c. of Bodies through the Air?

By what means the Air becomes the Medium of Sound, whether the more dense or rarify'd, moist or dry, transparent or opacous, be fittest for that Conveyance?

With what Velocity Sound is conveyed through the Air, whether it may not be conveyed swifter by Strings well stretcht, or solid Bodies?

Whether it proceeds by strait or curve Lines?

Whether it be not alter'd by Winds, &c?

By what means it becomes the Medium to convey Smells?

How it dissolves or licks up the odorous Steams and Effluvia of Bodies?

Whence it comes that so small a part of an odorous Body is able to tinge, or scent so great a Quantity of Air?

What are the several Temperatures of the Air, as to Heat and Cold, Dryness and Moisture in several Regions of the Earth, and at several Heights above the Surface of the Earth upwards and below the Surface, downwards in Wells, Mines, &c.

How many various ways there may be of making Thermometers and Hygroscopes to be visible at a great Distance, by the help of Perspectives, by which those Temperatures of the Air may be found without going up or down into those Places?

What is the Cause of the Congruity or Incongruity of the Air, and how many Phenomena of Nature may be solv'd thereby?

What is the comparative Gravity of the Air in several Climates and Regions, and Seasons of the Year?

The Degrees of the Elastick Power of the Air, how caus'd, augmented, destroy'd, &c.

What are the Degrees of Pressure in several Regions, Heights, Climates, &c. the Effects thereof, and Phænomena solvable thereby?

These few Instances, I hope, may serve for a Specimen of what I mean by the Method of propounding Queries on any Subject, to be examined by accurate Observations and Tryals, before the Writing a Natural History of it.

After the Queries have been thus propounded and ranged, the next thing will be to consider what Materials are to be got for the solving of them, and answering our Doubts, what Histories and Observations from abroad, and what Experiments, Observations and Tryals at home will be necessary to be obtained and made: What Instruments, Engines, and Contrivances, will be assisting to this End, how far the Senses themselves will help us, and where they leave us to seek other Helps, and this a serious and unprejudiced Meditation, and considering of the Nature of the thing will best hint. And accordingly we ought to set down under each Queries, what means can be thought of for resolving and answering of them, which Tryals and Ways ought to be prosecuted from beginning to end vigorously, with Diligence and Accurateness, and to be Registered as fast as made, that no considerable Circumstance may be forgotten. And always

§ 4th. The Method of answering the Enquiries.

K   ways

ways upon tryal as things occur, that seem to be assisting towards the solving of another Query, than they were intended for ; they ought to be registered under that, as an additional Help of solving that Doubt, for the Memory is frail, and may quickly forget even those things that are of most Importance, and does not without much Labour and Trouble at best, recal all Circumstances that are considerable at the time when they are most requisite. By this Method also, the Imperfections of History will be amended. And tho' indeed this Process of Reasoning and Inquiry may seem nothing else but what every Man would do, and does indeed continually practise in all kinds of Inquiry : Yet has it this vast Advantage above the common way, where the bare Powers of the Senses, Memory and Understanding are relied upon, that it perfects these Faculties to the highest pitch they are capable of, and that is indeed as much as can be hoped for from Art : Every thing being here reduced to Regularity, Certainty, Number, Weight, and Measure; for whereas in the common ways of Ratiocination, Examination and Inquiry, all things are trusted to the immediate Power of the Faculties of the Soul, *viz.* the bare Senses, Memory and Reason; in this they are none of them left, without their Armour, Engines, and Assistants, the Senses are helped by Instruments, Experiments, and comparative Collections, the Memory by writing and entering all things, ranged in the best and most Natural Order; so as not only to make them material and sensible, but impossible to be lost, forgot, or omitted, the Ratiocination is helped first, by being left alone and undisturbed to it self, having all the Intention of the Mind bent wholly to its Work, without being any other ways at the same time imployed in the Drudgery and Slavery of the Memory, either in calling particular things to Memory, or ranging them in Order, or remembring such things as belong to another Head, or in transposing, jumbling, ranging, methodizing, and the like; for first all things are set down in their Order, the ultimate End, the intermediate, and other Ends that are aimed at in order to the great one, the Steps and Ways that lead to each of these, then Engines and Helps are propounded ; the Progress, that has been made and the Distance to come, is plainly to be seen for all things are registred in their due Order, as fast as made.

Next, it is not troublesome to find what thing is to be done in the next place, the way of proceeding is chalked out, nor will the Mind be much troubled to run over all the particular Instances and Heads of Inquiry, they are all presented at once to the View: Their Order, Congruity, Disagreement, Similitude, *&c.* are all manifest to the Eye, quickly to be examined, recollected, reviewed, otherwise placed, blotted out, or the like, according to occasion, and nothing need be forgotten or omitted, or put in a false Order, if but a small parcel of Diligence be made use of.

The means of Collecting Observations. The last thing therefore is, to consider of the means of collecting Observations, and making such Experiments as seem likely to determine the Inquiry, either Negatively or Affirmatively, either in part or totally, from whence these Materials are to be collected, and by what means? For according to the choice of the Experiments, such most usually is the Information. Such Experiments therefore, wherein Nature is as 'twere put to Shifts and forc'd to confess, either directly or indirectly the Truth of what we inquire, are the best if they could be met with : But these being hard to find at the beginning, it will be best to be first a little acquainted with the Method of Nature, in her most evident Manifestations of her self, to follow her meerly upon the Light of common Observations and Experiments, such as are very obvious upon that Subject, till we are somewhat acquainted with the ways she seems most inclined to follow, and so by degrees can follow her closer and closer at the heels, for by this means we may be able to guess where she begins to make a Deflexion out of her common Road ; which way her Paths lie, at least whereabouts we lost her, and were able to follow her no longer with our bare Senses: And there we ought to make use of the Helps of our Senses, of Microscopes and Telescopes, for the discovering the minute Figure of divers kinds of Liquors and Menstruums; for discovering latent Tastes : Of Thermometers and Hygroscopes for discovering Degrees of Heat and Cold, Dryness and Moisture, and other tangible Qualities which our Senses are unable to distinguish: Of exact Scales, weighing in

Water,

Water, &c. for comparative Gravity, and Expanfion of Bodies : Of Barofcopes, for Gravitation and Preffure of the Parts of Fluids one upon another : And feveral other Contrivances which a good Mechanift will eafily invent upon occafion, as the Subject fuggefts : By which the Informations of the Senfes may be advanced and more certainly determined.

By thefe means are to be fearched out the Properties of Bodies, whereof the Hiftory is to be written, and where we can find no farther ways of proceeding to deeper Searches, and Nature feems to leave us in the Lurch, or pafs away by unfeen Paths, there ought to be fet up as it were a Land mark to direct us where to begin again to fearch, if making Tryal in one way we find our felves miftaken, and thus we may a fecond or third if poffibly we can by any means light upon fuch Experiments or Obfervations, as may inable us to guefs which way fhe was moft likely to take ; but if upon Tryal we find it to be a bufinefs of much greater Difficulty, the Progrefs how far we have gone is to be regiftred, and the *non ultra* together with it, and fo that kind of Inquiry may be laid by for a time, till fomewhat more of the fecret Workings of Nature are learnt from fome other Profecutions of her, in other ways, for Nature is fo very fubtle and referved, that there will need a very great Stock of Patience as well as Skill to be able to difcover her Paths and Methods. As in inquiring *An Inftance in the Caufe of Expanfion.* after the Adequate Caufe of Expanfion, we find that moft Bodies as well fluid as folid, Metals, Quick-filver, Stones, Glafs, Water, Spirit of Wine, Oyle, &c. are expanded by Heat, but finding alfo that the contrary Quality to Heat, Namely, intenfe Cold does produce the fame Effect as that Water frozen into Ice is more rarified than the Water : We are here at a lofs to find what way Nature fhould take with two quite contrary Agents, to bring forth the fame Effect, here therefore we fet up a Mark, and make an Attempt to find what way Expanfion is perform'd by Cold, we find that moft Ice when examin'd is all over befprinkled with diffeminated Bubbles ; till we have traced Nature a little farther, we inquire therefore, whether Nature has not taken that way of rarifying that Body, but we may find that even thofe pieces of Ice which through the beft Microfcope is perfectly clear and free from thofe fmall Bubbles, has a greater Expanfion than the Water out of which it was frozen, becaufe it will fwim in it, and next becaufe that the Refraction of Ice is lefs than the Refraction of Water. This laft feems to hint that Nature has taken this way of making Ice lighter than the common Water, by precipitating a groffer or heavier part of the Water to the Bottom, and by collecting the lighter and more rarify'd Parts and freezing them, as may be in part obferved in the freezing Salt Water ; but that neither is this the way that Nature has attempted, this Experiment will fatisfy us, that taking two clear pieces of Ice, and fuffering one of them to thaw and the other to remain frozen, the Ice will ftill fwim upon the Water, whence 'tis evident that the Water is the fame as to Weight. Befides we find that the whole Bulk is expanded, and not the frozen part made lighter and the unfrozen heavier ; for we find it to break the containing Veffel if it be fuch as will not freely give it room to expand ; fo that we muft here fet up a reft, till we may come to the Knowledge of it fome other way.

By thefe ways are we to proceed to collect all the moft common and obvious Experiments and Obfervations, that feem to have any thing of Information in them as to the Nature inquir'd after, or are very fignificant to any other Nature, yea though we cannot prefently forefee what ufe there may be of it, yet as in collecting Timber for a building, hewing off all the Superfluities and trimming it to be fit for the Repofitory ; we fhould lay it up in the place of things of uncertain Ufe.

But to proceed, the ways of difcovering the Properties and Powers requifite *Three ways of difcovering the Nature of Bodies.* to be well underftood and made ufe of in the compiling of a Philofophical Hiftory, may be thefe three following,

I. By the Help of the Naked Senfes.

II. By the Senfes affifted with Inftruments, and arm'd with Engines.

III. By Induction, or comparing the collected Obfervations, by the two preceding Helps, and ratiocinating from them.

Firft,

Article 1ſt. By the naked Senſes. Firſt, By the naked Senſes are diſcovered the more obvious and ſuperficial Proprieties of Bodies ſuch as theſe,

Shiningneſs, or not giving any Light.	Gravity, or Levity.
Tranſparency, or Opacity.	Coarſneſs, or Fineneſs.
Reflexiveneſs, or Refractiveneſs.	Faſtneſs, or Looſneſs.
Colour, or Colourleſneſs.	Stiffneſs, or Pliableneſs.
Sonorouſneſs, or Dulneſs.	Roughneſs, or Brittleneſs.
Smell or Taſte.	Clammineſs, or Slipperineſs.
Heat, or Cold.	Figure, or Motion.
Dryneſs, or Moiſture	Place, or Poſition.
Fluidity, or Conſiſtence.	Action, or Paſſion.
Denſity, or Rarity.	Parts, or Number.

Theſe are as 'twere the firſt Elements or Letters of Information, and therefore ought firſt to be learn'd and underſtood, before we proceed further into the deeper parts of Inquiry. But we are not here to ſtay ; for this, like the Knowledge of Letters, without knowing how to ſpell with them, or uſe them, is little worth ; for our Senſes are of ſuch a Conſtitution, that they are very apt to miſlead us in thoſe things where their Power reaches, and in many things they leave us without being able farther to aſſiſt us.

Article 2d. By the Senſes helped and aſſiſted. The Defects therefore being naturally two, we ought to provide againſt them with two Artificial Helps ; firſt, for the more certain determining and defining the Senſations, and reducing them to a Standard, and next for the Diſcovery of thoſe ſenſible Properties in Bodies, which our Senſes are not able to reach, and defining them alſo.

1ſt. Reducing Senſation to a Standard. Firſt, For the exact determining and defining of the Quality or Degree of the Proprieties, Powers, and Affections of Bodies, we ought to provide ſuch Inſtruments or Standards, as may be capable of receiving all Degrees whereof that Propriety is capable, after which Search is made : That ſo by making the Standard receive the ſame Degree of the Propriety with that in the Body to be meaſur'd, the Diviſion of the Standard may give the determinate Quantity or Degree, whether the Inquiry be after the Quantity of its Extenſion, Time, Motion, Action, or Paſſion.

Secondly, For diſtinguiſhing the Quality of ſome of them in anſwer to what kind, of this or that general Propriety they belong to ; there ought to be peculiar Contrivances that ſo every thing may be more exactly defin'd, and nothing may be left to the unaccurate and caſual Information of the Senſes, but that every thing that is taken into Philoſophical Hiſtory, may be capable of being accurately determin'd by Inſtruments. Now though it be very difficult to determine exactly in all ; there being ſome of them, ſuch as the Smells and Taſtes of Bodies, which never have been brought to any kind of Theory, and of which therefore we have ſo very imperfect Notions that we have not words for many, and even thoſe Names we have are very ambiguous and determine little, yet 'tis not impoſſible but that even theſe alſo may be reduc'd to a Theory and Standard ; for the Variety of Colours is not leſs than the Varieties of Taſtes and Smells, and yet 'tis not difficult to derive them all from two Heads, and the Degrees of them ; namely, from the Degrees of Yellow, and the Degrees of Blew, and from the Interpoſure of White or much Reflection, and Dark or little Reflection: For all the Colours in the World are made up of the Mixtures of ſome of theſe Degrees, with the Intermixtures of White and Black, which make them only appear more faint or foul. And it ſeems not improbable alſo, but that with Diligence there might be found out ſuch a Theory of Taſtes and Smells, as that from the Mixture of ſome few with their Gradations, might be explain'd all the Taſtes and Smells in the World. The well determining of which Inquiry, ſeems to be likely to afford us as great Aſſiſtance towards the Diſcovery of the Nature and Conſtitutions of Bodies, as to their Medicinal Uſe, as any way imaginable. Now though this nice diſtinguiſhing and defining the Degrees of ſome things be very neceſſary, yet in other things it is often times needleſs and
inſignificant,

inſignificant, for in ſuch things wherein Nature does not obſerve ſuch Nicety in making uſe of this or that peculiar Degree or Mixture, but ſeems indifferent to all; in ſuch things the diſtinguiſhing that Propriety in any one particular on which Experiment or Obſervation is made, will rather be prejudicial than aſſiſtant in diſcovering the Nature in general, but in other things where Nature ſeems to be bounded, and to act by a certain Method, and to keep within ſuch Limits, in thoſe the Limits and Bounds are to be obſerved, as in obſerving the Colour of any Terreſtrial Animal: 'Tis not very material to define exactly what Colour it is of, becauſe we find Nature uſes a Latitude; only this may be noted, that though the Colours of Terreſtrial Animals of the ſame Species are often very various, intermixt with White and Black, and no one Colour perfectly clear or bright is to be found amongſt them, yet in the Colours of Birds there are indeed to be found all Varieties of Mixtures, but generally the Colour is ſomewhat more fixt to the Species, and the moſt of them more clear and orient: Which laſt does diſcover ſomewhat of Diſtinction between the Parts and Subſtance of Hair and thoſe of Feathers, namely, that the Parts of Feathers are far more clear and ſmall, than thoſe of Hair, and conſequently 'tis not improbable, but that the conſtituent Parts may be more porous, defecated and fine. So likewiſe the Bounds of Heat, between which Nature has confin'd it ſelf for proportioning the Animal and Vegetable Life, and beyond either of which Life cannot ſubſiſt, are to be as exactly obſerv'd as can be defin'd, but the peculiar Warmth of this or that Animal is not ſo nice: So likewiſe for Gravity the lighteſt and heavieſt Animal, Vegetable, or Mineral Subſtance, and ſo for the reſt.

In other things where the exact Degree is very neceſſary and Fundamental to the Conſtitution of the Body, in that caſe the greater Diligence and Skill is uſed in the determining of it the better. Thus in determining the Specifick Weight, Denſity, Colour, Malleableneſs, &c. of Gold, or any of the other Metals: The more exact the Experiments are, the greater Information we receive from them of the Nature of thoſe Bodies.

For the making of theſe Standards and Meaſures, to determine the various Degrees of ſeveral Proprieties, there may be divers Contrivances for each peculiar Property, and ſome of them more fit, convenient, and exact than others. The Degrees of Light may be determin'd by Compariſon to the Light of a Candle, of a determinate Bigneſs, plac'd in a long dark Room or Gallery, and by examining the ſhining Body at ſeveral Diſtances from that Light; as ſuppoſe the Light or Shining of a Gloworm be to be determin'd in ſuch a dark Vault, I try at ſeveral Diſtances from the Candle whereabout the Light begins to be viſible; in departing from the Candle, and whereabout it begins to diſappear in approaching towards it, and that Place I mark for the Degree of the Light of Gloworms; by the like Method I try the Light of rotten Wood, decaying Fiſh, Diamonds, heated Metals, &c.

The ways of determining Colours, many ſkilful Painters and Dyers know *Obſervation* very well without Inſtruments, but by one not ſo ſkill'd, they may be defin'd *9th. and 10th.* by a way I have mention'd in my Micrography, which I therefore now omit to repeat.

The Acuteneſs and Loudneſs of Sounds, and Sonorouſneſs of Bodies, may be *Time of laſting,* eaſily enough meaſur'd by a ſound Pipe of a determinate Bigneſs, and by the *Velocity of Pro-* Strength of the Blaſt that is given by poiſed Bellows to blow it, other more *pagation, grea-* loud Sounds may be determin'd alſo by ſhooting ſmall Guns with various *teſt Diſtance of* Charges, or by the Diſtance they can be heard, and the like. *Extenſion.*

Smells and Taſtes being not yet reduc'd cannot be ſo exactly meaſur'd and defin'd, but they may be ſomewhat determin'd, by comparing them to the Smells and Taſtes of Bodies that are moſt common.

Heat and Cold may be many ways diſcover'd, by Weather Glaſſes and Ther- *The Diſtance* mometers of ſeveral kinds; the way of making and determining which, I have *and Velocity of* ſhewn in my Micrography, or elſe by Burning-Glaſſes, together with the help *Propagation,* of the Thermometers: For if a Burning-Glaſs of a known Number of Inches in *the Cold Air* Diameter be able to melt Gold, and Iron, and Copper, and Stones, &c. in ſuch *from Snowy* a determinate Quantity of Time; and that the Reflection from a part of it be *Clouds.* able to raiſe the Standard to ſuch a Degree, it follows, that thereby all De-

L

grees of Heat may be easily determin'd ; as suppose, for instance, it be desired to determine the Degree of the Heat of the Flame of a Lamp, intended by a strong Blast, we find that such a blown Flame is capable of heating Glass Red hot, and melting it in such a space of time.

To reduce it therefore to the Standard, 'tis easy to see what Aperture of the Burning Glass will produce the same Effect in the same time, and what Aperture at the same time (for this is very necessary to be known) will raise the Thermometer to such a Degree. The Degrees of Cold also may be easily determin'd by the Thermometer, as I have elsewhere shewn.

The Degrees of Dryness and Moisture in the Air, and sometimes also in other Bodies, may be distinguished by the Hygroscope, of which I have explain'd the way of making and using in my Micrography. Stiffness and Pliableness, Toughness and Brittleness, are sufficiently obvious, by comparing them to the Pliableness or Stiffness of pieces of unhardned Iron of peculiar Bignesses and Shapes, and to the Toughness of Wire of a determinate Bigness : Now though in all these things we cannot come to a Mathematical Exactness, yet it will be sufficient if we come as near to the Truth as the Matter is capable of ; for we find that Nature it self does not so exactly determine its Operations, but allows a Latitude almost to all its Workings, though as I said before, it seems to be restrain'd within certain Limits, and beyond those is neither excessive on the one hand or defective on the other.

The Specifick Gravity of Bodies may be determin'd by weighing in Water.

There are as many various ways also of determining all the other Proprieties, and reducing them to a Certainty or Standard, but these may suffice for an Instance, to shew what I mean by the determining the Degrees of the Proprieties in several Objects.

As for the determining of the Figure, Number, Motion, Velocity, Power, Time, and the like, the ways are sufficiently easy, and the ingenious Inquirer will upon the occasion, find various Contrivances to determine them.

2dly, By helping the Senses to discover what unassisted they could not, &c. The second way of assisting the Senses, is either first by enlarging their Power, or Sphere of Activity, and extending it much farther than that assign'd them by Nature ; or else secondly, by reducing other things to such a Constitution, as to bring them within the Power of the Sense. For the Performance of each of which there are various means to be used.

1st. By enlarging their Power. And first, for the enlarging the Power of the Sense, and making it capable of sensating many things, which without those Helps would not have been discerned or fallen within the reach of those Senses ; of these there may be many for the assisting of every Sense, but some of them have been more cultivated than others, and brought to a much greater Perfection, but yet not to the highest pitch they seem capable of, but they are every day more and more improv'd, and it may be hoped, that this Age may produce the perfecting of some of them.

As for the Sight Microscopes and Telescopes. Of this kind are Microscopes and Telescopes for the Sight, the one for discovering the Figure and Magnitude of the small Parts of such Bodies as are within our reach, the other for detecting the Figures and Magnitude of such Bodies as are by the Greatness of their Distance, reduc'd to so small a visible Appearance as that the naked Eye is unable to distinguish either their determinate Bigness or their Figure, these may be Helps both of Invention and defining : And as they are indeed the greatest Instance that can be given of the Improvement of the Power of the Senses ; So the perfecting of them is the most likely way to afford us the greatest help for the Detection of the Nature of Bodies. For the Eye is the most Spiritual and most capacious Sense we are endowed with, it affords us the most sudden, most distinct and instructive Information of all ; with this we expatiate through the Universe, and pass from the one end to the other in the twinkling of an Eye, by this we compare the Magnitude and Measure, the Distances, Motions, and the Velocities of all those vast Bodies which are disseminated up and down through it, and none of the other Senses tend so much to perfect the Imagination as this. Now whereas the Power of the Sight in Discovery was not able to distinguish of Objects that appear'd to the Eye under a less Angle than about a Minute, by the help of these it is able to distinguish such as would not appear bigger than a third. So that according to

this

this Calculation, the Power of the Eye is increased near 4000 times as much more as it was before, and we are capable of discovering things 4000 times further off, and 4000 times nearer the Eye than we were without them. And it seems not improbable to me but that each of them may be improv'd so far as to inlarge that Power 4000 times 4000 times the first Dimension, especially in such Objects where the imperfect Transparency of the Medium, or the Defect of Light does not hinder this Effect as in things very near the Eye, or in Objects very near the Zenith.

The Sense of Hearing does not altogether so much instruct as to the Nature *The Hearing.* of things as the Eye, though there are many Helps that this Sense would afford by a greater Improvement, there may be a Possibility that by Otocousticons many Sounds very far distant (I had almost said as far off as some Planets) may be made sensible, at least the Noises of Thunder might be discover'd at a much greater Distance than it can be by the Ear without these Helps, and hereby perhaps the Variations and Changes of the Weather might be predicted much longer before-hand than now they are, and Ships at Sea might perhaps discover an Enemy of Weather coming by the Hearing, as well as they can now discern an Enemy's Ship by the Sight. As for the hearing of Noises made as far off as the Planets, I cannot, I confess, my self so far throw off Prejudice, as not to look on it as a very extravagant Conjecture, but yet methinks I should have had the same Thoughts of a Conjecture to find out a Help for the Eye to see the smaller Parts and Rocks of the Moon, and to discover their Height and Shadow, before I had seen or known the excellent Contrivance of Telescopes. And though methinks from what Experience I have had of Sounds, I am apt to imagine them not capable of being propagated to so great a Distance; yet when I consider again, that by very ordinary and casual Tryals as it were, I have been able to hear Persons discourse distinctly where others in the same place have not heard any Noise or Whisper, I would fain perswade my self against concluding or building on the Impossibility of such things as I am not able demonstrably to prove not possible.

There may be also a Possibility of discovering the Internal Motions and A-*The Internal* ctions of Bodies by the sound they make, who knows but that as in a Watch *Motions of Bo-* we may hear the beating of the Balance, and the running of the Wheels, and *dies may be* the striking of the Hammers, and the grating of the Teeth, and Multitudes of *discover'd by* other Noises; who knows, I say, but that it may be possible to discover the *Sound.* Motions of the Internal Parts of Bodies, whether Animal, Vegetable, or Mineral, by the sound they make, that one may discover the Works perform'd in the severals Offices and Shops of a Man's Body, and thereby discover what Instrument or Engine is out of order, what Works are going on at several Times, and lies still at others, and the like; that in Plants and Vegetables one might discover by the Noise the Pumps for raising the Juice, the Valves for stopping it, and the rushing of it out of one Passage into another, and the like. I could proceed further, but methinks I can hardly forbear to blush, when I consider how the most part of Men will look upon this: But yet again, I have this Incouragement, not to think all these things utterly impossible, though never so much derided by the Generality of Men, and never so seemingly mad, foolish and phantastick, that as the thinking them impossible cannot much improve my Knowledge, so the believing them possible may perhaps be an occasion of taking notice of such things as another would pass by without regard as useless. And somewhat more of Incouragement I have also from Experience, that I have been able to hear very plainly the beating of a Man's Heart, and 'tis common to hear the Motion of Wind to and fro in the Guts, and other small Vessels, the stopping of the Lungs is easily discover'd by the Wheesing, the Stopping of the Head, by the humming and whistling Noises, the sliping to and fro of the Joynts in many cases, by crackling, and the like; as to the working, or Motion of the Parts one amongst another, methinks I could receive Incouragement from hearing the hissing noise made by a corrosive Menstruum in its Operation, the Noise of Fire in dissolving, of Water in boyling, of the Parts of a Bell after that its Motion is grown quite invisible as to the Eye, for to me these Motions and the other seem only to differ *secundum magis & minus,* and so to their becoming sensible they require either that their Motions be increased, or that the Organ be made more nice and powerful to sensate and distinguish them [to try the Contrivance about an Artificial Timpanum] as they are, for the doing of both which I think it not impossible but that in many cases there may be Helps found, some of which I may as Opportunity is offer'd make Tryal of, which if successful and useful, I shall not conceal.

Smelling. As for the Sense of Smelling, though it has been less cultivated than that of Hearing, and seems to be of much less Extent, and to have much less Influence upon our Knowledge than either of those I have already mentioned, it being only for the distinguishing of the Effluvia and Fumes of Bodies, which are dissolv'd by and fly upon and down the Air ; yet if we consider the Nature of it aright, we shall find that it is capable of a much greater Degree. We find that a Hound by this Sense is able for a good while after to discover where his Game has past, which possibly may arise from the Steams or Efflux of its Body, which perspiring through the Pores of the Skin, and coming into the Air are easily precipitated down upon the Track which the Creature has past over, and so lie loose upon the upper Surface of it, and thereby they easily touch the Nose of the Hound, which in following his Game he usually either rubs over the Grass, or Ground, or at least lays it so very near, that with drawing in the Breath at his Nose, by strongly sniffing ; the Volatile Salt, which is in the Effluvia of all Animals is easily rais'd and drawn in with the Air, and that Sense being very acute in this Creature, it easily perceives the smallest Impression on it.

There may be multitudes of ways of assisting this Sense, some of which I have already hinted in the Preface of my Micrography, as I have also concerning some Assistances that may be thought of for the helping of the Senses, of Tasting and Feeling, which may serve as a Specimen or Example to shew what my meaning is in this Particular.

2dly, By making the sensible Qualities in the Object more powerful. The Second way therefore of assisting the Senses in Discovery, is by making the sensible Qualities of the Object more powerful than naturally they are of themselves for affecting the Sense, or more proportionate to the Power and Faculties of them. This may be various ways performed according to the particular Nature of the Objects that are disproportion'd to the Sensory. For

1. First, Some are quite obscur'd and buried in the matter, so as not at all to affect the Sense, these therefore will need to be excited and made active and vigorous by Art ; thus the Tastes of Metals and divers other Bodies are discover'd, by opening and loosning the Bodies of them with appropriate Menstruums ; thus the Light of a Diamond is made visible by rubbing, The Inky Black Colours of Galls, or the Juice of Oak is made visible by mixing Coperas, The Sound of a Bell is discover'd by striking it, the Smell of Sal-Armoniack is freed by mixing Quick Lime, the biting Smell of Mustard-Seed is freed by bruising and grinding. The internal Heat of Corrosive Menstruums is made sensible by mixing dissoluble Bodies with them, the Gravity of the Air is manifested by being weighed in an evacuated Vessel, the Greeness of Gold is discover'd by being beaten very thin, the Greeness and Blueness of Copper by Dissolution, the Salt of Vegetables by calcining, and Multitudes of the like.

2. Secondly, Some are very languid and weak, and so affect the Sense to which they are appropriated so very little that they are hardly discernible, such as these therefore will need to be assisted by Art, and to be made more vigorous and powerful. Thus the Heat in the Air or Sun Beams, in the coldest time of Winter, is hardly sensible to the touch ; but if the Rays be united by a Burning-Glass, they will not only be able to warm, but also to burn the Finger; thus when the Air has very few Effluvia in it of an odorous Body, so that we can hardly smell them, if drawing in the Breath through the Nostril we make a great Quantity of that Air pass through it, those few that are collected and united out of the Air by this means become sensible. Thus the Smells of many other Bodies are so languid and faint, that they are hardly discernable without being either heated or rubb'd, the Flexibility of Glass is manifested by drawing it out into very small Threads. Thirdly, many things become insensible from their Slowness, these ought either to be accelerated or to be sought after by

other

other means which I fhall fhew in the third way of acquiring Information of the Effects of Nature. If they are fuch things as are within our Power to promote, their Motions are to be accelerated and promoted either really or in Appearance ; thus fuppofing the Experiment were true that fome Authors have delivered to us concerning the Acceleration of Sallets, we might poffibly be able to fee the Motion of Vegetation, as we might alfo, if that Story be true which *Clufius* tells us, of the ftrangely growing and rifing Tree; thus the Motion of the Hand of a Watch may be feen by making it go fafter: As to the making them appear fo though they really are not accelerated, this is done by the Telefcope for the Cæleftial Bodies, for by the help of long ones of that kind, the Motion of the Sun and Stars is almoft as plain as that of a Bowl, the like is done alfo by viewing the Shadow of the Sun when caft on the Ground, or a Wall, by a Body at a great Diftance from the fhadowing Body.

Thus alfo the Sound of a String very flackly ftrain'd is not to be heard, but by being ftrain'd harder it yields a very brisk Sound. Iron heated to one Degree of Heat has not acquir'd Motion enough to make it fhine, but if farther wrought on and agitated by Heat, it fhines very bright and clear.

Thirdly, Some Objects are too ftrong, and fo the Senfe is not able to indure the examining of them: In this cafe, the vigorous Influence of them on the Senfory is to be abated ; thus the Body of the Sun is fo bright as to be able to deftroy the Sight, but if it be veil'd with a Fog or Cloud, or the Sight be veil'd by a deep colour'd Glafs, or a fmall Aperture, or the Reflection of it be view'd in a Bucket of Water, the Eye may without much Trouble behold and view it. Thus the burning and corrofive Liquor of Oyl of Vitriol, or the like, which would burn the Mouth and fpoil the Senfory, when allay'd by the Mixture of much fair Water, becomes **a very pleafant Tafte,** and fuited well enough to the Organ: Thus the Sound of Bells in a Steeple is fo loud, that the Ear is hardly able to diftinguifh the differing Tones, but if the Ear be placed at a convenient Diftance it does plainly perceive the Harmony, and eafily diftinguifh each feveral Note and Tone.

Fourthly, Other Objects there are, which are fo minutely difpers'd through other Bodies, that unlefs there may be many of them collected together, or that that Matter through which they are difper'd be feparated from them they are not capable of affecting the Senfe. Thus Salts may lie invifible in Water, till by Evaporation the Water be feparated, and Coral diffolv'd into Vinegar becomes invifible, till collected by Præcipitation into a vifible Powder; thus Vapours difpers'd through the Air become fmall, and to the naked Eye invifible, till they are united clofer together in a Cloud or Mift, the invifible Stars which are difperfed through the Æther, become not vifible without being many of them united into a Galaxie, or cloudy Star, thus the Tinctures alfo of feveral Liquors are hardly vifible till much of the more Watery and Tranfparent Parts are evaporated.

Fifthly, There are other Objects of the Senfe, which though in themfelves very active and powerful, yet by being mixt and united with Objects more powerful, their Action on the Senfe becomes imperceptible, becaufe overpower'd by the ftronger Influence of the affociated Objects: Thus the Light of the fixed Stars in the Day-time becomes invifible by reafon of the greater Light of the Sun which fills the Air. Now the way of making thefe Objects fenfible, is by removing the Influence of the more powerful Object, either by deftroying, weakning, abating, or if it be capable of it, by ftrengthning the Powers of the weaker. Thus (if we may believe what is affirmed by many Authors) the Stars may be made vifible in the Day by placing the Eye at the bottom of a very deep Well, they may be alfo made vifible by a total Eclipfe of the Sun in the Day-time, and the like. Thus the Melody of a fweet Voice is not heard among a noife of Trumpets or Drums; thus the Pallate cannot diftinguifh the Sweetnefs and Variety of fuch Taftes as are mingled with others more ftrong and powerful ; therefore even the beft Drinks relifh ill after eating fweet things, thus 'tis commonly faid, that the fmelling of Hounds is fpoild by fuffer-

ing

ing them to fmell of ftrong fcented Bodies, thus the Light of a Gloworm, or Diamond, or the fparkling of a Cat's Back by rubbing is not to be feen but in the dark, and the Gravity of the Air feems Lightnefs when encompaffed with Water, which is much heavier and more powerful, but if the Water and all other incompaffing heavy Fluids be remov'd, the Gravitation of it becomes very manifeft.

6. Sixthly, There are other fenfible Qualities, which cannot be diftinguifh'd for want of Oppofites and contrary Qualities. Thus in a Full Moon the Irregularities of the Surface are not difcover'd, for want of dark Shadows to be intermixt with the brighter Reflections; thus the Tafte of Bodies is better perceiv'd by being tafted after other Subftances of a different Tafte, the Brightnefs of any Colour is better difcern'd by being interpos'd between Colours of another kind. And 'tis a Maxim in Mufick, that Harmonies become more pleafant and grateful, that is, affect the Senfory better by having Difcords intermingled: Thus Cold is better felt after Heat, Roughnefs after Softnefs, Drynefs after Moifture, Sweetnefs is better tafted after Sowernefs, and the like in all the Senfes. As for the Medicinal affifting of the Senfes, I leave that to the Phyficians.

There remains a third way of inquiring into the Nature of Bodies and Operations, by which we may be able to write a more accurate Hiftory of them, for all thefe Ways I have already mention'd, though in themfelves very requifite, and as it were the Letters or Elements to what follows; yet if the Natural Hiftorian proceeds no further in his Examination, his Information will be very imperfect, and he that fhall afterwards come to make ufe of it will find himfelf neceffitated almoft to begin the whole Inquiry anew, to make over again all thofe Experiments and Obfervations that he finds Regiftred, and to intermingle divers others to the end that he may find out that which ought to have been ready prepared to his hands; and in Truth, without profecuting this third way 'tis not poffible to make Experiments with any Judgment, that is, to know which Experiment is more or lefs fignificant, or of greater or lefs Concernment as to the Difcovery of the Proprieties fought, for moft Experiments are like fingle-Letters which feldom fignify but when they are joyn'd and compounded in Syllables or Words; nor can the Hiftory be freed from infinite Repetitions and Interpofitions of Experiments and Obfervations, which are either very infignificant or at beft indicate nothing elfe but what is much better manifefted in fome of the other Entries and Remarks, and fo ferve only to fill Room needlefly and perplex and weary the Ufer or Student of it: For 'tis not fit that every Experiment that is made fhould be regiftred, but of a Number of good Obfervations and Experiments, fuch ought to be chofen and pick'd which are as it were the Epitomy of the reft, and comprife in fhort and plainly all that is more largely and widely diffus'd and obfcur'd in others.

Art. 3d. or the Third Way of difcovering Nature by Induction.   That therefore which will regulate and rectify both the former ways of proceeding is this Third, which is an Inquiry into the Nature of things by the Effects produced at a greater Diftance, and more remote from immediately affecting the Senfe, and this is by putting of feveral Obfervations and Informations together, and collecting from them, and by reafoning and deducing from them, fo as to proceed, to the culling and chufing of the Experiments and Obfervations already made, and to the inventing of fuch farther Experiments and Ways of fearching, as fhall be moft fignificant to the Inquiry; for this will not only make the Hiftory much fhorter, and more compendious, but much plainer, fignificant, and full.

The third way therefore of difcovering Nature, is by the Obfervation of a great Number of Effects and Circumftances; and thefe, tho' very many, may be very well reduced under thefe two Heads.

Firft, By obferving the *Effects* themfelves produced.
Secondly, By obferving the *manner of Proceeding,* or means made ufe of.

Again, The *Effects* themfelves may be *Intermediate* or *Ultimate.*
1, 2, The *Intermediate* may be either, *conftant, neceffary,* and *always interpos'd* or *accidental,* and fometimes prefent fometimes abfent.   3, The

3, 4. The *Ultimate* alſo may be either *neceſſary* or *accidental.*

In the ſecond place, The *Manner* alſo of Natures proceeding may be either more *obvious* or more *ſecret*, and both theſe may be obſerved either in ſeveral Bodies, or elſe in ſeveral Operations.

The more *ſecret* are ſuch wherein the manner of proceeding is more obſcure and difficult to be found, and not yet diſcoverable by the Senſes, or any other known way.

Theſe more occult and ſecret Workings of Nature are diligently to be noted and examined. *The manner of the more ſecret workings of Nature.*

1. Firſt, The Operations of Bodies are to be more eſpecially noted which ſeem to produce Effects, by means of which we have not the leaſt Information immediately from our Senſes, ſuch as we call Sympathetical and Antipathetical, &c.

2. Next, Operations of Bodies at a much greater Diſtance, ſuch as we uſe to call Influences or Influxes.

3. Laſtly, we muſt obſerve the yet more ſpiritual and more ſubtile Operations of Phantſy and Imagination, Memory and Ratiocination : Both of ſleeping and waking living Creatures, how they work on their own Bodies, and whether they work on others?

The more obvious are ſuch wherein the Agents, Patients, and Means are more plainly to be diſcerned by the Senſes, or other commonly known ways, which may be ſuch as theſe following. *The manner of the more obvious workings of Nature.*

1ſt. In general, how Nature proceeds in generating, increaſing, weakning, and deſtroying the ſame Proprieties in ſeveral States of the ſame Body.

2ly, How Nature proceeds in diſtributing the ſame Proprieties in ſeveral Bodies, in what Bodies it has placed a dawning or beginning of it, in what a middle Conſtitution, in what the higheſt Perfection, in what a decaying, in what it has quite extirpated it?

3ly, How Nature proceeds in Conjunctions or Combinations; that is with what other kinds of Proprieties, the ſame Quality is joyned in divers Bodies? With which it flouriſhes moſt, with which it withers, with which moſt uſual, with which moſt ſeldom?

4ly, How Nature proceeds in Separations or Disjunctions, that is, what Propriety it ſeldom or never joyns in the ſame Subject?

5ly, To obſerve the Tranſitions of Nature, how from the Deſtruction of one Propriety it generates this, that, or another, whether that be the ſame in all Bodies, or how it varies? as ſweet into ſowre, &c.

6ly, To obſerve the ſeveral ways Nature takes in ſeveral Bodies to produce the ſame Effect.

7ly, To obſerve how, where, and when Nature makes uſe of the ſame Body or Means to produce differing Effects, as Condenſation and Rarefaction by Cold, &c.

8ly, To diſtinguiſh as near as may be, when there ſeem to be more than one Cauſe conducive to the producing of an Effect; which of them is moſt powerful, which leſs, which leaſt, and this by varying one and th' other of them, and obſerving the Iſſue. And by obſerving the Effects of each, when mixt with other Bodies in other ways.

9ly, To obſerve the Reſemblance and Diſcrepancy of Natures producing the like Parts in differing Kinds, Species, or Individuals?

10ly, To obſerve the Tranſition of Nature in the Forms and Proprieties of Creatures, how it paſſes from one to another, &c.

11ly, To obſerve where and how Nature ſeems ſometimes to be fruſtrated, and how and where it fails or miſſes in producing its uſual Effects.

12ly, To obſerve the Deviations of Nature in framing Specifick Bodies, and the ſeveral Circumſtances that attend upon ſuch Deviations.

13ly, To obſerve the Deviations of Nature in producing Individuals ſuch as Monſters, &c.

4ly, To

14*ly*, To obferve the concomitant Proprieties of Individuals in their greateft and loweft pitch of Perfection they feem capable of.

15*ly*, To obferve the various workings of Nature in various Places, and Times, how fuch Circumftances alter her Courfe, as Birds in the Air, and on Land, Fifh in frefh and falt Water, Men in *Guiney* and *England*, &c.

16*ly*, To obferve what things feem moft conducive to the Perfection or Imperfection of Productions.

17*ly*, In particular we are to obferve, especially and more attentively, the workings of Nature where fhe feems to be peculiar in her manner, and feems not any where elfe to follow the like Method.

18*ly*, To obferve and enquire after what middle way, or somewhat refembling Method can be found, which is as 'twere interpofited between this peculiar and the more common Method.

19*ly*, To obferve how much, and by what Degrees Nature is made to alter its Courfe by Art.

20*ly*, To obferve where and by what means Art caufes Nature to deviate where it affifts, promotes, perfects, impedes, diverts, deftroys the ufual Courfe of Nature.

21*ly*, To obferve the Natural and Artificial ways of producing the fame Effect, as diftilling falt Water, hatching Eggs by Artificial Heat, &c.

22*ly*, To obferve the Difference between Bodies produced by Nature and thofe by Art.

23*ly*, To obferve the differing ways of producing the fame Effect by Art.

24*ly*, To obferve with what Circumftances Nature and Art do fometimes exceed each other.

25*ly*, To enquire and try how many Mechanical Ways there may be of working on, or altering the Proprieties of feveral Bodies; fuch as hammering, pounding, grinding, rowling, fteeping, foaking, diffolving, heating, burning, freezing, melting, &c.

26*ly*, To enquire and try how many Mechanical Ways there may be of feparating Bodies; as winnowing, fifting, wafhing, filtering, ftraining, wringing, preffing, diftilling, evaporating, precipitating, Chryftallizing, burning, copelling, freezing, fhaking, knocking, &c.

27*ly*, To inquire and try how many Mechanical ways there may be of uniting and incorporating Bodies into one another; as by melting, Diffolution, jumbling, charring, digefting, Infolation, by mixing a third, by taking away a part, by Compreffion, by opening, by Time, &c.

28*ly*, To inquire and attempt by what means Bodies may be changed or tranfmuted, from one thing to another by a real change of all their former Proprieties and fenfible Qualities, and by having acquired new ones, being altered in their Confiftence, Colour, Bulk, Gravity, &c. as the Mixture of Tin and Copper, &c.

29*ly*, To obferve, or rather contrive, by what Means or Supplements Nature may be more fenfibly explained, that fo the Nature of infenfible Operations may be more eafily gueffed at and imagined.

In the making of all which Obfervations, Tryals, and Inquiries, great Care and Judgment muft be ufed in exactly determining the Quantity, Quality, Time, Place, Space, and feveral other Circumftances of the Ingredients, Effects, Proceffes, Doubts, &c. that all things may be reduced to fome Certainty of Number, Weight, and Measure, and that nothing may be left to doubting, Hefitation, or Gheffes, that no part of thefe Materials which are for the Foundation may be defective or faulty, which may endanger the whole Superftructure.

There are many other ways of makingufe of and deducing from Experiments and Hiftories, for the raifing of more general Axioms, and for the building of a Body of Philofophy, than thefe I have mentioned, which I muft refer to fome other Opportunity; thefe feeming to me fufficient to inable a diligent Inquirer to fet his hands to promote fignificantly this great Work of compiling fuch a Philofophical Hiftory, as fhall be both fufficient and adapted for the perfecting the Knowledge of the Works of Nature. And thefe being once well underftood stood and practised, all the other will easily follow : That therefore these may be the more plain and easy to be understood, I shall endeavour farther to explicate each of them, and to exemplify them with some easy and obvious Instances.

The first way therefore of discovering the Power and working of Nature more mediately, is by the constant and more necessary Effects, which are produc'd by the working Power, before it produces its final and ultimate Effect, and these serve as a Torch, Drum, or Light, by which we may be guided in our pursuit of Nature, and be inabled to distinguish by what Steps, and which way Nature proceeds.

1. For instance, Suppose it be inquir'd to know whether the Sun be a fired *Instances in* or burning Body, Here the Body to be examin'd is so far off, that we cannot *the Effects* make any Tryals or Examinations of it, and 'tis of that Bigness that it cannot *themselves.* be expected to be consum'd in many Ages, and so the ultimate Effect is not to be look'd after; the Helps therefore of knowing may be some such as these, what are the intermediate Effects of all Fire ? Heating, shining, emitting some kinds of Fumes and Vapours, wasting the Body it burns, and usually at last consuming it : These therefore are the things to be look'd after, and diligently examin'd; as first whether the warming of the Earth by the Sun Beams be not in the same manner perform'd as a Body ; suppose an Apple is warm'd by the Fire, whether the Cause of Subterraneous Fires and Earthquakes may not proceed from the Heat of the Sun, as Blisters and Eruptions on the side of an Apple that is roasted by the Fire. Next, Whether the Colour of its Light be not like that of Flame, especially that of Nitre and Sulphur. Thirdly, Whether it yield any Smoke or Fumes, and especially whether such *maculæ* and *faculæ* as have been discover'd in it, can be observ'd when at the Brink to be elevated above the Surface of the Sun: These must be made with great Diligence and very accurate Glasses, as must also this last, which could it be certainly known would afford us the greatest Probability, and that is the discovering of the Body of the Sun to diminish and grow less, which perhaps to After Ages may not be impossible, if with very accurate Telescopes this Age do exactly determine the Diameter of the Sun. Thus the Scorbute, and many other Diseases, are a long while discoverable by certain Symptoms almost insensible and scarce regarded, before it comes to rage with its more direful Effects : By which means a diligent Observer may detect the very Inclinations of Nature, and then surely much more easily turn them. Thus the Observations of the Change of the *Nuclei* of Comets is an Argument of the wasting and Consumption; thus also, by the daily Progresses of the Motion of the Comet, we may easily judge of the Distance and Velocity and way of it.

2. Secondly, Nature may sometimes be discover'd by comparing accidental intermediate Effects; these as they are for the most part not thought of, and are a Product of Providence, so do they generally afford very singular and excellent Information, and usually much more than the more constant and necessary and expected Circumstances. Thus by an abortive Birth, much more may be learnt of the manner of Formation in the Womb, than by only examining a perfect Infant: Thus the passing of the Comet very near some Star, so that the brightest part of the Tail seems to cover some Stars, and yet very little eclipse their Light, is a help to judge that the Substance or Consistence of it is very much rarify'd, and somewhat of the Nature of Smoke ; Thus also by the Curvity of the Tail of the Comet, and by the Deflection of it many times a good way out of the straight Line, which passes through the Body of the Comet, we may find that it cannot be caused by Refraction, as many suppose, but is rather a real Body.

3. Thirdly, Nature may be discovered by the constant ultimate End, or last Effect of a Principle. Thus somewhat of the Nature of a Comet may be discover'd by the end of it, and this we find always to be by degrees growing smaller and smaller, and fainter and fainter, till it disappears; and as it daily decreases in Bulk, so does it also in Motion, whence 'tis not improbable that

the

the Cause of both is from the Increase of Distance, and the Obliquity of the Line of its Motion to the Eye. Whereas, if it should accidentally happen, that the Comet should dwindle away and vanish, or be suddenly extinct when in its greatest Velocity and Brightness, 'twould be an Argument that its Constitution were of another Nature than what we shall hereafter indeavour to shew it probably to be, which may serve as an Instance to explain what we mean by our

Fourth Method of tracing Nature by the accidental ultimate Effects. An Instance of this 4th way may be this ; suppose the thing sought for be the Cause of Earthquakes, Here if we inquire after the End or Events of them, we shall find that they have sometimes ended in strange and monstrous Eruptions of Fires, and Smokes, and Waters, and the like, casting forth great Quantities of burnt and melted Sulphur, Sands, Stones, Earths and Minerals, together with new Rivers and Streams of boyling Waters, sometimes raising, otherwhile sinking Mountains, sometimes raising, sometimes sinking Islands, sometimes digging, sometimes filling Caves. Hence 'tis not improbable, but that Subterraneous Fires are the chief Cause of those direful Effects, and that those Fires may be fed by Supplies of Nitrous and Sulphureous Substances, with which those Places usually most abound, that are or have been subject to these Accidents ; for 'tis not else imaginable without the Supply of Niter, how those Fires should continue to burn, since I have not yet found any Substance whatsoever that would burn without a Supply either of fresh Air or Niter (the Reason of which I hope I have given in my Micrography) and 'tis very hard to imagine how such vast Fires should be supply'd with a sufficient Quantity of fresh Air, unless there be many Ventiducts under Ground, whereas we have no Knowledge of any : Or unless by the Influx of Springs and Rivers, the Vapours of the Water may serve to supply the Defect of Air, which whether so or not some further Inquiries and Experiments ought to be made ; and though they should not be found to be sufficient for this Effect, yet they seem very much to contribute to the Violence of the Commotion and Eruption, which the breaking of Æolipiles, and small Dubbles of Glass seal'd up Hermetically half fill'd with Water, seem further also to illustrate.

2dly, Instances in the manner and means of Natures Operations, first the more secret.   5. A Fifth way of discovering Nature, is by taking more especial Notice of such Operations and Effects of Nature as seem to be more secret and reserv'd, working on Bodies remov'd at some distance, such strange Effects as our Senses are wholly unable to shew us any probable Cause thereof ; for by discovering the true Reason of such Effects, we give our selves a new or Sixth Sense, which will open us a large new Prospect into Nature that we dreamt not of before. An Instance of this may be the Verticity or Direction of the Load-stone towards North and South; the Gravity and Attraction of the Earth towards its Center, the Influence of the Moon on the Waters of the Sea, or on Vegetable or Animal Bodies, the Attraction of Jet, Amber, Red-wax, and the like : we should very much labour to find out all the Assistances we are able for the perfecting of such Discoveries, by collecting all such Experiments together, and by comparing them one with another, that so the Mind may by some of those ways hereafter to be mentioned, discover first the Similitudes and Diversities of such Operations, and may the better be enabled to know what further Observations and Experiments are necessary for the Discovery of their Nature. Such Operations and Experiments therefore are to be sought after for from their Discovery, the Causes of much greater Effects may appear. The Verticity of the Loadstone may perhaps explain to us, why the Axis of the Earth keeps a Parallelism whilst it moves about the Sun; and the Explication of Gravity may shew us the true Cause of the Circular Motion of the Moon about the Earth, the Satellites about *Jupiter* and *Saturn*, and the Primary Planets about the Sun, and may also shew us the reason of the Currents, Ebbings and Flowings of the Tide, and the like, which I may hereafter more fully explain.

6. A Sixth way of discovering Nature, is by taking particular notice of such secret Proprieties of Bodies as cause them to unite or not unite with other Bodies,

or as cause them to operate, or not to operate on contiguous Bodies, these are Proprieties of Bodies of which the Sense can give us no other Information, but of the Effects ; and therefore the Discovery of the Causes of these will give us another, or a 7th Sense, whereby to watch and follow Nature. Of this kind is the Animation (as I may call it) of Iron by the touch of the Loadstone, the Dissolution of hard Bodies by appropriate Menstruums, the Congruity or Incongruity of Fluids with Fluids, or of Fluids with consistent Bodies [that is, a Propriety whereby Fluid Bodies will readily unite and intimately mingle themselves, or adhere to some kind of Bodies, and will by no means unite and mingle with or adhere to other] the raising Fermentation by Addition of Leaven or Yeast, the firing a Heap of Powder by a spark of Fire, the destroying many Thousands by the Infection of one Man, the Impregnation of a whole Cluster of Eggs by one treading of the Cock ; Experiments therefore and Observations of this kind should be carefully sought after, and all the Circumstances and Accidents diligently mark'd, measur'd and defin'd, for that these Proprieties whatever they be, seem to be some of the most considerable Instruments which Nature makes use of in all, or at least in some of the most considerable of its Productions. I have, I hope, made it probable at least, that Fire is nothing but the Dissolution or Corrosion of Sulphureous heated Bodies, by the Air as a Menstruum, and had I here a proper place, I hope I could shew that Fermentation is somewhat Analogus, or of the same kind with Dissolutions or Corrosion : If therefore we can by deducting from Observations and Tryals, find the true Nature of this Propriety, what a Multitude of things will there be explicable thereby, for though at first sight all these kinds of Experiments seem little instructive, because their Operations for the most part are such as fall not under our Senses, yet when their Nature is detected, that we know how to unlock those Mysteries, then we shall find their great Usefulness.

7. Further, Another way of discovering Nature, is by taking more especial notice of such of her Works, wherein she seems to act yet more secretly and farther remov'd from the Detection of our Senses, such as in the Formation and Configuration of Bodies : And here we are to observe all such things as vary and change those usual Methods, for if herein her Workings also can be detected to be Mechanical, it will not then seem impossible but that some of the most considerable Effects of Nature may be detected by Mens Industry, and to this end all kind of Impressions on the Phantcy are to be observ'd what kind of Alteration they make in the Body, as in the Formation of the Fœtus, in causing Miscarriages and Abortions, in curing or producing Diseases ; for these kind of Actions, we term more spiritual, because our Senses help us not at all in discovering of them, and they stand up as an Opprobrium to Philosophical Inquiry, as being generally believ'd impossible to be detected, and much less reduc'd to such a Degree of Science as might tend to practise, yet if we more seriously consider the Progress of Nature from the more simple and plain Operations to the more complicated and abstruse, we may from them deduce a great Argument of Incouragement. For we shall find it to make but very small Steps, and to add but a little more in one thing than in another, to make it a degree higher in Perfection ; there is but a small difference between Earth and strong Concretions, between such Concretions and Salt, between the crystallizing and shooting of Salt, and the Vegetation of Mould, and less between the Vegetation of Mould and Mushrooms, and but a very little between the Vegetation of Mushrooms and Moss, and as little between Moss and Grass, and between Grass and the most bulky Vegetable, and no great matter between the Vegetation of Plants and Zoophyts, and there is no great Difference between Maritime Zoophyts and Oysters, Blubbers and the like ; between those and Periwinkles, and other kinds of Shell-fish, between Shell-fish and crustaceous Creatures, between those and Fishes, between Fishes and amphibious Creatures, such as Morses and Sea-Calves, and the like, between those and Aerial Animals, &c. All such Operations and Experiments therefore as tend to the Illustration of one of these, are more diligently to be remark'd.

The more obvious workings of Nature explained.

1. To proceed to the more obvious workings of Nature ; *the firft way of difcovering them, is by obferving the Method or Progrefs of Nature in generating, increafing, weakning or deftroying the fame Propriety in divers States of the fame Bodies*, for hereby may be difcover'd what things and Circumftances are adjuvant, and what deftructive of this Propriety : As fuppofe Greennefs be the Propriety fought for, we may obferve that that Propriety is moft, and in its greateft Perfection when the Plant is fo, and that before the Plant is come to Maturity and is too moift, waterifh, and tender, it inclines or is ting'd too much with Blew, and afterward, as it decreafes in Moifture and grows more dry, the Yellownefs increafes ; and as it more and more dries and grows old, fo the Yellow is more and more heightned, till at laft it ends almoft in a Red. So that Blew feems more appropriate to Liquidity and Moifture, and Yellow to Drynefs and Sulphuroufnefs ; unlefs by comparing it with other Effects of the fame kind in other Bodies, as in the Generation of Colours on melted Metals, where Yellow beginning firft, then Red, and after Purple, according as the vitrify'd Skin grows thicker and thicker, we may fuppofe that the Blewnefs proceeds from the Thicknefs of thofe Parts which afford the Colour by their plentiful Supply of Moifture, and that as that Moifture decreafes and dries away, and thofe Colour-making Bodies grow thinner and clofer together, fo the Colour grows by degrees Yellower and Yellower, &c.

Again, Suppofe Liquidity be the thing to be obferv'd, we fhall find that Water for Inftance, when cold beyond fuch a degree grows very confiftent, folid, and hard, when it only fuffers a gentle degree of Heat or Warmth, it becomes liquid and moift ; but if Heated beyond that degree, it becomes Aerial, Fluid and Rarify'd. Suppofe Light be the Propriety to be trac'd, we may find that Fifh when frefh or newly dead fhine not or afford no Light, when they begin a little to taint and ferment as 'twere, they begin to fhine and glare, but as they grow more putrid and rot, fo again the Light decreafes and at laft goes quite out. So that it feems for the producing Light in fuch a Body there is requifite a determinate Degree of Fermentation or Corruption : Suppofe the ebbing and flowing of the Sea be inquir'd after, we find that the new Moon makes the ebbings and flowings very great ; as the Moon goes further and further towards the firft Quarters, fo thofe Motions do more and more decay, and are loweft or weakeft at the Quarters again, as the Moon goes further from that and nearer to its Oppofition to the Sun, fo the Tides again increafe, and after Decreafe to the laft Quarter, and after it again increafe to the New Moon : For this it remains yet farther to be obferv'd whether *cæteris paribus,* the Tides are greater at the Full or the New Moon, or whether lefs at the firft or laft Quarter ; for from the determining of thefe, there would be many helps afforded for the difcovering of the true caufe and reafon of them. Suppofe Specifick Gravity be inquir'd after, we are to inquire what Body there is which in feveral States of it hath feveral Degrees of it : And for this we may find Air, which according as it is more or lefs rarify'd, fo has it more or lefs Gravitation, whence we may deduce the Rarefaction and Condenfation of Bodies does diminifh or augment their Gravity, and 'tis not improbable as we fhall add by and by, but that this Propriety is general, that the comparative Gravity and Levity of Bodies depends upon their comparative Condenfation and Rarefaction.

2. *The Second way of difcovering Nature may be, by obferving how Nature proceeds in diftributing the fame Propriety in feveral Bodies.* As fuppofe Gravity be the Propriety inquired after, we may find among Fluid Bodies, that in Flame 'tis very little or nothing at all, in Air but very faint, in condenfed Air fomewhat more, in Oyl of Turpentine 'tis yet more prevalent, in ordinary rectify'd Spirit of Wine a little more, in Water greater, in feveral Saline and Chymical Liquors, yet more prevalent, as Oyl of Vitriol, Oyl of Tartar, &c. in Quick-filver moft of all, by which Progrefs we may learn that Gravity has little to do with Fluidity ; for that almoft the heavieft Body in the World is fluid as is alfo the lighteft, and there are few intermediate Degrees of which there may not be found fome fluid Subftance. And this will be farther manifefted alfo, if we confider the Difperfion of it among confiftent Bodies, for

there

there are confiftent Bodies almoft of all Degrees of Gravities. But on the other fide, we fhall find that Gravity has a great Dependence upon Rarefaction and Condenfation, for always the moft rarify'd Bodies feem to be the moft light, and the moft condens'd the moft heavy, for as in **Flame** it feems to be leaft, fo in Gold does it feem to be moft prevalent.

3*ly,* Another way of difcovering Nature, is by fuch Obfervations and Experiments as do manifeft the Method of Nature in Combinations or Conjunctions, that is, how and with what other ; the Propriety fought for is combin'd in feveral Bodies. As fuppofe the Propriety of Heat be inquir'd for, we fhall find that in the Sun and in Fire it is joyn'd with Light, but in Corrofion of Metals by Saline Liquors and in Fermentation, and in rubbing Motions, without it ; whence we may conclude Light or Darknefs not neceffary to Heat : Next Heat being produc'd by Oyl of Vitriol and Oyl of Turpentine mixt, and by two folid Bodies rubb'd together, fhews that neither is Fluidity or Confiftence effential in the Production of Heat; from the Heat in Flame, and boyling Water, we may conclude Drynefs and Moifture likewife not to be effential ; from the being able to make both Gold and Air hot, both Gravity and Levity, and Denfity and Rarity, appear not to be effential, but from a conftant Conjunction of an internal Motion of the Parts, where there is Heat, may be concluded, that thofe two have fome Dependance one upon the other. From the almoft conftant Combination of violent Heat and Light, we may conclude them to have fome great Affinity, as alfo becaufe in moft Bodies Fluidity is joyn'd with fome degree of Heat; we may conclude thofe alfo to have much Affinity, but how much, and in what manner muft be determin'd by fome of the other ways of Inquiry.

4*ly,* Another way of difcovering Nature, is by tracing her ways in disjoining or feparating Proprieties, that is, very feldom or never joining them together in the fame Body ; as Fluidity and Sonoroufnefs, Shining and abfolute Cold, Malleability and Tranfparency, Sweetnefs to Smell and Tafte, Hardnefs and Toughnefs, Levity and Denfity. Thefe and their Contraries are chiefly to be obferv'd, becaufe fuch as thefe do ftill lead us nearer and nearer to the Mark we aim at, and do as 'twere circumfcribe Nature, and bound it fo as that we know it cannot go beyond fuch or fuch Limits.

5*ly,* Another way of tracing Nature, is by obferving the Tranfitions it makes from one Propriety to another; of this kind of Obfervations and Experiments great Multitudes fhould be collected, that fo the Affinity and Dependance of one Propriety upon another may be the better underftood : For by this means the Circumftances alfo being well obferved, the Nature of any one of thofe Proprieties being known, the other cognate Propriety will eafily be difcover'd. As Sournefs and Acidity does ufually follow Sweetnefs in moft kinds of fermenting Liquors, as in Wine, Beer, Ale, Metheglin, *&c.* And in the making *Saccarum Saturni,* Sweetnefs feems to return again from Sournefs. Sweetnefs by Combuftion or Heat very often degenerates into Bitternefs : And Bitternefs by long keeping feems to turn into Sweetnefs, as in Hopt Beer long kept, Bitternefs, Acerbity, and Sowrnefs in unripe Fruits, by Maturity turns into Sweetnefs; the Bluifh Greenefs of Buds of Plants by degrees turns perfectly Green, and as they decay degenerates into Yellow, as I noted before; Plumbs, Grapes, Mulberries, and the like, being of a palifh Green at firft, by degrees turn Red, and at laft Blue ; the Colours on tempering Iron or Steel are firft of a Straw Colour, then Yellow, then Red, then Purple, then Blue, and fo onwards. To this Head may be referred many of thofe excellent Experiments of the Tranfmutation of Colours, publifht by the Incomparable Mr. *Boyle,* Cabages by an Inclination to Putrefaction do often produce a moft fragrant and Musk-like Odour, but fuffer'd to putrify quite, their Stink is not to be indur'd ; Apples alfo by Putrefaction do oft produce very pleafing Smells, Musk alfo is faid to be the Corruption of the Flefh and Blood of a kind of Dear : But generally all kind of putrify'd Subftances, efpecially Animal, ingender very loath fome Smells, which feem to be caus'd by a very penetrant and volatile Salt, which by the Diffolution of the Texture of thofe Subftances is let loofe, and being very Aerial

O   readily

readily mixes and joins it self with the Air, from whence at firſt it ſeems to have been taken.

6ly, Another way of diſcovering Nature, is by endeavouring to find by what ways Nature produces the ſame Effect in divers Bodies, whether always the ſame ways, or for the moſt part by differing, or by ſome few; and among all theſe Experiments and Obſervations, we are to make choice of ſuch eſpecially, wherein the Propriety ſought for is produced by ſome Cauſe that ſeems leaſt incumbred with perplexing Circumſtances.

As for inſtance, Whether Nature produces Heat in the Sun, in Fire, in Motion, in Fermentation, in Baths and hot Springs, in quick Lime ſlack'd with Water, in the Operation of corroſive Menſtruums, in Animals, &c. all the ſame way, or whether differing ways : That is, whether the Sun be not a Sulphureous and Nitrous Earth or Globule fir'd and conſum'd, or diſſolv'd either by it own Nitrouſneſs, or by the Circum-ambient Air, whether that and our common Fire be not much the ſame kind of Operation (but with differing Menſtruums and differing Diſſolubles) with that of corroſive Menſtruums ; and whether Fermentation be not a kind of Diſſolution or Corroſion, whereby the Parts work upon one another, and whether quick Lime ſlack'd by Water will not prove the ſame kind of Operation, Namely, the working of the Alkali in the quick Lime on the Body of the Water; whether Baths and hot Springs proceed not from Subterraneous Fires, and thoſe maintain'd by a nitrous and ſulphureous Fuel there plac'd ; whether the Heat in Animals be not caus'd by the continual working of the Liquors and Juices of the Body one upon another, and more eſpecially by the uniting of the Volatile Salt of the Air with the Blood in the Lungs, which is done by a kind of Corroſion or Fermentation, which to me I confeſs ſeems ſomewhat more than probable ; Firſt, Becauſe that only thoſe Animals that breath much are very hot, all other kinds of them are even cold to a Man's touch, as Fiſhes, Snakes, Frogs, Cameleons, &c. Next, That all thoſe Exerciſes which cauſe the Blood to circulate much, and conſequently to make the Animal breath much, do make the Heat to increaſe, and the expir'd Vapours to be more copious. Thirdly, That ſuch as ſtir little, and conſequently whoſe Blood does circulate but ſlowly, breath but little and ſeldom, and are generally moſt cold in Conſtitution and grow Flegmatick, and at laſt ſhort-breath'd, and are very apt to fall into Fevers or Exceſſes of Heat and Inflamations as it were ; becauſe thoſe Parts which ſhould have been wrought on by the Air, and thereby have been brought to another kind of Conſtitution and concoɛted, are in great Quantity laid up in the Blood : So that at laſt the Blood becomes over charg'd by them, and the Lungs become ſtuff'd and ſtopt, Whence wanting the Preſervative Salt of the Air, they upon all occaſions are apt to cauſe unnatural Fermentations and Putrefactions which inflame and deſtroy the natural Texture and Conſtitution of the Blood, Humours and Parts, and ſo vitiate oftentimes and deſtroy the very Principles of Life. Further, the Ebullition of Steams into the Lungs, which are carried out with the Breath by Expiration, may probably be cauſed by the Ebullition of the Blood upon the mixing of the Salt of the Air, ſomewhat after the Nature, as Oyl of Tartar will bubble by the Affuſion of Volatile and Acid Salts, now whether ſo or not, deſerves to be further inquir'd into. But this by the by ; Another Inſtance, to illuſtrate this Head, may be the Method Nature uſes in generating Colours : That is, whether the Colours in the Rain bow, in Triangular Cryſtal and Gems, in Bubbles and plated Bodies, in Flowers, Woods, Leaves, Stones, &c. In Liquors and Flame be all of the ſame kind, and from one and the ſame Principle diſguiſed under ſeveral Masks or Veſts ; or whether Nature has not almoſt in every of them taken a differing way. This will be found by reducing each of them to the moſt ſimple Principles, and by endeavouring to find out whether there be not ſome one Principle wherein they all agree ; for if it can be found that all of them do depend upon Tranſparency and Refraction, and that by deſtroying that Principle in any of them all the Colours will immediately vaniſh, 'tis a very great Argument that that is the chief Cauſe of all thoſe Appearances, and all the reſt are but accidental and circumſtantial, ſomewhat of this kind I have endeavour'd to explain in my Micrography. A Third thing

may

may be the Method of Nature, in producing Light, in ſome we find it to be effected by a violent Diſſolution of the Body, as in Fire, and perhaps in the Sun, in others we find it to be an Effect of a very gentle and ſcarce ſenſible Diſſolution, as in Fiſh and rotten Wood, and perhaps the Gloworm ; in others the Effect of a gentle Heat or Motion, as in a Diamond and *Bononian* Stone, from another Cauſe in the Scintillation of the Hair of a Cats Back when ſtrok'd much and quick in the dark, from another Cauſe in the ſhining of the Juice of a 100 legg'd Worm when kill'd in the dark. From another, the ſhining of *Ignes Fatui*, Dews, Sea-water, and the like. Now from the comparing of theſe ſeveral ways Nature makes uſe of for the producing of theſe Effects, it will not be difficult to find that there is one Principal Cauſe of all, which is in almoſt each of them conceal'd under a differing covering. Now by caſting away all thoſe Circumſtances, which by comparing them one with another, will be found needleſs and accidental as to the producing of Colour, we may quickly come to that which is the only true and adequate Cauſe.

7*ly*, Another Method of Diſcovery may be by taking notice of all ſuch Proceſſes of Nature, wherein by the ſame effective Principle it cauſes quite differing Products : For by diſtinguiſhing and defining carefully the conſiderable Circumſtances of ſuch Operations, the Nature of both of them will be the more eaſily found. As why Heat for inſtance, does in Bricks firſt by a gentle degree cauſe a Condenſation, and ſhrinking, and hardning, and afterwards by a more violent cauſes a Rarefaction, Liquefaction and ſoftning, if we obſerve well the Circumſtances we may find that the firſt is caus'd only by the flying away of the more watery and liquid Part that kept the other a little further disjoin'd, whereby thoſe more ſolid Parts ſlide and fall nearer together, whereas even then thoſe more ſolid Parts were not condens'd but rarify'd, as all other ſolid Bodies are by a ſenſible degree of Heat ; and as for the other Effects they are but a further Augmentation of the ſame Product. Another Inſtance may be the Condenſation and Rarefaction of Water by Cold ; the Reaſons of one of which Operations ſeem a little more abſtruſe, and deſerve to be farther inquir'd into ; Namely, why Water ſhould continue to condenſe more and more, till it comes to ſuch a degree of Cold, and afterwards according as the Cold increaſes, ſo does the Expanſion of the Water into Ice. The Diſcovery of the true Reaſon of which Experiment will very probably afford us a much larger Proſpect into the ways of Nature than we have yet been Maſters of, towards the finding of which it will be requiſite to take notice of and examine well all the Proprieties of Ice and Snow, ſuch as are the ſeeming Blebs or Bubbles generated, the Figures of falling Snow and the Figures of frozen Snow, both which are very ſtrange and extreamly pretty ; the Figures and manner of the freezing of Ice, the Refraction of Ice, and the Lightneſs of it, and the like.

8*ly*, Another way of Diſcovery, is by indeavouring to find out ſuch Experiments as may diſtinguiſh between two or more Principles, and ſhew what the Influence or Power of each of them is towards the producing of that Effect whereunto they ſeem both or all to concur : Of this kind there are Multitudes in Natural Operations, which Operations are very ſeldom ſo ſingle as to be perform'd and perfected by one active Principle only, but to the producing of almoſt all its Effects, Nature for the moſt part makes uſe of two, three, or more co-operating Principles ; the diſtinguiſhing the adequate Power of each of which is one of the moſt difficult things in all Philoſophical Inquiries, ſuch Methods and Rules therefore as aſſiſt us in this Performance, ought eſpecially to be look'd after. As for Inſtance, in the Fulmination of Gunpowder, what the ſeveral Offices of the three Bodies of which it ſeems neceſſary to be compounded are, what Part the Nitre, what the Sulphur, and what the Cole acts ; the like in the fulminating Powder, deſcrib'd by *Glauber*, made of Salt of Tartar, Sulphur and Nitre, whoſe Operation ſeems to be quite differing from that of Gunpowder, and nearer to approach to the Nature of *Aurum Fulminans*, which is a third thing of this kind to be obſerv'd, made of the Powder of Gold precipitated out of *Aqua Regis*, by Spirit of Urine, or Salt of Tartar ; and ſeeming to want the Sulphur, which ſeems neceſſary to the other two,

unleſs

unlefs the Gold may be faid to fupply it ; the like Inquiry may be made concerning the Caufe of Diffolution : As for Inftance, of Gold in *Aqua Regis*, whether the Gold it felf do not contribute as an active Principle, to the difperfing of it felf in the *Aqua Regis*, as well as the *Aqua Regis* doth to the Penetration or corroding the Gold ; and in the *Aqua Regis*, what the Sal Armoniack, and what the Nitrous Spirit contributes towards that Action. And herein the ways for Difcovery muft be by varying either the feveral Ingredients themfelves if it can be, and by obferving in what the new fubftituted ones differ from the other either in Quantity, Quality, Time, manner of operating, and the like, or elfe by indeavouring to vary and alter the Quantities of the Ingredients themfelves ; and by obferving diligently all the Circumftances of the fucceeding Effects. Or elfe Thirdly, fomething may be learnt by mixing one or two other Ingredients, and obferving and comparing their Effects to confider in all of them in what common Nature they all agree, and in what they moft of them differ, what Bodies feem to promote, and what to hinder thofe Operations.

9. Another way of tracing Nature is by obferving the Refemblance or Difcrepancy of Natures working in the producing the like parts in differing Kinds, Species, or Individuals. This Method is very luciferous, and produces very copious Matter of Information, for by obferving how Nature varies its Method according to feveral Defigns we may eafily by comparing, and rejecting, quickly arrive to fome pofitive Information, what the Ufe and Bufinefs of each part is ; as for inftance, by obferving the Keys of Sicamores, Maples, &c. and finding in them a tender, but perfect Plant wrap'd up and clos'd in a Box or Cafe, fo as to preferve it from taking Injury, which by being buried in the Ground in warm Weather does by degrees fwell and break the Shell, and grow up in a Plant : And comparing this with the like Procefs of moft other Seeds, though the Plant or Web of them be not fo vifible, we may conclude that they alfo have the fame Principle in them though fomewhat farther remov'd or hid from our Senfe : And by comparing thefe with the Eggs of Serpents, Crocodiles, Æftridges, Tortoifes, and Multitudes of other Oviparous Infects, who lay their Eggs in convenient Receptacles, that the Heat of the Sun or Air may hatch, we fhall find it very probable that Nature takes the fame courfe both in the one and the other ; but with fome difference, that in fome fhe feems to operate more openly, in others more fecretly and referved. And by comparing likewife the Method of Nature in the Formation of the Fætus in the Womb, we may find reafon to conclude, that all kinds of Vegetable and Animal Bodies are propagated by much the fame Ways and Methods, though fomewhat varied in Circumftances, the Obfervation and diligent Examination of which by Experiments will hugely promote this Inquiry. Thus alfo by comparing the Contrivances for Motion in the Leaves and Branches of the fenfible Plant, with the Mufcles and Inftruments of Motion in Infects, Birds, Beafts, Fifhes, fcaled, fhell'd, and cruftaceous, each of them feeming in fome particular or other to differ, and by joyning to thefe feveral other felf-moving Bodies, as the Beard of a wild Oat, the wreathed Seeds of Muskgrafs, the fhrinking of Gut-ftrings, the Expanfion of fired Gunpowder, the Corrofion of acid Liquors, &c. we fhall find many helps to judge of what is moft likely to be the true caufe of the Motive Power of the Mufcles : For every Difcrepancy in thefe brings us a ftep nearer to the thing fought for, by lefning the Bounds, or at leaft by fixing the Terms within which it muft be found.

10. Another way of Difcovery is by taking notice of the Tranfitions of Nature, by what degrees and fteps it paffes from one thing to another in the Formation of Species ; for this will afford very great Light, how to find out which Product of Nature is moft fimple, and which moft complicated, which the moft perfect, and which is fartheft from it, and wherein the Additions or Defects lie. And accordingly from this we fhall be the better inabled to find out the Significancy and Ufe of each part : As fuppofe from a Man Nature feems to defcend to an Ape, Monkey, or Baboon, which we may find in very many things to imitate Man very exactly, as in its Figure, Gate, and Jefture, as is teftified by ————— in his Natural Hiftory of the *Eaft Indies*, in frowning, grinning, and

laughing

laughing, as divers Travellers assure us, but seem to want the Use of Reason and Speech, the things wherein they differ in Figure from Men are chiefly these; that the comparative Bulk of their Brain is much less in Proportion to their Bodies than that of a Man, as has been excellently well observ'd by the Learned Physician Dr. *Willis*, that they are all over cover'd with Hair, that their Heads and Noses are flatted, and their Mouth thrust out, tending somewhat towards the Shape of other Beasts; that their Legs and Arms are much shorter in proportion to their Bodies than those of Men, and that their Spine, and consequently the Spinal Marrow is yet spun out longer and smaller into a long Tail : And which may be further taken notice of, that those which have naturally the longest Tails are usually *cæteris paribus*, the furthest remote from imitating the Actions of a Man, and do seem nearest approaching to the Capacity of other Brutes. And there is no doubt but that a diligent Observer may by accurately anatomizing each, and comparing them together, find divers other considerable Variations which are of a kind of middle Constitution, between those of a Man and those of other the most brute Creatures; which may much inable an Inquirer in finding what parts of a Man seem most to contribute to the Perfection of his Natural Parts. Another Instance may be this, to observe the Transition of Nature between the Figure of precious Stones, and the crystallizing of Salts, between the shooting of Salt, and the growing of Mould and Mushrooms, and its Transition from Mushrooms to Moss, and from Moss to Grass, *&c.* The accurate Observations of all which Transitions, together with all the Circumstances that attend upon them, will with a Clew almost lead us from the Explication of the most plain, single, and obvious Phænomenon, to the Understanding of the inmost and most secluded Process of Nature.

11. Another way of Discovery, is *by taking Notice of all such Experiments and Accidents as shew the Frustrations and Failings of Nature*; for all such Experiments as these, the Circumstances being diligently noted, afford very essential Distinctions, and do very much direct, circumscribe, and limit the Mind in its search : and, by shewing what things are destructive to it and over-rule and govern it, and what pervert it and turn it out of its Course, it very much fits the Mind for positive and affirmative Knowledge of the Causes of those Effects. For instance, Let the Nature of Fire be the thing sought for : Here we are to look chiefly after such Experiments as shew the failing of Nature in this Operation, such as these; the falling of Water on the Fire makes it immediately go out, query whether from the Coldness or Moisture; that 'tis not from the Coldness is evident, because boyling Water will produce the same Effect, nor is it from the Moisture, because then Spirit of Wine would do the same thing which yet it does not; query further therefore, whether it be by keeping off the Menstruum of the Air, if so, then the keeping of that Body any ways from coming to it will do the same Effect. To confirm this, we have many Instances of the Frustration of Nature; as that a Candle will presently go out if inclos'd in a Vessel, whereby the fresh Air is excluded : The like it will presently do, if it be included in a larger Vessel, and the Air drawn out. Coles likewise will do the same, if included in a close Vessel, nay though by a pair of Bellows included in the Box with them, they be all the time blown upon by them, as I have several times shewn before very many illustrious Spectators.

12. Another way of Discovery, is *by observing the Deviation of Nature in framing Specifick Bodies*, such kind of Operations wherein Nature seems to step a little aside out of its usual Rode, and seems to take up a new Method in forming : Now these though in themselves they seem at first to amaze and perplex the Mind, yet when by diligent Examination and Inquiry the Vail that covers them is remov'd, and it be discover'd to which of the more common Operations of Nature it belongs, and wherein it differs from them, then does it as the former, highly assist the Judgment in determining the true Nature of that Principle, by manifesting what great Influence these or those accidental Concurrents had in altering or disguising it so as to make it appear somewhat extraordinary and miraculous. As for instance, the Loadstone seems to be an Instance of the Deviation of Nature out of its usual Method, and seems to con-

tain

tain some Principles in it altogether extraordinary and very wonderful, but when we have taken this excellent Composition to pieces, and found that it is resembled in some of its Proprieties by the Motion of an Unison String, in others by the Attraction of rubbed Jet, Amber, Wax, &c. that both its Axis may be varied Mechanically into another Posture, and that its Poles may be turn'd end for end, and that its Vertue may be quite destroyed as well as Mechanically augmented ; that it has a Dependence on the Earth, and is mov'd by it, as having the first and chief Magnetical Principle which moves all the rest ; that the Sun, Moon, and all other the Planets, have the same or alike Vertue with this of the Earth, and that the Loadstone has given the occasion of the Discovery of all these : When we consider this Instance, I say, we may plainly see of what great Use Observations and Experiments of this kind are, for the finding out of the Methods and Ways of Nature which are somewhat beyond the Discovery of our Senses. Another Instance may be a Diamond, which for two or three Proprieties seems extraordinary, the first and chiefest is Radiation in the dark, after it has been gently rubb'd or struck, which gives us a new manner of producing Light seeming to depend on the other Property, namely, an extraordinary Hardness, and affords anew Difference or Help of Rejection : For since in this Experiment there is neither Combustion nor Flame as in Fire, nor Moisture and Putrefaction as in Fish and rotten Wood, nor a Motion of Animal Spirits, which some pretend to be the Cause in Glow-worms and Cats Eyes ; nor any previous Light, which some have imagined to inhere and remain like a Liquor in the Object till it be evaporated or dry'd, as in the Bononian Stone, by the help of this one extravagant Instance all these Suppositions are rejected, as not at all necessary to the Existence of Light, and only this one essential Propriety seems to be set up in the stead of them ; namely, a very quick Vibrative Motion, which a Body of that extream Hardness seems only capable of from so small and sudden a Percussion, as that has been observed to shine with. Another Instance of this Rule may be the Apparition of Colours in the Triangular or Sexangular Stiriæ of Crystal, for therein Nature seems to generate a lovely Variety of Colours after quite another way, than it seems to do in other Bodies whether Vegetable, as Flowers, Leaves, Woods, Fruits ; or Animal, as Blood, Gall, Hair, Feathers ; or Mineral, as Metals, Marchasites, Scoria, Vitriols, &c. in all which, some Authors will needs have a various Temperament of Sulphur and Mercury to be the chief and principal Cause. Now by this one Experiment or Observation of Crystal, these and divers other phantastical Hypotheses about Colour are overthrown, and by examining it thoroughly it may be found that this does demonstrate only one thing necessary, namely, a considerable Refraction enough to obliquate the Puls of Light, as I have in my Micrography indeavoured more fully to explain. Such Experiments as these do hugely strengthen the Discursive Faculty, and (at one Blow as it were) inables it to cut off all those numerous Heads of Hydra, which when cut off one by one do a fresh spring up again, and create new and greater Difficulties, but by watching Nature and taking hold of this opportunity of the Deviation of it, the Victory becomes easy and speedy.

13. Another way of Discovery, is *by taking notice of all such Productions of Nature, as are differing from the rest of the same Species*, and are therefore truly esteem'd monstrous and wonderful by the Generality, but a Philosophical Historian has somewhat else to do than admire them ; for these are indeed the most instructive and the richest Commodities he can meet with. His Business therefore is diligently to set upon examining of it both as to the Causes of it, and as to the particular Effects, and to indeavour to find out wherein lies the Deviation in what considerable Circumstances they differ from the most usual Effects, and wherein the Mysterie of Nature's proceeding after such a manner lies, what Cause it was made it thus deviate. One therefore that is fit to make Observation of this kind, must first be very well skill'd in the most usual ways of Nature of that kind, so as that he may be able readily to detect all the Aberrations of Nature : Nor is this Knowledge indeed sufficient, but he ought to be somewhat knowing also in the Uses and Designs of the parts of that Species whereof the thing under Examination is an Aberration ; for 'tis none of the

least

leaft Helps, towards the finding out the Nature of the thing fought for, to be able to know and judge what things are material and confiderable enough to be obferved; for 'tis not the fetting down of every little Variation, of which there be Multitudes in every individual of the fame Species, whereby they differ one from another, moft of thofe being to be paft over as the Effects of a *lufus naturæ*; that is, of many little Circumftances which perhaps 'tis impoffible ever to be able to take notice of, or find out, there being continually fuch Multitudes of them and thofe fo complicated: Nor again on the other fide are fmall, nay almoft unperceivable Variations in fome cafes to be paft by where the Caufes can be certainly found, or where thofe though never fo fmall Variations, become confiderable toward the producing greater Effects; for fometimes thofe Variations which feem greateft and moft confpicuous are very inconfiderable, and as to the promoting of Natural Knowledge fcarce fignificant. So that 'tis not every one that can be prefently fit for this Undertaking, but it requires a long and fedulous indeavour and accuftoming ones felf to obferve the Methods and Courfes of Nature; without which endeavour'd 'tis much to be fear'd that the Hiftory fo written will be full ftufft with Impertinencies, and contain very little of any thing folid, material and ufeful. Of this kind there are Multitudes of Inftances among Animals, Vegetables, and Minerals, all kind of extravagant natural Actions, Generations, Vegetations or Accretions, Difeafes, Cafualties, Conjugations, and Separations, and the like; being to be numbred under this, and every one in their feveral Kinds, if accurately examin'd, affording choice and rare Informations which affift us beyond any other way, how to command and regulate Nature, by either promoting or furthering it in its ufual Method.

14. Another way of Difcovery is, *by obferving the concomitant Proprieties of Individuals in their greateft or higheft, and in the loweft pitch of their Perfections or Exiftences.* As the former was of the extravagant and preter-natural Concomitants in a preter-natural State, fo this of a Natural: For though the former be an excellent Method of Difcovery, yet that alone, and of it felf is not fufficient, we ought as well to know what things and Circumftances accompany the natural Progreffes of Nature as well as the preter natural, that by the comparing thefe two together the Differences between them may more manifeftly appear. As for inftance, that in an Infant the parts are foft, moift and tender, and as very unfit for Animal Motion fo have they very little, till after a certain time moft of thofe parts begin to grow a little more dry and ftiff, but yet retaining Plenty of Natural Juice and Moifture, whereby all the numerous Parts of the Automaton (like thofe of a new and clean Clock, that has been a little us'd to take off the Roughnefs and is well oyl'd) eafily and glibly move and flip by one another and confonant hereunto, that Conftitution of Body is ever in Motion, eats much and acts much, is quickly wound up, and whurr 'tis quickly down again, and a new fupply of Aliment muft be had. And thus it continues to be wound up and run down, till by degrees the Oyl begins to be a little fpent, and to grow fomewhat more ftiff, and the Parts to be well worn and adapted one to another when it arrives at its beft going; the Child being become a Man, his Parts by much Exercife become very prompt and habituated, they move not fo much as at firft but more fteady and regular, the parts become more firm and confiftent, the *Humidum Radicale* feems to be perfectly concocted and brought up to its juft Confiftence, being neither too thin and watery, or too thick and clammy: But as he grows older the Parts grow dryer and ftiffer, and lefs fit for Motion; the Natural Moifture is grown too thick and flug, and the parts begin to fhrink and fhrivel, and to be clogg'd and worn, and all the Motions become flower and more heavy, and the parts grow quickly weary, a little Food ferves long; the Juice in many parts of the Body become fo charg'd with excrementitious parts thereof, that it turns into a kind of hard or ftony Confiftence: and like an old decayed and foul piece of Clock work, here a Pivot is worn loofe in his Socket, there the Oyl is thickned with Duft and Filth, as almoft to ftop the Motion: Here a Wheel is bent, and there a Tooth is worn out, and the like. Now as thefe things which are the common Accidents of Watches, and do generally happen to all

fooner

ſooner or later, according as they are better or worſe uſed, are very eaſy to be found by a diligent Obſerver, though altogether ignorant of Watches ; and by comparing the ſeveral Accidents one with another, he may at laſt be able to underſtand a Watch thoroughly, and know wherein the Goodneſs or Badneſs of one conſiſts, and what is good and bad for it, ſo may one that is wholly ignorant of the Fabrick of any Natural Body be able to learn the Nature of it, by obſerving the ſeveral Accidents that happen to it in the ſeveral States and Conditions of it.

15. Now as the Obſervation of the various Accidents of Bodies in ſeveral States is one way of Diſcovery, *ſo another way may be of obſerving ſuch Variations as happen to Bodies from their being produc'd at differing times, or in differing Places, of the ſame Medium, or in differing Mediums, or with a differing Quantity*; for each of theſe kinds of Obſervations do further manifeſt to us by what Rules Nature works, and by what things it becomes regulated and circumſcrib'd. Of this kind may be the obſerving of the difference between the Shape and Nature of a wild *Iriſh* Man (or ſuch a one as has nothing of Education to biaſs him) and one of *Saldania* or the *Cape of good Hope.* The Difference between the Stature, Age, Strength, Shape, &c. of Men at the beginning of the World and now. The Difference between the Fins of the flying Herring and the Wings of a Bird, between a Crab and a Spider, &c. the one being an Inſect of the Water, and the other of the Air. The Difference between Beaſts of the ſame Species under the Pole, and under the Line, &c.

16. Another way of Diſcovery is, *by obſerving what things moſt conduce to the Perfection or Deſtruction of any Production :* This is differing from the next but one preceding, in this, that there we conſidered only ſuch things as accidentally were found Concomitants with the ſeveral Conditions not ſo much conſidering them as Cauſes ; but here out of many of thoſe former, we ſegregate and collect ſuch as ſeem very active and contribute either to the better perfecting, or to the Deſtruction or Overthrow of ſuch a Body. As ſuppoſe that Fire be the Subject enquired into, we ſhall find Nitre or freſh Air, and ſome Sulphureous Body, to be that which moſt powerfully makes that Operations, and that nothing does deſtroy and hinder it ſo much, as the ſeparating of the intermediate Contract of thoſe two Bodies, by the throwing on of Water or any other incombuſtible and ſluggiſh Liquor.

17. Another way of Diſcovery is, to find out and enumerate *all ſuch Operations of Nature as wherein it ſeems to work after a peculiar manner, and very differing from her more uſual Methods;* for by this means many Circumſtances are cut off, which being generally the Concomitants in her more uſual Method, are therefore more liable to be thought eſſential to the producing of the Propriety ſought. For Inſtance, the Flying Herrings commonly obſerved flying in great Sholes in the Torrid Zone, may ſeem as an excellent Inſtance to manifeſt that to the Buſineſs of flying, there is no need of Feathers about the Body, nor in the Wings, nor in the Tail, as moſt imagine ; and the Poets ſeem to confirm it by the Story of *Dædalus* and *Icarus,* ſince this Fiſh has nothing but Fins and Scales: Nor ſecondly, is there any need of a flat Tail, ſuch as all kind of Birds have and Bats; for the Tail of this Fiſh ſtands edge-ways: Nor thirdly, is there any need of Joynts in the Arm, or Stems of the Wing, as in the Pinnions of Birds, and in the Fingers of the Bat ; nor is it ſo neceſſary that the Stem of the Wing muſt needs grow in the Center of Gravity, ſince this is not obſerv'd in this Creature, and divers other ſuch Circumſtances which were generally believ'd to be neceſſary Circumſtances to the Buſineſs of Flying by the Peculiarity of Nature, in Shaping this Fiſh after this kind, and induing it with the Power of Flying, they are all of them diſcovered to be only moſt proper for that peculiar Creature to which they were adapted, and where no ſuch Accompliſhment is beſtowed on a Creature by Nature, 'tis as proper if we would ſupply that Defect artificially to make uſe of one way as well as the other, and perhaps could there be made an Artificial Repoſitory or Magazine of Strength, which for Weight and Bulk would not be too cumberſome ; 'tis not

impoſſible

impossible to fit a Pair of Wings for a Man to fly with, which may be contriv'd somewhat after the manner of the long Fins of these flying Fish. Suppose Congruity be the thing look'd after, the thorough considering of the Nature of the peculiar Species of it between Iron and Magnets, will help to cut off many Circumstances which divers Instances in other Bodies do seem to make necessary.

18. Another way of Discovery is, *by inquiring after and diligently observing what middle way of Nature there can be found between those extravagant and the more common ones.* For such as these serve as a *Vinculum*, to conjoyn both these together by some common Nature, which is to be found in the third, and thereby hugely promote the Explication of both the other. As suppose, Congruity be the Nature sought, the more common ways of Congruity are between divers Homogeneous Fluids and Solids that are immediately contiguous; the more rare and singular is between two Load stones or two Magnetick Irons, or between a Loadstone and Iron contiguous and at a distance, between these too may be interposed the Attraction of Amber, Jet, Wax, *&c.* which as they sometimes act at a distance when they are rubb'd, and also on the Bodies contiguous, very much help to explain the Congruity both in the one and in the other.

19. Another way of discovering the Methods of Nature's working is, *by observing and comparing the Productions of Art with those of Nature.* And for this purpose it would be very requisite to have a perfect Account of all the Productions of Art, such as are dispers'd up and down in several Trades and Occupations of Men, whether for Profit or Pleasure; and especially all those excellent ways of working on Bodies by Chymical Operations, such as Menstrua, Mistion, Digestion, Fermentation, Distillation, Calcination, Fusion, Freezing, and the like; every of which as they admit of a vast Variety, so do each of them serve as so many Torches to light us in the dark Passages of the Labyrinth of Nature, where the Assistance of the common Works of Nature, like the Radiation of the Sun, cannot go along with us. For instance, suppose we compare an Automaton with an Animal, as I mentioned a little before by the by. Or suppose we compare Paper or Hats with the Skin of an Animal, because the Texture of those two seems of much Affinity with this, we shall find the Method of Nature prettily explicated by them: For in both those Artificial Products we find that the Artists endeavour first to cut, grind, or beat into small parts the Materials they are to use, then to make them soft, light, and supple with Water or other Liquor, then to dispose, place, or put it into such Forms or Moulds as may shape it into what Form they design it, then they there so work and order it, that the Moisture may by degrees waste, and the solid Parts unite more closely together, adding to it such glutinous Matter as may make it fit to stick, hold and grow stiff, firm, and strong together; and lastly, by several ways they smooth and colour, or beautify the Surface: All which Particulars may be understood more fully by my Descriptions of those Trades, and the Explication of their several Operations, which I must reserve for another Opportunity. Now Nature in preparing the Matter that does repair the Skin or Flesh of the Body, seems to proceed much after the same Method, the Food is chosen, then groun'd or chewed, then digested or brought into the Form of a Milk or Froth, then dispers'd over the Body, by degrees thicked, and lastly polished. Now though every Particular does not exactly hit, yet there are many that seem to have a great Affinity, and serve to prompt the Intellect, and very much to help the Fancy and Imagination to conceive of those things, and of the Method of Nature, and they will serve greatly to instruct the Mind what things are to be look'd after and examin'd in the Proceedings of Nature: And the more Variety there are of these Artificial Instances, the more will the Mind be quickned to Inquiry, and the more taken off from Prejudices, or an Imagination, that because the Process of Nature in one part may agree with one part of the Artificial Process; therefore that all the other parts of the one must agree with the other parts of the other, for when we see that even Art can use the same Beginning, but yet very differing intermediate Proceedings,

and

and yet at laſt by both produce the ſame Effects, we ſhall find cauſe to think that
Nature may do ſo much more.   And therefore I might have added to Paper
and Hats, Silks, and Cloths, and Linnen, and divers other ſuch Artificial Contextures which have every of them a differing way of proceeding to perfect the
End.

20. Another way of Diſcovery is, *by obſerving where and by what means Art
cauſes Nature to deviate or alter its uſual Courſe, where it aſſiſts, promotes and
perfects, and where it impedes, diverts, or deſtroys.* Of this there are Multitudes
of Inſtances in all things, about which Art has been uſed, and therefore needs
not exemplifying ; but certain it is, that this Method affords extraordinary Help
for Diſcovery of the true Nature of the efficient and material Cauſes of things : For
knowing what in Art is able to change, and divert the Proceedings of Nature,
and what to ſtay or promote them, it will not be difficult to find what they are
that are thus wrought upon, ſince it ſeems very probable that they muſt be ſomewhat of the Nature of thoſe in Art which promote them, and ſomewhat of a
contrary Nature to thoſe that do alter and impede them.   As becauſe 'tis found
by experienced Gardiners, that Artificial Heats ripen Fruit, 'tis not improbable
but that 'tis a convenient Degree of Natural Heat that contributes moſt to that
Effect.   Now as we ſhould obſerve diligently the Cauſes or Ingredients which
do co-operate with Nature, ſo ſhould we alſo obſerve in what Quantity it is
moſt aſſiſtant, by what Steps and in what Degrees it aſſiſts the Circumſtances of
Time, Place, manner of Application, Operation, and the like ; for without the Determination of theſe Particulars, the Informations will be lame and imperfect,
and nothing of Certainty can be built on them, for that which is aſſiſtant in one
degree, at one time, in one Place, or at ſuch a Diſtance, is perhaps deſtructive
and pernicious in another : This will not only help the Mind to judge of what
the cauſe is, but the Degrees and Circumſtances of Time, Place, Quantity, &c.

21. Another way of diſcovering Nature is, *by obſerving and comparing the Natural and Artificial ways of producing the ſame Effects.* For having the Artificial
way in our own Power, and being able to alter and change, and vary it : We
have much greater Helps to find out the true Reaſons and Cauſes of thoſe Operations, and having found them in Artificials 'twill be very eaſy to apply them to
Naturals, and this way of inquiring where the Subject is capable of it, is the moſt
eaſy of any I have yet mentioned, and the moſt inſtructive, and does more immediately inform the Senſe and the Imagination with a true Idea of it, oblite-
rating and diſpelling dark and confus'd Notions.   Thus, for inſtance, had we
not found an Artificial way of hatching Eggs by a gentle and equal Heat from
whatever cauſe it proceeds, we ſhould have been very apt to have fancied
ſtrange kind of irradiating and plaſtick Influences from the brooding Hen to the
hatching Eggs, but by the *Egyptian* Experiment of hatching them in Dung and
Ovens, or Stoves, which has been tried other ways very ſucceſsfully in *Denmark* (as *Bartholine* affirms) and in *England*, and elſewhere, with the gentle
Heat of Digeſting, and Lamp Furnaces ; and alſo by the hatching them oftentimes in Womens Boſoms, and divers other ways, 'tis evident that ſuch Phancies
will eaſily vaniſh.   Thus many People are ſtill very apt to fancy a certain attractive Vertue in the Sun, which by a kind of Magnetiſm does draw up the
freſh Water out of the Sea, leaving the ſalter part behind, and by that its Power does keep it ſuſpended in Clouds : Whereas if we conſider that any other
Heat to that Degree will do the ſame thing, whether the Heat be placed above
or below, or on one ſide or t'other, we ſhall then find cauſe to think that 'tis not
an attractive Vertue of the Sun that performs this Effect, but that 'tis the Heat
of the Sun which working on the ſuperficial and freſher parts of the Water
warms them, and by degrees rarifies them into the Form of Air, which having
much heat and Agitation in them, do ſo far expand themſelves as to make them more
rarify'd in *Specie* than the Circumambient Air, which being therefore heavier
than them cauſes them to aſcend in the ſame manner as Water makes Air, or
Oyl, or any other Liquor lighter than it ſelf to aſcend to the Top.   This way
does very much diſcover the naked Truth and Simplicity of things, by taking
away the Vizour under which it lay diſguiſed.   Much in the ſame manner as

Travellers

Travellers judge of the Beauty of the *Persian* or *Indian* Ladies, whom they never saw, by obferving and examining fuch as they have more Liberty to fee and converfe with.

22. Another way of difcovering Nature is, *by obferving the difference between the Products of Nature and thofe of Art.* And without this Head indeed the former way cannot be compleat, and therefore this has an immediate Dependance upon it: This way does farther affift the Mind to find out and fix the effential Differences and Proprieties of Natural Actions; for by comparing thefe kind of Obfervations with the former, we fhall be able to judge better of the differing Nature of thofe Operations, and what Propriety 'tis in the one that makes the Workmore perfect, and what 'tis makes the other mifcarry. Thus the Reafon why Rain Water feems to be more pleafant than diftill'd, feems to be partly from the Saline or Nitrous part of the Air which does fomewhat purify it, and partly alfo from the gentle or moderate Heat of the Sun which acts upon the Surface of the Water, and partly alfo from the greater Coldnefs of the outward Air, which being therefore heavier does fooner carry up the Vapours, though but a little rarify'd; the diftilled Water on the other fide contracts an Empyreume from the greater Heat, which is apply'd at the bottom, and fo the whole is much heated, and from the Pentnefs of the Veffel, whereby all thofe Parts that rife, though many of them are Saline and Terreftrial, are driven over with the Vapours, and muft neceffarily fall and unite again with the Water in the Recipient; whereas in the Air they ferve to another purpofe, for the Collection of thofe Parts together at the top of the Clouds, and there kindling, feems to be the caufe of Lightning and Thunder.

23. Another way of Difcovery is, *by obferving the differing Materials, and ways of producing one and the fame Effect by Art.* For this does mightily free the Mind from Prejudice, and from being too much imbued with any one Experiment or Method of proceeding, and each of them does much contribute to the Explication of the reft. Thus by obferving that the fpirituous part of Urine may be extracted out of it, either after it has ftood a confiderable time to putrify, or immediately after the Intermixture of quick Lime we may learn, that Putrefaction is nothing but a kind of Corrofion or a working of fome of the parts of the Urine upon others, and thereby a fetting others at Liberty. Thus the being able to make a very Volatile Spirit, and Salt with Horns, Bloods, Flefh, Hair, Hoofs, *&c.* of Animals, we may learn that all the parts of Animals feem to be much of the fame Nature, but only diverfify'd and dreft under feveral Textures and Schematifms; and by obferving that Spirit of Soot yields much the fame kind of Spirit, we may thence perhaps with fome Probability argue, that the caufe of thefe Effects may proceed from a Corrofion or mixing of the Salt of the Air with the Materials that yield thofe Subftances; the Operation of the one being made in the Chimney, and of the other in the Lungs or Heart, though indeed that which feems to be the Empyreume in all Liquors may perhaps not improbably be fuppos'd fome fuch thing as this Volatile Salt, and may perchance be caus'd only by the exceeding Violence of Heat.

24. Another way of Difcovery is, *by obferving with what Circumftances Nature and Art doe fometimes exceed one another.* For thefe kind of Obfervations as they difcover the Excellencies of the one, fo do they alfo the Defects of the other, and each of them contributes to the Explication of the other, and do put the Mind upon Inquiry how to fupply thofe Defects. For inftance, that Cryftal and Diamonds are made by Nature of an Hexangular Prifmatical Figure perfectly tranfparent and exceeding hard. Art on the other fide is able by Decoctions and Evaporations, to make a Body fomewhat tranfparent, and of the fame Figure, but very foft and brittle, and eafily either fufil or diffoluble again in Water, Namely, Salt Peter. This will prompt one to enquire what may be the caufe of the more perfect Tranfparency, and of the much greater Hardnefs; that is, to find out by what means Niter may be fo ordered as to be made perfectly tranfparent, hard, and fixt: Or elfe to inquire by what means Cryftal

may

may be made as eaſily liquefiable as Salt Peter, and by what Menſtruum it may be melted away, as that Salt is into warm Water. Somewhat like the former of theſe Inquiries may perhaps have formerly raiſed in the firſt Inventors of Glaſs a Deſire and Endeavour to find out ſuch a way, whereby theſe things might be performed, and thoſe Tryals perhaps might produce Glaſs ; as I think 'tis not to be doubted but that by this means the tinging of Glaſs into all kinds of Colours was ſought after and found. Another Inſtance wherein Art excels Nature, may be in Chymical Diſtillations and Separations which is no where naturally done, and the Inquiry how and where this is or may be perform'd by Nature, may prompt unto us perhaps ſomewhat of the ſtrange Operations perform'd in Animals, and ſtir us up to examine whether thoſe may not be Nature's Chymical Veſſels ; and to inquire alſo by what means thoſe combuſtible Subſtances that cauſe Lightning are ſeparated from other Vapours collected together, and afterwards kindled : A Collection therefore of all Experiments and Obſervations that ſeem to ſhew ſomething of this Nature, will greatly quicken and excite the Mind, and inform it of what things are material to be inquir'd, and what Circumſtances are very ſignificant and inſtructive.

25. Another way of Diſcovery will be, *to enquire after, to try and enumerate how many mechanical ways there may be of working on, or altering the Proprieties of ſeveral Bodies.* For the being well inſtructed and knowing in theſe, will exceedingly adapt and fit the Mind to trace the Method of Nature, and to judge which or likelieſt to which of thoſe ways Nature performs her Operations inquir'd after ; it will much rectify the Imagination, and take it off from an Inclination to unconceivable and confuſed Apprehenſions of things. Thus, methinks, the Operation of corroſive Menſtruums on Metals, or diſſoluble Bodies, may hint to us a way how the Air may operate on combuſtible Bodies, or ſuch as are diſſoluble by Air exceedingly heated. Thus the Obſervations that by the cutting off a part of any Stone from one ſide of it, does alter the Center of Gravity of it : And that a Muſical String, wherever it be ſtopp'd, if it be ſtruck does make the longeſt Vibrations in the middle, may prompt unto us perhaps ſomewhat of the Reaſon of the changing of the Poles of the Magnet upon the paring off one ſide. Were this way well practiſed, certainly Men would not have ſuch ſtrange, wild and unconceivable Notions of the Works and Effects of Nature : For as it ſeems to do nothing unintelligibly, ſo are there very many things that it manifeſtly performs mechanically : For inſtance, all Animal Motions and the Inſtruments thereto belonging. We ſhould therefore endeavour to be acquainted with all the various mechanical ways of Hammering, Preſſing, Pounding, Grinding, Rowling, Cutting, Sawing, Filing, Steeping, Soaking, Diſſolving, Heating, Burning, Freezing, Melting, and the like ; of which there are various other Species, and each of theſe have Multitudes of Individual ways, very much differing from one another, as many of which as can be attain'd unto, ſhould be underſtood and examin'd to inform and regulate the Conceptions of the Mind, and to remove thoſe Puerile and Childiſh Fancies that we ſuck'd with our Milk, and learnt with our Language.

26. Another Help of Diſcovery will be, *to inquire out, and try how many various mechanical ways there may be of ſeparating Bodies joyn'd and mixt.* Such as Winnowing, Straining, Wringing, and Preſſing, Waſhing, Diſtilling, Evaporating, Precipitating, Subliming, Cryſtallizing, Burning, Coppelling, Freezing, Shaking, Knocking, and the like ; each of which will furniſh the Mind with their differing Circumſtances and Proprieties, ſo as by comparing thoſe various kinds of Separations in the workings of Nature, with theſe it will be the better inabled to judge to which of them they have moſt Reſemblance, and will be better fitted to detect in what Circumſtances they vary, or are differing from them ; and the eaſier underſtand what Particulars are notable and what are not.

27. Another

27. Another Help of Difcovery will be, *to inquire and try how many various mechanical ways there may be of uniting and incorporating Bodies into one another.* Such as Jointing, Binding, Screwing, Pinning, Hooking, Shaking, Tumbling, Churming, Kneading, Melting, Diffolving (for the Diffolution of fome parts feem caus'd by the uniting of others) to which may be adjoyn'd Burning, in which there feems to be feveral Unitings as well as Separations; Digefting, Infufion, Freezing, Infolation, by mixing a third or fourth, &c. by taking away an Impeding part by Compreffion, by opening and divers other ways and Methods, fome of which are more obvious and vifible, others more fecret and obfcure, and themfelves will need further Explications: All which ways fhould, if poffible, be well underftood and reduc'd to a certain Theory, that fo by that means other more fubtile and curious workings of Nature, might by the Help of them be more exactly detected and defin'd.

28. Another way of Difcovery is, *to feek after and attempt by tryal all fuch ways, whereby Bodies are really chang'd from one thing to another.* And for this purpofe it matters not whether it be from worfe to better, or from better to worfe, or neither: For each, as to this Defign, may be alike ufeful. Of this kind may be fuch Bodies as are chang'd by all forts of Corruptions, Vegetations, Animations, Vitrifications, Incorporations, Combuftions, Digeftions, and feveral other Chymical Operations; or any other Mechanical and Artificial way whatfoever, whereby all or any of the former Proprieties or fenfible Qualities are really changed and deftroyed, and new ones generated in their Stead, fuch as the Alteration of their Confiftence, Colour, Bulk, Gravity, &c. An Inftance of this may be the Body produced by the melting together of Tin and Copper, which make a third Body quite diftinct in moft of its Proprieties from either of thofe other two; 'tas quite a diftinct Colour from either; 'tis of a Confiftence abundantly harder than either; 'tis exceeding brittle; whereas the others are both tuff, 'tis much heavier in Specie than either of them, and fo for divers other Proprieties, it feems wholly differing from either of the two Ingredients of which it is compounded.

And laftly, A moft general Help of Difcovery in all kind of Philofophical Inquiry is, *to attempt to compare the working of Nature in that particular that is under Examination, to as many various, mechanical and intelligible ways of Operations as the Mind is furnifht with.* For this will not only make the Mind very attent, and earneft, and circumfpect, in obferving, but will alfo hint many confiderable Circumftances to be inquir'd after, and Experiments for examining and explicating of them: And which is much more than either, will hugely affift the Ratiocination and Invention in detecting the true Caufes of things. As burning compar'd with Diffolution, &c.

Thefe are fome of the various ways by which Nature may be trac'd, by which we may be able to find out the material Efficient and Inftrumental Caufes of divers Effects, not too far removed beyond the reach of our Senfes, and which do not very much differ from fuch Effects as are more material and obvious to our Senfes. But as for the Difcovery of the more internal Texture and Conftitution, as alfo of the Motion, Energy, and operating Principle of Concret Bodies, together with the Method and Courfe of Nature's proceeding in them: Thefe will require much deeper Refearches and Ratiocinations, and very many Viciffitudes of Proceedings from Axiomes to Experiments, and from Experiments to Axiomes; and are indeed the Bufinefs of the Philofopher, and not of the Hiftorian, the Method of which I intend, God willing, to handle in the fecond part of this Philfophical Algebra; which explains the way of making ufe of the *Penus Analytica,* of raifing Axiomes, and more general Deductions from a fufficient Stock of Materials collected according to the Method of this firft part, with Integrity, Judgment, and Care.

Having thus paft over curforily the Methods and Means of Inquiry, we will next confider the Manner and Order of entring what things are to be Regiftred, and in what manner, and to be rejected as ufelefs or noxious.

In the making of all kind of Obfervations or Experiments there ought to be a huge deal of Circumfpection, to take notice of every the leaft perceivable

Circum-

Circumstance that seems to be significant either in the promoting or hindering, or any ways influencing the Effect. And to this end, as I mentioned before, it were very desirable that both Observations and Experiments should be divers times repeated, and that at several Seasons and with several Circumstances, both of the Mind and of Persons, Time, Place, Instruments and Materials : For all these do very much contribute to the Discovery of Circumstances. And an Observer should endeavour to look upon such Experiments and Observations that are more common, and to which he has been more accustom'd, as if they were the greatest Rarity, and to imagine himself a Person of some other Country or Calling, that he had never heard of, or seen any thing of the like before : And to this end, to consider over those Phœnomena and Effects, which being accustom'd to, he would be very apt to run over and slight, to see whether a more serious considering of them will not discover a Significancy in those things which because usual were neglected : For I am very apt to believe, that if this Course were taken we should have much greater Discoveries of Nature made than have been hitherto. For I find it very common for Tradesmen, or such as have been much versed about any thing, to give the worst kind of Description of it for this purpose ; and one that is altogether ignorant and a Stranger to it, if he be curious and inquisitive, to make the most perfect and full Description of it. And the like may be observed also in such as travel into other Countries, that they will give a better Description of the Place than such as are Natives of it ; for those usually take notice of all the things which because of their Newness seem strange, whereas a Native passes over those because accustom'd to them. I grant that a Native, or one that has been more accustom'd and vers'd in a thing or place, shall be able to answer Questions propounded much better : But a Stranger shall be best able to make the Queries ; every Experimenter and Observator therefore should endeavour to be himself both the Inquirer and the Answerer, he should indeavour to make himself as knowing and as much vers'd in any thing he is to describe, and to suppose himself as ignorant and unacquainted as if wholly a Stranger : For as the one will make him inquisitive, so the other will inable him to solve his Doubts. And that his Attention may be the more weakned and rous'd, it will be necessary that he should look upon every Circumstance as the most significant and essential to the producing the Effect, and to continue so to do till he find sufficient Reason to the contrary, by having thoroughly consider'd and examin'd it : For though I confess that this his Supposal will be often frustrated, yet I dare assure him, that it will divers times also prove much otherwise, as I have very often found. And 'tis one considerable Step towards Science, to know the Negative Properties of things, for by that means the Affirmative Properties are made somewhat more defin'd and circumscrib'd.

Of Registering Experiments.   Now what I have here spoken of, Attention and Diligence in making Observations and Experiments, the same I would have also in registring ; at first let all Circumstances be entred as considerable, unless they are so very obviously otherwise that they appear so at the first examining of them, but yet even in that case also 'tis good to be a little doubtful that possibly something may be at first overseen, which being discover'd would cause other Thoughts and Opinions of it ; they can be easily struck out, as soon as they are by further Observations or Experiments prov'd insignificant, and if entred in few words they will not take much room ; besides there are very many things, which though perhaps insignificant to the present End or Design, may yet be very notable to some other. If it be found such, 'twill be very good when obliterated in one place, to be inscrib'd in another, where at least it may keep its place till some other thing much more significant to the same purpose, may give occasion to displace it.

Now Observations, Experiments, or Circumstances are not to be esteem'd according to the common Opinion of the World, nor are they to be look'd upon as they are curious or not, or pleasant, or strange, or gainful, or sumptuous, or esteem'd by the great, the grave, the otherwise Learned part of the World, or any of those other kinds of Valuations which are put upon them for other ends, and by Persons altogether unable to judge of their Significancy as to this great and useful Design : But he that is a true Philosophical Historian, will

find

find quite other Reafons to advance their Value and fix his Efteem of them. He may perhaps fee Caufe to account thofe the moft precious and rich, which are generally efteem'd the moft vile and fordid; he may perhaps difcover that to be the richeft Ambergreafe, which another takes for Greafe fit for naught but to noint his Shoes: Thofe things which others count Childifh and Foolifh, he may find Reafons to think them worthy his moft attentive, grave and ferious Thoughts; and thofe things which fome are pleafed to call Swingfwangs to pleafe Children, have been found to difcover Irregularities even in the Motion of the Sun it felf. Other things which the Generality would account an Employment about Niceties and Trifles, he finds to be the fhorteft and eafieft way to his Journey's end, and from the miffing of the Hundred part of a Grain, perhaps in his Statical Experiment, finds the Mafs of Metal to be many Hundred Pounds worfe for Allay: And from the turning of a Straw, is able to forefee a Change in the great Ocean of the Air. He ought therefore to fortify himfelf againft thefe kinds of Prejudices, which are too to apt to obtrude into his Mind, and prepoffefs him againft a clear View and Obfervation of Circumftances as they are in their own Nature, or as they are fignificant to the Defign of perfecting Philofophy, and not to neglect or pafs by any of them as trivial, or childifh, or filthy, or bafe and mean, and the like; but having always his main End or Aim before his Eyes, to make that the Touchftone, whereby to find the Value of all his Inventions.

And as thefe things are not to fway him in the things of his own Invention, *What Influence* fo neither fhould they have any Influence upon him, as to thofe things which *Authority* he receives from others, Authority therefore fhould have no other Argument of *ought to have.* Prevalency, but as it was affirmed by an inquifitive, judicious, and moft ftrictly veracious Perfon; one that is not found to vent Affirmations rafhly or negligently, or for any other by Refpect, but meerly for the fake of Truth, and becaufe he had by Obfervation or Tryal found it fo, or for fome very confiderable reafon believed it fuch; one that is very circumfpect in chufing and placing his Words, and that is not obferv'd to ufe too much the Superlative Degree, nor to be too confidently pofitive in his Affertion. Wherefoever therefore any thing is regiftred upon the Authority of another, there ought to be put in the Margin a C, a P, or a D, according as the Authority is Certain, Probable, or Doubtful: Nor needs there any other Naming fince they are only to be refpected according to one of thefe Confiderations, or at moft nothing but the bare Name of the Perfon. For 'tis not Epithets taken from Antiquity or Novelty, or Honour, or Greatnefs, or Will, or Eloquence, or any other Learning but Experimental, that will be fignificantly added upon this Account: And therefore a Philofophical Hiftorian fhould indeavour to look through all thofe Vifards, and to fee only what Truth or Probability at leaft he can fpy underneath; befide, that fuch kind of Additions fill Space, and fo expand the Hiftory into a wider Space, whereas it ought to be compris'd, as I fhall afterwards fhew in as little room as poffible, fo as to appear and come under View all at once that the Eye may the more quickly pafs over it from one Particular to another, as I fhall afterwards more fully explain.

The next thing to be taken care of is the manner of Regiftring: And this, as *The third part* it ought to be done as faft as the Experiment is made, and as foon as the Ob- *of the manner* fervations or Circumftances occur, becaufe of the Frailty of the Memory, and *of Regiftring* the great Significancy there may be in fome of the meaneft and fmalleft Cir- *Natural Hifto-* cumftances; fo ought they afterwards to be feveral times reviewed and exa- *ries.* min'd, and rang'd into a better Method, and abbreviated in the manner of Defcription; fo that as nothing be wanting in the Hiftory, fo nothing alfo be fuperfluous in the words. In the Choice of which, there ought to be great Care and Circumfpection, that they be fuch as are fhorteft and exprefs the Matter with the leaft Ambiguity, and the greateft Plainnefs and Significancy, not augmenting the Matter by Superlatives, nor abating it by Diminutives, not inclining it to this or that Hypothefis, or accommodating it to this or that Author's Opinion; avoiding all kinds of Rhetorical Flourifhes, or Oratorical Garnifhes, and all forts of Periphrafes or Circumlocutions, omitting the Citations of Authors, or the Recital of Opinions, and Sayings, or the like; in the fecond Review and Writing of which, 'twill not be amifs to write it in a very fine piece of of Paper, and to enter it in the moſt compendious manner of writing that the Hiſtorian is acquainted with, ſuch as ſome very good Short-hand or Abbreviation, whereby the whole Hiſtory may be contracted into as little Space as is poſſible ; for this, as I ſhall more fully explain in my ſecond part, is of huge Uſe in the Proſecution of Ratiocination and Inquiry, and is a vaſt Help to the Underſtanding and Memory, as in Geometrical Algebra, the expreſſing of many and very perplex Quantities by a few obvious and plain Symbols : And therefore 'twere to be wiſht, that we could expreſs the whole Hiſtory in as few Letters or Characters as it has conſiderable Circumſtances, ſomewhat of the manner of doing which in my ſecond Part.

Now theſe Hiſtories being writ in brief, in a ſmall piece of very fine Paper, 'twill be very convenient to have a large Book bound after the manner of thoſe that are very uſual for keeping Prints, Pictures, Drawings, &c. in, to preſerve them ſmooth and in order : On the ſides of which, in the ſame manner as thoſe Pictures are kept, it would be convenient to ſtick on with Mouth Glew, or ſome ſuch Subſtance in the beſt Method that can be thought of for the preſent ; the ſeveral ſmall Schedules containing the abbreviated and complicated Hiſtories of Obſervations or Experiments, as they are laſt written on fine Paper, for by the Contrivance of this Book, which for Brevity's ſake I will call a Repoſitory, not only all the Hiſtories belonging to any one Inquiry may be placed ſo as to appear all at one View, there being two large ſides of Paper to be fill'd with theſe Schedules : But they may at any time, upon occaſion, be preſently remov'd or alter'd in their Poſition or Order, that which was plac'd firſt may be plac'd middle-moſt, or laſt, or tranſpos'd to another Head, or a little remov'd to ſuffer another to be interpos'd, the Convenience of which will quickly upon Tryal be found to be very great, as alſo it has another Convenience that many of thoſe Schedules which ſeem to be of the ſame Significancy may for a time be placed all one over another, and ſo at laſt the choiceſt and moſt excellent of them may be preſerv'd and plac'd in their room, and all the reſt as ſuperabundant, and in particular leſs ſignificant of the ſame thing may be remov'd elſewhere, of which an inquiſitive and diligent Hiſtorian will very often find great Uſe. On theſe large ſides he may place them either according to the Method of the Queries, which he has at firſt propounded to himſelf, or according to their firſt appearing Plainneſs, or Difficulty, or after any other Method of Inquiry, or Proceeding, which every one will be beſt able to adapt for himſelf, according to the Subject whereon he makes his Inquiry, or according to his particular Aim and Scope in examining it, or according to the Knowledge he has already acquir'd in it.

As for the Queries which he at firſt propounds to himſelf to be examin'd on that Subject, he intends the Hiſtory of, thoſe will be moſt conveniently written either in ſome other ſmall long Book, or elſe better in a ſingle Sheet of Paper, either of which may at the ſame time be expos'd to the View with the Schedules on the ſides of the larger Repoſitory, and as 'twill be no great Labour to write over the one anew according as further Information ſhall give occaſion to add or alter Queries, ſo 'twill be much leſs to tranſpoſe and range the Method and Order of the Schedules in the Repoſitory.

Now becauſe oftentimes much more may be expreſſed in a ſmall Picture of the thing, than can be done by a Deſcription of the ſame thing in as many words as will fill a Sheet ; it will be often neceſſary to add the Pictures of thoſe Obſervables that will not otherwiſe be ſo fully and ſenſibly expreſt by Verbal Deſcription : But in the doing of this, as a great Art and Circumſpection is to be uſed in the Delineation, ſo ought there to be very much Judgment and Caution in the uſe of it. For the Pictures of things which only ſerve for Ornament or Pleaſure, or the Explication of ſuch things as can be better deſcrib'd by words is rather noxious than uſeful, and ſerves to divert and diſturb the Mind, and ſways it with a kind of Partiality or Reſpect : Beſides that, it fills up room, and occupies the Mind with the Ideas of things which are little ſignificant in the preſent Inquiry.

And therefore all thoſe kind of Pictures of the outward Forms and Beauties, and Varieties of the Species of Nature, are to be referred to another Head,

where

where indeed they will prove very fignificant, but to a peculiar kind of Inquiry, as I fhall fhew more at large in my fecond part. All things indeed ought to be regiftred very exactly and defin'd and determin'd all according to their Proportions in Number, Weight, Meafure, Time, Place, and Circumftances; but all in brief, and yet fufficiently fignificant.

Together with thefe Schedules of Hiftory, 'twill be convenient to interpofe fmall Schedules of particular Deductions, or Conjectures, or Queries, or Caufes of Doubt, or receiv'd Hypothefes, and the like; but thefe, as they fhould be expreft in a very few words, fo that they may be the more obvious, and may thereby the lefs difturbe the Mind in its Inquiry: So 'twill be beft to have them written with an Ink of fome other Colour, as Red or Green, or the like; for this will much affift the Memory and Ratiocination, as I fhall afterwards manifeft more at large.

The Promife of our Author at the end of the foregoing Difcourfe of profecuting, and more particularly explaining the way of ranging Obfervations and Experiments, fo as to make them more convenient for Ufe, as occafion offers, was I believe never performed: For I never heard or met with any of that Subject, and as to the reafoning part of his Philofophick Algebra, that likewife was not wrote, only there is fomething to that purpofe in feveral of his Geometrick Lectures read Anno 1680. *wherein he fhews the Excellency of the Method obferved by* Euclid *in his Elements, which he enlarges upon; fhewing how from a few felf evident Axiomes and Definitions, and* Poftulata *eafy to be granted, a vaft Structure of undeniable Truths have been raifed, and that from the Method of not leaving any thing undemonftrated behind, but ftill proceeding on, fteadily and firmly a* Notioribus ad minus nota; *which Method, if exactly obferved in Philofophical Inquiries, the whole Pile would be founded and built upon fo fure a Foundation as never to be fhaken. And in order to this, he prefers generally the* Synthetick *Method as the moft inftructive and perfective of the Underftanding and Reafon, tho' he fometimes proceeds by the* Analytick, *Specimens of each of which will be feen in feveral of the following Lectures, wherefore I fhall forbear to enlarge upon them in this place, fince the Prefaces to the particular Lectures will with more Benefit inform the Reader what ufe he made of them: And likewife of what Ufe, if not Neceffity,* Theories *and pre-conceived* Hypothefes *are (contrary to the Opinion of fome Learned Perfons) in order to the making more proper Obfervations, contriving and ordering more convenient Experiments, and inventing more fit Inftruments for that purpofe, the more accurately and nicely to determine whether the fuppos'd Theory be true or falfe; all which Obfervations without fuch a preconceived Suppofition, would either have been paft by unheeded, and feveral material Particulars unobferved, and Experiments wanderingly made; or as Chance offered them, and not made with fo much Care and Circumfpection, and Inftruments and other neceffary Apparatus not well contrived for determining the Enquiry; yet he ftill afferts all fhould be done with great Candor, and without Fondnefs for any* Theory, *which fhould be taken up only to difcover Truth, and as eafily laid down again if found not agreeable to Truth. For a farther Account of his Opinion in this Matter, I refer the inquifitive Reader to the feveral places where this Subject happens to be difcourfed of, and more particularly to a Lecture about determining the Oval Figure of the Terraqueous Globe, and Encompaffing Atmofphere, whether it be an Oblong or a Prolated Spheroeid, and of determining the Queftion whether the* Axis *of the Earth's Rotation has or does fucceffively, tho' very flowly alter, which Lectures were read the beginning of the Year* 1687. *and follow in their proper place.*

I fhall only as a Specimen of thefe Geometrick Lectures above-mentioned, give the Reader fome few Abftracts of fome of our Author's Explications: Since I judge it needlefs to publifh his Lectures on that Subject at large, the Elements of Geometry having been already illuftrated and fet forth by feveral eminent Perfons and that in different Methods, and the firft I fhall offer is what our Author has delivered concerning the Definition of a Point, *viz.* R. W.

A Point is that which hath no part. This which fome would deem the moft inconfiderable thing in the World, feems yet the moft difficult to be under-

ftood;

stood; no Senfe, or Imagination, or Fant'cy, can reach it, nor words defcribe it, but by a Negative, to tell you what it is not: For it is not to be taken in the Senfe, that the whole Earth is called a Point in refpect of the Univerfe, nor in the Senfe that the End of a tapering thing is called a Point, as of a Pin or Needle, tho' they feem to be the fmalleft things we know, becaufe thefe later may be faid to have as many parts as the fore-mentioned; for fince all Quantity is divifible *in infinitum,* the leaft Quantity may be divided as often as the greateft, and therefore whatever is divifible muft have Parts, and therefore none of thefe can be properly called a Point, in the Senfe here named, unlefs this Point be underftood to be the *Apex* of a Mathematical Cone or Pyramid, where the Superficies of it is determined, for that will be a Mathematical Point: But it cannot be fuppofed of a Phyfical Point, or Material Cone, or Pyramid, for that will have Extenfion and Bluntnefs. And we find that Microfcopes will make thofe Points divifible even to Senfe, nay even almoft to difcover a new World in a Point, nay there is one now that affirms he has feen more than 10000 Living Creatures in the Bignefs of a very fmall Sand, which it felf indeed is but a vifible Point to the naked Eye, and each of thofe 10000 may have Worlds within them. We know not the Limits of Quantity, Matter, and Body as to its Divifibility or Extenfion, no Imagination can comprehend the *Maximum* or the *Minimum Naturæ,* our Faculties are finite and limited, and we muft content our felves within the Orb and Sphere of their Activity. And acquiefce in a Negative Definition, and underftand if we can fomewhat that is fmaller than the fmalleft, though that be alfo improper; for in that which is not Quantity, there is neither fmaller nor bigger, we muft endeavour to underftand fomewhat infinitely little, lefs than which there cannot be, fomewhat that has no Bignefs or Extenfion, or Quantity, but only Pofition and Refpect to Quantities circumjacent: From which, to this or that Body, there is a determinate Length and Diftance; and upon this account, wherever we endeavour to underftand this Notion, our Imagination will reprefent to us the fmalleft vifible Body, as an exceeding fine Sand, or a Mite, or the Point of a Needle, or the fmalleft vifible Body we have ever feen on Paper, or the like; which we muft be content with fince the Fantcy forms nothing but what is firft in the Senfe, though it be none of thefe. And in truth it can have no true Definition that will reach its Effence. Analogous to this Point, Sign or nothing in Quantity is the *Nought* Cifer, or *Zero* in Number, the never in time. The Reft or Quiet in Motion: For as no Aggregate of Points will ever produce a Line or a Quantity, fo the Multiplication of Noughts or Cifers will never produce a Number, and as the Addition of Nevers cannot make time, fo the Aggregate of Refts cannot produce a Motion. So that all thefe may not improperly be called the *Terminus* or Bound, from which they all begin, fo Quantity may be faid to begin from a Point or nothing. Number may be faid to beigin from Nought Cifer or Zero, Time may be faid to begin from Never, and Motion to begin from Reft: And as the *Minimum Naturæ* may be faid to be the firft Quantity, if at leaft there be a *Minimum* in Nature, fo a Unite may exprefs it in Numbers, Inftant in Time, and Moment in Velocity. It may poffibly be thought I have faid too much of nothing, but yet it feems to be of the greateft Confideration in Nature; for it feems to be the beginning of every Creature, even the greateft Creatures having been traced to begin from an Attom or Point, no Eye or Senfe can reach it, nor any Underftanding limit it, that the beginning of a very large Animal hath been feen alive 10000 times fmaller than a Mite may be proved, and yet how much fmaller it may have been is not determined.

Now as thefe exprefs Incomprehenfibles one way, as to their Beginning or Centrality, fo the Incomprehenfibles the other way which may be called Circumferential, may be expreffed by Infinity, Abyfs or Immenfity for Quantity or Extenfion, Innumerability for Number, Eternity for Time, and Inftantaneous for Motion: But thofe are beyond our Reach, and yet even of thofe there is a necef fary Ufe in Geometry; and without which feveral of the moft confiderable Demonftrations both in that and Arithmetick cannot be performed, but of thefe elfewhere. When I come to confider Infinity and Innumerability, when I fhall fhow that innumerable Points do make a Mathematical Line, innumerable Lines

do

do make a Mathematical Superficies, innumerable Superficies do make a Mathematical Body, innumerable Moments make a Velocity, innumerable Inftants make Mathematical Time, by fuppofing Motion joyn'd to them : For a Point moved makes a Line in a Mathematical Senfe, a Line moved makes a Plain, a Plain moved that makes a Body, and contrary Motion reduce them back again, which is expreft or perform'd by Multiplication and Divifion.

I fhall beg the Candid Readers Patience to add one Remark more of the Doctors on the Method of Euclid, *and that is of his Method of Demonftration, and that in two very eafy Problems, viz. the Prop. 1. and 2. Lib. 1. which I hope for fome Obfervations and Hints, particularly as to the Analyticks of the Ancients will not be altogether unacceptable.*

Euclid having premis'd his Principles, he begins his Method of Demonftration, in which he takes no more for granted than what he hath already laid down as eafy and felf evident. His firft Propofition then is upon a right Line, given to make an Equilateral Triangle. He hath defined in the 4th Definition what he means by a right Line, namely, that which lieth ftraight between the two Extremes of it which are Points, and what he means by an Equilateral Triangle, namely, fuch a one which hath all its three Sides equal to one another.

This firft Propofition is a Problem, which explains a way how to do and perform the thing required, as well as fhews how to manifeft the Truth and Certainty of the thing done: It contains therefore and fhews a double Invention, without which, or fome fuch other thing, the Propofition can neither be done, nor demonftrated; which Inventions are called Mediums or Means by which we attain to the end propounded or defired. The end here fought is how from the ends of a Linen give to draw two other Lines each equal to the given Line, which fhall meet in one and the fame Point: It is certain that thefe Lines muft begin from the ends of the firft Line given, but which of thefe to draw firft, and which way, with what Inclination to the former Line, that is, with what Angle, that is not yet known, and fome Invention muft be thought of how to direct our Ruler to draw it. Well, how fhall this be done, fince there may be infinite of Lines drawn from each of thofe Points which fhall every one of them be equal to this Line given? How then fhall we among thofe Infinite or Indefinite Number chufe out the right? 'tis impoffible, without fome Invention. Our Author therefore helps you to one, and one which you have already granted to be feafable in the third Petition upon the Center a, and Diftance, a b, draw a Circle, fays he, b g c h f b, what then? To what purpofe? Why this Circle then will give you a Line in which are contain'd all the *Plate 1ft. Fig.* Points or Ends of the infinite Lines, which may be drawn from the Point a any *2 d.* ways that fhall be equal to a b How fo? Why by the 15th Definition you are taught, that a Circle is a plain Figure bounded by or contain'd within one Curve Line, which is called the Circumference, to which every right Line drawn from a Point in the middle, which is called the Center, are equal to one another: But what are we yet the wifer? How do we know which of thefe infinite Lines we are to draw? To which of thefe infinite Points that are in this Circumference? To know this, you muft do the fame thing upon the Point b, that is, upon the Point b and Diftance b a. Draw or defcribe the Circle a d c e f a, which will give you all the poffible infinite Points in that Plain; to which the from the Point b right Lines may be drawn equal to b a. Now then fince thefe Circles contain all the poffible Points of the Lines equal to a b or b a, that can be drawn from a or b. It follows, that where thofe Circles interfect there only muft be the Point to which thofe Lines may be drawn; namely, at c and at f and no where elfe foever: Drawing therefore Lines from a and from b to either of thofe Points c or f as a c, b c, or a f, b f, you have done the thing that was propounded, namely, upon the Line a b, given you have made an Equilateral Triangle a b c or a b f, which was defired. This is the firft part of the Problem, and indeed the difficulteft to find out; namely, how to do the thing required, and in this part lie the greateft Difficulties of Mathematical Knowledge, to wit, in the finding out the proper and true Mediums or Means to perform the Problems requir'd to be done, which for the moft part are of the fame Nature with this, and confift in

the

Mind may acquire an Habit of Intention, and of examining the whole Chain of Confequents from the firft Principles to the Truth evidenced. For the want of which, fome fmall Error perhaps may flip into the Mind under the Appearance of Truth, and thereby make all the fubfequent Reafonings and Deductions unfound; and 'tis very much harder to clear and free the Mind from it when once received, than to prevent the Reception thereof. There cannot therefore (in this Study efpecially, not now to mention any other, where it is poffible it may be altogether as convenient, nay neceffary) there cannot, I fay, therefore be as I conceive too much Circumfpection and Caution ufed in admitting Principles, and furnifhing the Mind with the true grounds of Knowledge; becaufe for the moft part we are too prone to take up every thing we hear upon Truft: Without Examination, we are too apt to run away with a thing, and think we know it and fee it clearly before we are fure we do, and are impatient of Delay in examining and confidering, whereas if the Mind be a little at firft accuftomed to this leifurely and ftrict way of reafoning, after it has got a habit it will make as much Difpatch in receiving things with fufficient Examination, as another fhall without it. And the Patience only is needful for the moft part, at firft, to beget Attention: Nor is it peculiar to this Acquifition alone, but we fee it neceffary, and practifed in many other things where a good habit is to be acquired; as in Reading, Writing, Mufick, Drawing, and moft other Manual Operations. The Roots and Beginnings of Knowledge and Practice too are bitter and tedious, but the Fruits are fweet and pleafant; and whofoever attains the end, will never repent the time they fpent in the beginning.

Poffibly fome Readers may think thefe Abftracts, out of fome of our Authors Geometrical Lectures, too prolixe; but I hope they will not by all be judg'd wholly unneceffary, and ufelefs, at leaft I thought it not amifs to give this Specimen of our Author's Nicenefs, as to the admitting of things unproved, for real Truths: But if this be a fault, I hope what follows in the fubfequent Difcourfes of the Nature of Light, and other no lefs curious Subjects, will make fufficient amends.
R. W.

LECTURES of LIGHT,

EXPLICATING ITS

Nature, Properties, and Effects, &c.

SECT. I.

Containing those read about the beginning of 1680.

The CONTENTS.

1. *The Nature of Light not well explained by Authors hitherto, and is in it self as difficult and abstruse a Subject as any in Nature.* 2. *The Opinions of some of the more Famous Ancient Philosophers concerning its Nature, as* Anaximanders, Anaxagoras's, *&c. as likewise that of* Lucretius *and the* Atomists. 3. *Their Insufficiency shewn in six Particulars.* 4. Aristotle's *Definition of it wherein defective, yet capable of a more Mechanick Explication than any either of the Ancients or Moderns.* 5. *An Explication of the* Theory, *that Light is a propagated Motion, the greatest Difficulty seems to lie in the vast Extension thereof, which some have thought infinite* ; *Quantity infinite as to its Greatness and Smalness, can have no Bounds assigned to it by Man's Thought or Imagination, the inconceivable Distance of the Stars.* 6. *In the next place, as the Distance is immense, so the Motion is infinitely swift* ; Romers *Experiment questioned whether sufficient,* Light *the* Anima Mundi. 7. *This Propagation of Light the Action of a Body, not a Spirit* ; *the Action proportioned to the Expansion which is in duplicate Proportion to its distance reciprocally* : *This Action produces Heat, which is proportioned to the Light, why that of the Moon insensible to us.* 8. *The Propagation of Light in a Homogeneous Medium in strait Lines* in Orbem, *from the Lucid Point* ; *yet this hinders not, but that it may be bent by a difforme Medium into a Curve, which the Author publisht Anno* 1665. *and called* Microgr. *it Inflexion* ; *2dly, By Refraction* ; *3dly, By Reflexion* ; *4thly, A* p. 217. *Ray may be absorbed* : *This is called Mortification or Extinction* ; *5thly, A Ray is dispersed, split, or opened at the Superficies of the second Medium, &c. whereby the Appearance of Colours is produced* ; *6thly, A Ray is receiv'd or imbib'd by a Medium, and returned again from that Medium.* R. W.

1. **I** Intend, God willing, this Term to treat of *mixt Geometry*, as it is *The Difficulty* made use of for the Explanation and clearing of some Subject to which *of the Subject.* it is applyed, and by Example therein to shew of what Use it may be in any other Matter that falls within its Reach. And the Subject I have pitched upon as the first and most obvious, though yet the most abstruse of all others is *Light :* None that has Eyes can be ignorant of it, and yet there have

been

been very few, if any, in the World that have hitherto underftood and explained the true Nature and Caufe of it. And though it was the very firft thing in the World to which the Almighty Creator gave his *Fiat*, when he made the World, *fiat Lux*, Let there be Light ; yet it may be poffibly the laft and moft difficult of all fenfible things, that may be thoroughly underftood. And this Subject I have the rather begun withal, becaufe from a clear Explanation of this, feveral other Subjects, as thofe of *Gravity*, *Magnetifm*, *Rarefaction*, *Condenfation*, *Solidity*, *Fluidity*, and the like, will be demonftrably evidenced : Now though Nature hath not furnifht us with diftinct and appropriate Organs of Senfe, whereby we may immediately be made fenfible of all thofe Operations and Workings of Nature, as no Senfe informs us immediately of the Emanations of the *Magnetical* Vertue, no Senfe immediately informs us of the Inftruments or Powers imployed for driving Bodies towards the Center of the Earth ; no Senfe informs us of the *Gravitation* or continual Preffure of the *Air* ; no Senfe informs us immediately of the means of the Conveyance of Light, yet an inquifitive and obferving Man may find Helps enough to affift thofe Senfes which the Creator has furnifht him with, to difcover all thofe ways and means made ufe of, and to demonftrate their Proprieties and Powers as clearly, as if the Inftruments and manner of working were vifible and obvious immediately to fome of our Organs of Senfe.

To repeat to you all the Definitions and Defcriptions thereof in *Authors* that have treated of it would be endlefs, and inftead of making the Nature of it more perfpicuous, would quite darken and put it out : For the moft part of them have only fpoken of it as it were Metaphorically and by Smilitudes, feeming not to have underftood at all themfelves what they endeavoured to explain to others : Or at leaft have treated of it in fuch general Terms, that inftead of making it more intelligible, they have made it incomprehenfible. Such therefore I fhall omit to mention, the Science that they deliver being only ufeful for Allegories and Similitudes, and Rhetorical Embellifhments, and no way tending to the Phyfical Explanation of its Effects and Proprieties.

Certain it is, that the Nature of it feems to be the moft abftrufe of any thing we yet know in the Univerfe, and though moft feeing People do believe they thoroughly underftand it, yet if they fhall confider more attentively what their Knowledge of it is, they will begin to think themfelves a little in the dark, and to want fome further enlightning to difcover that which before they thought fo evident, which will now feem to differ from all other things in Nature.

The Opinions of the Ancients.   2. But before I come to thefe, I fhall determine the Opinions of fome of the moft eminent Philofophers and Mathematicians, which we find either in ancient or Modern Writings, to fee how far they have agreed, and in what they have been deficient in explaining the true Nature of Light.

Amongft thefe I fhall begin with the moft ancient, as *Anaximander*, *Anagoras*, *Leucippus*, *Heraclitus*, *Empedocles*, *Zeno*, and the *Stoicks*, *Plato* and his Followers. All which make Light to be Fire, or a certain Flame iffuing from the Lucid Body, as the Sun, which they fuppofe the Fountain of Light, and to be all Fire, Flame, or pure Light : And there *Anaxagoras* call'd it μύδον διαπυρόν a fiery Mafs, and καθαρώταον πῦς moft pure Fire, and πυρὸς ἀθροισμα μέγα a vaft Mafs of Fire. And wherefoever there was Light, there they fuppofe Fire, which produced the Effects of Fire if it were denfe enough ; but if it were not denfe, it only made things vifible, and produced the Effect that we call Light. This was their Opinion in general, but how they did more particularly explain the Nature of Light do not now appear ; fo that in effect we are as much to feek as to the Knowledge of the true Nature of Light as before : But 'tis but giving of it another Name, and calling Light by the Name of Fire or Flame, without telling us what that other thing is which they name. For who underftands what they meant by Fire or Flame, whether the ordinary Fire of Wood, Coles, &c. or an Elementary Fire, fuch as the Peripateticks afterwards fuppofe; or a third kind, fuch as the Mafs of the Sun and fixed Stars, or neither of all thefe : Becaufe they granted the Moon rifes to participate of it, and yet hath none of its own.

In truth we have no Information from it that is pertinent to this Inquiry I am now about : For call it Light, or call it Fire, or call it Flame, unless we knew the Proprieties and Causes of it, it comes all to one thing, it instructs us not ; for how come we thereby to know how this passes from the Sun? For instance, or from the fixed Stars, some Thousands of times further than the Sun to our Eye here placed upon the Earth, in an instant? Which Light really doth (as I shall afterwards endeavour to show.) How comes the Sun, or any one, nay all the fixt Stars, continually to give out so great a Quantity of Flame, as every moment to fill the whole Universe; which is an Extension or Space Millions of Millions of Millions of times bigger than the whole Globe of the Earth and Sea, and indeed incomprehensible in Greatness, and yet at the same time the Body of it not sensibly wasted ; nay, thus it hath done ever since the beginning of the World, in every moment of time, and yet by the best Observations we can find recorded in Natural Historians and Astronomers, we cannot learn that the Sun is diminished in Quantity : So that let the Flame be never so much rarify'd, yet considering it must fill so infinitely vast a Space every Moment, certainly it must have long before this have rarify'd this Body all away, this therefore cannot be a true Explication of the Nature of Light. Besides, we are yet to seek the true Nature of Flame, how that comes to make it self sensible at a Distance : For though we see a Stick of Wood, for instance, or a Candle, by means of Heat to be turned into Flame and to be consumed thereby, so that the whole Substance thereof by degrees is all converted into a successive Body of Flame, yet how this comes to affect our Sight at so many Miles distance in an instant, so that at the very Moment the Flame is kindled, or extinguished ; or discovered, or covered, though at 10, 20, or more Miles Distance, the Eye at the same instant is sensible of these Varieties. Now who can imagine, that the Body of Flame, which appears at one instant in the top of the Candle, should at the same instant fill a Hemisphere of the Atmosphere 10, 20, or more Miles in Diameter, and yet it must be concluded so to do if this be the cause of Light : For there is no Point in all that Hemisphere, in which if the Eye be placed, the Candle cannot be seen at the very instant 'tis lighted. This Explication therefore is to me, I confess, wholly inconceivable, and is complicated with such Difficulties as no true reasoning can make it possible and intelligible, and therefore as an Absurdity or Impossibility, I must reject it.

For as in pure Geometry nothing is to be let pass for a Truth, whose Cause and Principles are not clearly shown by the Progress of Reasoning, and the Process of Demonstration : So in Physicks Geometrically handled, nothing is to be taken for granted, nor any thing admitted for a true Conclusion, that is not plainly deduced from self-evident Principles, and those founded upon the immediate Objects of Sense disintangled from all the Fallacies of the Medium and Organ. To avoid then in part this unintelligible Expansion of Flame, so as to fill the whole Sphere of the true Medium incompassing the Lucid Object. Some later Authors have added, that this Expansion is only superficial, and not solid, and that the whole Medium is not at the same Moment compleatly fill'd with this rarify'd Flame, but that the Momentary Emanation of Flame from the Lucid Point makes a Spherical Superficies, which Spherical Superficies by an almost instantaneous Motion expands it self every way *in Orbem*, and successively becomes the Superficies of greater and greater Spheres, till it attain the Extremities of the Universe, or be at length lost in the Profundities of the Abyss of Matter. For Explanation of which, they bring the Similitude of the Rings or Circular Waves upon a stagnating Pond of Water, for as in that (say they) the Wave made by a Stone, or the like Body falling into the Water makes a Wave, which very Wave you see expands it self and moves from that place where the Stone fell, in a Circle that continually grows bigger till it touch the Extremities of the Pond, or *Stagnum* of Water ; so that very Flame which is emitted from the Lucid Body, does by successive Motion but yet very rapid, move it self from the Lucid Point to all the Extremities of the Material World in a Spherical Superficies, which does continually grow bigger and bigger, and that 'tis only a Superficies as it were that is at once fill'd by it, and not the whole Sphere ; from which Cause, say they, the Eye can be

Nothing is to be allowed in Natural Philosophy but what is solid.

U
no

no where plac'd in the ambient Sphere of Matter, but this increasing Sphere will affect it and move against it, and thereby make on it an Impression which we call Light. Now the Body so long as it burns continually emitting such Spherical Superficies of Flame, which continually follow one another, with the same, though it be an infinitely rapid Motion and swiftness.

> *Semper enim nova se radiorum Lumina fundunt,*
> *Primaq; dispereunt.*
>
>   **Says *Lucretius.***

And again in another Place of his Books he adds,

> *Suppeditatur enim confessim Lumine Lumen,*
> *Et quasi pro telo stimulatur fulgure fulgur;*
> *Qua propter simulacra pari ratione necesse est*
> *Immemorabile per Spatium transcurrere posse,*
> *Temporis in puncto.*

It follows therefore, that the whole Sphere must also be fill'd with them. This seems to be the Theory which *Epicurus* and the *Atomists* maintain, which is at large explained by *Gassandus*, and our Learned Dr. *Charleton.*

The Insufficiency of the Ancient Opinions.   3. But the Difficulties in it are very great; for first, *Epicurus* supposed that all the Space between the visible Cœlestial Bodies was a perfect Vacuity, and only made for the way of these Orbicular Superficies of Light, or Passage of those Troops of Atomes of which these Orbs consisted; for so *Lucretius* in his Second Book explains it, speaking of Atomes.

> *Quæ porro magnum per Inane vagantur*
> *Et cita dissiliunt longe; longeq; recursant*
> *In magnis Intervallis. Hæc aera rarum*
> *Sufficiunt nobis, & splendida Lumina solis.*

Now 'tis hard to conceive how such infinitely small Bodies, should with so rapid a Motion pass so vast a Space in an instant almost, and yet must continually in the way through every Point of Distance meet with crossing Spherical Surfaces of Light from infinite other Lucid Points, and yet the Passage of them not to be at all impeded or stopt.

2*dly*, 'Tis not yet proved, that there is any such thing as a *vacuum* in Nature; and *Descartes* supposes that Extension and Body is one and the same thing, and that there is no where Extension but there is Body, and no Body but is extended; for which he brings several Arguments, not easy to be fully answered, which I shall not now insist upon.

3*dly*, Though it might be granted, that there were an Extension without a Body to fill it, and a perfect Vacuity; and so the Atomes or Bodies moved through it, will pass without any Impediment from this Medium or Space, yet since we see that Light passes the most solid Bodies also instantaneously, or in a Velocity rapid beyond Imagination, here certainly it should meet with Impediments to stop it: For we find it pass through the hardest Body in the World, namely, a Diamond; and seems to pass more freely through it than through the Air or Water, or the most Fluid Body, as may be gathered from the greater Refraction of the Rays from the perpendicular in the more solid Body: Nor can I conceive how the Vacuity of the Pores of the Bodies can solve this Difficulty, since it will be hard to conceive how those Pores can be alike open every way to the Passages of the Atomes of Light.

4*thly*, Supposing there such a Vacuity or Medium not resisting Motion, and there were such Bodies as Atomes to be moved in it, yet 'tis difficult to conceive how they should receive so rapid a Motion from the Luminous Body:

For no such rapid Motion is there in being. Now 'tis a Rule, *Nil dat quod non habet*, that which hath no such rapid Motion cannot give it to the Atomes that proceed from it. Now that 'tis not necessary a Luminous Body should have so rapid a Motion, may be argued from the shining of a Diamond in the dark, only by gently striking it with the end of ones Nail, as I have often experimented, upon a large Diamond that had that Quality : Or from the shining of rotten Wood, or such other cold Substances which seem not to have any such kind of rapid Motion, and yet produce Light, which might be farther instanced in the new *Phosphori*.

5*thly*, If such a rapid Motion of fiery Atomes should be the cause of Light ; it would be very difficult to conceive, how so tender a part as the Eye should continually receive them concentrated in the *Tunica Retina*, and yet not be destroyed and batter'd in pieces by such continual Volleys of Atomes.

6*thly*, If there were such a constant Emanation of Atomes, and that it has continued ever since the Creation of Light : Certainly this supposed *Inane*, or void Space between the Cœlestial Bodies, must needs have been filled quite full long before this, and then the free and istantaneous Motion of the succeeding Emanations must have ceased, because they must find their way all stopt up by others, and consequently by this time we should have had no Light at all communicated from the Sun.

I could instance in many other Difficulties, as that of conveying the *Species* of things, and the like ; that this *Hypothesis* of the *Epicureans* or *Atomists*, who did not understand the Reason of Vision is encumbred with, which seem to make it impossible, and unfit for the Genuine Explication of their admirable Proprieties of Light ; but that these, I suppose, may suffice at present for this purpose, though on the other side there are many things that may be said for it, that have not been hitherto urged by any I have met with. Some of which I shall have occasion hereafter to mention.

4. *Aristotle* was aware of these Difficulties, and therefore goes somewhat *Aristotle's* more craftily to work in his Definition of Light : Giving you a Notion of it *Definition of* in such general Terms without particular Explication, that you make almost *Light,* what you will of it, φῶς δ᾽ ἐστιν ἡ ἐνεργεία τῦ διαφανῦς ἦ διαφανές. Light is an Act of a perspicuous Body, in as much as it is perspicuous. He affirms Colour to be the Cause why a coloured Body is seen, and this Colour, says he, does effectually move the Pellucid Body : But this Colour is not seen but with Light, therefore says he, Colour in the Light does effectually move the Pellucid Body, but Colour without the Light, though it be congenit with the Pellucid, yet it doth not actually move the Pellucid Body ; therefore, says he, the Body must be actually Pellucid that Colour may move it. Now it cannot be *actu* Pellucid without Light, therefore Light is that which *actu* by its Action makes a Pellucid Body : And therefore the Act of that pellucid Body is Light. Now says he, this Light is not Fire nor any other Body, nor the *Effluvium* of another Body, for so it would still be a Body ; but 'tis the Presence of Fire, or some such like, in the Pellucid, and the Absence or Privation of it Darkness : From which his Definition of Light, I cannot I confess, well judge what his Theory of Light was ; for this Definition is only made upon one Effect of Light, and doth not at all tell us under what *Genus* Light is put, nor what are its Differences, nor what are the many Proprieties of it . So that these are to be sought elsewhere. And when we have seen all he has said of Light, we shall find our selves as much in the dark as before, as to the Knowledge of the Nature of Light, he here considers Light only as it is in the *Medium* that conveys it, namely, in a Pellucid or Transparent Body, and so calls it the Act of the perspicuous Body ; but what this Act is, or how it comes into the Pellucid he tells not, that you must seek for elsewhere. However, though he has not so particularly and positively explained what he means by this Expression of his ; nor did perhaps understand any plausible or intelligible *Theory* of it, yet to me he seems to have light upon such an Expression as may possibly being

Mecha-

Mechanically and Geometrically explained, more naturally and truly make out the *Theory* of *Light* than any other Expreſſion or Explanation of any other, either Ancient or Modern Naturaliſt, Φῶς ἐϛίν ἡ ἐνεργεία τῦ διαφανῦς.   Light is the in-working of the Tranſparent Body or *Medium* ; that is, the internal Action of the Pellucid or Tranſparent Body, is that which is the Light of which we are ſenſible, or that Light which moves the Eye,   And this ἐνεργεία is nothing but Motion, and this Motion is impreſſed by the Motion of the Lucid Body, and that Body is Lucid that has ſuch a Motion in it : So that Light in the ſhining Body is a peculiar Motion of it, which can communicate it to the tranſparent Medium, that is, to ſuch a Body as is fit to propagate it, and Light in the Eye is this Motion impreſſed on the Eye, by which the Brain or *Anima* becomes ſenſible of it.   For if we conſider all the Appearances thereof, we ſhall at length be neceſſitated to come to ſome ſuch Concluſion : Nor can I conceive how the Phœnomena thereof, can be by any other Hypotheſis but this of a propagated Motion, be comprehended.   And though even this be not without its Difficulties, nor is it well conceivable how it ſhould be, if we conſider the almoſt infinite Difference between the Propagations of Light, and the Motion of any other ſenſible Body : Yet when we more attentively conſider and weigh all the Effects and Proprieties thereof, and compare them with the other Effects, and Proprieties of more groſs, tangible and ſenſible Bodies, we ſhall find that the *Lex Naturæ* is the very ſame, by which both the one and the other Motions are governed ; and that there is here the ſame *Regimen in Specie*, though they differ in Degrees.

A new Theory explained.   5. The firſt and moſt difficult Propriety of this Motion of all the reſt, is the almoſt incomprehenſible and unconceivable Extenſion thereof ; which is as boundleſs and unlimited as the Univerſe it ſelf, or the *Expanſum* of all Material Beings : The Vaſtneſs of which is ſo great, that it exceeds the Comprehenſions of Man's Underſtanding.   Infomuch that very many have aſſerted it abſolutely infinite, and without any Limits or Bounds, there being no bound ſet ; but it may be conceived, that Matter may ſtill extend farther and farther continually, being as infinite as Quantity, which is by all concluded to be ſo, both as to its Greatneſs and Smallneſs : The Limits of which, cannot be either conceived or expreſſed ; for whatever can be conceived, may be expreſſed and computed by Meaſure and Number.   Now here no Number can be aſſigned, but there may be given both a greater and a leſs : As Unity, let it ſignify never ſo great a Quantity, as a Foot, a Yard, a Mile, a Diameter of the Earth or of its Orb, may continually be increaſed by Multiplication or Addition, ſo as to repreſent Tens, Hundreds, Thouſands, Millions, and ſo onwards of its Quantity.   So be a Unity taken for never ſo ſmall a Quantity, as a Foot, an Inch, a Line, an Atome, its Quantity may be ſtill ſuppoſ'd diminiſhable, either by Subſtraction or Diviſion ; and ſo a Tenth, a Centeſme, a Thouſandth, a Millionth part of it may be conceived and computed.   Now the Propagation of this Motion is coextent with it, as I ſhall afterwards prove.

To avoid the Incomprehenſibleneſs therefore of this infinite Extenſion of the Univerſe, and yet to make it as extenſive as Quantity it ſelf, *Des Cartes* has found out a new Term or Expreſſion for it, which he calls indefinite ; which Notion differs only from infinite in this, that the one has abſolutely no Bounds or End, and the other that it can have none aſſigned.   But in truth, they have one and the ſame Signification, and that is that Quantity neither hath any Bound, nor can have any Bounds aſſigned to it by Humane Reaſon.   And if Quantity can have no Bounds, then Body and Matter can have none, according to the aforeſaid Author *Des Cartes* Opinion, Body and Extenſion, or Quantity being the ſame thing : So that wherever Extenſion can be ſuppoſed, there alſo muſt be ſuppoſed a Body, and where there is no Body there can be no Extenſion, and conſequently no ſuch thing as a Vacuum or Space devoid of Body.

Quantity boundleſs, or can have no Bounds ſet to it.

But whether his Notion be true or not, 'tis not much to our preſent purpoſe : For moſt certain it is, whether it be finite or infinite, the Vaſtneſs of it is ſo great that it exceeds our Imagination, to conceive of it truly as it is, and whoſoever has a finite and limited Conception of it, has a falſe one not grounded on Reaſon, but ſome precarious Opinion ; for if we conſider firſt the vaſt

Diſtance

Distance between us and the Sun, which from the beſt and lateſt Obſervations in Aſtronomy, is judged to be about 10000 Diameters of the Earth, each of which is about 7925 *Engliſh* Miles, therefore the Sun's Diſtance is 79250000 Miles; and if we conſider that according to the Obſervation, which I publiſh-ed to prove the Motion of the Earth, the whole Diameter of this Orb, *viz.* 20000 made the Subtenſe but of one Minute to one of the fixt Stars, which can-not therefore be leſs diſtant than 3438 Diameters of this great Orb, and conſe-quently 68760000 Diameters of the Earth: And if this Star be one of the near-eſt, and that the Stars that are of one Degree leſſer in Magnitude, I mean not of the ſecond, becauſe there may be many Degrees between the firſt and ſe-cond, be as much farther, and another ſort yet ſmaller be three times as far, and a fourth four times as far, and ſo onward; poſſibly to ſome Hundred De-grees of Magnitude, ſuch as may really be diſcovered by longer and longer Te-leſcopes, that they may be 100 times as far, then certainly this Material *Ex-panſum*; a part of which we are, muſt be ſo great that 'twill infinitely exceed our ſhallow Conception to imagine. Now by what I laſt mentioned, it is evi-dent, that Light extends it ſelf to the utmoſt imaginable Parts; and by the help of Teleſcopes, we collect the Rays, and make them ſenſible to the Eye, which are emitted from ſome of the almoſt inconceivably remote Objects: And ſince we find, that ſtill longer and better Teleſcopes do diſcover to us ſmaller and ſmaller fixt Stars, which in Probability are farther and farther removed from us, and that we cannot ſet Bounds to the Extent of it; it follows, I ſay, that the Extenſion of the Propagation of Light is indefinite, immenſe, and beyond our reach to conceive, yet nevertheleſs we ſee by clear Induction that ſo it muſt be, though we do not preſently well conceive how. Nor is it only the great Body of the Sun, or the vaſt Bodies of the fixed Stars, that are thus able to diſperſe their Light through the vaſt *Expanſum* of the Univerſe: But the ſmalleſt Spark of a Lucid Body muſt do the very ſame thing, even the ſmalleſt Globule, ſtruck from a Steel by a Flint, which is as ſmall as the Point of a Pin. For that produces as real Light as the other; and all Light propagating *in Orbem*, that Point muſt do the ſame thing with every Point of the Superfi-cies of the Sun. Now that every Point of the Luminous Superficies does emit Light *in Orbem* through the Diaphanous Medium, is evident from this, that there is no Point of the Ambient Tranſparent Medium in which the Eye be-ing placed, does not ſee every Point of the Lucid Surface, and conſequently every ſenſible Point of the Superficies of the ſhining Body, does really propa-gate its Light thus *in Orbem*. Nor is this to be limited to a Point big enough to be ſenſible to the naked Eye; for by the Help of Microſcopes viewing a Lucid and ſhining Body, as a burning Cole, or a red hot Iron, or the like; one is able to diſtinguiſh Parts that ſhine 1000 ſmaller than we can diſtinguiſh with the naked Eye, and yet theſe may be diſcover'd and are viſible, and con-ſequently muſt radiate *in Orbem*, as the bigger and more ſenſible Parts: So that hereby we are aſcertained by our Senſe, that the leaſt ſenſible Point of Body is able to affect the greateſt *Expanſum* of Nature. So it appears both to our Senſe and our Reaſon, and therefore we cannot doubt it, but ſet it down as an undoubted Principle.

6. But then ſecondly, In the next place, this Propagation of Light which is immenſe, is (in all Probability, and as far as Experiments, Obſervations and Reaſons can aſſiſt us) infinitely ſwift: Or we may ſay, that the Propagation thereof through the whole vaſt or immenſe *Expanſum*, as far as we can yet find, is made in a Point or Inſtant of time; and at the very Inſtant that the re-moteſt Star does emit Light, in that very Inſtant does the Eye upon the Earth receive it, though it be many Millions of Millions of Miles diſtant, ſo that in Probability no time is ſpent between the emitting and the Reception; for with this agrees all the Experiments that have been thought of for this purpoſe, and no one has yet proved it temporary, though many ways have been thought of for that purpoſe: And though the ingenious Monſieur *Romer* pretends to have found a way, by which he hath experimentally proved, that this Propagation is not inſtantaneous but temporary, and ſo there is ſomewhat of time ſpent in the Paſſage of Light, from the illuminating Object to the Eye or Body en-

The Diſtance of the Stars un-conceivable.

The Motion of Light infinite-ly ſwift.

Romer's Ex-periment doub-ted whether ſufficient.

X   lighted

lightned, yet if we examine his Experiment a little more confiderately we may find reafon to doubt, whether he hath from thefe grounds fufficient to make fuch a Conclufion.   Certain it is, whether by it he proves the matter he aims at, or not : His Ingenuity in the inventing the way was not lefs to be efteemed and valued, than if it had fucceeded ; nay, it is altogether as valuable, if by it we could prove that no fpace of time were fpent whilft the Light is propagated fuch a determinate Space, as if it proved it to be momentary and meafurable.   For in all Inquiries of this Nature Truth is the thing fought after, and the finding of that is the Reward of our Endeavours : And therefore I would not be thought to examine this Obfervation of this ingenious Man, with any defign to detract any thing from the Credit of the Obfervation, or the deferved Reputation of the Author.   But that I may firft explain it to fuch perhaps as have not heard of it ; Secondly, that I may put fome in mind of it, that perhaps may have forgot it ; and Thirdly, That I may excite both, or either, to be mindful to make fome farther Obfervations of their own of that kind, to fee if by any means they can thereby determine this Queftion, whether the Propagation of Light for fuch a determinate Diftance, or Length, be inftantaneous or temporary : For till that be proved pofitively, the true Theory cannot be proved, as we fhall afterwards fhew.   His Way then which is printed in the Journal *des Scavans* at *Paris*, and fince in *Englifh* in the 136*th* Philofophical Tranfaction, is by the Light of the Sun reflected from the Satellit of ♃, both when it enters and when it emergies out of the Shadow of the Body of ♃, by which he endeavours to demonftrate, that the time that Light fpends in paffing about 3000 *French* Leagues, or $7925\frac{17}{33}$ *Englifh* Miles, of 5280 *Englifh* Feet to a Mile, that is, in paffing a whole Diameter of the Globe of the Earth, is lefs than one fingle fecond, or the 60th part of a Minute of an Hour.

But to confider a little further this ingenious Way of Monfieur *Romer*, I do very much doubt, that we are as much to feek for a true Theory of this Satellit of ♃, as we are of our own Satellit the Moon, if not fomewhat more, by reafon that the Anomaly thereof may be complicated with more different Motions than even this of the Moon, which is affected only by two Bodies, *viz.* the Sun and the Earth ; whereas I am of Opinion, that the Motion of this inmoft Satellit may be acted on alfo by the other three exteriour Satellits, and confequently there will need other Equations and Allowances to be made in the Calculation of its true Place, befides the Allowances for the Influences of the Sun, and the Body of *Jupiter*, which whether he did conceive or take any Cognizance of, I know not : And therefore unlefs we are affured of the true intermediate times between the Eclipfes of it, we cannot make a certain Conclufion.

But fuppofing this may prove it to be temporary, and not inftantaneous, yet we find that 'tis fo exceeding fwift that 'tis beyond Imagination ; for fo far he thinks indubitable, that it moves a Space equal to the Diameter of the Earth, or near 8000 Miles, in lefs than one fingle Second of the time, which is in as fhort time as one can well pronounce 1, 2, 3, 4 : And if fo, why it may not be as well inftantaneous I know no reafon, unlefs it may be faid 'tis inconceivable any Body can be infinitely fluid ; which yet how it can be denied, I know not, unlefs we will allow a Vacuity, which the great Afferter of the Inftantaneous Propagation of Light, Monfieur *Defcartes* will by no means admit.   Now that either there muft be a Vacuity, or an infinite Fluid, or elfe no Motion can be made, every way, will neceffarily follow from Geometrical Demonftrations of the Proprieties of Figure : And therefore either infinite Fluidity muft be allowed in Matter, or a Vacuity.   Nor can this infinite Fluidity be evaded, by faying, that there is a Matter indefinitely fluid, becaufe if indefinitely fignifies any thing lefs than infinite, the Demonftrations holds good againft it, as well as if it fignify'd finite.   There is a neceffity therefore of admitting in Nature, either firft a Vacuity, which impugns the very ground of the *Cartefian* Principles, *viz.* that Body and Extenfion are the fame thing ; or fecondly, a Penetration of Dimenfions, which is likewife contradictory both to his and the Opinion of moft eminent Philofophers in the World ; or thirdly, a perfect *Plenum* but infinitely fluid, which I conceive cannot be difproved.   But being proved, I fhall after-
                                                                              wards

wards shew all the strange and unconceivable Phenomena of Light will be most clearly and evidently, and most demonstrably made out ; and not only the reason shown why its Extension is so vast, but why its Propagation is so instantaneous. Now though I cannot now stand to shew the Reasons of these Conclusions, yet by a Methodical and clear Process of Demonstration they will be shewn to be as necessary Consequences from undeniable Principles, as any Conclusion made by *Euclid* in his Geometry, of which I shall have occasion to speak more largely.

This being that we call Light, sure if any thing may be call'd the *Anima Mundi* : Its Action being so near of Kin to that of a Spirit, the whole Mass being in an instant acted by it, and made sensible as I may so speak, of what is done in any one Point : So that Light may be said to be *tota in toto & tota in qualibet parte*, possibly with some kind of Plausibleness. And yet after all this we may prove it to be purely corporeal, and subjected to the same Laws that bulky, tangible, and gross Bodies are subject to. This may inform us also, how even the very remotest Star, and every one of those indefinite Number of Stars may have an Influence every Moment upon this Ball of the Earth on which we tread, and every one upon every other, and all in Proportion Measure and Harmony, so they were made, and so they are preserved, Θεός γαρ άεί γνωμέτρει.

7. We come then in the third place to note, that this Propagation of Light, whether it be instantaneous, as most probably it is, or temporaneous, and requires a time someway proportion'd to its Distance, is not the Action of a Spirit but of a Body, and that it is subjected to the same Laws that other corporeal Actions or Motions are subjected to, and consequently is a Subject that falls under the Laws of Quantity, and there its Proprieties may be a fit Subject for Geometrical Exercitation.

Propagation of Light the Action of a Body.

And this appears first, for that its Power or Action is always proportionable to its Expansion ; now this Expansion in a free Pellucid Medium, is in a Duplicate Proportion to the Distance it acts reciprocally taken.

The Actions of Light are first, that effect it causes in the Eye, where it creates a Passion which makes us sensible of Light, which Effect or Action of Light is sometimes so very small and curious, that we should no way have been sensible of it had not the Creator given us an Organ Passive by it, and so fit to discover it, and had Mankind not had that Organ of Sight, no other part of our Body could have been sensible of that Effect, nor could it ever have entred into our Imagination to conceive what way it were possible the Mind or Understanding of Man should be informed of an Action a thousand thousand Miles off, at the same Instant that it was there done, nor though it were a shorter way that this Information came, *viz.* 8000 Miles which Monsieur *Romer* says he has proved, is passed in less than a second of time : We could have had, I say, no Imagination concerning it, nor any Conception of the Possibility of the Appearance of Light or Colours. Hence, To hint this only by the by, we cannot conclude but that possibly there may be many other Motions and Operations of Bodies at a distance, and several other ways by which the Bodies of the World may influence one another, though it has pleas'd God not to give us Organs or Senses to discover them, and thereby many things that are accounted Sympathetick or Magical may be done by Natural Causes and Powers, of which we have no Organs to make us sensible. Now from divers late Discoveries about the influencing Powers of Gravity and Magnetism, to name no other at present, of which we have no Sense that does immediately inform us ; but we become knowing and assur'd of them by other means, than immediately by peculiar Organs of Sense.

Now this Propagation of Light doth act duplicately proportionate to the Distance from the Lucid reciprocally ; that is, the Strength of the Light at one Foot distance from the Lucid Body, is to the Strength of the Light at two Foot as four to one, and to that at three as nine to one, and so forwards. So that the farther this Action is propagated, the more is it expanded, rarify'd, or weakned. To explain this, Let us conceive all the Medium incompassing the Lucid Body within the Compass of a Sphere of a Foot *Radius*, to be by the

The Propagation acts in a Duplicate Proportion to the distance.

Power

Power of Light in the Lucid Point, thrown out and opened into a hollow Orb, which shall incompass this emptied Globe of a Foot Diameter, possessed by the shining Body. The Thickness then of this incompassing Orb will be $\sqrt{c\,2}$ — $\sqrt{c\,1}$. the Expansion of this Orb causes the fluid Matter that was in its place before to expand into a bigger Orb: The Thickness of which will be $\sqrt{c\,3}$ — $\sqrt{c\,2}$. and so onward. So that the Rarefaction or weakening of the Power of Light increases in Duplicate Proportion to the Distance, and that this is so does plainly appear by Multitudes of Experiments, which I shall have occasion to make use of hereafter.

The Action of light carries with it a certain degree of Heat.
Next, Though so small a Degree of this Power or Action as does affect the Eye, doth not move or affect the other Senses of our Body, yet is it not without its effect upon other Bodies, besides that which it works on the acutely sensible Parts of the *Retina* of the Eye; for we find, that it also doth produce Heat, and every the least degree of it carries along with it some, though it be a small degree of Heat: Which degrees, if they are collected and concentred, do produce very sensible Effects both upon the touch, and also upon most other Bodies, whether fluid or solid: For we find it to rarify Fluids, and to melt, burn, and shatter to pieces the most solid Bodies: And therefore though the rarify'd, and smallest Degree of Light does not actually produce sensible Effects, yet since the Constipation, Multiplication, or collecting of many of those together. It follows, that the least Degree of Light has somewhat of Heat; and that the reason why it is not sensible, is only because of its Smalness, and that it is beneath those Degrees which are before actually in the Ambient, even as in the Day-time we are insensible of the Stars, because the Light of the Sun hath already fill'd the Air with a greater Light: Not that they do then less shine upon us than they do in the Night, for as I many Years since here shewed many of them may be seen at Noon day, by the help of Telescopes. And (as I shall afterwards prove more at large) there is no degree of Light, but has its degree of Heat proportion'd to those degrees of Light, which are concomitant to the degrees of the Light of the Sun. To this many have objected, that the Light of the Moon is so far from being actually hot, that it is actually cold, and the more those Rays are condensed the more is the Cold augmented: And to this purpose *Wepferus*, in his Treatise *De Apoplexia*, relates a Story how by the collecting the Rays of the Moon there was produced an actual Cold, which was very sensible to the hand held in the *Focus*. But this he relates not as tried by himself, but by another Person; but upon Inquiry further concerning this Matter, I cannot find there was any such Matter certainly observed. So that the Observation is suspected to have proceeded from some Mistake, and the Person said to have made this Observation, would not maintain any such Assertion, and therefore though it might well suit with the Relator's Theory, yet till we have some more positive Proof of Matter of Fact, and of the Curiosity and Circumstances of the Observation, I hope we may be dispensed with, though we are not of his Opinion.

Why the Rays of the Moon have no sensible Heat.
Besides, I have this to answer, That by divers Experiments purposely made, both by my self and divers others, we could not find that the Rays of Light from the Moon had any such Power of Cold as is pretended; nor indeed could we find, that they had any sensible degree of Heat, for having made the Tryals with reflecting Concaves, which collected a great Quantity of the Rays, and concentred them upon a Thermoscrope (which would be moved sensibly by a very little Alteration of Heat or Cold) I could not certainly perceive any sensible Variation, though the little accidental Changes of Heat or Cold in the Ambient Air, were very sensible by it; so that whatsoever may be pretended, I am sufficiently assured there is no such cooling Quality in the Light of the Moon.

Now that the degree of Heat, if proportion'd to the degree of Light, as in the Sun must be very small, and consequently wholly insensible to us will plainly appear, if we consider what Rarefaction of Light is caused by the Reflection from the Body of the Moon. And how small a Quantity of the Light of the Sun, which falls upon the Moon is reflected to us: For if we consider, that when the Moon is full, and so all the Hemisphere of it visible to us, is inlightned by the Sun, that the Quantity of Light which falls upon that Hemisphere mifphere of the Moon is rarified into a Sphere about 228 times bigger in Diameter than the Moon before it arrive to us, and confequently that the Light of the Moon is 104368 times weaker than the Light of the Sun; and confequently, that there muft be 104268 full Moons to reflect a Light as ftrong upon the Earth at Midnight as the Sun doth at Noon-day : And therefore 'tis no great Wonder, if a 104368th part of the Heat of the Suns Rays is not felt by us. This would be the greateft Strength of the Moon's Rays, fuppofing no part of the Sun's Light were loft in the Body of the Moon, but that all were reflected; but then if a part of it be there loft, it will make the Difproportion confiderable greater, and confequently lefs fenfible : Though therefore we are not fenfible of the Heat of that Light, yet we are not to conclude it without its due Proportion of Heat.

The fame Reafon may be valid, why the Light of Gloworms, rotten Wood, Fifh, and the Late invented *Phofphorus*, do not at all affect the touch with their Warmth : For though that degree of Heat be proportion'd to their degree of Light, yet their Proportion of Light is fo fmall, that 'tis not to be imagin'd it fhould produce any degree equivalent to that which is in the Air that incompaffes our Body.

8. This Inftantaneous Propagation of Light is in the next place in ftraight Lines, every way from the Radiating Lucid Point, through a uniform pellucid Medium. With this agrees the Judgment and Confent of all, both Ancient and Modern Authors, that have written of this Subject, all conclude it to radiate every way in ftraight Lines from the Luminous Point, whether they fuppofed it a Flame, as divers of the Ancients; or whether they fuppofed it a Flux of Atomes, as the *Epicureans*, or Species, as the *Peripateticks*, or the Motion of a ftagnant Body, as the *Cartefians*, and our Country-man Mr. *Hobbs*; they all fuppofed it to pafs in ftraight Lines, though fome of them fuppofed thofe Lines to be but Phyfically fuch, that is, fo that the whole made a ftraight Line, though the imperceptible parts thereof might be a little bended by the Pofition of the Pores, as the Atomifts fuppos'd, or by the Form of the conftituent Parts of the pellucid *Medium*; as the *Cartefians*, who imagined the faid *Medium* to confift of fmall Globules contiguous to each other. And with this alfo agree all Obfervations both in the Heavens, and on the Earth, nor have any Experiments or Obfervations hitherto contradicted it. Now though the Propagation of Light at a great Diftance fhould be temporaneous, and fo be fome confiderable time in coming from the Luminous Body to the Eye, and thence that the Morning Object fhould not be in the fame place that it appears to the Eye, yet this hinders not but that; that temporaneous Propagation may ftill be made in a ftraight Line, there being no Caufe affignable in a uniform ftagnant Medium why it fhould be otherwife.

The Propagation of Light in ftrait Lines in an homogeneous Medium.

But then this hinders not, but that this ftraight Line may be bent by a Difform Medium.

In the next place therefore, the Propagation of Light is various ways affected, and fo the Straightnefs of the Rays is changed and diverted another way.

1*ft.* By a Medium not uniform and homogeneous, the Ray is bent from a ftraight Line into a Curve, which I have long fince proved by many Obfervations and Experiments, and publifhed in the Year 1664. This Paffion of Light from a difform *Medium*, I have called *Inflection*; and fhall hereafter have occafion more fully to treat of it.

By a Difform Medium the Ray is bent into a Curve.

2*ly,* The Straightnefs of the way of Propagation is broken, fhort as it were, and diverted another way by its paffing out of one uniform Medium into another uniform *Medium*. This is call'd *Refraction* of the Ray, whereby the ftraight Line of Propagation is at the Superficies of the two contiguous tranfparent *Mediums* diverted fome other way within the fecond *Medium*, which makes an Angle at the Superficies w the former Rays contiuued.

3*ly,* The Ray is broken and diverted another way by its meeting with a *Medium* unfit for admitting the Propagation of Light through it felf, and thereby the Ray is kept within the firft Medium, but at the *Superficies* is with an Angle diverted and bent fhort another way, this is called Reflection.

Y

4*ly,*

4ly, The Ray is impeded, ſtopp'd, deaded, or abſorpt by meeting with a Body unfit either to propagate it through it ſelf, or reflect it into the firſt *Medium*, which may be called Mortification or Extinction, of this kind are blank Bodies, and divers others which retain and keep it for a long time, and do not whilſt they keep that Form, return or communicate it to any other.

5ly, The Ray is diſperſed, ſplit, and opened by its Refraction at the Superficies of a ſecond Medium, and from a Line is opened into a diverging Superficies, and ſo obliquated, whereby the Appearances of Colours are produced.

6ly, The Rays of Light are imbib'd into, and receiv'd by a ſecond Medium, and thence returned again by degrees after they have remain'd a conſiderable time in the recipient Medium, as in the *Bononia* Stone, and ſome of our late invented *Phoſphori.*

Of each of theſe, I ſhall more at large diſcourſe, and explain the particular Cauſes and Reaſons of theſe Affections, and the Rules, Laws, and Limits of their ſeveral Powers.

SECT.

SECT. II.

Containing the Lectures of Light read about Michaelmas, 1680.

The CONTENTS.

1. *The true Method of acquiring Knowledge, is first by examining the* ὅτι *that it is so, and then the* διότι *why it is so.* 2. *The Bodies from whence Light proceeds, as first the Sun ; its vast Bigness and Distance from the Earth, emits Rays every way equally* in Orbem, *is subject to Changes from its Spots which are at large described ; with their Motions and Nature, and of the Sun's Rotation.* 3. *That the Rays of the Sun carry Heat as well as Light, that the Sun has Heat really, and that it is not produced by the Reflexion of the Rays from the Earth ; why the upper Air colder.* 4. *That the Sun is incompassed with an Atmosphere, or something analogous to it, the Limb which appears to us is that of the Atmosphere, more of the Spots : The Sun agrees with the Earth in most Particulars except Light, why the Light of the Sun is most insisted on.* 5. *Farther Reasons that there must be a fluid Body incompassing the Sun, with a farther Explication of the Spots, that they are not Planets like the Body of* Venus *or* Mercury in Sole, *tho' there may possibly be Planets nearer the Sun than them which the Author sees no reason to believe, these Spots are within the Atmosphere of the Sun, and much of the Nature of Meteors, a farther Confirmation that there is a small transparent Shell or Atmosphere about the Sun.* 6. *That within this Shell is a solid Opaque Body, solid from its Rotation, Fixedness of its Axis, and its Power of Gravitation, Opaque from the Spots not appearing thro' it.* 7. *Eight Particulars, wherein the Sun and Earth agree, and three wherein they differ.* 8. *Supposing the Sun composed of Nitrous and Sulphureous Particles, and set on Fire, all the Phenomena thereof may be explained, the Proportion of the Diminution of the Action of Light in Proportion to the Distance from the Luminous Body demonstrated, and that the Light of the Sun is from an actual Fire, or Dissolution of the Superficial Parts thereof, with an Objection against it answered.* R. W.

1. **I** Have begun in my former Lectures to enumerate and explain to you some of the Proprieties of Light, and to observe to you what it effects and performs, which I have done in order to shew how, and by what means they are performed, and from what Causes those Effects proceed. First, to explain to you the ὅτι, and shew you that so and so it is, and then the διότι, how and why it is so.

This is the true Method of coming to the Knowledge of all the Operations *The true Me-* of Nature, and therefore whoever goes the other way to work, and begins *a thod of acqui-* priori to this first of the Cause, and then to deduce the Effects from it, as a *ring Knowledge.*

great

great Man has done, or at least would be thought so to have done ; begins at the wrong end, and at length when he came to the ultimate and most visible Effects, he found himself, or at least most Men have found it for him, that he was much at a loss and unable to get out, and extricate himself.

The Works of Nature are a great Labyrinth, which is already built and perfected, their ways are determined and bounded by impenetrable Walls ; and there are no new Passages to be made, other than what are already fixt: He therefore that shall think immediately to fly and transport himself over these Walls, and set himself in the very middle and inmost Recess of it, and thence think himself able to know all the Meanders and Turnings, and Passages back again to get out ; will find himself hugely mistaken and puzled in finding his way out again.

Whereas he, that would march secure, must first find some open and visible Entry, and there enter with his Clew and his Instruments, and take notice of what Turnings and Passages he finds, and see how far he can proceed in this and that way, before he finds a *ne plus ultra* ; then setting down and protracting all the ways he has there gone, and what he has there met withal, he must return by the help of his Clew and try another Passage, and do as much there, and so a third and a fourth, and so onward, setting down still and protracting his several Essays ; by comparing of all which together, he will at last be able to give you the true Ground plat of the whole Labyrinth, and thereby to tell you which is the right and which is the wrong way to find the middle or Center: Which is the nearest and which is the farthest way about, which is the plainest and easiest, and which the ruggedest and the most difficultest, which the lightest, and which the darkest Passage, and all the Occurences you will meet withal in the ways.

The most of our Philosophers that have hitherto written, have gone the other way to work. They have begun from some inward part of the Labyrinth, having made some small Entrance, and have thence thought they knew the whole Fabrick, and to have found the way out again by the help of their Memories, neglecting or despising the Clew, the Compass, the Circumferenter, and the Chain, whereby to observe Measure, and set down all they observed in their way : And have thereupon feigned a way, and have made to themselves a Labyrinth, and have presently given you a Design of the whole. But alas, this Labyrinth was in their own Mind, and not of Nature's making, and how perfect soever they are in their own Method, they are altogether to seek in that of Nature.

Thus the *Pythagoreans* were puzled with their Numbers ; the *Peripateticks* with their Four Elements ; the *Epicureans* with their Atoms ; the *Chymists* with their three Principles, Salt, Sulphur, Mercury ; *Ptolomy* with his Orbs and Epicycles ; *Kepler* with his Harmonicks ; *Guilbert* with his Magnetisms ; not to name many of the Ancients, some whereof would reduce all from Fire, others from Air, and others from Water, some from Heat and Cold, others from Light and Darkness, others from Good and Evil, but all fell short of the true Explication of Nature.

He therefore that would make a thorough Discovery, must begin from the most sensible, obvious and plain Effects of Nature ; of these he must make a diligent Inquiry, first what is done, and then as near as may be how 'tis done.

Our present Inquiry therefore being after the Nature of Light: To proceed according to the Method I have now been speaking of to you ,we must first inquire and search on the outside of this Labyrinth, and see what Entrances or Inlets there are by which we penetrate into it ; that is, we must inquire what are the most obvious and sensible Effects of it : These must be all, if possible, found out, enumerated, and set down. Secondly, Every one of these again must be more strictly examined, determined, and stated, and the Limits set, its *Maximum* and *Minimum* demonstrated ; its comparative Likeness and Unlikeness to the Proprieties of other Subjects taken notice of, and recorded ; its Congruents or Opponents, or its Promoters or Retarders ; its Contraries and Destroyers ; and the like must also be examined, and all these must be Methodically Disposed and Registred into fit Tables, that so out of these found Materials

chosen

chosen with Judgment, examined with Strictness, cleansed and fitted with great Sedulity and Reasonings, we may raise a sound and lasting Structure that no Age or right Reason shall overthrow or destroy.

Such are the Fabricks raised by Geometry, thus *Euclid*'s and *Archimede*'s Demonstrations, none since have been able to disprove. This Learning which was said to have been brought first out of *Egypt*, was possibly known before the Pyramids were built, and may last when not a Dust of those massy Piles may be left undevoured by Time; for Truth always was, is, and ever will be the same.

2. To find the Nature of Light we must examine first, what it is in the Luminous Body that is the Fountain, and emits or causes it; Secondly, what it is in the Medium that propagates and conveys it; and Thirdly, what it is in the Eye, or the subject that receives it, and is affected or acted by it. *The Bodies from whence the Light proceeds.*

The first thing then I shall take notice of, is of the Bodies from which Light proceeds, as from the Fountains, whence it has its Original and first Spring. Namely, of such as we have no sense that informs us, that 'tis brought into them from any other place, but seems to be there generated and produced.

These Bodies are very many, and very differing in their Constitutions, and therefore the Enumeration of them, and some of their Proprieties may be a great help to us to judge of the Nature of Light.

The greatest and most remarkable of all (at least *quoad nos*) is the most glorious Body of the Sun; which from the glorious, great, and powerful Effects of it upon this World or Earth, on which Mankind is placed, was by the Heathens, *Romans*, *Greeks*, *Persians*, &c. esteemed a God, and so worshipped and adored; but under various Names, as *Jupiter*, *Apollo*, *Phœbus*, *Phaeton*, and several other Names, all of which signified the Sun. As *Juno*, *Venus*, *Cynthia*, *Diana*, &c. signified the Moon. The things observable in this Body, besides its Light, are first, that 'tis the greatest Body we yet know in the World, of whose Magnitude we can have any tolerable Certainty : It being very much bigger than all the Planets together, *viz.* ♄, ♃, ♂, the Earth, ♀, ☿, and their Satellits, *viz.* those of ♄, ♃, and the Earth, and may be possibly bigger than any fixt Star, of which by and by. *The vast Bigness of the Sun and Distance from the Earth.*

The Bigness of it is collected from its Distance, and the Angle, under which it is seen. The Distance is by some of our late Astronomers, who have been more than ordinarily curious in their Observations, judged to be about 10000 Diameters of the Earth distant from us, and the Angle under which it is seen about half a Degree: Its Diameter therefore must be about $\frac{1}{114}$ part of its Distance, and consequently about 87 times bigger than the Diameter of the Earth, its Body therefore being Spherical, as I shall shew by and by, must be 87 times 87 times 87, that is, 658503 times bigger in Bulk than the Body or Globe of the Earth : And therefore the Surface of it, which is the part that gives Light, is 7569 greater than the whole Superficies of the Globe of the Earth. Now almost half this Superficies is seen at once, and therefore that part is near $3784\frac{1}{2}$ times bigger than the whole Superficies of the Earth. Now every part of the whole Superficies of the Sun does shine, and emit Light every way *in Orbem*, which will be probable from this, that a very large Zone of the Sun doth so; and therefore since all parts of the Sun seem to give Light alike, it is more than probable, that every other part of the Sun's Surface doth the same thing. Now before I demonstrate this, I must note to you another Propriety observed in the Body of the Sun, which is necessary for proving both the real Bulk of its Body, and the radiating every way of the Superficial parts of it. It is observed then, that there sometimes happen to be several dark and dusky Spots visible upon its Surface, whose Passage over the Sun have been by Telescopes and other Instruments curiously traced and calculated, by which it plainly appears, 1st, That this Body we see, which appears only as a Plain, is a Globous and Spherical Body; and this because the said Spots are observed to pass over its Face with a Motion proportion to a double Line of Sines, or as they must appear, supposing they were placed upon a Globe appearing under that Angle, and equally turning round upon an *Axis*. This is yet farther confirmed by the Alteration of the Shape of the Spots, when they are nearer the

Limb,

Limb, and so are posited obliquely from what they appeared in the middle, and so directly faceing us; which Alteration perfectly answers to the Shape of such a Spot, made upon the Face of a Globe, and by turning the Globe, altering the Position of it to the Eye. These tell us further, that this vast Globe makes a Revolution in 25 Days, or thereabouts, upon an Axis obliquely posited to the Ecliptick; whence it is plain, as I noted before, that all parts of the Sun's Surface do shine, for that they are sometime or other seen. 2dly, There being no part of the Sun's Surface lying between the two Tropicks of the Earth upon it, but is sometime or other seen in all the Positions of a Hemisphere, and yet continually seeming as far as we can discover, equally giving Light; it follows, that all those parts at least do emit Rays of Light *in Orbem* the like may with all manner of Probability, be concluded of all the rest.

The Sun subject to Changes and of the Spots seen in it.   The next thing then I shall observe is, that this great Body is subject to as great Changes in its superficial parts, as any that happen to the superficial parts of the Earth, and consequently may have Generations and Corruptions, or Alterations, as do happen here upon the Earth. This is evident by those great Spots which, as I have noted to you, do often appear upon the Face of the Sun, and move along with it.

These are of no certain Figure, nor of any certain Bigness, but sometimes bigger, sometimes less, sometimes more appear, sometimes fewer: Sometimes darker, sometimes dusky, sometimes brighter. Most of the dark have about them a Duskiness at a certain Distance, which does sometimes remain after the dark one be quite wasted, as they are found sometimes before the dark appear. Some of these Spots have been observed to turn into Spots brighter than the rest of the Sun's Surface, but especially when they approach the Limb of the Sun, where also many of the dusky ones appear, and more than usually upon the middle parts of the Sun. Both the dusky, and especially the brighter parts, are observed to stay some of them considerably longer in the Limb of the Sun than they ought to do, according to the Theory of moving upon and along with the *Superficies* of the Globe: But they are never seen to appear without the Limb, but within the edge or in the very edge of the Sun, without making any Protuberance. The brighter Spots are observed to appear brighter towards the Limb, and sometimes to appear in it very bright.

They are observed always to pass over the Face of the Sun, from the East-side towards the West, sometimes in a straight Line, and sometimes in an Ellipsis when they move regularly, but they are also sometimes observed to decline out of those Lines, and swerve sometimes towards the North, and sometimes towards the South, but never to go the contrary way.

Sometimes one of these Spots divides into many, which separate from one another, and sometimes many of them coaless, and joyn together in one.

From all which Appearances, it is very evident, First, That these Spots are Bodies moved upon, or in some fluid Body somewhat of the Nature of those we have upon the Earth, as to Fluidity, *viz.* Air or Water, though possibly the fluid, may differ from these Earthly Bodies in other Qualities.

Secondly, That these Bodies are either opaque, and so hinder the Light of the Sun to pass through them, or else they are incombustible and dark Bodies, which will afford no Light at all for a certain time, and do as it were quench and deaden that part of the Sun where they rise.

An Account of the Spots in the Sun.   So that though the Face of the Sun be the most glorious and vivid Light that we are sensible of in the World, yet since the Discovery and Use of Perspective Glasses it has been observed, not to be free from some parts that are dusky, and some perfectly dark, and some other parts that are observed to give a brighter Light than even the clear Face of the Sun it self: The former are called *Nebulæ* or Clouds, the second *Maculæ* or Spots, and the third *Faculæ* or Blazes. These have been observed by *Schiner*, *Galileo*, and others, to be generated up and down in various parts of the Sun's Face, and to increase and grow bigger sometimes, and sometimes to grow less, decay and vanish: Their Increase is sometimes from a small Cloudiness, to increase larger and larger, and then in the middle sometimes, and sometimes in various parts of it, to have perfect dark Spots, which also continue to increase sometimes so big as to co-

ver

ver a part of the Sun equal to all *Europe*, and fometimes to be bigger than all the Superficies of the Earth, thofe Spots do fometimes coalefs and joyn all into one, and fometimes divide and feparate into divers, and part afunder confiderably : And again, at other times many of thofe Spots which are generated feparately, do meet together and make one great one. Thefe appear fometimes of a dusky Red, fometimes Yellowifh, fometimes of a dusky Blew, and various other Colours ; their Shape is very irregular, and fcarce any two alike, not unlike the upper fides or edges of the great white Clouds we ufually fee here in the Summer-time : Yet generally the edges of the *Maculæ* or darkeft Spots, are very defined, and this Spot is perfectly Black to the very edges; but always about thefe edges to a certain Diftance, which is much the fame, be the Spot bigger or lefs there is a dusky bordering, which is likewife fhaped according to the edges of the Spot, and is all of an even Darknefs or Duskinefs. The *Faculæ* are not defined but uneven, and ufually appear brighteft towards the middle. The Shape of thefe Spots fometimes continue much the fame for fome Days, but yet feldom without fome Alteration: So that indeed they feem to be always in a State of Alteration, but fometimes quicker fometimes flower. From the Obfervation of them in feveral parts of the Sun, it is moft demonftrably evident, that they have fome kind of Thicknefs, but very fmall in comparifon to their Breadth ; for as they approach towards the Limb, they keep their extent toward the North and South, but diminifh towards the Eaft and Weft, in the fame manner as a broad flat Body would do if varioufly pofited to the Eye : Infomuch as fuch as are towards a round appear by degrees to turn to a longer Oval, almoft all in the edge appear a Line bended circularly, which is an evident Proof that the Motion of them is on a Spherial Surface, and not a plain, for if it were on a plain the Shape of them would receive no other Alteration at the Limb of the Sun than it would at the middle. And from hence alfo we have a good Argument, that the Body of the Sun is a Globe, and not a plain flat round Superficies, as fome of the ancient Philofophers are faid to have afferted it ; nor a round Hole bored through the dark Shell of the Univerfe, to let through the Light of the *Cælum Empyreum*, which fome others of them are faid to have afferted, fuppofing alfo the fixt Stars to be nothing elfe but fmaller Holes through this dark Shell. But thefe Conceptions as too rude, grofs, and favouring of vulgar Conceptions, I pafs over and proceed to obferve to you further, that thefe Spots of the Sun are obferved to move generally all from Eaft to Weft, and over the Face of the Sun, fometimes coming in at the Eaft Limb, and in 12, 13, 14, or 15 Days to move to the Weft Limb, and to perform this Motion regularly for the moft part, according to an order of Sins, the Radius of the Sun being for the Radius, and the Order beginning from the Center, which is another Demonftration that their Motion is on the *Superficies* of a Sphere, and that they move on it almoft equal Spaces in equal times, I fay almoft equal ; becaufe they have a kind of Motion of their own, whereby they are fometimes as it were promoted and fometimes hindered, fometimes carried a little towards the North, and fometimes a little towards the South. This Motion of theirs from Eaft to Weft, over the Face of the Sun, fometimes appears to us to be made in a ftraight Line, which happens when the Earth is in that part of the plain of the Ecliptick, which cuts the Plain of the Equinoctial of the Sun's turbinated Motion, which is twice a Year, *viz.* in the beginning of *June* and *December :* At other times the Line of the Motion of them is incurvated and bent into an Ellipfe, which is greateft when the Earth happens to be in thofe parts of the Ecliptick, which are the extream Limits of it, compar'd to the Plain of the Sun's Equinoctial, which is alfo twice a Year, *viz.* in the middle, between the Nodes, both Plains paffing through the Center of the Sun, that is, about the beginning of *March* and *September*. From whence alfo is deduced another undeniable Demonftration, that the Sun's *Superficies* is Globular, and that it moves round upon its *Axis* from Weft to Eaft, as the Earth and *Jupiter* alfo are proved to do. And another Remark is likewife evidenced, that this *Axis* of the Sun's turbinated Motion, remains fixt and directed toward the fame parts of the Heavens. In the fame manner as the *Axis* of the Earth is obferved to do, and likewife the *Axis* of ♃ and ♄, fo far as we can yet difcover by the Spots, Ring, and the Satellits of

thofe

thofe Bodies. So that the Method of Nature in moſt things agrees both in our and other Globous Bodies of the Univerſe. There is yet one Obſervation more concerning theſe Spots, which further confirms this Deduction, and that is that there is a certain torrid Zone, as I may call it from its Similitude to the torrid Zone of the Earth, *viz.* a certain Space or Breadth on each ſide of the Æquator of the Sun towards the North and South Poles, in which theſe Clouds, Smokes, Blazes, or Spots are obſerved to appear moſt : Whereas without thoſe Limits, or in the two temperate Zones, they appear more ſeldom, and thoſe which do are only *Nebulæ* or Clouds ; but in the two Polar Zones there appear none at all.

How great a Similitude there appears in this with the Globe of the Earth, I need not now inſiſt on, only I ſhall make this Remark by the by from this Similitude, that though all that have hitherto ſpoken concerning this Subject, have concluded that the time of the Revolution of the Sun's Body upon its *Axis,* is to be deduced from the Revolution of ſome Spots that have laſted more than quite round the Body of the Sun, and come to the ſame Place again, in which they were 29 Days before or thereabouts. I muſt upon this occaſion, I ſay, remark that here upon the Earth, between and near the Tropicks, we always have a continual Brieze of Air, which moves from Eaſt to Weſt ; which upon very good Reaſon is concluded by *Galileo,* and moſt of our Modern Naturaliſts, to proceed from the Earths moving from Weſt to Eaſt, and ſo leaving the Air behind, which lagging of the Air is yet much more conſiderably felt and perceived in the higher Parts of it by the Clouds, and by the Paſſage of it over the tops of high Hills. So that if theſe Spots be Clouds or Smoke, or ſomewhat Analogous to them, rais'd into the Air, Atmoſphere, or ſome Fluid Analogous to the Earth's Atmoſphere, as I ſhall obſerve by and by, then may the Motion of the ſolid Globe of the Sun be conſiderably ſwifter than thoſe Clouds appear to be carried, and inſtead of being 25 Days, poſſibly may make a Revolution in 20 Days or ſooner.

Theſe Particulars I have here mentioned, I could have more largely demonſtrated to you by Schemes and Figures, whereby every Particular I have aſſerted of this Matter might have been more fully ſhewn and explained. But I do rather avoid it ; Firſt, becauſe in Demonſtrations of that kind very few Auditors are able to go along with the Deſcription and Quotations of Lines and Letters in the Schemes ; and Secondly, becauſe it ſpends more time with much leſs Advantage to the Auditory.

The Suns Rays carry Heat as well as Light. 3. I ſhall then in the next Place remark to you, That the Rays of the Sun are obſerved to carry with them Heat, or to produce it in the Bodies upon which they fall, eſpecially if they be collected by the help of a reflecting or a refracting Burning glaſs : Inſomuch that by thoſe means it is eaſy to ſet Bodies into an actual Flame and Fire ; nay, not only to ſet Bodies on fire and conſume them, but even to melt the moſt ſtubborn Bodies. Inſomuch that none of the Metals, as Tin, Lead, Silver, Braſs, Copper, Iron, Gold, are able to indure it without being in a Moment almoſt melted, and nor only theſe, but Stones, Clay, Flints, Bricks, and almoſt all other Bodies that will not burn, will by the Power of the Sun's Rays, collected with a Burning-glaſs, be melted and turned into Glaſs to Admiration. Nay, 'tis poſſible by this means to augment the Heat to almoſt any aſſigned Degree, and poſſibly ſome hundreds times more than 'tis poſſible to perform by all the Artificial Fires that can be made with any combuſtible Materials we yet know : Of which Effects, and the Cauſes and Proprieties thereof, more hereafter. Now after all this, there have not been wanting divers Men who would needs perſwade us, that notwithſtanding all theſe Obſervations the Body of the Sea has no Heat, nor have the Rays themſelves, but that they produce Heat and Fire only by agitating the Body upon which they fall, and are reflected ; and this is the Reaſon (ſay they) why the upper Parts of the Air are ſo very cold, and the under Parts next the Ground are ſo very hot, for the Rays of the Sun, ſay they, being in themſelves perfectly cold in paſſing thorough the upper Air ; and being not reflected, they cauſe no Agitation or Heat, but being reflected from the Earth in the under Parts of the Air, the croſs Agitation cauſeth the Parts of the Air to beat one

againſt

against another, and this causeth Heat much in the same manner as a Flint and Steel being struck one against another, though neither of them be hot before they meet together; yet when they meet, produce both Heat, Fire, and Light, though there were no sensible Signs of any of these before, and so a piece of cold Iron may by being hammer'd on a cold Anvil with a cold Hammer, very nimbly and stongly, be not only heated so as to burn ones Fingers, and to fire Gunpowder, but to be visibly red hot : So that though the Hammer and the Anvil were both in themselves devoid of Heat, yet their Motion does produce it on the Iron. To this it may be answered, that as to the Warmth of the Air *Why the upper* at the bottom, and the Coldness at the top of the Mountains, or high Towers, *Air is colder.* the reason is plain from this, that the Air near the Earth is warmed by the Heat of the Earth, and being not so swiftly moved and changed for cold Air, as that which is at the tops of Mountains, or of very high Towers, which is also further removed from the warm Surface of the Earth : But that the Rays of the Sun will do the same thing as to burning of any Body by the help of a refracting burning Glass at the top of a Hill or Tower, there is no manner of reason to doubt. 'Tis, I think, sufficiently evident to all the World, that Heat is convey'd by the Sun Beams as well as Light, and that those Beams both of Light and Heat are emitted by the Sun, and therefore we have no more reason to believe, that the Sun has no Light than that it has no Heat.

4. All these Circumstances consider'd, it seems very reasonable to conclude, *That the Sun* that the Superficies of this great Body of the Sun is incompassed with an Air or *has an Atmo-* Atmosphere, or some other fluid Body or Menstruum, even as this Body of the *sphere, or some-* Earth ; and that this Atmosphere, though possibly 80 times thicker than the *thing like it.* Thickness and Height of the Atmosphere about the Earth, yet compared to the Vastness of the Diameter of the Body, it becomes wholly invisible to us, though assisted with our best Telescopes : And besides, 'tis not to be doubted, but that being very near the Body, and having reflective Parts in it, it must of it self look as bright as the very Body it self, and consequently that the Limb thereof which appears to us is really the Shell of the Atmosphere, Air, or fluid Menstruum about the Sun, and not the very solid Body it self that shines. Hence all the Phænomena of the *Maculæ* and *Faculæ* of the Sun observed will be solved, and these Spots of the Sun will be no other than our Clouds or Smokes, which rise into the Atmosphere; this I say, will plainly make out all their Appearances to be much the same as those of Clouds are here with us : For 'tis not to be doubted, but that we have sometimes Clouds big enough to hinder the Sun from shining upon as great a part of the Earth's Surface, as those Clouds of the Sun do hinder us from seeing of the Sun's Surface.

Hence 'twill be easy to know why they sometimes move a little Northwards, and sometimes a little Southwards, but still follow the general Course of the Sun's Body, why the black Spots generally vary their Shape, regularly as on a Spherical Surface, but that the bright ones do not, but seem to grow otherwise ; why the bright ones appear most near the Limb of the Sun, and not so often in the middle ; namely, where we come to see the Light reflected from the under sides of the Spot, or Cloud : This gives a clear reason why they stay so long about the Limb, and why they grow bigger, whereas the dark grow less and sooner vanish. And in short, there is no Observation of these Spots in the Face of the Sun that I have ever yet made my self or seen of others, but will hereby be clearly made out.

So that upon all that has been thus far said concerning the Body of the Sun, *The Sun in most* it plainly appears, that it agrees with the Terraqueo-Aerial Globe in divers of *Proprieties a-* its Proprieties, and I shall another time prove to you several other Particulars, *grees with the* by which it will plainly appear, that they perfectly agree in most other Pro- *Earth except* prieties except Light, and wherein that difference consists I shall likewise *that of Light.* show.

I am the more particular (upon this occasion) in my Description of the Sun, because as it is the very Fountain of all visible Light, and the most considerable Body in the World : So the Proprieties of this being explain'd, it will the more clearly discover to us what are the most considerable Proprieties of Light in

other

other Luminous Bodies, and thence we may be able fully to explain this Subject, which is the moſt operative and moſt conſiderable Ingredient of the Univerſe.

There muſt be a fluid Body encompaſſing a more ſolid in the Sun, with more concerning the Spots.

5. Having thus ſhewn you that it is neceſſary there muſt be a fluid Body incompaſſing the ſolid Body of the Sun, for otherwiſe thoſe irregular Motions of the Spots cannot be made out, and with the ſuppoſal of it, may be made out and explained very rationally, I ſhall now more particularly ſhew you the Reaſons thereof. All that have hitherto made accurate Obſervations concerning theſe Spots in the Sun, amongſt which, I think, none has been more diligent and curious than the Learned and Ingenious Jeſuite *Shinar*, in his *Roſa Urſina*, that the *Phænomena* of the *Maculæ*, *Nebulæ* and *Faculæ*, are much what I have already given you an account of: And though there be one or two who from ſome ſuperficial and ſlight Obſervations, and from much of Fantcy have pretended ſome other Motions of theſe Spots, and would thence conclude, that they are not Clouds but ſome ſmaller Planets, ſo near the Body of the Sun, as that they can never be ſeen, but when they are in their Perigean Conjunctions, and ſo come between the Sun and our Eye; yet ſince they are diſallowed of by the moſt diligent and curious Inquirers into theſe Matters, and ſince I could never meet with any ſuch my ſelf, I have good reaſon to ſuſpend my Aſſent to their Concluſion, till by manifeſt Obſervations it ſhall be made out to the contrary. Certain it is, that the Bodies of *Venus* and *Mercury* when they have appeared in the Face of the Sun, have been very differing in their form from thoſe of the uſual Spots: For Firſt, they appear round, which few or none of theſe Spots are obſerved to do. Secondly, They have not been obſerved to have any *Nebulæ* about them, which all the Spots that ever I have ſeen have always had. And Thirdly, Their Motions have been ſo ſwift as to paſs over the whole Face of the Sun in a very ſhort time, as in ſome few Hours; whereas theſe Spots are at leaſt 12 days, and ſometimes longer. Fourthly, They are obſerved to paſs over in a ſtraight Line, whereas theſe are very often obſerved to paſs in an Ellipſe, *quam proxime*, and but twice a Year in a ſtraight Line. Fifthly, They paſs over the Sun with an equal ſwiftneſs as to Senſe, whereas theſe paſs with very unequal, as I noted to you before, and according to the Proportions of Sins. Sixthly, They make no ſtay in the Limb, which theſe Spots oft-times are obſerved to do. It plainly follows therefore, that theſe Spots are very near the Surface of the Sun, if not upon it.

I do not deny but that it is poſſible there may be the Bodies of other Planets about the Sun, nearer than that of ☿, which by reaſon of their nearneſs to its Body, may never appear but only at ſuch time as they happen to be obſerved whilſt they paſs under the Sun: But I never yet met with any certain Obſervation from which I ſaw a neceſſity for making ſuch a Concluſion; for the Poſſibility thereof is no ways a ſufficient Argument for its Neceſſity, or ſo much as a Probability; for all the Obſervations that have been made of theſe Spots at the Limb make their ſtay rather longer than ſhorter than they ought to do, ſuppoſing them upon the very Superficies of the Sun, and therefore they are ſo far from being without the ſhining and bright Limb of the Sun, that 'tis manifeſt that they are within it, that is, within the Superficies of the Atmoſphere that incompaſſes the Body of the Sun.

Now the ſuppoſing of ſuch an Atmoſphere or fluid Body to incompaſs the ſolid Body of the Sun (for there is as great a neceſſity of a ſolid Body of the Sun as there is of a fluid about it to make out the reaſon and cauſe of divers other Proprieties of it, as I ſhall afterwards ſhew) will plainly and intelligibly make out all the *Phænomena* of the Spots, and make it almoſt demonſtrable that theſe *Maculæ*, *Nebulæ* and *Faculæ* of the Body of the Sun, are much of the Nature of the Meteors raiſed up into our Atmoſphere from the Earth, and, as I ſhall by and by make appear, will plainly ſhew unto us from what cauſe the Light of the Body proceeds. I have mentioned to you already, that the Spots are obſerved to ſtay conſiderably longer in the Limb of the Sun than they ought, according to the Rule of moving upon the Superficies of an opacous Globe, for it has been found that they appear, when according to that Rule they ſhould diſappear; it follows therefore, that either they muſt loſe their

Regularity

Regularity when they come to the apparent Limb of the Sun *quoad nos*, or elſe that the edge of the Limb is *aliquatenus* tranſparent; for the former there can be no imaginary Reaſon, there being no difference in that part of the Superfi- cies of the Sun from any other; becauſe every part of the Sun ſucceſſively is in the Limb, and Spots ariſe promiſcuouſly in any Part of its middle Zone: It muſt therefore of neceſſity be from the Tranſparency of ſome ſmall Shell, about the ſolid ſhining Body, and therefore probably of an Atmoſphere. But ſecond- ly, 'Tis manifeſt that this Atmoſphere is moved much as our Atmoſphere is; for by many Obſervations it has been certainly found, that theſe Spots which riſe in the middle Zone of the Sun have been obſerved to be longer in paſſing over the Sun's Disk, than thoſe which happened in the Intermediate, which perfectly agrees with the Motion of the Atmoſphere about the Earth, for the Air between and near the Tropicks is obſerved to lag and fall more behind the Motion of the Earth than the Air in the temperate Zones; for in the Torrid Zone the Air or Wind almoſt continually ſeems to blow from the Eaſt, or from ſome Point of it, which is generally now concluded to proceed from that Cauſe, I ſay for the moſt part from the Eaſt, or ſome Point of it, as Eaſt South- Eaſt, or South-Eaſt, Eaſt-North-Eaſt or North Eaſt, or the like, which ex- plains alſo why thoſe Spots of the Sun are obſerved to move ſometimes toward the North-Weſt, and ſometimes towards the South Weſt: But then thoſe in the intermediate Zones follow the Courſe of the Sun's Body more eaſily, as with us, where the Winds ſometimes blow from the Weſtwards, and ſeem to be moved faſter than the Earth it ſelf.

6. Having therefore as far as the thing is capable of Demonſtration ſhew'd, *That the Sun* that the Superficies of the Sun is fluid and ſomewhat tranſparent, and has *is a ſolid and* Motions in it analogous and very like to the Motions of our Atmoſphere: I *opacous Body.* come in the next place to obſerve to you, that the Body of the Sun it ſelf with- in this Shell is a ſolid Body and opacous. Its Solidity I prove from three Pro *Why ſolid.* prieties here obſervable, and thoſe are Firſt, the Conſtancy of its Rotation; Secondly, The Fixtneſs of its Axis; And thirdly, the Power of its Gravitation or Attraction to its Center. Firſt, I ſay, from the Conſtancy of its Rotation; this is an Argument ſo plain, as nothing can be more, for we need go no further than the Earth on which we tread, whoſe Rotation we find very certain and conſtant, and none can yet prove but that it is always equal and uniform; in that Motion whereas we ſee the fluid Bodies about it, as the Air, nothing is more uncertain and unconſtant than them, nay though it be guided by the Su- perficies of the Earth, nay the very Water which is contain'd in the Capacity of the Earth, and ſo has much more reaſon to move round, than if all fluid: Yet we ſee that this has great Varieties of Currents, Ebbings and Flowings, and the like; eſpecially in the great Ocean, though it be leſs in Seas incloſed, the ſame we ſhall find if we make tryal with Water in a Diſh, or Water about a Diſh, and the like, which will preſently confound a circular Motion that ſhall be impreſs'd upon it, and ſo muſt quickly ſtand ſtill, whereas we find it quite otherwiſe, and to continue the ſame as it was firſt obſerved to do. But then ſecondly, by reaſon of the Fixedneſs of the Axis of its Revolution, this is a ſtronger Argument than the former for its Solidity; for there is no body that we yet know that is fluid, has any ſuch Propriety as Magnetiſm or Dire- ction, and all that have a Magnetiſm are ſolid as the Earth, ♄, ♃, and the Moon, the Magnet and Steel; nay, Steel being either melted or diſſolved in *Aqua Fortis*, and ſo made fluid loſeth its Virtue [And Iron heated red hot does no more attract till cold, as having ſomewhat of Fluidity] and if it would loſe the Regularity of its turbinated Motion, then certainly much rather would it loſe the Direction of its Axis, if it were not a Solid: It follows there- fore that ſince 'tis evident from Obſervation, that this Axis keeps its Poſition and Direction, therefore that the Body of the Sun muſt be a ſolid and not a fluid Body. The third Argument drawn from its attractive or gravitating Power, to prove its Solidity, I cannot here ſtay to inſiſt upon the Explication of, becauſe the reaſon thereof cannot ſo plainly appear without the Explica- tion of a whole Theory of Gravity, which will come in more properly under another Head, and therefore I can only tell you, that the Explication of the
Cauſe

Cause of Gravity will clearly prove that the Body that has Gravitation strictly so called, must have also Solidity. Now that it has such an Attraction or Gravitation, I shall prove first from its Spherical Figure; 2dly, From the Motion of these Spots; and 3dly, From the Motions of all the other primary Planets, whose Motions as I have many Years since shewed in this Place, are all influenced and modulated by the attractive Power of this great Body. This also as the former, I must for the present refer to that Head to be more fully explained and demonstrated, and only name it at present.

Why Opaque. In the next place, that the Body within the Atmosphere or transparent Shell, is opacous, I argue from the disappearing of the Spots in the Limb, and their not returning backwards as they would seem to do if the Body were transparent as the Atmosphere is, or the Flame of a Candle, or the Radiations, or hazy Light about the Nucleus of a Comet, through which as through its Beard, I have seen small fixt Stars.

Eight Particulars in which the Sun and Earth agree. Three wherein they differ. 7. We find then, that thus far the Proprieties of the Body of the Sun do seem to agree with the Proprieties of the Body of the Earth: As first, in its Globular Figure; 2dly, In its Rotation; 3dly, In its Gravity; 4thly, In its Polar Directions; 5thly, In its Atmosphere; 6thly, In the Motions of that Atmosphere; 7thly, In attracting Planetary Bodies; 8thly, In the Fixtness of its Axis or Polarity, &c.

But then in the next Place they differ, first in Magnitude, the comparative Quantities of each I shew'd you before. 2dly, In the Make of the Surface, that of the Earth being rugged and unequal, but that of the Sun as far as yet can be discovered, very equal and smooth. 3dly, In their Qualities, the Sun's Surface being both hot and light, and that of the Earth dark and cold; that therefore which would afford these Proprieties to the Body of the Earth would make the Earth on which we tread a Sun. These two Proprieties then we find Fire to supply, if therefore the Surface of the Earth were made and compounded of Nitrous and Sulphureous Particles, or such like combustible Substances, and that they were once set on fire, I see no reason why the Earth should not be in all respects the same to the Moon as the Sun is to the Earth: Nor is there any reason why all the other Proprieties of the Earth that it now hath, excepting those of Coldness and Opacity, should not remain much the same. If therefore we further suppose (I say suppose for I do not now intend in this Place to prove that 'tis really and positively so, and not otherwise, though I shall afterwards from other Arguments demonstrably prove it) that the solid Body of the Sun is made or compounded of such Materials as will really work one upon another, and dissolve or burn each other, as we find Sulphur and Nitre do, or any Sulphureous Body, and the Air when rightly joyned. From this Hypothesis, I say, for I will not presume to call it more at present, I conceive all the Phænomena of the Sun will be made very easily intelligible, and be shew'd to be perfectly consonant with the other Processes of Nature, which is a very probable Argument at least that really it is even so done and not otherwise.

The Phænomena of the Sun explained. 1. First then I say, supposing the Superficies of a Body as big as the Sun to consist of such Materials as would really work upon each other, and consequently burn, as violently as some Materials which are here upon the Earth would do if once set on Fire, I say the Surface of such a Body at such a Distance so burning, must give to the Earth a very considerable Light and Heat.

First for Light, It is evident by Experiment that Nitre and Sulphur burning each other, make a very bright Light; insomuch, that few Eyes can indure to look upon it, and is as intolerable almost as the Light of the Sun. Now 'tis very probable, that the Materials that maintain the Fire of the Sun are yet much more adapted for that purpose, and therefore that this Light and Heat may much exceed it, but still this doth not make the Action of it differ, nor make it really differ in *Specie* from a Fire made with Earthy Materials but only in degrees, and therefore still supposing the whole Superficies of the Sun to afford as much Light in every visible part of it, as these Bodies so burning do, according to the Bigness of their Surface; it must necessarily very strongly affect the

Earth,

Earth, though placed at this Diftance; for all Light in the firft place propagates *in infinitum* in an Inftant. Now the *Medium* between the Sun and us being perfectly tranfparent, and fo nothing of the Light being loft but only rarify'd, it follows, that we muft receive the fame Proportion of the Light of fuch a Body as we do now of the Light of the Body of the Sun as now it is: So that thence the only Difference muft confift in the Proportion of the Light of the Bodies; that is, whether the Light of any one part of the Sun equal to an Artificial Fire fo made, be any thing brighter: For if they be equal, as 'tis very poffible they may, then the fame Effects will follow. Now the Queftion will be, how fhall this be proved or tried, whether this be fo or not? We cannot go to the Sun, nor fetch Fire from Heaven, as *Prometheus* is faid to have done: Nor can we fet or remove our Fire fo far diftant from us, as to make an equal Comparifon of the one with the other. I grant it, we cannot; but yet Art may help us to a way, by which we may be able to afcend thither by Reafon, and be as much affured of it as if we actually did it: And that is, by knowing in what Proportion the Quantity of Light does diminifh, according to the diftance it is propagated from the Luminous Body; for by that means, we may meafure *Hercules* by his Foot, from exact Obfervations made of the Power of Luminous Bodies in propagating Light here with us, we may calculate the Power of Luminous Bodies, though never fo far diftant. Light then, as I formerly hinted, doth decreafe in Duplicate Proportion to its diftance of Propagation from the Luminous Body, that is in the fame Proportion with the Superficies of the Spheres of Diftance.

For fuppofe A the Luminous Point, that emits a Quantity of Light to fill the Space A B B; this Light in the next Space fills B B c c, then c c d d, then d d E E: And at E E it is arrived at twice the Diftance of B B from A. The Power therefore of this Ray of Light which at B B was all contained within the circular Bafe of the Cone A B B, is by that it acts at the Diftance E E expanded into the circular Bafe of the Cone A E E; Namely, into the Circle E E, which Circle being twice the Bignefs of B B in Diameter, muft have its Area Quadruple to the Area of B B. And fo of F F, which is at treble the Diftance, the Area of the circular Bafe of the Cone A F F will be Nine times the Area of B B, and fo onward the Areas increafe in a Duplicate Proportion of the Diftance of them, from the Apex of the Cone, or which is the fame from the Luminous Point A. *The Proportion of the Diminution of Light. Fig. 4. Plate 1.*

The Power therefore of Light thus propagated will be diminifhed or rarified, fo that at twice the Diftance it will have but a Quarter of the Power at thrice the Diftance, but one Ninth at Four times the Diftance, but $\frac{1}{16}$ at five times the Diftance, but $\frac{1}{25}$ part of the Power which it had at one Space of Diftance: And confequently the Proportion of the Power of Light at any one Diftance, to the Power of the Light at any other Diftance, will be reciprocally Duplicate to the refpective Diftances, as the Power of Light at five Spaces Diftance to that at fix Spaces Diftance, will be as $\frac{1}{25}$ to $\frac{1}{36}$, that is as 36 to 25; for as $\frac{1}{25}$, $\frac{1}{36}$ :: 36. 25. which are the Squares of the Diftances reciprocally taken. This, I fay, is the Expanfion of Light according to the various Diftances of its Action from the Luminous Body, and according to this Rule all Light is found to act and diminifh its Power in Proportion to its greater Diftance. So that the Power of any Artificial Light, as Fire, Flame, &c. being found at any meafurable Diftance, the Power of it may be eafily found for any affignable Diftance be it never fo great: And on the contrary, the Power of Natural Light, as that of the Sun, Moon, Planet, or Stars, being found by Experiment at an affigned Diftance, though never fo great, the Power of it may be found by Calculation at any affigned Diftance, though never fo near, and confequently we have a means of truly calculating the comparative Power of Natural and Artificial Lights from Experiments made on each of them. But then fecondly, We have another thing to be taken notice of in our Calculation, to make the Comparifon compleat and exact, and that is of the Area of the Luminous Body, for 'tis not enough to calculate the Power of one

Point

Point only, but the Power of an Aggregate of them muſt alſo be taken notice of. And this is of the Cone inverted, and turned the other way, where the Apex of the Cone is the Eye, or the Point of the Subject inlightned, and the Baſe is in the Luminous Body, as the Disk of the Sun, and this by ſuppoſing the Ray in all Degrees of Diſtance equally ſtrong, does diminiſh the Power of inlightning in Proportion to the viſible Angle, under which it appears at greater or greater Diſtances. This therefore will alſo be in Dupli- cate Proportion to the Diſtance reciprocally taken ; for the Area of Light muſt ſubtend equal Angles or Cones to make an equal Light, and therefore at double Diſtance there muſt be Four times the Area of Light to make the ſame Effect, and at treble Diſtance Nine times the Light, and at Quadruple Diſtance Sixteen times the Luminous Area to produce the ſame Effect upon the Subject. A circular Area therefore of as bright a Light, or ſhining Body as the Sun, being placed at ſuch a Diſtance as that it may appear under much ſame Conical Angle as the Sun doth, *viz.* of ½ a Degree, muſt give as Light to the Subject as the Sun it ſelf.

From theſe two Conſiderations, 'twill be eaſy to calculate the comparative Power of naturally Luminous Bodies to the Power of ſuch as are artificially, or to compare the Light of the Sun with the Light of Coles, Flame, *&c.* and to ſee their Differences.

The Light from the Sun cauſed by an actual Fire. From which I queſtion not, but that there may be very cogent Arguments drawn to prove, that the Light of this Body of the Sun may be cauſed by an actual Fire, or Diſſolution of the ſuperficial Parts thereof ; partly by the At- moſphere or Air incompaſſing it, and partly alſo by the Conſtituents of it mix- ed together into one Maſs, which have Analogy with our Sulphur and Nitre, which do work upon and burn each other, and ſo the Sun will be found to be a vaſt Globular Body, whoſe whole Superficies is in a continual Diſſolu- tion or Fire ; partly by the working of its conſtituent Parts one upon another, and partly alſo by the Aſſiſtance of the Atmoſphere, Air, or Fluid Body, in- compaſſing it. And thence we may deduce, that the Phyſical or Natural Cauſe of its Light, is the actual Fire or burning of its ſuperficial Parts ; which being proved, or ſuppoſed ſo, all the Appearances that have been hi- therto taken notice of concerning Clouds, Spots, and Blazes, will be very na- turally and clearly ſolved ; and there is no one Obſervation I have yet made, or met with in other Authors, that do any way ſeem to croſs or thwart it. Matters of Fact none can deny, that ſuch Changes and Alterations do happen, and I conceive it will be as eaſily granted, that they have their Natural Cau- ſes. And therefore that which doth with moſt likelihood ſolve them, is at leaſt the moſt probable Cauſe.

An Objection anſwered. But ſome may object and ſay, that if this were ſo, certainly the Body of the Sun in ſo many Thouſand Years would have been all conſumed, at leaſt would have grown ſenſibly leſs. Suppoſe this were granted and ſaid, that it has grown ſome Minutes leſs ſince it firſt began to give Light, none could con- tradict it by any Obſervations we have upon Record ; for we have no Aſtro- nomical Obſervations of that kind 2000 Years at leaſt, that could evidence the contrary. But ſuppoſing we had Obſervations of 4000 Years ſtanding, and that they had found the Diameter of the Sun to be as many Minutes as 'tis now, yet that would have been no Argument but that the Sun might have every Year been a Mile leſs in Diameter than it was the preceding Year, and conſequently been 4000 Miles leſs in Diameter than it was 4000 Years ago. No Obſervation never ſo carefully made, either then or now, could have contradricted it : For if the Sun's Diameter be near 87 times bigger than the Diameter of the Earth, and the Earths Diameter be near 8000 Miles, the Dia meter of the Sun muſt be near 696000 Miles, and 4000 is but a 174 part of the Diameter, and conſequently could have diminiſht it but about ½ of a Minute, which is a much leſs Quantity than the Ancients pretended to ob- ſerve to. But ſuppoſing they could have obſerved even to Seconds, yet that could not have contradicted it, since as I shall upon occasion shew a Reason, why the Sun may have approacht as much as to recompence that Defect. But I have not now time to explain it : And shall only add, that this being so, it will thence very rationally follow, that the Stars also being very probably Bodies in most Proprieties the same with the Sun, will be Bodies also whose Superficies do actually burn consonant to which the Observation of the Noble *Tycho*, and others of the Stars that appear'd in *Cassiopeia*, in the Year 1572 will be judged to be all fir'd together, and so quite burnt out in one Year ; for it lasted no longer, and did never appear before, nor has since that I can hear of. Consonant to this Theory, will be the Appearances of Comets, of which kind I this Week observed one in the Sign of *Scorpio*. But of this Matter I have elsewhere discoursed somewhat already, and shall add more hereafter upon another Opportunity, when I come to explain what the Cause of Light is in Fire, and other Luminous Bodies here below within our reach ; the Explanation of which will manifestly demonstrate to us what 'tis in all other Bodies whatsoever that are out of our Reach.

S E C T.

SECT. III.

Containing the Lectures read in January *and* February, 168$\frac{0}{1}$. *being a Continuation of the same Subject of Light.*

The CONTENTS.

1. *Light the most admirable Effect of Nature, one of the principal Powers by which every part of the great Existence of Material Beings is united and made one. The Infiniteness or Indefiniteness of the active Power of Light already explained; the smaller the Stars appear, the greater is their Distance; the reason why some before invisible are made visible by Telescopes, because few Eyes can be affected by any Object under a less Angle than a Minute; thence several small Stars coalesce into one, and why some of the fixt Stars, though less than a Minute, as but of a second, are yet visible; an Objection against the use of Telescopes in Astronomical Observations answered, and why the Stars appear less through a Telescope than to the naked Eye.* 2. *An Explication and Confirmation of* Des Cartes *Hypothesis of Vision, and that the fixt Stars are really at different Distances, though they may be also of different Magnitudes, a farther Reason that the Propagation of Light must be instantaneous.* 3. *The innate Light of all Celestial Luminous Bodies proceeds from an actual and real Fire something like that on the Earth, though not altogether the same, the Fuel being possibly different.* 4. *By this the Subject of the Inquiry is brought nearer,* viz. *on combustible Substances, whereon we may exercise our Scrutinies with more Power, to find the Cause of Light and Fire, and by Analogy, what it is in the Sun: Which therefore is to be the Subject of future Discourses.* 5. *Of the Nature of Comets, which are another sort of Celestial Fire, which ought to be examined before the treating of Terrestrial and Culinary Fires, and whose Light is different from that of the Sun, Stars or Planets, their different Appearances have caused great difference in Writers of them. The three Opinions mention'd by* Seneca *in his Natural Questions enumerated, with those of other Ancient and Modern Philosophers.*

Light the most admirable Effect in Nature. 　1. I Began the last Term to explain to you several of the Proprieties of Light, as being one of the most admirable Effects of Nature which are subjected to our Senses, and consequently to our Speculation and Contemplation, as being one of the first and principal of the Powers of the great System of the World, by which the whole is united and made one; and every one part of that unconceivably great Existence of Material Beings is affected by every other, which may thence not improperly be called one Body, or the only Material or Corporeal Being, distinct from which no other Corporeal being is.

This

This by *Moses*, in the Hiſtory of the Creation, is comprehended under the double Name of Heaven and Earth, denoting both, one material Being ; but conſidered in its parts, Namely, fluid and ſolid Matter. After the Creation of which God ſaid, Let there be Light and there was Light, ſo that the firſt active Power was Light.

Some of the Proprieties of this active Power I have already explained : Namely, firſt its indefinite Extenſion to every part of the whole of Matter, which becauſe our Imagination can ſet no Bounds or Limits to ; I therefore call infinite or indefinite, not as ſuppoſing it to be really ſo, but for that, as our Senſes inform us of no ſuch Bound, ſo neither can our Imagination fix the *ne plus ultra*, beyond which no Material Being can exiſt. For wherever we put it, we preſently ſuppoſe Space and Extenſion beyond it, and that at leaſt if it be not Body, as *Des Cartes* would have it ; yet it has the inſeparable Propriety of Body and Matter, namely, Extenſion : And no one has yet told us, what Body is diſtinct from Extenſion, or what is the true Eſſence of Body or Material Being, beſides Extenſion ; and 'tis as eaſy to conceive indefinite Body, as indefinite Extenſion. Nor indeed can Extenſion be well conceived without the Notion of Body, no more than Body can without the Notion of Extenſion : for Extenſion is nothing but the abſtracted Notion of ſomewhat extended : And therefore if there be Extenſion, there muſt be ſomewhat extended. Now if it be not the Propriety of Spirits, as all Divines and Philoſophers conclude, but only of Body, then wherever there is Extenſion, there is really a Body extended ; and therefore ſince our Imagination can never limit Extenſion, ſo neither can they ſet Bounds to Matter or Material Being.

Now I told you, that our Eyes aſſiſted by the help of Glaſſes inform us that Light is propagated or communicated to us from utmoſt inconceivable Diſtances, at leaſt if we believe the vaſt Diſtances the Stars are placed from us, and that the ſmaller the Stars are the greater is their Diſtance : For ſtill the longer and better our Teleſcopes are the more are there diſcovered of ſmall Stars which were before, and without that Help inviſible ; not for that they did not affect the Eye with Light without, as well as with the help of the Teleſcope, but becauſe the Power of the Eye is limited to a certain Magnitude of Appearance, under which nothing can be diſtinctly perceived : Whatſoever Object therefore affects the Eye under a leſs Angle than that Eye can diſtinguiſh, becomes inviſible or not ſeen. Now whereas moſt Eyes diſtinguiſh not a leſs Angle than a Minute, or the 60th part of a Degree, or the 21600 part of a Circle, therefore whatever is ſenſated or ſeen by it, is ſeen of that Bigneſs or under that Angle : And ſo if there be 2 or 3, or 10 or 100 ſmall Stars ſo near together as that they are all compriſed within the Angle of one Minute, the Eye has a Senſation of them all, as if they were one Star, and diſtinguiſhes them not one from another ; ſo likewiſe is it, that if the Light be ſtrong and powerful ſo as to affect the Eye, it always appears of the Bigneſs of a Minute, though poſſibly its real Angle be not a ſecond. Thence every Star that ſuch an Eye diſcovers, appears to be of the Bigneſs of a Minute at leaſt, and ſo it is conceived really to be, though yet when we come to examine its Diameter by the help of Teleſcopes, we really find it to be but ſome few ſeconds or ſixtieth Parts of ſuch an Angle ; and hence it is, that it is told as a very great Wonder, and is indeed as a great Argument objected againſt the Uſe of Teleſcopes, that there can be no Truth in the Diſcoveries made by them : For that though they are found to magnify and increaſe the Appearance of all other Objects except the Stars ; yet when they are viewed through them they appear to be rather leſſened than increaſed in Bulk, whence they conclude of that Inſtrument that does ſometimes magnify and ſometimes not, and indeed both at the ſame time (as when one looks on two Stars 10 Minutes diſtant from each other, their Diſtance is really augmented though their apparent Diameters ſeem not to be at all) they conclude, I ſay, that all the Appearances through ſuch an Inſtrument are uncertain and imperfect, and real Miſinformations, and conſequently nothing but Phantomes and falſe Repreſentations ; and this Conſideration or indeed Inconſideration hath been the occaſion why ſeveral otherwiſe very ingenious and knowing Men have been prejudiced againſt the making uſe of Teleſcopes, and other Optick Glaſſes, for the Diſcovery of Nature, for not

C c

knowing

knowing how to anfwer to themfelves thefe and fome fuch other Objeftions as eafily anfwerable, if well confidered, they have fallen into a Disbelief of the whole Information thefe Helps afford us; and will therefore in all Obfervations on which they build any thing; only make ufe of the naked Eye: Whereas had they made ufe of thefe Helps, they would have been able to have made much greater Advances in their Difcoveries and Obfervations.

An Objeftion against the ufe of Telefcopes anfwered.

To anfwer this Objeftion therefore againft the Truth of the Difcoveries of Telefcopes, and thofe of Microfcopes, I fay, that thefe Inftruments do equally magnify the real Angle, under which any Objeft appears to the naked Eye, and fo doe equally magnify the real Angle of the Stars, as well as of any other Objeft, and that the Fallacy lies in the Eye and not in the Inftrument: For as I faid, fuch is the make of the fenfible part of the Eye, *viz.* of the *Tunica Retina,* that it cannot diftinguifh in moft Eyes an Angle lefs than a Minute (though there be fome that can to the third of a Minute, but thefe are very few) whence if there be any ftrong fhining Objeft that does very powerfully operate on the Eye, fo as to create a Senfation, and yet does really aft under an Angle only of fome few feconds; yet becaufe the Eye cannot diftinguifh a lefs Angle than a Minute, the Objeft is fuppofed to be a Minute in Bignefs: And fo if the Telefcope do not fo far increafe the real Diameter of the Objeft as to make it more than a Minute, it does feem indeed not at all to magnify it; becaufe it is ftill made to appear, but under the Angle of a Minute. *Des Cartes* has a very ingenious Explication of the *Tunica Retina,* or the way of Vifion, which does very intelligibly make out the reafon of this Propriety in the Eye: Which poffibly it may not be amifs now a little to explain, that fome Prejudices may be removed, againft Arguments that are deduced from Obfervations made with Telefcopes, and fome other Optical Glaffes.

Des Cartes Hypothefis of Vifion.

2. " He explains then (as *Porta, Kepler, Shinar, Galileo,* and many others
" that had treated of that Subjeft before him do) the Organ of Vifion the
" Eye, by the Similitude of it to a dark Room, into which no other Light is
" admitted but what enters by one round Hole, in which a convenient Con-
" vex refrafting *Lens* is placed fo, as to colleft all the Rays from Objefts
" without, and to unite them in their diftinft and proper places upon a Wall
" or Sheet of Paper at a covenient Diftance within; whereby the Pifture of
" all thofe Objefts that are without the Room, is made as it were and placed
" upon the Wall or Sheet within: This Sheet fays he in the Eye, is the *Tunica*
" *Retina,* on which the Pifture of all Objefts without the Eye are as it were
" painted and defcribed. Now this Pifture on the *Tunica Retina* is nothing
" but the Impreffion of the feveral Rays from the Objefts without, collefted
" by the help of the *Cornea* and *Cryftalline,* as by the Convex Glafs in the dark
" Room. And the *Retina* being like a piece of Plufh, with the ends of the
" Threads turn'd towards the *Cryftalline,* all the other ends of them being termi-
" nated in the *Brain,* there can be no more diftinft Senfations than there are
" diftinft Threads to convey the Impreffion on them: So that if the whole Pi-
" fture of the Objeft be fmaller than one fingle Thread of this Plufh, it can-
" not affeft or move a lefs part than one of thofe fmall Threads or Filaments
" of the *Retina,* and therefore the Senfation is the fame as if the Objeft did
" take up or cover the whole end of the Thread or Filament, though it affeft
" but a tenth part of it provided it be ftrong.

I have been the more particular in the Explication of this, becaufe fince my former explaining of the indefinite extenfive Power of Light, I have met with fome that have objefted againft the Reality of the Appearances through Telefcopes, as if no Arguments drawn from Obfervation, made by the Help of fuch were to be efteemed of any force, whereas indeed all fuch Objeftions do only proceed from an Ignorance of the Grounds of Opticks and of Vifion, we being equally as certain of the Appearances we difcover by them, as of thofe things which are difcovered and feen by the naked Eye. It was by fome of the Ancients conjeftur'd, that the *Galaxia* or Milky Way was nothing elfe but a great number of Stars, fo fmall as that they could not be diftinguifh'd: Telefcopes have difcovered the Truth of that Conjefture, and manifefted it to be fo, and

we

we have henceforth no more reason to doubt that it is so, than we have to doubt whether there are any Stars at all in the Heavens.

Others again I find to object, that though there really be such a great Variety *That the fixt* of Magnitudes in the Appearances of the fixt Stars, yet it is uncertain whether *Stars are at* those Magnitudes do wholly proceed from the Distances of them, and not ra-*different Di-* ther from a real Difference in their Magnitudes, and if so, then all those Stars *stances.* both great and small may be at equal or very near equal Distances from the Earth ; and if so, then the Extensions of the Heavens need not be supposed so vastly big, as if their appearing Magnitudes proceeded only from their Remoteness from the Earth : To which I say as I did before explain, that I do suppose their appearing Magnitude to be caused by both; that is, First by their real Difference in Magnitude and in Brightness; and secondly, by their differing Distance from us. The Visibleness of some proceeds from their extraordinary Vividness of Light, as that of the Great Dog-star, which though it be the most conspicuous Star in the Heavens, is yet found by the Telescopes to be less in Diameter than several others which appear not so conspicuous : As that of the Bull's Eye.

And this by the way seems to be the reason of the Appearance of the New Star in *Cassiopea*, observed by *Ticho Brahe*, and by divers other eminent Astronomers of that time, which from a Star of the third Magnitude increased to be of the Bigness of *Venus*, and more conspicuous than any other fixt Star in the Heaven, and yet in less than a Year it diminished by degrees and went out wholly, and hath not since appeared ; all which time of its Appearance it perfectly kept the same place without any Variation, so that in Probability it was a fixt Star before of a very dull Light, and so invisible till by some Constitution in its make, as some more combustible Shell or Orb of its Body, it then burnt or shined out more conspicuously, which Shell being once consumed, it again disappeared, and has since that time been no more seen.

Others again, that to the naked Eye appear one Star, and that very conspicuous, by the Telescope are discover'd to be two or more Stars, so near together as that the Eye cannot distinguish between them, both the Images of them falling upon one single Filament of the *Tunica Retina*, and so both of them making but one Impression on the Brain; of this kind the most remarkable is the Star in the Left Horn of *Aries*, which whilst I was observing the Comet which appeared in the Year 1664. and followed till he past by this Star, I took notice that it consisted of two small Stars very neat together : A like Instance to which I have not else met with in all the Heaven, they seeming to be both of them very near of equal Bigness, and yet so very near together, that you will need a Telescope of a considerable Length to see them both distinct and separate.

Others, I conceive, may be of equal Distance, and may yet appear of differing Magnitudes from their real Difference of Magnitude, the Body of the one being so much bigger than the other as they appear.

But after all this, I conceive it very probable, that the greatest Number of the small Stars appear such, not from any of these fore-mentioned Reasons, but only because they are further distant from us : It may be objected perhaps, that 'twill be very hard to prove, whether that be the Cause or not of such their Appearance : But to this I answer, that though it hath not yet been positively proved, yet as I mentioned in my Attempt to prove the Motion of the Earth by Observations, I there hinted somewhat to this purpose, and it shall not be long before I acquaint the World with what I have done in that kind. So that for the present I shall say, that upon the whole there is no reason to doubt, but that the extent of the Heavens is vastly beyond what we have hitherto imagined, and consequently that the extent of the Propagation of Light is equal with it, and therefore, notwithstanding these Objections that I formerly laid down, remains without any solid Reason against it.

I proceeded next to shew that this Propagation of Light was to all imagina-*Of the instan-* ble Distance in a Moment or Instant of Time, insomuch that every one part of*taneous Mo-* the Universe might by this means be affected by every other part of it, and though *tion of Light.* I then related some considerable Objections against it, and to prove its Propagation Temporaneous, that is to spend some considerable time in passing from

the

the Lucid to the enlightned Body, if at a great Diftance, yet as I fhall afterwards prove by the Effects of Light, the Propagation muft be inftantaneous.

After this I explained what Light was in the Lucid Body: And for that
end more particularly defcribed the Conftitution and Make of the Body of the
Sun, as the principal and moft confiderable Body for Light as to us, and fhewed
many Arguments to prove, that it is no other than a Body actually burning or
on Fire, that it has an Atmofphere that incompaffes it, which may poffibly be
the *Menftruum* that diffolves it, as the Air or Atmofphere about the Earth is
the *Menftruum* of burning Bodies here upon the Earth, that it did fometime
produce dark Spots or Clouds, which feem'd Analogous to our Smoke, and
fometimes brighter, which feem'd Analogous to our Flames. So that upon the
whole, I concluded it a folid Globous Body actually on fire in its fuperficial
Parts, and that from that Fire its Light and Heat proceeded.

The Light of the Moon and other Planets, both Secundary and Primary,
Telefcopes do plainly evidence to proceed from the Reflection of the Sun's
Light, and therefore none of thofe can be properly faid to be Luminous Bodies.
But the fixt Stars, as I have already mentioned, feem to be of the fame Nature
with the Body of the Sun, and therefore the fame Explanation that was given
of the Light in the Sun, will ferve alfo for the Light of the Bodies of thefe
Stars. And thence, as I juft now mentioned, a clear Reafon will be given of
divers new Stars that have appeared and difappeared.

The Light of   3. So that in Probability the Light of all the Celeftial Bodies proceeds from
the Stars from an actual Fire, much of the fame Nature with the Fires we here have burning
an actual Fire. upon the Earth ; and therefore if we find out what is the Nature of our Fire
here with us, we may from that explain how it is generated and how it operates in the Heavens.

Not that I fuppofe, that the Fuel of the Celeftial Fires is the fame with our
Fuel here upon the Earth, as Sulphur, Bitumen, Stone-Cole, or other combuftible Mineral Subftances ; or Woods, Refins, Oyls, or other Vegetable Subftances, or Fat, Bones, or fuch like Animal Subftances ; but that it may be of
Variety of other Subftances very differing from any of thefe ; for as all thofe
I have named are much different from one another, fo may there be a Hundred other Subftances diftinct from any one of thefe, and diftinct alfo one from
another, all of which may notwithftanding be of a Subftance fit for the Diffolution of that fluid *Menftruum* in which they fwim, in the fame manner as
thefe I have named are for the Diffolution of the *Menftruum* of the Air, and
fo may be fit Fuel to maintain that Celeftial Fire.

Of the Nature   4. We have therefore, brought our Inquiry into Subjects much nearer to us
of Fire. than either the Sun or fixt Stars, and into fuch as are within our Command
and Reach, into fuch as on which we may with more Power exercife our
Scrutinies and Examinations ; in which, if by our Tryals and Examinations we
can find out what the efficient Caufe of Fire and Light are, we fhall by Analogy eafily find out what is alfo the Caufe of the Light in the Sun, and in the
fixt Stars, which Examination and Scrutiny into the Caufe of Fire, and the
Light thereof, fhall therefore be the Subject of fome of our following Difcourfes.

Of Comets.   5. But before we leave the Contemplation of the Celeftial Bodies, and begin our *Examination* of Terreftrial or Culinary Fires, the late appearing Comet puts me in mind of another kind of Light, which is thought by moft to be
of a quite differing Nature from thofe of the Sun, Stars, or Planets, and not
to be at all Analogous to them.

The great Variety of Form there has been amongft thofe that have appeared
at feveral Times, and in feveral Ages of the World, and the great Alterations
there have happened almoft in every one that appeared before it difappear,
has fo much confounded Mens Judgments concerning them, that you fhall
hardly find two Men agreeing in all things, to the fame Opinion.

Seneca

Seneca in the Nineteenth Chapter of his seventh Book of Natural Questions, recites three Opinions concerning *Comets.* Some, says he, think that no Comet does really exist, but that the Appearance thereof is made only by the Conjunction of the Rays of several Stars or Celestial Bodys into one Point, and a Repercussion or spreading of them from thence : *Quidam nullos esse Cometas existimant, sed species illorum per repercussionem vicinorum siderum, aut per Conjunctionem vicinorum reddi.*

2. Some indeed do suppose them to have a real Existence, but to have peculiar and proper Courses of their own. And that after a certain time, the same Comets return again, and appear to us: *Quidam aiunt, esse quidem, sed habere cursus suos & post certa Lustra in conspectum mortalium exire.*

3. Some do also suppose them to have a real Being, but not such a durable one as may deserve the name of a Star, but of such a substance as does wast, and is dispersed and consumed after a certain time; namely, The time they appear which is but short. *Quidam, esse quidem, sed non quibus siderum nomen imponas quia dilabuntur, nec diu durant & exigui temporis mora dissipantur.*

So that the first of these Opinions did seem to suppose that they were either an Union of several small Stars which did really before exist, but being separate, made no Appearance 'till united; or else that the Rays of these meeting together in one Point by Repercussion or Reflection, did seem to make this Appearance. This might well enough agree with the Opinion of the Peripateticks, and those that supposed the Planets and Stars fixt in solid Orbs, whose Motions carried them round, and thence possibly they might allude to the Focus of a Burning-Glass, as if this Appearance were nothing else but the Rays of some Celestial Body, whether Sun, Planet, or fixed Star, which being collected into one Point, by Reflection, from the middle parts of the Concave of some of the solid Crystalline Orbs, might there make a bright Appearance, and then the Tail would be nothing else but the union of other Rays which fell further from the Middle or Axis of the Concave, which unite at several Distances from it; or else that some of these Spheres might have some parts of them of greater Refraction then others, and so by that Refraction, might collect a great Quantity of Rays diffused from that Luminous Body which was its cause, as most probably the Sun, as the most considerable Light of this part of the Universe; and unite the greatest Quantity in the Head of the Comet, and others in the Tail : And according to these Hypotheses, the Comet would really be nothing else but a Phantasm or Appearance, and not have any real Existence in Nature, and so would not be much differing from the appearing Meteors, such as Rainbows. The *Parhelii*, and the *Paraselenæ*, the Mock-Suns and Mock-Moons, and the like; all which have no other Existence than the Representation of a Body in a Looking-Glass; they being indeed nothing but a Reflection or Refraction of those Luminous Bodies which they represent, or are attributed to. As a Rainbow is nothing else but the Reflection and Refraction of the Rays of the Sun from the round Drops of Rain which fall from the Cloud, which at certain Positions to the Eye and Sun, do by Refraction and Reflection return an extraordinary bright and coloured Ray to the Eye, which very Drops so soon as ever they are out of that Posture return not at all; this is Geometrically demonstrated by *Maurolicus, Des Cartes,* and divers others, and may Experimentally be verified by an artificial Fountain, casting up and dispersing Water into the Air in a Mist, which will in the Sunshine make a Rainbow. The same may be Geometrically demonstrated of the *Parhelii* and *Paraselenæ.* That all these are nothing but the Phantoms or Appearances of some other Luminous Body, made by an extraordinary Collection and Repercussion of the Rays from some other place, than that Luminous Body should appear in, and so the Causes of them may be most certainly assigned and shewn, which being all Atmospherical and Aerial, and placed in the lower Region near the Earth, they become of no long continuance, but quickly vanish. Now if these Refracting and Reflecting Substances that may be supposed the cause of the Comets this way, be supposed to be Ætherial Substances, and so not subject to any suddain Change (as the Atmosphere is) the Cause re

maining

maining longer; the Effect also may have a longer Existence, and so a Comet may be supposed to last six Months or more.

Several have been the Opinions concerning this way, and those very differing; some have supposed the Head to be the Point where all these Rays concentred and met together, and there produced a kind of combustive Focus; through which the Rays of the Sun penetrating, did afterward refract various ways, and strike forth to a vast length, and from that Penetration of the fiery Focus of the Head, acquired such a Quality, as made them to become visible; by which means, according as this burning Point or Focus did refract more on one side than on the other; did the Stream or Tail of the Comet appear to bend from the strait Line continued from the Sun through the middle of this Focus. This they resembled to the Radiation of the Sun between dark Clouds upon a thick and foggy Air, which does indeed very much resemble the Appearance of the Blaze, or rather like the Rays of the Sun let in by one single Hole, or through a Glass into a dark Room.

I have only this more to add, That if such Reflecting or Refracting Bodies could be supposed, or that we had any other Argument to prove them than only the Appearance of the Comet it self, there would be some pretty Congruities in the Theory that would be of some cogency to perswade the Belief of this Opinion: As, First, That from the Geometrical Laws both of Refraction and Reflection, this Phantom would have a form much like that of a Comet; that is, it would have a Head brighter than the rest, it would have a Tail or Blaze spreading from it, it would have this Tail always pretty near, opposite to the Sun; that is, not always directly, but sometimes a little varying from the direct Line, though it would sometime also be directly opposite; it would sometime be strait, but sometime also be bended, sometimes clear, sometimes a little coloured, and the like; which, I cannot now stay to insist upon, but may some other time more fully explain. And this the rather, because I do not find that any one that has hitherto written of Comets, has in the least mentioned any Explication like this; nor does *Seneca* at all explain what the Opinion really was: But upon considering of various ways how to solve the Phænomena, and how also to explain the Words of *Seneca*, amongst others, I pitch'd on this, of which I shall upon another Occasion speak more fully, and shew wherein also the Objections lie against it.

Hevelius's Opinion examined.   Mr. *Hevelius* seems to give another kind of Solution of the Tail or Blaze of Comets, which though it does, *toto Cælo*, differ from this I have now explained; yet it may not improperly be made use of to explain this first Opinion mentioned by *Seneca*. He then supposes that the Tail or Blaze, is really nothing else but the Rays of the Sun, which in passing through a nebulous Body, such as he conceives the Head to be, are refracted, and reflected by the *Nucleus* or *Nuclei*, if it have more than one, by which Condensation, Decussation and Collection of those Rays he supposes the Blaze to be formed; now though, indeed, he does suppose the Head of the Comet to be a distinct Substance, and so falls in or agrees with the Third Opinion; yet as to the Tail, he supposes it a meer Phantom, and to have no real Existence in Nature.

This supposition concerning Comets refuted.   But against this Supposition there are many Objections; as first, though the Blaze of the Comet does sometime resemble the Radiation of the Sun between the Clouds, upon a thick Air below those Clouds, as it did in this present Comet, when the Blaze appeared brightest and longest, yet 'twill be very hard to make out the Similitude well in a Comet; for these Radiations under the Clouds appear brighter than the rest of the Air, because all the rest of this thick Air under them is shadowed and darkned by the interposition of the Clouds, and those that appear bright, do so, because the Sun shines clearly upon them between those Clouds. But in the Comet we want, first the Cloud, or somewhat that should darken the Æther round about the Blaze; I say the Æther, because, as I shall afterwards shew, all Comets that have been accurately observed, and thence, in probability, all Comets whatsoever have appeared, to be very far removed above the Air, then in probability this dark Body would hinder the view of some part of the Blaze. Secondly, We find that these Radiations between the Clouds never happen but when the Air underneath the Clouds is thick and somewhat opacous, without which they cannot appear; but when

shall

shall we find such an opacous Air to reflect the Light into the Heavens. It would be much more difficult to suppose such a vast space of the *Æther* to be thickned (as must necessarily be) to make out this Appearance; than to suppose only so much Matter as may just serve to make the Bigness of the Blaze it self, which though it be prodigiously long, as some thousands of the Earths Diameters, yet still 'tis easier to conceive how there may be matter enough to make a Cylinder, than to make so vast a Body as an Orb of the *Æther* of that thickness. But then, Thirdly, There is nothing in the shape of the Head of the Comet that does any ways resemble the perforation of a Body that should shadow the rest of the *Æther* about the Blaze. For as I shall afterwards shew you, Comets do generally appear to have a brighter Body in the middle, about which there is a kind of White Cloud, from which the Blaze does seem to issue. So that, in truth, they have no reason at all for this Supposition or Opinion, and it has in probability sprung, and had its first rise from those who supposed Comets to be nothing else but some small Appearance here in the Air below: But since, as I said before, It has been by so many and so exact Astronomical Observations found, that some of these Comets are very high in the Heavens, and far removed beyond the Bounds of the Air, that groundless Opinion may also be discharged, and yet I find most of our Astronomerrs and Philosophers do incline to be of that Opinion, as particularly *Des Cartes, Fromundus, Kepler, Cysatus, Ricciolus, Gremaldi,* &c. who though they do all assign the real Body to the Comet, yet as to the Blaze, that they suppose to be made by the transit of the Suns Rays through the Cloudy part of the Head   And *Hevelius* also, the latest Writer of Comets, is of this Opinion, not as if it were made by the passing of the Rays through a Hole, as in a dark Room, but by the Refraction and Collection of the Rays in the Cloudy, and yet transparent Body or Head of the Comet. Now this Body or Head he does not suppose Spherical or Globular, and to collect the Rays of the Sun beyond it into a Focus, as a Glass Globe full of Water would do; but to be of the form of a Dish or Boat, and to consist of various sorts of Bodies, some Round, and some Angular, which do variously Reflect and Refract the Rays of the Sun, and so make them unite and cross each other in various Ways on that side of the Comet which is opposite to the Sun, but because he could not well conceive how these Rays should come to be conspicuous, unless there were some opacous reflecting Body behind the Comet, as there is in the Air when the Radiations before mentioned are seen below the Clouds, therefore he has supposed a vast Collection of Vapours or halituous Substances, proceeding partly from the Sun, and partly from the rest of the Planets, as ♄, ♃, ♂, &c. to be made beyond the Body of the Comet, that is on that side that is opposite to the Sun, and these he supposes to be very much more thin than the Air or Atmosphere about the Earth; and therefore, that a little quantity of Matter will go a great way in that Collection: Upon this halituous Matter the Radiations falling, he supposes, are Reflected, and so the appearance of the Blaze is generated. *Kepler* was aware that there was a necessity of such a kind of halituous Substance as this mentioned by *Hevelius*; but yet, considering the vast extent of the Blaze of some Comets, namely, to 40, 50, 60, nay 90; and if we may believe —— to 110 Degrees in length; and that this Angle must be subtended by the Tail, as a strait Line, which in some Cases will run it out to a vaster length than if it were only a Circular Extent, he could not conceive whence all that matter should be brought. But *Hevelius* has found out whence to fetch it; namely, from the Orbs and Bodies of the Planets; for since, says he, we are assured, *Quod tam immensa materiarum Congeries, umbrarum scilicet primariarum circa maculas & circa ipsum Solem secundariarum in longe adhuc majori quantitate quandoq; reperiatur, utiq; non absurdum quoq; est etiam tales expirationes tenuiores etiam circa Cometas dari. Nam dum non raro pene omnium Planetarum Orbes trajiciunt, multum ubiq; materiæ attrahunt averruntq; secum, adeo ut brevissimo temporis Spatio cum motu velocissimo gaudent vastissimum subtilissimarum istarum exhalationum cumulum, ad caudam refringendam convenientem coacervare possint.* But to this Opinion of his, it may be objected, that, first, as to the Collection of halituous Substances, if such were made in its Passage then in probabiliy this would be in that part of it which came behind it in its Motion, and so consequently the Tail should always appear in that Line which the Comet has past; as we may often observe in the small Meteors to be seen in a clear Night called Star-shootings, many of which do leave a kind of Glade of Light behind them in the way through which they have past. So he gives no manner of Reason why it should be opposite to the Sun, nor indeed is his Explication at all natural, but altogether forced, and Extraneous from any other Method or Operation in Nature, nor is it built upon the Appearances, for as I shall afterwards shew, had he well heeded those, they would have hinted some other ways of explicating these *Phænomena.*

Anthelme's Opinion examined.
I should have here left this Opinion, but that I was this Week informed from *France* of a Person D. *Anthelme*, a *Carthusian* of *Dijon*, who pretends to have a true Theory of Comets, and to be able to predict them; and accordingly hath put out an Ephemerides of this present Comet, therein not only setting down what he had observed before the Publication, but what should happen afterwards 'till the time of its disappearing. This Man I mention not for his predicting of the Way and Motion of the Comet, for that I think may be much more exactly done than what he has, by the way I have published in my *Cometa*, which was invented by Sir *Christopher Wren*; by which, from any four Observations truly made, one may certainly find the Line, Distance, Motion, Inclination to the Ecliptick, its place among the fixt Stars, the length of its Tail, Brightness, *&c.* so long as it shall appear to the naked Eye; for so long that Theory will hold pretty near; I do not therefore mention this *French* Author for that, but to shew that he that is far out of the way in his Conjectures about the form of the Comet, which he supposes also to be made by the Refraction of the Sun's Rays, the Opinion we have now exploded, and shall hereafter more demonstratively confute from undeniable Arguments; this Man, in probability, is as much out in his Theory, which is only this, that the Head or Body of the Comet is Transparent, and that the Tail is made by the Refraction of the Sunbeams through it, but does not seem to have considered the Difficulty which *Kepler, Hevelius,* and divers others had taken notice of, and provided for in this Hypothesis.

I could relate to you the Opinions of many other Authors who have inclined to this Opinion, that the Blaze of the Comet is nothing but a Phantom or Appearance, but that as I find the very best of them that have imbraced this Opinion, to have been very dark and perplexed in their Explications; and as if they had not well understood it themselves, so there are others who only give a bare Assertion without any Explication or Reason at all: The Authority of such Men, I confess, weighs very little with me.

I shall therefore pass on to the second sort of Opinions, and that was of such as supposed them to be Aerial, Halituous and Sulphureous Bodies placed somewhere in or near the Atmosphere, which was raised out of the Earth, and fired in the upper Regions of the Air, and there continued 'till they wasted away. Of this Opinion was the great Philosoher *Aristotle,* and almost all his Followers; nay many of them, to this Day, who have not taken the Pains to be better instructed. Of this Opinion we find generally all the Stoicks, but that they suppose them elevated from the Air into the *Æther*; also the *Chaldeans* and all Historians, who have mentioned Comets in their Political History: Of this Opinion are almost all the Illiterate and Ignorant People of the World, and almost ever have been, and ever will be; because they are for the most part ruled by the most obvious Appearance to the Sense, without taking Pains to make use of their Reason to examine things strictly; so that if the majority of Votes be an Argument for the Truth of any Opinion, certainly this will carry it from all the rest, at least a Hundred Thousand to One. And yet, after all this, *Aristotle,* his Commentators, his Followers, the greatest number of Scholars, and particularly the Stoick Philosophers, as well as Peripatetick, the Historians, Divines, many Physitians, and all the Illiterate *Vulgus* in the World, will be found quite mistaken in their Opinion, and will easily be confuted by the Astronomers and modern Philosophers, who have clearly and plainly demonstrated their Mistake and Error. And that is, by undeniably proving the vast distance those Bodies are removed from the Earth by the Parallax, or rather want of Parallax, which they have been of later Ages certainly observed to have; for that does most certainly and infallibly shew that they are so far from being Aerial or Atmospherical, as *Aristotle* seems to suppose, that they are seldom,

if

if ever fo low as the Moon, many times as far off as the Sun, and fometimes perhaps much farther; I fay perhaps, becaufe the Evidence for that is not as yet fo eafily attainable, for no one has yet certainly proved the Parallax of the Sun, nor of *Mars* to any exactnefs; much lefs have they of the fuperior Bodies.

Johannes Regiomontanus, was the firft among the Moderns, who began to elevate the Pofitions of Comets above the Air or Atmofphere; for by his Obfervations of that which appeared in the Year 1472, he found it by its Parallax, diftant eight Semidiameters of the Earth at leaft, which is very far above the reach of the Air, which thofe, that with any probabilty judge of its Altitude, at moft make, not above Twenty Miles Perpendicular, but in all probability is yet much lefs. But *Ticho Brahe*, and at the fame time *Rothmannus* Mathematical Profeffor to the *Landgrave of Haffia*, *Michael Meftline*, *Cornelius Gemma*, *Maddeus Heggetius*, and many others (too many to be named at prefent) who had made Obfervations of the Comets that appeared in the Years, 1577, 1580, 1585, 1590, 1593. did all clearly find and prove that they had all of them lefs Parallax than the Moon, and confequently that they muft be far above it; and with them agree almoft all the Learned Aftronomers fince, only *Galileo* would feem to make it only a Phantom fomewhat like a *Halo*, which changed its place according to the Pofition of the Eye that faw it, and thence would give a Reafon why it could have no Parallax; for fince its being or Pofition depended only upon the Refraction and Reflection of the Sun's Rays; according to him, its Diftance or Angle with the Sun would appear the fame where-ever the Eye were placed to time it; and, confequently, it would obferve and keep the fame Pofition amongft the fixt Stars in the Zenith, as in the Horizon; fuppofing it elevated fo far only above the Earth, or at leaft, fo pofited, as not to fall in its Shadow. But this Explication of this great Wit, and moft excellent Philofopher and Mathematician *Galileo*, though it be very fubtil and curious, and has fome feeming probability, yet the ftrict Examination of the Appearances by the known Laws of Refraction and Reflection, will fufficiently fhew the Infufficiency of that Solution; and fhould the Examination of thofe not have been fufficient to have confuted this Suppofition from the endeavouring to folve the common Appearances of Comets to the Naked Eye; yet the Impoffibility to have folved the Appearances of them through the Telefcope would have fufficiently confuted it. But fetting him afide, all the confiderable Aftronomers who have fince written of Comets, do conclude them not to be Sublunary, but far removed above the Moon, and Æthereal. Such were almoft all thofe who writ of that great and very bright Comet which appeared to the World in the Year 1618. And fuch are thofe that have writ of Comets that have appeared fince; and more particularly, of thofe two great ones which appeared in the End of 1664, and in the beginning of the Year 1665. Many of which are comprifed in the *Theatrum Cometicum*, Printed in the Year 1667.

This is then the Third Opinion mentioned by *Seneca*, as the fecond to be held by divers of the Antients. Namely, That Comets were Æthereal Bodies, placed at a great Diftance from the Earth, and there moved according to Rules peculiar to them only, and diftinct from the fixt Stars, and conftantly appearing Planets.

What Arguments the Antients had to make them of this Opinion, does not appear any more, than it doth why they held divers others; many of which have been with great Applaufe, and very good Reafon taken up, and received by many of our late Philofophers: But certain it is, 'twas not without fome very good Grounds; otherwife, 'tis not to be conceived how they fhould be able to hit upon them: As, Particularly that of *Ariftarchus Samius* or *Philolaus*, who Afferted the Sun to be the Center of the Univerfe; and that all the Planets, and the Earth among the reft, which muft therefore be efteemed one of them, moved round about it, that remaining fixt. Which Opinion was received by *Copernicus*, and has been fince followed by the moft knowing Aftronomers. 'Tis not therefore to be doubted, but that the Antients might have fome of the fame Reafonings for them that we now have; and poffibly many other, which length of time has devoured; and 'tis not Improbable what *Simon Steven* has indeavoured to prove, and the learned *Hugo Grotius* has helped him to many Arguments for it; that there was before any of the Hiftories now extant, of

E e   Pro-

Prophane Writers, a learned Age and Place of the World far exceeding that of *Ægypt*, or *Greece*; of which we have no manner of Hiftory conveyed down to us, but fome few fcraps and hints here and there fcattered up and down in fome of the Writings of the Antients. 'Tis not improbable, but fome fucceeding Ages and Sects of Men might induftrioufly deftroy them (which was no difficult thing to do before Printing was in ufe) as 'tis faid of *Ariftotle*. But whatever was the caufe, is uncertain; It is therefore much eafier to find out the Truth by new Inquiry into the Nature of the Things themfelves, than to hunt for the Caufes of things among the Worm-eaten Volumes of Antiquity. We fhall therefore pafs over the feveral Branches of Opinions under this Head, of the Æthereal Nature of the Comets, and come to the various Opinions that have been afferted and defended by the Moderns, whofe Grounds and Reafons we may eafily know.

There are then under this Head, great variety of Opinions, as to the Sub-ftance, Light, Magnitude, Diftance, Motion, Duration, Generation, &c. of Celeftial Comets. But they may be reduced to thefe.

The firft was, That Comets were certain Planets or wandering Stars, the Laws or Rules of whofe Motions were not yet known, and which were diftant from the Seven Planets that were known. Of this Opinion were the *Chaldeans*, as alfo *Democritus*. And that thereupon, why they did but fometimes only appear, and then vanifh, was by reafon of their Approaching and Receding from the Earth in their proper Courfe, or by reafon of their nearnefs to the Sun. *Plutarch*, alfo, fays, that fome of the *Pythagoreans* alfo, were of that Opinion: *Seneca*, alfo, held the fame.

The fecond Opinion is, That the Body and Tail of the the Comet is made up only by the conflux of many fmall, and, before, imperceptible Stars; and that the Reafon of their difappearing is, becaufe thofe Stars are again difperfed.

The Third Opinion is, that the Comets are made *De novo*, out of the *Materia Cœleftis*. Every of thefe are varied by feveral Suppofitions about the Blaze, of which more hereafter.

N. B. *Here our Author breaks off, and leaves this Difcourfe of Comets imperfect, fo that I was in fome doubt whether I fhould publifh it; but confidering it contained a brief Explication of feveral Opinions of the Antients, and fome of the Moderns, of the Nature of Comets; I thought it might not be unacceptable to the Reader. I fhall in fome following Sheets prefent you with a pretty large Treatife of Comets; containing his own Theory and Explication thereof, from Obfervations made on thofe in 1680, and 1681.*
What follows is the Continuation of his Lectures of Light, wherein he profecutes his former Inquiries into the Nature thereof. R. W.

SECT. IV.

Being a Continuation of the Lectures of Light inter-rupted for sometime by our Author's Observations on the Comets in 1680. These were read about May, 1681.

The CONTENTS.

1. I Was the last Term diverted from proceeding with the Explication of Light I had begun to discourse of in some of my former Lectures, by the Appearance of the Comet; which seems to give a Light very differing from those of other Celestial Bodies : I was therefore the more willing upon that Occasion to discourse on the Light of that Body, having before discoursed of the Light of the Sun and Stars. But it was with a Design of Resuming the Discourse of Light in General; for that a clear Understanding and Explication of it, will very much facilitate the Knowledge and Science of many other abstruse and difficult Operations in Nature. For the doing of which as it ought,
much

much ufe muſt be made of Geometry. And, indeed, without it little can be done, that will any ways intelligibly inform us concerning it. General and indefinite Aſſertions and Deſcriptions do but imperfectly inform, and the Deduction from ſuch Propoſitions muſt be uncertain, and of a dubious Senſe; and defective of Form, becauſe they want the neceſſary Limits and Boundaries. Whereas, on the other ſide, where the Definitions are ſtrict and exact, and the Deductions cloſe and neceſſary, the Science thence derived is Poſitive and Demonſtrative, and will admit of no manner of Heſitancy, or Contradiction.

The Proprieties I have taken notice of were,

A Recapitulation of the Three Proprieties of Light.   1. The Incomprehenſible Extenſion of its Propagation, boundleſs and unlimited as the Univerſe, and yet really affecting every Attom or Point of the Medium or Maſs of Created Body, and this not only of the tranſparent Medium, but as I conceive, and ſhall hereafter explain and ſhew my Reaſons for it, even every Atom and Point of Opacous Bodies alſo; ſo that no one Atom or Particle of created Body is free from its Power; and be the Extent thereof never ſo Immenſe (as whoſe Imagination can ſet Limits to Extenſion) yet the whole, and every part thereof is really affected by the Power of Light.

Secondly, The prodigious Swiftneſs, or rather Inſtantaneouſneſs of this Propagation; ſo that it ſeems to exert its Power to all imaginable Diſtance in an Inſtant of time; ſo that at the ſame Inſtant that the Lucid Body emits its Light, or exerts it Power, the Receptive Body though never ſo far diſtant is affected by it; and this without any reſpect to the vaſt ſpace interpoſed, ſo that a Body a Million of Millions of Miles diſtant, is affected as ſoon as a Body diſtant but a Span, ſo that it may be ſaid to outpaſs the quickneſs of our Thought; for that we muſt think of one thing after another. And though ſome ingenious Men, as Monſier *Romer*, have indeavoured to prove it to be temporaneous, and to ſpend ſome time in paſſing from the Illuminating to the Illuminated Body, thereby thinking to make it more Intelligible and Adequate to other Powers and Operations of the Univerſe; yet he ſuppoſing that time to be ſo incredibly ſhort, in compariſon to the length of the Space it paſſes, as he allows but one ſingle ſecond of time, or the ſixtyth part of a Minute of an Hour for the time in which it paſſes the Diſtance of about 20000 Miles; it makes it much more difficult to conceive ſo rapid a temporaneous Motion, than the Inſtantaneouſneſs of that other. For the Motion of a Cannon Bullet is as much ſlower than this of Light, as the Motion of a Snail is than that of a Cannon Bullet.

The Third Propriety of Light which I took notice of, was, that though its Expanſion ſeems to be indefinite, and its Motion Inſtantaneous, or infinitely ſwift; yet that its Power was finite, and limited and ſubjected to the Laws of Quantity, and admitted of the Rules of Compariſon, of Majority, of Minority, and Equality, which nothing that is infinite is ſubjected to; and upon this Account it is, that it falls under the Conſideration of Geometry.

1. I ſhall now begin with a more particular Conſideration of Light; and therein I ſhall conſider what Light is, that has theſe admirable Proprieties. Reſerving the explication of ſeveral other Proprieties of it altogether as wonderful, 'till I have a little further explained theſe, and ſhewn how theſe are produced by it.

Light then will fall under a Threefold Conſideration; Firſt, As it is in the Luminous Body. Secondly, As it is in the *Medium* that conveys it. And, Thirdly, As it affects the Eye, by means of which, we come to the Knowledge of all the reſt.

A Three-fold Conſideration of Light.   The Luminous Objects are either Celeſtial or Terreſtrial; of each of which, there are ſome that ſhine by their own Light, and ſome that ſhine by Light reflected from them, but derived from another Luminous Body.

The

The Principal of the Celestial (at least as to us) is the Sun, which for ought we yet certainly know, is the Principal and Brightest Body in the World. I have already explained somewhat of the Nature of that Body as to its bigness, its turbinated Motion, its Atmosphere, its *Nebulæ, Macuiæ* and *Faculæ*, and their Proprieties and Motions, and thence gave some probable Conjecture of the Constitution and Substance of it, and concerning the manner how it comes to give Light ; and I shew'd you many Reasons why, in all likelyhood, the Light of the Sun might proceed from an actual Fire, somewhat Analogous to the Fire of Bodies burning with us ; whence from an understanding of the Nature of Fire, Flame and Light here within our Reach and Command, we might the better be inabled to examine and judge of the nature of Light in general ; for if the Celestial Lights are Analogous, and much of the same Nature with the Bodies that give Light with us, then the Knowledge of the one will explain the other.

Next, I began to shew some Reasons why in Probability the fixt Stars were of the same Nature with the Sun, as to this Propriety of Emitting Light : For, that first, they were Bodies some of them vastly Distant, as I have, I think, experimentally proved by the Observation I made of the passing of Stars near the *Zenith* ; and consequently they must be vastly big. Thence, Thirdly, They must emit a very strong and vivid Light, since at so vast a Distance they do so sensibly almost Dazle the Eye ; for the Power of Light, as I shew'd before, though it be instantaneous and indefinite in Extension, doth yet continually Diminish in its Power, the farther it acts from the Lucid Fountain ; and this not in a Simple but Duplicate Proportion to the Distance ; so that a Body a Hundred times further Distant, receives not a 10000 Part of the Light. But then, Secondly, 'Tis probable, that they are actual Fires, as I indeavoured to prove the same, from some remarkable Instances we have had of some of them that have, as it were, blazed out upon a suddain, and after a short space, quite burnt out, so as never to appear since ; as that remarkable Star in 1572, which was so accurately observed by the Noble *Ticho Brahe*, and some others of that Nature ; and by some others, which sometimes appear, and sometimes disappear again, as that in *Collo Ceti*.

Thirdly, I shew'd why also Comets were Bodies that shined by their own Light, and did not receive their Light from the Sun, but from a Principle of their own ; and this I have shewn to be very much of the same Nature with our Fire. And by very many Observations I have made of the last Great Comet, I am confirmed that the Light of that vastly great Blaze, which at sometimes was extended to so great a length, as to subtend an Angle of almost Ninty Degrees, and to be of the breadth of near Three ; was wholly from it self, and was not caused by the Reflections of the Light of the *Sun* ; and that all that Stream issued from the Body or Head, much after the same manner, as the flame of a Candle does issue from the Weik ; and therefore from all Circumstances I could observe of it, and from what I took notice of in the former Comets ; I judge it to be a Body actually on Fire, or in a State of Dissolution, and that it consists of burning Materials, but much differing from the Substance of the Sun and fixt Stars, which afford a more pure, strong and defecated Light, whereas this is more blended with a kind of Smoke, or Hetrogeneous Vapours, which are consumed whilst they are in the Blaze, in the same manner, as the Smoke of a burning Body here with us is consumed by the kindling of it into Flame, as it ascends from the smoaking or steaming Body ; as may be observed in the Burning of a Tallow or Wax Candle, or of Oyl, Spirit of Wine, or the like in a Lamp. These therefore are the Celestial Bodies that emit Light of their own ; in all which, the Original or Cause of it seems to be nothing else but an actual Fire, and to be Analogous, or very much of kin to the Fires, that consume Terrestrial Bodies, and therefore our Inquiry for the cause of Light is brought somewhat nearer to us, and more within our reach, and therefore we may with the greater Ease and Certainty find out the true Cause and Nature of it.

For as to all the other Celestial Bodies, *viz.* the Moon, and the rest of the primary and secundary Planets, 'tis very evident that they do not shine by their own proper Light, but by the help of that of the Sun, which is reflected from

them

them to us. For if we confider the Moon, 'tis very evident not only from the Increafe and Decreafe of Light, which make the Appearances and Phafes of the Increafing and Decreafing of the Moon, and from the Eclipfes both of the Sun and Moon, which have very long been Obferved and Explained by this Theory, the Dark Body of the Moon eclipfing the Sun, and the Interpofition of the Earth between the Sun and the Moon, eclipfing the Moon; but from the very Shadows of the Protuberant and Craggy Parts of the Moon upon the Surface of its Body ; for thofe Shadows may, with a Telefcope, be as plainly feen as the Shadow of the Stile of a Dial, and the Motion and Change thereof may be as plainly alfo feen, and the Progrefs of the Light of the Sun upon the Surface of that Body. But whereas fome object that the fecundary and faint Light of the Moon, which is fometimes remarkable in total Eclipfes, feems to be a proper Light of the Body it felf, 'tis now evident enough that, as *Kepler* well obferved, that Light proceeds from the Refractions of the Sun's Light in the Atmofphere about the Earth, where it is refracted towards the *Axis* of the *Umbra* of the Earth; and as for that of the New Moon, that is caufed by the Reflection of the Sun's Light from the Surface of the Earth ; for that 'tis very plain, that as the Light of that Decreafes, as it does when the Afpect is changed, and a lefs part of the inlightned Surface of the Earth reflects to the Moon, as from the firft to the laft Quadrature, that fecundary or faint Light vanifhes and is no more vifible.

Next, As to the Light of the other Planets, 'tis very clear that they Receive what they Reflect, from the Sun ; for 'tis plain, that *Mercury*, when it has paffed between us and the *Sun*, has appeared a fmall Dark Spot, and fome have affirmed to have feen the Phafe of it through a Telefcope, to appear Horned like a New Moon, though I never yet obferved it fo my felf. But as for *Venus*, I have very often obferved the Changes in her, and found her as fharp as the Moon, two days before or after the Conjunction, without the leaft Appearance of Light on the other part of her Body ; and *Mars* I have obferved a little wained, but as for *Jupiter*, I have divers times plainly feen the Shadow of one of the *Satellites* pafs over its Disk, as well as the *Satellites* eclipfed by the Shadow of the Body of *Jupiter* ; fo that both the Body of *Jupiter* and the *Satellites* about it, do fhine only from the Reflection of the Light of the *Sun*. We have no reafon to doubt but that the Light of *Saturn* and its *Satellites* proceed from the fame Caufe, and that becaufe as the Body of *Saturn* is fo much further removed both from the *Sun* and us, fo the Light is confiderably more Dull and Weak. And befides, I have feveral times plainly feen the Shadow of the Ring upon *Saturn*, which could not be, if the caufe of its Light did not proceed from the *Sun*. So that upon the whole, we have fufficient Grounds to conclude that the Light of all the Planets proceeds from the Light of the Sun reflected from them to us ; and confequently, that the emitted Light of all Celeftial Bodies is much of the Nature of the Lights of the Fires we have here upon the Earth.

Terreftrial Luminous Objects. 2. We come then in the next place to confider fuch Bodies as are within our reach, that emit a Light of their own ; that fo by a Scrutiny of them we may find out the Caufe and Reafon of Light.

Of thefe we have a vaft Number of all Bodies almoft, by fome means or other affording us Inftances of this Luciferous Nature, but they may all be reduced to a few general Claffes or Heads, under which Claffes they may be eafily ranged in fome refpect or other.

1. Sulphureous Bodies, &c. The Firft and Principal, and the moft general of all the reft, and which may moft properly be faid, of fuch Bodies as emit their own Light, or to produce Light from themfelves, are all Sulphureous, Unctuous, Refinous or Spirituous Bodies, which will being firft heated, be burnt or Diffolved by the Air, as a *Menftruum* ; for all fuch Bodies, whilft they are thus Diffolved or Burnt, emit a confiderable Light.

This Head therefore comprifes all combuftible Bodies, which are either Mineral, as *Sulphur, Cole, Afphaltum, Bitumen, Petroleum,* and the like ; or Vegetable,

getable; almoſt all Parts of which, except the Watry, are Combuſtible and Diſſoluble by the Air.

Or, Thirdly, Animal Subſtances; all the Oily or Fatty Parts of which are likewiſe Combuſtible, but the Watery and Earthy Parts are not.

Now all theſe Subſtances being firſt heated to a certain Degree, ſome more, ſome leſs, will by the Air be preyed upon and diſſolved, in which Action of Diſſolution or Burning, Light is produced: And 'tis very evident that that Action is neceſſary to the effect of Light, for that before the Conſumption or Diſſolution begins, and after it is finiſhed, there is no Light produced, but only during the time of the Diſſolution. And this may be farther argued from this, that the faſter and quicker the Diſſolution is made, the more ſtrong and vivid is the Light; and the ſlower; the more weak and languid; and therefore, the more of the *Menſtruum* of the Air is applied to the Diſſolving Body, the more quick is the Diſſolution performed, and the brighter is the Light, as is well known in the blowing of Fire with Bellows, whereby a quick ſupply of freſh Air, is brought to the burning Body, which is ſufficiently known to all People, though not under this Notion: Moſt People ſuppoſe it to be only for blowing away the Aſhes, and ſo by that means ſhewing or diſcovering the Fire that lies underneath them; but I have proved by divers Trials, that 'tis not the Motion of the Air by the Bellows, for removing the Aſhes or driving off the burning Parts that does any thing in this Effect; becauſe if the Air that is ſo blown be firſt ſatiated and then blown on it, it produces no other effect than to blow off the Aſhes, and blow out the Fire; for the more you blow the more dead is the Light, and the ſooner is the Fire quite extinct; inſomuch that in a very ſhort time the Coles all become perfectly Black, without emitting the leaſt glimpſe of Light or Shining, at which time if one blaſt of freſh Air be blown upon thoſe ſeemingly dead extinct and black Coles, they all immediately begin to Glow, Burn, and Shine afreſh, as if they had not been at all extinct; and the more freſh Air is blowed upon them, the more they ſhine, and the ſooner are they Burnt out and Conſumed. So that 'tis the freſh Air that is the Life of the Fire, and without a Conſtant ſupply of that it will go out and Die.

Somewhat like this is obſervable in the Life of Animals, who live no longer than they have a conſtant ſupply of freſh Air to breath, and, as it were, blow the Fire of Life; for ſo ſoon as that ſupply is wanting, the Fire goes out, and the Animal dies, and all the other vital Functions ceaſe; as any one may preſently ſee, if he puts a ſmall Animal as a Bird, or the like, into a ſmall Glaſs and covers it cloſe; for in a ſhort time the Air becomes ſatiated, and is no longer fit for Reſpiration; but though the Animal breath it as before, and Pant and move his Lungs as before; yet if the Air be not freſh, the Fire of Life will extinguiſh. Some Learned Philoſophers and Phyſitians have been of the Opinion, that the uſe of Breathing was for nothing elſe, but that by the Motion of the Lungs the Blood might be kept circulating which paſt through them, or that the Steams of the Blood might be carried off, which it could not do when it was full of Steams; but by many Trials I have proved that neither of thoſe are at all the Cauſe of the Death of the Creature, but only the want of freſh Air.

For whether the Lungs move or not move, if freſh Air be ſupplied, the Animal lives, if it be wanting, it dies. Again, If the Air be full of Steams or not full of Steams, it is all one, the Animal lives if it be freſh, but if it be not, it dies; nor does the heat or Cold of it do any thing. But this only by the by, being more proper to another Time and Diſcourſe; my preſent Inquiry being after the Nature and Cauſe of Light. This then is one of the Claſſes of ſhining Bodies; namely, ſuch as are Diſſoluble or Burnable by the Air.

The next Claſs are all ſuch Bodies as are not combuſtible, but are ſo fixt as to indure a great degree of Heat, without being ſubject to flie away or be diſperſed into Vapours; ſuch are all ſorts of Metals, Stones, Earths, Clays, Salts, Sands, White Burnt Bones, Aſhes of Vegetable and Animal Subſtances, and the like; Every one of which when heated to a certain Degree of Heat, will Shine or afford Light; but under a certain Degree will not ſhine at all.

2. Shining Bodies not Combuſtible, but heated.

Now

Now there are great Varieties of these Degrees, for that some will not begin to shine till, 'they have a very intense and violent Heat, others with a small Degree, insomuch that I lately saw the Pouder of a Stone which laid upon a Plate of Metal, and held over a Chafingdish of Coles, would presently, and with a small Heat begin to shine, but so soon as the Plate cooled, would leave off shining, but the Plate being warmed again, it would again shine; and almost every Body has a peculiar Degree of Heat, at which it begins its shining; so that there are almost as many Varieties of Degrees of Heat to make Bodies shine, as there are to make Bodies flow and melt; some will shine before they melt, as almost all the harder Bodies; as Gold, Silver, Copper, Brass, Iron, Stones, Earths, &c. others will Melt before they Shine, as Tin, Lead, Saltpeter, Allum, Vitriol, Tallow, Gums, &c.

3. Bodies shining without Heat. In the Third Class are all such Bodies as shine without Heat, by an inward Fermentation, in which though their Light be but small, yet does it become visible enough in a darkned Room or in the Night; such are Glow worms, *Scolopendra,* several kind of Flies, decaying Fish, as Whitings, Oysters, and many others, sometimes Flesh, as Veal; also rotten Wood, and some sorts of Putrifying Vegetables, also some Putrifying Urines; also the *Phosphorus* made out of the *Caput Mortuum,* or the Rob of Urine found out by Dr. *Kunkell,* and many others.

4. Bodies shining by an Impression of Light. In the Fourth Class are such as shine by the Impression of Light made upon them, by being exposed only to the Light of the Sun or the Day. Such are the Preparation of the *Bononian stone,* and the Preparation lately found out of common Chalk by Dr. *Baldwin;* these receive such a Power from the Influence of the Light, that being carried into a Dark Room after they have been exposed to the Light, they then appear to shine like a Cole of Fire, and continue so to do for a pretty while, but will by degrees lose their Light, and be extinct almost in the manner as a Piece of Red hot Iron; but being again exposed to the Light of the Sun, or a Window, they presently reassume their shining Quality.

5. Bodies shining by Motion. In the Fifth Class are all such as shine by Motion, Diamants, Sea Water, some sort of Dews, Sugar, Black Silk, the Back of a Cat, and clean warmed Linnen, as has been lately experimented by Dr. *Crone,* and several other Substances which will shine with a degree of Motion or a little rubbing.

To this Head also, may be referred several others also which require a great Degree of Heating or Rubbing, as Iron and some other Metals which may be made Red Hot, or to shine with Hammering only, two hard Stones as Flints and the like, struck one against the other, two Pieces of Wood which with Rubbing will take fire, and the like.

3. These several sorts of Lights are to be the Guides which must conduct us in our search after the true Nature of Light, nor can the Truth of the Theory be fully Discover'd, 'till every one of these Witnesses and Testimonies are thoroughly examined, and that by comparing the Evidences that each of them shall bring distinctly, with those of every one of the other, there being such Axioms and Maxims founded, as will open a way to the clear Knowledge of this most abstruse and difficult Science of Light. From which as all the visible Appearances derive their Original, so the greatest part of the Knowledge and Information of Mankind; for the Explication of which, the Theory of Vision, and the structure of the Eye, the Organ of that Sense, and all the Powers and Modifications and effects of the Rays of Light: And so the Theory of *Opticks,* *Dioptricks,* *Catoptricks,* Perspective and Projections, and Cromatick, or the Theory of Position, Modification and Effect of the Rays of Light, whether Direct, Refracted, or Reflected, or Compounded on the various Superficies on which they are incident; every of which I design (God Willing) fully to explicate. So also the Velocity and Modification of all the Motions of the Celestial Bodies, *viz.* both the primary and secundary Planets, have their Original and Cause, as I shall hereafter plainly and fully demonstrate.

It

It would be too long here to recount to you the whole proceſs of the Examination of theſe Evidences, and the whole proceeding, with thoſe Evidences ; by
comparing every one, with every other, ſingly ; and then, many together, with
ſuch a peculiar Number of many others ; whereby the Nature and Cauſe, and
the Charaﬅeriﬅick of Light in General is diſcovered ; and then, to diſcover
what is the peculiar cauſe of it in this, and that, and t'other particular Body,
from whence it proceeds. It will ſuffice at this time to tell you the Reſult and
Concluſion ; for that the Proceſs is long and tedious, and not attained but by
many Steps and Degrees. *Light then is nothing elſe but a peculiar Motion of* Definition of
the parts of the Luminous Body, which does affeﬅ a fluid Body that incompaſſes the Light, what
Luminous Body, which is perfeﬅly fluid, and perfeﬅly Denſe, ſo as not to admit of it is.
any farther Condenſation ; but that the Parts next the Luminous Body being mov-
ed, the whole Expanſum of that fluid is moved likewiſe. So that any aſſignable
Parts next the Luminous body being protruded a certain aſſignable Space, that
protrudes all the vaﬅ *Expanſum* of the fluid, every way *in orbem*, at the ſame
Inﬅant an aſſignable Space : So that no one Atom, or Point of it, to all imaginable Diﬅance, but is at the ſame time moved with it, or protruded forward : For Inﬅance, When a Luminous Part of the Sun is moved with the
Motion of Light, it does at the ſame Inﬅant, move the Parts of the Incompaſſing fluid, which is the proper *Medium* of Light, with the Motion of Light ;
which part cannot ſo be moved, but that all the Parts of that *Medium*,
to the extent of the World, muﬅ be moved at the ſame Inﬅant, and protruded
from the Luminous Point in a direﬅ Line ; ſo that at the ſame Inﬅant, that the
Apex of the Cone is moved, the ſpherical baſe of that Cone alſo is moved, and
every imaginary Spherical Superficies, that is parallel to that baſe, is moved likewiſe.

This Conſequence will follow of neceſſity, from the Definition of the Nature *The Medium of*
of the *Medium*, that is proper for the conveyance of Light. And that is, that *Light is perfeﬅ-*
it is a *Medium perfeﬅly Denſe* ; that is, ſuch as will not be by any Power forced *ﬅly Denſe.*
into leſs Dimenſions than it is contained in, but does compleatly fill and maintain that ſpace. And, Secondly, From its *perfeﬅ fluidity*, it does accommodate it ſelf to all manner of Forms, ſo as exaﬅly to ſhape it ſelf into the new
Form that is given to it, by the Motion of Light.

For Inﬅance, If we imagine A B C to Repreſent an hollow Conical Body, Fig. 5.
Indefinitely extended from the Point A, which is the Apex towards B C, and at Plate 1.
the ſame time imagine alſo this hollow Conical Body, fill'd with a Body perfeﬅly fluid, and perfeﬅly Denſe ; that is, ſuch as will perfeﬅly accommodate
it ſelf to the Figure of that Cone, and intirely fill the Cavity of it, ſo as not to
leave the leaﬅ Point of it unfilled ; and that will not admit of any manner of
Condenſation into a leſs Room : If then we imagine, that by the firﬅ ﬅroke
of the Motion of Light, the Parts of the fluid that fill th Apex *A d n*, be driven forward toward the baſe, into the ſpace *d n e o*, equal to it in quantity ;
it muﬅ at the ſame Inﬅant drive that part of the fluid that fill'd the ſpace *d n e o*,
into the ſpace *e o p f*, equal to it in quantity, and that which fill'd the ſpace
e o p f, muﬅ at the ſame time be protruded into the ſpace *f p q g*, of the ſame
quantity ; and ſo onward *f p q g*, into *g q r h*, and *g q r h* into *h r ſ i, in Inſi-*
nitum, or to the utmoﬅ extent of the Cone, and filling fluid Matter ; ſo that at
the ſame time that the Parts that made the imaginary Spherical Baſe, *d n*, of
the Cone *A d n* are moved into the imaginary Spherical Baſe *e o*, of the Cone
A e o ; will the imaginary Spherical Superficies, *l u*, of the Cone *A l u* be moved into the Place of the imaginary Spherical Baſe *m x*, of the Cone *A m x*,
though never ſo far removed from the Apex *A* : So that a Body perfeﬅly denſe,
and perfeﬅly fluid, muﬅ communicate ſuch a Motion begun, to all imaginable
Diﬅance in an Inﬅant. It being impoſſible that the Apex of the Cone *A d n* can
be moved into the ſpace *d n o e*, without moving at the ſame time, every part
of all the reﬅ of ſuch a Cone, to the utmoﬅ Extenſion.

The further conſideration then of this Cone, will give us the Reaſons, and
Grounds of the three I have already named, and of ſeveral other Proprieties of
Light, and make them very intelligible and plain to be underﬅood, and eaſy to
be demonﬅrated.

As, Firft, From hence we may underftand the Reafon of the Force and Pow-er of Light, at feveral Diftances from the Luminous Body; for according to the Increafe of the imaginary Bafes of the parts of the Cones, and according to the Decreafe of the Thicknefs of the feveral Parts; fo is the Decreafe of the Power of Light at thofe feveral Diftances. For, Firft, It is clear that the fame Quan-tity of Motion, and confequently of Light, that there is is in the firft Cone or Apex *A d n*, the fame is there in the laft part *l u x m*, and in every other inter-mediate Part, as *d n o e, e o p f, f p q g, g q r h,* and the reft; fo that if we compute it firft according to the Expanfion of the Imaginary Bafe; we fhall find that thofe increafe in a Duplicate Proportion, that is, as the Squares of the feveral Diftances, as at ten times the Diftance, the Expanfion is a Hundred times the fpace; and confequently the fame quantity of Motion is expanded into a Hundred times the fpace, and therefore an equal fpace of the Superficies of that, at ten times the Diftance, will have but $\frac{1}{100}$ Part of the Motion or Light that is upon the Superficies at once the Diftance. This therefore will be repre-fented by the Sections of a Conical Body, made by turning the Hyperbola round upon the Afymtot; for the Ordinates to the Afymtot being in reciprocal Proportion to the intercepted Parts of the Afymptot, the Squares or Circles of thofe Afymptots, muft be in Duplicate Proportion of the intercepted Parts of the Afymptot Reciprocally. This is the Proportion that the ingenious *Kepler*, allows to the Decreafe of Light, fuppofing it to be only in Duplicate Proporti-on of the Diftance Reciprocal; and according to this, he founds the Proportion of the Power of the Sun in moving the Planetary Bodies at feveral Diftances; but he ought to have confidered alfo another Decreafe of the Power of the Light, according to the Decreafe of Thicknefs, of the bafe Parts of the Cone. For fince in all the Imaginary equal Parts of the Cones, there is the fame quantity of Matter, if the fame be Expanded in Breadth, it muft be diminifh-ed in thicknefs. If therefore at ten Foot Diftance, for Inftance, it be fpread into a Breadth 100 times as big as at one foot diftance, then confequently to make the equality of Content in the one and the other, there muft be but $\frac{1}{100}$ part of the thicknefs.

For if at the Diftances ———————— 1, 2, 3, 4, 5, 6, 7, 8, &c.
The Superficies or Bafes expanded be as — 1, 4, 9, 16, 25, 36, 49, 64, &c.
Then the Thicknefs of thofe Bafes muft be as 1, $\frac{1}{4}$, $\frac{1}{9}$, $\frac{1}{16}$, $\frac{1}{25}$, $\frac{1}{36}$, $\frac{1}{49}$, $\frac{1}{64}$, &c.

Thefe then will give the Proportions of the length of the Pulfes or ftrokes of Light, at feveral diftances from the Luminous Body, and con-fequently the Velocity of thofe Pulfes. So that according to thefe Rules, the Force or Power of Light muft decreafe in quadruplicate Proportion of the Di-ftances reciprocally taken; that is, as the fquared Squares of the Diftances Reciprocally; and confequently, as I fhall afterwards fhew the effect of Light, or the Motion it caufes in other Bodies, will be in Subduplicate Proportion of the Powers, and therefore only in Duplicate Proportion of the Diftances Reci-procally taken.

So that thence it is evident, that Light does act according to the Proportion of a Body moved, obferving exactly the fame Proportions, and therefore can be nothing elfe but that; for what Thing foever hath all the fame Proprieties with another, muft be the fame,

It is not therefore what the Learned and Ingenious *Bulialdus* would have it to be; namely, a certain Subftance which is a Geometrical *Medium,* between a Body and a Spirit. *Lux eft,* (fays he) *media Proportionalis inter corpoream fubftantiam & Incorpoream :* Light is a middle proportional Subftance, between a corporeal Subftance, and an incorporeal. A middle proportional (fays he) is that which between two extream Lines, does equally divide the Rationes of both, and which does participate of the Exceffes and Defects, and communi-cates the fame Habitudes with both; and by how many of its parts it is exceed-ed by the Greater, by fo many parts of the Lefs does it exceed that. For In-ftance, fays he, Let *A E* be an incorporeal Subftance, and *C* a Corporeal. The incorporeal Subftance *A E,* exceeds the corporeal Subftance *C,* by the Excefs

D E,

D E, to wit, by inftantaneous Motion and Penetration of folid Bodies; but the corporeal Subftance *C*, is defective of the Incorporeal by its Termination and fucceffive Motion. Now we muft find a middle proportionate Subftance, which is defective of the Incorporeal, and exceeds the Corporeal, but a middle proportional does participate of the Excefs and Defect. Now *B G* (the Subftance of Light) is defective of *A E*, in Termination and fucceffive Motion, but it exceeds *C* in inftantaneous Motion and Penetration. Now that Subftance which is defective of one, and exceeds the other, is a Medium, but Light is fuch a Subftance, which by its Penetration and inftantaneous Motion, exceeds a corporeal Subftance; but it is defective of Incorporeal Subftance, in its Termination and Succeffive Motion. This is his Demonftration, but how much more inftructed we are by it, of the Nature of Light, I fhall leave to every Man to judge. It is, I confefs, above my reach to conceive what Subftance 'tis he fhould mean; it being perfectly new and not thought of before, that ever I could meet with; nor can I fee what need he had of fuppofing any fuch Subftance. For fince the fame Proprieties that are found in Light are found in Corporeal Subftances, or Bodies, as I have before mentioned; I fee no reafon why on this Account, we have any Reafon either to fuppofe an Incorporeal Subftance, or a Subftance of a middle Nature, between Incorporeal and Corporeal. 'Tis to me, I confefs, very difficult to conceive what a Corporeal Subftance is; nor can I have any more clear Conception of what is meant by that Expreffion, than what I would exprefs by thefe two Words; *fomewhat extended*, which how that differs from a *Vacuum*, or an Extenfion, without Subftance, or an extended Nothing, is not eafy to be underftood by one that throughly confiders his own Conceptions.

Des Cartes therefore makes Extenfion and Body, or corporeal Subftance, to be one and the fame thing; and that no other Subftance but Body, or Corporeal, can be extended.

But to leave thefe Metaphyfical Notions, 'tis clear from what I have fhewn, that as to this Subject, Light, there is no need of fuppofing any other Subftance, but Corporeal, or Body; and that, fo and fo qualified; that is, perfectly Fluid, and perfectly Denfe, and fo Receptive and Communicative, of all manner of Motion.

As to the Notion therefore of the Subftance of Light, I know not what can be farther added, that is more known or more Intelligible than that it is; Firft, A Subftance, or a fomething; that is infinitely fluid, or at leaft, indefinitely; if that be more conceivable, whofe leaft conceivable Part is free from cohefion with any other, and fo is fufceptible of any kind of Motion, without carrying or moving along with it the Lateral Bodies, whereby it only communicates the Motion it receives behind, to the Parts that lie immediately before it; whence follows that great Propriety of Light, that in a uniform Medium, it propagates its Motion every way in direct Lines or Rays, from a Center of a Sphere. *The true Notion of Light.*

And, Secondly, That it is a Subftance, or fomething that compleatly fills an Extenfion or Quantity every way extended, and cannot be condenfed, or forced into lefs Extenfion, Space, or Room, by any Natural Power; but that the fame Subftance will always have the fame Quantity, or Extenfion, one way or other; what it wants in one, it will have in one or both of the other Dimenfions; as what it wants in breadth it will have in thicknefs, or in length, that fhall recompence the whole, and bring it to equality.

Thirdly, That this, as all other Bodies, is fufceptive and communicative of all manner of Motion, but is more appropriated to Motion of fuch a Degree of Swiftnefs, which is in proportion to the Motion of other Bodies, whofe leaft part is folid and bulky, as the bignefs of the one, to the bignefs of the other, Reciprocally taken. This may ferve for the Explication of the Subftance of Light.

4. The next thing we are to confider, is, the Motion of Light, which is the principal thing confiderable in it; for the Subftance without the Motion has no effect, nor has the fubftance Light; 'tis that we are fenfible of, and not of the Subftance; fo that be the Subftance what it will, whether Corporeal, or Incorporeal, *Of the Motion of Light.*

corporeal,

corporeal, or Middle, Proportional, or None; provided we know what the Motion is, and the Rules, Powers, and Proportions of that, we need not much confider the Subftance of it.

In the Confideration then of Motion thefe thing are obfervable.

1. The Quantity.
2. The Quality.
3. The Power.

By the quantity of Motion, I underftand only the Degrees of Velocity exiftent in a certain Quantity of Matter.

By the Qualities of Motion, I mean the Modifications of it in Body, as whether it be Simple or Compound, Reflected, Refracted, Direct or Oblique, and the like.

By the Power, I mean the Act or Effect it produces upon other Bodies, in agitating or moving them.

In the Confideration of every one of which, I fhall indeavour to reduce the Theory to Calculation and Mathematical Exactnefs; without which, all other ways are but Random Gueffes, and make no certain and demonftrative Conclufions.

Sound how caufed. The Motion produced by the Lucid Particles muft be of a certain Degree of Swiftnefs; otherwife, it is not propagated in the form of Light, for 'tis not every Motion that produces that Effect; for 'tis in Light, as it is in Sound, that the Motion muft be of a certain Degree of Swiftnefs, before Motion will be propagated in the Medium that conveys it: we find that moving a Stick in the Air, if we move it but flowly, we hear no Sound; becaufe the Motion is fo flow, that the Parts of the Air that were before it do eafily move round the Sides of the Stick and come behind it; fo that only thofe Parts of the Air are moved that lie near the Stick, which do only receive fuch a circulating Motion as brings them from before to come behind, the ambient Parts of the Air having Power enough to reflect and keep in that Motion, fo as only to circulate about the Stick; but if the Motion of the Stick be fo fwift, as that the Particles before it over power the Refiftance of the ambient Air, fo that its Motion is not reflexed backwards, but propagated directly forward into the Air, then Sound is generated and propagated from the Stick, every way *in orbem*; whence if you give a very quick Motion to the Stick in the Air, you prefently hear a Noife.

A certain Degree of Heat produces Light. In the fame manner, if you take a piece of the moft fixed Body that will indure the Fire; as for Inftance, a piece of pure Gold, or refined Silver, which will not waft nor burn by heating; if you heat it but with a fmaller Degree of Heat, you will not perceive it to fhine or give any kind of Light; but if you continue to Augment the Heat to a certain Degree it will begin to fhine, and appear Red Hot, as we call it; and if it be heat more, it fhines brighter; but if you take it from the Fire, and permit it to cool, its Light grows fainter and fainter, and when it is come to a certain Degree of Heat, it ceafes to fhine at all, and emits no Light. Now Heat, as I fhall afterward prove, is nothing but the internal Motion of the Particles of Body; and the hotter a Body is, the more violently are the Particles moved, and with a quick Motion; but the Particles of Bodies, according as they are more bulky and clofe, fo do they require the greater Degrees of Motion, to make them move with an equal Degree of Motion, with that of fmaller Particles; as I fhall afterwards prove, when I come to give the Laws and Rules of Motion propagated from Body to Body. In the fame manner in fuch Diamants, as will fhine like a Gloworm in the Dark, (for all Diamants will not; but I have feen and tryed many Diamants that would;) the Stone will not begin to fhine 'till it has received a certain Degree of rubbing and Agitation, but beyond that Degree, the more you rub it the more it fhines, and any little ftroke upon it with the Nail of ones Finger, when it fo fhines, will make it feem to flafh. The like I have lately obferved in the Phofporus of *Kunkell*, that the rubbing it a little with ones Finger, does make it glow, and as it were flame. So if you take a Piece of Cold Iron, and

Ham-

hammer it on an Anvil, you muſt continue hammering it very ſtrong and quick a good while, before you will perceive it to begin to ſhine; but if you continue to work it with a Hammer for a certain ſpace, it will ſhine very briskly; and grow, as we call it, Red Hot. Now in all theſe Inſtances, and a Hundred more I could produce, 'tis evident that there muſt be a certain Degree of Hammering, Rubbing, or Heating, before the Body ſo wrought on will produce Light: All which do effect an internal Motion of the parts of the Bodies ſo Hammered, Rubbed, or Heated; 'tis therefore evident, that 'tis not every Motion of the Particles of Bodies that will produce Light, but a certain Degree of it; under which no Light is produced, and beyond which the Light is increaſed and augmented.

This kind of internal Motion therefore in the Parts of the Body, is that which produces Light; whatſoever therefore produces this Motion, produces Light; whether it be heat, as in all very fixt Bodys, or Fire, which, as I told you before, is a Diſſolution of the Body by the Air, as in all Unctuous, Reſinous, or Sulphureous Bodies; or Hammering and Strokes, as in Stones, Chryſtals, Diamants, Sugar, &c. or Fermentation and Corruption, as in Fiſh, Glow-worms, Rotten Wood; or the Motion of Light it ſelf, as in the Bononian Stone, and Dr. *Baldwin*'s Phoſphoros, and in almoſt all other Bodies held in the Focus of a Burning Glaſs. Light therefore in the Object, is a peculiar kind of Internal Motion of the Particles.

The propagation of this Motion into, and through the incompaſſing Medium is that we call Light in the Medium, or the ſpace between the Inlightning and Inlightned Body. This propagation of Motion, as I ſaid before, is every way *in orbem*; and it may be cauſed either by an Immediate pulſe of the Particles of the Body againſt the Parts of the incompaſſing Fluid, as a Stone ſtriking againſt the Water, from whence the Waves of Motion are there propagated in Rings; or elſe by the extruſion of the Part of the Fluid Medium of Light that lies between the ſolid Particles of the ſhining Body; as Water ſqueezed out of a Spunge into Water, or Water forced out of a Syringe, or Pipe, into Water, which will produce the ſame Rings in the Surface of the Water. It ſeems to be in ſome Caſes One way, and in ſome Caſes the other. In burning Bodies, it ſeems to be the firſt way, where every Particle of the Body Diſſolved flies aſunder, and is rarified or diſperſed into a bigger ſpace, in the manner as we may obſerve in the firing of a Grain of Gunpouder, which we ſee expands into a Sphere of Flame, which extrudes and evacuates a Sphere of Air round about the fired Grain. But in hammered Bodies, and ſome other I have named, it ſeems to be the other.

What Light is in the Medium.

If we therefore conſider what Effects follow in theſe ſenſible Examples, we may the more certainly conclude what muſt follow in the more inſenſible.

The Grain of Gunpouder, then, when it is fired, rarifies it ſelf into a Sphere near a Hundred times as big in Diameter, or one Million times as big in Bulk; this extrudes all the Air that was contained in that Sphere into a Space or Orb without it, and incompaſſing it, large enough to contain it; and conſequently muſt remove the Air that fill'd that ſpace into another ſpace without that, and that the next, and ſo onward ſucceſſively to a certain Diſtance; 'till at laſt the Medium of the Air being a Springy, Rarified, or Yielding Medium, and not a Denſe and Unyielding Medium, the Motion is at length loſt, and ſo this ſound audible but to a certain Diſtance. Whereas in the propagation of Light, the *Medium* being perfectly Denſe and Unyielding, that Propagation is continued *in Infinitum*, or to the utmoſt extent of the *Medium*. The ſolidity therefore of the incompaſſing Spheres, will be to one another as 1, 2, 3, 4, &c. in Arithmetical Progreſſion; and conſequently the Diameters of thoſe Spheres will be as $\sqrt{c\,1}.$ $\sqrt{c\,2}.$ $\sqrt{c\,3}.$ $\sqrt{c\,4}.$ and ſo onwards; and conſequently if you take the Diameters of the contained, from the Diameters of the containing, the Remainders will be the thickneſs of the containing ſhell; that is, the $\sqrt{c\,1}.$ will be the length of the ſtroke of the Pulſe of Light in the firſt ſpace; $\sqrt{c\,2}.-\sqrt{c\,1}.$ the

H h   length

length of the ftroke of that Pulfe in the fecond fpace; $\checkmark$ c 3.—$\sqrt{}$ c 2. the length of the ftroke in the third; $\sqrt{}$ c 4.— $\sqrt{}$ c 3. in the fourth, *&c.* fo that thofe indefinitely continued, will be very near to a Series of Numbers in the fame Proportion, with the fuperficies of the Spheres reciprocally taken, and confequently the length of the ftroke of the Pulfe of Light, will be in duplicate Proportion to the diftance reciprocal.

I have been the more particular in the Explication of this Power of Light, becaufe, as I fhall afterwards prove to you, this is the Power of Celeftial Bodies by which they Act upon, and attract each other; and by which all the Primary Planets that move about the Sun are regulated in Velocities, Diftances and Motions, whether circular or Oval. As alfo all the fecundary Planets, as the Moon about the Earth, and the Satellites about *Saturn* and *Jupiter*, make their Periods. And from the true ftating of this Power, and the Effects of it on Bodies at feveral Diftances, all the Theory of Aftronomy will be deduced a *Priori*, with Geometrical Certainty and Exactnefs; and confequently the Tables and Numbers will be eafily adapted, which will tend to the Perfection of that Noble Science.

SECT.

Sect. V.

A Continuation of the former Subject of Light. Being the Lectures read in June, 1681.

The CONTENTS.

1. *Having shewn what Light is in the Luminous Body and* Medium, *the Author comes in the third Place to shew the Operations it hath on the Subject; the chief of which is, that Effect it has on the Eye; to which End he gives a particular Explication of the Fabrick of this admirable Organ, in which there are infinite receptive Points within, to receive all the Rays from the Infinite Points without. Vision is made by reuniting all the Rays proceeding from one Point of the Object, after they have been scattered into one Point again.* 2. *A Second Way of conceiving how the Eye multiplies the Power that was by the* Hypothesis *before explained, i. e. that according to the length of the Stroak or Pulse, so is the Power or Strength of Light. Effects of Burning Glasses explained and applied to this purpose; that the length of the Pulse at the* Focus *thereof is the same with the length of the Pulse at the Sun.* 3. *The Action of the Eye much the same with that of a Burning-Glass; so that the impression on the* Retina *is the same, as if the Action of the Object were really there.* 4. *Why the Eye is not hurt by the Object, tho' it, as it were, feels and touches it: And this is, because it takes in, the* Basis *but of a very small* Cone *of* Rays *from the radiating Sphere; so that tho' the Velocity or length of the Pulse be the same, yet there being but few, their collected Power is less; and this is perform'd by the Contraction of the* Pupilla; *whence the Eye becomes weakned by bright Objects, and why we can look on the Sun thro' a very small Hole.* 5. *The Fabrick of the Eye and all its parts, as far as relates to Opticks, examined, and is necessary to the present Design; the more particular Examination of the Parts, and its Humours, being refer'd to the Nature of Refraction.* 6. *An artificial Eye very useful for the thorough Understanding of Vision. The Description and use of a Perspective Box, instead of a dark Room, which will explicate all the* Phenomena *of Vision as they are represented in the bottom of the Eye. An Explication of Shadows or the defect of Light.* R. W.

I Have in some of my former Lectures in this place, explained to you the Nature and Proprieties of Light; and shew'd to you what it is in the Luminous Body from whence it proceeds, and what it is in the Medium, through which it is propagated: I shew'd you how it came to be propagated every way *in Orbem,* to all imaginable distance in an Instant, and with what proportion of Strength it was so propagated to all assignable Distances from the Lucid Object; and thence I deduced with what Power it operated, and thereby produced Effects on those Subjects, on which it was impressed.

The

What Effect Light has on the Eye.   The firſt and Principal of all the Operations it hath on Subjects, is that effect which it hath upon the Organ of the ſeeing Eye, wherein it maketh ſuch an Impreſſion as becomes ſenſible to the Animal Faculty. This then is the next thing I ſhall indeavour to explain ; namely, the Action or Effect of Light upon the Eye.

For the doing of which, I ſhall firſt conſider the Fabrick and Make of that Organ. Secondly, The manner how Light comes to operate upon it.

An Explication of the Eye.   Firſt, For the Fabrick of the Eye, It is in it ſelf ſo truly admirable, that there is nothing in the whole Creation better deſerves our Contemplation, and wherein the Wiſdom and Deſign of the Great Creator more ſenſibly appears ; for as of all created Beings, thoſe which are animated ſeem to have the greateſt Contrivance ; every thing in each of them ſeeming to be contrived on purpoſe, and with a Deſign, reſpecting the end of their being and well-being, and continuation either in the individual, or in the Species propagated. So among thoſe animated Bodies, Animals ſeem to abound with more excellent contrivances than Plants ; and of Animals ſome are yet more curious and perfect than ſome others ; that is, have more Contrivance and Perfection of Organiſation and Mechaniſm than others ; though every thing in its kind be furniſh'd with thoſe Faculties which are requiſite to perform thoſe Functions which are neceſſary to their Preſervation. Now of all the Organiſations of Animals, none are more admirable than thoſe of the Senſes, and of thoſe, none, that we know, more wonderful than that of Sight, wherein we ſhall find every thing ſo adapted for Matter, Form, Situation, Motion, and the like, that it does far exceed the Contrivance of the Wit of Man to come near it, even in Imitation. And yet we find that all things are Conſonant and Congruous to our Underſtanding, and we cannot chuſe but approve and admire the great Wiſdom and Contrivance of the Maker ; ſo that we may even from thence clearly and demonſtratively ſee, that the Reaſon of Man is a ſpark of the Divine Influence, and that whatever is done in the World is adequate to the Principles and Ground of Reaſon implanted in our Underſtanding and Knowledge ; and that all things are formed and act with Deſign and Reſpect to the End, and not fortuitouſly and by chance.

For an Inſtance of this, we cannot in Nature pitch upon a better than the Fabrick of the Eye, in which we ſhall find every thing adapted and formed for that particular part of performing Viſion, which is to be performed by it ; and every part has its neceſſity to make up the perfect Effect, and no one is redundant, and there is no part defective.

The Radiations of Light I have formerly Explained, are continually Propagated from every Luminous Object, and from every Point of every Luminous Object, every way from every one of thoſe Points *in Orbem* ; as the Rays from a Sphere : So that as there are infinite of thoſe radiating Points in the World, ſo from every one of thoſe infinite Points there are infinite of thoſe Radiations ; ſo that the Luminous *Medium* has infinite Radiations in every Point thereof ; to wit, a ſingle Radiation from every one of thoſe infinite Radiating Points. Now theſe Radiating Points are not only all ſuch as ſend out their own Light which is generated in themſelves, but all ſuch likewiſe, as by Reflection or Refraction, are the Cauſes of reflecting or diſperſing the Light, received from other Luminous Bodies. Now the Eye is an Organ or Inſtrument by which all thoſe infinite Rays that are thus jumbled and blended together, and ſo might be thought impoſſible to be ſeparated, are ſo curiouſly ſifted, culled, ſeparated, and parted from each other, that they are all again made diſtinct, and every one of them appropriated, as it were, to is diſtinct Point or Cell. So that as there are infinite of thoſe Radiating Points without the Eye that emit thoſe Beams ; ſo there are infinite of thoſe receptive Points within the Eye that receive them, each of which Points do only receive the Radiations from one of thoſe infinite Points without, and from no other whatſoever at the ſame time. Now it is not only a Separation of theſe Rays thus paſſing in one ſingle Point only

*

                                              only

only of the Luminous Medium, for that would feem to be more eafy, but it is a Separation of all thofe infinitely infinite Rays that pafs through the infinite Points that are in a Superficies as big as the Pupil, or Black Hole of the Eye, and a Reunion of all thofe radiations that come from any one Point, into one Point again ; fo that the Eye may not improperly be called a Microcofm, or a little World ; it having a diftinct Point within it felf, for every diftinct Point without it felf in the Univerfe ; and when a Hemifphere of the Heavens is open to its view, it has a Hemifphere within it felf, wherein there are as many Refpective Points for Reception of the Radiations, as there are differing Points for emiffion of Radiations, and all thofe infinitely infinite Radiations, which proceed from that whole Hemifphere of the Univerfe, and pafs through the *Area* of the Superficies of the Pupil of the Eye, are by this truly wonderful Contrivance of the Eye, feparated from each other, and conveyed to the diftinct cells of the Microcofm of the Eye. For the exact and curious Performance of which Work, the Fabrick of the Eye is fo curioufly contrived, that 'tis beyond the Wit of Man to imagine any thing could have been more compleat. Nay, It could never have entred into the Imagination, or thought of Man to conceive, how fuch a Senfation as Vifion could be performed, had not the all Wife Contriver of the World endued him with the Faculty and Organ of feeing it felf. How could it have entred into the Imagination of Man to conceive, how it fhould be poffible for fuch an Atom of the Univerfe as Man is, to be informed at the Inftant that a thing is done, how and where it is done, though Million of Millions of Miles diftant ? Certainly no more than we can now imagine how it fhould be poffible for any Man here in *London* to know the particular Thoughts and Inclinations of any one fingle Man in *China* or *Japan*, or of all the *Chinefe* or *Japanefe* together, at the fame Inftant they are thought there.

Now the contrivance of the Eye is not more admirable for its Power of feparating differing Rays from differing Points, one from another, than it is for congregating and culling all the infinite Rays that come from one Point, and Reuniting them again into one Point ; for by this, principally, is Vifion made. This is that which makes the Rays produce fo powerful an Effect as to be fenfible to the Animal. Now this will appear more plain if we confider the Explication I have formerly given of the Caufe of Light in the *Medium*, and the manner of its inftantaneous Progreffion through it. This I fhew'd you was a Motion or Pulfe caufed by the Protrufion of the Bodies about the Center, a certain fpace every way in *Orbem*, towards the Circumference. Now though the length of this Pulfe at the Luminous Body, as the Sun, from the Center outwards, fhould be an Inch perhaps ; yet fince the length of that Pulfe doth decreafe continually in duplicate Proportion of the Diftance, reciprocally taken from the Luminous Body ; the length of the Pulfe of Light here with us would not be the 1000000 Part of the thicknefs of a Hair ; now what can we imagine or conceive could be fo curioufly fenfible as to be moved thereby, or that the animated Body, or any part of it, could be fenfible of it, or affected by it ? certainly it could not, and therefore the all Wife Creator contrived the Eye to be an Organ to reftore again the Strength of that Pulfe, which was deftroyed by the great interpofed Diftance ; for by the means hereof, the Pulfe that was, by diftance, fhortned Million of Millions of times of the length it had at the Luminous Point ; is by the reunion of them by the Eye again, reftored to a good part of its firft Power, in the correfponding Point in the Eye : for as, whilft Rays are diverging and fpreading from the Luminous Point into a uniform *Medium*, the Pulfe grows fhorter and fhorter in a duplicate Proportion to the Diftance reciprocally ; fo in converging Rays (or Rays drawn to a Point, from a Superficies) do the lengths of the Pulfes increafe in a contrary order : So that in probability, in the Point of Reunion in the Eye, the Pulfe may be almoft as long, as at the Point of Emiffion or Emanation. That this may be the better underftood, I would difcourfe a little upon a very common and obvious Experiment of fetting Fire to a Body by the Rays of the Sun, collected by a Burning Glafs, whether Reflecting or Refracting, it matters not much to our prefent Reafoning.

Suppose then we have a Burning Glass of a Foot Diameter, or breadth; which will collect all the Rays from the Sun, and unite them at fourteen Inches from the Glass, into a Focus or circular Figure of the Sun of ½ of an Inch in Diameter, we see first by Experiment, that the Rays so collected will set Fire to Wood, and several other Combustible Bodies and consume them, whereas the Rays of the Sun before this Union of them, were very hardly, perhaps, if at all sensibly warm. If therefore we consider the Reason of this Effect, we shall find that all the Rays which were before expanded into a Circle of a Foot Diameter, are, by this Constipation made by the burning Glass, crowded and thrust together into the space of a Circle ½ of an Inch in Diameter; we must conclude that all that warmth that was in the Circle of a Foot Diameter, is now in a Circle of half a quarter of an Inch. Now the Area of the greater Being, to the Area of the less, as 9216 to one, it follows that the Heat of the greater to the Heat of the less, must be Reciprocal to the Area, that is, as 1 to 9216, and consequently the impression of the Light at the *Focus*, must be more than at the Glass, no less than 9216 times; and consequently the same as the direct Rays of Light from the Sun would be, at one 96th part of the Distance of the Earth from the Sun; and consequently as strong as it would be upon a Planet about the Sun, which should appear to us at the Distance from the Sun of 36 Minutes, or a little more than the Diameter of the Sun. Now in the same manner as this Burning Glass acts upon the Rays of the Sun in constipating and driving them together into a smaller room, does the Eye for all other Rays of Light from Luminous Objects. Where that Impression or Action of the Light, though in it self it be very small, and wholly insensible even to that part of the Eye, which is the most sensible and curious of all the Parts of the Body, namely, the *tunica Retina*, as I shall afterwards shew, yet is made sensible by the Multiplication of its Force upon the Constipation of the Rays into a *Focus*, which Acts and Terminates in that most curious Substance.

This is one way by which we may conceive somewhat of the Reason of the curious Fabrick of the Eye for the Multiplication of the Action or Power of Luminous Bodies, upon the sensible Animal Part.

How the Eye Multiplies the Power of Light. 2. The other way we may conceive how this Fabrick of the Eye does cause this Impression to be Multiplied, Augmented, and become sensible, Depends upon the consideration of the Hypothesis, which I propounded the last Term for the explanation of Light, and that was by a Pulse or Stroke, according to the length of which, I shewed you at that time, the Power or Strength of the Light was.

This I explain'd to you by a sensible Experiment made by firing Gunpowder. For a Corn or Grain of Gunpowder expanding it self, when fired in a Sphere .1000000 as big as its own Bulk, must necessarily act accordingly on the encompassing Medium; but I need not repeat what was then said. Therefore to return to the Instance of the Burning Glass.

Now by the Refraction or Reflection of a Burning Glass, all those Rays which before were Diverging and spreading wider and wider from a Point, and so grew weaker and weaker in the proportion I mentioned (that is, according to the Superficies of the Sphere, or Basis of the Cone) by this Action I say of the Burning Glass, they are made converging and approaching nearer and nearer together; and so of consequence augmented and increased in Power and Effect, and the Strength lost or rarified by the diverging, is renewed and revived by the converging. And whereas in the diverging, the Diminution was very slow and long, in this converging, the Increase and Augmentation is very quick and short; for as the distance of the Burning Glass from the Sun, is to the distance of the Burning Glass from its Focus; so is the Increase of Constipation, by the effects of that Burning Glass upon the Rays, to the decrease of Expansion of them in their Progress from the Sun to the Glass; so that the Rays of Light at half the Distance of the *Focus* from the Burning Glass, is the same with the constipation of the Rays, at half the distance of the Sun from the Burning Glass; and consequently the length of the Pulse, and strength of the Ray is the same; and so at a tenth Part of the distance from the Focus, the
                                                                            Power

Power or Action of Light, is as strong as it is at a tenth part of the Distance of the Sun from the Burning Glass. So that if the distance of the Sun be 10000 Semidiameters of the Earth, and the Focus 14 Inches; the strength of the Light, or the length of its Pulse or Stroke shall be the same at $1\frac{2}{5}$ Inch from the Focus, that it is, at 1000 Diameters Distance from the Sun; and consequently, the length of the Pulse in the very *Focus*, must be the very same with the length of the Pulse at the Sun.

3. Now the Action of the Eye being much the same upon the Rays of Light, from any Luminous Object with this of the Burning Glass; it follows that the Eye does by its Power bring all visible Objects into the bottom of it, and make an Impression on the *Retina*, the same, as if the very Action of the Object were immediately there.

3. So that the Substance of the *Retina* is affected or moved by the very same *These applied to* Action, as if it touched the Object; and the Eye does continually make the *the Eye.* Hemisphere of Actions or Motions within it self, the same with the great visible Hemisphere without it. And these Impressions are communicated to the Brain, or sensated by the Animal Soul, if that Substance be in Health and Sound; if not, the Impression is Defective, and the Sight or Sensation Imperfect. As it sometimes happens in some Distempers of the Brain and nervous Parts, in which Cases the sight fails, though the Organ of the Eye it self be perfectly formed, as in a *Gutta Serena.*

There is a very remarkable observation of Monsieur *Mariotte* about Vision, that the sensation of Light is not made in the *Tunica Retina*, but on the *Choroeides*; That that part of the bottom of the Eye which the *Choroeides* does not cover is wholly senseless and blind, though the Impression of Light upon the Place be the same as on the Parts that are contiguous, and lie about it.

Now this Gentlemans Observation is, that that part of the Eye, where the Optick Nerve enters into the Cavity of it, which is not in the Axis of its Figure, but at a pretty distance from it nearer to the Nose, namely, at about 25 Degrees from the Axis inward, is not cover'd with the *Choroeides*. And that we have no sense of the Impression of Light made upon it.

The Experiment is this, take two small Candles in the Night, or in the Day time, two small bits of White Paper of about the bigness of a Shilling, let the Candles be set on a Table at two or three Foot distance, so that the Flames may be about the height of the Eye from the Floor; let the Papers in the Day time be stuck against a dark Wall, or dark coloured Hangings, at about the same distance, and the same height; then placing your self just before them, and looking towards them, close one of your Eyes with your Hand; as suppose your left Eye, and look directly on the Candle or Paper on your left Hand, and you will see both the Objects very plain, that you respect, very clear and distinct, and the other somewhat more Imperfectly; keeping your Eye thus shut, and the right Eye respecting the left Hand Object, by Degrees go backwards, 'till at length you will perceive that the Right Hand Object vanishes, and is no more visible; mark that Distance and you will find it to be at about $3\frac{1}{4}$ times the Distance of the two Objects, going yet farther backward, you will again begin to see them both as before, viz. at the distance of about $4\frac{1}{2}$; then again going in this Posture nearer the Objects, you will find the Right Hand Object disappear when you come to the former Distance, and when nearer, they will both again appear, and so continue 'till you come close to them. Now the reason of this Appearance is, that the Axis of the Right Eye being always kept directed to the Left Hand Object, when you are at the aforesaid Distance, the impression from the Right Hand Object falls on that part of the bottom of the Eye where the Optick Nerve is inserted, over which there is no part of the *Choroeides* expanded, and the sensible part being wanting, the Sensation is not made, though the Impression be the very same; as on each side of it, as I shall prove more particularly, when I come to explain the several parts of this most curious Organ, and what the Function and Use of each part is, which I may make the Subject of some of my succeeding Lectures.

This

This Deduction of his was disapproved by Monsieur *Pequet*, tho' the Experiment was allow'd, who gave his Reasons for maintaining the *Retina*, the chief Organ for receiving the Species. This Dispute may be seen in the *Philos. Transact.* Numb. 35, & 59. whether it be the one or the other, is not much to our present purpose, therefore I shall leave it, and proceed.

4. I have endeavoured to explain to you that admirable contrivance of the Organ of Sight, the Eye, whereby it Collects the Rays of Light, so as to make an Impression upon the sensitive Part of it, of the Action, Motion, or Power of the Luminous Object upon the immediately incompassing *Medium*, though *Why the Eye is* this Luminous Object be never so far distant, and by that means, as it were in *not hurt by the* an instant, to touch, or feel any such Object, as if it were contiguous to it, but *Action of Light.* yet so as not to hurt or offend the sensible part; for the Eye taketh but a very small Cone, or part of the Radiating Sphere; and thereby, though the Motion be the same as to Velocity and Length of Pulse in every the smallest Cone or Ray, that it is in the whole Sphere; yet being but a small part of the whole incompassing *Medium*, it contains but a part of the Action of the Luminous Point; for which Reason we are able to look upon the Sun, or a Fire, or an exceeding bright Flame; as melted Silver, or Iron, or Sulphur burning upon melted Niter, without much offending the Organ, if it be strong and vegete; but if the Eye be weak, and the Impression be continued, it will much offend it, and dull the Sense, whence it is that looking much upon Fire, or any such bright Object, does very much decay the Sight, and makes it more insensible of the weaker Impressions made by other less Luminous Objects: And hence we find, that we are unable for a time to perceive Objects in a House or Room, immediately after we come in out of the Sunshine. Now by reason of the great Variety that there is in differing Objects, as to the Quantity and Strength, and that the *Retina*, or sensating part is capable only of receiving Impressions to a certain Degree of Strength, without being hurt by it, there is a contrivance in the Eye, which I shall afterwards more fully explain, by which the Quantity of the Rays admitted is moderated, so as to keep it, that the impression does not exceed that limit: And this is the Aperture or Hole through the *Iris*, which is the black Hole that appears in the middle of the transparent part of the Eye; for this Hole which admits the Rays to pass into the Eye, is contracted or dilated, according as the Object is brighter or darker; that a lesser Quantity of the stronger Rays, and a greater Quantity of the weaker Rays may be admitted, and hence it is, that a brighter Object among dimmer Objects, does cloud and darken them, because the aperture of the *Iris* being contracted protionable to the Strength of the brighter, the Rays, admitted from the fainter and more dim Objects, are not sufficient to make a sensible Impression. So that the effect of the Rays are by this means proportion'd to the Ability of the sensible Part of the Eye to bear the Impression, and where notwithstanding the utmost contraction of this aperture of the *Iris*, the Rays make too strong an impression upon the *Retina*, we are forc'd to wink and close the Eye Lids nearer, to shut out part of that quantity of Light which would otherwise have entred into the Eye; or to look through a small Hole, or through an opacous Body. And hence it is, that any one may with ease look upon the Sun, if he look through a small Pin-hole in a Plate, by which means one may with pleasure see an Eclipse of the Sun, without using any opacous Glass; though if the *Cornea*, or any other part of the Eye, be any ways opacous, this way discovers the Defects of them, and does somewhat vitiate the Figure of the Object. But of this, and the manner of contracting of the Pupil, more, when I come to explain that part of the Eye; that which I mention it for at present is, only to explain how the Eye becomes as it were a Hand, by which the Brain feels, and touches the Objects, by creating a Motion in the *Retina*, the same, and at the same Instant, with the Motion of the lucid Object it self. For the make of the Eye is such, in all its Contrivance and Parts, that the Conical Ray of Light proceeding from a Point of the Object, and terminating with a Divergency in the Aperture, or *Cornea* of the Eye; is by the Refraction thereof again reunited into a Point at the *Focus*, which is in the *Retina*; and consequently, whatever the Motion or Power of the Light was in the *Apex* of this Cone, which is at the

Luminous

Luminous Body the fame is the Motion or Power of Light, at the Point or *Apex* of the Cone, made by the Refraction, and terminating in the *Retina*, fo that the Eye does, as it were, invert and fhorten the conical Radiation, and contracts a Cone 10000 Semidiameters of the Earth in length, into the length of an Inch or thereabout in a Man; from which Explication all the Appearances of Vifion, whether by the naked Eye, or by Telescopes, or Microscopes, will be very naturally, and I conceive very truly explained; and the wonderful Wifdom of the Great Creator more manifeftly fhewn.

5. We are therefore in the next place to confider the Fabrick of the Organ it felf, of what Parts it confifts, and of what ufe each of them is toward the compleating this Effect.

1. In the Confideration whereof, the firft thing that reprefents it felf to our View, is the tranfparent part of it that is placed outwards, which is the entrance by which the Rays pafs into it.

I fhall not need to mention the pofition of it in the Face, nor the Duality of them, nor the Cells of the Skull in which they lie, nor the Lidds that cover it when Senfation ceafes, as in Sleep; fave only that I fhall afterwards fhew you the ufe of them for moyftning, glazing, and clearing the *Cornea* from Duft and other Fowlnefs; no nor of the various Mufcles that ferve to Rule it to and fro every way, and direct and fix the *Axis* of it upon the Object to be viewed; the contrivance of which is truly admirable, nor fhall I take notice of any Anatomical Obfervation concerning it, fave only fuch as tend to explain the Make and Fabrick of it, for performing this Effect of Collecting Diverging and parallel Rays, and refracting them into a Point or *Focus*: Other confiderations thereof being more proper to be handled upon the confideration of other Subjects.

Having taken the Eye out of its place, or Socket in the Skull, and having taken off carefully all the Mufcles that ferve for its Motion, as being not now confidered, we have a round Ball fhaped fomewhat like that reprefented in the fixt Figure *A B E B F A*. This Body is in a Man of about an Inch Diameter, and to *B A B*, is very near of a globous Figure, though in divers other Animals it be of divers other Figures; fome of them more depreft at the middle, and nearer to the fhape of a Turnip, and at about 25 Degrees from an imagined Axis, which paffes through the middle of all its parts, is inferted into it the Optick Nerve *F F*, which Infertion together with all the Globous part of the Ball, is covered with a thick, ftrong, and pretty ftiff Coat, or Shell, which ferves as a folid Wall, to preferve the fhape and figure of the Parts within, to which alfo the Mufcles, for its outward Motions, are faftned; and likewife the Mufcular Parts within the Eye, which ferve for the inward Motions; this is called the σκληρώδης, or *Tunica Sclerotica*, or hard Coat; and is a continuation of the *Dura Mater*, or the outmoft ftrong hard Bag that contains the Brain; and by a curious Diffection may be found quadruplicate, as is alfo the *Cornea*. This for the moft part is white and opacous, and fo permits no light to pafs it any way, though in fome Creatures I have obferved it to be pretty Tranfparent, fo as to fhew the Picture of Objects without, made at the bottom of the Eye, as in Young Kitlings: The formoft part of this is of a more protuberant Figure, and feems fomewhat Elliptical; rifing confpicuoufly prominent above the Superficies of the Sphere *B A B*, continued this Prominent part *B E B*, is perfectly tranfparent, though it be of a flexible Subftance, and fiom fome kind of Refemblance it has to Horn, is called the *Cornea*, or horny Coat: This, as it is more round in the middle about E, than it is at the fide *B B*; fo I have obferved it alfo to be thinner in the middle, than at the fides, fo that it refembles the defcription in the Figure. The Ellipticalnefs of the Figure, as it may plainly be difcovered by the Eye, without any other help, fo more certainly by the Reflection of Images from its Surface, and by the refraction of it when filled with Water, and looked through toward any near Object. Through this tranfparent Coat or *Cornea*, the Rays enter into the Eye, and receive their firft and greateft Refraction towards their converging and meeting at the bottom

Plate 1. Fig. 6.

The Fabrick of the Eye.

K k tom

tom of the Eye. This is much larger in some Animals, as in Cats, Owls, Leopards, and other Creatures that seek their Prey in the Night; and so is able to receive a greater Quantity of those faint and dim Rays dispersed from Objects at that time, in which Creatures also the Pupil of the Eye is capable of a much greater Expansion and Contraction, as I shall by and by observe. This may give a very good hint of the possibility and practicableness of seeing in the Dark, of which I have many Years since made divers tryals with very good Success; and I have known several Men who have had such a Constitution of their Eyes by Nature, that they would be able with Ease to see every Letter distinct, when other Men, that otherwise had very good Eyes, could not see the Lines.

The inside of this thick and hard Coat of the Eye, is covered with another Coat, being in various Eyes of various Colours, as Black, Blue, Brown, Green, Yellow, and the like; it covers also the Optick Nerve, and is joyn'd to the *Sclerotica*, by an infinite company of little Veins, and Arteries and Vessels; this immediately joyns to, and, as it were, lines the Insides of the hard outward Coat, so far as the vitreous Humour extends; namely, to *B B*, and is called the *Choroeides*. But above this place it is separated from it in the aqueous Humour, and is called the *Uvea*. The use of this, as to Opticks, seems to be for the imbibing of the Rays of Light after they have imprest their Motion upon the *Retina*, though I have observed in some Creatures, a strong reflection from the bottom of the Eye, which could be from no other than the *Choroeides*. What its Use is for conveying necessary supply and Nourishment to the Parts of the Eye, is not my Subject.

To the inside of this Coat is joyned the *Retina*, which is that which immediately covers the vitreous Humour, and is the same Substance with the Substance of the Brain, which is also the *Medulla*, Marrow, or Pith of the Optick Nerve. This by *Des Cartes* and most others, is supposed to be the sensible part of the Eye, which receives the impression of the Pencils of the Rays of Light; though there are others of another Opinion, that the *Retina* being the same with the substance of the Brain, has no sense in it, as the Brain it self hath not, but that the *Choroeides*, as being the same with the *Pia Mater*, and consequently of the most acute Sense, is that which receives, and is sensible of the Impression of the Rays of Light: And to confirm this, the Experiment I shew'd and explain'd to you the last day is brought as an Argument by Monsieur *Mariotte*, which carries in it indeed very much of probability; for by that Experiment you have a sensible Proof, that in that part of the Eye where there is no part of the *Choroeides*, as at the *Medulla* of the Optick Nerve, there you are blind as it were, or insensible of the Light; whereas in that Place there is the greatest Plenty of the *Retina* or *Medullary* Part; within this Coat is contained the Vitreous or Glassy Humour of the Eye which fills the whole lower Cavity of it; it is called the Glassy Humour, not that 'tis so very hard; but because it being very transparent and clear, it is of a greater consistence than the watery, being like a Jelly, and yet is softer than that which from its exceeding clearness, not hardness, is called the *Chrystalline*; this is delineated by the Figure *G G*. This Humour on the upper side of it has a Cavity in it, where it receives the *Chrystalline* Humour, which is somewhat of the Figure delineated by *I H*: the under part of which in a Man, and in most other Terrestial Animals, is much more convex than the uppermost which is more flat; but in most Fishes it is of a perfect Globular form; its of a pretty solid Consistence so as to keep its Form after it is stript of the Coat or Skin, that covers it both above and below, called the *Aranea* or Cobweb Coat, which is very thin, strong and transparent, and is joyn'd to the *Choroeides* by the Edges, by means of the *Ciliares B H*, *B H*, which seems to be Muscular, all the space between the Crystalline Humour and the Cornea is filled with a very clear and liquid Water, the Figure of which Cavity, and consequently of the Water contained is exprest by *I I*, contain'd within the Cavity *E B H B E*.

In this Water between the Chrystalline and the Cornea, is placed a Skin with a Perforation in the middle of it, that is called the *Uvea*, exprest by *B I*, *B I*, the outermost side of which is of various Colours, in various Eyes, as blackish, blueish, greenish, yellowish, brownish, and the like; the Hole of it in several

Animals

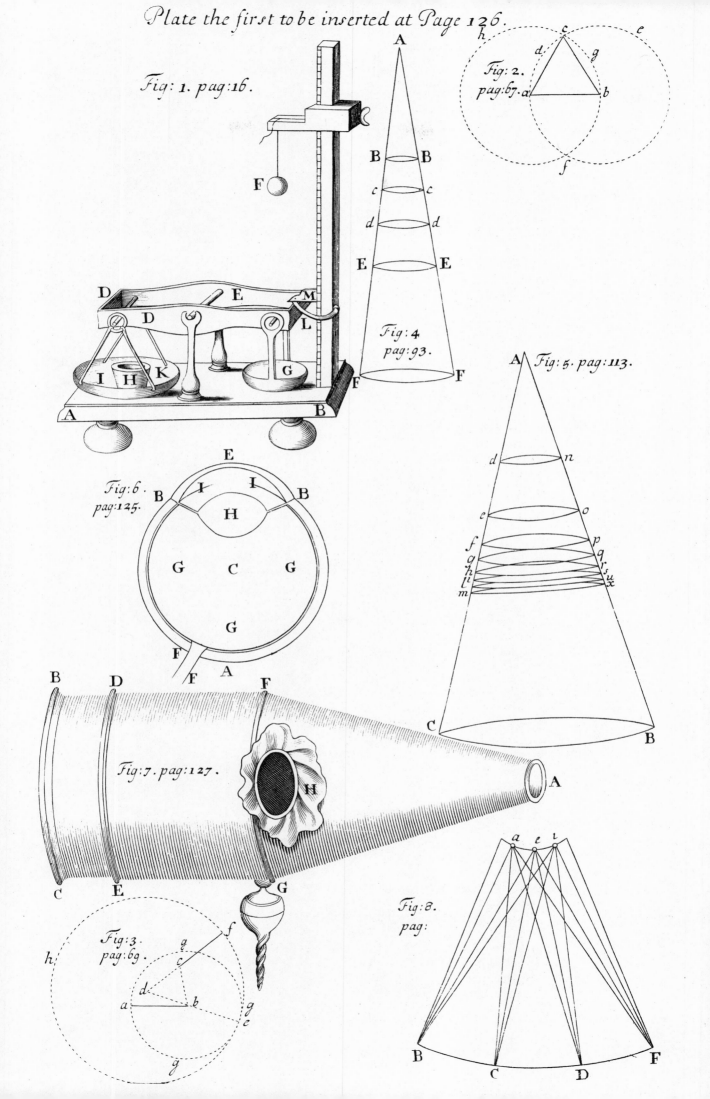

Plate the first to be inserted at Page 126.

Fig: 1. pag: 16.

Fig: 2. pag: 67.

Fig: 4. pag: 93.

Fig: 5. pag: 113.

Fig: 6. pag: 125.

Fig: 7. pag: 127.

Fig: 3. pag: 69.

Fig: 8. pag:

Animals is of feveral fhapes, but in Men it is perfectly round, in Sheep of an oblong Oval, in Cats like a flit; in other Creatures of other Forms, the bigneſs of which is more or leſs, according to the brightneſs or dimneſs, the nearneſs or remoteneſs of the Objects feen, and has in it a kind of natural Motion not voluntary, which is moved only by the various Impreſſions of the Objects. And we have no other Power to open it than by looking upon dark Objects, or of ſhutting it, than by looking upon bright and near Objects: The Limits of which Motion in Men is not very great, but in Cats and other Creature, that fee in the Dark, very great.

This Watery Humour does fometimes breed a kind of Mother in it, fo as to become thick, and look White, and fo hinder the Rays of Light in part, or in whole, from paſſing through it, and when it is grown to a fenfible Thickneſs, is call'd a *Cataract*, but the Sight may be again recovered by couching that *Cataract*, which is nothing but thruſting in a fine Needle through the *Cornea*, and with the Point of it breaking and cruſhing down to the bottom of the Eye this Mothery Subſtance. This Humour, though it be all let out, will prefently be renewed again, and filled with Water as before, without deſtroying the Sight of the Eye, as has been often experimented.

Thus I have ſhewed you all the parts of which the Eye confiſts, and the form and manner of their Pofition in order to compleat this curious Organ to make it fit for Vifion; having omitted all thofe other confiderations of it, which belong more properly to Anatomy and Phyfick, my aim being only to take notice of thofe things only ferve for the explication of Opticks and Light.

It would be too long for this prefent Exercife to explain to you the exact Figure, and the various Refractions of the feveral parts of the Eye, and to ſhew you the particular ufe of every part of it, for compleating the collection of Rays proceeding from the Points of the Luminous Object, and terminating them in as many diſtinct Points at the bottom of the Eye, which I defign, God willing, to compleat, when I come to explain Refraction and the Laws thereof. And therefore, I ſhall at prefent only mention to you, that that Collection or Termination is made at the *Retina* or *Choroeides*, which, as I have ſhew'd, you are the Coats that line the bottom of the Eye, and encompaſs the vitreous Humour, on which they do defcribe, as it were, a perfect Picture, or Repreſentation of all outward Objects, as may be plainly feen by the Eye of a Kitling; the *Sclerotis* or bottom of which is tranfparent, or by any other Eye, if the *Sclerotis* be carefully ſhaved off fo as to leave it tranfparent: And as I have done by a large artificial Eye made with Glaſs, Water, and Jelly, figured according to the ſhapes reprefented in the Scheme, which is a Section of the Eye, made by the Optick *Axis*; that in this Picture are remarkable not only all the Lines and Proportions, but the Lights, Shadows, Colours, Motions of the Objects themſelves. So that from a clear Underſtanding of this, the Reafon, Caufe, and Manner of Vifion will be clearly underſtood.

5. Now becaufe the Structure and Making of fuch an Artificial Eye is very difficult, and the ufe thereof notwithſtanding, very neceſſary for a through Knowledge of Opticks; I having only mention'd this at prefent, that fuch as have a Mind to be curious in it, may, if they pleafe, prepare the like.

I ſhall rather as a Supplement to it, make ufe of a darkned Room, or Perſpective Box, in which all the Appearances that are made in the Eye are in ſome manner reprefented. Prepare therefore a Box of the ſhape in the feventh Plate 1. Figure, let it be four or five Foot long from *A* to *D E*, and make the bottom Fig. 7. of it *B C*, Concave towards the End *A*, and the bottom of the Box *B D E C*, being made Cylindrical, and not Tapering, as the part *A FG* is, that the movable bottom *B C*, may be placed nearer to or farther from the End *A*. At *A* place a Convex Glaſs of the length of the Box in a Hole as large as the Glaſs, which the larger it is the better, becaufe of feveral Tryals that may be made with it, which cannot be made with a ſmaller. To this Hole cut feveral, as eight or ten Pieces of Paſt board that may each of them ferve to cover it, and in every of them cut a Hole of a Round, or other Figure you would ufe, and either in
the

the middle of it, or out of the middle of it, and of a greater or lefs Figure; according to the Tryals you defign by them; let the infide of the Concave bottom be made very White, to receive and reflect the Points of Light, and make a Hole in the fide of the Box *H*, covered about with Leather, or thick Wollen Cloth, with a Hole large enough to put ones Face into it, fo as to fee the Species or Picture of outward Objects upon the bottom, then turning the end *A* where the Glafs is placed toward the Object (if the Sun fhines upon it, it is the better, becaufe of the great Reflection of Light from fuch Objects,) flide the moveable bottom *B C*, to or fro, 'till by looking in at the Hole *H,*you perceive the Reprefentation of the outward Objects very perfect, then take notice of the diftance of the Object, and likewife the diftance of the bottom ;. the Pofition, Magnitude, Brightnefs, Colour, and all the other Remarks that appertain to the explaining the feveral Appearances that may happen to the Eye, then fit it for reprefenting Objects at a greater diftance, and take notice of the diftance of the bottom, and all the other Remarks neceffary for explaining your Inquiry : The like may be done with the various apertures of Paftboards, which may ferve to explain all that might happen to the Eye, by the contracting and dilating the Pupil, by obferving the definednefs of the Species on each fide the *Axis*, and where they are moft diftinct ; and fo for all other Queftions that may happen concerning what Light is in the Eye, and what Effects it there produces. It may be convenient to fix a Ball and Socket underneath it to make it more eafy to be managed.   It may alfo be made fquare as well as Cilindrical, provided the bottom of it, *B C*, be a Concave of a part of a Sphere of the length of the Boxes Radius.

Let this therefore fuffice at prefent for explication of the firft Principle of the Emanation of Light from the Luminous Body, and for the Reception therof upon the fubject ; that the Light is conveyed from every Point of the Luminous Body, to every Point of the Body inlightned, through a uniform tranfparent Medium by direct Emanations, or in imaginary ftraight Lines.   The fame Rule holds in all Light that proceeds from an Object inlightned, that promifcuoufly reflects the Light caft upon it every way, for fuch a Body may be faid to fhine, as it were, by the Light of another Body, and may therefore upon that account be faid to be a fecundary Luminous Body, and the Light a fecundary Light, fuch as that of the Moon, and the other Primary and Secundary Planets, fo that the fame Rule will hold in both, and the inlightning and the inlightned Cones are to be confidered in the calculation of Rays from Bodies fhining by a fecundary Light, and the Proprieties and Proportions to be obferved in both, in their Power and Propagation, will fall under the fame Rules as I fhall afterwards more at large explain and manifeft.

Next, As light is thus propagated by imaginary ftraight Lines, fo is alfo Shadow, which is nothing but a Defect or want of a peculiar Light, taken off or intercepted by an opacous Body, or of a Body that will nor permit the Rays to pafs onwards in its direct Courfe, which is only vifible by Accident ; that is, by finding from that part a defect of the Influence of Light, which we are fenfible of, every where about it.   And by this means it is that we fee the dark or fhaded fide of the Moon in an Eclipfe of the Sun ; that is, we perceive fuch a part of the light of the Sun taken off by the opake Body of the Moon coming between that and us, but of it felf it is no ways vifible ; for though we may be faid to fee that fhaded part of it which hides part of the Sun, yet we cannot fee any part of it which is without the Suns Limb, fo were the Body of the Moon in an Eclipfe of the Moon, perfectly within the fhadow of the Earth, and that no manner of Light by the refraction of the Sun-beams in the Atmofphere were conveyed to it, we fhould fee no other appearance of it, but only that fometimes this, fometimes that Star would difappear which was covered by it, and it is only diftinguifhed by the Light about it.

This therefore comes under confideration only relatively with refpect to Light, and is to be calculated as a Defect, though the fame Rules in calculation of the two before mentioned Cones will here hold alfo; but as Defects or like Quantities in Algebra marked with a Minus.

SECT.

SECT. VI.

A farther Continuation of the Lectures of Light. Read about April *or* May, 1682.

The CONTENTS.

1. *Light, the* Medium *by which all or most part of the Knowledge we have of the Celestial Bodies is conveyed to us. A farther confirmation of a* Plenum. *Mr.* Romer's *Observation of a temporaneous Propagation of Light not conclusive. That the* Medium *is absolutely Dense, and where the Parts are immediately contiguous, the propagated Motion must be instantaneous.* 2. *Tho' this propagation be instantaneous, yet the impression of this Motion is Momentary, or Temporaneous; therefore every Pulse of Light is Momentary, and requires some time, tho this is inconceivably short. Mr.* Hobb's *Expedient of a* Conatus ad Motum *insufficient. That there must be an actual local Motion, and that able to break the most solid Bodies. What Light is in the Agent, Medium, and Patient, is explain'd by a familiar Example: All Motions local, and differ only in the lengths of Spaces, and Moments of Time.* 3. *How Light is instantaneously propagated in Orbem, evinced by a cogent Example, by which all the Proprieties of its Motion are clearly explained. Two different Cones may be considered between the illuminating and illuminated Bodies. Why the Light of the Sun exceeds that of all the Stars collected, if the Stars were brought nearer, tho' their Areas remain'd the same, yet their Light would be greater.* 4. *The Proprieties of Light propagated in a transparent uniform Medium to the Eye, reduced to four Considerations, each of which are enlarged upon and exemplified. How the same Corpuscle may communicate different Motions several different Ways, in the space of a Human Moment.* 5. *Every sensible Moment of Time, as well as every sensible Particle of Matter composed of infinite lesser; so that in the same sensible Moment, the same sensible Point may be successively moved infinite Ways, when the Vibrations of a string can be no longer discerned, they become the Objects of another Sense, the Hearing; the sensible Moments of Creatures proportioned to their Bulk. Short lived Creatures may have as many sensible Moments as longer lived, and in some Sense be said to live as long as Man. That there are infinite Spaces in the least sensible Space to be moved; and lastly, the Velocities may be infinitely swift in each of these Spaces. The bigger the Body is, the slower are its Vibrations. Lesser Animals see those Vibrations which we can only hear. A Continuation of that Subject of the Propagation of Light. That the vast Number of successive Impulses in a Human Moment is no Objection; so that upon the whole, there may be assigned to the Propagation of Light, a real local Motion.* 6. *From the former Reasons, the Author deduces the Cause of the perfect fluidity of the vast Expansum of Matter or Æther, between*

the

*the Planetary Bodies.   Why one fluid Body hinders Motion thro' it, more
than another, instanced by some Experiments.   R. W.*

*Light the Me-
dium to convey
all Celestial
Knowledge.*

I Have formerly explain'd here several Properties of Light, which I have been
the more particular in because it is the *Medium*, by which all the Knowledge
we have of the Heavenly Bodies is conveigh'd to us: for though we are affected
also by the Heat, yet it seems to be conveyed to us by no other Medium than
that of Light ; for Light, as I have shew'd you, seems to be nothing else but
an Internal Motion of a Transparent, first begun, or imposed by the Luminous
Body, upon the Parts of the Uniform, or Transparent *Medium* ; and then propagated through that *Medium*, to the utmost Extent, or Limits of it.   Now
from the boundlessness of its Propagation, and the Instantaneousness also of it,
I conceive that the Parts thereof are absolutely Contiguous, and make a P*lenum* ;
so that at the same Instant that a part is moved by the Lucid Body, at any one
part of the *Medium*, the utmost Extreams of the *Medium*, on that side towards
which the Motion is impressed, are moved also.   And this agrees with the most
curious Observations that have been hitherto made concerning it ; and though
Monsieur *Romer* indeavours to make it otherways by Observations made about
the *Satellites* of *Jupiter* ; yet, as I have formerly shew'd you, they are not sufficient
to prove his Theory ; because, supposing his Observations and Calculations exact, yet there may be other as probable Causes assigned to solve the Appearances,
as this which he has assigned . So then if the Propagation be instantaneous, it
will follow, I say, that the *Medium* is perfectly Dense, or the Parts immediately contiguous one to another ; for if there should be Vacuities intersperfed,
and so the Parts behind should be necessitated to move through that Space, before
it could touch the next, and that another space, before it could touch the third,
and that third another Space to pass, before it could touch a fourth, and so onwards ; it would follow, that the passing of every one of these Spaces would
take up some time, and consequently would make the Motion temporaneous
but where the Parts are immediately contiguous, the first cannot move without,
at the same Instant, moving the second, nor that without moving the third,
nor that without moving a fourth, fifth, sixth, and so forward, to an innumerable Series, or to the utmost extent of the Medium.   The ingenious *Descartes*,
therefore, compares it to a solid Rod or Stick, whose Parts being all contiguous, the one End cannot be thrust forward, but that at the same Instant, the
other end is also thrust forwards, which is a plain and very sensible Explication
of what is meant by Instantaneous Propagation in the *Medium*, *viz.* a moving
together of all the Parts of the *Medium*, and not a successive.

*Its Impression
on the Medium
momentary.*

2. Now though the Propagation be thus instantaneous, yet the Impression of
this Motion on the *Medium* is Momentary, and though it be never so short a
Motion, and never so quick, yet it must be temporary ; for if the moving Luminous Body does move, or remove the *Medium* before it ; it must remove it
some space, and that Space cannot be passed without some time ; and therefore,
I conclude, that every Stroke, or Pulse of Light is Momentary, and lasts for
some space 'till a second Pulse or Stroke is impressed, though the Duration
of each Pulse be never so short ; as suppose, but the thousand thousandth part
of a Second of time, yet a Thousand Thousand of such Pulses will make a Second
of Time, and though the space that it moves be but the thousandth Part of
a Hairs Breadth, yet even that is a Space, and has a *terminus a quo*, and a *terminus ad quem*, and an interjacent space, through which the Motion must be

*Hobbs's Expe-
dient insuffici-
ent.*

performed in such a Space of time.   Nor will the Expedient which Mr. *Hobbs*
has found out, to save a Local Motion, serve the turn ; for he would have it to
be nothing but a *conatus ad motum*, an Endeavour to move, and not a Real Motion, and *Descartes* would have it a Propension to Motion, and not a Motion ;
but what the one means by *Conatus*, and the other by Propension, if it be not
an actual Motion, I understand not ; but as I shall hereafter prove, it must be an
actual *Loco*-Motion, for the Experiments I shall bring for that purpose, will
manifest it to the Sense to be a Local Motion, and that very considerable too.
in as much as it is able to break in Pieces even the most solid Body in the
Wolrd :

World. Now when I see a Mason holding the Edge of a Steel Chizzel hard against a very solid Marble Stone with his Left Hand, and with his Right, striking upon the Top, or Head of that Chizzel, with an Iron Hammer, so as to break off a piece of the Stone, I cannot but conclude that that Chizzel must have had more than a *Conatus ad Motum*, to make the Marble break, and that there was a real Local Motion of the whole Chizzel together forwards, so far as the Edge thereof did penetrate the Marble before it brake it. And this, I hope, may serve as a sensible Similitude, by which I would inform the Understanding what kind of Action or Motion it is by which Light is first generated in the Luminous Body. namely, like the Motion of the Hammer against the Head of the Chizzel ; next, how it is propagated through the transparent *Medium*, viz. the Medium is all moved together, even as the Body of the Chizzel : And, Thirdly, How that acts upon the Subject inlightned, and that is, after the manner as the Marble is broken by the Chizzel. This may, perhaps, seem but a coarse Similitude, for the Explication of the Motion or Action of Light, which is the most curious and spiritual of all sensible things. But yet, I have this to answer, that the more plain and obvious it is to be understood, the better it is to inform the understanding of the manner how, an Operation, which is too curious and fine to be reached by our Senses, is performed. And though I cannot have an imagination of a Space, but the thousandth Part of the breadth of a Hair, yet, by my Reason, I can be certainly informed that such a Space there is, and even by Microscopes we can make such a Space visible, and yet our fancy will diminish no farther than the least sensible Point to the naked Eye ; as the point of a sharp Needle or the like : But we are not less certain of it, though we cannot imagine it, that is, make an Image or Representation of it to the Mind. Now we are by the Eye assured that there is Light, and consequently, I say, there is a Motion impressed thereby upon that Sense, because there is no Sense but what is made by an Impression of some Motion, and that Motion is not impressed but by a Body moved with Local Motion, (for I cannot understand any other Motion,) and Local Motion must have a Space to pass, and that Space must be passed in some time ; and therefore Motions can only differ in lengths of Spaces and Moments of time ; if therefore I understand, comprehend, and imagine one Local Motion that falls under the reach of my Senses, I can by similitude comprehend and understand another that is ten thousand Degrees below the reach of them, they having both the same Proprieties, and differing only in the Spaces and the times ; whosoever therefore, endeavours to explain any insensible Way of producing an Effect, by somewhat that is less intelligible than that which he would explain, acts preposterously, as I could have instanced in the Explications of very famous Men, which instead of informing, do much confound and perplex the Understanding ; but it would be too long for this place.

A familiar Example to explain these matters.

3. I shall therefore proceed, and that is, to explain, how the Motion of Light is propagated *in Orbem*, for so we find it, which this Similitude I have here used does not reach, but only that of a direct Ray ; to make this therefore plain to the Understanding, I would propound a hollow Cone of Brass, or some other strong close Substance, whose bottom should be made of a yielding Substance and Spherical, and the *Apex* should have a Cylindrical Hole, by which it might be filled with Water, Quickfilver, or some other fluid Substance : Into this Cylindrical Hole or Syringe, I would have fitted a Cylinder so close as not to let the Water pass by it, having filled this hollow Conical Vessel, I strike against the end of the Cylinder with a Hammer, and force it to move the whole length of the Cylindrical Hole ; In this case it is clear, that the Water which filled the whole Vessel, and Cylindrical Hole must be all moved towards the bottom, and at the same Instant that I force in the Cylindrical Plug ; now supposing the Water not capable of Condensation, and the sides of the Cone not subject to stretch, and only the bottom capable of being moved ; I find that the Plug must have driven all the Water in the Cylindrical Hole into the Cavity of the Cone, and so must have driven forward as much as lay next to it of equal space, into the space of another equal Quantity of Water, and so onward ; 'till that which touches the bottom must drive the bottom so much

How Light is propagated in Orbem shewn.

much lower, as to inlarge the Capacity of the Cone enough to receive the Quantity of Water in the Syringe, forced into the Cone by the Plug. Now if we confider this Similitude, it will explain fome other Proprieties of the Propagation of Light. For, Firft, it is clear that every part of the Water muft be moved at the fame Inftant. Secondly, That there is no reafon why the Motion of all Parts that lie at equal Diftances from the end of the Syringe, fhould not have the fame Degrees of Motion. Thirdly, Why the Parts that lie more remote from the Syringe, have ftill the lefs proportion of Motion communicated to them. Fourthly, It fhews us plainly what that proportion is; namely, a Proportion reciprocal to the Square of the Diftances; for every of thofe Spaces muft be equal to the firft, as therefore the fame quantity of Motion is expanded into a bigger and bigger *Area*, fo muft its Power upon an equal fpace of any two Diftances, have its Power reciprocal to the *Areas* of thofe Bafes; fo that hereby we fee clearly the reafon why the Power of the Light at feveral Diftances is diminifhed in Reciprocal Proportion to the Expanfion of it. And this may ferve for the Explication of the Propagation of Light, from any fingle Point of a Luminous Objeƈt. Now the fame, thing that we underftand of any one fhining Point of a Luminous Objeƈt; the fame thing I fay, we are to conceive of every one of the whole Luminous Body; for evey point of it doth in the fame manner propagate its Influence, Power, or Motion; for if inftead of one Syringe at the end of the Cone, there were Two, Three, or more fuch Syringes, if any of them were moved, the Effeƈt would be the fame, as in that I have mentioned already, and if all were moved together, every one would have its Influence on the bottom, as if it had aƈted fingly, and fo evey Point of the bottom would be affeƈted, or moved by it, as well as every of thofe Points would alfo be affeƈted, or moved by every one of the other Syringes; as

Fig.8. Plate 1. fuppofe, *a, e* and *i*, were the three Holes of thefe Syringes, and *B, C, D, F,* were the bottom of the Cone; if the Syringe *e* were moved, it would propagate a Motion, or force to every point *B, C, D, F,* of the bottom *B, F,* fo likewife if the Syringe *a,* or the Syringe *i*, were moved fingly, each of them would propagate their Motion to every one of thofe Points, *B, C, D, F,* of the Bafe *B, F,* and to every other Point of it. And confequently, all thofe Syringes being moved together, muft every of them influence or move every Point of the Bafe, *B, F,* with its own diftinƈt Influence. Now the fame thing that will happen in this Cafe, in the Preffure or Motion of the Water againft the bottom, will alfo be in the Cafe of Light; for if we fuppofe *a, e, i,* to reprefent the Body of the Sun, and *B, C, D, F,* the Surface of a Body inlightned by it; It is moft certain, that every Point of the Bafe or Objeƈt, *B, C, D, F,* is influenced by every Point of the Superficies of the Sun that fhines; fo that there may be confidered in the Radiation of Light, between a Luminous Body, and an inlightned Body, two forts of Cones, each made up of infinite Radiations; namely, the inlightning Cone, and the inlightned Cone; the inlightning Cone I call that, which is propagated from one Point of a Luminous Body unto all the Parts of the Body inlightned, fuch are *B, a, F, B. B, e, F, B. B, i, F, B.* the active, or inlightning Point being the *Apex* thereof, as *a, e* and *i.* And, **2ly**, The inlightned Cone, I call that, which has the inlightned Point for its *Apex,* and whofe Bafe is terminated at the Luminous Body, and all terminate in the inlightned Point, fo if *a, e, i,* reprefent the Body of the Sun, then *a, B, i, a. a, C, i, a. a, D, i, a,* and *a, F, i, a.* do each of them reprefent a Cone, whence it will clearly follow, that the bigger the inlightning Body is, the more Radiations there will fall upon it, and the more the Cone will be inlightned; and this is one of the Reafons why the Light of the Sun does fo much exceed the Light of all the Stars, becaufe that in the Hemifphere of the Sun that Shines upon us, there are more Luminous Points or Radiations than from all the Stars of a whole Hemifphere of the Heavens; but there is alfo a fecond Caufe, and that is to be fetcht from the greater Diftance of the inlightning Bodies of the Stars; for, as I fhew'd before, the Power of the Light doth decreafe reciprocally to the fquares of the Diftance. For fhould all the Luminous Bodies of the Stars be diminifhed in Diameter, according to their differing Diftances, and be brought fo near us, as the Sun, and fo appear all under the fame Angle they now do, their Light would be confiderably ftronger, and greater to us in the Night, and even in the

Day

Day than now it is; though the *Area* of them all put together, would be no bigger than now it is; for the Light from the brighteft Star, as of the great Dog Star, though in a Dark Night it feem very vivid, yet could it be feen with the Light of a part of the Sun appearing of the fame Diameter with it, it would look very faint and weak. And when I have viewed a Star in the Day-time, with a Telefcope, though by the help of the Telefcope I have mightily fortified that Light, and fo centuplicated its Power, yet after all, I found that the Body of it has appeared fainter than the Body of the Moon at Noon.

4. Thefe then are all the Proprieties we need to take notice of in a fimple Propa-*Proprieties of* gation of Light through a tranfparent uniform *Medium.* Namely, firft, that there is a *Light to be ob-* Propagation of Light from every Point of the Surface, in every part of the tranfpa-*ferved.* rent incompaffing Medium *in orbem,* that they each of them exert their particular Influence in that Orb, as if they were all fingle and diftinct. And, Secondly, That the more of thefe fingle Rays there fall upon an inlightned Point, the more it is inlightned, and that each of thefe Rays does act upon the inlightned Body with the fame Power, as if it acted fingly, though at the fame time, Millions of Radiations from other Points do act upon it.

This does feem fomewhat difficult to be underftood how it fhould poffibly *How a Body* be fo: But yet if we confider, that though we cannot by Senfe apprehend the *may communi-* very Manner of its Acting; yet we are not without fenfible Examples of fuch *cate different* kind of Actions naturally performed: For if on the fmooth Superficies of a *Motions diffe-* ftanding Water, we let fall a Drop of Water, we fhall, I fay, plainly fee how *rent ways.* the Motion made by the fall of that Drop is every way propagated in Rings or Waves increafing and fpreading further and further from the Point where the Motion was begun; and this every way with equal Velocity; which may be argued from the perfect circular form of fuch Rings. But that which comes yet nearer to the Similitude of Light, and for which Property only I mention it, is, if we let fall at the fame time 10 or 20 Drops in feveral diftances one from another, we fhall find that every one of them will produce Rings about it; each of which will continue to be propagated equally every way as regularly, as if there had been but one Drop let fall: And though they varioufly crofs one another, and fo, one would imagine, fhould confound the regular propaga-tion of each others Rings; yet whoever fhall obferve any one of them in the time of fuch propagation, fhall find that they are not in the leaft difturbed by the Action of any other, though they may be croft with 20 fuch differing Con-fecutions of Rings. And though, I confefs, after all this, it does feem not a little difficult to comprehend how one and the fame Particle of Matter, or of the tranfparent *Medium,* fhould at the fame Inftant propagate through it a thou-fand differing Motions, a thoufand differing Ways; yet fince we are affured by the laft Similitude of the Rings or Waves upon the Surface of the Water, that it is actually done in Nature, and that vifible to Senfe, though we cannot fo clearly comprehend the Metaphyfical Reafon thereof: yet 'tis enough for a Principle to build upon, that we are affured it is fo, and that fuch and fuch are the Effects that flow from it. So tho' it be difficult to comprehend the Metaphfical Reafon, why a Body which is by another moved with a certain Degree of Velo-city, fhould continue to move forwards in a right Line with the fame Velocity it received, till it be ftopt by meeting with other Bodies, and communicating that Motion to them: (For who can underftand what it receives, and what it parts withal, and what it is diftinct from the Effence of a Body that fo moves it or ftays it?) Yet fince we are fenfibly informed that really it is fo, it will be enough for a Phyfical Principle of Nature, of which we can have no further Light or Information, that will make it more plain and certain to us. Now though it do feem thus difficult to be explain'd, yet 'tis not wholly impoffible. I do confefs, the Confideration they have about it, of the neceffity of the Pro-pagation of it many various Ways through the fame Body, in the fame Inftant, does much confound the Imagination; becaufe who can imagine a Body to com-municate Motion to another, without its being actually moved it felf? And if it be actually moved it felf, how can it move more than one way at once? And if it moves but one way, how can it move all the oppofite Bodies with their peculiar Propagations?

5. But to this it may be answered, first, that there are in every *sensible* Point of Matter a sufficient number of distinct Particles to convey every one of those Motions distinct, without interfering one with another : For as there may be Millions of Motions communicated to a *sensible* Point, so there may be as many Millions of distinct Particles to receive each of them distinctly.

But besides that every sensible Moment of time is composed of infinite Instants, or of an indefinite number of other Moments of time of a shorter duration; so that within a moment of time that is sensible to a Man, the same sensible Point may be moved many Millions of ways successively, and so communicate each of those Motions distinct, without being confounded with any two : And the next human Moment may have and convey as many others, as many several ways. Now that this may be so, we may yet farther consider, that Motions may be infinitely swifter than sensible Motions ; that is, than those Motions that we can see a *Prius* and *Posterius* in : For the swiftest Motion that we can see, is that wherein we can distinguish the Body moving from the *Terminus a quo* to the *Terminus ad quem*, in a sensible time, or a sensible moment : For if it be in both within the least moment of time we are able to distinguish, it seems to us as if it were in both the terms and the interjacent space altogether. For instance, take a long String, and stretch it out between two Pins ; if it be long and but slack, we are able to see and distinguish it, as it moves from one side to the other, and how it returns again, because it makes its Vibrations within the compass of several human Moments of time ; and if it come within three sensible Moments, we seem to see it in three sensible Places. But if it be strain'd yet straighter, so as to make its whole Vibration within one human Moment, we see it as if it were in all parts of its space and in the two *Termini* at once, about which time, and not before, it begins to sound. Upon the same account it is, that if you take a Coal of Fire in the Night, and move it to and fro pretty quick, it seems to make a perfect Line of Fire ; whereas if it be moved slow, you see it distinct as a Body moved. I could give a hundred Instances by which I could make it manifest, that the *Phænomena* thereof proceed only from the length of time there is in the shortest Moment of a Man.

And I do not at all doubt but that the sensible Moments of Creatures are somewhat proportion'd to their Bulk, and that the less a Creature is, the shorter are its sensible Moments ; and that a Creature that is a hundred times less than a Man, may distinguish a hundred Moments in the time that a Man distinguishes one. For when I hear a Fly moving his Wings to and fro so many times, with such a Swiftness as to make a Sound, I cannot but imagine, that that Fly must be sensible of and distinguish at least 3 Moments in the time that it makes one of those Strokes with his Wings, for that it is able to regulate and guide it self by the Motion of them. And the like may be said for the quick Motions of other lesser Creatures. So that many of those Creatures that seem to be very short lived in respect of Man, may yet rationally enough be supposed to have lived, and been sensible of and distinguished as many Moments of time as a Man ; because within that space of time it has lived, it has had as many distinct Moments of time, and has had as many distinct Differences of Moments, as a Man hath in the Age he lives. But this only by the by.

But farther, in the third place, as there are infinite Parts in the least sensible Part, and infinite Moments in the least sensible Moment ; so there may be infinite Parts of Space in the least sensible Space to be moved. For since all Space is infinitely divisible into lesser, we cannot say how little a Space is necessary to be moved to make a sensible Propagation of Light. Possibly the thousand thousandth Part of the least sensible Space, may be sufficient to be moved, to make the continuation of the Propagation of Light through a Particle. Now we are sensibly informed by the Microscope, that the least visible Space (which is that which appears under an Angle of half a Minute of a Degree) may be actually distinguished into a thousand sensible Spaces : And could we yet further improve Microscopes, 'tis possible we might distinguish even a thousand more Spaces in every one of those we can now see by the help of those Microscopes we have already. Now possibly a less Space than the least of these may be be enough for a Body to be diflocated in the Motion that is neceffary to produce the Propagation of a Ray of Light.

But then in the fourth place, Velocities may be infinitely fwift in thofe Spaces : For who can imagine the fmallnefs of time that a Motion can be performed through the fmalleft of thofe Spaces ?

To explain which a little further, I fay, 'tis evident firft to the Senfe of Seeing, that the bigger the Body is, the flower is its Vibration, and the fmaller, the quicker : Which is evidenced to the Eye in all pendulous Motions, and in the Recurfions and Vibrations of Pieces of Timber, which the longer and bigger they are, the more flow are the Vibrations made by them ; and the fmaller and fhorter, the quicker. But then where the Eye is unable to affift us any further in diftinguifhing the fwiftnefs of Vibrations, there the Ear comes in with its affiftance, and carries us much further : And as I fhewed before in the Vibrations of Strings, fo now I inftance further in Bells, where we find by the Tone, that the fmaller the Bell, the fharper and more fhrill its Sound ; and this carries us on to a Sound fo fharp, that we only call it fcreeking, and at length it becomes offenfive to the Ear, becaufe beyond that it cannot endure the Senfe of a fhriller Note or quicker Vibration : For that the Shrillnefs of the Note depends upon the quicknefs of the Vibration, I think I need not inftance. Hence I conceive that there may be yet beyond the reach of our Ears infinite fhriller and fhriller Notes, which may be diftinguifhed by Ears or Organs of Hearing adapted by their leffer Bulks and finer Parts, to diftinguifh thofe quicker Vibrations : And therefore thofe leffer Creatures that we difcover, tho' poffibly they cannot hear thofe Sounds which we hear, but are able to diftinguifh every Turn and Return of the Vibrations of them by the quicknefs and aptnefs of their Sight ; yet they may have as great variety in the differences of Sounds wholly imperceptible to us, as we have within the reach of our Ears. And as the Voice of Man is limited to a certain number of Notes, lower or higher than which no Human Voice can reach ; fo may it be in the Voices or Sounds made by thofe fmaller Creatures. That this may be fo, we may argue yet farther from the Curiofity and Make of their Sight ; for we plainly enough fee, that the fmaller the Eye is, the fmaller is the Picture of the vifible Object that is made at the bottom of it upon the *Choroeides* or *Tunica Retina.* And this, as I may hereafter explain, is as demonftrable from the Principles of Refraction and Opticks, as any one thing in that Science : Which if fo, how fmall will be the Picture of the Object that is painted at the bottom of one of thofe Eyes which by a Microfcope we difcover in the Clufter of the Eyes of Flies, and other fmall Infects ? And yet after all this, we have no reafon to doubt that thefe Creatures are able to diftinguifh as many fingle Parts in thofe Pictures, as a Man can in a proportionate Picture at the bottom of his Eye. For as the Senfation of a Man's Sight is limited to a certain bignefs, lefs than which none can diftinguifh ; which, as I have elfewhere fhewed, is not lefs than what is comprifed within about a half a Minute of a Degree, at moft, of the Orbicular Part of the bottom of the Eye ; which in all probability is from the bignefs of the fmalleft fenfible Part receiving the Image, or of the Optick Nerve that is capable of conveying a diftinct Motion or Senfation to the Brain, as *Des Cartes* has very ingenioufly explained : So in thefe fmall Creatures, where every thing elfe is proportionably fmaller, 'tis not at all to be doubted but that thofe Fibres that convey the Senfation to their Brain, are proportionably alfo fmaller ; and confequently that they muft have at leaft a Faculty of diftinguifhing the Parts of that Picture, which whole Picture may poffibly be made upon much lefs than half a Minute of a Degree of the Orbicular Part of the bottom of their Eyes only : For as the Space of thofe Fibres is fhorter between the bottom of the Eye and the Brain, fo may their bignefs be proportionably fmaller. All which Particulars confider'd, it does feem that Nature has as it were ballanced the Gifts beftowed upon them by fome other Means adapted more particularly to each of their Conftitutions ; as were it proper for this Time and Place, I could more particularly explain and demonftrate. But thefe Speculations being only by the by, I fhall rather proceed with my Difcourfe concerning the Nature of Light, fo as to make the manner of its Operations mechanically and fenfibly intelligible ; by confidering further, that if there be a real Motion neceffary for

every

every diſtinct Propagation of Light, then it will ſeem to follow, that every luminous Point muſt have its diſtinct Moment to be propagated this way and that way within the ſpace of a ſenſible Moment : Which if it be affirmed to be ſo, I ſee no Reaſon in Nature why it may not be poſſible, and that from thoſe four Conſiderations I before ſpecified. So that though the whole Hemiſphere ſhould be filled with lucid viſible Points, as we find in a clear ſtarry Night, that it is pretty thick ſet with Stars, and by Teleſcopes we diſcover it to be yet thicker : Why, I ſay, Impreſſions may not be made from every one of them diſtinctly and ſucceſſively upon one ſingle ſenſible Point of Matter in one human moment ; and conſequently why the ſame Chime of Impulſes may not be again repeated the next Moment, and ſo perpetually in every human Moment: For 'tis not the Number of them that would at all impede ſuch a Concluſion, no, not if there ſhould be ten thouſand times as many more ; for there might be found ſmaller Moments enough within that Space of a ſenſible or diſtinguiſhable Moment, to fit every one with one at leaſt : ſo that the ſame point of Matter might communicate every one of their Impreſſions diſtinct and ſucceſſively within that Period : And beſides this, there might be found diſtinct Parts enough, within the Orb of this leaſt ſenſible Point, to propagate every one of thoſe Motions diſtinct, their various ways, by appropriated Parts, all at the ſame Inſtant.

So that upon the whole, we may aſſign to every Propagation of Light through the leaſt ſenſible Space, a real temporary local Motion. And if Monſ. *Des Cartes* by his Propenſion to Motion, and Mr. *Hobbs* by his *Conatus* or Endeavour to Motion, do not mean ſuch a real local Motion, their Notions are neither of them intelligible to others, nor did they really underſtand them themſelves. For bare Propenſion to Motion, is not Motion, and conſequently cannot propagate Motion : And Endeavour to move is not moving, and ſo cannot propagate Motion : But for the Propagation of Motion, Motion is neceſſary. And this I hope has ſhewed a Poſſibility at leaſt, if not a Probability, how it may be made.

The Cauſe of the Fluidity of the vaſt Ex-panſum.   6. If then this be ſo, we may hence deduce the Cauſe of the perfect Fluidity of the vaſt quantity of Matter which fills the whole *Expanſum* of Space between the ſolid Cæleſtial or Luminous Bodies of the Univerſe. And we may thence bring a demonſtrative Reaſon why it becomes ſo free from impeding the Motions of the Planetary or Cometical Bodies that are moved through it. For if every one of theſe Luminous Points, the Fixt Stars, which fill almoſt every Point of the Heavens in a clear Night (as is made yet much more viſible by the help of long Teleſcopes) be as glorious and Luminous Bodies as the Sun it ſelf, though they here appear incomparably leſs, and of a fainter Light, by reaſon of their Diſtances indefinitely almoſt more diſtant from us than that is : If, I ſay, every one of thoſe Fixt Stars, or glorious Suns, be ſtuck up and down here and there in the vaſt *Expanſum* of Matter that fills the whole of Nature, not at equal but various Diſtances one from another ; and every one of thoſe do really once at leaſt within the ſpace of one human Moment of time, really move the whole *Expanſum* of the Ethereal Matter (as 'tis moſt evident and demonſtrable they do ;) then what can there poſſibly be more rationally contrived to make and preſerve the perfect Fluidity of the *Æther* ? For every Point of Matter is Millions of ways, and conſequently with incredible Velocity moved to and fro within the compaſs of one ſingle Moment, and ſo muſt neceſſarily have its Parts indefinitely divided, and looſe one from another ; and conſequently being thus fluid, and the minute Motions ballancing each other in every Point of Matter, and theſe Motions being proportionably ſwifter than the ſwifteſt Motion of the more bulky Maſs : It follows, I ſay, that the Impediment to any bulky Bodies moving through it, muſt be inconſiderable, or almoſt nothing. For the Parts of this Matter being indefinitely ſmaller than the leaſt ſenſible Point, and the Motion of each of them, though never ſo ſmall, being within the compaſs of a human Moment determined every way, or infinite ways, the Motion of them one way muſt ballance that of others another, and conſequently give no Impediment to the ſenſible or bulky Body moved through them. I could have proceeded further from one and the ſame Principle to have

explain'd

explain'd how this continued Chime of Motions from every Part do create various forts of harmonical Motions in concrete Particles, which have their various and admirable Effects in producing the Harmony which is in Nature. But of that fome other time, this will be enough at prefent, to intimate that every one of thefe Cæleftial Bodies have their fhare in the Motion of the Matter of the World, and every one of them act more or lefs powerfully, according as they are nearer and nearer pofited to the Parts acted upon; and confequently the Sun, as I before hinted, becomes in our Parts more confiderable than all the other Cæleftial Bodies. 'Tis poffible there may have been in fome former Ages of the World, a Notion fomewhat like this; but not fo well underftood by thofe that we are beholden to for the Hint of it : Which may be argued both from the *Platonick* and *Pythagorick Theorys*, and much more from thofe Scraps we have of the Philofophy of *Confucius*, the *Chinefe* Philofopher, who was contemporary with *Pythagoras*, but wrote of the Philofophy of an Age fifteen hundred Years before him . But the regaining of it is not to be hoped from any of their Hints, but from a clear and fteddy Geometrical Method of Reafoning, proceeding from the more fenfible to the more abftrufe and infenfible Caufes and Effects of things.

Nor can I conceive any other Notion why one Body fhould refift or hinder Motion more than another, than that the one is lefs fluid than another; that is, that the folid Parts of the one fluid Body are fmaller than the folid Parts of the other fluid Body. And we find it evident to Senfe in fenfible Fluids, where we may fenfibly be affured, that the groffer the Particles of the fluid Body are, the more impediment does that Body give to the Motion of another Body through it . As upon the evaporating of Liquors that have folid Bodies in them, in the mixing of Pouders with Water or other Liquors, and in the mixing of Salts and Sugars; which give a much greater impediment before they are diffolved into Fluidity than afterwards. If then from fenfible Experiments we proceed to Effects infenfible yet evident to Reafon, we may conclude that the Æther muft be abundantly more fluid than any other Body, and indeed may be faid to be indefinitely fluid; and fo the Refiftance that it muft give to bulky Bodies, muft be indefinitely fmall, becaufe there is fo mall a Part of it diflocated by the tranfit of a Body, being indeed nothing but a meer Superficies, or the Parts of it that are next contiguous to the Body moved through it. But of this I fhall upon onother occafion fay more, when I fhew the Caufe why the Bodies moved through them, though they do really every moment diflocate as much Body as is equal to them in Bulk, do notwithftanding receive little or no impediment to their progreffive Motion.

Why one Fluid hinders Motion more than another.

N n   S E C T.

SECT. VII.

The CONTENTS.

BEfore I give the Contents of this Section, I think it may be convenient, in order to the better understanding of what follows, to premise, That our Author having thus far prosecuted his Inquiries into the Nature of Light, What it is in the Luminous Body, to wit, a certain Vibrative Motion of its Parts, of a determinate Velocity. 2dly, What the Medium is, how it is acted upon by Light, and how Light is thereby propagated, with all the necessary Qualifications of this Medium. 3dly, What this Action is on the Eye, and how the Powers of Light are exerted upon the sensible Part thereof, to cause Vision: Instead of proceeding farther in the Method he had proposed to himself, of explaining how the Rays or Pulses of Light from the Luminous Bodies are Reflected, Refracted or Inflected, by a successive Refraction, bending the Ray into a Curve; which several Subjects I suppose he design'd to treat of, though I do not find he ever did (except of Inflection, of which see Micrography, p. 217.) being diverted by other invervening Subjects, which carried his Thoughts other ways: And indeed the Field of Nature is so large, and so plentifully adorn'd with tempting Curiosities, that it is a Restraint upon the Collector, not to leave one before it is thoroughly examined, to reach at another. I say, when our Author had treated on these Heads so far, he leaves this Subject, I must confess, in some sense imperfect; and taking occasion from his having mention'd Time and a Human Moment, he wrote the following Discourse, wherein,

1. The Author attempts to shew how we come by the Notion of Time, tho' the Impressions on the Senses are all momentary. The Communis Sensus not sufficient for this purpose, therefore there is a necessity of supposing some other Organ. This he conceives to be what we call Memory, and then he proceeds to give an Hypothesis to explain Memory, and how it is performed: That Memory is organical: That the Soul, tho an Incorporeal Being, yet in performing its Actions makes use of Corporeal Organs: That Memory is the Repository of Ideas form'd by the Senses, or rather by the Soul it self. 2. The Action of the Soul in ordering and storing up Ideas, is call'd Attention. The Author's Notion what it is: That the Place of the Repository is somewhere in the Brain, whose Substance is the Material out of which Ideas are formed, the Chain of which is coyled up in the Repository, the Soul being at the Center where the present Idea is made, which is the present Moment; and hence comes the Notion of Time and Duration, and is apprehended as a Quantity. 3. A Mechanical Representation supposed for the better Understanding the several Operations of the Soul, viz. Apprehending, Remembring and Reasoning. That there may be some certain Point in the Brain, where the Soul has its chief Residence, and there receives its Informations, and gives its Orders. This Repository is furnished with

adapted

adapted Matter for the Uses of the Soul: Five sorts of Matter for the Impressions of the Five Senses: That for Sight explain'd by the Bononian Phosphorus: That for Sound by the Vases in antient Theaters and Unison-tuned Strings. Smelling, Tasting and Feeling also after the same manner are explained. 4. Out of this adapted Matter the Ideas formed are material and bulky, of determinate Figures, Sizes and Motions. That the Soul forms one Idea each Moment, which Moments differ in duration in different Men. A Computation of the number of Ideas that may be form'd in a Man's Life. That the Number will not be found to be an Objection against this Hypothesis. That Attention is the Action of the Soul in forming Ideas, and what they are. That they continually protrude each other from the Center. That the Soul by its Radiation and the Re-action of the Ideas, becomes sensible of them, and so of Time. How it is sensible of many concomitant Ideas. How some Thoughts lost may be recovered. That this Radiation and Re-action weakens in a duplicate proportion to the distance of Time. That the Soul may exert its Power on any particular Idea according to its own Will. That there is a continual Radiation of the Soul in the Repository of Ideas, and is in some sense reacted upon by them ; whence comes what we call a bringing to remembrance. 5. The Action of the Soul called Thinking, is a more particular Radiation thereof to this or that part of the Repository. Thinking is partly Memory, and partly an Operation of the Soul in forming new Ideas. Reason a more compleat Action of the Soul from comparing Ideas. As the Repository is better stored, so the Soul acts better. The Soul a self-moving Principle and Primum Movens. The Soul compared to the Sun in the Great World. If the Sun had Understanding, it would be sensible of the Resistance its Rays meet with. This explain'd by Hearing and Seeing. A double Influence from the Sun on Bodies and their Motions. Tho' we cannot conceive how the Soul, being spiritual and incorporeal, acts upon Ideas that are corporeal, or can be acted upon by them ; yet we are assured such Effects are performed. That the Soul is not confin'd to act only upon these Ideas, but may extend its Power to every part of the Body, and possibly to some considerable Distance from the Body. R. W.

BEfore I come to the discussing of the particular Matters treated of the last *How we come by the Notion of Time.* Section, I would a little further consider what I have been discoursing of, viz. Time : And here, since it is a general Maxim in the Schools, that *Nihil est in Intellectu, quod non fuit prius in Sensu,* I would query by what Sense it is we come to be informed of Time ; for all the Information we have from the Senses are momentary, and only last during the Impressions made by the Object. There is therefore yet wanting a Sense to apprehend Time ; for such a Notion we have : And yet no one of our Senses, nor all together, can furnish us with it, and yet we conceive of it as a Quantity. For this therefore, since we cannot find any external or outward Sense, we must seek within, and we shall find there is somewhat like that which is called *Communis Sensus,* which is receptive of all the outward Impressions of the other Senses. But still this is insufficient to afford us the Notion or Knowledge of Time ; for the Impressions on that can be no other than the Impressions from the other Senses, conveyed by the *Media* of the sensory Nerves, which must be also momentary, as well as the first Impressions, and consequently do not yet sufficiently inform us of the Notion of Time. Considering this, I say, we shall find a Necessity of supposing some other Organ to apprehend the Impression that is made by Time. And this I conceive to be no other than that which we generally call Memory, which Memory I suppose to be as much an Organ, as the Eye, Ear or Nose,

and

and to have its Situation fomewhere near the Place where the Nerves from the other Senfes concur and meet.

Memory Orga- nical.

Now that it is really Organical, I argue from this, that it may be both im- improved and impaired, it may be deftroyed and exalted to a great Perfection. It is at fome times fenfible, and at other times wholly infenfible, as particularly in Sleep : And whenever 'tis fo, we have no Senfe of Time, but we pafs over all that Space of Time, as if it had not been, and we only come to under- ftand it by other Circumftances. Befides, we have often known that the Me- mory has been quite deftroyed by a Fall, or great Blow upon the Head, by a Fever, or other great Sicknefs ; nay often by Excefs of Drinking, all which affect not the Soul : And in probability, this might be caufed by fome Wound, Hurt, Bruife, or fome orher Diftemper of that Part, which we conceive to be the Organ of Memory ; which makes it an unfit Organ for the Soul to make ufe of for that effect; and confequently the Soul can no more remember with- out the Organ of Memory, than it can fee without the Organ of Sight, the Eye, or hear without an Ear. For the Soul, or firft Principle of Life, tho' it be an Incorporeal Being, yet in performing its Actions, makes ufe of Corporeal Organs, and without them cannot effect what it wills.

Memory then I conceive to be nothing elfe but a Repofitory of Ideas formed partly by the Senfes, but chiefly by the Soul it felf : I fay, partly by the Senfes, becaufe they are as it were the Collectors or Carriers of the Impreffions made by Objects from without, delivering them to the Repofitory or Storehoufe where they are to be ufed. Which Impreffions being actual Motions, as I have plainly proved in the Explication of the Organ of the Eye, and the Operation of Light, thofe Motions conveyed to this Repofitory become Powers fufficient to effect fuch Formations of Ideas as the Soul does guide and direct them in : For I conceive no Idea can be really formed or ftored up in this Repofitory, without the Directive and Archiectonical Power of the Soul ; and the Actions or Impreffions ceafe and fail without the concurrent Act of the Soul, which regulates and difpofes of fuch Powers.

2. This Action of the Soul is that which is commonly called *Attention*, by which what is meant no one does further or more intelligibly explain, than on- ly by giving the fame Notion by fome other ways of Expreffion, which, it may be are as little intelligible. My Notion of it is this, that the Soul in the Action of Attention does really form fome material Part of the Repofitory into fuch a Shape, and gives it fome fuch a Motion as is from the Senfes conveyed thither ; which being fo formed and qualified, is inferted into and inclofed in the com- mon Repofitory, and there for a certain time preferved and retained, and fo becomes an Organ, upon which the Soul working, finds the Ideas of paft Acti- ons, as if the Action were prefent.

The Author's Notion concern- ing Ideas.

This Repofitory I conceive to be feated in the Brain, and the Subftance there- of I conceive to be the Material out of which thefe Ideas are formed, and where they are alfo preferved when formed, being difpofed in fome regular Order ; which Order I conceive to be principally that according to which they are formed, that being firft in order that is firft formed, and that next which is next, and fo continually by Succeffion, from the time of our Birth to the time of our Death. So that there is as it were a continued Chain of Ideas coyled up in the Repofitory of the Brain, the firft end of which is fartheft removed from the Center or Seat of the Soul where the Ideas are formed ; and the other End is always at the Center, being the laft Idea formed, which is always the Moment prefent when confidered : And therefore according as there are a greater number of thefe Ideas between the prefent Senfation or Thought in the Center, and any other, the more is the Soul apprehenfive of the Time interpofed.

Thefe are the *Supellex* of the Soul, and thefe are the Inftruments it makes ufe of in the apprehending of things or Actions paft ; and by thefe it becomes fenfible of all that it really knows, and according to the Perfection or Imper- fection, the Multitude or Paucity, the Regularity or Irregularity of the Order and Difpofition of thefe Ideas in the Repofitory or Memory, the Aptitude or Ineptitude of the Subftance for Formation, Radiation, Difpofition, &c. fo is the Soul the better enabled, Firft, to form new Ideas aright, or rightly to ap- prehend the thing to be known. Secondly to apprehend the Order according

to

to which they have been formed, and are ranged ; that is, to know the time, or, to speak in the common Phrase, to remember what is past; as if it were present, and how long it is since it was done, by the number of Ideas beween. The Soul therefore understands Time, or becomes sensible of Time, only by the help of the Organ of the Memory, which Organ is this Repository of Ideas, and by means of the Order, Situation and Distance of the said Ideas, from the Center, or one among another, so it becomes sensible of Time : And Time, as unnerstood by Man, is nothing else but the Length of the Chain of these Ideas, between any two that are at any time apprehended together : And according to the Number of the Links in this Chain, so is the Impression made to the Soul that apprehends it, of a longer or shorter time interposed ; and the Notion of Time is the Apprehension of the Distance of Ideas from the Center or present Moment. And so Time comes to be apprehended as a Quantity, and so falls under the Consideration of Geometry and Mensuration.

3. Now because nothing is so well understood or apprehended, as when it is represented under some sensible Form, I would, to make my Notion the more conceivable, make a mechanical and sensible Figure and Picture thereof, and from that shew how I conceive all the Actions and Operations of the Soul as Apprehending, Remembring and Reasoning are performed. *A sensible Representation of the Matter.*

I suppose then that there may be a certain Place or Point somewhere in the Brain of a Man, where the Soul may have its'principal and chief Seat.

I will not now enter upon Arguments or Reasonings from Experiments or Observations, to determine the precise Place, though concerning the definitive Position thereof, I have much that I may at another time produce : But I will only suppose at present, that there may be some such Place whereinto all the Impressions made from the Senses upon adapted Matter may be deliver'd ; which Impressions, as I have elsewhere explain'd, are no other but actual Locomotions given to the Parts of Matter or Bodies so or so moved.

I suppose then this Repository to be furnished with variety of Matter adapted for the Uses to which the Soul applies them, which I call the Elements out of which Ideas are made ; among which Variety there are principally five sorrs fitted and adapted to receive the Impressions from the five Senses ; that is, one peculiar Kind for the Impressions of Sight, which is of such a Quality, Form, Make, Bulk, or other Constitution, as makes it Receptive and Retentive of the Impressions of Light and Colours, which none of the other Bodies are capable of. Which may a little be explain'd by the Matter of the Phosphoros made of the *Bononian* Stone, or that found out by *Baldwinus* made of Chalk and Niter ; which Matters are so made and adapted by the Chymical Preparations of them by the force of Fire and Mixtures made in their Processes, that they, so soon as exposed to the Impressions of Light, receive and retain those Impressions, though for no long time, yet enough to shew us a Specimen of a certain Qualification not to be found in most other Bodies, which may yet possibly be done much more powerfully and effectually by the Chymistry of Nature in the Digestions and Preparations made in the wonderful Elaboratory of the Animal Body ; where all things are are ordered and adapted by the All wise Creator, for the Work to be done : So that nothing can be imagined wanting or redundant to perform what is by his Intention design'd to be done.

Another sort of Matter I suppose to be that which is fitted to receive the Impressions of Sound, somewhat like those Bells or Vases which *Vitruvius* mentions to be placed in the antient Theaters, which did receive and return the Sound more vigorous and strong ; or like the Unison-toned Strings, Bells or Glasses, which receive Impressions from Sounds without, and retain that Impression for some time, answering the Tone by the same Tone of their own. And though in these Examples (which I am fain to bring for Explication only) there seems wanting the great Requisite of a Power to retain for a long while those Impressions which are so given, they all of them losing them in a very short time ; yet, as I shall by and by shew, they do and will each of them retain their several Impressions long enough to make them sufficient for producing the same Reactions whenever they are again acted upon. And such an Impression I shall prove is again given both by the Soul and by succeeding similar Sen-

sations,

fations : For having Potentiality of receiving, and being excited by fuch Impreffions, they do again renew their former Impreffion, and afrefh fhew their Power, in the fame manner as the Mufical String or Bell, or the well prepared *Bononian* or *Baldwin* Phofphorus do each fhew their Natures, when the one is ftruck or agitated by Motion, and the other acted upon by Light.

The like appropriated Materials I fuppofe alfo for the Impreffions of the other Three *Senfes, viz.* Smelling, Tafting, Feeling ; each of which are qualified to receive and retain the Impreffions from the other Senfes. As for inftance, the Smell being caufed by a fubtil and curious Exhalation from the odoriferous Body imbibed by the Air, the Olfactory Nerves are prepared with an aerial Body fit to diffolve or imbibe that Subftance in the fame manner as the Air does from the odoriferous Body ; which aerial Body, by means of the Olfactory Nerve, having an immediate Intercourfe and Paffage to the Brain, does immediately convey it thither : And according to the nature of this aerial or fpirituous Subftance with which the Olfactory Nerve is furnifhed, fo does it diffolve or imbibe this or that Exhalation out of the Air. Whence I conceive that it is of diftinct Natures in every Species of Animals, and thence that every one of them have diftinct Senfations of the fame *Effluvia*, and that which is congruous and agreeing to one, is of a contrary nature to another ; and thence what is grateful to one is odious to another. And again, what is fenfible to one fort of Creature, who has an aerial Subftance fitted to diffolve and imbibe fuch or fuch a Steam, is wholly infenfible to another that wants that aerial Subftance, and is furnifht with one of a differing Nature. Which I conceive to be the reafon, why Dogs and other Creatures have fo ftrong a Faculty of fmelling the Scent of Animals, or the Flefh of them, which are very hardly difcoverable to a Man. On the other fide, in probability Man is fenfible of many things, as the Smell of Flowers, Herbs and Fruits, which poffibly a Dog does very little, if at all fcent.

The like may be faid of the Tafte, which I conceive lies only in the Nature of the watery Liquor conveyed by the Nerves of Tafte to the Tongue, according to the Nature of which for diffolving this or that Subftance of the Bodies touching it, is the Impreffion of Tafte conveyed to the Brain. And fo we may fee a clear Reafon why one Tafte may be tafted by one, which is not by another, and why one Tafte is pleafant to one Creature which is not fo to another, and how a Body becomes guftable or taftelefs, and how that which is taftlefs in it felf may be made taftable, and why that which is taftable may be made taftelefs. Of both which kinds I could give hundreds of Inftances which would much confirm this my Theory, and fhew what Improvements of this kind could be made. The like, I conceive, is to be faid of an adapted Matter for receiving and retaining the Impreffions of Feeling, fomewhat after the nature of the warming Stone, and feveral other fuch Subftances, which do imbibe thofe Impreffions more readily, and retain them for a longer time. Now I do fuppofe, that the Repofitory is continually fupplied with a fufficient quantity of thefe kinds of Subftances, with which the Senfe does continually form Ideas, and difpofe of them into the Repofitory of Memory, and that without thofe Materials, and the concurrent Impreffions of the Senfes, it cannot form them : For otherwife a blind Man would have Ideas of Colours, which yet he has not, and a fick Man would have a true Idea of Taftes, which yet he has not.

But to return to the confideration of the Place or Repofitory where thefe Ideas are form'd and retain'd.

The Ideas material and bulky.

4. I fuppofe there may be about this place, which I will henceforward call the Center, a certain Sphere of Capacity fill'd with adapted Matter, for the Formation, Reception, and containing of all the Ideas which fhall be emitted from the faid Center. Thefe Ideas I will uppofe to be material and bulky, that is, to be certain Bodies of determinate bignefs, and impregnated with determinate Motions, and to be in themfelves diftinct ; and therefore that no two of them can be in the fame fpace, but that they are actually different and feparate one from another ; and as they have their diftinct Figures, fo have they each of them their diftinct Qualifications of Motions and Conftitutions.

I

I will suppose further, that the Soul may every moment, partly by its own immediate Power, and partly by the help of the Impressions produced by the Senses, form one of these Ideas, and insert it into the Repository. Which Moments in some Men may be more, in some may be less, within the same compass of time, according to the Activity of the Soul it self, and according to the Aptitude or Unfitness of the Matter to be wrought upon. So that in some there may be Four of them formed in a second Minute of Time, in others possibly not One in two Seconds of Time : And according to the Perfection and Aptness of the Matter to be formed, and the Activity of the Soul in performing its Effects, so are there more of these Ideas formed within the same Space of time. So that a Man of an ordinary Constitution of Soul and Body, that is, one of a middle Degree between the more active and quick, and one of the more slow and dull, may within the compass of his Life, supposing he should live to a hundred Years of Age (which yet not one of a hundred thousand thousand does arrive to) form within that compass of time, and store up in his Repository, a thousand Millions of distinct Ideas ; all which may have followed each other in a continued Series, beginning with the time of the first Advertency of the Child, and continuing to the time of the actual Separation of the Soul and Body at Death, Which I thus compute : A hundred Years contain 36525 Days, and 36525 Days contain 876600 Hours, and 876600 Hours contain 3155760000 Seconds. Now one with another, when the Soul is intent and acting, there may be 3600 formed within the compass of an Hour, and so one in a Second of Time. So that if the Soul could through the whole Course of 100 Years be continually so intent, and so acting and forming these Ideas, and inserting them into this Repository or Organ of Memory, there might be there reposed 3155760000 Ideas. But by reason of Sleep interposed, one third Part of the Number will be taken off, the Soul then for the most part ceasing to form Ideas, or when it does, they are only imperfect and lost. So that there will remain but 2103840000, or to take a round Sum, but 21 hundred Millions. Now if we examine this remaining two thirds of Time or Moments, and therein consider what part of the time remaining is lost in Infancy, Old Age, Sickness and Inadvertency, we may well reckon that two thirds of these remaining Moments are lost, and no Ideas at all formed in them ; and so instead of 21 hundred, there will remain but the number of 7 hundred Millions. And if we again consider how small a part of these are industriously and carefully stored up, we may very well agree, that not above a seventh Part of these are stored up : And so one hundred Millions may be a sufficient Number to be supposed for all the Ideas that may have been treasured up in the Organ of Memory through the whole Course of a Man's Life, though of a hundred Years continuance ; and consequently one Year with another may be supposed to add to this Store about one Million of Ideas. But if we consider how much this will amount to for every Day, we shall find that yet the Number is very much too big, and must be yet very much diminished : For when we consider that this will still make 2738 Ideas for every Day of the hundred Years ; and if a Man considers with himself how many he conceives he may have added to his Store in one Month next last past, I am apt to think he will conclude, that one with another, it will be enough to allow one Tenth of that Number for the Number of Ideas that have obtained a Place in this Repository, the Organ of Memory. So that if a Man allows but two or three hundred a Day, nay, but one hundred for every Day he hath lived, since he was born to his present Moment, he will find that Number large enough to contain all the Ideas he has really stored up in the Organ of his Memory. As supposing a Man of fifty Years of Age, who according to that compute must have lived 18262 Days ; and consequently if you reckon but a hundred for each Day, must have 1826200. It will be very hard, I conceive, for a Man of that Age perfectly to remember so many distinct things, though yet I will not say it is impossible. But supposing he could by recollecting remember 100 Millions, and consequently must have as many distinct Ideas, I see no Reason why all these may not actually be contained within the Sphere of the Activity of the Soul acting in the Center. For if we consider in how small a bulk of Body there may be as many distinct living Creatures as here are supposed Ideas, and every of these Creatures per-

fectly

fectly formed and endued with all its Vegetative and Animal Functions, and with sufficient room alfo left for it to move it felf to and fro among and between all the reft, fo as to pafs by every one and touch none, we fhall not need to fear any Impoffiblity to find out room in the Brain where this Sphere may be placed, and yet find room enough for all other Ufes, of which we may afterwards affign fome very neceffary.

But to return to the Defcription of this Organ. I do fuppofe that what we call Attention is nothing elfe but the Action of the Soul in forming certain Ideas, which for the prefent I will call little Images, which bear the Stamp, Seal or Mould according to which the Soul formed it in the Center of the Repofitory. I fuppofe further, that thefe are continually formed by the Soul in the Center, and the prefent always protrudes thofe that were formed before it further into the Repofitory. So that the greater the number of Ideas are that have fucceeded any ones Formation, the greater is the Space of Time of which we have a Senfe : and the Ideas become further and further removed from the Center, and more and more new-form'd Ideas interpofe themfelves between the Center and the faid Ideas placed in Orbs at a greater diftance, by the intrufion of frefh Ideas between the Center and them.

I fuppofe further, that all thefe Ideas, though they may for a long time retain the Forms and Motions imprefs'd on them by the Senfes, and by the Action of the Soul ; yet notwithftanding they being material, and fo fubject to change, I conceive, that as the Motions may in time decay, fo the Form may (by fhifting and changing place in the Repofitory or Organ of Memory, and being protruded farther and farther from the Center or Seat of the Soul, and crouded into Orbs, though further off, yet clofer and clofer ftuffed and crouded together) be in time alter'd, and fometimes quite loft.

I fuppofe further, that the Soul being feated in this Center, and there acting, as I faid, by the help of the Information and Impreffions of the Senfes, and forming continually new Ideas, and fo protruding them onwards, and filling the Sphere of the Repofitory fuller and fuller from the Center, increafing outwards. I fuppofe, I fay, that this Soul by its Radiation does actually apprehend, or as it were feel, or is fenfible of any Idea that remains treafured up within this Repofitory : And this it becomes fenfible of, partly from its own Power of Radiation, and partly from the Re-action of the Ideas. It becomes, I fay, fenfible of them, wherever placed within the Repofitory ; partly by its own Radiation, by which it acts upon the fluid Spirits incompaffing it, propagating from it felf every way *in Orbem*, a Radiation like the Sun, by which, as by a Stick, it becomes fenfible of all thofe Ideas that are yet unwafted within the Repofitory, feeling as it were their Form, their Refiftance, and their Re-action to its Radiations : Partly, I fay, only by their lying in the way of the Radiation, and partly alfo by their re-acting and repercuffing a Radiation back upon the Soul. By the Diftance of it from this Center the Soul becomes fenfible in fome meafure of the time in which the Idea was made, and how long fince it was inferted, there being fo many Orbs of later or more inner Ideas formed and lying between them, which have been fince inferted.

By this means it becomes fenfible of many Ideas that accompanied that Idea, when made, many of them having kept the fame Order in which they were made ; though oftimes other Ideas, not formed immediately before or after, intrude and thruft in themfelves between, out of the order they did really fucceed in, fo as often to interrupt and break the Chain or Order of Infertion.

I conceive further, that befides the natural Decay there may be of the Form and impreft Motion of the Ideas, there may be alfo an Impediment to this Radiation of the Soul, by the Interpofition of other Ideas between the Center and the Idea fought, much after the manner as the Earth interpofing between the Moon and the Sun, hinders the Sun from radiating upon the Moon. And in fuch cafe the Idea may fometimes be thought to be loft, which yet may afterwards be found again when the Obftacle is removed.

Again, as in the Radiation of the Sun, which is as it were a Reprefentation of the Soul of the World ; the Radiation of the Soul is more powerful upon Ideas at a nearer than at a further Diftance ; and their Reaction is alfo more powerful back again, and that in a duplicate proportion to their Diftance reciprocal,

procal much the same with that of Light, which is the most spiritual Action of all we are sensible of in the World. And thence it is, that the Memory of things long since done is for the most part very faint, unless in some cases, where the Impressions made upon those Ideas were at first very powerful, or often recalled, which may be said to be a new forming of them.

I suppose further, that though by means of the continual Radiation of the Soul into this Repository or Organ of Memory, it has at all times sense of all the Ideas that are there reposed, yet that Sense is but imperfect and confused by reason of the Multitude; yet can it readily exert its Power more particularly and strongly to this or that Idea, according to the Determination of its Will. And whensoever it is upon the Action of Thinking, that is, of fixing or darting its Radiation more powerfully upon this or that Idea placed in the Repository, it does according to the Power of its Radiation receive a more sensible Impression or Repercussion from those Ideas upon which it radiates, and thereby it does not only apprehend their Qualifications more distinctly, but also it does as it were renew or refresh the former Impressions, and add to them a further degree of Perfection. And so though they are in a Place farther distant from its Center, and by the length of time or the number of Ideas that have been since inserted, and so lie in the way of Communication, it be become more faint and weak in the retaining the first Impression, and consequently in its re-acting Power; yet by this second Action or Radiation of the Soul upon it, its Form and Qualifications are renewed and perfected, and for the future it becomes more powerful than the rest of those at the same or lesser Distances, that have not been by such second Radiations so renewed and invigorated; and besides every such Action of the Soul does create and form a new Idea at the Center, which has Impressions that are the Result of those renewed Actions: And this having somewhat the like Figure and Motions or Qualifications, it has a Sympathetick Agreement with the other; and the Impressions from the one do more readily make the Impressions from the other more sensible, in the same manner as a Musical String being moved, does make another String that is unison or harmonious with it, move also, and so together make the Sound the louder, or the Impression the stronger.

There is a continual Radiation of the Soul into the Repository.

Next, as I suppose there is a continual Radiation of the Soul into the whole Repository of Ideas, so I do conceive likewise that every Idea so placed being so qualified as above, by particular Impressions of Motions, which continue for a long time so to move, as they were at first impregnated, does from such its Power so retained, radiate a Motion of its own, which may in some manner also act upon the Soul, so as to excite it to Attention; and by this means also whenever any Idea is created and impregnated with Motions or Qualifications similar to those of other Ideas placed at some distance in the Repository, the concurrent Impressions or Re-actions of those similar Ideas upon the Soul at that time do make the fainter to be the more notable, and so excite the Soul to Attention or Radiation that way also; and by that means it has an Excitement to be more sensible of the other also at that moment: And this I take to be that Impression which we are sensible of, when we say, This brings to my Mind, or This puts me in mind, or this makes me remember, &c.

5. I do further conceive, that that Action of the Soul which we call Thinking, is a more particular Radiation of the Soul to this or that part of the Repository, or on this or that Idea placed in it, and at the same time forming new Ideas in the Center of the Repository; which Action of the Soul in framing new Ideas at the Center, is continued almost every moment: And though it doth not every moment make a distinct Idea, yet may it be perfecting of one, and giving new Impressions every moment: And thence I conceive the Body of one Idea (for as I before mention'd, I suppose them to be really corporeal and material) may have many and various Impressions and Motions annexed to it, possibly of 100, nay of 1000 Moments, whence that Idea may be supposed to be more compleat and perfect in it self: And when it again comes to be acted upon by the Radiation of the Soul, all the Impressions or Qualifications thereof become of Power to affect the Soul with those Impressions which it had formerly received from the Soul.

What Thinking is.

So

So that Thinking is partly Memory, and partly an Operation of the Soul in forming new Ideas.

Another and more compleat Action of the Soul, is the forming new Ideas from the comparing the Re-actions from several Ideas placed here and there in the Repository, and its being sensible of the Harmony or Discord of them one with another, which does produce an Idea wherein all those various Respects are in some means united and impressed upon one and the same Idea. This is an Idea of greater Perfection, and according to the Attention of the Soul in being sensible of more and more variety of former Ideas, and the Regularity and Order of its proceeding in that Action, and the more steddy and distinct manner in the Course and Progress of it, so is the Idea more compleat, as well as more compounded : And this I conceive to be that Action of the Soul which is commonly called Reasoning ; and the Conclusion is the new Impression made upon the Idea informing from the comparison of other Ideas which may be contain'd in the *major* and *minor* Propositions.

Now according as the Repository is stored with more and more Ideas, so has the Soul a greater variety to range and expatiate into, whether these Ideas are only the first and more simple, such as are the Results from the Impressions of the Senses ; or the more compounded, such as are made by the Result of comparing several together : And therefore accordingly the Ideas that are made from fewer and more simple Ideas, are less compounded Ideas ; and those which are made from a greater number, and those more compounded Ideas, are yet more and more compounded, and more and more accomplish'd and perfect. This will give some Reason why the younger and first Results of the Actions of the Soul in forming Ideas, are more simple and less perfect, and from whence the Results of the Actions of the Soul in the elder Years, become the more compounded and perfect.

The Soul a self-moving Principle. The Soul then is the *Primum movens,* the self-moving Principle, which has in it self a Power of radiating every way *in Orbem* from its Center of being every instant and for ever, and so is always by means of that Radiation every where as it were actually present, in every point of the Sphere of its Radiation, though yet it may be supposed to be more immediately and powerfully present in the Center of its Being. It is not, I conceive, possible to be truly understood or described, but only by Similitude ; and the best Similitude for that purpose, I conceive, is the Sun in the great World.

Compared to the Sun. Now if we consider the Sun in the Great World, we shall find it first a Being which has in it self a Power of radiating or dispersing Light into the Whole of Nature, and (consequently by this its Influence) of being as it were every where present, and of being sensible of all those other Bodies that are placed any where throughout the whole *Expansum* : For as it doth by its Radiation influence and affect every Point of the Universe, so must there be a kind of reflex Influence upon it self from every such Point : For as any one, and every one Ray it sends forth, does meet with and affect any Body in its way, so consequently must that End of the Ray that touches the Sun, have a greater or less Resistance to be moved forwards ; and consequently if there were Understanding in the Sun it self, it must be sensible that this or that Ray does somewhere in its Progress receive such or such an Impediment to its Propagation or moving forwards that way. And be not only sensible, that somewhere that Ray meets with an Impediment, but it may be sensible also at what distance that Impediment or Re-action is given to its Progress : For supposing the Resistance or Re-action of all those impeding Objects, where-ever placed, to be in themselves equal, the Impediment or Resistance to that End of the Ray that is moved by the Sun, must receive a Resistance proportion'd to the nearness of the impeding or re-acting Object ; and consequently the Impediment made thereby upon the End of the Ray protruded by the Sun, must be reciprocally proportionate to the Distances of the impeding Object ; and consequently by the proportion'd Resistance or Re-action of the Objects, there is a manifest Distinction at that End of the Ray that touches the Sun, of the Distance of the Object touched by it. Next by the number of the Rays that receive Impediment from that Object, there is a manifest Distinction of the bigness of that Object ; for if the Angle of the Cone of Rays that receive Resistance from any Object,

be

be actually made and has its Being at the Sun, and that the Diftance of that Refiftance be likewife diftinguifhable at the Apex of it at the Sun, then is there a Manifeftation or Indication at the Superficies of the Sun (by means of this Radiation) both of the Diftance of the affected or affecting Object, and of the Angle or Magnitude of it at that diftance, and not only of the Magnitude and Diftance, but of the differing nature of the Refiftance or Re-action of the Object of fuch a bulk and fuch a diftance, by the confecution of momentary Impreffions. This I could plainly demonftrate by a Similitude drawn from the Action made upon the Organ of Hearing, from which the Ear is not only inabled to judge of the Magnitude and Diftance of the Sound, but of the Flatnefs and Sharpnefs, the Muficalnefs and not Muficalnefs by the like Diftinctions in it.

But it may be much better explain'd by the Eye, wherein we find, that though there be no Radiation immediately emitted by the Eye, which would make the Reactions to the Center the ftronger; yet is the Eye able by the reflected Reactions only of Objects that are acted directly upon by the Sun, to difcover the Figure, Colour, Magnitude, Diftance, &c. of all Objects from which there can come to it felf that free Radiation. So that the Soul in the Center of the Repofitory, is fenfible of all the Ideas placed in it, as the Eye is fenfible of all things that are placed before it.

Next, if we confider the Sun in the Great World, we fhall find it to be placed in the Center of a Space, all which Space, and all Bodies placed within that Space, it does more particularly influence by an attractive Power of drawing all bulky Bodies to it, or of commanding all the Motions of them; and confequently may have fenfe of the Renitency of Bodies, as well as of the Motions and Diftances of each of them. So that all Bodies, more efpecially within the Sphere of its Activity, do receive a double Influence from it; firft of being radiated, inlightned and vivified; and fecondly of being regulated and govern'd in their Motions by it. And hence the Bodies fo placed, as they have each of them peculiar Properties, Shapes and Motions of their own, fo have they alfo particular Influences, Radiations, Excitations and Regulations communicated to them from the Sun, which gives them not only their regulated Motions and Pofitions, but alfo a kind of new Being or Activity, by which they become vifible and fenfible to the reft of the World, which would otherwife be dark and infenfible, and vagrant here and there uncertainly in the *Expanfum* of the Univerfe. So that the Soul forms to it felf a Microcofm, or Picture of the Macrocofm, in which it radiates, and is fenfible of every thing contain'd therein, in the fame manner as the Sun in the Macrocofm.

Somewhat of this kind is the Influence of the Soul upon the Ideas placed within the Sphere of its Radiation : And though I cannot cenceive how the Soul, which is incorporeal, fhould move and act upon the Ideas which are corporeal, or how thofe on the other fide fhould by their Proprieties, Qualifications and Motions, re-act upon and influence the Soul; yet I am affured, that fuch Effects are performed both by the one and the other Beings; and without them, neither the Senfation, Cognition, Remembring, nor Ratiocination, could be performed; all which are plainly the Refults of the conjunct Influences of the Soul, and the Ideas or Bodies placed within the Repofitory or Sphere of its Activity.

Now though by what I have been faying, I have endeavour'd to fhew that the Soul has by its Radiation a more than ordinary and commanding Power over all the Ideas placed within the Repofitory; yet I would not be underftood fo to limit its Sphere of Radiation, as not to fuppofe that it may have a much bigger Sphere of influencing Power, and thereby may extend it, not only to all and every Point of the Body inlivened and preferved by it; but poffibly it may extend even out of the Body, and that to fome confiderable Diftance, and thereby not only influence other Bodies, but be influenc'd by them alfo. And upon this account I could produce a Multitude of Obfervations and Reafons, to prove not only the Poffibility, but the Probability, nay almoft Certainty of fuch an Influence, and this from the Senfiblenefs of others Ideas, *Lupus in Fabula*, *Fafcination*, &c. of which poffibly fome other time.

Here

Here our Author leaves off, nor as I can find, ever reaſſumed this Subject ; and though poſſibly ſome Perſons may imagine that the foregoing Explication of theſe abſtruſe Actings of the Soul is too mechanical, and tends to the making the Soul a material Being, yet I hope the candid Reader, peruſing it without prejudice, will not find the leaſt Cauſe for ſuch an Imputation, it being throughout the whole Diſcourſe aſſerted and ſhewn to be a Spiritual, Immaterial and Self moving Principle ; and it is granted by all Men, that it both acts and is reacted upon by Body, only our Author ſuppoſes the Pictures conſerving the Ideas to be material, which I hope cannot juſtly give offence : However, as I have ſaid in the Preface, I hold my ſelf not in the leaſt obliged to defend or maintain any of his Opinions or Diſcourſes, but fairly preſent them to the Ingenious as he left them.   The next that follows is a Diſcourſe of Comets wrote about Mi-chaelmas in the Year 1682, containing a Phyſical Hypotheſis and Explication of them, from Obſervations made of one that appeared in Auguſt 1680, and on that very unuſual one apppearing in December the ſame Year, and the beginning of the next Year, and on the following in Auguſt 1682.   Wherein, after an Intro-duction, and ſetting down ſeveral Opinions of Authors that have wrote of Co-mets, he gives us his own Obſervations, Hypotheſis and Explication.   R. W.

A

A
DISCOURSE
OF THE
Nature of Comets.

Read at the Meetings of the ROYAL
SOCIETY, foon after *Michaelmas* 1682.

The CONTENTS.

At the End of the Year 1680. *there appearing a very great, and indeed the most remarkable Comet that the Heavens have shewn us in our Age, the Author was diverted from prosecuting his Theory and Explication of Light in the several other useful and necessary Disquisitions relating to Reflected, Inflected and Refracted Rays; though something of the two last was formerly publish'd by him in his* Micrography, p. 47, & 217. *In the present Disquisition, he does not so much relate and confute the Opinions of others (though there is something of that also) as plainly give us his own Observations of the Appearances, as he viewed them through several Telescopes, night after night, when he could. By the way, I must in all gratitude acknowledge, that the Figures relating to this Discourse were generously communicated by the Ingenious Dr.* Woodward, *who purchased them, (put in loosely into* Bayer's Uranometria*) at the publick Auction of Dr.* Hooke's *Library. Though indeed these Figures were all very rudely designed, only as Helps to his own Memory, which the Author himself could much better have fitted for the Graver; yet I have endeavoured to supply this Defect as well as I was able, and hope the Reader will pardon the Failures. I think they pretty well answer his Descriptions, those being my chief Directors in perfecting the Draughts. I need not be particular in the Contents of this Discourse, the Marginal Notes which I have added will sufficiently inform the Reader: Therefore I shall only give some account of what is immediately annext to it, and which indeed the Thread of the Discourse led him to; that is, a short Treatise of Gravity: For there being a Gravitation of all Bodies to the Sun, it seemed a difficult Problem (at least according to his Hypothesis of Comets) to give a reason of the Blaze or Tail's being nearly opposite to the Sun. We have then here annext a pretty large, and (if I may be allowed to speak) an ingenious Discourse of Gravity or Gravitation. The*

Qq

Running

Running Title will direct the Reader to it. In this he considers the most known Proprieties of the Celestial Bodies, and having made several Deductions from Observations, as to the Nature of the Æther, Air, and the like, in which in transitu *he explains Thunder and Lightning, asserting a Levitation, as well as Gravitation (or a receding from as well as tendency towards the Center) having also shewn that the Æther or vast fluid* Expansum *is the* Medium *to convey the Motions of Gravitation as well as Light; he comes in the next place to treat more particularly of Body and* Motion, *explaining what he understands by each of them, and then treating of Motion, says, that the two great Laws of Motion are* Light *and* Gravity, *and having before treated of the former, he comes to explain the latter more particularly, when having shewn that there is such a thing as Gravity, with the Limits and Proportions of its Power, and that it exerts it in all Bodies, he comes at last to the Principal Part, the* Cause of Gravity, *and after the Enumeration of its Proprieties, gives his* Explication *and* Hypothesis *of the Cause thereof. The Author designed to have answered several Objections against this his Hypothesis, but having reply'd to one only, the Discourse ends. To supply this Defect, I have added some Fragments which I found relating to the same Subject, which the Reader will find immediately annext.* R. W.

Of COMETS.

The Introduction to the following Discourse of Comets.

I Have formerly in this Place read several Discourses concerning the Nature and Proprieties of *Light*, and have therein explain'd some of the most wonderful Qualifications thereof. I should have proceeded farther in that Disquisition, after another Method than what I now take, had I not been diverted by an extraordinary and unusual Light, which since offer'd it self to my View, and exacted a more nice Observation and Contemplation upon it; and that was the Comet in *August* last. This new appearing *Light* caused me sooner to fall upon the Contemplation of this Subject, than according to my *intended Method* I should have done, tho' I designed to have come to it hereafter in its due Place and Order, wherein I design'd also to have given an account of what I observed concerning those of 1680 and 1682.

THO' the Frequency of *Comets*, and some of them very considerable, has excited the Lovers of Astronomical Learning to search and find out what they are; yet I have not hitherto met with any (tho' I have seen and perused the *Theorys* publish'd by very many Ingenious Men) that has given such an account of them, as to me seems natural and satisfactory. For tho' these Bodies seem very heterogeneous, singular, and of a distinct Nature from all the rest of the Celestial Bodies we contemplate; yet I am very apt to believe, that whenever we attain a true Knowledge of them, we shall find them to be the Product of the same regular Course of Nature. 'Tis true our Knowledge, even of the most conspicuous, is very imperfect, and not brought to the utmost Perfection of Improvement that the Helps which Nature has afforded us may seem to require; tho' even then we shall be to seek after divers other Proprieties of them, which are by other Helps afforded to the Inquiry after the Qualification of terrestrial Bodies. For whereas we have for the Examination of Terrestrial Bodies all the Five Senses, for those of the Heavens we have but Two at most, or indeed (the Information of the second being so very little) but one; and that is the Sight, the other, viz. that of Feeling, being so very little, that 'tis almost inconsiderable in all, except the Sun. This may be argued from the Experiments that have been made to find whether the Rays of the Moon convey any Heat, by the help of Burning-glaffes, whereby tho' the faid Rays have condenfed the Beams above 500 times, and confequently augment their Power accordingly, yet I could never find the leaft fenfible Alteration as to the heating or cooling Quality of them ; and this try'd, not only by cafting them on the back of the Hand, as on a Part of the Body very fenfible, but by throwing them upon the Ball of a Thermometer made with Air, which would be rarify'd with the leaft degree of increafed Heat, and condenfed with the leaft degree of Cold. Whence we may very rationally conclude, that if the Alterations of Heat and Cold caufed by the Rays of the Moon, when full and wholly inlightned, be fo very infenfible and inconfiderable, certainly the Influence of the other Planets, as to the Alterations of Heat and Cold, muft needs be very much lefs : For if the Sun's Light reflected from a whole Hemifphere of the Moon, which is firft abundantly more near to us than any of the other Celeftial Bodies, and fo appears an illuminated *Area*, which is bigger than the *Areas* of all the other Celeftial Bodies put together, both Fixed Stars and Planets, does produce no fenfible Alterations as to the Degrees of Heat and Cold, how much more infenfible muft the Alterations be which are caufed by fome other Body, which alters not in its Light a 10000 part of the Light of the Moon, as thofe Alterations of the other Planets will be found to be upon ftrict Examination ? Next, if the Reflection of the Sun's Light from a Body fo near us as the Moon is, in comparifon of the other Planets, works no fenfible effect, how much lefs effect muft the other Planets produce, which are vaftly much farther from us. Again, if the Reflection from the Moon, whofe Diftance from the Sun is much the fame with that of the Earth, produces no effect, how much lefs fignificant muft be the Reflection from *Saturn*, *Mars* and *Jupiter* be, which in the neareft Approach to the Sun are much further off from the Body of the Sun, than ever the Moon can be. So that upon the whole, we may conclude, that tho' it cannot be denied, but that the Celeftial Bodies may have fome kind of power and effect in the Alterations of Heat and Cold, yet compared to the Influence which the Sun hath in that Particular, it may be faid to be almoft nothing, or at leaft wholly infenfible. I do not fay that the Fixed Stars and other Planets, befides the Sun and Moon, are wholly infignificant, or without effect, as to the Body of the Earth ; for that, as I fhall in another place fhew, they may and have all fome Influence ; but to be found out by other *Media* than the immediate Senfes . But as to fenfible Effects, as to Heat and Cold, I conceive them fo fubtle and curious, as not ro be diftinguifhed by the more grofs Organs of our Senfe in any of the Planets, nay of the Moon it felf, fave only of thofe of the Sun.

So then the Sight being the chiefeft Senfe that can inform us concerning the *What the Sight informs us as* Nature of Celeftial Bodies, we may next confider what kind of Information *to Comets.* concerning the Nature of Comets this Senfe can afford us, and fee whether we can find in all or any of the Authors that have yet written of them, fo full an Account as for this purpofe were very defirable, and, as I conceive, might, if care had been accordingly taken, without much difficulty have been attained. For my own part, I muft confefs, tho' I have read and examined a great many, and confider'd and compar'd them together, to find Anfwers to thofe Queftions I propounded to my felf concerning them ; yet I was fo far by this means from procuring to my felf a fatisfactory Anfwer to them, that I was more to feek after this my Enquiry, than I was before : For I found the Accounts of feveral Hiftorians concerning them fo very different one from another in moft things, that I knew not which to rely upon. Which I fuppofe might be caufed, either from their differing way of obferving, or from the difference of the goodnefs of their Sight, or for the moft part from the differing Hypothefes they had made to themfelves, or been prepoffeft withal from the Writings or Doctrines of other Men. 'Twas a long time that the Opinion prevailed in this Part of the *No Accounts* World, that they were nothing but fublunary Meteors toffed and blown to and *in Authors* fro by the Winds or Motions of the fuperior Regions of the Air, and the Accounts *fatisfactory,* we find given of them by Men of that Perfuafion to be very fuitable to that Suppo-*and why.* fition. So that for all the time that the *Peripatetick* Philofophy and the *Ptolomean* Aftronomy prevailed, all the Accounts concerning them are idle and infignificant to this purpofe, and feem only fuited to the Ufe which they defigned for them, which

which was to make them only as Meſſengers, to foretel, by the help of their own Chimeras and Fancies joined with them, what Alterations were like to happen in human Affairs, and thence I doubt not, proceeded the ſtrange Shapes of them which they have painted out unto us of Targets, Shields, Spears, and Daggers, with Hands, &c. of Dragons and Serpents, and ſuch like. A great variety of which kind of Figures you may find in Authors that have written concerning them ; and you may ſee a great many of them together in *Hevelius*'s *Cometagraphy*, moſt of which, I confeſs, I look upon only as the Pro-

The Appearan-ces different from what they make 'em.

ducts of a prejudicate and prepoſſeſt Poetick Fancy in the Hiſtorians : For of thoſe five which I have obſerved, I could not obſerve any thing like them, no more than I could any of thoſe Figures of them which are delivered to us by the ſaid *Hevelius*, as Obſervations of his own : For the Figures of them, which I obſerved both with my naked Eye, and with the beſt Teleſcopes I had (ſome of which I am ſure were very good) I found the Appearances of them much of another kind. And of theſe Figures I was not aſſured by the Appearances of one or a few Obſervations, but by the Repetitions of them ſome hundreds of times, and by changing the Poſition of the Tube, Apertures, Eye glaſſes, Poſture of my Head, and the viewing of them with the Right Eye, and ſometimes with the Left, that if thoſe Appearances had been cauſed by any thing peculiar either in the Glaſſes or the Eyes, I might have found them out. And leſt ſomewhat in the Air or Atmoſphere might cauſe them, I examined them when at a good hight above the Horizon, and continued ever now and then to obſerve them, even to the very ſetting of them at the Horizon ; in all which Obſervations I plainly ſaw and took notice of the true appearing Figure and Shape thereof. Wherefore this imperfect and differing Account I found concerning Comets, made me reſolve to throw aſide all manner of Hypotheſes concerning them, and to obſerve them as if there never had been any ſuch Appearance before, and to attend wholly to what the Appearances themſelves would teach me :

The Author's Candidneſs in Philoſophical Matters aſ-ſerted.

And this I have done in every one that I have yet obſerved ; for tho' I have al-ready publiſhed my Conjectures, which were grounded upon thoſe Obſervations I had made on the three preceding Comets, yet I did not at all confine my ſelf to be of that Opinion, or not to ſeek farther to inform my Judgment by other Ap-pearances I ſhould happen to obſerve in my future Trials ; nor ſhould that at all have prevailed with me to defend a former Conjecture, that I had owned ſuch an Opinion to the World, and had brought ſeveral Arguments to make it more probable, fetch'd from other collateral Agreements in the Operations of Nature. For in things of this nature, where the Informations are but few, and at beſt but imperfect, and where a little unheeded Circumſtance may be of great importance in determining the Significancy of it, and where there is oftentimes ſo great a Similitude between the Effects produced by Cauſes and preceding Circumſtances vaſtly differing, 'twould be a high Piece of Arrogance and over valuing ones own Judgment poſitively to aſſert the trne Cauſe of ſuch appearing Effects to be this or that, and not another. And therefore as in the former, ſo in this, what I deliver as my Opinion, I would have no farther to be rely'd on than as the Reſult of my Ratiocination and conjecturing from the beſt Information I could hitherto obtain ; only I do poſitively affirm, that the Obſervations I here ſhall mention were made with all the Care I could, and that the Appearances to me were ſuch as I here expreſs them ; and that I do verily believe that there was no kind of Fallacy in them, but that any other Perſons might have ſeen the ſame, had they heedfully attended what they ſaw ; which to do, nothing is more advantageous than the preſent deſigning and drawing what is ſeen, and writing a Deſcription thereof. Now tho' I did in this Enquiry throw off all Prepoſſeſſion of other Hypotheſes, ſo as not to be biaſs'd by them, yet was I not ſo unmindful of them, as not to make ſome good uſe of them ; and that was, to conſider them as propounded by their ſeveral Authors, and thence by Synthetical Ratiocination to conclude what the Appearances ought to be, if ſuch or ſuch an Hypotheſis were true, and conſonant to the thing it ſelf, and thereupon to examine whether any ſuch Appearance could be diſcovered. To this end I conſider'd thoſe of *Galileo*, *Hevelius*, and divers others, who ex-plain the Blaze or Tail by the Light of the Sun, refracted in the Head, and ſo conſtipated into a Stream, to make the Appearance of that light Emanation

which

which is on the Side oppofite to the Sun; and putting fuch Suppofitions, as if real, I deduced what muft probably then be the Appearances that would follow from them; and then making Obfervations afrefh, I inquired whether I could difcover any Appearances that would favour fuch or fuch a Suppofition: But upon the whole, I muft needs fay, I found no one Remark that did any ways incline me to be of fuch Opinions, though I had many that for the prefent convinc'd me, that the Blaze muft needs proceed from fome other Caufe. It would be too long to recount here the feveral Hypothefes I did for this purpofe confider, and the particular Remarks I made to fatisfy my felf concerning them, that they were not in fuch Particulars agreeable to the Theory fuppofed: And therefore I fhall rather give an account what the Particulars were which I my felf did obferve.

My Obfervations of the firft, which appeared in *November* 1680, were but few, having the opportunity but of two Mornings to fee it, which were the 22d and 23d of the faid Month; at which times being in the dawning Light of the Morning, and the Air above not fo clear, I could not make any certain Determination of its Place, but by comparing its Pofition with the Stars that appeared near it, of the greater Magnitude: For on Monday Morning, *Nov.* 22d 1680, at half an hour after 6 a Clock, it was almoft in the Line that paft through *Spica Virginis* and *Cor Leonis*, but not full fo much toward the South; and its Diftance from *Spica*, as near as I could judge by my Sight, for I had then no Inftrument ready, was very near the fame with that of *Algorab* in the Right Wing of *Corvus*, or rather fomewhat more. Whence (by the Globe) I conceive it was about 3½ Degrees enter'd into *Scorpio*, and about 3½ Degrees South of the Ecliptick. Its Blaze was but fhort, but pointed towards *Spica Virginis*, not directly, but a very little on the South of it. It reached more than half way towards it, and fometimes by Glances it would feem of the whole length almoft. Its Appearance was but faint, as was alfo that of the Head, which though it feemed bigger than any Star of the firft Magnitude, yet it had but a faint, hazy and duskifh Light, like the Appearance of a Star of the firft Magnitude, through a hazy or foggy Air. I then viewed it with a fix-foot Telefcope, and found the Head of it to appear very large, but very feint; and though it were confiderably brighter in the middle, yet the *Nucleus* thereof was not fo defined as I had feen fome of the former, but feemed inveloped in a Cloud or Fog, not well defined: The Hazinefs about which fomewhat brighter Middle part, was pretty well defined, and round towards the Sun; but the other part feemed to fpread parabolically, or rather hyperbollically from the Sun. The dawning Light increafing apace, and the Air thickning, I had not long to obferve it; however I followed it as long as I could, till it appeared but like a faint hazy Star with little or no Tail.

The next Morning, which was the 23d, I faw it again; but it was got much farther into the dawning Light of the Morning, and the Air was much more hazy: It was then got to the South-Eaft of *Lanx Libræ*, and by placing it according to its Pofition to thofe Stars I could fee, I judged it to be removed more Eaftward about 4 or 5 Degrees, than it was the preceding Morning, and I conceived it to move pretty near in a Parallel with the Ecliptick, or rather to be got fomewhat more Southward. The Appearance through the fix-foot Telefcope was much the fame with that I faw the Morning before, and the time being very fhort, the Air thickning, and the Light increafing, I could add no more Remarks, hoping fome other clear Morning would better accommodate me; but though I attended, yet I could not from that time fee it again: Though by others I find it was obferved a good while before, and by others feveral days after. Mr. *Thomas Hill* of *Canterbury* faw it firft the 12th of *November*, at half an hour after Five in the Morning, and by its Diftances from *Cor* and *Cauda Leonis*, taken with an Inftrument of four Foot and a half Radius, he found it then, as he fays, in 12 Degrees of *Virgo*, and in two Degrees of North Latitude, with a flow Motion, having not paffed above four Degrees in three days. Its Tail was then about 30 Degrees long. Sigr *Montanari* at *Venice* in *Italy*, on the 19th of *November*, faw it at 4 Degrees diftance from *Spica Virginis*, and about the fame Latitude with that Star. He judged it in 23 of *Libra*, with about one Degree and half of South Latitude: Its Tail directed towards *Spica*, not directly, but a little to the Southwards of it. Its Head appeared as big as a Star of the first Magnitude, but of a dusky Light, and pale like a *Stella Nebulosa* : Its Tail was very short, and reached not much more, than two Degrees towards *Spica*.

Afterwards viewing it with a Telescope 17 *Venetian* Feet in length, he saw the Head of it three times as big as that of *Jupiter*, which was seen that Night, only its Figure was not so well and round defined, but of a smoaky dusky Colour which caused several of those that viewed it to differ somewhat in their Judgments about this Measure : And (he says) that one thing was very remarkable, that he could not in this see any distinct round *Nucleus* more shining than the rest of the Head, as was plain to be discovered in those of 1664 and 1665, wherein they were pretty clear, and not without a roundish Termination. But in this the Light was considerably greater in the middle than towards the Extremes, but without any certain Boundary, whence it had more the resemblance of a little illuminated Cloud, than of any thing else, illuminated but with a dusky Light. This he resembles to the Appearance of Smoak issuing out of a Chimny or Furnace, wherein there is a great Fire, when seen at some distance in the Night ; for there the Smoak seems to be a kind of Flame tapering to some distance, and there to vanish. *Note, the Latitude of* Venice *is* 45°. 27'.

The 21st it was distant from *Spica Virginis* 8°. 28'. the 22d in the Morning 13°. 10. the 23d he could not see it for Clouds ; the 24th it was distant 23°. 30'. the 25th it was distant 28°. 13'. From which Observations he concludes its Longitudes to be, the 21st in 27°. 51'. of ♎ ; the 22d in ♍ 2°. 33'. the 24th in ♍ 12°. 52'. the 25th in ♍ 17°. 45'. Its Latitude was South, and it moved almost parallel to the Ecliptick, and seemed to tend towards the Sun, so as he hoped it might be seen to pass through, or eclipse the Sun : And the straight Line from the Comet through *Spica Virginis*, passed very near *Cor Leonis* all the times he saw it. Comparing the Spaces that it passed the several Days which he saw it one with another, he found it to accelerate in its Motion ; for between that of the 21st and 22d, it passed but 4°. 42'. whereas in the next two Days it had passed 10°. 19'. So that he supposed its greatest Acceleration would be pretty near its Conjunction with the Sun, which would be on the 28th of the same Month ; and thence he conceived it might re appear, after it had past the Sun in the Evenings, and be seen for a good while. Which whether it did or

Observations of the great Comet in December 1680.

not, I cannot learn from any Place since that time, for I find no mention of any Comet till the 10th of *December* following, when the Tail of a Comet was seen to rise out of the West South-West, above the Horizon, to a great length, by some in *Oxford*. And Dr. *Wallis*, at the same Place the Night following, being the 11th of *December* about seven of the Clock at Night, saw the Tail of it very bright and long, which he judged to be about three quarters of a Quadrant, but narrow upwards ; the Head of it he judged, by the Position of the Tail, to be about the Head of *Sagittary* ; the Point reached as high as the *Swan*, but somewhat to the Eastward of the bright Star therein, pointing towards the Constellation of *Perseus*, from which time forward it was continually observed.

Whether it were the same with the former in November.

Some are of opinion, that this was the second Appearance of the same Comet, after it had past the Sun, though there are more of the contrary Opinion, and suppose them to be two differing Comets, and that because of the differing Tendency of both their Motions: The Comet of *November* daily increasing its Latitude to the South, as several of the Observators make it ; but other Observations make it to be at its greatest South Latitude on the 23d or 24th of *November*, and that from that time, till it disappeared, its Latitude continually diminished. But which of the two observed best, I know not ; but sure I am, that the Observations I have hitherto met with of it, are so uncertain, that 'twill

NB. *This the Author never performed.*

be hard to say which of them is right. However, somewhat more concerning this matter shall be added hereafter, when I come to speak of the Motions of Comets in general ; for however strange the differing Observations of several Men, who possibly may not be sufficiently skilful to make the Observations, and of others who though they may have Skill enough, may yet want fitting Instruments for that purpose ; yet by all that I have observed my self, and by

The Nature of all Comets the same.

what I have found in the Observations of Learned Astronomers, I conceive they are all of them of the same kind, and are moved with the same regular Motions,

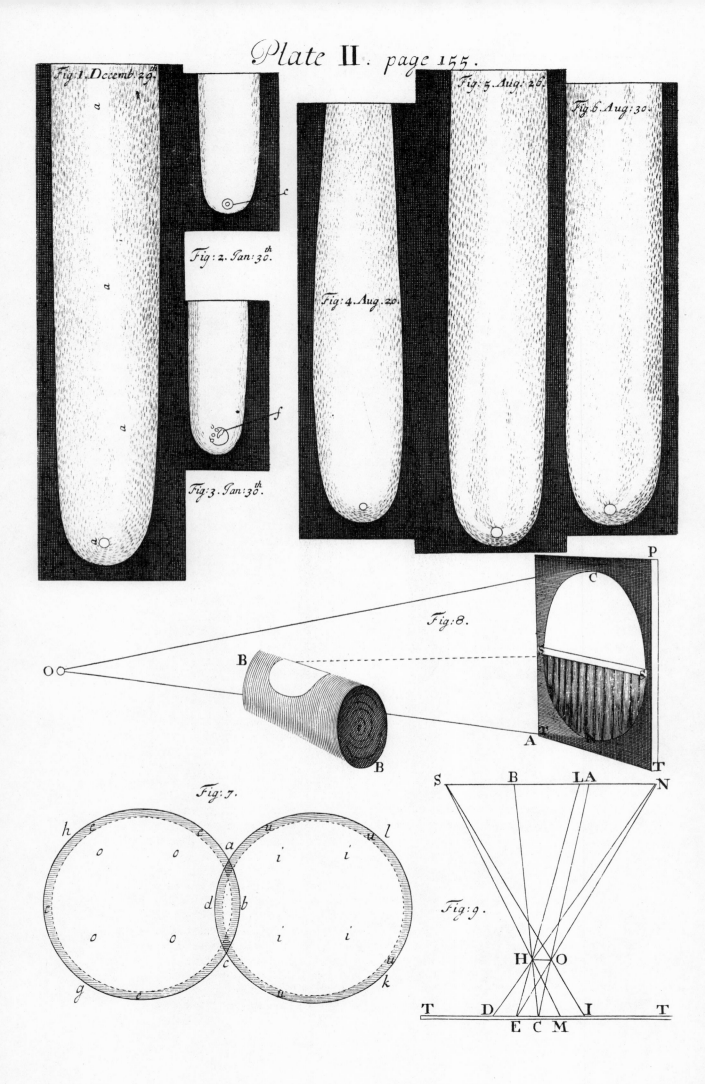

Plate II. *page* 155.

Fig: 1. *Decemb:* 29.th

Fig: 2. *Jan:* 30.th

Fig: 3. *Jan:* 30.th

Fig: 4. *Aug:* 20.

Fig: 5. *Aug:* 26.

Fig: 6. *Aug:* 30.

Fig: 8.

Fig: 7.

Fig: 9.

tions, and for the moſt part agree in their other Affections and Proprieties. I ſhall therefore, by reaſon that all the Obſervations I meet with of this firſt are but very few, and ſcarce any one that may certainly be rely'd on, rather leave any further Diſquition upon this, and proceed to the Obſervations and Appearances of the 2d, the Blaze of which, as I ſay, began to be ſeen the 10th of *December* 1680, riſing up above the Horizon, and on the 11th was ſeen by Dr. *Wallis* at *Oxford* to riſe above the Horizon ſo high as the *Swan*, and was conceived to come from a Head below the Horizon in ſome part of the Heaven near the Head of *Sagittarius*. I find alſo by Mr. *Caſſini*'s Relation of the Comet, that Mr. *Flamſtead* at *Greenwich* ſaw the Tail of it on the 10th and 11th, a little after the Setting of the Sun, and took notice, that on the 10th it paſſed through the middle of the Conſtellation of the *Eagle*, and terminated at 3 Stars mark'd by *Bayer* with *A w* and *b*, and that on the 11th the Tail extended to the extremity of the Dart. The 12th he ſaw the Head of it at 4 of the Clock and 40 Minutes, in 5 deg. 9 min. of *Capricorn*, with 9 degrees and 4 Minutes of North Latitude. The ſame day Mr. *Caſſini* ſaw the Tail of it riſing above the Clouds near the Horizon, and appearing bent like a piece of a Rainbow; whoſe Convexity, which was ſenſible, reſpected the South: It ſeem'd terminated with two Circles concentrick to each other: At 24 ½ Minutes after Five, he ſaw the Head 4 ½ degrees high, in the ſame Verical with *Aquila*. The Tail roſe, oblique to the Vertical, declining towards the North; ſo that the 3 Stars of the *Eagle*, which are in a right Line, were as much to the South of it, as they were diſtant one from another; and it paſt by the moſt Weſtern Stars of the *Dart*, and tended towards the Tail of *Cygnus*: It ended at the Milky Way, and was of a pale Gold Colour. The Length of it was about 40 degrees. From that time it continued to be obſerved almoſt every Night ſomewhere or other, as I find by comparing the ſeveral Accounts of it which I have ſeen; but moſt of the Obſervations are ſo imperfect, that nothing certain can be built upon them. I ſhall therefore paſs them by, and only take notice of thoſe of Mr. *Caſſini* made at the *Obſervatoire* at *Paris*, and only ſuch Obſervations of his as are Phyſical, omitting at preſent thoſe which are purely Aſtronomical, and ſhew the Place and Motion of it, which I ſhall have occaſion to uſe hereafter, when I ſhall alſo take notice of the like Obſervations made here by Mr. *Flamſtead*.

The 17th of *December* I find that Mr. *Caſſini* viewed the Head of it with the *Caſſini's Phyſical Obſervations.* Teleſcope of his Quadrant, but found the bigneſs of the *Nucleus* not to exceed the bigneſs of a Star of the 3d Magnitude to the naked Eye; not of a determinate Figure, but confuſed and irregular; and obſerving it through a Teleſcope of 35 Foot, it appeared of the bigneſs of the Ball of *Saturn*, but confuſed alſo and irregular, which he aſcribes to the Vapors near the Horizon which encompaſſed it, for that the Bodies of the Planets near the Horizon are ſo confuſed likewiſe. The Length of the Tail he judged 48 Degrees.

I ſaw it ſeveral times between the 18th and 19th Days of *December*, but in Places *The Author's own Obſervations. Plate 2. Fig. 1.* where I had no Convenience of making any good Obſervations of it; but the 29th at 7 in the Evening, I view'd the Head with a 14 Foot Teleſcope, and found it of this Form: There was a hazy Brightneſs, which ſeem'd through the Teleſcope about half a Degree in Magnitude, or as big as the Moon would appear to the naked Eye. This was fainter and fainter, as it was farther from the middle, but no where certainly defined; yet the half of it, which reſpected the Sun, was pretty round, and beyond that the Sky was dark and clear, without any Light: Toward the middle it grew lighter and lighter, and about a 6th or 8th part of it was pretty near of an equal Degree of Light, not defined any way, but ſomewhat like a whiter part of a Cloud: Out of this there was plainly to be ſeen a kind of Stream iſſuing out, not directly oppoſite to the half round Part, but a little to the Northward of a brighter ſmall Stream, which paſſed through the reſt of the Head into the Blaze; and though it ſeem'd to iſſue out of it towards the North Pole, yet it ſuddenly bent into the middle of the Blaze, and aſcended a good way into it like a Pith. The half-round part alſo toward the Edges of it, ſtruck into the Tail, making the Outſides of the Tail or Blaze both brighter than the reſt of the Blaze, except the Pith: Theſe were a little diverging upwards, and ſo bounded the Sides of the Blaze. The Stream out of the middle, as it appear'd through the Teleſcope, ſeemed as if there had been a brighter Stream of

ſome

some more shining Matter that had issued out of it, not perpendicularly, but a little inclined to the Right Hand, and imitated a Stream of Water, if it had run out of a Vessel a little inclined to the Perpendicular: For it bent quickly into the Axis of the Blaze. This is represented in the Figure by the bright Part issuing from the round *Nucleus, aaaa.* This appeared sometimes more plain and sometimes more faint, so as sometimes to be much like the rest of the Blaze: But for the most part, so much of the Head as I could see at once, was brightest of all in the middle, and then brighter on the Edges than the rest of the Blaze. Its Blaze or Tail then extended to a very great Length and Breadth, and ended between the two Stars in *Perseus* marked by *Bayer* with γ and *n.* At first it seemed to turn off at φ and υ on the Right Hand, or towards the North; but as the Evening grew darker, I plainly saw it to reach the Stars γ and *n.* As concerning its Place at that time, and the tendency of its Tail as to the Sun, we shall speak of them hereafter in their due Places: For I shall now only mention to you what I observed in its Shape and Appearance.

December the 30th, at half an hour after 8, I observed the Comet both with my naked Eye, and with a Glass of six Foot: Its *Nucleus* was hardly distinguishable, only there was a cloudy Whiteness in the middle, with a hazy Light about it, which by degrees grew fainter and fainter; but still it was more defined towards the Sun, yet as before very imperfectly, though the outermost Edge had somewhat considerably more light than the Sky, and had a rounding like a Cloud. This Haziness spread from the Head on that Side that was opposite to the Sun, somewhat like a Parabolick Figure, and made up the Blaze or Tail; but the Head was considerably lighter than the Blaze. Looking often upon it, and diligently inquiring, and remarking what I could discover, I saw the same Stream of Light issue out of the *Nucleus* as I had the Night before, and this in the manner of a sudden Spouting of Water out of an Engine to quench Fire, which would presently again disappear, and be much like the rest of the Blaze. These Dartings I could perceive to rise to a considerable height into the Blaze or Tail. I often saw the Telescopical Stars through the Blaze, and this Night I observed one almost up to the very Haziness about the Head of the Comet, appear through the Blaze. After I had discovered this issuing of Light through the Telescope, I diligently attended the Appearance of the Comet with my naked Eye, and I could plainly perceive such a kind of Darting of Light from the Head, which did sometimes seem to dart almost the whole Length of the Blaze or Tail, which I have some hundreds of times since taken notice of.

Jan. 5. I hoped to have seen it eclipse ♪ of *Pegasus* in *Bayer*; but it passed very near it, but missed it.

Jan. 7. I observed it about 11 a Clock at Night, I could not see the Length of the Blaze for the Clouds. It tended towards *Perseus*, but seemed not to reach it. It was grown very faint, and seemed much wasted. It was very strange that there appeared little or no Halo or Atmosphere about the Head on that Side that respected the Sun; but the Parabolick Edge seemed to touch the very *Nucleus* or light Cloud in the middle. The brighter Dartings out of Light at some times more than at others, now manifestly appeared; and I was then assured by above 20 several times taking notice of it, and examining it with all imaginable care through my 14 Foot Telescope, that these Appearances were no Optical Fallacies. I thought the Alteration in the Air might have been some way a Cause of this Appearance; but then I should have discovered some such thing in the Fixed Stars, which yet I could not: And therefore I judge it a true and real Appearance of the Mutation in the Comet it self, how instantaneous soever it appeared; of which I shall shew more in my following Observations. I this Night also took notice of the Stream, as before, issuing out of the *Nucleus* into the Blaze, with a brighter Pith or Axis of Light, and it seemed to issue in the same manner as before, by spurts, and then as suddenly disappearing. The Appearances were neither caused by the Eye; for I saw it both with the Right and with the Left Eye, and with several Inclinations of my Head, and so altering the Postures of each of them, I turned the Telescope, and varied the Glasses and Apertures, to see if any of these would make them not to appear, or alter any of them; but I found them in every Trial, and therefore they must be caused by a real Effect in the Object it self.

Jan.

Jan. 9th, from 9 till 12, I obferved the Places, Motions, Pofitions and Appearances of the Comet. The Places of it I fhall not mention here. The Blaze of it was fometimes pretty clear and bright, efpecially about the Girdle of *Andromeda*; which was juft within the Rays to the naked Eye, but through the Telefcope it was fometimes clear of them, though fometimes in the Glafs alfo it was manifeftly within them: They fpread alfo fo wide upwards, as to touch the Foot of *Andromeda*, a little beyond which they feem'd to terminate, though at other times they reacht even to *δ* of *Perfeus* in *Bayer*, fo that *δ* feem'd to be in the very middle or Axis of the Blaze. This Night again, as I had feveral Nights before, I very often obferved the fudden Radiations or Flafhings from the *Nucleus*, but efpecially in the middle of the Pith or Blaze. It was exeeeding wonderful, and, all things confider'd, it feems very difficult to be explained from what Caufe, or by what means it was effected. I oftentimes obferved the Head with very little Radiations, and then upon a fudden a bright Stream iffued from the *Nucleus* or light Cloud in the middle, and afcended into the Blaze, fometimes ftraight up from the middle, and almoft as big as the *Nucleus*, and would fhoot fometimes to a good diftance from the Head into the Blaze, which I difcover'd by viewing a part of the Blaze at a pretty diftance from the Head, with the Telefcope, without feeing the Head it felf. Sometimes it would iffue from one fide, and fometimes from another, and fo fhoot upwards into the Pith of the Blaze. Sometimes it would be difperfed, as it were, into a broad Light, and undefined, whilft the other afcended ftraight, and defined; and that alfo fometimes on one fide, fometimes on the other, and feemed fomewhat like the flaring of the Flame of a Candle or Torch. Thefe Appearances I am farther *The Appear-* certain were not caufed by my Eye, or by the Glaffes of the Telefcope, or by *ances were* the Alterations of the Air: Not by my Eye, becaufe I faw the fame Appear- *real.* ances, whether I looked with my Right, or my Left Eye, and changed the Pofture of my Head when I looked; fometimes feeing them with my Head upright, fometimes with my Head inclined horizontal on one fide, and then on the other; and fo in all variety of Poftures, in which I ftill faw them. Nor were they caufed by my Glafs, for I faw them with the fame-Glafs changed with feveral Apertures, and turned every way round, fo as fometimes one Side of the Tube was upwards, fometimes another; yet the Appearances were the fame, as they were alfo through 4 or 5 other Glaffes, through which I faw them in the fame manner. Nor were they caufed by the Air, for the Fixed Stars near the Head of the Comet had no fuch Alterations. Again, if it had been the Alterations of the Air, the Flafhings would have been feen to defcend fometimes, and fometimes to crofs the Blaze; but thefe always iffued from the Head, and fhot upward into the Blaze, and never any other way, that I could obferve. And I have hundreds of times obferved fuch Flafhings with my naked Eye, darting from the Head even to the whole Length of the Blaze, almoft in a moment. Befides, when thefe Flafhings ceas'd, as they often did, I could fee divers fmall Telefcopical Stars in the middle of the Blaze very plainly: Whereas when the *Telefcopieal* Flafhing appeared, they could not be feen for the Light, efpecially the fmaller *Stars feen* of them; and I faw them on the one fide that was without Emanation, clofe *through the* up to the Pith, but on the other fide of the Pith that had the light Emanation, *Blaze.* I could not perceive them, and fo after a little time *vice verfa.* Sometimes alfo I could fee them on both fides up to the Pith, in the middle of the Blaze, and fometimes they would be all hid. This Night I exactly obferved its Progreffes *No Paralax to* among the fmall Telefcopical Stars, to fee if I could have found any fenfible *be obferved.* Parallax of it, but I could difcover none.

I took notice of the fame Appearances on the 16th of *January*, and the 23d and 24th but very little, as alfo on the 26th and 27th.

January the 30th at 11 at Night, I obferved the Pofition of the Comet, and feveral other Particulars. I obferved this Night alfo, as I had done feveral Nights before very often and very plainly, that the Appearance was perfectly a Refemblance of Flame, but that exceeding thin and rarify'd, and of a faint Light: That it waved, flared, or undulated to and fro: That it fometimes feemed to burn clearer and ftronger, and fometimes fainter and more dim; fometimes on one fide, and then on the other, and fometimes in the middle of the Blaze alfo, or in the Part oppofite to the Sun: And which I took more no-

tice

tice of, as more confiderable, it would be fometimes more on the Side next the Sun, and fometimes lefs: Sometimee it appeared with little or no *Halo* about it, but only the *Nucleus* or white Cloud with a little Stream or Blaze iffuing from Plate 2. Fig. 2. it like the 2d Figure.   At other times, for the twinkling of an Eye, or fmall moment, I could fee a very fmall bright Point of Light in the middle of it, as at *c*, which appeared no bigger than a Telefcopical Star, which was very near it, which immediately difappeared, and feemed to be covered with the white cloudy *Nucleus*.   This cloudy *Nucleus* was alfo much bigger and brighter than at other times, and fometimes feemed to have feveral bright Parts in it, as in the Plate 2. Fig. 3. 3d Figure at *f*.   Every one of thefe Remarks I obferved at leaft half a fcore feveral times, and the Changes were very quick ; fo that I was fully fatisfied in my felf, by all the ways of examining I could think of, that thefe Mutations and ftrange Appearances, poffibly never heeded by any before (for I never met with any mention of them in any Author, or from any Perfon that had taken notice of Comets, but only I have been told by fome antient Men that faw that in 1618, that it did perfectly fparkle and fhoot forth Fire ; but I confefs I did not then give credit to them, but attributed the Caufe of their having fuch an Idea or Remembrance of it to their having poffibly more dreadfull Apprehenfions of it in their younger Years, and alfo to the great Brightnefs of the Tail of that Comet) : I fay, I was fully fatisfied that they were real Mutations in the very *Phænomenon* it felf.   And this I was the more fatisfied of, becaufe I had hundreds of times taken notice with my bare Eye, of the Glancings and Dartings out of the Light of the Head into the Blaze ; in which 'tis almoft incredible with what Swiftnefs the Flafh or darting of Light paffes from the Head to the very Extremity of the Blaze : For I never obferved the Dartings of the Lightning (which I have often diligently remark'd and computed to move above a Mile in lefs than half a Second of Time) to move more fwiftly from Place to Place, than I did fee through the Telefcope fuch kind of Dartings from the Star to move : I mean the actual Flame of the Lightning, and not the fpreading of the Light it felf, which I conceive rather to be inftantaneous ; and though it do feem to be fucceffive, and to fpread in a very quick time from the Center *in Orbem*, and that the more remote Parts are inlightned after the nearer ; yet I take that to proceed partly from the weaker Impreffion made by the remote parts on the Eye, and partly from the Yieldingnefs of fome parts of the *Medium* through which it is propagated.   Now if this Appearance be really in the Object, as I am fatisfied it is, and that this Object be at fo vaft a diftance from us, as by all the accurate Obfervations that have been hitherto made for this purpofe, 'tis certainly prov'd to be ; we fhall find by comparing the diftance of the Lightning with the diftance of the Comet, how incredibly much fwifter thefe Dartings of Light in the Comet will be than the Dartings of the Flame of Lightning it felf: And yet after all, how incredible foever it feem, I am fatiffied by my often repeated Obfervations, that the Matter is really fo.   It feem'd to me upon my viewing them often, that 'twas not improbable but that thefe Flafhes or Sparklings were caufed much after the fame manner as the fudden Kindlings of Steams or Smoke in a Fire, beginning at the Head, and kindling like a Train into the Tail, which may poffibly be made up of fuch a Stream of combuftible rarify'd Parts, and that the whole Light of the Head and the Blaze was from the actual fhining of the Head and the Parts of the Blaze ; but of this more hereafter.   However, this I think is very plain, that the whole Blaze proceeded and iffued from the Head in material Steams, and that it is not at all produced by any manner of Refraction of the Rays of the Sun paffing through the Head, as many are very apt to fuppofe and affert ; for which I fhall add, I obferved all the fame Appearances again the 3d of *February*, and continued to fee them till 12 of the Clock at night ; fo that I was fufficiently confirmed in the reality of the Appearance, and that it was not a *Deceptio Vifus*.   I obferv'd it again in its Progrefs the 7th and 9th, and diligently fet its Place among the Fixed Stars that lay near it in its way.

The laft time I faw it was on the 10th of *February* at Night, when I fixed its Place among the Telefcopical Stars, with the Direction of its Blaze, which to the laft I all along obferved very confpicuous.   I this Night alfo, through my 14 Foot Telefcope, difcover'd all the before-recited *Phænomena*, as before, tho'
they

they were very much fainter and paler, and every thing diminished as to its Vividneſs ; ſo that I did not expect that it would laſt much longer : However, I believe I might have followed it for a Fortnight or Three Weeks longer, had not partly other Occaſions, and partly the Cloudineſs and Thickneſs of the Air, prevented me from ſeeing it for 7 or 8 days after, till which time I continued ſo often as I had Opportunity, to look for it. Monſ. *Caſſini*, it ſeems, follow'd it ſome days longer, till it arrived at the Foot of *Perſeus*, where he alſo loſt ſight of it. I do not yet hear that any one has certainly ſeen it beyond that time, and Mr. *Caſſini* ſeems not to be very ſure of ſome of his laſt Obſervations.

Thus I have given you in ſhort the Sum of what Phyſical Obſervations I have made concerning theſe Comets, which as they are new, ſo they may poſſibly ſeem the more ſtrange, for that no other that has writ concerning them, has mention'd any ſuch Appearances, and for that ſeveral Appearances mention'd by ſome very famous Writers, ſeem very differing, if not contradictory to theſe. However, what I did obſerve I have ſet down, that ſuch as cannot find cauſe to believe them from what I have here ſet down, may by their future Opportunities and Obſervations better inform themſelves, and more critically ſearch and find out the true Appearances, and at leaſt the probable, if not the true Reaſons thereof. For I am perſwaded, that there was ſcarce any Appearance in this Comet, but may in ſome degree, more or leſs, be found in every one that ſhall appear for the future ; for that I look upon them to be all of the ſame nature, and to have all the ſame Proprieties in ſome meaſure ; and I ſhall be content not to be believed, if making the Obſervations in my way, and with as good Inſtruments, they do not find the like Appearances.

Theſe Obſervations had ſtill lain by me neglected, had not the Appearance of this laſt Comet in *Auguſt* made me find them out ; which put me in mind again of repeating my former Care and Scrutiny after the true Appearances thereof. I did therefore, ſo ſoon as ever I had diſcover'd it, put my Glaſſes in order, (which had lain by neglected ſince that time) and reſolved in this wholly to mind thoſe kind of Obſervations, for that I hoped I ſhould from other hands receive ſufficiently exact Aſtronomical Obſervations thereof, of which I ſhall afterwards have more occaſion to make uſe, when I come to enquire concerning the Diſtance, Courſe, Velocity, Magnitude and Original of them. And tho' the *Determination* and *Demonſtration* of all theſe do require a great Stock of accurate Obſervations purpoſely and pertinently made, which is hardly to be obtained from all that have hitherto writ concerning them ; yet from ſuch as they are, I ſhall ſhew ſome Conjectures, which to me ſeem to have ſomewhat of probability in them, which may ſerve at leaſt as Hints to ſuch as have Opportunity to obſerve them, and are furniſhed with better Abilities and better Inſtruments than I have hitherto been furniſhed with.

NB. *Theſe Aſtronomical Obſervations, and our Author's Remarks upon them, I have not met with amongſt his Papers ; ſo that I verily believe he never procured them, or at leaſt never made any Animadverſions, as is here mentioned.* R. W.

But to proceed to the Obſervations I made of this laſt Comet, which appear'd *Auguſt* the 16th 1682. The Forepart of the Night being exceeding clear overhead, looking upon the Heavens, I diſcover'd a Comet in the North a little above the Horizon, glancing its Blaze toward the South-Eaſt, between ſome thin Clouds that were near the Horizon, and preſently fetching a ſix-foot Teleſcope, and viewing the Head of it, I remarked its Poſition to ſome Teleſcopical Stars that were near it, and with my naked Eye found the Place of thoſe Stars, as to the Stars about them ; the moſt conſpicuous of which were two little Stars of the 3d Magnitude, in the Fore Foot of the Great Bear, marked by *Bayer* with *s* and *x*, and 'twas near in a Line with *s* and *T* ; 'twas pretty vivid, and through the Teleſcope ſeemed to have a bright and ſtrong *Nucleus*, though ſmall, not very defined, and the Light or *Halo* about the Head was much of the Form of all the other I had ſeen, when very conſpicuous. The Side next the Sun was pretty round, and at a good diſtance from the *Nucleus*, and the Blaze ſtruck from it in a Parabolick Figure.

I

I had not the Opportunity of obferving it again till *Auguft* the 20th at 9 at Night, at which time I took its place.

Plate 2. Fig. 4. Through the Telefcope it appeared of a Shape which is fhewn in the Draught or Picture. See *Fig.* 4.

The *Nucleus* was the fmalleft, but the brighteft I have feen ; the hazy Light about it was fo much the brighter, the nearer it was pofited to the *Nucleus.* The brighteft part of the Head diminifh'd to about 5 or 6 Diameters of the bright Star, as I may call it, in the middle, without which was a thinner *Halo*, which was about twice as broad without it, which was of a pretty equal Light ; and this towards the Sun was terminated in a rounding Figure, not very defined, yet fo much, that immediately beyond the Sky look'd black, and was clear of it. The brighter part about the Star or *Nucleus* feemed to fpread more or brighter towards the Blaze than any other way, a little tapering ; but the thinner part was much more fpread that way, aud extended about eight or ten Degrees, which made up the Blaze. This feem'd to be a kind of Smoke or Steam, which taper'd towards that length from the Sun ; fo that the brighter part feem'd fomewhat like a thin Flame, and tapering a little into the Blaze, but was foon fpent, and the other thinner part, or Flame, made up all the reft of the Blaze.

Aug. 21. I faw it again, and noted its Place, but was diverted by accident from making Telefcopical Obfervations, and fetting them down.

Aug. 22. I noted the Pofition, Shape and Length of its Blaze, but nothing elfe.

Plate 2. Fig. 5. *Aug.* 26. At 7 in the Evening, I delineated the Figure and Shape of the Comet exactly like that I faw through my 14 Foot Telefcope, which will appear more plain by the 5th Figure than I can otherwife well exprefs it. It had a pretty bright round *Nucleus*, and about that was an Atmofphere of thinner Light, which was terminated towards the Sun with a round Figure. That part of this *Halo* or lighter Atmofphere towards the Sun, was not fo bright and radiant as another kind of Light, which feemed to iffue from the *Nucleus* or Star both ways at Right Angles, with the Axis through the Sun ; which lighter Iffuings bent into a kind of Parabolical Figure within the former *Halo* or Atmofphere, and was terminated within it, and feem'd to form as it were a 2d Parabolical Termination towards the Sun, in the *Apex* of which *Parabola* was the bright *Nucleus*, and this brighter Parabolical Line of Light feemed as grofs or thick as the *Nucleus* it felf. This iffued on both fides, but that on the Right Hand, or the Northermoft, was much more confpicuous ; infomuch, that that on the Left Hand, or towards the South, was to be feen but fometimes, but that of the other fide was very plain and confpicuous, and feem'd like a Stream of Flame blown out of a Candle by a Blowpipe afcending or bending upwards juft as fuch a blown Flame of a Candle will do, if it be made by a gentle Blaft. This I remark'd very carefully, to fee whether I could find by any fucceeding Obfervations, any Alteration of the Magnitude, Figure, Brightnefs or Pofition in refpect of the Comet's *Axis.*

Thefe two brighter Spoutings of Flame or Light turned or bent upwards from the Sun, and after a fhort fpace feemed to unite into the *Axis* or Middle of the Blaze, and form the Shape of the outfide of the Flame of a Candle tapering to a point ; the fainter part alfo without it feemed to taper much in the fame manner. I faw alfo feveral Corrufcations or Flafhings of the Flame fhooting out to a great diftance into the Blaze.

Aug. 29. I noted the Place and Pofition of the Comet at ½ an hour after 8 at night. Its Blaze pointed exactly at the bright Star in the Crown.

I obferved the Body of it through a 14 Foot Telefcope, and faw the Spoutings out of the brighter Streams from the *Nucleus*, but efpecially of that on the Right or Northern fide, which was very large and confpicuous, that on the Left or South fide being much fainter and lefs confpicuous. They feemed not now at Right Angles with the *Axis*, but to be fomewhat more towards the Sun, both of them ; but clofe by the *Nucleus* they turned about again, and extended into the Blaze with a kind of tapering Form, as on the 26th, and in all other Particulars it feemed to be much the fame as it then appear'd. For it feem'd, as I faid before, like a Stream of Light, or Flame, or Fuzee, iffuing more efpetially on the Right or Northern fide, and turning about into the Blaze, where

it

it made a kind of tapering Light; but the oppofite Side was not near fo plain or eafy to be feen.

Aug. 30. I viewed it again with my 14 Foot Tube, and found its Figure fuch as I have defcribed in the Draught. The *Halo* or Atmofphere about the Head, on that fide which was next the Sun, was thinner than the laft time I faw it, not fpreading fo far that way as then. The Fufe or Stream on the North fide of it was very plain and bright, but feemed not to iffue now at Right Angles with the Axis of the Blaze, but, as it were, at 45 degrees with it, and then bent into the Blaze with a kind of Parabolick Figure, and fo ran Parallel with the Axis to a great length, and did not taper in towards it, as on the 29th. The iffuing on the oppofite fide was hardly at all vifible, only it feemed a little bright-er in that part, than in the middle part of the Blaze near the Head.

Aug. 31. I took its Place and the Direction of its Blaze by the 14 Foot Tele-fcope. The bright *Nucleus* appeared much as it had done the preceding Nights, and the Fufe or Stream of Light had much the fame Inclination to the *Axis* as laft Night, only it feemed now to run farther parallel to the *Axis* into the Blaze. The Hazinefs of the Head about the *Nucleus*, on that fide which was next the Sun, was now much thinner and nearer to the *Nucleus*, and pretty well defined.

There was a little Emanation anfwering to it on the Left Hand, but that was exceeding faint; yet the Sides were brighter than the middle part near the *Axis*. I faw the flaring of the Light, and the Corrufcation, as I had done almoft every time I faw it. The *Nucleus* was not a tenth part of the bignefs of the *Halo* or *Haze* about it.

September the 1ft, I viewed it again with my 14 Foot Telefcope. I could fee no fmall Stars near it; the Fufee or Stream of Light appeared much as it had done the two preceding Nights. I ftill plainly faw the Flaring or Flafhing of the Light, and fometimes alfo faw a Shooting or Spouting as it were of Light from the *Nucleus* directly into the Blaze, which as quickly difappeared.

I began to fee it *September* the 4 at 7 ½, the *Crepufculum* being yet very bright. The *Nucleus* was pretty clear and round, but the Blaze from it was only two Emanations of a kind of Parabolick Figure on each fide, as in the Figure; but the Northern Side was brighter than the Southern ftill, and they feemed to fpread one from another with an Angle of about 60 Degrees, fo far as I could fee them then; for they extended but a little way from the *Nucleus*. The middle part of the Blaze between them was hardly vifible. But as the *Crepuf-culum* diminifhed, it appeared much brighter and fuller, and then I could fee its Light alfo in the middle part of the Blaze. Scarce any *Halo* between the *Nucleus* and Sun appear'd, at firft, and but little more when it appear'd brighteft. I obferved alfo the flaring or flafhing of the Light, and a kind of moving of the Fufee on the North fide. It was at its brighteft about 8, when I obferved alfo its Pofitions. I followed it with my Telefcope downwards towards the Horizon near half an hour after it difappeared to my Sight; and I was able to fee it almoft to the very Horizon, even till it went behind a Steeple a little above the tops of the Houfes, though the Smoke much thickned the Air. As it grew lower and lower, the Blaze difappeared by degrees, and at length alfo the Hazinefs about the Head; fo that I conld not fee the two Streams, but only now and then by glances; but the *Nucleus* it felf I faw very plain, but verymuch fmaller than before, and feemed about the bignefs of *Oculus Tauri*, but very dull and faint, in comparifon even of the fmall Fixed Stars which were not far from it.

The Figure of it when brighteft this Night, was much of the fhape of the Flame of a Candle clofe fnuffed, the *Nucleus* reprefenting the End of the Snuff; tho' that in a Candle fo order'd looks perfectly black, but the *Nucleus* was very light.

Sept. 8. I faw it from 7 ½ till almoft 8; I took notice of its *Nucleus*, and of the Emanations on each fide, as alfo of the flafhing and flaring of the Light. The Beams were darted on each fide parabolically, and feemed at firft almoft like two Sides of an equilateral Triangle, but when it was cleareft they were much longer. The Clouds near the Horizon hinder'd me, that I could not fee it till 8.

Sept 9. at 7 h. 28 m. I faw it perpendicularly over the top of *Bow* Steeple; it was 3 times the length of the Dragon above the top of it. The Fufee or Stream

T t

feemed

seemed juſt above it in that poſture, as if it had been the Blaze it ſelf bended, the oppoſite ſide being ſo faint, that I could only now and then perceive it. The Blaze was at Right Angles with a Line from *Arcturus* through the Head. I ſaw very plainly now alſo the flaring, flaſhing and wavering of the Light. I continued to obſerve it and make my Remarks till it almoſt toucht the Horizon, though the Air was very ſmoaky near the tops of the Houſes.

Sept. 10. I firſt diſcovered it with a 4 Foot Teleſcope, at 7 ¼. It appeared very faint : There was nothing beſides the *Nucleus* and the Parabolical Edges of the Blaze, or the two Emanations from the *Nucleus*; the Northern ſide was ſtill the brighter and longer. It was very much ſmaller and fainter this Night than Yeſter-night and yet the Sky clearer and darker. I could not find any Fixed Stars near it through the Teleſcope, nor could I ſee any Stars with my Eyes, the Sky being very cloudy all above it, it juſt appearing under and be-tween ſeveral Clouds : Nor could I, nor I believe any body elſe, ſee it now with his naked Eye; and yet through my 14 Foot Teleſcope I perceived very plainly the Streams, with the Flaring, Flaſhing, and ſometimes a perfect Lightning, as it were, in the parts of the Blaze pretty far diſtant from the Head ; which I 6 or 8 times took notice of to be almoſt in the very *Axis* or middle of the Blaze. I by many trials this Night alſo ſatisfied my ſelf that theſe Appearances were no Deluſions of the Sight, but proceeded from real Mutations in the Body it ſelf.

Since which time I have never been able to make any farther Obſervations of It, by reaſon of the cloudy thick Air.

An Explication of the Appear-ances. Now by all theſe Obſervations it appears very evident to me, that a Comet is a Body moſt probably round, ſituate in the middle of that part we call the *Nu-cleus*, or the brighter part in the middle of the Head, which is inveloped by a kind of Atmoſphere of thick Clouds or Smoak : That a lighter or thinner kind of parts, like Vapours, ſpread from it to a much greater diſtance, poſſibly 8 or 10 times as far towards the Sun, which by their Limitation in reſpect of the Sun, are driven back again, and return upwards, and oppoſite to the Sun. Of theſe kind of Emanations there ſeem two ſorts : One that goes to a greater diſtance, and is but very fine and thin, which makes the outmoſt Edge of the *Halo* about the Head, when the Comet appears biggeſt and brighteſt, and is in its neareſt Approach to the Earth. The other, which is a thicker and groſſer, which deſcends not ſo far towards the Sun, but is poſſibly more firey, and ſo recoiles upwards ſooner, and makes the Parabolical Emanations that appeared on both ſides of it. The biggeſt and brighteſt of which was that towards the North, or that part which was the hindermoſt in its way of Motion, the Fore-ſide thereof being very thin, and but at ſome times viſible; whereas the other was always very conſpicuous. As it went farther and farther off from the Earth, ſo the thinner part more and more diſappeared (which was very viſible when it it was in its neareſt Approach): So that all the time I ſaw it in *September*, the ſecond or thinner *Halo* diſappeared, which I ſuppoſe was cauſed, firſt by the greater diſtance of it from the Earth, and ſecondly the Light of the *Crepuſcu-lum*, in which it was always placed. And this I judge, becauſe even when it was much more viſible, if I viewed it pretty early before the Day-light was much ſpent, I could only ſee thoſe two Radiations from the *Nucleus*, without ſeeing the thinner *Halo* about the Head ; which yet I ſaw afterwards when the Evening was darker, which I ſeveral times took notice of, and which did recon-cile what I had obſerved concerning the differing Appearance of other Comets towards the latter end of their Appearance.

The white Cloud about the Body, which I call the *Nucleus*, I take to be ſomewhat analogous to a thick Smoak or Steam before it was fired, which only inveloped the firey Body in the midſt of it, which I take to be the Solid, through which I very often perceived a ſudden ſmall bright momentary Glance of Light, which I conceive was either the bright Body in the middle, or elſe ſome kind-ling of the Smoak or luculent Flame about it ; but I rather took it to be the for-mer. The two Emanations I take to be the under Edge of the actual, though thin Flame, which, as I have noted, did perfectly reſemble the Shape of the Flame of a Candle tapering above the Comet towards the *Axis*, and ſometimes meeting in it pretty near the Head, though at other times it were prolonged to a much greater diftance, and feemed to afcend almoft parallel. The thinner hazy part without this, which made up the Head, and a great part of the Blaze or Tail, I take to be a kind of Halituous Subftance, that did not actually kindle into Flame, but appeared by the Light of the Sun, and in part alfo by the Light of the Comet it felf, that is, of the fhining Cloud or luculent Flame. The fudden Flafhings I fo very frequently faw, I think are evidently a certain kindling of fome parts within the compafs of the Flame, which like Lightning, the one End of them near the Comet taking fire, a whole Train of them fol-low, as one may alfo commonly fee in the Flame of a Fire. The flaring of the Light, now on one fide, and then on another, I take to proceed only from the nature of the Emanations, which fometimes proceed on one fide, and fometimes on the other, which are more apt to take fire and turn into Flame. The fudden Dartings out of Light, which feemed to extend, to the naked Eye, even to the whole Length of the Blaze, I take to proceed partly from fuch a kind of kind-ling as I juft now mentioned, and partly alfo poffibly from a temporaneous Pro-pagation of Light, which, as I fhall afterwards fhew, in a yielding or fpringy Body, is temporaneous, and not inftantaneous. So that poffibly fome fuch fud-den Glance of bright Light, which I often faw break through the middle of the *Nucleus*, might be propagated to the reflective parts of the whole length of the Blaze, and fo be reflected fucceffively ; which is otherwife fo exceeding rapid and quick, that confidering the vaft length of the Blaze, it feems unconceivable how it fhould be moved : For the quicknefs of Lightning is nothing to be compared to it, though by many Obfervations I have feen it move near a Mile in a quarter of a Second Minute of Time, but this muft neceffarily move many thoufands of Miles in a fhorter time.

To conclude, all the *Phænomena* did fo perfectly refemble the Appearances of a burning, flaming and fteaming Body here in the Air near the Earth, that fo far as I can yet inform my felf, I fee no reafon to doubt, that it is a Body qua-lified much in the fame manner as a Body on fire, or burning in the open Air with us. Though if Fire be only a Diffolution of a Body by the nitrous part of the Air, it may feem pretty difficult to explain how there fhould be any Fire in thofe Places through which Comets have been obferved to move. Next, though the Exiftence of fomewhat analogous to Fire and Flame, fhould be fhewn probable in Comets, and in the Places through which they pafs, yet it may feem difficult to conceive how the Flame and Steams thereof fhould chiefly iffue and move towards thofe parts of the Space that are fartheft off from the Body of the Sun ; for fo it has been obferved to do by all the lateft and beft Ob-fervations : And thence it has happen'd, that almoft all that have written more particularly concerning them, have explain'd the Appearance of the Blaze, not by a Matter iffuing from the Head of the Comet, but by a certain Collection of the Sun Beams made by a Refraction of them in the Head of the Comet ; fome without any confideration of a denfer Matter fit to reflect thofe Rays fo col-lected back to our view ; though there be fome others, among which is Monf. *Hevelius*, that have feen the neceffity of fuch a reflecting Matter, befides the meer Refraction of them in the Head. But in fhort, I have not yet met with any Hypothefis of that kind that has given fuch an Explication of the manner of thofe Reflections and Refractions, as will accord with the vifible Appear-ances that any one that will be diligent and circumfpect may eafily obferve. For taking Refractions and Reflections to be made as they fuppofe them, and con-fidering what the Figures of the Appearances muft then of confequence be, they will be found exceeding different from what they really are, and will give no fatisfactory Explanation to a ftrict Enquirer. Leaving therefore the further Exa-mination of thefe Hypothefes to their Affertors, or to fuch as may think them to contain fomewhat more of probability than what I am here willing to allow them ; I fhall rather proceed to the confideration of that Hypothefis which the Obfervations I have made do more incline me to embrace. Now though I con-fefs there may at firft confidering of it appear feveral, and thofe no ordinary Dif-ficulties in this my Suppofition, yet when I have a little further explained the Reafons and Caufes, which I conceive of the Celeftial Appearances, they may appear to have fomewhat more of probability than poffibly fome may imagine.

That Reflection and Refraction of the Sun-beams are in-fufficient to ex-plain the Ap-pearances.

The

Five Difficulties in this Hypothesis.

The greatest Difficulties that I conceive in this Hypothesis, are Five, namely,

First, If the Comet be a burning Body, or a Body in dissolution, how comes it, that it can supply so vast a quantity of Flame or steaming Emanations, as to form an Appearance of so prodigious a bigness and length, as those of necessity must be which have been so often and so exactly observed; as in those, to instance in no more, which were observed by all the Northern World in 1618, and lately in 1680, and yet notwithstanding, last, without a sudden and total Dispersion or Consumption of that exceeding small Body in the Head, from whence they are supposed to be all supply'd.

Secondly, Next if the Blaze of Comets be from the Head, and that the Comets are Bodies which are moved with a pretty swift Motion through the Spaces of the *Æther*, how comes it to pass that this Flame or Steam does not follow after or point directly to the way through which the Head or Body it self has past?

Thirdly, If the Blaze be in part an actual Flame, and the Head be a Body actually on fire, or in a State of Dissolution, and that all the Fires and Flames we know have need either of actual Nitre, or of a Nitrous Air to make them, which being satiated, the Fire or Flame will no longer continue, without a farther Supply either of actual Nitre or Nitrous Air; how comes there to be either such a quantity of actual Nitre in the Body of the Comet, or of Nitrous Air in the *Expansum* in which the Blaze is observed to extend, and yet neither the Head of the Comet be supposed a terrestrial Body, nor the Nitrous Air be supposed to extend beyond the Limits of the Atmosphere about the Earth, which those that have given it the greatest Extension, do assign to be not above 50 Miles above the Surface of the Earth and Sea, and those others that think this too great, will not allow it to be a 5th part of that height?

Fourthly, Supposing there could be found a Reason or Cause, why the Body of the Comet should be supposed to contain some such Substance as Nitre, and that there might also as probably be supposed such a Substance dispersed through the *Æther*, as would produce a Flame like that of a Candle, or other flaming Body here in the Air; yet what Cause can be assigned why it should not equally disperse it self every way from the burning Body, as we find Flame here with us to do every way from the Center of the Earth? And why does it always extend it self towards that part of the *Æther* only that is farthest off from the Sun in respect of the Head of the Comet?

Fifthly, If this Appearance of the Blaze were an actual Flame, yet how should it be possible, that it should continue a Flame so long, as to extend to so vast a length, as possibly of some hundred thousand, nay of some Millions of Miles, and not be extinct in some very short Space, as the flaming Parts of Bodies here with us are observed to be, which are suddenly kindled and converted into Flame, and that Flame as suddenly wasted and dispersed, as indeed every part of the Flame we see of a Fire or Candle is? For though the Flame of a Candle seems to last till the whole Candle be burnt out, yet 'tis not really two moments the same Flame, but the parts of the Flame are every moment annihilated, and others in the same place every moment afresh supplied from the Steams that are continually issuing out of the Wieke. Now it seems inconceivable how it should be possible, either that Steams should be carried to so great a distance, or that Flame should last so long a Journey, as from the Head to the utmost Extent of the Blaze.

The Explication continued, to prove the Author's Hypothesis.

These and some other Difficulties there are, which when one has well considered, of the vast Distance of them, even when nearest to us, which all the accuratest Observations do most manifestly evince, and consequently the exceeding Magnitude of their Body, and prodigious Extent of their Blaze, and as a consequence of these, the great Swiftness of their Motions, 'twill be enough to startle one, and make one despair of ever being able to render a true Explication

cation of the Causes of thefe Effects. And 'tis very apt to make feveral Perfons to have recourfe to an immediate, extraordinary and divine Power acting, not according to the general Laws and Methods of the reft of Nature, but according to a fingular and particular Determination of that Power for the exhibiting thofe Appearances extraordinarily to Mankind: Whence fome afcribe them to the miraculous Power of good Angels immediately directed by the Will of the omnipotent Creator: Others (of which we have lately a Treatife on purpofe, upon the occafion of the great Comet in 1680.) to affert them to be produced and moved by the Power of Evil Spirits or Devils. But thefe, as the Subterfuges of Ignorance, and the want of Induftry, we leave to their Affertors. And though I muft confefs it to be a very difficult Attempt to manifeft and demonftrate the true Theory of them, yet I fhall endeavour from that fmall Stock of Obfervations I have hitherto met with, and thofe Imperfect and mean Helps I have hitherto had, to fhew at leaft a probability, what they are, and how moved, and that they may be fome fuch kind of Bodies as I conjecture them to be; and that in many Proprieties they may be confonant and agreeable to the other Celeftial Bodies. Now to do this as it ought, one fhould be acquainted with what thofe Proprieties are, which may be known of any other Celeftial Bodies: For if they be found agreeable in thofe, we may more rationally fuppofe a further Agreement in other unknown Properties.

Now there feem to be but two forts in general of Celeftial Bodies, and thofe are either fluid or folid. By folid I underftand all thofe Bodies that appear, and are made fenfible to us, either by their own Light, or by the Light of another Body reflected from them. So that thefe Solids do feem of two kinds, that is, either Bodies appearing by their own Light, or Bodies appearing by the help of fome other Light. And poffibly the Comets may be a third fort, that is, fuch as appear partly by the help of their own Light, and partly by the help of other Light reflected from them.

The fluid parts of the World I here fuppofe of two kinds, that is, one whofe *2. Fluids of two* Parts are in fome fort folid, and may have determinate Figures, Magnitudes and *kinds.* Motions; and the other, which hath no one Part that may be called a Solid, but its Parts are infinitely or indefinitely fluid.

The firft I call the Een-fluid, or almoft-fluid *Æther*; the fecond, the quite fluid *Æther*.

The former part of this Divifion of Mundane or Æthereal Bodies, I fuppofe is eafy enough to be underftood and granted: And the fecond, though it feems a meer Chimera, and without real ground in Nature, yet by thofe Obfervations and Experiments I fhall afterwards produce, I hope it may appear, at leaft to be poffible, though there may be no one found that can pofitively demonftrate it to be fo, and not otherwife.

And this poffibly may be the utmoft that Man's Senfes and Reafon will ever *The moft that* inable him to perform, in the acquiring of the Knowledge of fuch Caufes, *Man's Senfe* Principles and Operations; the Method and Inftruments wherewith they work *and Reafon will* being far removed beyond the reach of our Senfes: And therefore the beft and *enable him to* utmoft we can do towards the difcovery of them, is only accurately to obferve *perform.* and examine all thofe Effects produced by them, which fall within the Power of our Senfes, and comparing them with like Effects, produced by Caufes that fall within the reach of our Senfes, to examine, and fo from Senfibles to argue the Similitude of the nature of Caufes that are wholly infenfible. And this is the utmoft Bound and Limit of our moft exalted and regulated Reafoning, beyond which that Power cannot carry us. We may therefore reft fatisfied with what that will furnifh us; and 'twill furnifh us with a great deal, and far more than poffibly any one has thoroughly fhewn and demonftrated, or perhaps fo much as ever conceived it could, if a right Method be followed in the making of Obfervations pertinent, and of ufing them fo as they may exert their utmoft Power toward producing the Difcovery. The Power of Man's Faculties in this kind, has not, I fear, been fufficiently thought upon, much lefs difcovered, and all that has been hitherto produced feems rather to be fome lucky hits of chance, than the neceffary Products of a regular Art grounded upon the unerring Indications and Dictates of Nature. But this only by the by. I return then to the Explication of the Comet, and in order to the removing

V v

thofe

Anſwer to the former Difficulties.

thoſe Difficulties that I have named, and ſome other, it will be neceſſary to conſider what are the moſt known Proprieties of the ſolid Celeſtial Bodies, to ſee how far this Body, we are conſidering, will agree or diſagree with them.

Of the Solid Celeſtial Bodies.

All ſolid Celeſtial Bodies then have two Proprieties; firſt a Faculty of emitting or reflecting Light; ſecondly an Orbicular Figure.

1. They have or reflect Light.

The Sun and Fixed Stars, by the beſt Obſervations I can yet make, ſeem to have the Power of emitting Light, the Planets, both primary and ſecondary, of reflecting the Light caſt upon them from other Bodies; among which the Earth may be reckoned for one. This moſt certainly does, as well as the other Planets, reflect the Light of the Sun; one Evidence of which is the inlightning of the Moon thereby, when it is near the Conjunctions.

2. They are Orbicular, and thence have a Gravitation to them. Theſe the two chief Principles in Nature.

The ſecond Propriety of their Orbicular or Spherical Form, is an Indication of another active Principle, which I conceive univerſal to all ſolid Bodies in Nature, and that is, of a Gravitation or Power of attracting ſimilar ſolid Bodies towards their Centers. Which two Principles I take to be the moſt conſiderable and the moſt active in Nature, and thoſe from which the moſt conſiderable Effects are produced; and when they are underſtood and explain'd as they ought, I queſtion not but that they will afford us Solutions and Reaſons for a 1000 *Phænomena*, the Explication of which do now ſo much puzzle and perplex us.

In his Lectures of Light.

Concerning the firſt of theſe I have already pretty largely diſcourſed, and explain'd thereby the manner of its Production and Propagation, and what Effects are thereby produced; how it comes to produce Senſation in the Eye, and how it cauſeth Heat, Rarefaction, Liquefaction, Ignition, and the like; and ſomewhat alſo I have mentioned concerning the Refraction, Reflections, Inflection, deadning and quickning of the Radiations thereof; as likewiſe of compounding, dividing, and variouſly blending of them in the Production of Colours. But I ſhall not now farther enter upon the Explication of them, referving them to ſome other parts of my Diſcourſe, which are yet behind, concerning the Nature of Light. That which I have at preſent to conſider, is rather how Light comes to be produced in the Head and Blaze of Comets.

How Light is produced in the Head and Blaze of Comets.

Now theſe Bodies being ſo far removed from our reach, and appearing ſo ſeldom, and the Helps we have hitherto met with affording us ſo very little that is to this purpoſe, I hope it will not be expected that I ſhould be able to bring ſuch powerful Arguments as may not be at leaſt doubted of, if not poſitively contradicted. I confeſs my great want of ſuch; however, I find from thoſe few Obſervations I have made, ſome Arguments that do much incline me to think, that what I have conjectured of them is very conſonant to the appearing Effects of them, though in every Particular it does not ſo exactly agree.

1ſt Suppoſition, that there is a denſe bright Body in the Nucleus.

Firſt then for my firſt Suppoſition, that there is in the middle of that white cloudy part near the middle of the Head, which we call the *Nucleus*, another more denſe and bright ſhining Body than what is ordinarily taken notice of; I argue from two Particulars. The firſt is, that I hundreds of times have taken notice of ſome ſhort and momentary Appearings of ſuch a Star-like Spot, as I have mention'd in my Obſervations; which is almoſt an ocular Demonſtration; I ſay almoſt, becauſe poſſibly it may be ſaid, that thoſe were but (like ſome of the reſt) Flaſhings or Kindlings of ſome parts of that Cloud of Smoak. And I confeſs I was often of that opinion my ſelf, when I compared them with the other Flaſhings and Spoutings of Light I have mention'd: But then when I conſider'd the ſecond Argument, that there muſt be ſomewhere a very ſolid Body, otherwiſe it could not be moved with ſo ſwift, and ſo regular and uniform a Motion, as all Comets that have been accurately obſerved, have been found to do; I conceived there was more likelihood to conclude, that it might be ſome part of the Star it ſelf through ſome Chaſms in the ſmoaky Atmoſphere. For unleſs there were ſome ſuch Body, 'tis not to be imagined, that a Cloud, ſuch as *Hevelius* has ſuppoſed, ſhould be able to be moved ſo vaſt a Space ſo regularly, and with ſo ſwift a Motion; nor that it ſhould be able to afford Matter enough to make and ſupply ſo vaſtly big and long-extended a Blaze. For there cannot be allowed to it an *Æther* moving along with it, in which it ſhould ſwim like a Cloud in the Air, or Froth on the Water: For if ſo, how could

that

that in 1664 go Retrograde, and quite contrary to the Motions of the Heavens, if it paſſed between the Earth and *Mars*, as I have ſeveral Arguments that make me believe it did? Nay, how could all of them move Retrograde to the Motions of the Planets, which I hope I may ſhew ſome Arguments to prove? Thoſe that hold ſolid Orbs, will afford it no room, nor thoſe that hold *Vortices*. Thoſe indeed that ſuppoſe Demons, may ſuppoſe what they will, but to little purpoſe.

Next, unleſs there were ſome very denſe and very violently burning Body ſomewhere in the Head, it could not afford ſo vaſt a quantity of Steams, Smoak, Vapours and Flame, as muſt neceſſarily go to the making up of ſo vaſt a Blaze, which is not a conſtant abiding Body like a Cloud; but, as I manifeſtly diſcovered, rather of the Nature of Smoak, Steams, and Flame, from a burning Body, which are continually in a State of Diſſolution and Waſting, and are continually ſupply'd by ſome Fountain or burning Body in the Head; and this Body can be no where placed but within the cloudy *Nucleus*.

Thirdly, if there were not ſome ſuch Body within the cloudy *Nucleus*, the Roundneſs of that ſide of the Head, that is next the Sun, could not be, nor the greater Denſity of the Light about and near it: For we ſee that Clouds and Smoak, and the like unconjoin'd Bodies, have irregular difform Shapes; but the ſolid Body in the middle muſt be that which made the uniform Roundneſs thereof, as I ſhall afterwards more fully prove, when I come to explain the Nature of that other univerſal Principle, Gravity, in the proceſs of my enſuing Diſcourſe.

But (which ſeems to make the thing yet more probable than all the other Arguments) I have made a Ball of combuſtible Subſtances mixed together, which being ſuſpended by a Wire in the open Air, and there kindled, would ſo very well repreſent all the Appearances in little to the Sight, that the very Reſemblance thereof ſeems to be a very perſwaſive Argument, that the Effects and *Phænomena* of both were produced from like and homogenous Cauſes. And ſince the *Phænomena* of the Ball are produced by the Fire, and by the Gravitation towards the Center of the Earth of the ambient *Medium* of the Air, it ſeems not incongruous to conclude, that the *Phænomena* of the Comet may be produced by a ſolid combuſtible Ball actually fired, and by a Gravitation of the ambient *Æther* towards the Center of the Sun. But I know it may be ſaid, that *Omne ſimile non eſt idem*: And I will readily grant, that it is not a poſitive Proof, however 'tis poſſibly as poſitive as the thing it ſelf will bear: For in a Subject where we cannot obtain ſuch ſufficient Proofs as we can deſire, we muſt be contented with what we can obtain. And let me add this Conſideration, that all the Theorys of the Heavens and of Celeſtial Bodies, we have hitherto had, are ſubject to the ſame Objections that this is; for which of all the Motions of the Celeſtial Bodies hath not been explicated by various Hypotheſes? Some ſuppoſing the Annual, others the Diurnal Motion of the Earth neceſſary: Others ſuppoſe neither of them, others only one: Some ſuppoſe both the Earth and the Sun alſo to be moved; others again ſuppoſe neither of them, but that both the Earth and the Sun may ſtand ſtill, and only the Heavens of the Fixed Stars may move round them, as *Cocceus* in his Hypotheſis: Others have ſuppoſed the Moon to ſtand ſtill, and all to move about that, as ——— : Others have placed ♄, ♃, ♂, ♀, and ☿, as the Central Body, and ſolved the Appearances by ſuppoſing all the other to move about ſome one or other of them: And others, imaginary Points here or there in the *Æther*: And yet every one of them, grant them but their Suppoſitions, will make a ſhift to ſolve the Appearances. But then there will be found ſo many Inconcinuities in their Suppoſitions, which yet will be found neceſſary to be granted to ſolve the Appearances, that at firſt hearing we reject them as very improbable, and readily bend to that which avoids them, and hath all things very conſonant and congruous: Which is the reaſon why the *Copernican* has obtained with all the modern and beſt Aſtronomers, againſt all the other, as being the moſt ſimple, and the leaſt incumber'd of any; eſpecially as it is improved by the Incomparable *Kepler*. All the Reaſon of which is from this Maxim, that *Natura nihil egit fruſtra, ſed fruſtra fit per plura quod fieri poteſt per pauciora*. The Simplicity therefore of the Hypotheſis to be granted,

and

and the Concinuity of it with the known Operations of Nature, is as cogent an Argument as can be urged for any Hypothefis of this nature, and that I hope I fhall be able to manifeft in this I have pitched on.

In the mean time, I fhall now only hint, that thofe vifible Appearances of Comets which I have with much care and circumfpection obferved and examined, with what ftrictnefs and unprejudicatenefs I could, do incline me to deduce them from thefe following Particulars, which I fhall more particularly endeavour to prove hereafter.

Several Dedu-ctions from the Obfervations. **1.** *The Medi-um muft be ex-ceeding thin and fluid.*

First, That thofe Parts of the Heavens through which Comets do pafs, muft be a very thin and rarify'd, and an exceeding fluid Medium ; otherwife fo very thin a Body as the Halituous Steams about the Head, and efpecially the more thin Halituous Steams which make up the Blaze or Tail, could not be moved through it with fo fwift a Motion, and that in all Particulars fo regular, without much altering or varying the true Form and Pofition thereof ; I fay, without much altering and varying the true Form thereof, becaufe, as I fhall afterwards fhew, it does really fomewhat alter both the Form and Situation of the Head and Blaze, which would otherwife in probability appear of a fomewhat different Shape.

What I underftand by rarify'd and condenfed, I fhall afterwards manifeft, when I come to the Explication of the Conftitution of the *Medium*, that fills the Spaces between the folid Globular Bodies : For though it freely permits a Body to be moved through it, it cannot be thence argued, that it contains a lefs quantity of Body within the fame Dimenfions, but only that there is a lefs quantity of folid Body, or uniform and united Motion.

2. *There is a Gravitation to and Levitation from the Sun.*

Secondly, That there is a Gravitation towards, and a Levitation from the Body of the Sun : For as I have by many of the Obfervations fhewn, though there be a Defcent of the Steams from the *Nucleus* towards the Sun, yet I always plainly faw, that they quickly returned, and went contrary and oppofite to the Sun, and that fometimes to a prodigious Extent.

3. *This Gravi-tation and Le-vitation ex-tends to and beyond the Earth.]*

Thirdly, That this Gravitating rnd Levitating Power, in refpect of the Sun, doth extend even to the Earth, and beyond it, as will neceffarily follow from the Comet which appeared in the Year 1664, (to inftance in no other) For 'twas evident, that the Motion of that Comet was in a Line, without the Orb of the Earth ; and yet we found, that that Body was regulated in the fame manner as all the other Comets, and that its Blaze was extended in oppofition to the Body of the Sun, and, as I fhall afterwards more particularly prove, was moved oppofite to it.

4. *A flaming Body may be beyond the At-mofphere.*

Fourthly, That there may be a Fire or Flame, and a burning or flaming Body, in part of the Heavens far beyond the Atmofphere, nay much farther off from the Earth than the Body of the Moon it felf ; and confequently that there may be other Bodies of the fame nature with the Earth, which may be much farther off from the Earth than the Body of the Moon, nay much farther off the Sun than either the Earth or Moon : And therefore it may be no great Abfurdity to fuppofe, that the Body of the Moon may be of a Subftance not much differing from the Subftance of the Earth, and fo may have many Proprieties, if not the fame, yet probably not much differing from it.

5. *The Power of Gravitation is extended far into the Æther, &c. The Æ-ther the Caufe of Gravitation.*

Fifthly, That the Power of Gravitation is extended into the *Æther*, without the Atmofphere of Bodies, and confequently that the Atmofphere or Air is not the Caufe of Gravitation, but rather the *Æther*, in which the Atmofphere or Air is but a kind of Diffolution, as Salt or Tinctures are diffolved in Water or other Liquors, and that from thence comes even the Gravitation of the Atmofpheres to their incompaffed Bodies ; which we obferve by many other Experiments made here upon the Earth : For 'tis evident that Bodies in a Receiver, exhaufted or emptied of the Air by means of the exhaufting Engine, or any other ways, have not lefs of Gravity towards the Perpendicular or Center of the Earth, than Bodies in the open and free Air ; nay they are found to be proportionably

tionably heavier, by how much a Body of the Air, equal to them in bulk, has been found to be lighter than them; which is an Experiment that has been often try'd.

Sixthly, That the Air it self is no farther the *Menſtruum* that diſſolves Bodies by Fire and Flame, than as it has ſuch a kind of Body raiſed from the Earth, as has a Power of ſo diſſolving and working on Unctuous, Sulphureous or Combuſtible Bodies : And this is the Aerial or Volatile Nitrous Spirit, which, provided it be ſupplied in the Body to be ſo diſſolved, as by Fire, will work the ſame effect, even without Air. This is obvious in Compoſitions made with Salt of Nitre and other combuſtible Subſtances, as in Gunpowder, and the like, which will actually burn without the help of Air, as may be tried with it under Water ; nay in an exhauſted Receiver, as I have often tried, wherein the Effects are much the ſame, as if the ſame Accenſions had been made in the open and free Air ; though where this Nitrous part is wanting, no Combuſtion, Diſſolution or actual Fire will be produced, be the Heat never ſo great. Whence we may deduce, *6. The Air the Diſſolvent of Bodies by Fire, ſo far as it has a Nitrous Spirit.*

Seventhly, That in the Steams that iſſue from the Cometical Body, there are two ſorts at leaſt of Particles or particular Subſtances : Namely, firſt a Nitrous, ſuch as is every where to be found in our Air, and is perhaps that part which may moſt properly be called the Vital part thereof, which ſupplies the *Menſtruum* to burning and flaming Bodies ; and that which continues the Life, Heat and Motion of all Animals and Vegetables. Secondly an Unctuous or Sulphureous Body, that is to be diſſolved by it. Both which kinds of Bodies may be actually in the Star or ſolid Body, which I have ſuppoſed placed within the cloudy *Nucleus*, which may ſerve to continue the actual Fire once begun, and may both be rarify'd into the Halituous Steams that compoſe the cloudy or hazy Head and Blaze (which Particles, when emitted from the Body, may be ſeparated, and afterwards by convening together again, may produce an actual Flame) and make thoſe Flaſhings and Flarings, which I ſo often took notice of. *7. Two ſorts of Particles in the Steams of Comets; 1ſt A Nitrous.* *2dly, A Sulphureous.*

That there may be ſuch kind of Effects produced, I would argue from Obſervations which are commonly made here in the Atmoſphere near the Earth. Every one has ſeen the Lightning and heard the Thunder here in the Air, and many have endeavour'd to give a Solution and Explication thereof. But though there be a vaſt variety of Opinions and Hypotheſes concerning it, yet to me they ſeem every one of them to have miſſed the right. I ſhall not trouble you to relate them here, ſince I have already declared my Opinion concerning them; nor ſhall I at preſent trouble you with ſetting down many abſurd Conſequences that would follow from ſuch their Hypotheſes, which would be quite incongruous to the manifeſt, if heeded, Appearances : But I ſhall only tell you what, from all the Obſervations I have made concerning it, I conceive Thunder and Lightning to be, which whether it be congruous to the *Phænomona*, and ſufficient to explain them, I leave to the curious Obſerver to judge. I have ſhewed already, that the Atmoſphere about the Earth doth abound with a ſpirituous Nitre, or Nitrous Particles, which are every where carried along with it ; beſides which ſort of Nitrous Particles, there are alſo other Particles raiſed up into the Atmoſphere, which may be ſomewhat of the nature of ſulphureous, unctuous, or other combuſtible Bodies; as we ſee Spirit of Wine, Spirit of Turpentine, Camphire, and almoſt all other combuſtible Bodies, will by Heat be rarify'd into the form of Air or Smoak, and be raiſed up into the Air ; all which, if they have a ſufficient degree of Heat, will catch fire, that is, be diſſolved and turned into Flame by the Nitrous Parts of the Air, as thouſands of Experiments might be brought to prove. There are alſo other ſorts of theſe ſulphureous Steams, which are raiſed up from ſubterraneous and mineral Bodies, which only by their coming to mix with the Nitrous Air (though they have no ſenſible Heat in them) will ſo ferment and act one upon another, as to proudce an actual Flame ; which has been often found in Mines; and more eſpecially if any part of them be kindled, the whole Train of them, intermingled with the Air contiguous, will immediately take fire, like a Train of Gunpowder, and run from one end *An Explication of Thunder and Lightning.*

to the other of thofe Vapours, be they never fo long, as I could prove by a Multitude of Relations from the Cole-mines and feveral other Mines. The Accenfion of which Vapours is fo fudden, and with fuch violence and fwiftnefs runs
from one end to the other, as often to kill the Miners, to blow up their Props,
Stays and Houfes, and do as prodigious Effects as if a great quantity of Gunpowder had been fired in the Mine. Now Lightning here in the Air I take to
be much of the like nature, that is to fay, the Air or Atmofphere about the
Earth is continually furnifht with the fpirituous Nitrous Parts : Now the Heat
of Summer, whenever very extraordinary (as 'tis always obferved to be before
Thunder and Lightning) raifes up alfo out of the Earth a great quantity of ful-
phureous Vapours, which are of fuch a nature, as that meeting with the Nitrous of the Air, they work upon each other, and thereby begin a farther degree
of Heat, which increafes by certain Degrees fo long, till it arrive at a certain
pitch, at which pitch they actually fall on each other, and produce an actual
Fire or Flame, which fo foon as ever it kindles, whereever it be placed in the
Train, it almoft inftantaneoufly fires the whole Train, and runs to the End with
fo great a Swiftnefs, that though I have obferved the Progrefs of it at three or
four Miles diftance, as I have judged by the coming of the Sound to me, yet
have I feen this Train kindle or pafs at leaft a Miles diftance in little more than
the quarter of a Minute of time. Now the Progrefs of the Flafhes or Dart-
This applied to ings of Light out of the Comet do feem to be much of the like nature ; and
the Comets fla- though the Progrefs of the Flafh in the Comets be poffibly a thoufand times
shing. more fwift ; yet confidering the vaft difference there is between the Air and the
Æther, I know not but that the Progrefs of the Accenfion of Flame in the Lightning may be accounted as quick through the thick *Medium* of the Air, as that
of the Comet in the thinnner and more fluid *Medium* of the *Æther*.

8ly, The Mo- Eighthly, From the great Diftance of the Comets, and the great Variation
tion of Comets of Place they feem to make, we may collect that the Motion of them muft needs
very rapid ; be very rapid, and to equalize the Swiftnefs even of the Earth it felf, if not
therefore they much to exceed it ; and confequently to continue that Motion fo regular, one
are folid. would rationally fuppofe it muft be as folid as the Earth it felf; or elfe that
the *Æther* has very little, if any, impeding Power to the Motion of folid Bo-
ies through it.

9thly, Yet the Ninthly, That notwithftanding this, yet there feems to be reafon to fuppofe,
Parts of the that there is a greater Denfity even of the Parts of the *Æther* it felf; for other-
Æther are wife it feems hard to conceive how there fhould be a Levitation of the flaming
denfer. Parts, and a Gravitation in refpect of the Sun, of the other more folid, as I
fhall afterwards prove more clearly by Confequences drawn, not only from the
Form of their Motion, but from the more indifputable Motion of the Planets.

10thly, An Ac- Tenthly, That there feems to be a vaft Acceleration in the Motion of Levi-
celeration in le- tating Bodies (where the Motion is continued upwards) as well as there is of
vitating Bodies Gravitating Bodies, where the Motion is continued downwards, and towards the
upwards. attracting Center : For though (as I have before mentioned) the exceeding fwift
Dartings and Flafhings of the Light do rather feem to be made by a fucceffive
Accenfion, like a Train of Gunpowder (and, as I have fuppofed, if not proved,
Lightning) ; yet to maintain fuch a Succeffion of Steams, there muft needs be
an exceeding quick Supply from the Head, even to the utmoft Extremity of the
Blaze : And it looks not unlike to a kind of actual Levitation, or a driving
outwards of certain halituous Parts from the Sun, as if the Rays of Light of
the Sun were carried with a local Motion rapidly fwift, and in their Paffage by
the Star of the Comet, did carry with them fuch kind of halituous or fiery
Steams. The often obferving with my bare Eye thefe fudden Dartings of Light,
which feemed to pafs almoft in a Second from the Head even to the End of the
Blaze, did often make me confider, whether the Rays of Light might not thence
be fuppofed to be moved away from the Sun with this excceedingly violent and
rapid Motion ; efpecially fince there are fome Obfervations of Mr. *Romer's* a-
bout the Eclipfes of *Jupiter* Satellites, which feem to make probable fuch a
Theory. But whether that does well accord with other Appearances, and whether

ther it may be allowed in the Theory of Light I have fuppofed, I fhall leave all Perfons free to judge. And as I defire they would give me the liberty to fatisfy my felf in trying to make a Solution of the Appearances that I have hitherto taken notice of by fome Suppofitions of my own, fo I fhall not endeavour to perfuade any of them to leave their own, or be of my Opinion, where the Appearances themfelves, that I have mentioned, or they fhall obferve, fhall feem not to make it pofitively neceffary: Since I doubt not but a more experienced, more thinking, and more judicious Man, may plainly difcover what to me is as yet undetected.

For demonftrating thefe 10 Particulars I have named, and feveral others confequential upon them, I judge it neceffary to demonftrate, as plainly as I am able (by the fmall Stock I have of Obfervations and Experiments, and fome few Deductions I have made therefrom) *Four Particulars.* *Proofs of the 10 foregoing Particulars.*

Firft, That the vaft *Expanfum* of the World, that is, the whole Interftice between the greater globular folid Bodies thereof, is a Body exceedingly fluid, and fo fluid, as hardly to be able to hinder the Motion of any Solid through it, much lefs of a Body of any confiderable Bulk or Magnitude. *1. The vaft Expanfum is exceeding fluid.*

Secondly, That this exceedingly or indefinitely fluid *Medium*, though it do not at all, or at moft very little, hinder the Motion of Bodies through it, is yet notwithftanding the *Medium* by which the Communication of the harmonious or inharmonious Motions of the more folid Parts and Particles are communicated to others at a confiderable diftance; and that by means thereof both the Motion of Light is propagated outwards, or from the folid Body to all imaginable Diftance in Radiating Lines or Orbicular Pulfes, with unimaginable Celerity: And alfo the Gravitation or Motion of Defcent from all imaginable Diftance towards the Radiating Body, of all folid Bodies, is caufed and produced by the like Radiating Lines or Orbicular Pulfes reverfed, with an unimaginable Celerity and prodigious Power. *2. 'Tis the Medium by which Motions are communicated both of Light and Gravitation.*

Thirdly, That this indefinitely or exceedingly fluid Body may be, and is a *Medium*, in which a folid compound Body of proper Materials may be fired and kindled into an actual Fire and Flame, and may be continued in that State fo long as the faid Materials fhall laft, and other Circumftances do not hinder; and may have its Flame and Steams afcend, and its more folid Parts defcend. *3. A Body may burn in it.*

Fourthly, That the Motion of Afcent and Defcent herein is continually increafed and augmented in a proportion more than duplicate downwards, and lefs than duplicate upwards, of the proportion of the Times; which Proportion fhall be determined and demonftrated. *4. The Proportion of thefe Motions.*

For the proving, or at leaft making very probable of which four Proprieties of fo vaft a Body, and of the Parts of it at fo great a Diftance, and of a Body fo altogether infenfible to our Organs, any otherwife but by a Series of feveral Confequences, it cannot be expected I fhould produce a fenfible and undeniable Demonftration; and yet when the Coherence of all the Confequences, that will neceffarily and naturally flow from this Doctrine and Theory, fhall be confider'd, I hope it may produce other Thoughts and Arguments, in other Mens Minds, far more cogent than I am able to produce.

Now that I may not be miftaken in my Expreffions, and that the Words I make ufe of, which are commonly ufed, but by various Men are underftood to fignify various and very differing Notions, I would willingly explain in what fenfe I underftand them, and what Notions I would willingly have them to communicate, when made ufe of by me.

I conceive then the Whole of Realities, that any ways affect our Senfes, to be Body and Motion. By Body I conceive nothing elfe but a Reality that has Extenfion every way, pofitive and immutable, not as to Figure, but as to Quantity; and that the Body, as Body, is the fame, whatever Figure it be of: As a Quart of Water is a Quart of Water, or a certain quantity of Body, though contained in a Globe, Cylinder, Cone, Cube, Quart Pot, or any other figured *Whatever affects our Senfes is Body and Motion. Body what.*

contain-

containing Veffel: And as Body, it is indifferent to receive any Figure whatever; nor has it more Extenfion in one than in the other Veffel, nor can it have lefs; nor is it more effentially a Body, when folid, as Ice, than when fluid; that is, the Minims of it are equally difpofed to Motion or Reft in pofition to each other; and therefore Body, as Body, may as well be, or be fuppofed to be indefinitely fluid, as definitely folid; and confequently there is no neceffity to fuppofe Atoms, or any determinate part of Body perfectly folid, or fuch whofe Parts are uncapable of changing pofition one to another; fince, as I conceive, the Effence of Body is only determinate Extenfion, or a Power of being unalterably of fuch a Quantity, and not a Power of being and continuing of a determinate Quantity and a determinate Figure, which the Anatomifts fuppofe. Thefe I conceive the two Powers or Principles of the World, to wit, Body and Motion; Uniformity of Motion making a Solid, and Difformity of the Motion of the Parts making a Fluid, as I fhall prove more at large by and by.

Motion what.   By Motion I underftand nothing but an Alteration, or Power of Alteration, of the Minims of a Whole, in refpect of one another, which Power may be increafed or diminifhed in any affignable Quantity; but the natural Ballance of the Univerfe is reciprocal to the Bulk or Extenfion, or to the Quantity of the other Power, Body.

Thefe two Powers immutable, but by the Power that made them.   Thefe two I take to be two fingle Powers, which co-operate in effecting the moft of the fenfible and infenfible Effects of the World. Of the fenfible Effects I am afcertain'd by fenfible Experiments and Obfervations; and of the infenfible I have a Probability from the Similitude, Harmony and Uniformity in the Operations of Nature.

Both thefe Powers I take to be the immediate Product of the Omnipotent Creator, and immutable in themfelves, without a like Command of the fame Power; and always to act in a regular and Uniform Geometrical or Mechanical Method; which Method by diligent Obfervations and curious Scrutiny may by natural and artificial Means be difcovered, and, as I conceive, reduced under certain Rules, and Geometrically demonftrated. The doing of which I take to be the true end of the Science of Phyficks, or of Natural and Experimental Philofophy; and all artificial Inquiries tending hereunto, I conceive to tend to the Advancement of the Knowledge of Art and Nature.

The firft Principle, Matter.   Thefe are as it were the *Male* and *Female* of Nature, from the Co-operations of which the moft of Natural Productions are effected. The firft is, as it were, the Female or Mother Principle, and is therefore rightly called by *Ariftotle* and other Philofophers, *Materia*, Material Subftance, or *Mater*; this being in it felf, abftractly confider'd, without Life or Motion, without form, and void, and dark, a Power in it felf wholly unactive, until it be, as it were, impregnated by the fecond Principle, which may reprefent the *Pater*, and may be call'd *Paternus*, *Spiritus*, or hylarchick Spirit, as fome call it, without whofe Conjunction nothing, or no Alteration can be produced: For neither can Matter without Motion, nor Motion without Matter, produce any Effect. As for *Matter*, that I conceive in its Effence to be immutable, and its Effence being Expatiation determinate, it cannot be alter'd in its Quantity either by Condenfation or Rarefaction; that is, there cannot be more or lefs of that Power or Reality, whatever it be, within the fame Expatiation or Content; but every equal Expatiation contains, is filled, or is an equal quantity of *Materia*; and the denfeft or heavieft, or moft powerful Body in the World contains no more *Materia* than that which we conceive to be the rareft, thinneft, lighteft, or leaft powerful Body of all: As Gold, for inftance, and *Æther*, or the Subftance that fills the Cavity of an exhaufted Veffel, or the Cavity of the Glafs of a Barometer above the Quickfilver. Nay, as I fhall afterwards prove, this Cavity is more full, or a more denfe Body of *Æther*, in the common Senfe or Acceptation of the Word, than the Gold is of Gold, Bulk for Bulk; and that becaufe the one, *viz.* the Mafs of *Æther*, is all *Æther*; but the Mafs of Gold, which we conceive, is not all Gold, but there is an Intermixture, and that vaftly more than is commonly fuppofed, of *Æther* with it: So that the Vacuity, as it is commonly thought, or erroneoufly fuppofed, is a more denfe Body than the Gold as Gold. But if we confider the quantity of the whole Content of the one with that of the other, within the fame or equal

quantity

quantity of Expatiation, then are they both equally containing the *Materia* or Body.

This poſſibly may at firſt hearing ſeem a little paradoxical, if not abſurd; however I doubt not but that by the Sequel of my Diſcourſe I ſhall be able to make it ſomewhat more plauſible, if not poſitively and undeniably demonſtrate it ſo to be.

The ſecond Principle or Power, which is *Motion*, is of a quite differing na- *The ſecond Principle, Motion.* ture, and may be rarified and condenſed, diminiſhed or increaſed, within the ſame quantity of *Body* or *Matter*, in any proportion aſſigned; that is, the ſame quantity of the 1ſt Power *Body*, or part of *Matter*, may receive any aſſignable quantity of the 2d, that is, any aſſignable Degree of *Motion*; and being poſſeſt of it, it may communicate or loſe any aſſignable part of what it has, and ſtill the Body, as Body, remain unalter'd and the ſame: For as it may be moved with any Motion, how ſwift ſoever it be ſuppoſed; ſo may it move with indefinitely ſlow Motions, and that ſo far, as that the next ſtep one would ſuppoſe it muſt loſe all its Motion, and remain in intire Reſt, and unalterable of Poſition, as to the contiguous Body.

It may poſſibly be ſtill demanded, what is *Matter*, and what is *Motion*? To which I can only anſwer, That they are what they are; Powers created by the Omnipotent to be what they are, and to operate as they do; which are unalterable in the whole, either by Addition or Subſtraction, by any other Power but the ſame that at firſt made them to be what they are; and what partial Alterations or Compoſitions are by them produced, they flow from that Omnipotent Wiſdom, that ordered them ſo to do: And theſe are thoſe which we call the Laws of Nature; which though at firſt glance they ſeem wholly unſearchable and incomprehenſible, yet God has planted in Man a Faculty by which, I conceive, he has a Power of underſtanding and finding out, by and according to what Order, Rule, Method, or Law, they act, and produce the Effects that are produced by them. And this I conceive to be that we call Natural Knowledge, and our Advance in this Inquiry, I conceive to be that which we call the Improvement of Natural Knowledge; and the nearer we can approach from the loweſt and moſt ſenſible Effects, to higher and higher Steps of Cauſes, the nearer ſhall we be to the higheſt and utmoſt pitch that human Nature is capable of arriving at.

I have in my Inquiries various and ſundry ways attempted to aſcend by the *Synthetick* Method, and as many ways attempted the contrary, or *Analytick* way, and ſhall therefore in ſome of my enſuing Diſcourſes give ſome *Specimina* of each, which though they may have their Failings, and come ſhort of what may be done by others, yet I hope they may appear to have been regularly and ſtrictly proſecuted: And this I am now upon, though it ſhould not prove the true, may yet be of ſome ſuch uſe, as the Rule in Arithmetick called falſe Poſition, for the finding by the wrong Product what is more likely to be the true one.

Various have been the Attempts of ſeveral Philoſophers, both antient and modern, to begin this *Analytical* way, which would be too tedious to repeat at this time; yet whether it be for that we have not a true, or at beſt but a very imperfect Account of what they were, we do not find that Satisfaction from the Product of them in the concluſion, which an inquiſitive and ſtrict Examiner would expect, the String and Series of the *Analyſis* being broken and imperfect, and not carried on through all the Steps of Deſcent, as it ought to be; which will be more difficult to ſupply than the Effect will poſſibly be valuable, unleſs we had a more full Account of what were their firſt and fundamental Poſitions. And though even this has been an Undertaking not left unattempted by ſeveral of the more modern Writers, yet whether ſuch Attempts have been altogether ſo ſucceſsful as is deſirable, I muſt leave to thoſe that have examined them to judge.

Others there have been, and that much a greater number, who have gone the other way, and have been dabling in this or that particular Subject, and have been ſo blinded with ſome little things they have therein met with, that they preſently ſquare all the reſt of Nature to their Rule. Such as theſe are too haſty in their Concluſions, and think to run away with that which they are far enough from attaining. The 4 Elements, the 3 Chymical Principles, Magne-

tiſm,

netifm, Sympathy, Fermentation, Alkaly and Acid, and divers other Chimera's, too many to repeat ; which having been embraced, nothing elfe will be heard, or go down with them ; whereas, alafs, Nature perhaps knows no one of thefe for a Principle in any fenfe, much lefs in that which they underftand it. Of which I fhall fay more elfewhere.

But to proceed, this Suppofition of the two fundamental and primary Powers, to wit, that of *Matter*, and that of *Motion*, which I have here delivered, feems to me very confonant to the Senfe I underftand of the Hiftory of the *Genefis* of the World, delivered by *Mofes* in the firft Chapter of *Genefis :* And though the Words of that Hiftory be by divers Authors very differingly explain'd and applied, yet by ferioufly confidering of them, I conceive they may genuinely bear this Senfe alfo in which I fhall here mention them.

A brief Inter-
terpretation of
the beginning
of Genefis.
The words of the 1ft Verfe, as render'd in our *Englifh*, are : In *the beginning God created the Heaven and the Earth :* In the *Hebrew* 'tis, *the Heavens* ; but the *Greek, Samaritan* and *Arabick* render it only the *Heaven.* The *Syriack* renders it, *the Being of Heaven, and the Being of Earth :* But the *Arabick* renders it thus : The firft thing that God created was *Heaven* and *Earth.* Which Expreffion does feem to fignify the firft Power that I have mentioned, namely, the *Matter* or *Mater*, the whole Subftance of the Heavens and the Earth ; that is, that Subftance, which being afterwards informed and qualified by *Motion*, conftituted the Heavens and the Earth. For it feems by the next Verfe to be for fome time without the Impregnation of the fecond Principle, *Motion* ; for 'tis faid, *the Earth was without form, and void, and Darknefs was upon the Face of the Deep*, or the Abyfs. The *Hebrew* is, *Defertnefs and Inanity.* The *Greek* renders it *invifible and incompofed.* The *Targum, defert and void.* The *Arabick* renders it, *covered with the Abyfs, and overwhelmed with the Sea.* And the Original, and all the Tranflations, agree in the Darknefs upon the Face of the Abyfs. All which Expreffions feem to fignify, that the *Mater* of Heaven and Earth was yet without any kind of *Motion* in it, but like that imaginary Entity we call Vacuity or Space ; which was without any moving or acting Power in it, but had as yet only the Power of Expanfion, Extenfion, or Expatiation : For this is what we underftand by the Notion of *Vacuum* or Space ; and fo is Darknefs, namely, a Defect of the Motion of Light : For Light, as I have already by many Arguments and Experiments proved, is a Motion, and that a regular, uniform, and truly Geometrical Motion. So that the Senfe of the fecond Verfe to me feems to be this, That the *Mater* out of which the Earth, or all the Solids in the World were afterwards made, was yet only a pure *Mater*, or extended Subftance, and of the fame nature with the Abyfs, which had not in it the 2d Power *Motion* ; but was dark, without the Motion of Light, without Form ; that is, without the Power of Motion, that makes Forms ; defert of Quality, Life, Action, or Diftinction ; wanting yet Motion, which maketh all the Diftinction, Quality and Action that is in the World. Then follows the next Words, which feem to fignify the Creation, or Infufion of this fecond Power *Motion. And the Spirit of God moved upon the Face of the Waters.* The Original is, *And the Spirit of God did move upon the Faces of the Waters.* The *Targum* is, *And a Spirit from the Confpectu of God did blow in upon the Face of the Waters.* The *Samaritan* renders it, *And the Spirit of God was carried upon the Face of the Waters.* The *Syriack* renders it, *And the Spirit of God did incubare, or brood, upon the Superficies of the Waters.* The *Arabick, And the Winds of God did blow upon the Face of Water.* All which feveral Readings do feem to fignify the Creation and Production of the fecond Power, *Motion.* For firft, 'tis moft properly called a *Spirit*, fignifying its Power of moving, by which Property only we know it. Next, it is faid to move, or be moved, or blown in or carried upon the Face or Superficies of the Waters. The *Mater* was now no longer dead, and unactive, and Earth , but it became a Fluid, fignified by Water . For, as I fhall afterwards fhew, it muft in this Place be fo taken, and not only for the Subftance Water, but that God joining the fecond Power *Motion*, and impregnating the *Mater* with it, made every *Minim* of it to move with infinite Varieties of Motions : And fo all thofe which before lay ftill, and changed not their Places and Pofitions in refpect of one another, and were therefore called Earth, are now by this Infufflation, Incubation, or acting of the Spirit of God upon the Superficies,

ficcies, become a perfect Fluid, or a Water. No two contiguous *Minims* yet agree in Unity or Uniformity of Motion. And hitherto seems to be the History of the Creation, or making of the two first Powers, *Matter* and *Motion*, *Body* and *Spirit*, or *Matter* and *Form*.

In the next place follows the Description of the two great Laws of Motion, *The two great Laws of Motion, Light and Gravity.* which constitute the Form and Order of the τὸ πᾶν, or World. The first is that of *Light*, and the second is that of *Gravity.* *1. Light.*

First for that of *Light*, which is the first regular Motion, or Rule of Nature, which is that regular Propagation of Motion, which, as I have formerly explain'd, extends it self instantaneously through the Whole of Matter. We find in the third Verse, *And God said, Let there be Light, and there was Light, and God divided the Light from the Darkness.* Whereby we find, that the first Regulation of Motion was the Principle of *Light*; which seems to signify, that this Propriety of the fluid Matter was then first implanted, by which the similar Parts of it were made fit to propagate the Pulse of *Light* to all imaginable Distance; and this Substance was distinguished from that other Substance, which would not propagate it, which was opaque and dark: For as yet we find neither the *Sun* nor *Stars* were made, nor the *Earth* it self formed but only a Qualification of Matter fit for the performing of those Functions, which were accordingly made distinct, and secondarily implanted: *And God said, Let there be an Expansum, or a Firmament, and let it divide the Waters from the Waters.* This seems to signify the second general and grand Rule of Natural Motion, namely, *Gravity.* For this Expansion or Firmament is said to *2. Gravity.* divide the Waters from the Waters, or one Fluid from another; for so the Word *Maim* seems to signify. And this made all those Fluids which were of a Terrestrial Nature, to congregate or gather together into the Mass of the Earth, or Earths; and the other of a more Celestial Nature, to gather together in the Sun and Stars. And this Expansion or Firmament, which was the extensive Power of Gravitation, was that which caused those Effects. These two Powers seem to constitute the Souls of the greater Bodies of the World, *viz.* the Sun and Stars, and the Planets, both such as move about the Sun, and such as move about any other Central Body: And both these are to be found in every such Body in the World; but in some more, in some less; in some one is predominant, in others the other; but no one without some Degree of both: For as there is none without the Principle of *Gravitation*, so there is none without some degree of *Light.* And though some doe not shew its Effects in producing Light immediately, yet I shall make it probable that it has that Motion blended with others, which hinder it from producing Effects, but yet do not wholly destroy the Principle. And this I shall make the more probable, when I shall shew how both these Powers are but distinct Effects produced by one and the same Power, and that this Power is implanted in every such great Globular Body in the World. I could go on through the whole History delivered in this first Chapter of *Genesis*, but that I only aimed at present to shew, that nothing of what I have hitherto supposed, does any ways disagree with Holy Writ, but rather, that it is perfectly consonant to that, as well as it is to Reason, and the Nature of things themselves.

I have often made use of the Words *Maximum* and *Minimum*, or of the *Maximum and Minimum, in what sense taken.* Greatest and the Least; and because there are various Opinions concerning the Significancy of those Expressions, some understanding them in one sense, and some in another, I would willingly have it understood in what sense I make use of them.

By the Words *Maximum* and *Minimum*, or the Greatest and the Least, I understand then only the greatest and the least Extension or Motion we have need to make use of in speaking or supposing, which will still be bounded: For Infinite or Unbounded cannot have an Idea formed in our Imagination or Memory, which must always have a bounded Idea, being material: And this bounded Idea, however by comparing and reasoning we may suppose it differing; yet it is never bigger or less in reality, than the biggest Appearance we have had of the Heavens, or the least Appearance we have had of a visible or other sensible Point. These Ideas therefore of *Maximum* and *Minimum*, made use of in Discourse and Reasoning, are compound Ideas, and consist of the simple Ideas of the sensible

Maximum

Maximum and *Minimum*, with a Proportion annexed. For, as much as the Idea of the *Maximum* does exceed the Idea of the *Minimum* brought in by the Sense; so much do we suppose the *Minimum* to exceed another *Minimum*, of which we would make a single Idea, but we cannot; but it will always be a compounded or comparative Idea; and so *vice versâ* of the *Maximum*. For neither can we form a simple Idea of any thing that is a Million of Millions of times less than the Idea of the least visible Point; nor can we form an Idea of a *Maximum*, which is Millions of Millions bigger than the imaginary bigness of the Heavens we see; but by Composition, and Comparison, and Proportion, we make the compounded Ideas, which suffice for a Material to be made use of in Reasoning. And when all comes to all, we do but reason upon the τὸ πᾶν in our own Repository or Memory, which contains certain Ideas, Forms, Pictures or Marks, we our selves have made of simple Sensations; which are originally begun from Motions without, but compleated, finished and disposed of within our selves, by the Power and Activity of the Soul; from whence proceeds that Difference which is to be found in the Imaginations and Reasonings of several Men: For the things of Nature are the same, and the Informations are conveyed by the same *Media*, and in the same Manner; yet partly the Organs of Men differ considerably in their Perfections; but chiefly the inward Parts of the Organ of Memory, and the natural or acquired Habits of the Soul in Imagination and Reasoning, are exceeding different. Some men have a more piercing Sight, and can distinguish a much smaller Point than others, possibly from the Tunicles and Humours of the Eye, their exceeding Clearness and Transparency, and Exactness of Figure; possibly also from the Fineness and excellent Structure of the sensible Part, and Optick Nerve, and Parts of the Brain serving to that purpose, and from the Habit, Use and Exercise of those Parts and Faculties: But still in the best, the *Minimum* and the *Maximum visibile* is limited, it can be no more than a Hemisphere of the Eye, nor smaller than a Point of the Eye, which to every Man is assignable; and whatever other Idea is formed to express a less or a bigger, is a compounded or proportionate Idea, and will be plainly discover'd so to be by any one that will but seriously so consider it.

But to leave this Digression, and proceed by various Enquiries in the Synthetick way, or by reasoning, and proceeding from sensible Observations and Experiments, to the more insensible Operations of Nature; I have already shewed Light to be a continued Pulse or Motion propagated through a Diaphanous *Medium* to all imaginable Distance *in orbem*; and by this means to continually agitate and make fluid, vivify and regulate the greatest part of the Universe. I have already shewed all its various ways of moving and crossing each other, and the harmonious Chime, as it were, of the Pulsations of several Luminous Points or Bodies, and therefore shall not here repeat them any further than only naming, As first, that Light makes all things sensible to the Eye; next, that such a Motion causes Heat, produces and contiues Fluidity and Solidity; producing Union and Separation; Union of homogeneous, and Separation of heterogeneous Bodies. These, I say, I have already pretty largely explain'd; and therefore I shall leave the further Explanation of it to a more proper Place, and proceed to the next Principle, *Gravity*, because I find that Principle to seem the more new and strange to some Persons; and I would willingly remove such Difficulties as occur, before I proceed, because otherwise there will be a hesitancy in all that follows.

Some Effects of the Motion of Light.

By *Gravity* then I understand such a Power, as causes Bodies of a similar or homogeneous nature to be moved one towards the other, till they are united; or such a Power as always impels or drives, attracts or impresses Motion into them, that tends that way, or makes them unite. The Universality of this Principle, throughout the whole and every thing therein, I shall afterwards have more occasion to explain, when I come to the Effects of Nature in lesser Bodies. At present I shall only proceed to shew it in the greater Bodies of the World.

What is understood by Gravity.

First then, that there is such a Power in the Earth, in respect of terrestrial Bodies, I think no one will deny in the general. Some Disputes there have been, I confess, among Philosophers, concerning the Nature of the Power it self, and some concerning the Subject in which it is inherent: Some supposing it to

1. That there is such a thing.

be

be a *Spirit*, an *hylarchick Spirit* ; others suppofing it an *innate Quality*, or inherent tendency to the Center of the World, not as 'tis the Center of the Earth, but as it is the loweft Place in the Univerfe, and fartheft removed from the Heavens, and from the more Spirituous and moving Bodies ; and fo is fuppofed the worft of Places, and made fit only to receive the Dregs of the Univerfe : And were the Body of the Earth there, or not there; yet thither would all thefe dull and earthy Bodies, that we now find defcend, tend, and there remain. Others fuppofe this Power placed in the *Æther*, and that by the Rotation thereof making it tend outward, the more folid Bodies, which confift of more bulky Parts than the *Æther*, are driven downwards. Others place it in the *Earth* it felf, which they fuppofe like a great *Loadftone*, and to fend forth certain Chains of uncous or hooked Particles, which pull down all Terreftrial Bodies out of the Air, or from any higher to any lower Place : And many other fuch Fictions and *Chimera's*, which ferve only to inform us what kind of Notions and Imaginations thofe Men had in their own Minds ; but in no wife to inform us of what the Power is, or in what manner it operates. Only this farther we may collect from them all, that every one of them took it for granted, that heavy and terreftrial Bodies were by fome Power moved towards the Center of the Earth, whether their particular Notions concerning that Power were right or not.

Next, there have been as many differing Opinions concerning the Limits of *Of its Limits* this Power : Some extending it too far, and others as extravagantly too little : *upwards.* Some fuppofing, that wherefoever in the Univerfe a terreftrial Body fhould be placed, there it would have a tendency towards the Center of the World or Earth ; and therefore that in the Creation, all the Terreftrial Matter of the *Chaos* met together, and made up the Body of the Earth. Others, on the other hand, have been too penurious in limiting its Power to fome few Miles ; fome to 50 Miles, others to a Boundary, that a Cannon well charg'd with Powder would be able to fhoot a Bullet out of its reach. But though they are both enough miftaken, yet they agree in this, that this Power of Gravitation does act at fome diftance above the Surface of the Earth.

Others differ again about the Modes and Limits of its working within the *Of the Modes* Body of the Earth below its Surface ; but no one I have yet met with feems to *and Limits of* me to have hit upon a right Notion concerning it; and yet all agree in this, that *its working be-* there is fuch a Power fomewhere placed, that does act regularly, and within fome *low the Surface* certain Limits. I could proceed farther to mention their Explanations ; but I *of the Earth.* conceive they would be too long, and not much to my prefent purpofe.

In the next place, this Power acts regularly and uniformly. I argue its Regu *2. It acts regu-* larity or Uniformity of acting on all fides or fuperficial Parts of the Earth, from *larly.* the Spherical Surface of the Sea ; and that from the Shadow of the Earth in Eclipfes of the Moon, where the Picture or Shadow of it is found to be round : And therefore though I cannot without very much trouble here upon the Earth, be afcertain'd of the Uniformity or Equality of the Power of Gravity working every way nearly towards the Center of the Earth; and though I cannot afcend high enough, tho' I fhould get to the top of the higheft Mountain in the World, to have a certainty from Infpection or Sight : Yet this alone, of the roundefs of the Shadow in Eclipfes, is Argument enough to perfuade any unprejudiced Perfon from disbelieving it, as a Matter very unlikely ; though it be not fufficient to prove its Geometrical Roundnefs, which muft be proved by other *Mediums*. Befides, we find that it muft be very near round, and confequently have very near uniform Gravitation, from the general Obfervations of Navigators, who do find, that fo many Leagues failed Northwards or Southwards, do alter a Degree of Latitude; which were the Gravitation not pretty near equal, it would not fo happen. 'Tis poffible, by very accurate trial, the Truth and Certainty thereof might be pofitively proved and determined ; but 'twill require more than my Opportunities will reach unto at prefent, to do it, though I can fhew how. It were defirable however, that it were once for all accurately tried.

The reafon why I infift fo much upon this Argument of the Roundnefs of the Figure of the Earth, is, becaufe I take this Roundnefs to be as convincing an Argument as any, to prove that there is the like Power in every Globular Celeftial Body, as there is in the Earth. For fince all the Celeftial Bodies, whofe

Shape

Shape we are able to difcover, are found to be of a Globular Figure, as is the Earth, and that feveral of them do turn round upon their *Axes* (as we find beyond doubt that the Sun and *Jupiter* do) were there not in them fuch a gravitating Power, all the loofe Parts of their Bodies muft he fhot out from them, or thrown away like a Stone out of a Sling fwung round, or the loofe Parts fticking to a Wheel or Top, when whirled round ; and confequently they muft in a little time be difperfed and fhattered to pieces. But no fuch Appearance has ever been obferved : Therefore it is an Argument that there is fuch a Power in thofe round Bodies of the *Sun* and *Jupiter*, which keep thofe moveable Parts from flying off. For that the Sun has moveable Parts, is evident by the Difcovery of our Telefcopes, which fhew us various forts of Spots ; which Spots, whether they be Clouds of Smoke, or more opaque Parts that rife out of the Body it felf, and only float on a fluid part of the Body of the *Sun*, like the *Scoria* or Drofs of red-hot melted Mettal, is not yet determined : And 'tis moft probable they are of the former nature, by the various Circumftances that have been taken notice of ; but be they which foever, yet the whirling of the Sun would throw them off, were there not fuch an attra&ting Power that kept them from receding, fince 'tis evident they are loofe from the reft of the Body. The like may be faid for *Jupiter*, in whofe Phafes great Alterations have been obferved by feveral ; and Monf. *Caffini* judges fome of thofe Appearances to be caufed by fome kind of Waters. The like I conceive may be faid for the Body of *Saturn*, though our Telefcpes have not yet certainly diftinguifh'd *Phænomena* fufficient to prove its Rotation.

I fay moreover, that this Power is not only placed in the Earth, but that there is the like Power in every Globular Body in the Univerfe, whether Sun or Fixed Star, Planet primary or fecondary, and in the Cometical Body included, as I have fuppofed, within the *Nucleus* or white Cloud appearing in the Head.

3. Its Power a&ts indefinitely upwards. In the third place, I fay, that this Power of Gravity, which is fufficiently evident on the Superficies of the Earth, and a&ts fo regularly every where round the Surface of the Globes, is not fuddenly extinguifhed, nor lofeth its Power at a little height above us : But, as I conceive, it is extended to a vaft diftance upward, even indefinitely ; and though it may be faid to be fenfibly finite, yet this fenfible Boundary has its Limits prodigioufly large ; and when the Degree of its Power, which fhall be called fenfible, is ftated, then thefe Limits alfo or Diftance of fuch an imaginary Surface, may be Geometrically determined, and the Proportion of the Semi-Diameter of it to that of the Globe of the Body in the middle, exa&tly determined and demonftrated. I conceive further, that this Power thus extended, does a&t with various Degrees at feveral Diftances from this Body, which Degrees I fhall alfo endeavour to ftate, and, as I conceive, evidently demonftrate from my Hypothefis, founded, as I conceive, upon the *Phænomena* of Nature, and not taken up at random, or by chance. Thefe my Conceptions (as being, I think, wholly knew, and not yet afferted by any Perfon whatfoever) may feem ftrange and extravagant, and I muft be content to have them fo efteemed, by fuch as may either have a Prepoffeffion for fome other Hypothefis, or fhall not allow of the Arguments I fhall bring to confirm them as fufficient for that purpofe. It cannot, I fuppofe, be expe&ted that I fhould try or fhew Experiments at Diftances fufficient to prove it experimentally and pofitively ; and therefore all that I can bring is only this, that I find a certain Agreement and Coherence of this my Suppofition with other Operations in Nature, and that hereby the Appearances of Nature's working are explain'd :

Several Opinions concerning the Motions of the Planets. Whereas I cannot find that by any other Hypothefes that have been hitherto made known, the *Phænomena* of the Heavens can be intelligibly and clearly folved, without the granting of many fuch A&tions or Motions, as are very abfurd, diffonant, and contrary to the natural Motions, A&tions and Effe&ts of Powers and Motions, which are within our reach to examine. Whence fome of them, that they may give a Caufe of the undoubted Appearances, have been fain to fuppofe underftanding Beings, Spirits or Intelligences, to be the Movents or Caufes of fuch Extravagancies. Others have fuppofed various forts of folid Orbs, Orbits, Epicycles, and I know not what other Wheel-work, to make out the fenfible Inequalities, and yet regular Periods ; which being too grofs,

and

and contradicted by the Motion of Comets, others have rejected, but instead thereof, have supposed Magnetism, as *Kepler* and his Followers, who have to that end feigned a Friendly Side and an Enemy Side to be planted in the circumgyrating Celestial Bodies: And because the Moon always keeps the same Side very near, respecting the Earth, and so its Appearances contradicted this Supposition ; therefore they supposed a *Nucleus* within the Moon, which had a differing Motion and Position in respect of the Parts of the Shell, or outward superficial Parts of the Moon which appeared. To help this yet farther, for this was not enough to do the business, they supposed a radiating Species to stand always stiff, like the Spokes in the Nave of the Wheel, and to turn round as the Body placed in the middle is turned ; which radiating Species or Spokes, like a kind of Besom, sweep along the Planet with them, not so fast as they themselves are moved, but with a somewhat slower Pace; and that so much the slower, as the Body to be sweeped forward was farther distant. But beside this, another Actor is needed, and that is, a second sort of Spokes made of the Rays of Light ; these also are supposed to help to sweep it on. Nay, besides all these there is another Help wanting, and that is, Magnetism, like that of the Dipping Needle ; by which means there is feigned also to be a kind of Libration, sometimes of the Body, sometimes of the Orbit. And after all these and several other lame Helps supposed, we find they are fain to be most thrown aside, when they come to Calculation. Others, as *DesCartes* and his Followers, have supposed a Whirling of the *Æther* round each Star, or Planetary Body, and a swimming of the Planet that moves round it in this *Vortice* : But how uncertain Effects and Motions of the Planetary Bodies must this way be produced, any one that considers well the Hypothesis, will quickly find, and as readily conclude, that if this Hypothesis be true, there can be no Astronomy ; besides, that were it granted, the *Phænomena* themselves could not be solved. It may still be said, that the disproving of all these will still be no Argument why what I have here supposed should be true.

But then it may likewise be farther urged, 1st, That this Hypothesis or Assertion which I have laid down, doth not create or suppose any new or unheard of Powers or Motions, but supposes only such as are altogether uniform and similar to Powers, Operations, Effects or Motions, which are within our reach and command, which we daily try, see, and find the regular working of.

My Arguments therefore to prove this Supposition, are only these.

Arguments to prove the Supposition.

First, That what I here suppose in all Bodies, I can prove to be in some, and so suppose nothing absurd or impossible.

Secondly, That the Principles I ground it upon, are (according to the working of Nature in all things) the most simple and the shortest that can be : And 'tis generally asserted so to be by all Philosophers, and found by all inquisitive Searchers into Nature. *Natura nihil agit frustra, sed frustra fit per plura, quod fieri potest per pauciora.*

Thirdly, That Nature seems to take similar Ways for producing similar Effects ; without granting of which we cannot reason or make any Conclusion from similar Operations. And then it would be no Absurdity to say, a Man grew out of the Earth like a Plant, or a Plant had Understanding and spoke.

Fourthly, That more or less of these Principles is to be found in every Body in Nature, but more remarkable in some of the Bodies in which I here suppose it, and that there is nothing that I have met with that does seem to shew a contrary or contradicting Quality in any one of them.

Fifthly, That from these most single and easy Principles of Body and Motions here asserted, there will follow such a Regulated Motion, as will *a priori* shew what are, have been, or shall be at any time assigned the true Places and Motions of the Celestial Bodies, consonant to the Appearances themselves : And this not in one, but in all, as I hope I shall shortly make more evident.

First

That Planetary Bodies have a Gravitation to them.

First then, that what I here suppose to be in all Celestial Globular Bodies, I can demonstrate to be in some; I think will readily enough be granted, when I prove that the Earth, on which we live, is one of those Celestial Bodies : And that Part I think I have proved by the Observation which I made of the Parallax of the Orb of the Earth to the bright Star in the Dragon's Head, which passes very near the *Zenith* of *London* ; an Account of which I have already given in my Attempt to prove the Motion of the Earth, which Attempt (how *trivial* soever it may be supposed, yet considering, that without some such Proof we were condemned to the worst Place in the Universe, and so thought unfit and unable to understaud any thing of Celestial Bodies) has given Mankind one Argument at least to believe somewhat better of their Mother Earth and themselves, than they did before, *viz.* that she hath *Origo Cælestis*, and that we our selves are *Incolæ Cælestes*. And so being granted able, at least, to consider, examine and reason about the Nature of the Earth on which we live, we are at the same time granted to be able to consider, examine and understand the Nature of some Celestial Body. This being granted, all the *Ptolemaick* solid Orbs immediately vanish, and all the ingenious Clockwork which has since that time been added to his. For since we are assured by this Observation, that the Body of the Earth is moved round the Sun once in a Year, and that the Earth swims or is incompassed with a fluid Air only, or a more fluid *Æther*, and that the other Planetary Bodies are moved about the Sun in the same manner as the Earth, and have the same Passions and Affections as the Earth hath of acceding towards and receding fromwards the Sun, of moving swifter and slower, according to several Distances from that Body, of turning round upon their *Axes*, of carrying peculiar lesser Planets along with them, which move about them as the Moon doth about the Earth, of eclipsing and being eclipsed by those Bodies, of being inlightned by the Beams of the Sun, and of being dark where that Light cannot shine, and the like ; why should we any more suppose it necessary that the other Planets should have solid Orbs to guide their Motions, than we find the Earth it self, which is one of them, really hath ? not now to urge the Arguments drawn from the Motions of Comets. This *trivial* Observation then was necessary to introduce us into the *Expansum* of Heaven, and to manifest to us how great a Voyage we make in a Year, and what we also do in the space of twenty four hours, and to inform us what Opportunity we have of surveying and knowing more of the World than before we thought our selves capable of. And though the Notion was perhaps fully understood and believed long before the other of *Ptolemy* was broacht ; yet being only a Probability, there could be no positive and undoubting Assent given unto it, without some such Experiment or Observation as I have formerly produced. The Earth then being found to be a Planetary Body, it will be no difficult matter to prove, that it hath that Propriety which we call Gravity ; that is, that all Terrestrial Bodies, or such Bodies that seem to be part of it, or that are of a like nature with it, are continually moved, or have an Endeavour to move towards the Center of the whole, which Endeavour is called the Gravity of such Bodies : And consequently a Planetary Body is proved to have Gravity, and 'twill not be difficult to prove the same in all the other.

An Inquiry into the Cause of Gravity. Some of its Proprieties enumerated.

It remains only to enquire what is the Cause or Principle of this Gravity, and what invisible or insensible Power it is that causes this Endeavour. Various have been the Attempts of several to explain it, but no one, that I have yet met with, to me seems satisfactory ; nor would they make out the *Phænomena*, tho' all they have supposed, how extravagant soever they be, should be granted ; whatever the Power be that doth thus cause Bodies to move towards the Center.

1st, It is wholly insensible by any other Means than by the Effects. There are no hamous Particles underneath to be discover'd to pull down the Body, nor any hammer Particles above to beat it down. A Body is not less heavy though there be never so thick, nor never so dense a Body placed between that and the Earth to break the Chains, or above it to hinder the Strokes of the Hammers or striking Particles ; nay though included every way within the densest Body ; as the middle Parts of a great Stone, or Piece of Mettal, weigh as much when whole, as when the same is broken in pieces.

2dly, The

2dly, The Endeavour of Gravity acts or tends always towards the Center of the Globe of the Earth, as far as any Observation has been made. This is generally granted and believed by all, though I doubt whether it hath been ever proved ; for though I believe it nearly probable to be so, yet I am not assured of it by any Experiment yet so much as attempted to be made. The best way that I know how to prove it, is, to measure the parts of a Meridian upon the Earth from Pole to Pole, and compare them with Celestial Meridional Altitudes : For if they every where correspond and answer one another, then the Perpendicular Line is true in all those Places ; but if otherwise, not. And till this be done, we are not by any certain Experiment assured, that the Body of the Earth it self is perfectly Globular ; for it may be somewhat either of an Egg-form, the longest Diameter being in the *Axis*, or else of a Turnep-form, the longest Diameter being in the Equinoctial. Nor is the Shadow of the Earth eclipsing the Moon, sufficiently distinct to determine this Point. This Gravitating therefore to a Central Point, though it be probable, is not yet positively proved by any Observations hitherto made, nor is it very easy to be made to sufficient exactness. But though we have no Experiment here made on the Earth, that does positively evince it ; yet this fetcht from the other Planets, may do something towards it : Namely, that most of the rest of the Planets (some of which are certainly bigger than the Earth it self, and, as I but now mentioned, have the same Qualifications) are observed to be very near Globular. Here by the by, I cannot but take notice, that there are in Philosophy many things that are generally taken for granted, which yet when we seek for the grounds of those Opinions, none certain are to be found, and thence all that is built upon them must be uncertain. For instance, in Experiments that have been made to prove the Magnitude of a Degree, 'twill be insufficient to prove the Magnitude of the Earth, till by comparing several made in several Latitudes, they are all found to agree, and shew the same Quantity : For if the Earth be Oval, as there seems to be good reason to suppose, then the Length of a Degree in one Latitude will not be equal to the Length of a Degree in another Latitude, and the Perpendicular of Gravity will not always point to the Center of the Earth. For if the Principle or primary Cause of Gravity, which I conceive an internal Motion in the Earth, be every way uniform, and so cause an equal Attraction to the Center, then any other Cause that alters the Dispositions of Bodies to receive this Power, or that superinduces another Power that in some parts of the Earth has a greater Renitency against the Power of Gravity than it hath in other Parts ; then the uniform Effect which Gravity alone would operate, will be altered by the adventitious Power. Now the Diurnal Rotation of the Earth doth superinduce such a Power ; for the Parts near the Equinoctial must have an Endeavour outwards, or from the Center ; whereas the Parts nearer the Poles must have less, and so much the less, by how much the nearer they approach the Poles : And this Renitency, as it will be directly opposite to Gravity under the Equinoctial, so will it be in all other Parts oblique unto it. Wherefore from the consideration of these two Causes, there seems to be a probability that the Perpendicular does not always and every where point to the Central Point of the Earth, how generally soever that Opinion be received which asserts the contrary ; and may possibly deserve some further Enquiry, as opportunity shall offer ; and there must want a Demonstration till this Question be determined. And by the way 'tis very remarkable, that by comparing of former with later Observations of the Magnitude of a Degree, the Earth seems to have continually grown less. But of these and several other Remarks I shall speak more, when I come to read concerning the Earth it self : I shall therefore return to the consideration of Gravity in general. This believed Roundness of the Figure, shews Gravity to act regularly in every part of the Earth's Superficies, otherwise it could not be nearly round.

In the 3d place then, the tendency of Grave Bodies respects the middle Parts of the Earth, though these Central Parts be carried with a very swift Motion from West to East by an annual Motion about the Sun. And therefore 'tis probable that it carrys with it the Principle or Power that acts ; and thence, that it

3dly, This Gravitation and Levitation extends to and beyond the must *Earth.*

A a a

muſt there be ſought for. This will need no other Proof, its Motion being already proved by the Perpendicular Obſervation.

4*thly*, Gravity is a Power which at all times acts equally; that is, a Body which remains the ſame, will always be found to have the ſame weight. This I conceive, none will doubt, but yet 'tis not very eaſy poſitively to prove it; for Scales cannot examine it, becauſe if the gravitating Power alter, the Counterpoiſe will be affected as well as the Weight; nor can it be try'd with my Philoſophical Scales made by a Spring, becauſe it may be ſaid, the Alteration is in the Spring, and not in the Weight. The only way that I conceive it may be try'd, is by the Deſcent of Bodies, compar'd with the time of their deſcending a certain Space, or becauſe that will be very nice, by the Vibrations of a Pendulum, whoſe time and number of Vibrations may be ſtinted: But here alſo will come ſome Objections, that there may be other Cauſes of altering the Velocity of the Vibrations, beſides Gravity, as the ſhrinking and ſtretching of the Rod; the thickning or thinning of the Air or Medium in which the Pendulum moves, unleſs it be in *Vacuo*, and the like. Yet I conceive theſe and others may be obviated, and the Matter determined, if that were neceſſary; but another Argument hereafter to be mentioned of the Moon, will better clear it.

5*thly*, Gravity is obſerved to accelerate the Velocity of deſcending Bodies with equal Accelerations in equal times. This hath been ſufficiently proved by falling Bodies and Pendulums, to certain Degrees pretty near, but not exactly. And therefore in the

6*th* place, Gravity is a finite Power, and acts with a determinate Degree of Force; that is, the Gravitating Power can never accelerate any Body beyond its own Velocity. That it is finite, we eaſily find from the Power we have of throwing or ſhooting Bodies upwards, which could not be, did not the Power of the Arm, Bow or Gun exceed it: And comparative to other Powers of Nature, 'tis weak.

7*thly*, That it acts on all Bodies promiſcuouſly, whether fluid or ſolid: So that the ſame Body which can be made fluid or ſolid, provided nothing be added to it or taken from it, will have, in both Forms, the ſame weight *quam proxime*.

8*thly*, The Bodies moſt receptive of it are ſuch as have their Particles of the greateſt bulk and of the cloſeſt Texture. This the whole Series of grave Bodies will ſufficiently manifeſt; and I ſhall afterwards prove, when I come to ſhew the Texture of Body, what it is that cauſes Bodies to be grave or heavy, and what makes them light, and that 'tis not the quantity of Matter contained within the ſame Space, but the Modification of that Matter, and the Receptivity it hath of Uniform Power.

9*thly*, I cannot find by any certain Experiment, that grave Bodies do ſenſibly decreaſe in Gravity, tho' further removed from the Surface of the Earth; which was the Intent of an Experiment I formerly tryed at the top of the Steeple of St. *Paul*'s and at *Weſtminſter-Abby*, and may now again be repeated with much more conveniency and greater advantage at the Column on *Fiſhſtreet-Hill*. For by counterpoiſing two Weights in a curious Pair of Scales, firſt at the top of the Steeple, and then letting down one of the Weights by a Wire of two hundred and four Foot in length, the Counterpoiſe remaining at the top in the Scale, the *Æquipondium* remained; whereas if the Gravity of the Body had increaſed by Approximation to the Earth, the Weight let down to the bottom muſt have weighed the heavier. But though the Difference were inſenſible in ſo ſmall an height, yet I am apt to think ſome Difference may be diſcovered in greater heights, and by ſome more curious ways than thoſe I then uſed, even in that height: For I ſhall in my following Diſcourſes plainly ſhew, from the Theory thereof, that there is neceſſarily a Difference, and that the Power of Gravity does decreaſe at farther and farther Diſtance from the Center of the Earth, and conſequently that the Line of a projected deſcending Body is not truly Parabolical, but Elliptical,

though

though it fhould be made *in vacuo*, where the Impediment of the *Medium* could make very little or no Alteration.

Having enumerated fome of the moft remarkable Proprieties of Gravity, we come in the next place to confider what may be the Caufe thereof.

And firft, I believe I fhall not need to fay much againft the Opinion of *Intelligent Matter*, which fuppofes every part of Matter to act underftandingly; for that being fuppofed, all Philofophy is vain, and there needs no farther Inquiry into Nature.

And fecondly, I have as little to fay to its Coufin-german Opinion, *viz.* the *Regimen* of an *Hylarchick Spirit*.

And 3ly, The *Epicurean* Atoms feem to me to give as little of Explanation almoft as either of the former.

And 4ly, For the *Peripatetick* Doctrine of tendency to the Center of the Univerfe, befides that the Foundation is falfe, the Earth being proved not to be in the Center, 'tis not yet underftood what the tendency is.

5ly, The *Cartefian* Doctrine, and that of Mr. *Hobbs*, are both infufficient, becaufe they do not give any reafon why Bodies fhould defcend towards the Center under or near the Poles.

6ly, Nor will the *Magnetifm* of *Gilbert* or *Kepler* ferve; for, as I fhall afterwards fhew, that is a Propriety diftinct from Gravity, and of quite another nature.

It muft therefore be fomewhat elfe differing from all thefe, which by reafon of its acting by the means of fome very infenfible Body, it will be very hard to demonftrate, yet not altogether impoffible. *What the Caufe of Gravity is.* We find then that a Propriety fomewhat like this is to be found in the Attraction of the Magnet and Iron. Another fomewhat like it is to be found in Amber, Jet, Glafs, Chryftal, Diamonds, and feveral hard Bodies upon Rubbing: And more inftructive yet to this Inquiry is the Experiment of Mr. *Newton*, of rubbing a Plate of Glafs, which is laid over fome fmall bits of Paper, or other light Bodies, at fome diftance, by which Rubbing the Papers are made to rife up towards the Glafs, and ftick faft to it. Now in all thefe Experiments there is a fenfible Attraction of Grave Bodies to the refpective attracting Bodies, or at leaft a Motion of thofe Bodies towards one another; though in all, the *Medium*, that caufes this Endeavour of Motion, be infenfible. Some have fuppofed for Amber, that the fame being a very unctuous Body, certain ftringy unctuous *Effluvia* are fent out, which fticking to the light Bodies, are drawn into the Amber again, and fo bring back with them the light Bodies. But this is very hard to be fuppofed of Glafs or Chryftal, and leaft of all of a Diamond, which yet will have a confiderable Electricity, as 'tis called, upon Rubbing; Befides, 'tis evident by Mr. *Newton*'s Experiment, that the greateft Electricity of Glafs is at the very time when it is hardeft rubbed, which fhould be the time when thefe unctuous Strings fhould be fent out; 'tis neceffary therefore that fome other Medium muft be found than thefe unctuous and ftringy Emanations.

If we farther confider of thefe Experiments, we fhall find that there is in all thefe a neceffity of an internal vibrative Motion of the Parts of the Electrick Bodies; and that fo foon as ever that Motion ceafes, the Electricity alfo ceafes: We may therefore conclude, that there may be fuch an internal Motion of the Parts of fome Bodies, as may caufe an Electrical Virtue in them, whereby they will be able to draw, with fome fmall Degree of Power, fome Bodies to them.

I have already here produced feveral Experiments, whereby I have fhewn how mechanically to produce fuch an Attraction towards the acting Body. The firft was that of a Body placed upon a wooden Rod, the one End of which was kept in its place by a Spring, and the other was ftruck by a Hammer, whereby it plainly appeared, that at every Stroke the Body was moved on the Rod towards the Hammer that ftruck. Here the *Æther* was refembled to a Solid. By the fecond Experiment, where a Ball poifed in Water defcended toward the ftriking Part, I fhewed how the fame Effect might be done by a fluid Medium, as in the other was done by a Solid. In the third was fhewn how a Fluid alfo might

be

See more Experiments in the Author's Life.

be affected by a like Pulse ; for that the Water it self, by means of a vibrative Motion in the Parts of the Glass, acquired a Motion towards the vibrating Parts. I should have proceeded, if not interrupted, to have experimentally proved the Effect of this Power in *Media* much more insensible. The Obviousness possibly of these and such like Experiments may make them be looked upon as slight and trivial ; and the Paucity of them, for that they come not in by whole Shoals, but are only caught singly, may make them not regarded. But as the Miracle was not less of the single Fish catched by a Hook, with the Tribute in his Mouth, than of the Shoals which were ready to sink the Vessels, and brake the Nets : So some one plain but pertinent Experiment, apply'd with Judgment, may be more significant than thousands of such as are pompous, amusing, and excite Admiration. And I am satisfied that more Discoveries in Nature may be made by the most plain, obvious and trivial Experiments to be every-where met with, than by the far-fetcht and dear bought Experiments which some seek after.

Nor is this way of working at a distance, by means of the internal Motion of the Particles of the Body ; so strange a thing in Nature, that we need much to insist upon these few Experiments to prove it. For if we consider the *Totum Sensibile* in Nature, we shall find it to be little else than what is this way produced. I have already, I think, fully proved in Light and Colour, the Object of Sight, that the Motion which is produced in the Eye, proceeds from an internal Motion made in the Sun so many thousands of Miles distant, or from the same in some Stars so many thousand times as much farther off. I could also as easily prove, that Sound in the Ear, which is a real Motion in some part thereof, is produced by the internal Motion of the Parts of the Bell some Miles perhaps distant. Somewhat like to this may also be said of the Smell, and of the other Senses; but the Instances of the first two will be sufficient ; especially the latter is the most evident ; and that because both the Motion in the Bell, and the Motion in the Ear, or some other Body there placed, is discovered by the other Senses, namely, by the Sight and Touch, as well as by the Ear.

These Particulars I could more largely explain by particular Experiments, and plainly evince, that the Motions of several Bodies at a distance, are caused by the internal Motion of the sounding Body ; and that this Power of moving is every way propagated by the ambient *Medium*, which excites in solid Bodies at a distance, a similar Motion. I could farther also prove, that every one of these distinct internal Motions of Bodies, as that of Light, and that of Sound, have distinct and differing *Mediums*, by which those Motions are communicated from the affecting to the affected Body : And so I conceive also that the *Medium* of Gravity may be distinct and differing both from that of Light, and from that of Sound. I conceive then, that the Gravity of the Earth may be caused by some internal Motion of the internal or central Parts of the Earth ; which internal and central Motion may be caused, generated and maintained by the Motion of the external and all the intermediate Parts of its Body : So that the whole Globe of the Earth may contribute to this Motion, as it will happen to a Globe of Glass or solid Mettal, to any part of which no internal Motion can be communicated, without at the same time affecting the whole with the same Motion. And I shall most plainly and evidently prove, when I come to the Explication of Magnetism, that this is undeniably performed and effected by this means.

The Hypothesis of the Cause of Gravity.

Suppose then that there is in the Ball of the Earth such a Motion, as I, for distinction sake, will call a Globular *Motion, whereby all the Parts thereof have a Vibration towards and fromwards the Center, or of Expansion and Contraction ; and that this vibrative Motion is very short and very quick, as it is in all very hard and very compact Bodies : That this vibrative Motion does communicate or produce a Motion in a certain Part of the Æther, which is interspersed between these solid vibrating Parts; which communicated Motion does cause this interspersed Fluid to vibrate every way in* Orbem, *from and towards the Center, in Lines radiating from the same. By which radiating Vibration of this exceeding Fluid, and yet exceeding dense Matter, not only all the Parts of the Earth are carried or forced down towards the Center ; but the Motion being continued into the Æther, interspersed between the Air and other kinds of Fluids, it causeth those also to have a tendency towards the Center ; and much more any sensible Body whatsoever, that is any*

where

where placed in the Air, or above it, though at a vast Distance ; which Distance I shall afterwards determine, and shew with what proportioned Power it acts upon Bodies at all Distances both without and within the Earth : For this Power propagated, as I shall then shew, does continually diminish according as the Orb of Propagation does continually increase, as we find the Propagations of the Media of Light and Sound also to do ; as also the Propagation of Undulation upon the Superficies of Water. And from hence I conceive the Power thereof to be always reciprocal to the Area or Superficies of the Orb of Propagation, that is duplicate of the Distance ; as will plainly follow and appear from the consideration of the Nature thereof, and will hereafter be more plainly evinced by the Effects it causes at such several Distances.

This propagated Pulse I take to be the Cause of the Descent of Bodies towards the Earth. But it way perhaps seem a little strange how the Propagation of a Motion outward should be the cause of the Motion of heavy Bodies downwards. To make this the more intelligible, I shall mention an Observation very commonly known amongst Tradesmen ; and that is, the driving of a Hammer or Axe upon the Helve, which to do the easiest way, they commonly strike the End of the Helve, holding the Helve in their Hand, and the Axe or Hammer at the lower End hanging downward, by which means they not only make the Axe to go on upon the Helve, but make it ascend, if they continue striking, even to their very Hand. To apply which Observation to my present Theory, I say, that the *Medium* of Propagation is the Helve, and the Axe or Hammer is the grave Body that descends: So that at every Stroke that is given by the Globe of the Earth to the propagating *Medium*, one Degree of Velocity of Descent is given to the Grave Body, which is as it were the Axe. Now according to the Velocity of this vibrative Motion of the Earth, so must the Power it communicates be stronger or weaker. Suppose for instance, there should be 1000 of these Pulses in a Second of Time ; then must the Grave Body receive all those thousand Impressions within the space of that Second, and a thousand more the next, and another thousand the third Second ; so that in equal Times it would receive equal Degrees of Acceleration. And if a Second of Time were again subdivided into a thousand Moments of Time, the Body would receive one Degree of Acceleration in the first moment, one more in the 2d, a 3d in a 3d, and so onwards : So that the compounded Acceleration would be as one the first Second, three the next Second, and five the next, and so onwards ; according as it is observed in the Motion of descending Bodies.

The Medium *that propagates this Motion, I suppose to be one part of that which permeates most Bodies, which we call by the general Name of* Æther, *and thence it proceeds that the Motion is communicated to every part thereof : And so the* Momentum *of every Body becomes proportioned to its Bulk or Density of Parts, disform to the fluid* Medium *that communicates the Pulse.*

The Objections that I expect against this Hypothesis may be some such as these.

1st. How does it appear there is any such Motion in the internal Parts of the Body of the Earth ? For who can descend thither, and if they could, how should they find it, it being from the Hypothesis supposed not within the reach of Sense ?

To this I answer, that though this be hypothetical, yet that there is some such Motion in those Parts, I shall prove clear enough, when I come to the Explication of Magnetism. In the mean time, there is nothing absurd or contradictory to the rest of Nature. The solidest Body in the World can receive an internal Motion of its Particles from an outward Impression ; as has been found in Diamonds, which upon Rubbing would shine, and upon so rubbing would become Electrical, and attract Bodies to them ; as I observed in the Diamond which was formerly shewed this Society by Mr. *Henshaw.* Besides, that it is receptive of internal Motion, is farther evident by the splitting or cleaving of a Diamond by a smart Stroke ; which is well enough known to our Jewellers and Lapidaries. The hardest Chrystal, Porphyrys, Agates, Flints, &c. that I have yet met with, will receive an internal Motion, as may be plainly argued from the Tone they give upon being briskly struck. The hardest of Mettals always give the best and longest Sounds, and consequently are the less hindred by the ambient *Medium. The Author breaks off here abruptly.*

B b b

The

The following DISCOURSE is a Lecture of Light, which I found among the Authors Manuscripts : And tho' I found by another Paper that it was read before the foregoing Lectures of Light ; yet I judged it would not prove unacceptable for the Experiments related in it ; from which it will appear, that the Picture of the Sun transmitted through a small Hole into a dark Room, does not answer to what it ought to be by the received Laws of Opticks ; and also that the Rays of Light do not proceed in strait lines, as he endeavours to shew by Experiment. I shall not venture at any Deductions, but leave that matter to the more intelligent Reader.
R. W.

Experiments the best way to find out Truths. THERE is no means in the World for the attaining the true Knowledge of things more certain and more instructive, than the accurate Observation and strict Examination of them by Trials and Experiments. And though, I confess, it is a much speedier and more easy way to collect and understand what is already known, to read and study such Notions of them as are already deliver'd in Authors treating of that Subject ; yet, as 'tis that way quickly attainable, so you will as quickly find your self at a *non plus ultra* in your Information, and much fuller of Doubts and Queries as to a perfect Knowledge of the thing you seek, than possibly you were, when you first enter'd upon that Inquiry. For the more you are informed, the more able you are to inquire for and seek after what is considerable to be farther known concerning that Subject ; and that Knowledge is much more apt to slip out of the Memory, and be forgotten : Whereas that Knowledge which is attained by a Man's own Observation and Study, as it always remains fixt in his Memory, so it so thoroughly informs his Imagination with a true and right Idea of the thing he inquires into, that he is able thereby readily to solve many Doubts and Difficulties that may at first occur to him; and it puts him in a capacity of pertinently inquiring farther into the Nature and Cause of the thing he seeks after. And let me tell you, whosoever has a Knowledge of things made up only of what he finds in Bocks of that Subject, shall find it to be very little, confused and imperfect ; especially if he comes to converse with such as have experimentally and sagaciously enquired thereinto. And in very many cases he will not only find his Knowledge little, confused and imperfect, but notoriously and dangerously false and erroneous: So that this kind of Knowledge, instead of leading and directing of him in the right way, oftentimes seduces him, and hurries him into the broad Way of Error and conceited Ignorance. I could give you many Instances of this Truth in Physicks, nay even in Mechanicks, whose Principles seem most obvious ; and shew you, that for want, I suppose, of accurate Trials and Experiments, several Axioms, which have been received and builded on as Truths, both by all the antient and modern Philosophers and Mathematicians, are yet notwithstanding by some few Trials and accurate Observations, found notoriously false : But these I shall reserve for some other Opportunities. I shall now rather chuse to give you an Instance in another Subject.

I have formerly endeavoured to explain several things concerning the Nature and Essence of Light, which I shall not now repeat; but having still many Doubts in my own Thoughts concerning the same, I have made it my aim, according as I had opportunity, to examine and inquire farther into the Nature thereof, by such Observations and Experiments as I judged might be any ways helpful to the Manifestation thereof. And herein I have not been altogether unsuccessful, having discovered several Proprieties therein, whereof before I had no Notion or Information.

To this purpose I prepared a Room fit for Trials of this nature, by so perfectly stopping all ways by which the Light could find its Entrance into the same, that the whole remained perfectly dark ; at least so much, that though a
Man

Man ftaid a long time in the fame, yet the Eye could not perceive any Light. For though that in many cafes be not abfolutely neceffary, yet in moft 'tis generally very convenient, and fit to make the Trial more accurate and certain. For as in a Mixture of divers Liquors, 'tis very difficult to diftinguifh and determine the true Tafte of any one of them ; fo the Effects and Properties of any one Ray is more obfcurely perceived, when it is blended and mixed with the Effects of a thoufand others. In this darkened Room I provided fuch Conveniency for admitting or excluding the Rays of Light, that I could let in what quantity of Light I pleafed, and in what manner ; and thereby had the opportunity of finding feveral Proprieties thereof, which are not otherwife difcoverable. Having then thus darkened a Room, by a very fmall Hole through a Brafs Plate in part of the Shutter, I let through the Light of the Sun, which by degrees fpreading it felf, feemed to make up a Cone, whofe *Apex* was in the Hole, and whofe Bafe was on the Paper expofed to receive the fame at a diftance. In this Image of the Sun thus painted on the Paper, it was very obfervable that the Middle thereof was very much brighter than the Edges, and that there was a kind of dark *Penumbra* that went round about the Limb of the fame, about a 16th part of the Diameter of the Circle ; the which *Penumbra* could be no ways afcribed either to the leffer Light of the Parts of the Sun near the Limb thereof; or to any thing defective in the make of the Hole or Paffage through which it was admitted ; but to fome other Caufe, or Propriety of Light, which I fhall hereafter explain. Having obferved this, at about the diftance of two Inches I let in another Cone of Light, and receiving the Bafes of them upon a Piece of Paper, at fuch a diftance from the Holes, as that the Circles did interfect each other ; I did manifeftly obferve, that there was not only a *Penumbra* or darker Ring incompaffing the lighter Circle, but a manifeft dark Line or Circle, which did manifeftly appear even where the Limb of the one interfered with the Limb of the other.

A new Property of Light difcovered.

As in the Figure, where *a b c g h*, *a d c k l* reprefent the Bafes of thofe Cones of Light, whofe middle Parts *ii ii oo oo*, appear brighter ; but the Parts thereof next the Limb, *e e e e*, *u u u u*, appear much darker, with a kind of *Penumbra*, or Faintnefs of Light; and the extream Circumference, or terminating Lines of each, appear perfect dark Strokes ; nay though the parts thereof *a b c* and *a d c* intermix with the brighter Parts of the other Bafe, as at *b* and *d*. Examining the bignefs of this Bafe with the diftance of it from the *Apex* or Hole, I found it no ways anfwer to that Proportion it ought to have, fuppofing the lateral Rays from oppofite Parts of the Limb of the Sun's Disk, did interfect each other in the above-mentioned Hole, and did proceed on by ftrait Lines to the Paper or Bafe ; but according to the various bigneffes of the Holes, and according to the various diftances of the Receiving Papers from thofe Holes, fo were the Proportions of the Diameters of thofe Circles to their Diftances varied: Which in Aftronomical Inquiries will produce no fmall Errors, if not carefully prevented by proper Remedies. I proceeded farther to make Experiments concerning the Nature of Light ; and holding an opacous Body between the Hole or *Apex*, and the Bafe or Paper, I obferved that there was, notwithftanding all the care I ufed to exclude other Light than what came in by that fingle Hole, a certain faint Light caft even into the Shadow of the Body ; and in that part of the lucid part of the Bafe, which was not fhaded by the opaque Body, there was a certain *Fafcia* or *Zone* of Light which went parallel along with the terminating Line of the Shadow of the opacous dark Body ; the which Zone of Light was manifeftly much lighter than any part of the lucid Bafe befides. Nay this lucid Zone did not only crofs the Circle of the Bafe, but did manifeftly proceed and extend it felf a good way beyond the lucid Circle of the Bafe, ftriking pretty far into the incompaffing opaque *Medium*. To make this more evident to you by a Scheme, let O reprefent the Hole in the Shutter of the Window, through which the Light of the Sun is let pafs: Let C O N reprefent the Cone of Light tranfmitted, and P A the Paper upon which the Circle or Bafis of the Cone is caft : Let B B reprefent the opaque Body interpofed between the Hole and the Papers, and S S T T the Shadow thereof upon the Paper. That which I obferved was this: The Shadow of the opaque Body B B was fomewhat all over inlightned, but feem'd moft inlightned towards the Edge thereof. Several Perfons

Plate 2. Fig. 7.

Plate 2. Fig. 8.

fons that were prefent, and faw and diligently obferved thefe *Phænomena*, conceived and objected, that the lucid Zone, or brighter part, which edged the Shadow of the opaque Body, was produced by fome kind of Reflection from the Side of the faid Body by which the Light paffed ; it being indeed a round Body, and fo fome of the Rays might poffibly reflect, fo as to fall upon the lucid Zone : But I could fee no reafon why it fhould not as much inlighten any other part of the bright Bafe or Figure of the Sun on the Paper; for the fhading Body being only a round Piece of Wood, not bright and polifht, nor of fo certain a Reflection, as to direct the Rays that fell on it exactly to a determinate Place, I could not conceive any reafon why that fhould produce fuch a lucid Zone. Others fuppofed that it might proceed from fome Reflection of the Brafs Hole through which the Light was admitted into the Room. But to obviate both thefe Objections, and to inquire farther into the Nature of this *Phænomenon*, I placed inftead of the Cylinder of Wood, a very fharp and fmooth edged Razor, fo that the Edge of the Razor was that which caft the ftrait Line of Shadow which divided the lucid Bafe ; from which there could be no Reflection, at leaft fo very little, that if we do fuppofe a Flatnefs or Breadth in the Edge thereof, it could not amount to a 500th part of the breadth of the lucid Zone ; and confequently there could be no imaginary Reafon drawn from the Reflection thereof to folve the *Phænomena* : And it was believed that the Appearance would have been confiderably differing, but upon trial thereof, the fame *Phænomena* were as obfervable as before, without any fenfibleVariety. The fame Appearance alfo was vifible, when inftead of the Razor, a piece of Paftboard was ufed for an opaque Body. And to obviate the other Objection, inftead of the piece of Brafs placed in the Shutter, which by a Hole in it let in the Light, there was placed a piece of Paftboard, with a fmall black Hole burnt through it : But upon trying over all the aforefaid Experiments with it, we found the very fame Appearances as when the Light paffed through the piece of Brafs. So that upon the whole matter it was very manifeft, that it was fome new Propriety of Light much differing from the common Rules and Laws thereof deliver'd in Optical and Phyfical Writers. Having difcovered thefe Proprieties, I proceeded farther to examine into the Nature of Light, by placing the Razor as before, fo as to divide the Cone of Light into two Parts, the tranfmitting Hole remaining as before : And I placed the Paper (expofed to receive the Circle of the Bafe) fo as that none of the enlightned part of the Circle fell thereupon, but only the Shadow of the Razor or opaque Body ; and to my wonder, I found a very brisk and vifible Radiation ftriking down upon the Paper, of the fame breadth with the Diameter of the lucid Circle, or at leaft (if the Shadow did not divide the Circle into two equal Parts) as big as the Subtenfe made on the faid Circle by the Shadow ; and this Radiation always ftruck perpendicularly from the faid Line of Shadow, and did not only extend fo far as the bredth of the remaining part of the Circle ; but like the Light or Tail of a Comet, extended more than 10 times that length, and in probability more than a 100 times ; nay, as far as I could find by many Trials, the Light from the Edge did ftrike downards into the Shadow very near to a Quadrant, though ftill I found, that the greater the Deflection of this new Light was from the direct Radiations of the Cone, the more faint they were.

It was hereupon objected by fome, that this Deflection of the Light was to be afcribed either to the Reflection of the Particles of Duft flying to and fro in the Air of the lucid Cone, or to fome kind of Tranfparency and Refraction in the Edge of the Rafor.

But to obviate thefe Objections, I took care firft fo to hide that part of the lucid Cone that was between the Hole and the Razor, that little or nothing thereof could come to fhine on that part where the Radiation appeared : And next by changing the Sides of the Razor, I placed the thick Back thereof inftead of the Edge : So that if there were any thing afcribable either to the Tranfparency, or Figure and Superficies thereof, all thofe Proprieties might be altered, and confequently the Effects producible thereby : But upon all the variety of Changes and Alterations and Examinations of it, this way and that way, I found the Effects and *Phænomena* the fame ; fo that it was manifeft, that the Effect was afcribable wholly to a new Propriety of the Rays of Light, and not at all to

The Effect wholly to be afcribed to a new Property of Light.

any

any Reflection or Refraction, or any other common Propriety of Light.

I proceeded yet farther to examine into the Nature of Light, and finding *These Radiations of Light might be moved.* that there were several brighter Parts of this Radiation into the Shadow, and others that were darker and more obscure, and that they did all strike perpendicularly into the Shadow ; and finding also that these brighter and darker Parts would be moved to and fro, and disappear, and other new ones appear, according as I moved and slipt the Razor or shadowing Body to and fro : After several Trials I found, that wheresoever there was a part of the shadowing Body more high than the rest of the Superficies, there the Radiation into the Shadow was brighter and more strong ; and wheresoever there was a Notch or Gap in the said Superficies, there a darker Stroke or Radiation would be : Insomuch that if I fixt upon the Side of the shadowing Body, a Piece of Lead, or the like (whether reflecting or not reflecting Body, 'twas the same thing) there would strike a brisk Radiation from the Shadow thereof into the Shadow of the opaque Body perdendicularly to the Line of Shadow. If the Superficies or Bulk of the Knob was considerably big, the Radiation would strike perpendicularly to the Sides thereof; so that if the shadowing Body were circular, it would strike towards a Center ; and if it were concave, it would strike with Radiations, as it were, from a Center : If it were a sharp Angle, or Corner, it would strike by a Line dividing the Angle into two equal Parts. This also, after several Examinations and Trials thereof, by varying Experiments, I found to be ascribable to a new Propriety of the Rays of Light, and not at all to Reflections or Refractions, or any other commonly known Propriety of Light.

Proceeding farther to make Observations of the bigness of the Figure of the Sun, painted by the Rays of Light admitted through the small Hole in the Brass Plate, upon the Table or Paper exposed to receive them ; I observed that the Limb of that Figure was always much darker than the middle Parts, and that it was not only darker, but ragged, and not neatly and distinctly defined, by reason of a kind of *Penumbra* which fringed the edge thereof. Comparing this *Penumbra* with the bigness of the Hole in the Plate through which the Light was admitted, I found that it was considerably broader than that, sometimes five or six times as broad ; so that I was sufficiently satisfied that it could not proceed from a *Penumbra* caused by the bigness of the Hole upon the common Principles, that is, from the Supposition of the Rays from every point of the Sun proceeding in strait Lines : For had that been supposed, the *Penumbra* could not have been broader than the Diameter of the admitting Hole, as it will be made very evident, if we examine the Progress of the Rays Geometrically, supposing them to move always exactly in strait Lines.

Let SN in the 9th Scheme represent the Diameter of the Sun shining through *Plate 2. Fig. 9.* the Hole HO, and painting upon the Table TT the round Figure of the Sun, whose Diameter suppose is DI, terminated by the Rays SOI and NHD, proceeding from the Extreams of the Sun's Diameter SN, to the opposite Sides of the Hole HO. Draw then from the Extremes of the Sun's Diameter S and N, two other Rays, SM and NE, passing by the corresponding Sides of the Hole H and O, and terminating at the Table or Paper at M and E ; which last Rays, with the preceding, will cut off from the shining Circle of the Sun MI and ED. And because of the vast Distance of the Body of the Sun from us, those Rays which we have here drawn diverging, will notwithstanding be Physically and sensibly parallel ; and consequently the breadth of the *Penumbra* MI and DE, must be equal to HO the Diameter of the Hole, by the 34 *pr. 1st Euclid.* the Paper or Table being supposed parallel to the Diameter of the Hole HO ; or if we will proceed according to the strictness of Geometry, the Breadth of the *Penumbra* MI will be so much greater than the Diameter of the Hole HO, as the Distance SI is to the Distance SO. For as SI is to SO, so is MI to HO, by the 4th of the sixth of *Euclid*; the which Proportion being, as to the greatest accurateness of *Sense*, a Proportion of Equality, it follows that the *Penumbra* of the Disk must be equal, as to all sense, to the Diameter of the Hole; and to make the *Penumbra* double to the Diameter of the Hole, the Distance of the Hole and Paper must be equal to the Distance of the Sun from the Hole; that is, as SI is double to SO, so will MI be double to MO. It follows therefore that this extraordinary *Penumbra* can no way be ascribable to the common Principles of

Light;

Light, but to some new Propriety, whereby the Light doth deflect from strait Lines, contrary to what is hitherto asserted by Optick Writers. Nor will the bright *Zone* which I mention'd, be explicable by any of the common Rules of Opticks : For according to the common Principles of Opticks, all the Parts of the shining or light Picture of the Sun, which lie between M and E, must be equally inlightned ; that is, supposing the Light to proceed only by right Lines : For every Point between E and M will be inlightned by an equal Space of the Diameter of the Sun. From the Point E of the Sun draw the Line EHL ; then shall LN represent such a part of the Diameter of the Sun, as can at once inlighten the Point E through the Hole. Then take any other Point in the Picture of the Sun between M and E, as suppose the Point C, and from the Point C draw two Lines touching the Extreams of the Diameter of the Hole H and O ; that is to say, CHB and COA, terminating at the Points B and A of the Sun ; I say, that BA shall be equal to LN. For since SN, HO, and TT are Parallels, HC will be to BC, as HE to LE. But as HE to LE, so is HO to LN ; and as HC to BC, so is HO to BA. Therefore as HO is to LN, so is HO to BA ; and consequently BA and LN are equal ; and consequently every Point of the Picture of the Sun painted by the Rays on the Table TT, between the Points E and M, ought to be equally inlightned by the Rays passing through the Hole HO ; since every of them is inlightned by an equal part of the Diameter of the Sun's Disck, which is contrary to the Observations that I have made ; and therefore the Rays of the Sun which cross each other in the Hole of the Shutter HO, do not proceed on in strait Lines, but deflect, some this way, some that way, as I shall hereafter more at large declare, when I shall shew divers other strange *Phænomena* of Light, both in Direct, Reflected and Refracted Rays ; whereby are produced Colours, Light and Heat, and various Pictures of the Objects without : For according to this or that Variety of the quantity of Light admitted, so would the Effects be exceedingly differing as to Light, Heat and Colours. And I also further observed, that the widening or streightning of the Hole would alter the *Penumbra,* and that a smaller Hole would make a larger *Penumbra,* which is contrary to the common Principles of Opticks : For if the Rays went in strait Lines, the bigger the Hole were, the bigger would be the *Penumbra.* These things I have deliver'd to you as briefly and succinctly as I could. The other *Phænomena,* God willing, I shall hereafter deliver to you more at large.

"IN reference to the foregoing Experiment of Light, I found a Paper to this
" purpose. On the 18th of *March* 167$\frac{3}{4}$ Mr. *Hooke* read a Discourse con-
" cerning the Nature and Properties of Light, in which was contained several
" new Properties of Light not observed, that he knew, by any Optick Writers :
" These were, That there is a Deflection of Light differing both from Reflection
" and Refraction, and seeming to depend upon the unequal Density of the con-
" stituent Parts of the Ray, whereby the Light is dispersed from the Place of
" Condensation, and rarify'd or gradually diverged into a Quadrant. 2dly, He
" observed that this Deflection is made toward the Superficies of the opacous
" Body perpendicularly. 3dly, That in this Deflection of the Rays, those Parts
" of diverged Radiation that are deflected by the greatest Angle from the strait or
" direct Radiations, are faintest, and those that are deflected by the least, are
" strongest. 4ly, That the Rays cutting each otehr in one common *Foramen,*
" do not make the Angles *ad Verticem* equal. 5ly, That Colours may be made
" without Refraction. 6ly, That the true bigness of the Sun's Diameter cannot
" be taken with common Sights. 7ly, That the same Rays of Light falling
" upon the same point of the Object, will turn into all sorts of Colours only
" by the various Inclination of the Object. 8ly, That Colours begin to appear,
" when two Pulses of Light are blended so well and near together, that the
" Sense takes them for one.

The two following Fragments of Gravity *and* Magnetism, *I found amongst some other loose Papers, which I suppose the Reader will accept of, tho' he should judge them of little worth.* R. W.

Of GRAVITY.

ALL folid Bodies take in and emit Fluids for their Suftentation. All fuch fluid Bodies have fomewhat of Solidity in them, when admitted, but are emitted more fluid.

The Sun and Stars continually emit; they muft therefore admit, otherwife a *Vacuum*.

The Earth, Planets, Moon, and Secondary Planets, admit, therefore muft emit; otherwife Penetration; neither poffible therefore a Circulation.

All Animals and Plants fenfibly admit and emit.

Of Minerals. The Magnet admits and emits. Electrical Bodies the fame, and the fhining Diamond.

All Bodies are in motion : Motion and Body equipollent.

Similars work moft powerfully on each other.

Similar Bodies join together more eafily.

All Solids have a tremulous Motion, as Bells, &c.

The tremulous Motion of Solids work on or move the incompaffing Fluids, and comminute, grind or divide the included or interfperfed.

All Fluids by degrees without this Comminution, become more folid, Part agreeing with the Part in Motion, as Saline Liquors, Waters, Air, &c.

Coherence nothing but Similitude of Parts and Motions.

Where the Motion of the denfer prevails, Coagulation; where of the fluid, Diffolution.

The more fluid, the quicker the Motion is; the more folid, the more flow.

The vibrating Motion of all Globular Bodies is from the Center to the Superficies, and *vice verfâ*. This fhewn by the Bell, Water in a Glafs, &c.

The Motion to and fro at the Center infinitely fwift, becaufe condenfed conically.

The comminuted Parts receive a rapid Motion according to their Smallnefs, fhewn by the Burning Glafs, &c.

They muft recede or be emitted with that Velocity. Their Recefs every way equal.

The Earth turbinated and roafted by the Sun; whilft Equinoctial Parts contract, Polar recede.

This Recefs not at once, but fimilar; whence a circular vibrative Motion, or Pulfe of Gravitating Matter. This confirmed by Magnetifm, Bell, Water in a glafs, &c.

Central Parts of the Earth poffibly fluid.

Heat or Excefs of Motion fhakes the Parts of Solids fo, as to make them Fluids, which is when a minute Fluid can get between.

Thence more eafily divifible by Supreme Fluid, which is Fire.

Supreme Fluids always recede from the Center radiating; leffer Fluids follow in their place.

Of

Of MAGNETISM.

After the Explication of Light and Gravity, I come in the 3d place to the Explication of Magnetifm. Magnetifm then is a certain Power in the Body of the Earth, or any other Celeftial Globulous Body, by which a certain Motion is produced in an appropriate *Medium*, that affects or moves certain Bodies capable of receiving the Impreffions thereof according to determinate Laws.

The Power in the Body of the Earth is the vibrative Motion of the internal Parts thereof from North to South, and from South to North.

The *Medium* appropriate for receiving and communicating this Motion, is an Æthereal fubtil Matter, which penetrates and pervades, and fills the Interftices of all Terreftrial Bodies.

The Bodies capable of receiving Impreffions or Motions from the Motion of this *Medium*, are thofe we call Magnetical, *viz.* Loadftones and Iron, *&c.* which are homogenious or unifonous, or equally great with the Magnetick, or fo vibrated Parts of the Body of the Earth.

The Caufe of this Motion is firft from the Circular Motion of the Body of the Earth, or other Globe upon an *Axis*.

And fecondly, the Obliquity of this *Axis* to the Plain in which it is moved, with a Motion of Lation.

This imperfeſt Fragment is all I find of this Hypothefis, tho' there are other Matters relating to Magnetifm fcattered in his Difcourfes. R. W.

This Difcourfe

This Discourse gives an Explication of a Glade of Light first observed in the Heavens by Dr. Childrey, *about the* Vernal Æquinox, *and by Monf.* Caffini *and others. This Lecture was read before the* Royal Society, June *the* 3d 1685.

DOctor *Childrey*, at the End of his *Britannia Baconica*, which he pulished in the Year 1660, containing feveral very curious Obfervations made by himfelf and others, has this Advertifement to the Curious and Ingenious. There is a thing which I muft needs recommend to the Obfervation of Mathematical Men, which is, that in *February*, and for a little before, and a little after that Month (as I have obferved feveral Years together) about 6 in the Evening, when the Twilight hath almoft deferted the Horizon, you fhall fee a plainly difcernable way of the Twilight ftriking up toward the *Pleiades*, or Seven Stars, and feeming almoft to touch them. It is to be obferved any clear Night. There is no fuch Way to be obferved at any other time of the Year, that I can perceive, nor any other Way at that time to be perceived darting up elfewhere. And I believe it hath been and will be conftantly vifible at that time of the Year: But what theCaufe of it in Nature fhould be, I cannot yet imagine. So far theDoctor difcourfing with this Gentleman about a Year or two after this Publication, he could not then think of any Caufe of it, unlefs perhaps it might be fome extraordinary Reflection of the Sun Beams, caufed by fome part of the Weftern Ocean ; but could not be pofitive, but doubted whether this might be a Caufe or not. This Tract of Dr. *Childrey's* was tranflated into *French*, and printed in the Year 1667, as appears by the *Mifcellanea Curiofa Academiæ Naturæ Curioforum* ; and by that means the Advertifement was fpread in *France*, and the reft of *Europe*. In the 11th Journal *des Scauans* of the Year 1683. we have an Account of a Sight the moft rare that has been obferved in the Heavens, defcribed by Mr. *Caffini* thus. "A Light, like that which blanches the Milky Way,in Page 183.

Mr. Caffini's *Obfervations.*
" but more clear and fhining in the middle, but more faint towards the Ex-
" treams, was expanded over thofe Signs which the Sun was fhortly to pafs
" through. I began to fee it at the *Royal Obfervatory*, the 18th of *March St.N.*
" two Days before the *Æquinox*, upon the occafion of turning the Telefcope
" (with which I had been viewing the Changes of *Saturn*) to fee the 1ft Star
" of *Aries*, which is compofed of two, diftant only the Sum of their Dia-
" meters. I faw this Conftellation, and that of *Taurus* more light than ordi-
" nary, about ¼ after 7 of the Clock, which was ½ an hour after the Evening
" Twilight. The Weft End of this Light was terminated by Horizon-Clouds
" about 3 Degrees high, the Breadth of the cleareft part was about 8 or 9
" Degrees: It was extended obliquely near the *Zodiac*, and fheer'd by the North
" fide of the two brighteft Stars in the Head of *Aries*, comprehending all the
" Body. It extended in Length over the 7 Stars, and ended infenfibly in the
" Head of *Taurus*. That part of the Heaven was fo very clear, that Stars of
" the 6th and 7th Magnitude could be plainly feen, even in the middle of it,
" which was the brighteft, as is fometimes feen in the Tails of Comets. But
" 'twas too great for the Tail of a Comet, tho' it refpected the Sun, and defcen-
" ded behind the Clouds, without altering its Situation among the Stars. It
" continued to appear for fome Days, but alter'd not its Pofition, tho' it grew
" fainter by degrees. The 26th of *March* (*St. N.*) which was the laft
" Night he then faw it) it feemed to be moved fomewhat more towards the
" North than at firft, which fome Obfervations of it in *April* following farther
" confirmed. I pafs over his comparing of it to other *Phænomena*, becaufe I
" take them to be of another nature. As for the Caufe of it, he takes it to be
" either from the Head of fome Comet hid under the Sun's Rays, which yet he

doubts

" doubts to affert, becaufe of its Breadth, or from the Sun's Body it felf ; but
" determines nothing.   He takes its Diftance to be great, approaching towards
" the Fixed Stars, above the Planets, becaufe it chang'd its Place fo very little
" in the time it appear'd.

In the *Nouvelles des Livres* of *March* laft, is inferted a Letter of Mr. *Chouët*,
Profeffor of Philofophy at *Geneva*, giving a further Account of the Obfervation
of it at that Place the laft Spring, *viz.* 1684. by Mr. *Fatio de Duillier*, to this
effect.   " That 'tis a great Light, like the Tail of fome Comet, whofe Head
" is abfconded in the Sun's Rays, appearing fometime in the Weft, fometime in
" the Eaft, after and before the Twilight, but always near the Sun.   'Tis al-
" ways near the Plain of the Ecliptick, and refpects the Sun.   The End next
" the Sun is about 14 Degrees broad, at about 40 Degrees from the Sun, and
" from thence goes about 30 Degrees farther, diminifhing in Breadth and Bright-
" nefs, and ending in almoft a Point.   It is brighteft through the middle, yet
" even through that fmall Stars may be feen.

This admirable Appearance, fays he, was firft obferved by the Illuftrious
Caffini in *March* and *April* 1683, where Mr. *Fatio* was prefent and affiftant in the
Obfervation : And returning to *Geneva*, he obferved it in *March*, but was much
furprized to find it again by chance in *Feb.* 1684. which made him frame the
following *Hypothefis*, *viz.* that he was in part of the fame Opinion with Mr.
Caffini, that the Light was caufed by fome more reflecting or refracting Parts
expanded into the *Æther* in that place which conveyed the Sun's Beams to our
Sight : But differ'd alfo from him, 1ft, In that Mr. *Fatio* fuppofes it fpread about
the Sun's Body moft about the Plain of the Ecliptick, extending far beyond the
Orb of *Venus*, and even almoft to the Orb of the Earth.   2ly, In that he fuppofes this Luminous Matter about the Sun not to be a Globe, but only a tapering Circle in the Plain of the Ecliptick : So that it is much thicker near the Sun,
where it doth to a great thicknefs inclofe him ; but as it fpreads further and further from it, fo it grows thinner.   3ly, That this Matter is carried round about
the Sun by the Motion of the Heavens, in the Plain of the Ecliptick, and terminates at the Orb of *Venus*.

To make out which *Hypothefis*, he affirms to have feen the like Glade of Light
in the Morning before the Twilight in *September*, and both before the Morning
Twilight, and after the Evening Twilight in *December*.   But this I do not find
obferved by any one elfe.

But thefe Hypothefes, tho' ingenious, do not give fo fatisfactory an Account
of this Appearance, as I conceive ; efpecially the firft, which is indeed not limited enough to make it deferve the Name of an Hypothefis ; and for the 2d, I
conceive no reafon why it fhould not every Night and every Morning that is clear,
and without much Moonlight, be vifible round the Year ; efpecially in the Torrid Zone, where the Ecliptick rifes more perpendicular.   Which I do not find
hath been noted, nor does it appear every Year : For I my felf (for two or three
Years after I firft faw the beforemention'd Advertifement of Dr. *Childrey*, which
was, as I remember, in 1662, 1663, and 1664) looked diligently for it, but
found it not.   And Dr. *Childrey* himfelf told me, that he had never found it at
any other Time of the Year : However it will be very well worth looking after.

The Author's   Comparing all thefe Obfervations together, my Conjectures are, that this Ap-
Opinion of its pearance is caufed by fome *Effluvia* from the Body of the Earth it felf, produced
Caufe.   by the near Approach of it to the Sun, when in and near its *Perihelium*, which
Perihelium being about the 5th or 6th Degree of *Taurus* for the Sun's Place, or
of *Cancer* for the Earth's Place, is on the 16th or 17th Day of *December*.   By
which Approach of the Body of the Earth to the Sun, I conceive that a more
than ordinary Rarifaction is made of the Parts of the *Atmofphere*, and the
Dimenfions thereof accordingly extended to a much greater diftance than at any
other times of its periodick Revolution : And the annual Motion being then alfo
proportionably increafed in Swiftnefs, many of the more than ordinarily rarify'd Parts of this *Atmofphere* may be for a time converted into a kind of *Æther*,
and be thereby intimately mixed and united with it, and fo be left by the fwiftly moving Ball in the Vicinities of its Paffage through the *Æther*, where for
fome time after it may remain perfectly incorporated with the Parts of the
Æther : But the extraordinary Heat reflected from the Body of the Earth, hav-

ing

ing left it for some time, these Aerial Vapours begin to lose that Form, and condense again into a Substance somewhat like the rarify'd Air, out of which they had been generated by the Coaction of the Sun and Earth. Which Condensation makes them of a differing **Transparency** from the rest of the Æther, and thereby capable both of reflecting and retracting the Rays of the Sun passing that way, and so make them to become visible to the Earth in that place of its Orbit where they had been left, and so continue, till by Degrees they be dispersed and scatter'd into a greater space or quantity of the Æther, and at length wholly disappear. To make this the more conceivable, and also more sensible and probable, I could produce an Experiment in more sensible and tangible Bodies, that would perfectly represent all the Particulars remarkable in these Observations, making use of Fire to represent the Heat of the Sun, of Water to represent the Air or Atmosphere, and of Air to represent the Æther; whereby the same Phænomena, at least very similar, would be plainly visible, respect being only had to the proportionate Differences between the Bodies representing and represented, and the Times of producing the Changes necessary to exhibit the mention'd Phænomena both of the one and the other Observation. But that I think will not be necessary, since none that has made any Observations at all, can be ignorant of them. 'Tis known to all, that Heat, whether of the Sun, Fire, or an Animal Body, will make Water so incorporate with the Air, as to waste away into it, without being at all visible, or altering the Transparency of it, as we every moment are sensible of it in our Breathing. 'Tis as well known likewise, if the Air be very cold into which we breath, the Vaporous Parts will presently condense, so as to become visible. 'Tis as well known also, that such Vapors, if the Air be warm, do spread themselves into the circumjacent Parts of the Æther, and will by degrees be wholly lost and dispersed. 'Tis likewise known, if such a reaking Body be moved through the Air, it will leave the Air through which it passes, infected by it; which Infection will spread laterally, and be broader than the Line of Motion. And the like may be said of all the other Phænomena necessary to make a sensible Representation of this notable Appearance.

Supposing then that this is the Cause of this Appearance, the Reason will be plain, why it appears at that Place, at that time of the Year, of such a breadth at the West end, and so sharp at the East; why of such a Length, why 'tis brightest in the middle, why fainter towards the Edges, why extended in or near the Plain of the Ecliptick, why it varies this way or that way, why it keeps its place among the Stars so long, and the like; which I am ready to explain more fully, if any Doubt.

Against this Hypothesis several Objections may be made, as

First, If this were the Cause of this Appearance, the *Atmosphere* of the Earth, and consequently the moist or watery part thereof would in time waste and be consumed, and so the World would be unfit for the Uses it was designed, of nourishing Vegetables and Animals. *Objections against the Hypothesis answered.*

To which I answer, that it may possibly be true, that the Moisture of the Earth may have always for the time past, and may also at present, and for the future, proceed to waste; and consequently the Earth may have grown drier, and continue so to do. There is sufficient ground to believe, that a great part of the Land that is now dry, and a considerable height above the Level of the Sea, hath been in former Times covered by the Sea, which the Shells now found do sufficiently evidence; and by what means it comes to be so, is not so well known or proved. There are other Parts, as *Palestine*, which have in former Times been much more succulent and fruitful than they are at present, being now Rocky, Sandy, and Barren.

But secondly, To supply this Wasting, it may be alledged, that the continual Gravity of the Earth doth make the heavier Parts thereof to get lower, and closer together; and thereby the Watery and Aerial Parts, that have fill'd the former Cavities and Interstities thereof, may be squeezed out into the Sea and *Atmosphere*: And so as the Body of the Earth may have by this means shrunk, and

and be grown leſſer and ſhrivelled; ſo the Watery and Atmoſpherical Parts about its Surface, may in ſome proportion to its preſent bigneſs be ſupplied.

Thirdly, 'Tis not unlikely, but that, as the extraordinary Heat of the Sun upon the Earth, when it is in its *Peribelion*, may for a time convert ſome parts of the *Atmoſphere* into *Æther*, and the extraordinary Swiftneſs of the Earth may leave them behind; ſo the leſſer Heat of the Sun upon the Earth, when in its *Apbelion*, may ſuffer the Parts of the *Æther* to be converted into Air, and by the ſlower Motion of the Earth in that part, be taken hold of and carried with it, and afterwards be further converted into Water, and ſo repair what was loſt in the *Peribelion*. I ſhall not mention that we find further, that Waters do petrify, and petrify'd Subſtances again revert into watery, that being more proper to another Head.

Secondly, It may be objected, That if this were the true Cauſe, why ſhould not the like happen to the other Planets, as particularly to the Moon, whoſe Glade would be ſeen every New Moon, eſpecially in *November*, *December*, and *January*.

To this I anſwer,

Firſt, That 'tis not undeniably proved, that any of the primary Planets have Water, or Atmoſphere about them; and ſo though they may have as great or greater Viciſſitudes than the Earth in reſpect of the Sun; yet this Tail would not be produced without an Aerial or Atmoſpherical Subſtance fitly prepared to receive theſe Changes. And for the Moon, 'tis moſt probable it hath none, and if it ever had, may have been thus waſted, and be now grown dry and rocky.

But ſecondly, Suppoſing they really have the ſame Subſtances about them, as the Atmoſphere is about the Earth, and that ſuch a Tail ſhould be really produced by them; yet for two Reaſons they could not be ſeen by us. The firſt is from the great Diſtance of them from our Sight in the Primary Planets; and ſecondly, the direct View of ſuch a Tail, if it were produced by the Moon: For the Moon moving about the Earth, the Eye on the Earth muſt always look upon ſuch a Tail or Stream tranſverſly, and ſo being but thin, cannot be ſeen: But in this of the Earth, the Eye looks upon it endways; and ſo, though rare of it ſelf, yet the Length of it being turned towards the Eye, it appears much the more denſe, and becomes viſible in a dark and clear Evening.

This *Phænomenon* I thought the more worthy conſideration, becauſe it was firſt diſcovered and publiſhed to the World, by an *Engliſh* Gentleman, and becauſe, that if the Reaſon thereof be what I have here ſuppoſed, it may help to give an account of abundance of other *Phænomena*, whoſe Cauſes have been aſcribed to very differing Principles and Agents.

I propounded the laſt Wedneſday an *Hypotheſis* for the Solution of that *Phænomenon*, that appears in the Weſt after the Twilight, like the Tail or Glade of a Comet. And having ſince met with ſeveral other Objections againſt it, beſides thoſe I then anſwer'd, I thought it might not be impertinent to give a further and more compleat Explication of it; and that the rather, becauſe I find that ſeveral of them have proceeded from a miſtaken Conception of the Theory it ſelf.

I ſhall therefore explain all thoſe Particulars more exactly by Schemes and Delineations, which may ſerve to give a more perfect Idea thereof.

Plate 3. Fig. 1.   The firſt repreſents the Ball of the Earth encompaſſed with an Atmoſpherical Shell or Cover, compoſed the greateſt part of *Æther*, but tinctured by rarify'd Particles of Water, Vapours or Air, which are ſtill more rarify'd and expanded, and fewer; and the nearer to the Nature of the *Æther*, the further they are diſtant from the Surface of the Earth.

Fig. 2.   The ſecond repreſents this enveloped Ball moving by its annual Motion in a part of its proper Orbit or Line about the Sun, and ſo paſſing through the Body of the *Æther*, which I ſuppoſe altogether ſtagnant, and not moving round with

it

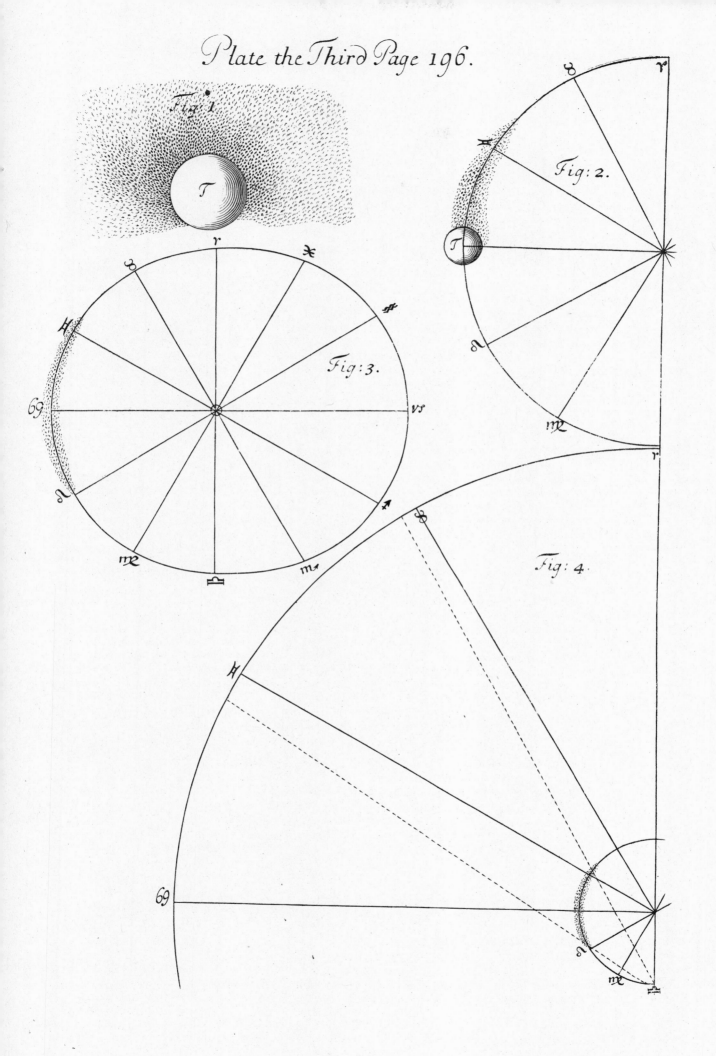

it in a *Vortice*, as *Des Cartes* fuppofed ; but quiefcent, according to that Theory of Celeftial Motions which I long fince have explained and fhewn to this Society, which deduces the Caufe of their periodick Motions from an impreft direct Motion, and an attractive or protruding Impulfe towards the Center of the Sun.

By means of the fwift Motion of which Body thro' this ftagnant *Æther*, I conceive there may be fome of the higher and more rarify'd Parts of the *Atmofphere* left behind, and not carried along with it, they being for that time more intimately united to the *Æther* ; but that thofe Parts, after they have for fome time been feparated, may alter or lofe their Rarefaction, and fo become for a time vifible to the Eye upon the Earth, now removed at a great diftance from them.

The third reprefents the fame in the Orbit of the Earth about the Sun, fhewing this Subftance left in that part of the Orbit which neareft approaches the Body of the Sun, where its Power and Heat is more intenfe, and where the Motion of the Body of the Earth is much more rapid than in other Parts of its Orbit. From which two Caufes, I conceive, the Earth leaves an Impreffion or Sign of its way through the *Æther*, fomewhat like the Froth left in the Wake of a Ship paffing fwiftly through the Water, which may be feen by one looking from the Poop of the Ship a good way behind, like a white Line, and has fometimes in a dark Night appeared to fhine.

Nor is this the only Inftance ; for I conceive there are very few, if any, here prefent, who have not feen the fhining Line left behind by the Meteors called Falling Stars, or Star Shootings.

This alfo reprefents the Pofition or Angle of it in refpect of the Sun, as alfo the Length of it, and the manner how that End of it which is next the Sun, fpreads, and the other End is fharp, and how the middle becomes more bright and confpicuous than the reft.

The 4th reprefents the fame Orbit of the Earth drawn in fmall, and fo manifefts the Reafon why that part of the Orbit appears to the Earth in *Virgo* and *Libra*, amongft the Fixt Stars of the Conftellation of *Aries* and *Taurus*.

The right underftanding of this Theory will plainly fhew a Reafon why it had fo little, if any Parallax at all; which made *Caffini* fuppofe it higher than the Planets, and *Chouet* that it was about the Sun : For by the Scheme it plainly appears, that it muft be for the moft part of it further diftant than the Sun.

The chief Objections that I have fince met with are thefe.

Other Objections anfwered.

1. How the *Æther*, which is fo exceeding thin and fluid a Body, can detain or ftop any part of the Atmofphere in the Tranfit of the Earth, and why the Gravity of the Earth, which carries along with it the Moon, according to my Theory, which is fo vaftly much more diftant, fhould not be able to carry with it all the Parts of the Atmofphere.

2. Tho' the *Æther* fhould thus retain part of the Atmofphere, as I fuppofe, yet why this retained Subftance fhould not appear fooner, and how it fhould continue fo long after, without being wholly difperfed into the *Æther*.

3. Why this Separation, or marked Way, fhould be left only when the Earth is in its *Perihelion*, and not all the Year, in every part of its Orbit.

4. Why this Glade fhould not appear the fame every Year, fince the Earth moves the fame Trace through the fame *Æther*, and fo at the fame Times or Places of its Orbit, it has the fame Influences both from the Sun and the *Æther*.

To the firft I anfwer, That tho' the *Æther* be exceeding fluid, yet both from Obfervation and Experiments it affords fome Refiftance to Bodies moved through it. Firft by Obfervation it has been, I think, always found that the Tail, Blaze or Glade of Comets, has not been exactly directed or pointed from the Sun, but hath always had an Inclination backwards, that is, towards the Place from whence the Comet is moved, as I have publifhed in my Obfervations concerning Comets ; the Blaze of a Comet in this fomewhat refembling the Afcent of the

Flame of a Candle, when it is moved fideways through the Air. But fecondly, by experiment we find, that though the Motion of a *Pendulum in vacuo* will be much more free, and laft a confiderable time longer than the Motion of a *Pendulum in pleno Aëre* ; yet even this will in fome fhort time alfo lofe its Motion, and ftand ftill, as I have manifefted to this Society by former Experiments purpofely made. 3ly, Tho' the gravitating or attracting Power of the Earth be able to retain and carry the Moon along with it in its annual Orbit, the Moon being a Body of a vaft Bulk of Solidity, compar'd to the Fluidity and fmall Refiftance of the *Æther* through which it moves : Yet, as I fhall afterwards prove in my Theory of Lunar Motions, the Impediment of the *Æther* hath a very confiderable Influence upon it, and produceth very fenfible Effects, tho' they are afcribed to differing Caufes. But on the other hand, the Solidity of the Parts which ferve to exhibit this *Phænomenon*, are fo very fmall, and fo near approaching to the Nature of the *Æther*, that the Stagnancy of the *Æther* hath a confiderable Influence and Effect upon them.

For anfwer to the 2d Objection, 1ft, I fay, that I fuppofe it when feparated from the Atmofphere, to be fo near of the fame Nature of the *Æther* with which it is mixed, that it difcovers not its effential Difference, till it hath been for fome time feparated from the Atmofphere ; but then when the Reflective Influence of the Earth hath been for fome time wanting to it, it doth by degrees re-affume its preceding Form, and by degrees revert into the Form of Air, Vapours or Water, and fo becomes of a differing Nature from the *Æther*, and ferves to reflect the Rays of the Sun towards the Earth.

2ly, The Nearnefs of its Qualification to the *Æther*, makes it more flow in altering its Form. Of this we have Inftances enough in the Atmofphere in a dry Seafon, as at this prefent, when though the Air be plentifully charged with watery Vapours and Exhalations, yet they continue for a long time in the form of the Air, being not difcoverable from the more permanent Body of the Air it felf, by any difference of Refractivenefs, till by fome other Caufe unknown, they be converted again into the Form of Water in fmall Globules, or Drops, and fo appear in form of Clouds, many of which Drops uniting into one, form a Drop of

Of Rain.

Rain, and fo fall down to the Earth. This unknown Caufe feems to be fometimes extraordinary Heat, whereby one part is converted into Lightning, upon which another prefently reverts into Water or Rain, and falls down in Thunder Showers. At other times it feems to be extraordinary Cold, as one may judge by the falling down of thofe Drops in the form of Ice, as in Hail Showers.

3ly, If we confider the vaft height from the Surface of the Earth, to which the Parts of the Atmofphere afcend, which exhibit the Twilight, which *Cardan* believes to be almoft 800 Miles, tho' *Ricciolus*, and others more moderate, fuppofe it not above 100 Miles high ; we may eafily affent, that fome of thofe Parts may be left in the *Æther*, confidering the Stagnancy of the *Æther*, and the exceeding great Swiftnefs of the folid Globe of the Earth through the fame. But then if we confider the Parts of the Atmofphere not Refractive, they may be fuppofed very much more elevated, even to the height of a Diameter of the Earth. But if they are fuppofed lefs than 50, which the moft moderate allow, yet they will be high enough to be left behind by the fwiftly moving Ball of the Earth.

To the Third Objection, why this Train or Stream fhould be left when the Earth is in its *Perihelium*, and not as well at all other Times and Places of its Revolution, I anfwer, That there being a manifeft difference of a Caufe, 'tis rational enough to fuppofe there may be a fenfible difference of Effect. 'Tis by other ways proved that the Earth is in that part of its Orbit nearer the Sun, and that its Motion is then and there proportionably fwifter ; if then we can obferve a different *Phænomenon*, 'tis rational to afcribe it to that different Caufe, till a more certain be found. Now that fuch a Caufe may have fome confiderable Influence, I fhall produce an Obfervation of the before-mentioned Dr. *Childrey*, in the fame Book, viz. his *Britannia Baconica*,

Moon's Influence on Floods.

pag. 97 & 98. " I forgot (fays he) to fay, that feveral great Inundations fpeak " in favour of my Opinion touching the Moon in *Perigeo*, her greatning the
" Tides

" Tides ; for I can affure you, that for that great Flood *Anno* 1532. *Novemb.* 5.
" on which was made this Diftick.

Anno ter deno cum fefqui mille Novembris
Quinta ftat falfis Zelandia tota fub undis.

" That in the Year 1551 and 1552, *Jan.* 13th ; that horrible one 1570, on *All*
" *Saints* Day, the firft of *November* ; and that notable one 160⁵⁄₇, *Jan.* 30th,
" the greateft that ever was known in *Severn*, and fo fatal to *Somerfetfhire*,
" *Glocefterfhire*, and *Monmouthfhire* ; they were all when the Moon was in
" *Perigeo*, as he that lifts to calculate, or fearch the *Ephemerides* for thofe
" Years, will find.   And the fame Doctor, in the beginning of his Book, adds
an Advertifement of an Obfervation he made before that Book was quite prin-
ted off, *viz.* " That on the 1ft of *November* 1660, between 10 a Clock at
" Night, and 5 next Morning, happen'd an unufual fhifting of the Tides in the
" *Thames* at *London* ebbing and flowing three times, as 'tis reported, in that
" fpace ; which, fays he, was when the Moon was almoft in the very place of
" her *Perigæum.*

To which let me add one Obfervation more to the Doctor's, That all thefe
Phænomena hapned when the Earth was very near its *Perihelium*, and within the
Limits of this fuppofed Luminous Glade or Wake, as I may call it, of the
Earth ; and 'tis not impoffible but that this greater Nearnefs of the Body of the
Earth to the Fire of the Sun, may make it emit more copious, and other na-
tured Steams than at other times, when not fo much roafted by the Heat of the
Sun.

As to the 4th Objection, why this fhould not appear every Year the fame ; I
anfwer, that there may be many Caufes or Reafons to make one Year confiderably differ from another, as is fufficiently manifeft by the Variety of Weather of
one Year from another.   But to determine pofitively what is the Caufe, does
require a greater number, and more exact Obfervations than have been hitherto
made of it.

Having underftood that there yet remains one Objection againft the *Hypothefis*,
I have propofed for folving the Glade of Light appearing in the Weft in *Februa-*
ry, *March*, and *April* ; and that is, againft the Stagnancy of the *Æther*, and
its ftaying of Atmofpherical Parts within it from following the Motion of the
Earth. I fhall thereupon mention two *Phænomena*, which I conceive, when they are
well confidered, will give fome probable Argument for this Opinion ; and thofe
are two of the fame Kind or Nature, but obferved at different Times and Places.   The firft I fhall mention, tho' the laft in time, was the *Fax* or *Lampas* Of a Lampas
Volans obferved after Sun-fet the 1ft of *March* 1676, at *Fau*---- by *Petrus de* Volans.
Lauina ; at *Rome* by Monf. *Auzout* ; at *Florence* by *Matthias del Arpi* ; at *Ve-*
nice by *Jo. Jacob Hertz*, and in feveral other Cities of *Italy* ; in all which it
was feen alfo by very many others, and at the fame time alfo was obferved in
the Lower Parts of *Germany*, as at *Triers* by the *Jefuits* there ; Places very far
diftant one from another ; yet the Time and Manner of Appearance in all was
much the fame.   It feemed to rife out of the North Eaft, and to pafs by the
Meridian to the South Weftern Parts of the Heavens, near the fame Tract that
the Sun had gone that Day, and difappeared behind thick Clouds, where with
a mighty Noife it was fuppofed to be blown to pieces and difperfed.   It appeared about the bignefs of the Full Moon, and left behind it a Tail about 3
Diameters, of a reddifh Flame at firft, but turning bluifh towards the laft.   It
lafted about a Minute or two.   Its Noife at laft was like the Noife of an Earthquake at a diftance, and made the Glafs in the Windows fhake.   From the
comparing of feveral Obfervations, 'twas fuppofed about 90 Miles high, and
near a Mile in Diameter.   The feveral Authors that have writ concerning it,
have explicated it by an Hypothefis very different from mine.   My Conceptions
of it are thefe.

Firft, That it was a vaporous Steam much of the fame nature with that which
makes Lightning raifed into the Superior Parts of the Air by means of its own

innate

innate Heat and Rarefraction, which might poffibly proceed from fome fubterraneous Operation in fome Parts of the Eaft lying far diftant from _Italy_, as _China,_
or fome other Part where there might be fome Earthquake, or poffibly fome Ir-
ruption, by which it might be fent out in great plenty, and forced up with
great Power and Swiftnefs, that remaining there fome time, it might from the
Cold or want of Heat of thofe higher Regions, by degrees be condenfed and
conglobated nearer together, and by the Operation of the more Æthereal part
of the Atmofphere, be prepared for Accenfion.; and fo being kindled, it would
continue fome fmall time before it fet fire to the middle Parts thereof, at which
time it feemed to imitate the Noife of Thunder afar off. Now that Particular
for which I mention it, is the way of its apparent Motion, which was faid to be
much the fame with the Sun that Day, rifing Eaftward, and paffing by the Meridian towards the Weft. This, I conceive, was caufed by the Diurnal Motion
of the Earth, whereby the Parts where it was feen being moved very fwiftly
towards the Eaft, _viz._ about 12 or 14 Miles in a Minute, the higher Parts of
the Atmofphere in which it was kindled, being left behind, it appeared as if it
had been carried by a fwift Motion of its own from Eaft to Weft. And by reafon, I fuppofe, that even that part of the Atmofphere was moved a little towards the Eaft, thence was the Appearance of the Tail or Blaze it had that way,
of about 3 times its own Diameter : Which will, I conceive, give a probable
Caufe of its apparent rapid Motion, and very well agree with the Hypothefis I
lately mentioned.

And the fame _Hypothefis_ will folve a like _Phænomenon_, which, as well as I
can remember, was fome 10 Years before obferved, both here in _England_, and
in _Holland._ It was feen by Sir _Robert Murray_, if I mifremember not, and by
Mr. _Shortgrave_, and I think alfo by Monf. _Hugens_ in _Holland._ It was as big as
the _Italian_ Meteor, and was judged to be of an exceeding great height in the
Atmofphere, being feen at Places fo far diftant at the fame time. It appeared
firft about the North Eaft, and paffed by the North Weft, not rifing, as I remember, fo high as 10 Degrees above the Horizon. For fuppofing that in the fame
manner to be left behind by the fwiftly moving Parts of the Earth, the _Phæno-
mena_ will be very naturally folved ; and therefore deferve, I conceive, to be
taken notice of in the Hiftory of Nature.

An Account of Dr. Isaac Vossius's Hypothesis of GRAVITATION, with some Animadversions thereupon.

HAving perus'd a Discourse of the Learned Dr. *Vossius*, wherein he endeavours to explain the true Reason and Cause of the *Gravitation* of Bodies towards the Center of the Earth, I thought it might not be unacceptable to give an account of my Thoughts concerning it, it being a Subject well worthy the consideration of this Society, there having not been to this day any one *Hypothesis* given by any Writer, that is sufficient to solve the *Phænomena* thereof, or to explain the Multitude of Effects produced by it, much less to demonstrate the Power and Limits thereof, concerning which I have heretofore somewhat more largely discoursed in this Assembly. I shall not now spend time in the enumeration of the various *Hypotheses* of several other Authors, but confine my self only to the consideration of that which is propounded by this Worthy and Ingenious Person. He conceives then, that the sole reason why heavy Bodies descend towards the Center of the Earth, and why light Bodies ascend from it, is the Diurnal Rotation thereof upon its *Axis*, and wonders that it was never found out before, even by those who patronized the *Copernican Pythagorick* (or, as he affirms, the *Chaldean* and *Egyptian* Opinion, long before *Pythagoras*) of the Motion of the Earth. The Reasons he assigns, why this Motion must infallibly and necessarily produce this Effect, is because heavy Bodies having an inaptitude to Motion, do therefore endeavour towards the Center, where there is none, or the least that can be. This he explains by two sorts of Experiments tried or observed by him; the first is that of a *Vortex*, or Whirl of Water in a large Tub, the second that of a large Top. By the first, he says, he found that the Water being put into a swift Circular Motion, all those Bodies which were heavy, and sunk to the bottom, were drawn to the middle, and the heaviest of them got nearest to the Center; and those less heavy were removed farther and farther off, according to their proportionate Degree of Gravity, as Lead would get nearest, Iron next, then Stones, or other less heavy Bodies. On the other side, such Bodies as were lighter than the Water, and so swam upon it, would recede and fly off to the Sides of the Tub. The like *Phænomena* he observed also in Whirlwinds of the Air. His second Experiment of the Top, he produces to answer some Objections which are usually made against the Motion of the Earth, and so will consequently be against this *Hypothesis*: For 'tis usually, says he, objected, that if the Earth move, then all such Bodies as are loose upon it, would be so far from growing more heavy towards the Center, that they would all of them be rather thrown off into the Air or *Æther* with a great violence, and tend outwards or upwards from it, since 'tis plain, that a Body put into a Wheel, and turned swiftly round, has a tendency from the Center, and not at all to it. For, saith he, tho' it be true, that a Wheel turned thus perpendicularly, do's cause the heavy Body to recede; yet if the Wheel were moved Horizontally, as a Top is, with its *Axis* erect, and at right Angles with the Plain of the Horizon, it would not. But I conceive both these Arguments are *gratis dicta*, as are all the Conclusions deduced therefrom, and the *Phænomena* they exhibit are to be ascribed to quite different Causes to those he assigns. For first, as to Whirl-winds and *Vortices*, 'tis clear, that by the violent Circumrotation of the Air or Water, the Endeavour of those Bodies is to recede from the Center of that Rotation, and by that means there is less Resistance in the Center for Bodies, whether heavy or light (for both will move towards it) to get into it; but the lighter much easier than those that are heavy, as 'tis common to see small Whirles of the Wind to gather together Leaves and Straw, and light Dust, and raise them up into the Air; but Stones and heavier Bodies are not at all

F f f   stirred

stirred by it. And for the same reason, I suppose, it is, that large and violent Whirlwinds upon the Sea do cause the Water to rise up from the Sea, and ascend upwards, and the Clouds on the other hand to descend downwards into the Center, now made almost like an empty Pipe by the recess of the Air in whirling round, as is observed in the Spouts at Sea; which quantity of Water so raised, suddenly falls again, so soon as the whirling Motion ceases. Now, as in Whirlings of the Air, the Water rises in the *Axis* or middle, so 'tis very obvious in Whirl-pools of Water, the Air descends, and fills that Cavity that is deserted by the Water in the middle. But neither of these afford any Argument, as I conceive, of *Gravitation* to the Center of the Earth: For 'tis not here the fluid *Medium* that is whirled round faster than the solid Body of the Earth, but this Body is whirled round faster than the Air; and that is supposed to be the reason why the Winds in the *Torrid Zone* do for the most part move from the Eastern Parts of the Earth towards the Western, making that Wind they call a Trade Wind. Now both Monf. *Des Cartes*, and Mr. *Hobbs* have been of this opinion, that the Diurnal Motion of Rotation might be the cause of this Tendency of Bodies to the Center of it; but neither of them have explained the manner how, supposing the *Æther* to be the most compact Body, and so to be thrown off by this Rotation, and thence the more sensible and tangible Bodies of the third Element to be forced towards the *Axis* of Rotation: They have not, I say, explained how these lighter Bodies come to tend towards the Center; for granting what they suppose, those Bodies would not tend to the Center of the Globe, but to the Center of each Parallel Circle of Latitude, and consequently under the Pole there would be no Tendency at all. Now tho', 'tis true, it would be a hard matter to confute them, to assert experimentally a Gravitation at the Pole; yet 'tis evident enough in all other Degrees of Latitude, that the Tendency is not to the Center of the Parallel of that Latitude, but always towards the Center of the Globe. Again, if the Rotation of the *Æther* were the Cause of this Tendency towards the Center, and that this Rotation were differing from the Rotation of the Earth, that is, either faster or slower, which seems to be the Cause supposed in the first Experiment of the *Vortex* of Water, then falling Bodies would not descend in a Line tending to the Center, but in some Oblique Line, either inclined towards the East or the Westward of it. If, on the other side, it were from the swifter Rotation of the Body of the Earth, as seems to be hinted by the 2d Experiment of the humming Top, then would falling Bodies not descend and fall perpendicularly, but to the Westward of it in the same Parallel of Latitude. Again, whereas Dr. *Voffius* says, that a Vertiginous Motion, whose *Axis* is perpendicular to the Horizon, does not throw off Bodies from it, as the Motion of a Wheel, whose *Axis* is parallel to the Horizon; 'tis clear by Experiment that it doth, in the same manner, which may be plainly seen, if Water be dropt upon the top, whilst in that turbinated Motion; for it will disperse it every way with great violence. And as to the standing still of the Top upon its End, when it is so violently moved round upon it, and of its running away with a great Swiftness so soon as its Sides touch the Ground, I conceive the Reasons of both are so plain, that I need not insist upon them. Again, whereas Dr. *Voffius* lays great stress upon the Perpendicularity of the *Axis* of the Earth to the Plain of its annual or progressive Motion. It is evidently otherwise; for the *Axis* is always declined 23 ½ Degrees from that perpendicularity. So that I fear we are yet to seek for the true Cause of Gravity, as well as we are of the Degrees of its Power, and the Limits of its Extent: For tho' there have been many that have supposed its Power not to extend beyond the Air or Atmosphere, and upon that have given the reason of the Suspension of Water in the Clouds, and of the flying of Kites, and other Fowl, to a great height into the Air, and the like; yet 'tis very evident by many Arguments I produced in my Lectures about the Comet, that the Power thereof is not limited within so small an Extent, but rather that it hath a strong and powerful Effect, not only as far as the Moon, but vastly far beyond it; and that it is one of the most essential Properties of all the large Globular Bodies of the Universe.

this approaches very near Newton

Of

Of Dr. Dee's Book of Spirits.

Tho' this Discourse be of a quite differing nature from all the other Subjects treated of in this Book, yet I thought it would not be unacceptable for the newness of it, since it gives a quite different Explication of that unusual sort of Treatise of Dee's Converse with Spirits, from all other Interpreters. This Paper was bought by a Gentleman in the said Book, at the Auction of Hook's Library, who was pleased to send it to me. To him therefore my self and the Reader are obliged for this Tract. To which is added an Account of Dr. Dee and his Studies, transcribed by Dr. Hooke out of Mr. Ashmole's Theatrum Chemicum.

HAving lately met with a Book, which though it hath been published now above 30 Years, I never had the Curiosity to examine further into, than upon opening here and there to read some few Lines, which seeming for the most very extravagant, I neglected any further Inquiry into it: Yet having not long since met with a small Pamphlet of the same Author, intituled, *A Letter, containing a most brief Discourse Apologetical, with a Plain Demonstration and Fervent Protestation for the lawful, sincere, very faithful and Christian Course of the Philosophical Studies and Exercises of a certain studious Gentleman, an antient Servant to her Most Excellent Majesty Royal.* Written to the Most Reverend Father in God, the Lord Arch-Bishop of *Canterbury*, Primate and Metropolitan of all *England*, and one of her Majesty's most Honourable Privy Council, *&c.* And subscribed by *John Dee*: Wherein, besides his Protestation before Almighty God, upon the peril of his Soul's Damnation, if he lied, or took his Name in vain therein, that with all his Heart, with all his Soul, Strength, Power and Understanding (according to the measure thereof which the Almighty had given him) for the most part of his time from his Youth hitherto, he had used, and did still use, good, lawful, honest, Christian, and Divinely prescribed Means, to attain to the Knowledge of those Matters which were meet and necessary for him to know, and wherewith to do his Divine Majesty such Service, as he had, did or should call him unto during his Life, for advancing his Honour and Glory, and for the Benefit and Commodity Publick of this Kingdom, so much as by the Will and Purpose of God should lie in his Skill and Ability to perform, and of his Profession of being a Christian. Besides this Profession (I say) I found it contained a Catalogue of most of his Works, either published before that time, or then in Manuscript; by the Titles whereof he seeming to be an extraordinary Man, both for Learning, Ingenuity and Industry, I had a desire to peruse the Book with a little more Attention than I had formerly Thoughts of; to see if by the Contents thereof it might have contained any of those Subjects, which he, in the said Apologetical Discourse, had asserted himself to have written concerning. Nor was I frighted from this my Purpose, either by the six pretended Conjurers prefixt to the Title, *Mahomet, Apollonius Tyaneus, Kelly, Friar Bacon, Paracelsus,* and Dr. *Dee* himself; nor by the Title, viz. *A true and full Relation of what passed for many Years between Dr.* John Dee *(a Mathematician of great Fame in* Queen *Elizabeth and King* James, *their Reigns) and some Spirits, tending* (had it succeeded) *to a General Alteration of most States and Kingdoms in the World,* &c. Since I conceived both these to have been the Ingenuity of the Publisher, to make the Book sell the better: No, nor thirdly by the long and frighting Preface of the Publisher, Dr. *Merick Casaubon,* who certainly did believe him the said *Dee*, to be a Conjurer or Witch, and to have dealt with the Devil all along through the whole Course of this Relation of his Travels into *Germany, Poland,* and other Parts of *Europe*; he understanding the same all

along

along in the plain literal Senſe, as indeed moſt Readers have, and do as yet conceive of it, as he, beſides what he hath ſaid in his Preface, doth more particularly ſhew in his Contents of the ſeveral Sections of it, and his ſeveral Notes diſperſed here and there in the ſaid Book. But proceeding to peruſe the ſaid Diſcourſe, I upon the firſt View and Conſideration of the 3 Copper Sculptures prefixed, immediately conjectured what the Subject of the Book was likely to be, which by divers other Circumſtances afterwards I was more confirmed in, as I ſhall by and by ſhew.

But firſt, it may ſeem needful that I premiſe ſome Diſcourſe Apologetical for my ſelf,

Firſt, for peruſing a Book ſuppoſed to be a Book of Conjuration, and dealing with the Devil and his Imps.

Next, For diſcourſing in this Place concerning a Book which has been publiſhed ſo many Years, and paſt under the Cenſure and Judgment of moſt Learned Men, and ſo is at beſt but ſtale, and what every body knows, or may have known already.

3dly, That it contains a Diſcourſe of a Subject ſo much beſide the Deſign of the Inſtitution of this Honourable Society ; this ſeeming to have nothing to do with the Improving Natural Knowledge.

4thly, For that it ſeems not to have relation to the Hiſtory of Nature or of Art, and ſo falls not within the Limitation of the Subject of this Lecture.

5thly, For my Preſumption in interpoſing my Conjectures and Sentiments concerning the Subject Matter of the ſame, after it hath been cenſured by ſuch Eminently Learned and Judicious Men, as Bp *Uſher*, Dr. *Caſaubon*, and others.

As to the firſt of theſe, I found in the very Title Dr. *Merick Caſaubon*'s Opinion ſpecified to be, that the Relation was real (as to the Point of Spirits) and that a ſober Chriſtian might make ſeveral good Uſes of all : And in the Preface it ſelf the Doctor hath very much inlarged upon this Subject, and ſays in the firſt Page of his Preface, that he was the more confirmed in his Sentiments concerning it, when he was told at firſt by thoſe that knew very well, that the moſt Reverend, Pious and Learned Arch Biſhop of *Armagh*, then lately deceaſed, upon reading the ſaid Book before his Death, had declared himſelf to the ſame purpoſe, and wiſhed it printed. His firſt Uſe is for an Argument againſt Atheiſts, and ſuch as do not believe Spirits and Devils. 2dly, Againſt Enthuſiaſts, who altogether depend upon new Revelations, zealouſly and fervently praying for ſuch Inſpirations and extraordinary Aſſiſtances, ſaying, that this Buſineſs of Prayer and Praiſing is a Buſineſs, as of great Comfort, ſo of much more Danger and Deluſion than many do believe ; upon which account he tells many ſtrange Stories. 3dly, For to deter Men from preſumptuous unlawful Wiſhes and Deſires ; and thence of making uſe of Witches, Conjurers, Aſtrologers, and Fortunetellers, and all Books of thoſe Subjects, which he conceives were the Cauſe of Dr. *Dee*'s Deluſion : So that I was ſatisfied there could be no great Danger or Harm in the looking farther into the Contents of it. But more than this, I conceived it not reaſonable altogether to depend upon the Opinion and Sentiment of others concerning it, when the Book was by, to give Teſtimony of it ſelf ; for that divers Books have been condemned for ſuppoſed Crimes, of which yet, upon further Inquiry, they have been found innocent, and to have quite a differing Deſign from what they ſeemed at firſt ſight to intend. Witneſs the *Steganographia* of the Abbot *Trithemius*, which was ſo fiercely accuſed of Conjurations by *Carolus Bovillus* his Contemporary, by *Wierus* his Follower, alſo by Cardinal *Bellarmine*, *Antonius Paſſerinus*, and by moſt others ſince, who underſtood not the Art and Ingenuity of the Book ; but others more judicious and knowing have vindicated and cleared him from thoſe Calumnies, and proved the Art and Ingenuity of the Book, as above all other, *Guſtavus Selenus*, or *Auguſtus* Duke of *Lunenburgh*, pag. 37. *Ut profanum Vulgus ab occulte ſcribendi hac Arte arceret, atq; adeo quibuſdam Terriculamentis abſterreret, ingenioſiſſimus noſter Abbas, eam Magiæ, vulgo inviſi & odioſi Nominis ſpecie venditavit, quaſi infernalium Spiritum ope, dirisq; Incantationibus, ſub horrido confragoſo, atq; ad terrorem pene conficto idiomatiſmo res perageretur, quem Scopum non ob-*
ſcure

scure innuit in duabus ad Electorem Palatinum Philippum Præfationibus. Addamus nos ipsum porro tali involucro ingenuum Ingenii Lusum cogitasse, in gratiam Eruditorum artem hanc filo Ariadnes fido adepto addiscentium. Ludit enim sub Nomine Spirituum ad Literas, quibus occulte aliquod Negotium alteri significatur; vel quod illæ sunt Animi & Spiritus nostri indices voluntatem nostram absenti quo vox non penetrat, fideli & mirabili modo perferentes; vel quod inter plures literas (quæ pro occultando instituto in Epistola aliud Thema tractante transmittenda adhibentur) istæ, quibus quasi aliud agendo Secretum alteri indicatur, uti Spiritus, Vita & Anima; cætera vero eo non pertinentes, pro Mortuis habendæ sint. And so he proceeds to shew the Reason, why he calls some of those Spirits Dukes or Princes, others Captains, others ministring and subservient; and in short, detects the whole Artifice of the whole Book, which had nothing of that Design for which the illiterate and unskilful Readers did generally condemn it.

But secondly, As to the Staleness of the Book, it having been now printed and published about 32 Years, I answer, that as to my self, tho' I had often seen the Book, and heard many Discourses of it, and of its Contents, yet as to my own knowledge of it, it was perfectly new, and possibly it may be so to a great many others, considering the Subject of the same, and the manner of the Delivery thereof, which indeed seems to be (bating some Parts that relate to a kind of History of *Dee*'s particular Affairs and Transactions with some Great Men) a Rapsody of incoherent and unintelligible Whimsies of Prayers and Praises, Invocations and Apparitions of Spirits, strange Characters, uncouth and unintelligible Names, Words and Sentences, and Relations of incredible Occurrences. So that wherever you open and begin to read, you may find cause enough in a very little time to throw it aside and neglect it, till you have quite forgotten what you then met with, as it happen'd to me, who had in that manner several times seen and read here and there a few Paragraphs.

But next I answer, that there are many Books that have been a long time printed; nay some so long, that they are many of them almost quite lost, and very hardly and rarely to be met with, which yet deserve to be looked into, and an account given of, as much as many new Books, which now almost every Day are brought forth into the World; upon which Subject I need not inlarge, because I believe I may have many others of the same Opinion: For there are many things which are now produced for Novelties and new Discoveries, which yet may be found to have been long since published, and either have not been taken notice of, or through Length of time have been forgotten and lost, as if they had never been. Again, there are many Books, that have slipt into the World at such times, as no body, or very few, at least, have taken notice of them upon their first coming, by reason they were of Subjects then not much regarded, or in vogue, or when Mens Minds were taken up or more concerned for other Subjects, or Matters of greater import, which by the Time of the Printing might possibly be the Fate of this very Book, which probably at another time would have made more Noise, and, it may be, have met with more Notice, if not also more Opposition. And it has been the Fate of many good Books to be neglected for some time after their first Publication, which yet in time come to be better look'd into, and the Usefulness of them understood, and then to begin to be prized, as I understand was the Fate of Mr. *Purchas* his Pilgrims and Pilgrimage, and several others.

As to the 3d Objection that may seem to need an Apology, namely, the *Heterogenity* and Unfitness of the Subject for the Consideration of this Society, as being reputed a Treatise about Supernatural Effects or Productions, I must confess, that if it be to be understood according to the plain literal Meaning, it would be truly so; but whereas I conceive the true Meaning and Design of the whole to be quite another Matter, I think it may be as properly referred to the Improvement of Natural Knowledge to understand it, as of any other Book that has plainly and expresly treated of the History of Nature and Art. For I take it to be a concealed History of that kind, which may also apologize for my treating of it upon this occasion in this Lecture.

It may also serve for my 5th Apology: For tho' I confess it may seem to favour of too much Confidence, to differ from the Sentiments of most Men concerning it; yet since what I propound is not positive, but rather as Queries to

　be

be refolved by fuch as have better Abilities and Opportunities to folve them than I have, and that I am ready to fubmit to fuch well-grounded Determinations. I hope my Attempt in this kind will not appear to exceed the Limits of the Charter of *Philofophia libera*, nor be repugnant to the Doctrine of *Nullius in Verba* : For whatever may feem rational to others to judge of the faid Book, to me, I confefs, it feems to be defigned to comprehend another Meaning than what is plainly legible in the Words of it, which poffibly many others that have read it, may have no Sufpicion of; neither may they have ever feen or confidered the Cryptography of *Trithemius*, or any other Author on the like Subjects. *Non omnia poffumus omnes.* Thus much by way of Apology.

To come then to the Book it felf. Upon turning it over, and comparing feveral Particulars in it one with another, and with other Writings of the faid Dr. *Dee*, and confidering alfo the Hiftory of the Life, Actions and Eftate of the faid Author, fo far as I can be informed, I do conceive that the greateft part of the faid Book, efpecially all that which relates to the Spirits and Apparitions, together with their Names, Speeches, Shews, Noifes, Clothing, Actions, and the Prayers and Doxologies, &c. are all *Cryptography*; and that fome Parts alfo of that which feems to be a Journal of his Voyage and Travels into feveral Parts of *Germany*, are alfo *Cryptographical*; that is, that under thofe feigned Stories, which he there feems to relate as Matters of Fact, he hath concealed Relations of quite another thing; and that he made ufe of this way of abfconding it, that he might the more fecurely efcape difcovery, if he fhould fall under fufpition as to the true Defigns of his Travels, or that the fame fhould fall into the hands of any Spies, or fuch as might be imployed to betray him or his Intentions; conceiving the Inquifition that fhould be made, or Profecution, if difcovered, would be more gentle for a Pretended Enthufiaft, than for a real Spy.

What his Defigns or Bufinefs with the Emperor, the King of *Poland*, and others, was, is hard to determine, *i. e.* firft whether he were fent upon fome private Meffage by the Queen, or any of the then Minifters of State, to inquire into and difcover the fecret Defigns or Actions of that Court, is hard now to determine; but 'tis likely. For in his Apology he alledges, that the Lord Treafurer had by the Queen's Order written to the Arch Bifhop, to fignify that he went beyond Sea by her good Favour and Licenfe; and we find alfo that the Queen did fend feveral Letters and Meffengers to call him home, and that upon his Return the Queen received him kindly at *Richmond*, and that fhe ufed to call at his Houfe at *Mortlack*, and fhewed herfelf courteous to him upon all occafions, and againft *Chriftmas* 1590, fent him 200 Angels to keep his *Chriftmas*, and 100 Mark for the fame purpofe 1592. We find alfo, that in his Return for *England*, he prefented the Landgrave of *Heffe* with 12 *Hungarian* Horfes; which feems too much for any Man in a private Capacity. And when he returned, he left *Kelly* with the Emperor, who for feveral Years after kept Correfpondence with Dr. *Dee* here, which might poffibly continue to execute the fame Defign; *Kelly* being now grown Sir *Edward Kelly*, and the Emperor's Chymift. And in probability Dr. *Dee* might have fufficiently furnifhed him with *Cryptography* enough to fend what Intelligences he pleafed, without fufpition, which was eafily conceived under any other feigned Story. I will not determine whether this were his Bufinefs, I fay, or whether it might not be upon his own account, to fee if he could make a Fortune under the Emperor by means of Chymiftry, or Mathematicks, or Aftrology, or Mechanicks, all which I find by his Writings he was well verfed in, and efpecially in the Bufinefs of Opticks, and Perfpective and Mechanick Contrivances; an effect of which I conceive his Chryftal, or Angelical Stone, or *Chryftallum Sacratum*, as he terms it, to have been, for that it was of a confiderable bignefs, and was placed upon a Pedeftal, or Table, which he calls a Holy Table, which might contain the *Apparatus* to make Apparitions, when he had a mind to be feen in it, as likewife to produce Noifes and Voices, if there were occafion. All which might be done by Art, as has been fhewn, both formerly by *Roger Bacon*, and of late by the Echoing Head. He likewife pretended to the Philofophers Stone and *Elixir*, for which I take *Kelly* to be his Engine. I find alfo, that he affirms to have had 2 Ounces of the *Pouder of Projection*, which, as Mr. *Afhmole*, in his Notes upon the *Theatrum Chymicum*, publifhed by him 1652, fays, was fo rich in Virtue (being

One

One upon 272330) that they at firſt loſt much by making Projections for Trials, before they found out the true height of the Medicine. He was like-wiſe well verſed in *Cabaliſtical* Learning and *Cryptography*, as appears by the Title of a Treatiſe written by him upon that Subject and by that Book which he ſeems to have prized ſo much, and calls the Book of *Enoch*, which I take to be of no other uſe, than for *Cryptography* and *Cabaliſms.* I will not deter-mine, I ſay, whether his Deſign might not be by theſe and ſome other ſuch In-genuities (as particularly a Glaſs, which he mentions, *Pag.* 256. (the Secret of which he opened to Dr. *Curtz* the Emperor's Phyſician) for *Battering* in a dark Night, &c. which what he means by it I underſtand not ; but Dr. *Curtz* told him that Concluſion would be very acceptable to the Emperor. He had alſo written Six Books *deSpeculis Comburentibus,* Two Books of the *Aſtronomical Ring,* or *Ring Dial,* and two Books alſo of *Clockwork*) to find Entertainment and Encou-ragement from the Emperor. But I do rather conjecture, that he was employed by Queen for ſome private Affair of State, and that he made uſe of theſe his In-ventions, in order to obtain the freer and more unſuſpected Acceſs to the Empe-ror ; which having not ſucceeded as might have been expected, he was recalled, and returned into *England* in *Nov.* 1589. That a great part of this Treatiſe is *Cryp-tography,* I conceive is very probable from theſe and divers other Conſiderations : Firſt, for that he took ſuch care to preſerve the Book of *Enoch,* which I con-jecture to contain the Methods and Keys of what was concealed in this Book. Next, for that the Method and Manner thereof is ſo like to that of *Trithemius* his *Cryptography,* that I conceive (were it worth while) it would not be difficult to decipher a great part of it, by analogy thereunto. Now tho' at that time the Key or Method of that Book were not ſo well and commonly known, yet I do not doubt but this inquiſitive Man had got Knowledge of it in his Travels and Enquiries in *Germany,* poſſibly when he preſented his *Monas Hieroglyphica* to the Emperor *Maximilian* 1564 ; and poſſibly it might be upon the ſame ac-count, that he made choice of this way of Invocations and Revelations to con-ceal his Meaning, that I ſhewed before *Trithemius* had done in his. *Trithemius* alſo pretended to Revelation, as may be ſeen in the Hiſtory of his Life, tho' not ſo frequent as this Author has done in this Book, at leaſt if the Senſe thereof be underſtood literally ; but that I conceive to be nothing but the outward Form, Appearance or Dreſs of the Subſtance and Subject of the Book, which lay abſcon-ded from common Diſcovery under that Mask or Diſguiſe ; tho' yet I am apt to believe he had ſome artificial Contrivances to perform this alſo, when he ſaw cauſe. Thirdly, for that there are very many plain Inſtances of *Cryptography,* both by changing and putting ſome Letters for others, and Numbers for Letters, and Num-bers alſo for Words, and Tables for diſpoſing or placing Letters according to ſe-veral Orders and Methods, to be ſeen in the Book it ſelf : And the Book which he calls the Book of *Enoch,* ſeems to be nothing elſe. Beſides, the Words that he ſets down, as delivered by his Spirits, are many of them inarticulate, accord-ing to the commonly accepted Sounds or Pronunciation of thoſe Characters they are written with, and therefore were not put to ſignify thoſe Letters. It would be too long to give Inſtances out of the Book it ſelf of theſe Particulars, and 'tis needleſs, ſince they are ſo very many and frequent in every part of the Book. He hath likewiſe divers Polygonal Figures, as I conceive, for the ſame purpoſe, and many other ſuch Indications of *Cryptography.*

And to conclude for the preſent, any one that does without prejudice peruſe the *Libri Myſtici Apertorii Cracovienſis Sabbatici,* pag. 115. will ſee a hundred Arguments to convince him of the Probability, if not Certainty of this my Con-jecture : And ſome other time I ſhall give ſome other Arguments, which may poſſibly give fuller Satisfaction. But I would not detain too long upon this Subject.

Out of the Theatrum Chemicum Britannicum, *collected into one Volume,*
with Annotations.   By Elias Afhmole *Efq;* London, *printed* 1692, 4to.

PAG. 480. [Mr. *Afhmole's* Notes.] As touching Dr. *Dee*, he chiefly bent his
Studies to the Mathematicks, in all Parts of which he was an abfolute
and perfect Mafter ; witnefs his Mathematical Preface to *Euclid's Elements*,
wherein are enumerated many Arts of him wholly invented (by Name, Definition, Property and Ufe) more than either the *Grecian* or *Roman* Mathematicians have left to our Knowledge ; with divers Annotations and Inventions Mathematical added in fundry places of the faid Book, together with feveral Pieces
of Navigation Perfpective, and other rare Mathematical Works of his in Ma-
nufcript.

His Epiftle prefixed to *John Field's Ephemerides* 1557. de U*fu Globi Cæleftis*,
to *Edw.* 6. *de Nubium, Solis, Lunæ, & reliquorum Planetarum, &c. Diftantiis,
&c.* to *Edw.* 6. *Aftronomical and Logiftical* Canons to calculate *Ephemerides* by ;
de Stella admiranda in Caffiopeæ Afterifmo ; an Advice and Difcourfe about Re-
formation of the Vulgar Year ; fpeak him a Learned *Aftronomer.*

Laftly, He was a good *Aftrologian*, and a ftudious Philofopher : His 300
Aftrological Aphorifms ; his 120 Aphorifms *de preftantioribus quibufdam Naturæ
Virtutibus ;· Monas Hieroglyphica* ; *Speculum Unitatis* (being an Apology for
our famous Friar *Bacon*) ; his *Cabbalæ Hebraicæ Compendiofa Tabula*, with many
others, afford no fmall Evidence to the World.

All which, and many more in feveral kinds of Learning, as Hiftory, Heral-
dry, *&c.* written by him before the Year 1583. Some time he beftowed in Vulgar *Chymiftry*, and was therein Mafter of divers Secrets ; amongft others he
(*Dec.* 28. 1519.) revealed to one *Roger Cook*, the great Secret of the *Elixir* (as
he called it) of the Salt of Metals, the Projection whereof was one upon a
hundred.   His great Ability in *Aftrology*, and the more fecret Parts of Learning
(to which he had a ftrong Propenfity and unwearied Phanfy) drew from the En-
vious and Vulgar, many rafh, hard, and lying Scandals upon his moft honeft
and juftifiable Philofophical Studies, and many times forced him, out of the
Bitternefs of his Soul (which was even crucified with the Malice of impudent
Tongues) moft ferioufly and fervently to apologize : Nor-could he enjoy Tran-
quility in his Studies, but was oft difquieted and vexed with the fower Difpofitions of fuch as fcandalized moft injurioufly both him and them : Infomuch
that (1581) the Year he went beyond Sea, his Library was feized on, wherein
were 4000 Books, 700 of them Manufcripts. (*A Caveat for all Ingenious and
Eminent Philofophers to be more wife than to keep any dear or excellent Books in
their own Houfes.*)   And 'tis moft probable that at this time his *Speculum Unitatis* might fall into fome Hands that would never fince fuffer it to fee Light ;
which might occafion the Learned *Selden* to fay [in the Preface to *Hopton's Con-
cordance*] this Apology was long fince promifed by him, but intimating it was
never writ. *Anno* 1592, [*Novemb.* 9.] Mr. Secretary *Walfingham*, and Sir *Tho.
George*, were fent to his then Dwelling houfe at *Mortlack* (by virtue of a Com-
miffion) to underftand the Matter and Caufes for which his Studies were fcandalized ; and for fome things in the like nature, was he neceffitated to fend his
Apologetical Letter to the Arch-Bifhop of *Canterbury.*

Thefe kind of Perfecutions were ftill multiplied upon him, and he fometimes
perfonally aggrieved by them : For about the Year 1594, he was under fome
Reftraint, which occafioned him to write to the Lady *Scudamore* [*Oct.* 28. 1594.]
to move the Queen, that either he might declare his Cafe to the Body of the
Council, or elfe under the Broad Seal have Liberty to go freely where he pleafed.

——'Tis generally reported, that Dr. *Dee* and Sir *Edward Kelly* were fo
ftrangely fortunate, as to find a very large Quantity of the *Elixir* in fome Parts
of the Ruins of *Glaftenbury* Abby, which was fo incredibly rich in Virtue (being one upon 272330) that they loft much in making Projection by way of
Trials, before they found out the true height of the Medicine.   And no fooner

were they Mafters of this Treafure, then they refolved to travel into foreign Parts, when falling into acquaintance with one *Albertus Lasky*, a *Polonian* Prince, which came into *England* in the beginning of *May* 1583, on the 21ft of *September* following, they, their Wives, Children and Families, went beyond Sea with the faid Prince. And whether they found it at *Glaftenbury*, as is aforefaid, or however elfe they came by it, 'tis certain they had it : For at *Trebona* in *Bohemia*, whither they were come to dwell [*Sept.* 4. 1586.] Sir *Edward Kelly* made Projection with one fmall Grain thereof [*Dec.* 9. 1586.] in proportion no bigger than the leaft Grain of Sand, upon one Ounce and a quarter of common *Mercury*, and it produced almoft an Ounce of moft pure Gold. This was done to gratify Mr. *Edward Garland* and his Brother *Francis*, and in their Prefence ; which *Edward* was lately come to *Trebona*, being fent thither to Dr. *Dee* from the Emperor of *Mofcovia*, according to fome Articles before brought by one *Thomas Symkinfon*. I alfo find this Note of Dr. *Dee's*, *Jan.* 9. 1586. *Donum Dei* 2 Ounces, *E.K.* Moreover, nearer the later *Teftimony*, I have received it from a credible Perfon, that one *Broomfield* and *Alexander Roberts* told him, they had often feen Sir *Edward Kelly* make Projection, and in particular upon a Piece of Metal cut out of a Warming-pan, and without Sir *Edward's* touching or handling it, or melting the Metal, only warming it in the Fire, the *Elixir* being put thereon, it was tranfmuted into pure Silver. The Warming-pan, and this Piece of it, was fent to Queen *Elizabeth* by her Ambaffador, who then lay at *Prague*, that by fitting the Piece into the Place from whence it was cut out, it might exactly appear to be once part of that Warming-pan. The aforefaid Perfon hath likewife feen in the hands of one Mr. *Frye* and *Scroop*, Rings of Sir *Edward Kelly's* Gold, the Fafhion of which was only Gold Wire twifted thrice about the Finger ; and of thefe fafhioned Rings he gave away to the value of 4000 *l.* at the Marriage of one of his Servant Maids. This was highly generous ; but to fay truth, he was openly profufe beyond the modeft Limits of a fober Philofopher.

During their abode at *Trebona* they try'd many Chymical Experiments, to fee whether they could make that Jewel they poffeft ; (The particular Account of their Operations I need not here relate.) yet I cannot hear that ever they accomplifht any thing : Only I find the 27th of *April* noted by Dr. *Dee* with feveral Expreffions of Joy and Gladnefs, as, *Hæc eft Dies quam fecit Dominus* : Again, *Mifericordia Dei Magna* ; and laftly, *Omne, quod vivit, laudet Dominum.* And to teftify what they meant, he writes upon the 30th Day following, *Mr.* Edward Kelly *did open the Great Secret to me, God be thanked.* While they lived at *Trebona*, Sir *Edward Kelly* went divers times to *Prague*, and the 15th of *Jan.* 1587, he went into *Poland*, but returned the 9th of *February* after. And 'tis probable thefe Journies were made in queft after fome famous Chymifts. Things were not carried here fo privately, but Queen *Elizabeth* had notice given her of their Actions ; whereupon fhe ufed feveral means by Letters and Meffages to invite them back into *England*, where it was believed fhe had fo far prevailed, that Mr. *Symkinfon* and Mr. *Francis Garland's* Brother *Robert* coming from *England* to *Trebona* [*Dec.* 8. 1587.] fuppofed they had been ready to come over to *England* upon the Queen's Letters formerly fent them. And tho' Sir *Edward Kelly* ftaid behind, yet Dr. *Dee* left *Trebona* [*May* 1. 1589.] and came for *England*. But whether occafioned by fome Unkindnefs received from Sir *Edw. Kelly*, or falling out of their Wives, or Sollicitation of Queen *Elizabeth*, or all of thefe concurring, I am not yet certain. Not unlike but each of thefe might contribute to their Separation. For that there was fome great and wonderful Unkindnefs paft from Sir *Edward Kelly*, appears by his fending for Dr. *Dee*, the beginning of *Jan.* 1588, under fhew of Reconciliation, and difcovering more than ordinary Intimacy and Complacency about that time ; which fair Shews the Good Doctor notes with thefe Prayers, *God lead his Heart to all Charity and Brotherly Love.* As alfo Letters fent by Dr. *Dee* to Sir *Edward Kelly* and his Wife the end of *March* following, requiring at their hands mutual Charity ; which [*May* 9.] after, upon Mrs. *Kelly's* receiving the Sacrament, fhe gave her Hand to Dr. *Dee* and his Wife in token of Charity. But it feems things were not cordial, but only outward : For the 6th of *September* following, the Lord Chancellor coming to *Trebona*, the Rancour and Diffimulation was more evident to him, and it feems grew up to a greater height than he could bear. And thereupon he thought wifely to avoid the further Danger by leaving *Germany*, which occasioned him [*Jan.* 4. 1589.] to deliver to Sir *Edward Kelly* the Powder, the Books, the Glass, with some other things, and thereupon received his Discharge in Writing under his Hand and Seal. While these Discontents continued, several Letters past between Queen *Elizabeth* and Dr. *Dee*, whereby perhaps he might promise to return. At length it so fell out, that he [*March* 1. 1589.] left *Trebona*, and took his Journy for *England*. The 9th of *April* he came to *Breame*, and had not staid there 3 Days, but the Landgrave of *Hesse* sent Letters of civil Complements to him, and within 3 Days after Dr. *Dee* presented him with his 12 *Hungarian* Horses, that he bought at *Prague* for his Journy. Here (*June* 27. 1589.) the Famous *Hermetick* Philosopher, Dr. *Henric Kunrath* of *Hamburgh* came to visit him. The 16th of *Novemb.* he went thence to *Stade*, where he met with Mr. *Edward Dyer* going Embassador for *Denmark*, who the Year before had been at *Trebona*, and carried back Letters from the Doctor to Queen *Elizabeth*. He was a great Correspondent of Dr. *Dee's*, and as earnest a Searcher after the Stone. The 23d of *Nov.* following he arriv'd at *Gravesend*, having been out of *England* 6 Years, 2 Months, and 2 Days ; and the 9th of *Dec.* presented himself to the Queen at *Richmond*, where he was favoured with a kind Reception.

Being settled again at *Mortlack*, the Queen used to call at his House to visit him, and shewed her self very courteous to him upon all occasions. Against *Christmas* 1590, she sent him 200 Angels wherewith to keep his *Christmas*, and 100 Marks against *Christmas* 1592. She likewise sent him word by Mr. *Thomas Candish*, to do what he would in Alchymy and Philosophy, and none should controul or molest him : And not unlike, by the Queen's Example, divers Personages of Honour at Court frequented his Company, and sent him many Gifts from time to time ; amongst others Sir *Tho. Jones* most nobly offer'd him his Castle of *Emlin* in *Wales* to dwell in free with all Accommodations.

His Favour was fair at Court, the Queen her self bad him find out something for her to bestow ; yet all the Preferment he gained was (*Dec.* 8. 1594.) the Grant of the *Chancellorship* of St. *Paul's* ; and the 27th of *May* 1595, his Patent past the Great Seal for the *Wardenship* of *Manchester*, whither he, his Wife, Children and Family came the 14th of *Feb.* 1596. and the 20th Day following was installed, and in this Wardenship, (wherein he had the Unhappiness to be often vext with the turbulent Fellows of that College) died, deserving the Commendation of all Learned and Ingenious Scholars. and to be remembred for his remarkable Abilities.

After Dr. *Dee* came to *England*, as is before remembred, Correspondence was still maintained between him and Sir *Edward Kelly*, in Letters sent by Mr. *Francis Garland* and others (and some Expectancy of Sir *Edward's* coming over (*Dec.* 23. 1589.) Mr. *Thomas Kelly* his Brother putting the Doctor in hopes thereof likewise.) But at length Sir *Edward* was clapt up close Prisoner by the Emperor (for he had so unwarily and openly managed the Secret, that it had given the Emperor occasion to carry a strict eye over all his Actions, out of a desire to be Sharer with him in his good Fortune) yet it seems the Emperor set him at Liberty (*Nov.* 4. 1593.) and Dr. *Dee* had notice of it the 5th of *December* after. And tho' he began to grow into the Emperor's Favour, in hopes to be entertained into his Service (for so he certify'd Dr. *Dee* by Letters in *August* 1595.) nevertheless he was clapt up again into Prison, and attempting to make his Escape out of a high Window, by the tearing of his Sheets, which were ty'd together to let him down, he being a weighty Man, fell and broke his Leg, and thereof died. This is one Report of his Death. Others there are, but Dr. *Dee* mentions none at all, of the manner thereof, only this : *Nov.* 25. 1595. *News that Sir E. K. was slain.*

Note, *That Two Presses being employed in Printing these Tracts, has caused a Chasme in the Pages.*

Lectures and Discourses

OF

EARTHQUAKES,

AND

Subterraneous Eruptions.

EXPLICATING

The Causes of the Rugged and Uneven Face of the EARTH;

AND

What Reasons may be given for the frequent finding of Shells and other Sea and Land Petrified Substances, scattered over the whole Terrestrial Superficies.

THE Treatise our Author mentions in the beginning of this Discourse I have not had the happiness to meet with among his Papers; possibly he might formerly have read some Discourses upon these Subjects, but if so they are lost, as I am satisfied some other valuable Papers are; if not, I know not well what he means, except some Hints in his Lectures of Light, and at the end of his Tract of Comets; Tho' I am rather of Opinion some of the following Papers were wrote before that of Comets: But of this Matter I can affirm nothing positively. This Discourse more particularly relates to the rugged and unequal appearance of the Earth's Surface, which he here endeavours to solve by successive Earthquakes and Inundations. I shall not (were I able) attempt to prepossess the Reader, nor longer detain him from the Authors own Discourses; only desire it may be observed, that the following Papers were read at several distinct times to the Royal Society, and upon that Account not so methodically digested as they would have been had they been published by himself.

R. W.

A Discourse of Earthquakes.

The Introduction to the following Discourse, giving some account of its Design.

I Have formerly endeavour'd to explain several Observations I had made concerning the Figure, Form, Position, Distance, Order, Motions and Operations of the Celestial Bodies, both as to themselves, and one with another, and likewise with respect to the Body of the *Earth* on which we inhabit. But conceiving it may more nearly concern us to know more particularly the Constitution, Figure, Magnitude and Properties of the Body of the *Earth* itself, and of its several constituent Parts, I have endeavour'd to collect such Observations and Natural Histories of others, as may serve to give some Light toward the making a compleat Discovery of them, so far as the Power, Faculties, Organs, and other helps that Nature has furnish'd Man with, may assist us in performing and perfecting thereof.

The Subject is large, as extending as far as the whole Bulk included within the utmost limits of the Atmosphere: And 'tis not less copious and repleat with variety, as containing all the several Parts and Substances included within those Limits, namely, The aerial, watery and earthy Parts thereof, whether Superficial or Subterraneous, whether Exposed or Absconded, whether Supraterraneal, Superterraneal, or Subterraneal, whether Elemental or Organical, Animate or Inanimate, and all the Species and Kinds of them, and all the constituent Parts of them, and the Composits constituted of them; of which also there will fall under Consideration, the Artificial as well as the Natural Causes and Powers effective of things; then their Generation, Production, Augmentation, Perfection, Vertue, Power, Activity, Operation, Effect, Conservation, Duration, Declination, Destruction, Corruption, Transformation, and in one word, the motion or progression of Nature sensibly exprest, or any other ways discernable in each of those Species. Which Subject, if we consider as it is thus represented, doth look very like an Impossibility to be undertaken even by the whole World, to be gone through within an Age, much less to be undertaken by any particular Society, or a small number of Men. The number of Natural Histories, Observations, Experiments, Calculations, Comparisons, Deductions and Demonstrations necessary thereunto, seeming to be incomprehensive and numberless: And therefore a vain Attempt, and not to be thought of till after some Ages past in making Collections of Materials for so great a Building, and the employing a vast number of Hands in making this Preparation; and those of several sorts, such as Readers of History, Criticks, Rangers and Namesetters of Things, Observers and Watchers of several Appearances, and Progressions of Natural Operations and Perfections, Collectors of curious Productions, Experimenters and Examiners of Things by several Means and several Methods and Instruments, as by Fire, by Frost, by Menstruums, by Mixtures, by Digestions, Putrefactions, Fermentations and Petrifactions, by Grindings, Brusings, Weighings and Measuring, Pressing and Condensing, Dilating and Expanding, Dissecting, Separating and Dividing, Sifting and Streining; by viewing with Glasses and Microscopes, Smelling, Tasting, Feeling, and various other ways of Torturing and Wracking of Natural Bodies, to find out the Truth or the real Effect as it is in its Constitution or State of Being.

To these may be added Registers or Compilers, such as shall Record and Express in proper Terms these Collections; add to these Examiners and Rangers of Things, such as shall distinguish and marshal them into proper Classes, and denote their Excellencies or Gradations of differing Kinds, their Perfections or Defects, what are Compleat, and what Defective, and to be repeated, and the like.

So that we see the Subject of this Enquiry is very copious and large, and will afford Work enough for every Well-willer to employ his Head and Hands, to contribute towards the providing Materials for so large a Fabrick and Structure, as the great quantity of Materials to be collected do seem to denote. However, 'tis possible that a much less number may serve the turn, if fitly qualified and done with Method and Design, and it may be much better and easier.

When this mighty Collection is made, what will be the use of so great a Pile? Where will be found the Architect that shall contrive and raise the Superstructure that is to be made of them, that shall fit every one for its proper use? Till which be found, they will indeed be but a heap of Confusion. Who shall find out the Experiments, the Observations, and other Remarks, fit for this or that Theory? One Stone is too thick, or too thin, too broad, or too narrow, not of a due colour, or hardness, or grain, to suit with the Design, or with some other that are duly scapled for the purpose: This Piece of Timber is not of a right Kind, not of a sufficient Driness and Seasoning, not of a due length and bigness, but wants its Scantlings, or is of an ill Shape for such a purpose, or was not fell'd in a due time: 'Tis Sap-rotten, or Wind-shaken, or rotten at Heart, or too frow, and the like, for the purpose for which 'tis wanted.

The Use of pre-design'd Theories, and Modules of Enquiry.

I mention this, to hint only by the by, that there may be use of Method in the collecting of Materials, as well as in the use of them, and to shew that there may be made a Provision too great, as well as too little, that there ought to be some End and Aim, some pre-design'd Module and Theory, some Purpose in our Experiments, and more particular observing of such Circumstances as are proper for that Design. And though this Honourable Society have hitherto seem'd to avoid and prohibit pre-conceived Theories and Deductions from particular, and seemingly accidental Experiments; yet I humbly conceive, that such, if knowingly and judiciously made, are Matters of the greatest Importance, as giving a Characteristick of the Aim, Use, and Significancy thereof; and without which, many, and possibly the most considerable Particulars, are passed over without Regard and Observation. The most part of Mankind are taken with the Prettiness or the Strangeness of the Phænomena, and generally neglect the common and the most obvious; whereas in truth, for the most part, they are the most considerable. And the greatest part of the Productions of Nature are to be seen every where, and by every one, though, for the most part, not heeded or regarded, because they are so common. I could wish therefore that the Information of Experiments might be more respected, than either the Novelty, the Surprizingness, the Pomp, and Appearances of them.

Of figured Stones.

The obviousness and easiness of knowing many Things in Nature, has been the Cause of their being neglected, even by the more diligent and curious; which nevertheless, if well examined, do very often contain Informations of the greatest value. It has been generally noted by common, as well as inquisitive, Persons, that divers Stones have been found, formed into the Shapes of Fishes, Shells, Fruits, Leaves, Wood, Barks, and other Vegetable and Animal Substances: We commonly know some of them exactly resembling the Shape of Things we commonly find (as the Chymists speak) in the Vegetable or Animal Kingdom; others of them indeed bearing some kind of Similitude, and agreeing in many Circumstances, but yet not exactly figured like any other thing in Nature; and yet of so curious a Shape, that they easily raise both the Attention and Wonder, even of those that are less inquisitive. Of these beautifully shaped Bodies I have observed two sorts: First, some more properly natural, such as have their Figures peculiar to their Substances: Others more improperly so, that is, such as seem to receive their Shape from an external and accidental Mould.

Of Chrystals, and the like Stones, shot into Figures.

Of the first sort, are all those curiously figured Bodies of Salts, Talks, Spars, Crystals, Diamonds, Rubies, Amethysts, Ores, and divers other Mineral Substances, wherewith the World is adorned and enriched; which I at present omit to describe, as reserving them for a Second Part, they seeming to be, as it were, the Elemental Figures, or the *A B C* of Nature's working,

rectly exhibiting the Impressions of the several Holes, Sutures, and Cracks that appear upon the top of one of these Stones. The 5th and 6th Figures represent another Helmet-stone of the same kind with the former, but less look'd upon against the bottom and side, exhibiting the Impressions of the several Holes, Sutures, and Cracks, that were in the imprinting Shell from which these Stones receiv'd their Shape: These were both of a kind of grey Flint. The 7th Figure represents the bottom of another sort of Helmet-stone, where the Vents *a* and *b* are placed in another manner, than they were in the 1st, 2d, 3d, or 5th Figures. The 8th and 9th Figures represent the bottom and top of another sort of Helmet-stone, which seems to be the filling up of a kind of *Echini*-shell, very like to those found in *Devonshire* and *Cornwal,* one of which I have delineated in the 10th Figure: This last kind' was of Chalk. I have several other sorts, which I have not now time to delineate, some of transparent Pebbles, some of Marble, some of a Stone as hard as *Portland,* some of black, red, grey, and other Flints, some of Coperas-stone, some of other kinds of Stone, none of Spar. I would to this have added the Description of a great Variety of *Echini*-shells, divers of which I have by me in the Repository of the Royal Society, and others that I have met with elsewhere, but that I shall do it elsewhere: They are indeed almost infinite, but all concur in these Properties which all Helmet-stones likewise have. First, that they are distinguish'd into five Parts, by Sutures, Ribs, and Furrows. Secondly, that they have two Vent-holes: They have divers of them also little Edges, being the Impressions of the Sutures, and divers little rows of Pins, being the Impressions of the small Holes; and any one that will diligently and impartially examine both the Stones and the Shells, and compare the one with the other, will, I can assure him, find greater reason to perswade him of the Truth of my Position, than any I have yet urged, or can well produce in Words; no Perswasions being more prevalent than those which these dumb Witnesses do insinuate.

TABLE IV.

THE Figures of this and the next Table were left undescribed by Dr. Hooke, which Defect I have endeavoured to supply in some measure. Fig 1st and 2d represent a sort of Shell, of which I think we have no Species now described; they are very thick and heavy: Of this sort I found one upon the Sand, on the side of the Severn about 8 or 10 Miles from Glouceſter; it was a perfect Stone. *'Tis figured by Dr. Plott, in his Natural History of Oxfordshire; Tab. 4. Fig. 1.* Fig. the 3d, another unuſual shaped Stone exceeding thick and heavy. I know not what the 4th is, it shews something like the Spine of some Fish. Of the 5th Figure I have seen several, and is well represented; they call them in that Country Screw-stones. *The rest of the Figures in this Table shew several sorts of Sharks-teeth, except the 18th and 19th, which seem to be the Shells of some Fish. The 10th Figure shews the Make of the inside of one of those long Teeth, if they are so, of which I think not many now doubt; in this the manner of the Fibres radiating from the Center, is very conspicuous. † At the Baſis of the 8th Figure, is observable the very great Cavity, as likewise the largeneſs of it. The 14th Figure represents one of thi largeſt Gloſſopetræ that has been ſeen. Upon the 16th and 17th Figure Dr. Hooke makes this Remark, that there are 220 of them in the Fishes Mouth. What the 15th is I know not, except it be a petrify'd Grinder bedded in Stone.* † *'Tis true these have by former Writers been thought Lapides ſui generis, and call'd Belemnites. I shall wave the Diſpute.*

TABLE. V.

FIGURE the 1st, the petrified Grinder of some large Animal, possibly of a Whale or Elephant. Dr. Grew, in his Muſeum, ſays of a Sea-Animal. Fig. 2. a petrify'd Crab, very much reſembling the Fish it ſelf. Figure the 3d, 4th, 5th, 6th, 7th, 8th, and 9th, I take to be Pieces of petrify'd Wood, tho' I know they have been otherwiſe eſteem'd by some Writers. Whether the 14th may not be the same, I will not determine. The 10th, 11th, 12th, and 13th, I take to be some sorts of petrify'd Fruits, or poſſibly some of them Seed-veſſels. The 15th and 16th Figures are the Aſtroites or Star-stones, of which one is given

Cccc   ſeparate

separate in the 16*th. Thefe in our Author's Opinion were Pieces broken off from the numerous Legs of that fort of Star-fifh, of which one was many Years fince fent from* New England, *if I miftake not, and is now in the Society's Repofitory : It is de-ſcribed in the Philoſophical Tranſactions, publiſh'd by Mr.* Oldenburg *by the Name* Philoſ.Tranſ. *of* Piſcis Echino-ſtellaris Viſci formis. *The* 17*th Figure I take for a fort of* N.50.p.1153. Fungus *petrify'd.*

　　It is a great Misfortune that the Deſcriptions of theſe two Tables are wanting a-mongſt the Papers, if they were ever drawn up, which I ſomewhat queſtion ; for the Figures were not number'd : For had he done it himſelf, he would have made ſe-veral very conſiderable Remarks ; which if I could, is not ſo proper for me to at-tempt ; nor do I know any thing of the Hiſtory concerning the Places where they were found, or the like : However I judged it not convenient they ſhould be loſt ; and therefore ordered them to be graved, and have ventured this imperfect Deſcrip-tion. What follows next, is the Abſtract of a Letter I ſent him from Briſtol, 1687.

R. W.

Briſtol, Aug.
17. 1687.

S I R,

IN anſwer to ſome of your Enquiries, as to the *Cornua Ammonis,* and other Shell-like Stones found about *Keinſham*, and other Places, I ſhall give you this ſhort Information of my Diſcoveries, and preſent you with the Draughts of ſome I happen'd to meet with there, and in other Places not very far diſtant, that is, in Part of *Gloucester* and *Somerſetſhire.*

　　The *Cornua Ammonis,* near *Keinſham,* lie moſt of them upon a little Hill, or riſing Ground, above *Keinſham*-Bridge ; the Place, as I take it, is about 18 Foot above the River : The River there runs half round the Foot of the Hill, where they lye very thick almoſt to touch each other, and are all of the large ſort bedded in an hard Rock or Stone ; ſome alſo I found near a Mile from thence in the Stone-walls of their Fields, and on the way in the Lanes ; and at *Stowey,* four or five Miles from *Keinſham,* I ſaw ſome Snake-ſtones, Oyſter, and Cockle-ſhells petrified and bedded in hard Stone, where is alſo a petri-fying Spring incruſtating the Moſs and Graſs, and all the wooden Troughs, by which it is conveyed with a ſtony Subſtance. Where they are not found faſtned to a Rock, I found them encompaſſed in a pretty large irregular Maſs of Stone, not ſandy, but rather like a whitiſh Clay harden'd, and theſe ſtony Maſſes bedded in a loamy kind of Earth ; in which ſoft Earth are alſo found Star-ſtones, and a ſort of petrified Cockle-ſhells, ſuch as Fig. 7. Tab. VI. I found none of the Snake-ſtones to have above 6 Turns, except one Mr. *Beaumont* ſhewed me of ſeven, and another amongſt Mr. *Cole*'s Rareties. But that which I eſteemed the greateſt Curioſity, was a large Stone of the true Shape and Figure of the common *Nautilus,* or Mother of Pearl-ſhell, which tho' but a part of the whole Shell, weighs about 30 pound : This I found in one of the dry Walls, near *Keinſham,* and not far from it another Piece of the ſame ; theſe are figured in the VIIth Table, Fig. 1, 2, 3, 4 ; and in theſe not only the Diaphragms are very viſible, but the Holes alſo in the middle of them, by which the Gut or String paſſes from one to another, in all reſpects anſwering to that of the *Nautilus*-ſhell ; which, I think, will evince this at leaſt to be a petrify'd Shell, tho' much larger than any of that kind that have been yet mention'd. Going down from *Mendip*-hills to *Okey*-hole, I found a ſmall Muſcle-ſhell petrify'd, on this the Shell was yet diſcoverable in ſome Places ; this is figured, Tab. VI. Fig. 1.

　　On the Face of the Rocks that are on the ſides of the *Avon,* not far from St. *Vincent*'s Rock, I found ſeveral wood-like Pieces of Stone ſtanding out a little from the Rock it ſelf ; ſome of which I have broke off, and have repre-ſented them in the Figures, Tab. VII. Fig. 5, 6, 7, and 8, and ſome ſuch like Bits of Wood in the Earth between the Layers of Stone unpetrify'd. But I ſhall at preſent detain you no longer, but for a more exact Information refer to the Figures themſelves ; which I can aſſure you are truly deſign'd, and are all Stones or Petrifactions, except the 6th Figure.

Tab.

Tab. VI. Fig. 1. reprefents two Views of a fort of Mufcle-fhell found near *Okey*-hole.

Fig. 2. a fort of Cockle, on this likewife part of the Shell was vifible.

Fig. 3. a Piece of a *Belemnites,* thefe are of the true bignefs.

Fig. 4. a large *Cornu-Ammonis,* about 18 Inches Diameter ; there are much larger to above 2 Foot, but this was one of the moft perfect and neat I could find ; on this the curious Foliage (as I may call it) of the Diaphragms was very vifible, as is reprefented in the Figure, and near the Center feveral fmall Shells petrify'd : This I had from *Keinfham.*

Fig. 5. I know not what to make of, except it be one joint of the Spine of the Back of fome Fifh ; fomething like it I have feen in the Backs of Salmons.

Fig. 6. a fort of *Nautilus*-fhell not petrify'd, being ftill vifibly a Shell broken, fqueezed and flatted to the thicknefs of an Half-crown ; the feveral Fragments were each roundifh, and ftuck together with a kind of blewifh Clay. This was given me by Mr. *Cole,* who told me there had been feveral of them found amongft the Rocks and Stones in Quarries.

Fig. 7. another fort of Mufcle or Cockle ; thefe are frequently found about *Briftol,* particularly on the top of St. *Michael's* Hill on the Road, and near the Gallows bedded in the Earth, not Stone, but are themfelves an hard Stone, and very thick and ftrong.

Fig. 8. a Piece of a broken *Cornu-Ammonis,* in which feveral of the Diaphragms are very vifible, the hollows not being fill'd up, but fhot on the fides with a fort of flinty, hard, and tranfparent Spar.

Fig. 9. a fmall *Cornu-Ammonis* of but three Turns, yet feems perfect and unbroken ; I know not whether it has any Diaphragms.

TABLE VII.

FIG. 1. fhews the large Stone of the Common Nautilus-fhape, in which *d d d d* fhews the Diaphragms to be feen on the outfide of the Stone ; as far as *f* is the larger Piece, which weigh'd near 30 Pound ; from *f* to *g* is a leffer Piece, in which alfo the Diaphragms are vifible on the outfide *d d d,* and likewife on the infide, where the Piece was broken crofs, fome of the Diaphragms appear ; as at *a a a, e e,* fhews part of the Shell ftill fticking to the outfide : *i i i* is a fmall Piece of the Center of the Stone, being only as much as makes 3 Diaphragms ; the prick'd Lines *b* and *c* fhew where the Stone fhould have been to have made it perfect : This is drawn not a quarter fo large as the Stone it felf.

Fig. 2. another Piece of the fame fort found at another Place in *d d d,* are the Diaphragms, *e* a part of the Shell remaining : Thefe fhelly Parts are of a different Subftance from the reft.

Fig. 3. a Piece of the fame Stone near the Center, with the leffer part *c* ; thefe have at *a* and *c* a protuberant part, being the hole of the Diaphragm.

Fig. 4. a Piece taken off from the former, in which at *a* and *c* are two fmall Cavities, anfwering the Protuberances *a* and *c* in the third Figure ; *e* the edge of the thin Shell which covers all the part from *e* to *a.*

Fig. 5, 6, 7, 8, Pieces of Stone refembling Wood petrify'd, of which the 6th is of feveral fmall Bits fticking to the hard Stone ; this I broke off from the Rock ; as alfo the 7th, wherein the crofs Lines fhew the ends of the long Fibres cut aflope ; this exactly refembled a fmall Stick cut flanting. In the middles of the 5th and 7th was a Cavity in the place of the Pith. The middle of the 8th was filled with a ftony Concretion very hard, as were all thefe Pieces, but fomething different from the reft of the Stone.

Yours, R. W.

Thefe, and the like Shapes, becaufe many of them are curious, have fo far wrought on fome Men, that they have endeavoured to give us an Explication of the manner of their Formation ; in doing of which they have fo far rambled from the true and genuine Caufe of them, that they have left the Matter much more difficult than they found it. Amongft the reft, *Gaffarel,* a
French

French Writer, seems not the least mistaken, who has transferr'd them over to the Confirmation, as he thinks, of his Astrological and Magical Fancy; and thinks that as they were produced from some extraordinary Celestial Influence, and that the Aspects and Positions of the fix'd Stars and Planets conduc'd to their Generation, so that they also have in them a secret Vertue whereby they do at a distance work Miracles on things of the like Shape. But these, as fantastical and groundless, I shall not spend time on at present to refute, nor on the Conjectures and Hypotheses of divers others; which though perhaps somewhat more tolerable than that I last recited, yet most of them have recourse to some vegetative or plastick Vertue inherent in the Parts of the Earth where they were made, or in the very parcels of which they consist, which, to me, seems not at all consonant to the other workings of Nature; for those more curiously carved and beautiful Forms are usually bestow'd on some vegetable or animal Body. But my Business at present shall not be so much to confute others Conjectures, as to make probable some of my own; which tho' at the first hearing they may seem somewhat paradoxical, yet if the Reasons that have induced me thereunto be well consider'd and weigh'd, I hope at least they may seem possible, if not more than a little probable.

Enumeration of the Phenomena.
The particular Productions of this kind that I have taken notice of my self in my own Enquiries, and which I find dispersed up and down in the Writing of others, may be reduced under some one or other of these General Heads or Propositions.

1.   First, That there are found in most Countries of the Earth, and even in such where it is somewhat difficult to imagine (by reason of their vast distance from the Sea or Waters how they should come there) great quantities of Bodies resembling both in Substance and Shape the Shells of divers sorts of Shell-fishes; and many of them so exactly, that any one that knew not whence they came, would without the least scruple firmly believe them to be the Shells of such Fishes: But being found in Places so unlikely to have produced them, and not conceiving how else they should come there, they are generally believed to be real Stones form'd into these Shapes, either by some plastick Vertue inherent in those Parts of the Earth, which is extravagant enough, or else by some Celestial Influence or Aspect of the Planets operating at a distance upon the yielding Matter of the Parts of the Earth, which is much more extravagant. Of this kind are all those several sorts of Oyster-shells, Cockle-shells, Muscle-shells, Periwinkle-shells, and the like, which are found in *England, France, Spain, Italy, Germany, Norway, Russia, Asia* and *Africa*, and divers other Places; of which I have very good Testimonies from Authors of good Credit.

2.   Secondly, That there often have been, and are still daily found in other Parts of the Earth buried below the present Surface thereof divers sorts of Bodies, besides such as I newly mention'd, resembling both in Shape, Substance, and other Proprieties, the Parts of Vegetables, having the perfect Rind or Bark, Pith, Pores, Roots, Branches, Gums, and other constituent Parts of Wood, though in another posture, lying for the most part Horizontal, and sometimes inverted, and much differing from that of the like Vegetables when growing, and wanting also, for the most part, the Leaves, smaller Roots and Branches, the Flower and Fruit, and the like smaller Parts, which are common to Trees of that kind; of which sort is the *Lignum Fossile*, which is found in divers Parts of *England, Scotland, Ireland*, and divers Parts of *Italy, Germany*, the *Low Countries*, and indeed almost in every Country of the World.

3.   Thirdly, That there are often found in divers other Parts of the Earth, Bodies resembling the whole Bodies of Fishes, and other Animals and Vegetables, or the Parts of them, which are of a much less permanent Nature than the Shells abovemention'd, such as Fruits, Leaves, Barks, Woods, Roots, Mushrooms, Bones, Hoofs, Claws, Horns, Teeth, &c. but in all other Proprieties
prieties

prieties of their Subſtance, ſave their Shape, are perfect Stones, Clays, or Earths, and ſeem to have nothing at all of Figure in the inward Parts of them. Of this kind are thoſe, commonly call'd Thunder-bolts, Helmet-ſtones, Serpentine-ſtones, or Snake-ſtones, Rams-horns, Brain-ſtones, Star-ſtones, Screw-ſtones, Wheel-ſtones, and the like.

Fourthly, That the Parts of the Earth in which theſe kinds have been found, are ſome of them ſome hundred of Miles diſtant from any Sea, as in ſeveral of the Hills of *Hungary*, the Mountain *Taurus*, the *Alpes*, &c.

4.

Fifthly, That divers of thoſe Parts are many Scores, nay, ſome many Hundreds of Fathoms above the Level of the Surface of the next adjoining Sea, there having been found of them on ſome of the moſt Inland, and on ſome of the higheſt Mountains in the World.

5.

Sixthly, That divers other Parts where theſe Subſtances have been found, are many Fathoms below the Level both of the Surface of the next adjoining Sea, and of the Surface of the Earth itſelf, they having been found buried in the bottoms of ſome of the deepeſt Mines and Wells, and incloſed in ſome of the hardeſt Rocks and tougheſt Metals. Of this we have continual Inſtances in the deapeſt Lead and Tin-mines, and a particular Inſtance in the Well dug in *Amſterdam*, where at the Depth of 99 Foot was found a Layer of Sea-ſhells mixed with Sand of 4 Foot thickneſs, after the Diggers had paſt through 7 Foot of Garden-mould, 9 Foot more of black Peat, 9 Foot more of ſoft Clay, 8 of Sand, 4 of Earth, 10 of Potters-clay, 4 more of Earth, 10 Foot more of Sand, upon which the Stakes or Piles of the *Amſterdam* Houſes reſt; then 2 Foot more of Potters-clay, and 4 of white Gravel, 5 of dry Earth, 1 of mix'd, 14 of Sand, 3 of a Sandy Clay, and 5 more of Potters-clay mix'd with Sand. Now below this Layer of Shells immediately joining to it, was a Bed of Potters-clay of no leſs than 102 Foot thick; but of this more hereafter.

6.

Seventhly, That there are often found in the midſt of the Bodies of very hard and cloſe Stone, ſuch as Marbles, Flints, *Portland*, and Purbeck-ſtone, &c. which lye upon, or very near to the Surface of the Earth, great quantities of theſe kind of figured Bodies or Shells, and that there are many of ſuch Stones which ſeem to be made of nothing elſe.

7.

Theſe Phænomena, as they have hitherto much puzled all Natural Hiſtorians and Philoſophers to give an Account of them, ſo in truth are they in themſelves ſo really wonderful, that 'tis not eaſie without making multitudes of Obſervations, and comparing them very diligently with the Hiſtories and Experiments that have been already made, to fix upon a plauſible Solution of them. For as on the one ſide, it ſeems very difficult to imagine that Nature formed all theſe curious Bodies for no other End, than only to play the Mimick in the Mineral Kingdom, and only to imitate what ſhe had done for ſome more noble End, and in a greater Perfection in the Vegetable and Animal King-doms; and the ſtricteſt Survey that I have made both of the Bodies them-ſelves, and of the Circumſtances obvious enough about them, do not in the leaſt hint any thing elſe; they being promiſcuouſly found of any kind of Sub-ſtance, and having not the leaſt appearance of any internal or ſubſtantial Form, but only of an external or figured Superficies. As, I ſay, 'tis ſome-thing harſh, to imagine that theſe thus qualified Bodies ſhould, by an imme-diate plaſtick Vertue, be thus ſhaped by Nature contrary to her general Me-thod of acting in all other Bodies; ſo on the other ſide, it may ſeem at firſt hearing ſomewhat difficult to conceive how all thoſe Bodies, if they either be the real Shells or Bodies of Fiſh, or other Animals or Vegetables, which they repreſent, or an Impreſſion left on thoſe Subſtances from ſuch Bodies, ſhould be, in ſuch great quantities, tranſported into Places ſo unlikely to have re-ceived them from any help of Man, or from any other obvious Means.

How the Diffi-culty may be ſolved.

Dddd

The

The former of thefe ways of folving thefe Phænomena, I confefs I cannot for the Reafons I now mention'd, by any means affent unto ; but the latter, tho' it has fome Difficulties alfo, feems to me not only poffible, but probable.

Object. 1. The greateft Objections that can be made againft it, are, Firft, by what means thofe Shells, Woods, and other fuch like Subftances (if they really are the Bodies they reprefent) fhould be tranfported to, and be buried in the Places where they are found ? And,

2. Secondly, Why many of them fhould be of Subftances wholly differing from thofe of the Bodies they reprefent ; there being fome of them which reprefent Shells of almoft all kinds of Subftances, Clay, Chalk, Marble, foft Stone, harder Stone, Marble, Flint, Marchafite, Ore, and the like.

In anfwer to both which, and fome other of lefs Importance, which I fhall afterwards mention, give me leave to propound thefe following Propofitions, which I fhall endeavour to make probable. Of thefe in their Order.

1.
Anfwered by thefe Propofitions.
My firft Propofition then is, That all, or the greateft part of thefe curioufly figured Bodies found up and down in divers Parts of the World, are either thofe Animal or Vegetable Subftances they reprefent converted into Stone, by having their Pores fill'd up with fome petrifying liquid Subftance, whereby their Parts are, as it were, lock'd up and cemented together in their Natural Pofition and Contexture ; or elfe they are the lafting Impreffions made on them at firft, whilft a yielding Subftance by the immediate Application of fuch Animal or Vegetable Body as was fo fhaped, and that there was nothing elfe concurring to their Production, fave only the yielding of the Matter to receive the Impreffion, fuch as heated Wax affords to the Seal ; or elfe a fubfiding or hardning of the Matter, after by fome kind of Fluidity it had perfectly fill'd or inclofed the figuring Vegetable or Animal Subftance, after the manner as a Statue is made of Plaifter of *Paris*, or Alabafter-duft beaten, and boil'd, mixed with Water and poured into a Mould.

2. Secondly, Next that there feems to have been fome extraordinary Caufe, which did concur to the promoting of this Coagulation or Petrification ; and that every kind of Matter is not of it felf apt to coagulate into a ftrong Subftance, fo hard as we find moft of thofe Bodies to confift of.

3. Thirdly, That the concurrent Caufes affifting towards the turning of thefe Subftances into Stone, feem to have been one of thefe, either fome kind of fiery Exhalation arifing from fubterraneous Eruptions or Earthquakes ; or fecondly, a Saline Subftance, whither working by Diffolution and Congelation, or Cryftallization, or elfe by Precipitation and Coagulation ; or thirdly, fome glutinous or bituminous Matter, which upon growing dry or fetling grows hard, and unites fandy Bodies together into a pretty hard Stone ; or fourthly, a very long continuation of thefe Bodies under a great degree of Cold and Compreffion.

4. Fourthly, That Waters themfelves may in tract of time be perfectly tranfmuted into Stone, and remain a Body of that Conftitution without being reducible by any Art yet commonly known.

5. Fifthly, That divers other fluid Subftances have after a long continuance at reft, have fettled and congealed into much more hard and permanent Subftances.

6. Sixthly. That a great part of the Surface of the Earth hath been fince the Creation transformed and made of another Nature ; namely, many Parts which have been Sea are now Land, and divers other Parts are now Sea which were once a firm Land ; Mountains have been turned into Plains, and Plains into Mountains, and the like.

Seventhly,

Seventhly, That divers of these kind of Transformations have been effected in these Islands of *Great Britain*; and that 'tis not improbable, but that many very Inland Parts of this Island, if not all, may have been heretofore all cover'd with the Sea, and have had Fishes swimming over it.

7.

Eighthly, That most of those Inland Places, where these kinds of Stones are, or have been found, have been heretofore under the Water; and that either by the departing of the Waters to another part or side of the Earth, by the alteration of the Center of Gravity of the whole Bulk, which is not impossible; or rather by the Eruption of some kind of subterraneous Fires, or Earthquakes, whereby great quantities of Earth have then been rais'd above the former Level of those Parts, the Waters have been forc'd away from the Parts they formerly cover'd, and many of those Surfaces are now raised above the Level of the Water's Surface many scores of Fathoms.

8.

Ninthly, It seems not improbable, that the tops of the highest and most considerable Mountains in the World have been under Water, and that they themselves most probably seem to have been the Effects of some very great Earthquake, such as the *Alpes* and Appennine Mountains, *Caucasus*, the Pike of *Tenariff*, the Pike in the *Terceras*, and the like.

9.

Tenthly, That it seems not improbable, but that the greatest part of the Inequality of the Earth's Surface may have proceeded from the Subversion and tumbling thereof by some preceding Earthquakes.

10.

Eleventhly, That there have been many other Species of Creatures in former Ages, of which we can find none at present; and that 'tis not unlikely also but that there may be divers new kinds now, which have not been from the beginning.

11.

There are some other Conjectures of mine yet unmention'd, which are more strange than these; which I shall defer the mentioning of till some other time; because tho' I have divers Observations concurring, yet having not been able to meet with such as may answer some considerable Objections that they are liable to, I will rather at present endeavour to make probable those already mentioned, by setting down some of those Observations (for it would be tedious to insert all) I have collected, both out of Authors, and from my own Experience.

The First was, That these figured Bodies dispersed over the World, are either the Beings themselves pretrify'd, or the Impressions made by those Beings. To confirm which, I have diligently examin'd many hundreds of these figured Bodies, and have not found the least probability of a plastick Faculty. For first, I have found the same kind of Impression upon Substances of an exceeding differing Nature, whereas Nature in other of her Works does adapt the same kind of Substance to the same Shape; the Flesh of a Horse is differing from that of a Hog, or Sheep, or from the Wood of a Tree, or the like; so the Wood of Box, for Instance, is differing from the Wood of all other Vegetables; and if the outward Figure of the Plant or Animal differ, to be sure their Flesh also differs: And under the same Shape you always meet with Substances of the same kind; whereas here I have observed Stones bearing the same Figure, or rather Impression, to be of hugely differing Natures, some of Clay, some of Chalk, some of Spar, some of Marble, some of a kind of Free-stone, some like Crystals or Diamonds, some like Flints, others a kind of Marchasite, others a kind of Ore. Nay, in the same figur'd Substance I have found divers sorts of very differing Bodies or kinds of Stone, so that one has been made up partly of Stone, partly of Clay, and partly of Marchasite, and partly of Spar, according as the Matter chanced to be jumbled together, and to fill up the Mould of the Shell.

The first Proposition confirmed.

Another Circumstance, which makes this Conjecture the more probable, is, that the outward Surface only of the Body is form'd, and that the inward

Part

Part has nothing of Shape that can reasonably be referr'd to it ; whereas we see that in all other Bodies that Nature gives a Shape to, she figures also the internal Parts or the very Substance of it, with an appropriate Shape. Thus in all kinds of Minerals, as Spars, Crystals, and divers of the precious Stones, Ores, and the like, the inward Parts of them are always correspondent to the outward Shape ; as in Spar, if the outward Part be shap'd into a Rhomboidical parallepiped, the inward Part of it is shap'd in the same manner, and may be cleft out into a multitude of Bodies of the like Form and Substance.

Another Circumstance is, that I have in many found the perfect Shell inclosed making a concave Impression on the Body that inclosed it, and a convex on the Body that it did inclose ; which I have sometimes been able to take out intire, and found it to be both by its Substance and Shape, and reflective shining, and the like Circumstances, a real Shell of a Cockle, Periwinkle, Muscle, or the like.

And farther, I have found in the same place divers of the same kinds of Shells, not fill'd with a Matter that was capable of taking the Impression, but with a kind of sandy Substance ; which lying loose within it could be easily shook out, leaving the inclosing Shell perfectly intire and empty ; others I have seen which have been of black Flint, wherein the Impression has been made only of a broken Shell, which stuck also into it ; the other Part of the Surface of that Stone, which was not within the Shell, remaining only form'd like a common Flint.

And which seems to confirm this Conjecture much more than any of the former Arguments, I had this last Summer an Opportunity to observe upon the South-part of *England*, in a Clift whose Bottom the Sea wash'd, that at a good height in the Clift above the Surface of the Water, there was a Layer, as I may call it, or Vein of Shells, which was extended in length for some Miles : Out of which Layer I digg'd out, and examin'd many hundreds, and found them to be perfect Shells of Cockles, Periwinkles, Muscles, and divers other sorts of small Shell-Fishes ; some of which were fill'd with the Sand with which they were mix'd ; others remain'd empty, and perfectly intire : From the Sea-waters washing the under part of this Clift, great quantities of it do every Year tumble or founder down, and fall into the Salt-water, which are wash'd also by several Mineral-waters issuing out at the bottom of those Clifts. Of these founder'd Parts I examined very many Parcels, and found some of them made into a kind of harden'd Mortar, or very soft Stone, which I could easily with my Foot, and even almost with my Finger, crush in Pieces ; others that had lain a longer time exposed to the Vicissitudes of the rising and falling Tides, I found grown into pretty hard Stones ; others that had been yet longer, I found converted into very hard Stone, not much yielding to the hardness of Flints. Out of divers of these, I was able to break and beat out divers intire and perfect Shells, fill'd with a Substance which was converted into a very hard Stone, retaining exactly the Shape of the inclosing Shell. And in the part of the Stone which had encompass'd the Shell, there was left remaining the perfect Impression and Form of the Shell ; the Shell it self remaining as yet of its natural white Substance, though much decay'd or rotted by time : But the Body inclosing and included by the Shell, I found exactly stamp'd like those Bodies, whose Figures Authors generally affirm to be the Product of a Plastick or Vegetative Faculty working in Stones.

Another Argument, that these petrify'd Substances are nothing but the Effects of those Shells being fill'd with some petrifying Substance, is this, That among those which are call'd *Cornu-Ammonis*, or Serpentine-stones, (found about *Keinsham*, and in several other Parts of *England*, and in other Countries, as at the *Balnea Bollensia*) which are indeed nothing else but the moulding off from a kind of Shell which is much shap'd like a *Nautilus*-shell, the whole Cavity being separated with divers small Valves or Partitions, much after the same manner as those Shells of the *Nautilus* are commonly observed to be. Among these Stones, I say, I have, upon breaking, found some of the Cavities between those Partitions remain almost quite empty ;

others

others I have found lined only with a kind of Tartareous, or rather Cryſtalline Subſtance, which has ſtuck to the ſides, and been figured like Tartar, but of a clear and tranſparent Subſtance like Cryſtal ; whereas others of the Cavities of the ſame Stone I have found filled with divers kinds of Subſtances very differing : Whence I imagine thoſe Tartareous Subſtances to be nought elſe but the hardning of ſome ſaline fluid Body, which might ſoak in through the Subſtance of the Shell. Others of theſe I have, which are quite of a tranſparent Subſtance, and ſeem to be produced from the Petrifaction of the Water that had fill'd them ; others I have found fill'd with a perfect Flint, both which I ſuppoſe to be the productions of Water petrify'd : And I may perhaps hereafter make it probable, that all kinds of Flints and Pebbles have no other Original.

I could urge many other Arguments to make my firſt Propoſition probable, that all thoſe curiouſly ſhaped Stones, which the moſt curious Naturaliſts moſt admire, are nothing but the Impreſſions made by ſome real Shell in a Matter that at firſt was yielding enough, but which is grown harder with time. To this very Head alſo may be referr'd all thoſe other kinds of petrify'd Subſtances, as Bones, Teeth, Crabbs, Fiſhes, Wood, Moſs, Fruit, and the like ; ſome of all which Kinds I have examin'd, and by very many Circumſtances, too long to be here inſerted, judge them to be nothing elſe but a real petrifaction of thoſe Subſtances they reſemble.

My Second Propoſition will not be difficult to prove, That if theſe be the Effects of Petrifaction or Coagulation, it muſt be from ſome extraordinary Cauſe. And this becauſe we find not many Experiments of producing of them when and where we will ; beſides we find that moſt things, eſpecially Animal and Vegetable Subſtances, after they have left off to vegetate, do ſoon decay, and by divers ways of Putrefaction and Rotting, looſe their Forms and return into Duſt ; as we find Wood, whether expoſed to the Air or Water, in a little time to waſte and decay ; eſpecially ſuch as is expoſed to the alteration of both, and even in thoſe Places where theſe petrify'd Subſtances are to be met with. The like we find of Animal Subſtances ; and we have but ſome few Experiments of preſerving thoſe Bodies, to make them as permanent as Stone, and fewer of making them into a Subſtance of the like Nature. *The ſecond Propoſition confirmed.*

The Third thing therefore, which I ſhall endeavour to ſhew, is, That the concurring Cauſes to theſe Petrifactions ſeem to be either ſome kind of petrifying Water, or elſe ſome ſaline or ſulphureous Mixture, with the concurrence of Heat, from ſome ſubterraneous Fire or Earthquake ; or elſe a very long Continuation of thoſe Bodies under a great degree of Cold and Compreſſion, and Reſt. That petrifying Waters may be able to convert both Animal and Vegetable Subſtances into Stone, I could, beſides ſeveral Trials of my own, bring multitudes of Relations out of Natural Hiſtorians : But theſe are ſo common almoſt in all Countries, and ſo commonly taken notice of by the Curious, that I need not inſtance. *Cambden* and *Speed* will tell you of abundance here in *England*, as the *Peak* in *Derbyſhire*, and in ſeveral other ſubterraneous Caverns in *England*. The Water it ſelf does, by degrees, produce ſeveral conical pendulous Bodies of Stone, ſhap'd and hanging like Icicles from the Roof of the Vault ; and dropping on the bottom, it raiſes up alſo conical Spires, which, by degrees, endeavour to meet the former pendulous *Stiriæ*. And indeed I have generally obſerv'd it, that wherever there is a Vault made with Lime under Ground, into which the Rain-Water ſoaking through, a pretty thickneſs of Ground, does at laſt penetrate through the Arch ; I have in ſeveral places, I ſay, obſerv'd that that Water does incruſtate the Roof with Stone, and in many places of it generate ſmall pendulous Icicles. This Water I have found in a little time to incruſtate Sticks, or the like Vegetable Subſtances with Stone, and in ſome places to penetrate into the Pores of the Wood, filling them up with ſmall Cylinders of Stone. This I have obſerv'd alſo in divres of the Arches of St. *Paul's* Church, which have been uncover'd and have lain open to the Rain, though there be *The third Propoſition confirmeds* no Earth for it to foak through. And tho' I have never yet been able to petrify a Stick throughout, yet I have now by me feveral pieces that retain fo perfectly all the Figure of Wood, and are yet fo perfectly in all other propreties Stone, that I find not the leaft Reafon of doubt to believe that thofe pieces have been actual Wood, having ftill the Bark, the Clefts, the Knots, the Grain, the Pores, and even thofe too which, for their fmalnefs, I have elfewhere call'd Microfcopical; tho' I confefs fome of thefe more perfect pieces feem to have been petrify'd from fome more fubtile and infinuating petrifying Water, than thofe I newly mention'd ; and 'tis not improbable but that fome Subterraneaous Steams and Heat may have contributad fomewhat towards this Effect. But firft I fhall endeavour to make it probable, that thefe petrify'd Bodies may have been placed in thofe Parts where they are found, By fome kind of Transformation wrought on the Surface of the Earth, by fome Earth-quake : And to this end, I fhall by and by mention fome ftrange alterations that have been made by Earthquakes, after I have firft made probable my fourth Conjecture.

The fourth Propofition confirmed. The Fourth Propofition therefore to be explain'd and made probable is, That Waters themfelves of divers Kinds, are, and may have been tranfmuted perfectly into a ftony Subftance, of a very permanent Conftitution, being fcarcely reducible again into Water by any Art yet commonly known. And that divers other Liquid or Fluid Subftances have in tract of time fettled and congealed into much more hard, fixt, folid and permanent Forms than they were of at firft.

The probability of which Propofition may appear from thefe Particulars.

I. That almoft in all Streams and running Waters there is to be found great quantity of Sand at the bottom, many of which Sands both by their Figure in the Microfcope, and tranfparently, feem to have been generated out of the Water.

1ft. Arg. Firft, I fay, That their tranfparency which they difcover in the Microfcope is an Argument, becaufe I believe there is no tranfparent Body in the World that has not been reduc'd to that Conftitution by being fome ways or other made fluid, nor can I indeed imagine how there fhould be any. All Bodies, made tranfparent by Art, muft be reduc'd into that Form firft ; and therefore 'tis not unlikely but that Nature may take the fame Courfe ; but this as only probable I fhall not infift on. Next, I fay, that the Figures of diverfe of them in the Microfcope difcover the fame things ; for I have feen multitudes of them curioufly wrought and figured like Cryftal or Diamonds, and I cannot imagine by what other Inftrument Nature fhould thus cut them, fave by Cryftalizing them out of a Liquid or Fluid Body, and that way we find her to work in the formation of all thofe curious regular Figures of Salts, and the Vitriols (as I may call them) of Metals and divers other Bodies, of which Chymiftry affords many Inftances. Sea-Salt and Salgem chryftylizeth into Cubes or four-fided Parrallelipipeds ; Niter into triangular and hexangular Prifms. Alume into Octoedrons, Vitriols into various kinds of Figures, according to the various kinds of Metals diffolved, and the various *Menftrua* diffolving them ; Tartars alfo, and Candyings of Vegetables are figured into their various regular Shapes from the fame Method and Principle. And in truth, in the formation of any Body out of this mineral Kingdom, whofe Origine we are able to examine, we may find that Nature firft reduces the Bodies to be wrought on into a liquid or foft Subftance, and afterwards forms and fhapes it into this or that Figure. But this Argument drawn from the Sand, found in all running Streams, I fhall not infift on, becaufe fome imagine it to be only wafht off from the Land and Shores the River paffes over, and perpaps much of it may : But yet that Sand may be made of clear Water, this fecond Argument will manifeft, and that is this:

That

That 'tis a usual Experiment in the making of Salt in the Salterns, by 2d. *Arg.* the boyling up, or evaporating away the fresher part of the Sea-water, to collect great quantities of Sand at each corner of the Boyler; which, after it has been well washt with fresh Water, is, in all particulars, a perfect Sand; and yet the Water is so order'd before it is put into the Boyler, that nothing of Sand or Dregs can enter with it, the Brine being first suffer'd to stand a good while and settle in a very large Fat, so that all the Sand and Dregs may sink to the bottom; after which, the clearer Water at the top is drawn off, and suffer'd to run into the Boyler. 'Tis not impossible, perhaps, but that Substance which made this Sand, might be dissolved in Water, and afterwards by evaparation coagulated; which, if so, makes not at all against, but rather argues strongly for my fourth Proposition.

But that the other Solution is something more probable, namely, That 3d. *Arg.* 'tis made out of the very Substance of the Water itself, this third Argument will make probable; and that is, that any Water of what kind soever, tho' never so clear and insipid, may, by frequent Distillations, be all of it perfectly transmitted into a white insipid Calx not again dissolvable in Water, and in nothing differing from the Substance of Stone; this I have been assured by an eminent Physician, who has divers times made tryal of it with the same success. If therefore the whole Body of any Water may, by so easy an Operation in so very short a time, be transmuted into a stony Substance, what may not Nature do that can take her own time, and knows best how to make use of her own Principles?

But 4*thy.* we have many Instances by which we are assured that Nature realy 4th. *Arg.* does change Water into Stone, both by forming in a little time considerable Stones out of the distilling Drops of Water soaking through the Roofs of Caves and subterraneous Vaults, of which we have very many Instances here in *England*; as to name one for all at the Peak in *Derbyshire*, the pendulous Cones of this petrify'd Substance directly point at, and oftentimes meet and rest on the rising Spires, generated by the drops of Water trickling through the Roof, as I mention'd before

And 5*thy.* there are divers other Waters which we need not seek after in 5th. *Arg.* Caves that have a petrifying vertue, and incrustate all the Chanel they pass through, and the Substances soak'd in them with Stone; these are so common almost in all places, that I need not instance in any; only I cannot pass by one, which is taken notice of by *Kircher* in his *Mundus Subterraneus*, being Observations made by himself, and it has in it two Circumstances very considerable; the first is, That Vegetables should grow so plentifully in a very hot Water. The second, that only such Herbs as grew in it, and not such as were Steeped in it, will perfectly, after drying, be turned into Stone, of which I shall afterwards have occasion to make more use. I shall give the History in his own Words, as they are set down in the 7th Paragraph of the 2d Sect. of the 5th Book of his *Mundus Subterraneus*, *Hæc* (says he) *experientia didici in Itinere meo Hetrusco, in quo prope Roncolanum. senensis territorii Oppidum* (a Town near *Siena* in *Tuscany*) *duos fontes calidos observavi, quorum aqua per Canales ad molares Rotas vertendas ducebatur. In hisce canalibus cyperus, junci, ranunculus similesq; herbæ tanta adolescebant fæcunditate, ut quotaunis eas, ne aquæ motum interturbarent, extirpare oporteret. Extirpatas vero projectasq; in vicinum locum herbas omnes in Lapidem conversas non sine admiratione spectavi. Cujus rei causam cum a molitoribus quærerem. Responderunt aquas istiusmodi hujus virtutis esse, ut quæcunq; inter canales, aut ipsa aqua excreverint herbæ mox ac extirpatæ fuerint, Lapidescant; quæcunq; vero extra aquam in campis patentibus excreverint herbæ, istas extirpatas nunquam Lapidescere.* I pass by his Reasons and Explications, because I think them very little to the Purpose: But the Observations themselves are very considerable, and serve for the explaining of severeal Phenomena I have observ'd in petrify'd Bodies, as I shall indeavour hereafter to shew, as in Corals, both Red, White, and the several Rarities of them, in Coral-
lines

lines also, and petrify'd Mushromes, of each of which I have examined a very great variety. But this only by the by.

6th *Arg.*   6thly. Therefore 'tis observable, that these petrifying Waters are for the most part very clear and limpid ; so that to the Sight 'tis not distinguishable from other Water : But only by the Effects, and therefore by the newly mention'd Observations of *Kircher*, we find that Vegetables, that upon drying turn'd into Stone ; whilst green and growing flourished and spread faster than others ; so that the petrifying Substance past through the finest and closest Pores of the living Vegetables, and therefore must certainly be very intimately mixt with the Water that could not be separated by so fine and curious Strainers.

7th. *Arg.*   But 7thly. To confirm this Proposition yet further, there are found in several parts of the Earth, such Waters will be intirely converted into Stone. Of this kind there are several Histories in the newly-mention'd Book, which I pass over, and shall only take notice of one for all, and that is in an Account sent to the *Roman* Coledge of Jesuits from the Masters, Surveyors and Clerks of the *Hungarian* Mines, in Answer to some Queries propounded to them. Page 183. of *Kircher's Mundus Subterraneus*, to the Query concerning the Properties and Metallick Experiments about Meneral Waters, they answer, That *Datur in fodinis aquæ genus quod in Figuram saccaro haud absimilem degenerat*, viz. *in Lapillos albas.*

And again, Page 185. of the same, from another Prefect of the Emperial Mines in *Hungary* in answer to the same Query, we have this Account. *Reperitur quoq; aqua quædam alba quæ in Lapidem durum abit. Si vero hæc aqua ante suam coagulationem mineram cupream transiverit, tunc generatur ex ea lapis qui Malochites vocatur, quando vero aqua illa perfluit cupream mineram continentem argentum fiet ex ea pulcher lapis ceruleus similis Turcoidi. Hæc aqua autem nullibi frequentius reperitur quam in mineris Lapidibus siliceis copiosis, & cuprum cum argento continentibus.* Whence I am apt to think, and I have many Observations and Arguments to confirm my Conjecture,

8th. *Arg.*   That 8thly, All kinds of *Talk* and *Spar*, most *Ores* and *Marchasites. Alumen Plumeum, & Asbestus; Fluores, Cryftalls,* Cornish-*Diamonds, Amethyfts* and divers other figured Mineral Bodies, may be generated from their Cryftalization, or Coagulation, out of some Mineral Waters.

9th. *Arg.*   And to make it yet more probable, I could in the 9th place add divers Experiments, by which several of these Concretes may be in a short time made artificially by several Chymical Operations, which would very much illuftrate the former Doctrin. But I hope what I have mention'd may suffice to make the fourth Proposition probable, that Waters of divers kinds may be turned in time to Stone, without being reducible again to Water by any Art yet commonly known, which being granted, my

The fifth Proposition proved.   Fifth Proposition will follow of consequence, *viz.* That divers other fluid Substances, have, after long continuance of rest, settled and congealed into much more hard and permanent Substances : For if Water it self may be so changed and metamorphosed, which seems the farthest removed from the nature of a solid Body, certainly those which are nearer to that Nature, and are mixt with such Waters, will more eafily be coagulated : I shall not therefore any farther insist on the Proof of this, than only to mention two Particulars, and that because we have almost every where so many Instances and Experiments ; and the first is that of *Pliny* in the 13th Chap. of the 35th Book of his Natural Hiftory, in all which Chapter he gives us divers Instances of several kinds of Earth, which, by the Sea-water and Air, converted into into solid and hard Stones ; his Words are these : *Verum & ipsius Terræ sunt alia segmenta. Quis enim satis miretur pessimam ejus partem ideoq; pulverem appellatam in puteolanis collibus oppone maris fluctibus, mersamq; protinus fieri lapidem unum inexpugnabilem undis, & fortiorem quotidie, utiq; si cumano misceatur Camento.*
                                                                          Eadem

Eadem eſt Terræ Natura & in Cizicena Regione, ſed ibi non pulvis verum ipſa Terra, qualibet magnitudine exciſa & demerſa in mare, lapidea extrahitur : hoc idem circa Caſſandriam produnt fieri : Et in fonte Gnidio dulci intra octo menſes Terram lapideſcere. Ab Oropo quidem Aulidem uſque quicquid Terræ attingitur mari, mutatur in Saxa, &c. to the end of the Chapter he goes on to relate divers Places where Earths, &c. are turned into Stones. Alſo in the 10th Chapter of the of the 31ſt Book, ſpeaking of the Nature and Kinds of Niter, he tells about the middle of the Chapter. *Nitrariæ egregiæ Ægyptiis nam circa Naucratim & Memphim tantum ſolebant eſſe, circa Memphin deteriores ; nam & lapideſcit ibi in acervis, multiq; ſunt Tumuli ea de causa Saxei, fiuntq; ex his vaſa, &c.*

The Second is an Obſervation of my own, which I have often taken notice of, and lately examined very diligently, which will much confirm theſe Hiſtories of *Pliny*, and this my preſent Hypotheſis ; and that is a Part of the Obſervation I have already mentioned, which I made upon the Weſtern Shore of the Iſle of *Wight*. I obſerved a Cliff of a pretty height, which, by the conſtant waſhing of the Water at the bottom of it, is continually, eſpecially after Froſts and great Rains, foundering and tumbling down into the Sea underneath it. Along the Shore underneath this Cliff, are a great number of Rocks and large Stones confuſedly placed, ſome covered, others quite out of the Water ; all which Rocks I found to be compounded of Sand and Clay, and Shells, and ſuch kind of Stones, as the Shore was covered with. Examining the Hardneſs of ſome that lay as far into the Water as the Low-Water-mark, I found them to be altogether as hard, if not much harder than *Portland* or *Purbeck*-ſtone : Others of them that lay not ſo far into the Sea, I found much ſofter, as having in probability not been ſo long expoſed to the Viciſſitudes of the Tides : Others of them I found ſo very ſoft, that I could eaſily with my Foot cruſh them, and make Impreſſions into them, and could thruſt a Walking-ſtick I had in my Hand a great depth into them : Others that had been but newly foundered down, were yet more ſoft, as having been ſcarce waſh'd by the Salt Water. All theſe were perfectly of the ſame Subſtance with the Cliff, from whence they had manifeſtly tumbled, and conſiſted of Layers of Shells, Sand, Clay, Gravel, Earth, &c. and from all the Circumſtances I could examine, I do judge them to have been the Parts of the Neigbouring Cliff foundered down, and rowl'd and waſh'd by degrees into the Sea ; and, by the petrifying Power of the Salt Water, converted into perfect hard compacted Stones. I have likewiſe ſince obſerved the like *Phænomena* on other Shores. And I doubt not but any inquiſitive Naturaliſt may find infinite of the like Inſtances all along the Coaſt of *England*, and other Countries where there are ſuch kind of foundering Cliffs. I ſhall not now mention the great Quantities of toothed Spar, which I obſerved to be cryſtallized upon the ſides of theſe Rocks, which ſeem'd to have been nothing elſe but the meer cryſtallizing or ſhooting of ſome kind of Water, which was preſs'd or aroſe out of theſe coagulating Stones ; For the Hiſtory of theſe kinds of figured Stones belong more properly to another Diſcourſe ; namely, of the Natural Geometrical Figures, obſervable in Oares, Minerals, Spars, Talk, &c. of which elſewhere.

One Inſtance more I cannot omit, as being the moſt obſervable of any I have yet heard of ; and that is, (Dr. *Caſtle*'s Relation) of a certain Place at *Alpſly* in *Bedfordſhire*, where there is a corner of a certain Field, that doth perfectly turn Wood and divers other Subſtances in a very ſhort time into Stone as hard as a Flint or Agat. A Piece of this kind I ſaw, affirm'd to have been there buried, which the Perſon that buried it had ſhot ſmall Shots of Lead into ; the whole Subſtance of the Wood, Bark and Pith, together with the Leaden Shot it ſelf was perfectly turn'd to a Stone as hard as any Agat, and yet retain'd its perfect Shape and Form ; and the Lead remain'd round, and in its place, but much harder than any Iron. Of this I am promiſed a Sample, but have not yet receiv'd it.

But to ſpend no more time on the proof of that of which we have almoſt every where Inſtances, divers of which I have already mention'd, I ſhall proceed to the 6th Propoſition ; which is, That a great Part of the Surface of the *The 6th Propoſition confirm'd.*

F f f f Earth

Earth hath been since the Creation transform'd, and made of another Nature: that is, many Parts which have been Sea are now Land, and others that have been Land are now Sea; many of the Mountains have been Vales, and the Vales Mountains, &c.

For the proving of which Proposition, I shall not need to produce any other Arguments, besides the repeating what I find set down by divers Natural Historians, concerning the prodigious Effects that have been produced by Earthquakes on the superficial Parts of the Earth; because they seem to me to have been the chief Efficients which have transported these petrify'd Bodies, Shells, Woods, Animal Substances, &c. and left them in some Parts of the Earth, as are no other ways likely to have been the Places wherein such Substances should be produced; they being usually either raised a great way above the level Surface of the Earth, on the Tops of high Hills, or else buried a great way beneath that Surface in the lower Valleys: For who can imagine that Oysters, Muscles, and Periwinkles, and the like Shell-fish, should ever have had their Habitation on the Tops of the Mountain *Caucasus?* Which is by divers of our Geographers accounted as high in its perpendicular Altitude, as any Mountain in the yet known World; and yet *Olearius* affords us a very considerable History to this purpose of his own Observation, which I shall hereafter have occasion to relate, and examine more particularly. Or to come a little nearer home, who could imagine that Oysters, *Echini,* and some other Shell-fish, should heretofore have lived at the tops of the *Alps, Appennine,* and *Pyrenian* Mountains, all which abound with great store of several sorts of Shells; nay, yet nearer at the tops of some of the highest in *Cornwal* and *Devonshire,* where I have been informed by Persons whose Testimony I cannot in the least suspect, that they have taken up divers, and seen great Quantities of them? And to come yet nearer, who can imagine Oysters to have lived on the Tops of some Hills near *Banstead-Downs* in *Surry?* Where there have been time out of Mind, and are still to this day found divers Shells of Oysters, both on the uppermost Surface, and buried likewise under the Surface of the Earth, as I was lately informed by several very worthy Persons living near those Places, and as I my self had the Opportunity to observe and collect.

The Effects of Earthquakes. To proceed then to the Effects of Earthquakes, we find in Histories Four Sorts or *Genus's* to have been performed by them.

First sort or Genus of Effects. The first is the raising of the superficial Parts of the Earth above their former Level: and under this Head there are Four Species. The 1st is the raising of a considerable Part of a Country, which before lay level with the Sea, and making it lye many Feet, nay, sometimes many Fathoms above its former height. A 2d is the raising of a considerable part of the bottom of the Sea, and making it lye above the Surface of the Water, by which means divers Islands have been generated and produced. A 3d Species is the raising of very considerable Mountains out of a plain and level Country. And a 4th Species is the raising of the Parts of the Earth by the throwing on of a great Access of new Earth, and for burying the former Surface under a covering of new Earth many Fathoms thick.

Second Sort or Genus of Effects. A second sort of Effects perform'd by Earthquakes, is the depression or sinking of the Parts of the Earth's Surface below the former Level. Under this Head are also comprized Four distinct Species, which are directly contrary to the four last named.

The *First,* is a sinking of some Part of the Surface of the Earth, lying a good way within the Land, and converting it into a Lake of an almost unmeasurable depth.

The *Second,* is the sinking of a considerable Part of the plain Land, near the Sea, below its former Level, and so suffering the Sea to come in and overflow it, being laid lower than the Surface of the next adjoining Sea.

A *Third,* is the sinking of the Parts of the bottom of the Sea much lower, and creating therein vast *Vorages* and *Abysses.*

A

A *Fourth*, is the making bare, or uncovering of divers Parts of the Earth, which were before a good way below the Surface ; and this either by suddenly throwing away these upper Parts by some subterraneous Motion, or else by washing them away by some kind of Eruption of Waters from unusual Places, vomited out by some Earthquake.

A Third sort of Effects produced by Earthquakes, are the Subversions, Conversions, and Transpositions of the Parts of the Earth.

Third Sort or Genus of Effects.

A Fourth sort of *Effects*, are *Liquefaction. Baking, Calcining, Petrifaction, Transformation, Sublimation, Distillation,* &c.

Fourth Sort or Genus of Effects.

The First therefore of the Effects of Earthquakes, which I but now named, was, that divers Parts of the Surface of the Earth which lay before, either below or level with the Sea, have been raised a good height above that Level by Earthquakes. Of this *Pliny* gives us several Instances in the 85th Chapter of the 2d Book of his Natural History, *Eadem nascentium Causa terrarum est, cum idem ille Spiritus attollendo potens solo non valuit erumpere. Nascuntur enim nec fluminum tantum invectu sicut Echinades Insulæ ab Acheloo amne congestæ ; majorq; pars Ægypti a Nilo, in quam a Pharo insula noctis & Diei cursum fuisse Homero credimus : Sed & Recessu Maris sicut eidem de circeiis. Quod accidisse et in Ambraciæ portu decem Millium passuum intervallo, & Atheniensium quinq; Millium ad Piræeum memoratur : Et Ephesi ubi quondam ædem Dianæ alluebat. Herotodo quidem si credimus, mare fuit supra Memphin usq; ad Æthiopum montes. Itemq; a planis Arabiæ. Mare et circa Ilium et tota Teuthrania quaq; campos intulerit.*

The First Species of Effects under the first Genus or Sort.

Meander, and *Sandys* also, in his Travels thro' *Italy*, and the Parts of the *Levant*, gives this Instance, *pag.* 277. speaking of the new Mountain, which was produced in the Kingdom of *Naples*, in the Year 1538. *The Lake* Lucrinus, says he, *extended formerly to* Avernus, *and so unto* Gaurus, *two other Lakes ; but is now no other than a little sedgy Plash, choaked up by the horrible and astonishing Eruption of the new Mountain, whereof, as oft as I think, I am apt to credit whatsoever is wonderful. For who in* Italy, *says he, knows not, or who elsewhere will believe, that a Mountain should arise partly out of a Lake, and partly out of the Sea in one Day and a Night, to such a height, as to contend in Altitude with the high Mountains adjoining.*

In the Year of our Lord 1538 *on the 29th of September, when for certain Days foregoing, the Country thereabouts was so vext with perpetual Earthquakes, as no one House was left so intire, as not to expect immediate Ruine, after that the Sea had retired* 200 *Paces from the Shore, leaving abundance of Fish with Springs of Fresh Water rising at the bottom, this Mountain visibly ascended about the second Hour of the Night, and so forwards.* And again, *pag.* 281, speaking of the same Place, he says, *The Sea was accustomed, when urged with Storms, to flow in thro' the Lake,* Lucrinus *driving Fishes in with it ; but now not only that Passage, but a Part of* Avernus *it self is choaked by the Mountain.* In which Histories I take notice only of these two Particulars at present. First, That that Part of the Land which lyes between *Lucrinus* and the Sea, that was oft-times before overflowed by the Sea, since this Earthquake, has been so far raised, as that now such Effects are no longer to be found. To confirm the rising of which the more, the other Circumstance of the Sea's departing from the Shore 200 Paces does much contribute. But not to insist on this, Mr. *Childry* in his *Britannia Baconica*, a Book very useful in its kind, being a Collection of All the Natural History of the Islands of *Great Britain*, to be met with in *Cambden*, or *Speed*, and some other Historians, together with such of his own as he had opportunity to observe, relates to us many considerable Passages to this purpose. In his History of *Norfolk*, he saith, That near St. *Benet*'s in the *Holm*, are perfect Cockles and Periwinkles sometimes digg'd up out of the Earth, which makes some think it was formerly overflow'd by the Sea. The Fenny Grounds also of *Lincolnshire* and *Cheshire*, seem to have proceeded from the rising of the Ground ; and those in *Anglesy*, where lopp'd Trees are now dug up with the perfect Strokes of the Ax remaining on them, seem to have

been

been firſt ſunk under Water, then overturn'd and buried in their own Earth, and afterwards the whole Earth ſeems to have been raiſed again to its former height. Of the raiſing of the Surface of the Earth, by the overflowings and ſtopping of Rivers and Waters, I ſhall afterwards ſpeak.

Linſchoten gives us a Relation of the like Effects of an Earthquake that hapned in the *Terceras.* The Relation, as I find it epitomiz'd by *Purchas* in the 1677 Page of the 4th Part of his *Pilgrims,* is this: ʻIn *July,* Anno 1591. ʻ there happen'd an Earthquake in the Iſland of St. *Michael,*which lyeth from ʻ *Tercera* South-Eaſt about 28 Miles, an Iſland 20 Miles long, and full of ʻ Towns, which continued from *July* 26. to *Aug.* 12. in which time none durſt ʻ ſtay within his Houſe, but fled into the Fields, faſting and praying with ʻ great Sorrow, for that many of their Houſes fell down, and a Town, called ʻ *Villa Franca,* was almoſt razed to the Ground, all the Cloyſters and Houſes ʻ ſhaken to the Earth, and therein People ſlain. *The Land in ſome Places roſe* ʻ *up,* and the Clifts removed from one Place to another, and ſome Hills were ʻ defaced and made even with the Ground. The Earthquake was ſo ſtrong, ʻ that the Ships that lay in the Road, and in the Sea, ſhaked as if the World ʻ would have turn'd round. There ſprang alſo a Fountain out of the Earth, ʻ from whence for the ſpace of four Days there flow'd a moſt clear Water,and ʻ after that it ceaſed. At the ſame time they heard ſuch Thunder and Noiſe ʻ under the Earth, as if all the Devils had been aſſembled together at that ʻ Place,wherewith many dy'd for fear. The Iſland of *Tercera* ſhook four times ʻ together,ſo that it ſeem'd to turn about ; but there happen'd no other Miſ- ʻ fortune unto it. Earthquakes are common in thoſe Iſlands: For about 20 ʻ Years paſt there happen'd another Earthquake, when a high Hill that lyeth ʻ by the ſame Town *Villa Franca* fell half down,and covered all the Town with ʻ Earth, and killed many Men. I have tranſcribed here once for all the whole Relation, becauſe there are many other conſiderable Circumſtances in it beſides the riſing of the Earth, which I ſhall have occaſion to refer to, under others of the Heads or Propoſitions to be proved, and therefore ſhall not need repetition. Two other Relations I find collected by *Purchas,* confirming this and ſeveral of the other Propoſitions: The one is that of *Dithmar Blefken*'s, in his Hiſtory of *Iſland,* Page 648 of the 3d Part of his *Pilgrims.* ʻOn the 29th ʻ of *November* about Midnight, in the Sea,there appear'd a Flame near *Hecla,* ʻ which gave Light to the whole Iſland: An hour after the whole Iſland trem- ʻ bled, as it would have been moved out of the Place: After the Earthquake ʻ follow'd a horrible Crack, that if all warlike Ordnance had been diſcharg'd ʻ it had been nothing to this Terror. It was known afterwards that *the Sea* ʻ *went back two Leagues in that Place, and remain'd dry.*

A Second Hiſtory *Purchas* has collected out of the Hiſtory of *Joſeph Acoſta* of the *Weſt Indies,* Page 940 of the 3d Part : omitting for the preſent divers other Circumſtances he takes notice of, I ſhall only mention that of the receding of the Sea. ʻ Upon the Coaſt of *Chile,* (ſays he) I remember not well ʻ in what Year, there was ſo terrible an Earthquake, as it overturn'd whole ʻ Mountains, and thereby ſtopt the Courſe of Rivers, which it converted into ʻ Lakes: It beat down Towns,and ſlew a great number of People, cauſing the ʻ Sea to leave her Place ſome Leagues,ſo as the Ships remain'd on dry Ground ʻ far from the ordinary Road, *&c.* An Example ſomewhat like this happen'd lately in the *Eaſt-Indies,* as I was inform'd by a Letter ſent thence to Mr. *D.* on *London-Bridge.* The thing in ſhort was this : At a Place, about 7 Days Journey from *Ducca,* the Earth trembled about 32 Days ; and the Sequel was, that it raiſed the bottom of a Lake, ſo as to drive out all the Water and Fiſh upon the Land, ſo that a Place which was formerly a Lake is now dry Ground. This was written from *Ballaſore, Jan.* 6. 1665. The Words of the Letter I ſhall give afterwards

The Second Species under the firſt Head or Genus of the Effects of Earthquakes. The ſecond Species of Effects of Earthquakes, is the raiſing of a conſiderable Part of the bottom of the Sea, and making it lye above the Surface of the Water, by which means divers Iſlands have been generated. Of this *Pliny,*in the 86th and 87th Chap. of the 2d Book of his Nat.Hiſt.gives us ſeveral Inſtances. *Naſcuntur,* ſays he, *& alio modo Terræ,* (having in the preceding

ding Chapter fpoken of the Shore's rifing above the Water, or the Water's deceding from the Shore, *ac repente in alto mari emergunt, veluti paria fecum faciente Natura, quæque hauferit hiatus alio loco reddente. Clara jam pridem Infulæ Delos & Rhodos memoria produntur enatæ. Poftea minores, ultra Melon Anaphe,* (of which *Strabo* makes mention in his Tenth Book.) *Inter Lemnum & Hellefpontum Nea. Inter Lebedum & Teon, Alone: inter Cycladas, Olympiadis* CXXXV *ann.* 4to *Thera & Therafia. Inter eafdem poft ann.* CXXX *Hiera: & ab ea duobus Stadiis poft ann.* CX *in Noftro ævo Thia.* Two of which Hiftories are alfo confirm'd by *Seneca,* in the Sixth Book of his Natural Queftions and twenty firft Chapter, where explicating the effects of Earthquakes by the commixture of Fire and Water, he fays, *Theren & Therafiam & hanc noftræ ætatis infulam, fpectantibus nobis in Ægeo mari enatam quis Dubitat quin in lucem Spiritus vexerit. Sandis* fpeaking of the *Jolian* Iflands, faith, ' Of thofe ' there were only Seven, now there are Eleven in Number, which heretofore ' all flamed, now only *Vulcano* and *Strombylo,* two of that Number do burn. *Vulcano* is faid to have firft appear'd above Water about the time that *Scipio Africanus* died. But we have much later Inftances to confirm this our Affertion : for about twenty eight Years fince, an Ifland was made among the *Azores* by an Eruption of Fire ; of which divers have related the Story. But *Kircher* in his *Mundus Subterraneus,* from the Relation of the Jefuits, has added the moft particular one. Having fpoken of the exceeding height of the Pike of *Teneriff* in the *Canaries,* and of the Eruptions of Fire in it, and the hot Springs found about it, he adds, that in the Azores alfo there are found places having almoft the fame Proprieties. The *Pico de Fayal de Santo Gregorio,* being almoft of equal hight, and St. *Michael's* Ifland having heretofore had feveral Vulcans, and having been troubled with many Earthquakes, and very notably about thirty eight Years fince, wherein all the Ifland was fo terribly fhaken, that the utter Ruin and Submerfion of the whole was feared. The Hiftory of which, in fhort, is this; That ' *June* 26. ' 1638. the whole Ifland began to be fhaken with Earthquakes for eight days, ' fo that the Inhabitants left Cities, Caftles and Houfes, and dwelt in the ' Fields, but efpecially thofe of a Place call'd *Vargen,* where the Motion was ' more violent. After which Earthquake, this Prodigy followed; At a place of ' the Sea, where Fifher-men us'd to fifh in Summer, becaufe of the great ' abundance of Fifh there caught, call'd *La Femera,* about 6 Miles from *Pico* ' *Delle Carmerine,* upon the firft *Sunday* in *July,* a fubterraneous Fire, notwith- ' ftanding the weight and depth of the Sea in that Place, which was 120 Foot, ' as the Fifhermen had often before that found by founding, and the multi- ' tude of Waters which one would have thought fufficient to have quenched ' the Fire : A fubterraneous Fire, I fay, broke out with a moft unexpreffible ' violence, carrying up into the Clouds with it Water, Sand, Earth, Stones, ' and other vaft great bulks of Bodies ; which to the fad Spectators, at a di- ' ftance, appear'd like Flocks of Wool or Cotton, and falling back on the Sur- ' face of the Water look'd like Froth. The Space of this Eruption was about ' as big as a Space of Land, that might well be fown by two Bufhels of Grain. ' By great Providence the Wind blew from the Land ; otherwife the whole ' Ifland would, in all probability, have perifhed by the mercilefs Rage of thefe ' devouring Flames, fuch vaft bulks of Stone were thrown up into the Air, ' about the height to feeming of three Pikes Lengths, that one would rather ' think them Mountains than Rocks. And which added further Horror to ' this dreadful Sight, was, that thefe Mountains returning again, often met ' with others afcending or being thrown up, and were thereby dafht into a ' 1000 Pieces ; divers of which Pieces being afterwards taken up and bruifed, ' eafily turn'd into a black fhining Sand. Out of the great multitude and va- ' riety of thefe vaft rejected Bodies, and the immenfe heaps of Rocks and Stones, ' after a while was form'd a new Ifland out of the main Ocean, which at firft ' was not above 5 Furlongs over ; but after a while, by daily acceffes of new ' Matter, it increafed after 14 Days to an Ifland of 5 Miles over. From this ' Eruption, fo great a quantity of Fifh was deftroy'd and thrown upon the next ' adjoining Ifland, that 8 of the biggeft *Indian* Galeons would not be fuffici- ' ent to contain them; which the Inhabitants fearing, left the Stink of them

' might

, might create a Plague, for 18 Miles round collected and buried in deep Pits. , The Stink of the Brimstone was plainly smelt at 24 Miles distance. Thus far he. But we have one Instance more of the Generation of an Island out of the bottom of the Sea, by an Eruption; which because it happen'd very lately, namely in 1650, and near an Island in the *Archipelago*, which *Pliny* relates to have been heretofore after the same manner produced, I shall in short relate, as it is more largely recorded by *Kircher*, in his *Mundus Subterraneus*, from the Mouth of Father *Franciscus Riccardus*, a Jesuit, who was at the same time in the adjoining Island, and was an Eye-witness of all the *Phænomena*.

‘ From the 24th of *September* to the 9th of *October*, 1650, the Island of *San-*
‘ *terinum*, formerly call'd by *Pliny Thera*, was dreadfully shaken with Earth-
‘ quakes, so that the Inhabitants expected nothing but utter ruine; and were
‘ yet more amazed by a horrid Eruption of Fire out of the bottom of the
‘ Sea, about 4 Miles to the Eastward of the Island : Before which the Water
‘ of the Place was rais'd above 30 Cubits perpendicularly, (I suppose he means
‘ as to appearance from the Island, otherwise 'tis but very little) which
‘ Wave spreading it self round every way, overturn'd every thing it met, de-
‘ stroying Ships and Galleys in the Harbour of *Candie*, which was fourscore
‘ Miles distant. The Eruption fill'd the Air with Ashes and horrible sul-
‘ phureous Stinks, and dreadful Lightnings and Thunders succeeded. All
‘ things in the Island were covered with a yellow sulphureous Crust, and the
‘ People almost blinded as well as choak'd. Multitudes of Pumice, and other
‘ Stones were thrown up, and carried as far as *Constantinople*, and to Places
‘ at a very great distance. The Force of this Eruption was greatest the
‘ two first Months, when all the Neighbouring Sea seem'd to boil, and the
‘ *Vulcan* continually vomited up Fire-balls. Upon the turning of the Wind,
‘ great Mischief was done in the Island of *Santerinum*, many Beasts and Birds
‘ were kill'd : And on the 29th of *October*, and 4th of *November*, about 50
‘ Men were kill'd by it. The other four Months it lasted, tho' much abated
‘ of its former Fierceness, yet it still cast up Stone, and seem'd to en-
‘ deavour the making of a New Island ; which though it do not yet perfectly
‘ appear above Water, yet 'tis cover'd but 8 Foot by the Water ; and the
‘ bubbling of the Water seems to speak another Eruption, that may in time
‘ finish Nature's Birth. And in the Year he writ this, which he says was
1656, there was an extraordinary boiling of the Sea, and an Eruption of Smoke. And though our Natural Historians have been very scarce in the World, and consequently such Histories are very few ; yet there has been no Age wherein such Historians have liv'd, but has afforded them an Example of such Effects of Earthquakes. And I doubt not, but had the World been always furnisht with such Historians as had been inquisitive and knowing, we should have found not only *Thera* or *Santerinum*, and *Volcano* and *Delos*, and that in the *Azores*, and one lately in the *Canaries*, but a very great part of the Islands of the whole World to have been rais'd out of the Sea, or separated from the Land by Earthquakes : for which Opinion I shall afterwards relate several Observations both of my own and others, which seem to afford probable Arguments.

The third Spe-
cies under the
first Genus of
Effects.
But to proceed to the third Kind or Species of Effects produced by Earthquakes, which is the raising very considerable Mountains out of Plains. Of this I shall add a few Instances ; but none more notable, than that of the new Mountain near *Naples* of which I said somewhat before out of *Sandys*'s Travels. In the Year 1538. *Septemb.* 29. this Mountain visibly ascended about the 2d hour of the Night, with a hideous roaring, horribly vomiting Stones, and such store of Cinders, as overwhelm'd all the Buildings thereabout, and the salubrious Baths of *Tripergula*, for so many Ages celebrated, consuming all the Vines to Ashes, and killing Birds and Beasts, and frighting away all the Inhabitants, who fled naked and defiled through the dark : And has advanced its top a Mile above the Basis : the Stones of it are so light and pory, that they will not sink when thrown in the Sea. This new Mountain, when new rais'd, had a number of Issues, at some of them smoking, and sometimes flaming;

ming; at others difgorging Rivulets of hot Water, keeping within a terrible rumbling; and many perifhed that ventured to defcend into the hollownefs above. But that hollow at the top is at prefent an Orchard, and the Mountain throughout bereft of its Terrors. 'It is reported, faith *Childrey*, that in a 'Parifh by the Sea-fide, not far from *Axbridge* in *Somerfetfhire*, within thefe 50 'Years, a Parcel of Land fwell'd up like a Hill; but on a fudden clave afun-'der, and fell down into the Earth, and in the place of it remains a great 'Pool. Our Englifh Chronicles fay, at *Oxenhal*, in the Bifhoprick of *Durham*, on *Chriftmas* Day 1679, the Ground heav'd up aloft like a Tower, and continued all that day immoveable, till Evening, and then fell with a horrible noife, finking into the Earth, and leaving three deep Pits, call'd Hellkettles. *Varenius* tells us of a new Mountain likewife raifed in *Java*, in the Year 1586, with the like Effects of thofe I formerly named of the new Mountain; firft fhaking the Earth, then heaving up and throwing up into the Air the upper Parts of the Earth, afterwards the Rock and inner Parts, then fiery Coals and Cinders, overwhelming the circumjacent Fields and Towns, and killing above 10000 Men, and burning what was not overwhelmed. I have not time to reckon up the multitude of Inftances I have met with in Authors; fuch as *Ætna* in *Sicily*, *Vefuvius* in *Italy*, one in *Croatia*, near the City *Valonia*, the *Pike* in *Tenarif*, and the *Pike* in the *Azores*, *Hecla*, *Helga*, and another in *Ifland*: The Mount *Gonnapi* in one of the Iflands of *Banda*, which made an horrid Eruption at the fame time with that in *Java*: The Mount *Balavane* in *Sumatra*: Others in the *Molucca* Iflands, in *China*, *Japan*, and the *Philippines*, and in fome of the *Maurician* Iflands, and feveral other Parts of the *Eaft Indies*. In the *Weft Indies* alfo we have multitudes of Examples, feveral in *Nicaragua*, and all along the Ledge of Mountains in *Peru* and *Chile*, and in *New Spain* and *Mexico*: In the Iflands of *Papoys*, difcover'd by *Le Mair*, joining to the South Continent in *Mar Del Zur*: All which are as fo many fhining Torches to direct us in the fearch after this Truth. There are many other Inftances of Mountains, that have but lately as it were left to burn, and are cover'd with Wood and grown-fruitful. So the new Mountain I formerly mention'd, has an Orchard growing where the Fire at firft flamed. Another in the Ifland *Quimeda*, near the River *Plat* in *Brafill*: The Iflands alfo of St. *Helena*, and *Afcenfion*, difcovered by the great plenty of Cinders, and the Fafhions of the Hills to have formerly contained *Vulcanoes*, and probably were at firft made by fome fubterraneous Eruption, as indeed moft of thofe Iflands in the main Ocean; fuch as the *Canaries*, and the *Azores*, and the *Eaft Indian*, and the *Cariby* Iflands and divers others feem to have been. A Paffage, to make this Affertion fomewhat more probable, I have met with in *Linfchoten*'s Defcription of the Ifland of *Tercera*, which as *Purchas* has epitomized I have here added. Pag. 1670. of the 4th Part of his Pilgrims (he faith, fpeaking of the Ifland of *Tercera*) 'The Land is very high, and as it 'feemeth hollow; for that as they pafs over an Hill of Stone, the Ground 'foundeth under them as if it were a Cellar. So that it feems in divers Pla-'ces to have holes under the Earth, whereby it is much fubject to Earth-'quakes, as alfo all the other Iflands are; for there it is a common thing: 'and all thofe Iflands, for the moft part, have had Mines of Brimftone; for 'that in many Places of *Tercera* and St. *Michael*, the Smoke and Savour of 'Brimftone doth ftill iffue out of the Ground, and the Country round about 'is all finged and burnt. Alfo there are Places wherein there are Wells, 'the Water whereof is fo hot that it will boil an Egg, as if it were over a 'Fire. Befides which, the fhape of the Hills, and feveral other Circumftances mention'd in *Linfchoten*, do make it probable that thofe have been all *Vulcano's*.

But to proceed to the Fourth Species of Effects of Earthquakes under this *Fourth Species* Head; and that is, the raifing of the Parts of the Earth by the throwing on *under the firft* a great accefs of new Earth: Of this I have already given many Inftances in *Genus of Ef-* the newly mentioned Hiftories of Eruptions, where I mentioned the over-*fects.* whelming of Fields, Towns, and Woods, and the like, by Materials thrown out by thefe Eruptions. I fhall only add one Inftance or two more to confirm

this

this Head, and then proceed. The firſt is that mentioned by *Olaus Wormius,* in the 5th Chapter of the 1ſt Section of the 1ſt Book of his *Muſæum,* wherein he gives an Account of an extraordinary Earthquake in *Iceland,* which fill'd the Air with Duſt, Earth, and Cinders, and overwhelmed Towns, Fields, and even Ships a good way diſtant on the Sea; and which ſent ſorth its Fumes with ſuch violence and Plenty, as covered all the Decks and Sails of Ships lying on the Coaſt of *Norway,* ſome hundred Leagues diſtant. His Words are Page the 18th thus, *Alterum portentoſæ Terræ genus, &c.* And to make this of *Wormius* the more probable, I have now by me a Paper of Duſt, which was rained out of the Air upon a Ship lying at *Algier* upon the Coaſt of *Barbary,* upon a great Eruption of *Veſuvius* in the Year 16--- The Relation of which, as I received it together with the Paper of Duſt from that eminent Virtuoſo, *John Evelyn,* Eſq; I ſhall here annex. * But which is beyond all, is the late Eruption of *Mongibell* or *Ætna.*

And to confirm this Propoſition yet further, I cannot paſs by a very remarkable Rain of Earth and Aſhes, that happen'd in *Peru, Anno* 1600, mentioned by *Garcilaſſo De la Vega,* one of the Off-ſpring of the *Incas* of *Peru,* in his Hiſtory of *America.* The Epitome of which by *Purchas,* is this, pag. 1476 of the 4th Part of his *Pilgrims.* ' I might add, ſays he, the great Earthquakes, *An.* 1600, in *Peru* at *Arequepa,* the raining of Sand, as alſo of ' Aſhes, about 20 days from a *Vulcan* breaking forth: The Aſhes falling in ' Places above a Yard thick, in ſome Places more than two, and where leaſt ' above a quarter of a Yard, which buried the Corn-grounds of Maize and ' Wheat, and the Boughs of Trees were broken and fruitleſs, and the Cattel ' great and ſmall dy'd for want of Paſture. For the Sand which rained covered ' the Fields 30 Leagues one way, and above 40 Leagues another way, round ' about *Arequepa,* they found their Kine dead by 500 together in ſeveral Herds, ' and whole Flocks of Sheep, and Herds of Goats and Swine buried. Hou-' ſes fell with the weight of the Sand; others coſt much Induſtry to ſave them; ' mighty Thunders and Lightning were heard and ſeen 30 Leagues about *A-*' *requepa.* It was ſo dark whilſt thoſe Showers laſted, that at mid-day they ' burned Candles to ſee to do buſineſs.---I could add divers other Inſtances to confirm this Propoſition; but theſe may at preſent ſuffice.

But this is but one way by which divers things have been buried: there is another way which I can only at preſent mention, and muſt refer the Probation and Proſecution to ſome other occaſion; and that is, that very many of the lower ſuperficial Parts of the Earth, have been and continually are covered and buried by the acceſs of Matter, tumbled and waſhed down by Exceſſes of Wind and Rain, and by the continual ſweepings of Rivers and Streams of Water. Under this Head, I ſhall ſhew ſeveral Places and Countries in the World, that are nothing elſe but the Productions of theſe Cauſes. To this purpoſe, *Peter de la Valle* gives ſome Obſervations which he made in *Egypt,* in the 11th Letter dated from *Grand Caire, Jan.* 25. 1616. ' Of the ' former ſeven Mouths of *Nile* (ſays he) there are only four left, and of ' thoſe but two Navigable; the reſt are either fill'd, or run no more, or are ' ſmall Streams not taken notice of, or only Torrents in the time of great ' Rains; but I could learn nothing of them, becauſe the great Expence of ' the Ancients for cleanſing the Ditches, has been intermitted for ſeveral ' hundreds of Years. He is likewiſe of Opinion with *Herodotus,* that the *Delta,* and all the Lower *Egypt,* where the *Greeks* navigated in his time, was in the firſt Ages of the World made by the Sand and Mud of *Nile.*

All which Hiſtories and Particulars do manifeſtly enough evince, that there have been in very many Parts of the World conſiderable Mutations of the ſuperficial Parts, ſince the beginning; and that therefore thoſe Places where theſe figured petrify'd Bodies are found; though they now ſeem never ſo much foreign, and differing from the likely native Places of ſuch animated Bodies, may notwithſtanding heretofore have been in ſuch another kind of condition, as was moſt ſutable to the breeding and nouriſhing of them: Which I ſhall yet further manifeſt, by comparing the other Effects produced by Earthquakes; ſuch as the ſinking, and burying, and tranſpoſing, and overturning of the ſuperficial Parts of the Earth.

Another

Another Sort of Effects, is the sinking of the superficial Parts of the Earth, and placing them below their former Position, both in respect of some Parts newly raised, and in respect of some other adjacent Parts not displaced. And this seems to be caus'd by the subsiding or sinking of those Parts into such Caverns, as by the strength of the Eruption passing below before it breaks out are made underneath : For so great is the Violence of these subterraneous Fires, that nothing almost is able to resist their Power of expanding ; but spreading themselves, and rushing that way which is most easy, they carry along before them Earth, Sand, and Rocks, and Mountains, and whatever lies in their way, and raise the superficial Parts of the Earth whilst they pass underneath. And if the Parts of the Earth underneath are so loose or obnoxious to the Force of the Fire, as to be dislodged, unless the remaining Parts are very strong and constitute a very firm Stony Arch, the Earth does easily tumble into the Holes and Hollows made by the Fire. Now it cannot be imagin'd but that all those vast Congeries of Earth, which I have already mention'd to have been thrown up, and to create new Islands and new Mountains, and the like, must leave vast Caverns below them, to be fill'd either with the Parts of the Earth that hang immediately over them, or with the Sea, or other subterraneous Waters, if the Roofs of these Cavities be strong enough to sustain the Earth above them from sinking. And some such Power as these subterraneous Fires, seems to me to have been the Cause of the strange Positions and Intermixture of the Veins of Ores and Minerals in the Bowels of the Mountains, where, for the most part, they are now found ; and even of bringing those Substances so near the Surface of the Earth, which, from the Consideration of very many Circumstances, seem to me to be naturally situated at a much greater Depth below within the Bowels of this Globe. And hence may be rendred a Reason of the Figures of these Minerals, and other Substances mix'd with them, and of the compounding and blending of several of those Substances together, whereby some of them are very strangely united and alter'd. But this I mention only by the Bye, and shall not insist on it, belonging more properly to another Head. To proceed then under this General Head, are comprised several Kinds of Effects, differing only according to the Parts of the Earth they have been wrought upon.

The second sort or General Head of Effects of Earthquakes.

The first is, The sinking of several Inland Parts, which were before eminent, and laying them much lower into Vales. Sometimes, the sinking of a Part of the Earth to a very great Depth, and leaving behind, instead of a firm Ground, a Lake of Salt or Sea-water. Of these we have several Instances in Natural Historians. And, to pass by many others, I shall only mention such as have lately happen'd. Of this kind Mr. *Childrey*, in his *Britannia Baconica*, has collected several Instances ; two out of our English Chronicle. His Relations are these, *Pag.* 62. ' *August* the 4th, 1585. after a ve-
' ry violent Storm of Thunder and Rain, at *Nottingham* in *Kent*, Eight miles
' from *London*, the Ground suddenly began to sink ; and Three great Elms
' growing upon it, were carried so deep into the Earth, that no Part of them
' could any more be seen. The Hole left (saith the Story) is in Compass 80
' Yards about, and a Line of 50 Fathoms plummed into it finds no Bottom.
Also,
' *Dec.* 18. 1596. a Mile and half from *Westram*, Southward (which is not
' many Miles from *Nottingham*) a Part of an Hedge of Ashes, 12 Perches
' long, were sunk 6 Foot and an half deep ; the next morning 15 Foot more ;
' the third morning 80 Foot more at least, and so daily. (And presently af-
' ter, he says) Moreover, in one Part of the Plain Field, there is a great Hole
' made by sinking of the Earth, to the Depth of 30 Foot at least, being in
' Breadth in some Places 2 Perches over, and in Length 5 or 6 Perches.
' There are sundry other Sinkings in divers other Places, one of 60 Foot, a-
' nother of 47, and another of 34 Foot ; by means of which Confusion it is
' come to pass, that where the highest Hills were, there be the lowest Dales,
' and the lowest Dales are become the highest Grounds, &c.
And again, *Pag.* 131. he gives an Instance, upon his own Knowledge, much to the same purpose, which lately happen'd ; namely, ' *July* the 8th 1657.

The first species of those Effects, under the second general Head or Genus of Earthquakes.

' about

' about 3 of the Clock, in the Parifh of *Bickly*, was heard a very great Noife
' like Thunder afar off; which was much wonder'd at, becaufe the Sky was
' clear, and no Appearance of a Cloud. Shortly after (faith the Author of
' this Relation) a Neighbour came to me, and told me, I fhould fee a very
' ftrange-thing if I would go with him. So coming into a Field, called the
' *Lay-field*, we found a very great Bank of Earth, which had many tall Oaks
' growing on it, quite funk into the Ground Trees and all. At firft we durft
' not go near it, becaufe the Earth, for near 20 Yards about, was exceeding-
' ly much rent, and feem'd ready to fall: But fince that time, my felf and
' fome others have ventured to fee the bottom, I mean to go to the Brink, fo
' as to difcern the vifible Bottom, which is Water, and conceived to be about
' 30 Yards from us; under which is funk all the Earth about it, for 16 Yards
' round at leaft, 3 tall Oaks, a very tall Awber, and certain other fmall
' Trees, and not a Sprig of them to be feen above Water. 4 or 5 Oaks
' more are expected to fall every moment, and a great Quantity of Land is
' like to fall, indeed never ceafing more or lefs; and when any confiderable
' Clod falls, it is much like the Report of a Cannon. We can difcern the
' Ground hollow above the Water a great Depth; but how far hollow or how
' deep, is not to be found out by Man. Some of the Water, (as I have been
' told) drawn out of this Pit with a Bucket, was found to be as falt as Sea-
' water, *&c.*

A confiderable Circumftance alfo to confirm this Propofition, is a Paffage
in that Hiftory I have mention'd out of *Linfchoten*, of the Ifland of *Tercera*;
where he fays [*and fome Hills were defaced, and made even with the Ground.*]

Kircher in the Preface to his *Mundus Subterraneus*, Chap. 2. tells us a very
remarkable Hiftory of the finking of a Town, and the Land about it, and the
Generation of a Lake inftead of it. *Contigit* (fays he) *hac eadem hora res æter-*
na ac immortali Memoria digna, fubverfio videlicet celeberrimi oppidi quod Sanctam
Euphemiam dicunt, erat hoc in extrema Sinus ora fitum fub equitum Melitenfium
Jurifdictione. Cum itaq; ad Lopicium ex vehementi Terræ fubfultatione veluti exa-
nimes in terra proftrati tandem fubfidente Naturæ paroxyfmo, oculis in circum ja-
centia Loca conjectis, ingenti nebula, paulo ante memoratum oppidum circumdatum
vidiffemus; ter fane poft Meridiem, hora tertia præfertim Cœlo fereno mira & in-
folita nobis videbatur. Diffipata vero paulatim nebula, oppidum quæfivimus fed
non invenimus. Mirum Dictu, Lacu putidiffimo in ejus Locum enato. Quæfivi-
mus Homines qui de infolito rei eventu nonnihil certi nobis enarrare poffent, fed for-
midabilis cafus tantaq; ftragis nuncium non reperimus, &c.---- Nos itineri infiften-
tes Nicaftrum, Amanteam, Paulam, Belviderium tranfeuntes nil aliud ad 200
Millia paffuum nifi cadavera Urbium, caftallorum, ftrages horrendas reperimus, Homi-
nibus per apertos campos palantibus & præ timore veluti exarefcentibus. That is,
' At this very time happened a thing worthy never to be forgotten, *viz.* the
' Subverfion of the moft famous Town, call'd St. *Euphemia*: 'twas fituated at
' the fide of the Bay under the Jurifdiction of the Knights of *Malta.* When
' therefore we had come to *Lopiz*, almoft dead from the vehement fhak-
' ing of the Earth, and lying proftrate on the Ground, at laft the *Paroxyfm*
' of Nature remitting, cafting our Eyes towards the Neighbouring Places,
' we faw the forementioned Town encompaffed with a great, wonderful, and
' unufual Cloud, which was feen by us three times, efpecially at Three-a-clock
' in the Afternoon, the Heavens being clear. This Cloud being, by degrees,
' diffipated, we look'd for the Town, but found it not, a ftinking Lake (to
' our wonder) appearing in the Place of it. We fought for fome Perfon or
' other, to give us fome certain Account of this unufual Event; but could
' not find one to tell any News of this dreadful Accident and great Deftru-
' ction, *&c.* We profecuting our Journey, paffing by *Nicaftrum, Amantea,*
' *Paula,* and *Belvedere,* found nothing for 200 Miles, but the remaining Car-
' caffes of Cities and Caftles, and horrid Deftructions; the Men lying in
' the open Fields, and, as it were, dead and withered through Fear and
' Terror.

To this purpofe, give me leave to adjoin an Extract of a Letter, fent from
Balafore in the *Eaft Indies*, *Jan.* 6. 1665. ' The fame Star appeared in our
' Horizon, about the fame time 'twas feen with you. The Effects in part

' have

' have already been felt here by unseasonable Weather, great Mortalities a-
' mongst the Natives, *English*, and others. We have had several Earth-
' quakes unusual here, which, with hideous Noises, have in several Places
' broke out and swallow'd up Houses and Towns. But about 7 Days Journey
' from *Ducca*, where were at that time 3 or 4 *Dutch*, they and the Natives
' relate, That in the Market-Place the Earth trembled about 32 Days and
' Nights, without Intermission. At the latter end, in the Market-place, the
' Ground turn'd round as Dust in a Whirlwind, and so continued several
' Days and Nights, and swallow'd up several Men who were Spectators, who
' sunk and turned round with the Earth, as in a Quagmire. At last, the
' Earth worked and cast up a great Fish bigger than hath been seen in this
' Country, which the People caught : But the Conclusion of all was, that the
' Earth sunk with 300 Houses, and all the Men, where now appears a large
' Lake some Fathoms deep. About a Mile from this Town was a Lake full
' of Fish, which in these 32 Days of the Earthquake cast up all her Fish on
' dry Land, where might have been gather'd many, which had run out of the
' Water upon dry Land, and there died : But when the other great Lake ap-
' peared, this former dried up, and is now firm Land.

To the same purpose also we have several other Instances, some later and
some nearer home. ' Near *Darlington* (says *Childrey*, in his *Britannia Baconi-*
' *ca*, speaking of the Rarities of the Bishoprick of *Durham*) are three Pits,
' whose Waters are warm (hot, says *Cambden*) wonderful deep, call'd Hell-
' Kettles. These are thought to come of an Earthquake, that happen'd
' *Anno* 1179. For on *Christmas* Day, says our Chronicles, at *Oxenhall*, which
' is this Place, the Ground heaved up aloft like a Tower, and so continued
' all that Day, as it were immovable, till Evening, and then fell in with a
' very horrible Noise, and the Earth swallow'd it up, and made in the same
' Place 3 deep Pits. The same in the Section of *Brecknock*, says, ' Two Miles
' East from *Brecknock*, is a Meer, called *Llinsavathan*, which (as the People
' dwelling there, say,) was once a City ; but the City was swallowed up by
' an Earthquake, and this Water or Lake succeeded in the Place : The Lake
' is encompassed with high steep Hills, *&c.*---

' Near *Falkirk*, saith *Lithgow*, remains the Ruines and Marks of a Town,
' *&c.* swallowed up into the Earth by an Earthquake, and the void Place is
' fill'd with Water.---- *Pliny* also, in the 88th Chap. of his 2d Book of Nat.
Hist. records a like Instance. *Mox & in his Montem Epopon cum repente flam-*
ma ex eo emicuisset campestri æquatum planitie. In eadem & oppidum haustum pro-
fundo alioq; motu Terræ Stagnum emersisse. Et alio provolutis Montibus insulam
extitisse Prochytam, &c. ' Presently the Mountain *Epopon* (when suddenly a
' Flame had shon out of it) was levelled with the Plain ; and in the same
' Plain a Town was swallow'd up into the Deep, and by another Motion of
' the Earth became a Lake. And in another Place, the Mountain being
' tumbled down, the Island *Prochyta* arose, *&c.*

The Dead Sea also in *Palestine*, was the Production of a most terrible Earthquake, and a Fire sent from Heaven : For, methinks, the Relation of the sad
Catastrophe of those Four Cities, *Sodom, Gomorrha, Zeboim* and *Adma*, mentioned in Scripture, seem somewhat like that I have newly related out of *Kircher* of
St. *Euphemia*. There are a multitude of other Instances which I could bring
on this Head, of the sinking of Mountains and Hills into Plains, and all these
into Lakes : Of which *Pliny* gives several Instances, in the 90, 91, and 92 Chap.
of his Second Book. The *Pico* in the *Moluccas*, accounted of equal Height
with that of *Tenariff*, was by a late Earthquake quite swallow'd into the
Earth, and left a Lake in its Place. *Vesuvius* and *Strongylus*, are by late
Earthquakes reduced to almost half their former Height. Many of those vast
Mountains of the *Andes* in *Chile*, were by an Earthquake, *An.* 1646. quite
swallow'd up and lost, as *Kircher* relates. I could add many Histories of the
fatal Catastrophe's of many Towns, and other Places of Note ; but these, I
hope, may suffice to shew this kind also of Mutation in the superficial Parts of
the Earth, to be effected by Earthquakes.

The second Spe-
cies of those
Effects under
the second Ge-
neral.

Nor does Earthquakes only sink Mountains and Inland Parts; but such Parts also as are near to, equal with, and under the Surface of the Sea. Of this we have Instances near home, of *Winchelsea* and of the *Goodwin-Lands,* and of the Towns in *Freezland,* that have been about 400 Years since swallow'd up by the Sea; and nothing but some Towers, and the *Goodwin-Sands,* are now to be found of them. The like happen'd to several Parts of *Scotland,* as *Hector Boethius* relates. *Linschoten,* in his History of the *West-Indies,* relates among many other Histories of the Effects of Earthquakes, this considerable Passage. ' Since, in the Year 1586. in the Month of *July,* fell another
' Earthquake in the City of *Kings,* the which, as the Vice-Roy did write,
' had run 170 Leagues along the Coast, and athwart in the *Sierra* 50 Leagues.
' It ruin'd a great Part of the City. It caus'd the like Trouble and Motion
' of the Sea, as it had done at *Chile,* which happen'd presently after the
' Earthquake; so as they might see the Sea to fly furiously out of her Bounds,
' and to run near 2 Leagues into the Land, rising above 14 Fathom. It co-
' ver'd all the Plain, so as the Ditches were filled and Pieces of Wood that were
' here, swam in the Water. There are multitudes of Instances of the like Effects in several other Parts of the World, which have been wrought by Earthquakes, which may be found in Natural Historians; which, for Brevity-sake, I omit, they serving only to prove a Proposition, which, I suppose, will be granted by any that have either seen or heard of the Effects of Earthquakes.

The third Spe-
cies of Effects
under the se-
cond General.

Now, though I find a general Deficiency in Natural Historians, of Instances to prove that the submarine Parts have likewise suffer'd the like Effects of sinking, they lying out of view, and so cannot without some Trouble and Diligence be observed; yet if we consider from how great a Depth these Eruptions proceed, and how little Distinction they make between Mountains and Plains, as to the weight of removing, we may easily believe, that the Bottom of the Sea is as subject to these Mutations, as the Parts of the Land. And since, by the former Relations, we have many Instances of the raising of the Bottom of the Sea, 'tis very probable that what Quantity of Matter is thrown to and raised in one Place, is sunk and falls into that Cavity left by another. An Island cannot be raised in one Place, without leaving an Abyss in another. And I do not doubt, but there have been as many Earthquakes in the Parts of the Earth under the Ocean, as there have been in the Parts of the Dry Land: But being, for the most part, till of late unfrequented by Mankind, and even now but very thinly, 'tis almost a 1000 to 1, that what happen are never seen; and a 100 to 1, if they have been seen, whether they be recorded: For how few Writers are there of Natural History? There is somewhat of Probability in the Story related by *Plato,* in his *Timæus,* of the Island *Atlantis* in the *Atlantick* Ocean, which he says was swallow'd up by an Earthquake into the Sea. And 'tis not unlikely, but that most of those Islands that are now appearing, have been either thrown up out of the Sea by Eruptions, such as the *Canaries, Azores,* St. *Helena, &c.* which the Form of them, and the Vulcanes in them, and the Cinders and Pumice-stones found about them, and the frequent Earthquakes they are troubled with, and the remaining Hills of extinguish'd Vulcanes, do all strongly argue for: Or else, that they are some of them at least some Relicts of that Great Island which is now not to be found; and yet we have no Records hereof. That there is as great Inequality in the Depth of the Sea, as there is in the Height of the Land, the Observations of Seamen, experimented by their Sounding Lines, do sufficiently inform us: For Hills, we have deep Holes; and for Mountains and Pikes, Abysses and Malstroons: And that these must have in all Ages been filling with Parts of the Earth, tumbled by the Motion of the Waters, and rowling to the lowest Place, is very probable; and so they would in time have been fill'd up, had not Earthquakes, by their Eruptions and Tumblings, created new Irregularities. And therefore that there are still such Places, is an Argument, that there have been of later Ages Earthquakes in some of them. Of these I shall mention one or two Instances, which I meet with in Voyages, and Relations of Travellers.

In

In the Relation of the Circum-navigation of Sir *Francis Drake*, speaking of the Straights of *Magellane*, he says, Pag. 35, 'They saw an Island with a very high *Vulcano* ; and the next Page, he says, 'They had need to have carry'd no- 'thing but Anchors and Cables, to find Ground, the Sea was so very deep: 'Which Depth is explain'd more express, Pag. 42. where 'tis said, 'Being 'driven from our first Place of anchoring, so unmeasurable was the Depth, 'that 500 Fathoms would fetch no Ground. And in Page 99. of the same Relation, the Author tells, how their Ship struck upon a Rock, which Page 102. he says, at low Water was but 6 Foot under Water, and just by it no Bottom to be found, by reason of the great Depth.

Mr. *Ricaut*, in a Letter of his to the Royal Society, dated from *Constantino-ple, Nov.* 1667, says, 'That the Water runs out of the *Euxine* Sea into the *Pro-* 'pontis with a wonderful swiftness, which is more wonderful in regard of the 'depth of the *Bosphorus* being in the Channel fifty or fifty five Fathom Wa- 'ter, and along the Land in most places the Ships may lye on the Shore with 'their Heads, and yet have twenty Fathom Water at their Sterns.

Besides these effects of raising and sinking the parts of the Earth, there is *The third Ge-* a third sort, which is the transposing, converting, subverting and jumbling *neral Head or* the parts of the Earth together ; overthrowing Mountains, and turning *the third sort of* them upsidedown, throwing the parts of the Earth from one place to another, *effects of Earth-* burying the superficial parts, and raising the Subterraneous. Of these kinds *quakes.* of changes there are many instances in the former Relations I have mention'd, as particularly that of *Linschoten* of the Earthquake in the *Terceras*, and that of *Josephus Acosta*, of the Earthquake upon the Coast of *Chile*. And there are a multitude of others I could here set down, but I shall only mention some of them. 'Soon after, (says *Josephus Acosta*, in the same place I mentioned be- 'fore) which was in the Year 1582, happened that Earthquake of *Arequipa*, which in a manner overthrew the whole City. And a little before in the same place, he tells of a terrible Earthquake in *Guatimala*, in the Year 1586, which overthrew almost all the City, and that the Vulcan for above six Months together continually vomited a Flood of Fire from the top of it. And a lit- tle after, the same Author, in the same place, says, 'In the Year of our Lord '1581, in *Cugiano*, a City of *Peru*, otherwise call'd the *Pear*, there happen'd 'a strange accident touching this Subject ; a Village call'd *Angoango* (where 'many *Indians* dwelt that were Socerers and Idolaters) fell sudenly to ruine, 'so as a great part thereof was raised up and carried away, and many of the '*Indians* smothered ; and that which seems incredible (yet testified by Men 'of Credit) the Earth that was ruined and so beaten down, did run and slide 'upon the Land for the space of a League and a half, as it had been Water or 'Wax melted, so as it stopt and fill'd up a Lake, and remain'd so spread all 'over the whole Country.

Nor are there wanting Examples of this kind even in this Island. Mr. *Chil-drey* in his *Britannia Baconica* has collected several out of *Cambden* ; as that in *Herefordshire*, 'Where, in the Year 1571, *Marcley* Hill in the East part of 'the Shire, with a roaring noise, remov'd itself from the place where it stood, 'and for three Days together travell'd from its old Seat. It began first to 'take its Journey *Feb.* 17. being *Saturday*, at six of the Clock at Night, and 'by seven the next Morning it had gone forty Paces, carrying with it Sheep 'in their Cotes, Hedge-Rows, and Trees, whereof some were overturn'd, 'and some that stood upon the Plain, are firmly growing upon the Hill ; 'those that were East were turned West, and those in the West were set in 'the East ; in this remove it overthrew *Kinaston* Chappel, and turn'd two 'High-ways near a hundred Yards from their old Paths : The Ground that 'they remov'd was about twenty six Acres, which opening itself with Rocks 'and all bore the Earth before it for four hundred Yards space, without any 'stay, leaving Pasturage in places of the Tillage, and the Tillage overspread 'with Pasturage. Lastly, overwhelming its lower parts, it mounted to a 'Hill of twelve Fathoms high, and there rested after three Days travel.

' At *Hermitage* in *Dorsetshire*, says *Stow* in his Summary, *January* the third
' 1582, a piece of Ground of three Acres remov'd from its old place, and was
' carried over another Close where Alders and Willows grew, the space of
' forty Rods or Pearches, and stopt up the high-Way that led to *Cerne*, a
' Market-Town, and yet the Hedges that it was inclosed with enclose it
' still, and the Trees stand bolt upright, and the place where this Ground
' was is left like a great Pit.' And tis not a little observable, that at the
same time that these changes happened in *America*, the like also happened in
England, of which I shall hereafter give divers other Instances, and shall also
deduce Corrolarys, that may otherwise seem very strange, and yet I question
not to prove the truth of them. *Maximus* (says *Pliny*, Cap. 48. Lib. 2. Hist.
Nat.) *Terræ memoria mortalium extitit motus Tiberii Cæsaris principatu. XII. urbibus
Asiæ una nocte prostratis.* ' The greatest Earthquake that ever hapæn'd in the
' Memory of Man was in the Reign of *Tiberius Cæsar*, twelve Cities of *Asia*
' being thrown down by it in one Night.' And again, (*Cap.* 83. ibid.) *Factum
est semel* (says he) *quod equidem in Hetruscæ disciplinæ voluminibus inveni, ingens
terrarum portentum L. Martio, Sex. Julio Coss. in Agro Mutinensi namq; montes duo
inter se concurrerunt, crepitu maximo assultantes recedentesq; inter eos flamma fumoq;
in cœlum exeunte interdiu, Spectante evia Æmilia Magna equitum Romanorum fami-
liarumq; & viatorum multitudine: Eo concursu villæ omnes elisæ, animalia per-
multa quæ intra fuerant exanimata sunt, anno ante Sociale bellum. Quod haud scio
an funestius ipsi terræ Italiæ fuerit quam Civilia. Non minus mirum ostentum &
nostra cognovit ætas. Anno Neronis Principis Supremo, sicut in rebus ejus exposuimus,
pratis oleisq;, intercedente via publica in contrarias sedes transgressis, in Agro Marru-
cino Prædiis Vectii Marcelli Equitis Romani res Neronis Procurantis.* Thus English'd. ' There happen'd once (which I found in the Books of the *Tuscane*
' Learning) within the Territories of *Modena*, *L. Martius* and *S. Julius*, be-
' ing Consuls a great wonder of the Earth; for two Hills encountred each
' other charging one another with a great crash, and retiring again, a great
' Flame and Smoak in the Day-time issuing out from between them to the
' Sky, while a great many of the *Roman* Knights, their Friends and Travel-
' lers beheld it from the *Æmilian* Road. With this conflict and meeting to-
' gether, all the Country Houses were dasht to pieces, many Animals that
' were between them perish'd. This happen'd before the *Social* War. I
' know not whether it were not more pernicious to *Italy* than the Civil-Wars.'
' No less a wonder was that in our Age, in the last Year of *Nero* (as we have
' shewn in his Acts) when Meadows and Olive-Trees (the publick Road lying
' between them) went into the contrary places, in the *Marrucine* Territory, in
' the Lands of *Vectius Marcellus*, a *Roman* Knight, Procurator under *Nero*.

There are many the like Instances to be met with in Authors, of the placing Parts perpendicular or inclining, which were before horizontal; so the
turning of other parts upside downwards, of throwing parts from place to
place; of stopping the Passage of Rivers, and turning them another way;
of swallowing some Rivers, and of producing others a new; of changing
Countries from Barren to Fruitful, and from Fruitful to Barren; of making
Islands join to the Continent, and separating parts of the Continent into I-
slands. There are other Relations that mention the vast spaces of Ground
that have been all at once shaken and overturned, some of five Hundred Miles
in length, and a hundred and fifty in bredth. Of the communication of Vulcanes (which are as it were the Nostrills or constant Breathing places of these
Monsters) tho' plac'd at a very great distance one from another by Subterraneous Caverns. Other Relations furnish us with Instances of the Substances
they vomit out; such as Pumice Stones, and several other sorts of calcin'd and
melted Stones, and Rocks, Ashes, Minerals, hot Water, Sulphur, Flame,
Smoak, and various other Substauces.

The fourth ge-
neral Head of In others we find instances of Liquefactions, Vitrifications, Calcinations,
Sublimations, Distillations, Petrifactions, Transformations, Suffocations and
the Effects of Infective or deadly Steams destroying all things near them, which possibly may
Earthquakes. be one cause of the scarcity of Relations where 'tis probable there have been
so very many effects wrought in the World of this kind. But these I shall
not

not infift upon, having I fear too long digrefs'd on this part to fhew the variety of effects produced by Earthquakes.

There is only one thing more that I think pertinent to our prefent purpose, and that is the univerfality of this active Principle: There is no Country almoft in the World but has been fometimes or other fhaken by Earthquakes, that has not fuffered fome, if not moft parts of thefe Effects. *Seneca* fays in the Preface to the 6th Book of his Natural Queftions. *Omnia ejufdem fortis funt, etfi nondum mota tamen mobilia; erramus enim, fi ullam terrarum partem, exceptam immunemq; ab hoc periculo credimus, omnes fub eadem jacent lege, nihil, ita ut immobile effet, Natura concepit: Alia temporibus aliis cadunt; & quemadmodum in urbibus magnis nunc hæc domus nunc illa fufpenditur, ita in hoc orbe Terrarum, nunc hæc pars facit vitium nunc illa. Tyrus aliquando infamis ruinis fuit. Afia duodecim Urbes fimul perdidit. Anno priore Achaiam & Macedoniam quæcunque eft ifta vis mali quæ incurrit, nunc Campaniam læfit: Circuit fatum, & fiquid diu præteriit, repetit. Quædam rarius, folicitat, fæpius quædam. Nihil immune effe & innoxium finit. Non homines tantum, qui brevis & caduca res nafcimur; Urbes oræque terrarum & Litora & ipfum mare in fervitutem fati venit. Quo ergo nobis permanfura promittimus bona fortunæ, & fælicitatem (cujus ex omnibus rebus humanis velociffima eft levitas) habituram in aliquo pondus & moram credimus? Perpetua fibi omnia promittentibus in mentem non venit: Id ipfum fupra quod ftamus ftabile non effe. Neque enim Campaniæ iftud aut Achaiæ, fed omnis foli vitium eft, male cohærere & ex caufis plurimis refolvi; & fumma manere partibus ruere.* Which I Englifh thus. ' All things are fubject to the fame chance; tho' they are
' not yet moved, they are movable; for we err, if we believe any part of
' the Earth excufed and free from this hazzard; all are fubject to the fame
' Law; nothing is made by Nature fo fixt as to be unmoveable; fome fink at
' one time, fome at another: And as in great Cities, now this Houfe, now
' that Houfe hangs tottering on Props; fo on the great Face of the Earth,
' now this part fails, now that: *Tyre* formerly was remarkable for its De-
' ftruction: *Afia* loft at once Twelve Cities. Whatever the Power may be,
' the former Year *Achaia* and *Macedonia* felt it now *Campania*: Fate goes
' round, and repeats what it had long before acted: It brings fome things
' often on the Stage, fome feldom; but fuffers nothing abfolutely free and
' untouch'd. Not we Men only are brought forth fhort Liv'd, frail Beings:
' Cities, Countries, Shores, nay the Sea itfelf are the Slaves of Fate. Why
' therefore do we flatter our felves that the gifts of Fortune will ftick by us,
' or that Happinefs will obferve any Rule or Meafure, Happinefs the moft
' fleeting of all humane Things? They that promife to themfelves all things
' fixt, furely never think that the very Ground we ftand on is it felf unfixt.
' Nor was that the frailty only of *Campania* or *Achia*, 'tis the fame in all
' Soils and Countries, to be loofely join'd and compacted, but eafily and by
' many ways diffolved; the whole remains while each part changes and finks
' into Ruine and Alteration.'

Thus we fee all Countries in the World are fubject to thefe Convulfions, but thofe moft of all that are moft Mountainous: Such are ufually all the Sea Coafts, therefore *Pliny* fays, That the *Alps*, and *Appnnine* Mountains have very often been troubled with Earthquakes. *Maritima autem maxime quatiuntur* (fays he) *nec montofa tali malo carent. Exploratum eft mihis Alpes Appenninumq; fæpius tremuiffe.* Martine places are moft fhaken, nor do the Mountainous efcape, for I have often found the *Alpes* and *Apennines* tremble.

For moft probably thofe that are moft Mountainous, are moft Cavernous underneath them; to countenance which Opinion, I remember to have taken notice in certain very high Cliffs towards the Sea fide, where the Hills feemed, as it were, cleft afunder, the one half having been probably foundred and tumbled down into the Sea, and the other half, as it were remaining, that at the bottom, near the Water, for almoft the whole length, there were very many large Caverns, which, by feveral Circumftances, feem'd to be made before the accefs of the Sea thereunto, and not by the wafhing and beating of the Waves againft the bottom of thefe Cliffs; for I obferv'd in many of them, that the Plates or Layers, as I may fo call thofe parts between the Clefts in

Rocks-

Of the Univerfality of this active Power or Principle.

Rocks, and Cliffs to lean contrary ways, and to meet, as it were, at the top like the Roof of a House, and others of them in other forms, as if they had been Caverns left between many vast Rocks tumbled confusedly one upon another. And indeed I cannot imagine, but that under these Mountains, Islands, Cliffs or Lands, that have been much rais'd above their former level, there must be left vast Caverns, whence all that Matter was thrown, where probably may be the Seat or Place of the Generation of those prodigious Powers. But this only by the Bye; for I intend not here to examine the causes of their beginnings, force, and powerful Effects, nor of their remaining, ceasing, renewing, or the like. It being sufficient, for my present purpose, to shew, That they have been certainly observ'd to produce those extraordinary Effects from what Cause soever they proceed. That they have been heretofore in many places where they have now ceas'd for many Ages; and that they have lately happen'd in places, where we have no History that does assure us they have been heretofore. That they have turn'd Plains into Mountains, and Mountains into Plains; Seas into Land, and Land into Seas; made Rivers where there were none before, and swallowed up others that formerly were; made and destroy'd Lakes, made Peninsuls Islands, and Islands Peninsulas; vomited up Islands in some places, and swallowed them down in others; overturn'd, tumbl'd and thrown from place to place Cities, Woods, Hills, &c. cover'd, burnt, wasted and chang'd the superficial Parts in others; and many the like strange Effects, which, since the Creation of the World, have wrought many very great changes on the superficial Parts of the Earth, and have been the great Instruments or Causes of placing Shells, Bones, Plants, Fishes, and the like, in those places, where, with much astonishment, we find them.

Concerning the Vicissitudes that places are subject to, in relation to Earthquakes, I find a memorable Passage sent by *Paul Ricaut* Esquire, now Consule of *Smyrna*, Dated *November* 23. 1667. ' *Constantinople*, says he, is not now so
' subject to Earthquakes as reported in former times, there having not hap-
' pen'd in the last seven Years, in which I have been an Inhabitant there, above
' one of which I have been sensible; but within these twenty Days in *Smyrna*
' fell out an Earthquake which dangerously shook all the Buildings, but did
' little or no harm; the Ships in the Road, and others at an Anchor, about
' three Leagues from hence, were sensible of it. It is reported that this
' City hath been already seven times devoured by Earthquakes, and it is pro-
' phesied, that it shall be so again so soon as the Houses reach the old Castle
' upon the top of the Hill, on the side of which remains the Ruins of the old
' City and the Tomb of St. *Polycarpus*, St. *John*'s Disciple, still preserv'd by
' the *Greeks* in great Veneration.

The Motion of the Water another cause of alterations on the Earth. Another Cause there is which has been also a very great Instrument in the promoting the alterations on the Surface of the Earth, and that is the motion of the Water; whether caus'd 1*st*. By its Descent from some higher place, such as Rivers and Streams, caus'd by the immediate falls of Rain, or Snow, or by the melting of Snow from the sides of Hills. Or, 2*dly*. By the natural Motions of the Sea, such as are the Tides and Currents. Or, 3*dly*. By the accidental motions of it caus'd by Winds and Storms. Of each of these we have very many Instances in Natural Historians, and were they silent, the constant Effects, would daily speak as much. The former Principle seems to be that which generates Hills, and Holes, Cliffs, and Caverns, and all manner of Asperity and irregularity in the Surface of the Earth; and this is that which indeavours to reduce them back again to their pristine Regularity, by washing down the tops of Hills, and filling up the bottoms of Pits, which is indeed consonant to all the other methods of Nature, in working with contrary Principles of Heat and Cold, Driness, and Moisture, Light and Darkness, &c. by which there is, as it were, a continual circulation. Water is rais'd in Vapours into the Air by one Quality and precipated down in drops by an other, the Rivers run into the Sea, and the Sea again supplies them. In the circular Motion of all the Planets, there is a direct Motion which makes them indeavour to recede from the Sun or Center,

and

and a magnetick or attractive Power that keeps them from receding. Ge-'neration creates and Death deſtroys; Winter reduces what Summer produces: The Night refreſhes what the Day has ſcorcht, and the Day cheriſhes what the Night benumb'd. The Air impregnates the Ground in one place, and is impregnated by it in another. All things almoſt circulate and have their Viciſſitudes. We have multitudes of inſtances of the waſting of the tops of Hills, and of the filling or increaſing of the Plains or lower Grounds, of Rivers continually carrying along with them great quantities of Sand, Mud, or other Subſtances from higher to lower places. Of the Seas waſhing Cliffs away and waſting the Shores: Of Land Floods carrying away with them all things that ſtand in their way, and covering thoſe Lands with Mud which they overflow, levelling Ridges and filling Ditches. Tides and Currents in the Sea act in all probability what Floods and Rivers do at Land; and Storms effect that on the Sea Coaſts, that great Land Floods do on the Banks of Rivers. *Ægypt* as lying very low and yearly overflow'd, is inlarg'd by the ſediment of the *Nile*; eſpecially towards that part where the *Nile* falls into the *Mediterranean*. The Gulph of *Venice* is almoſt choak'd with the Sand of the *Po*. The Mouth of the *Thames* is grown very ſhallow by the continual ſupply of Sand brought down with the Stream. Moſt part of the Cliffs that Wall in this Iſland do Yearly founder and tumble into the Sea. By theſe means many parts are covered and rais'd by Mud and Sand that lye almoſt level with the Water, and others are diſcover'd and laid open that for many Ages have been hid.

Of this kind the Royal Society received a memorable Account from the Learned Dr. *Brown* concerning a petrified Bone of a prodigious bigneſs, diſcover'd by the falling of ſome Cliffs; the words of the Relation are theſe. ' This Bone (which he preſented the Royal Society, and is now in the Re-' poſitory) was found laſt Year 1666. on the Sea Shore, not far from *Win-*' *terton* in *Norfolk*; it was found near the Clift after two great Floods, ſome ' thouſand Loads of Earth being broken down by the rage of the Sea, as it ' often happens upon this Coaſt, where the Cliffs conſiſt not of Rock but of ' Earth. That it came not out of the Sea may be conjectur'd becauſe it was ' found near the Cliff, and by the colour of it, for if out of the Sea it would ' have been whiter. Upon the ſame Coaſt, but as I take it, nearer *Hasbo-*' *rough*, divers great Bones are ſaid to have been found, and I have ſeen a lower ' Jaw containing Teeth of a prodigious bigneſs and ſomewhat petrified. All ' that have been found on this Coaſt have been found after the falling of ſome ' Cliff, where the outward Cruſt is fallen off, it clearly reſembles the Bones ' of Whales and great Cetaceous Animals, comparing it with the Scull and ' Bones of a Whale which was caſt upon the Coaſt near *Wells*, and which I ' have by me, the weight whereof is 55 Pounds.' Thus far he on this Sub-' ject. To this may be added the *Chartham* News, or the diſcovery of River-' horſe, or the *Hippopotamus* Teeth printed in the *Philoſ. Tranſactions.* N. 272. ' p. 882

Nor are theſe Changes now only, but they have in all probability been of as long ſtanding as the World. So 'tis probable there may have been ſeveral viciſſitudes of changes wrought upon the ſame part of the Earth; it may have been of an exact ſpherical Form, with the reſt of the Earths or Planets, at the Creation of the World, before the eternal Command of the Almighty, that the Waters under the Heaven ſhould go to their place, which before cover'd the Earth, ſo as that it was ἀόρατος κỳ ἀκαλαοκεύασος κỳ οκόλος επάνω τῦ αβύσε κỳ πνεῦμα θεῦ ἐπεφέρελο ἐπάνωτῦ ὑδ'αλος, inviſible and incompleated, and the Darkneſs of the Deep was over it (being all over cover'd with a very thick ſhell of Water which environ'd it on every ſide, it being then in all probability created of an exact Spherical Figure, and ſo the Waters being of themſelves lighter than the Earth, muſt equally ſpread themſelves over the whole Surface of the Earth) and where the Breath of the Lord moved above or upon the Surface of theſe Waters. It may, I ſay, in probability have been then a part of the exact Sphœrical Surface of the Earth, and upon the command that the Waters under the Air or Atmoſphere (which ſeems to be denoted by ςεςέωμα or Firmament; for the Hebrew Word ſignifies an Expanſum)

K k k k   ſhould

should be gathered together into one place, and that the dry Land should appear. It may have been by that extraordinary Earthquake (whereby the Hills and Land were rais'd in one place, and the Pits or deeper places, whether the Water was to recede and be gathered together to constitute the Sea were sunk in another) rais'd perhaps to lye on the top of a Hill or in a Plain, or sunk into the bottom of the Sea, and by the washing of Waters in motion, either carried to a lower place to cover some part of the Vale, or else be cover'd by adventitious Earth, brought down upon it from some higher place; which kind of alterations were certainly very great by the Flood of *Noah,* and several other Floods we find recorded in Heathen Writers. If at least there were not somewhat of an Earthquake which might again sink those Parts which had been formerly raised to make the dry Land appear, and raise the bottom of the Sea, which had been sunk for the gathering together of the Waters (which Opinion *Seneca* ascribes to *Fabianus*) *Ergo* (says he) *cum affuerit illa necessitas temporis multa simul fata causas movent nec sine concussione Mundi tanta Mutatio est ut quidam putant inter quos Fabianus est.* His description of the Manner and Effects of a Flood, is fine and very suting to my present Hypothesis. This Part being thus covered with other Earth, perhaps in the bottom of the Sea, may by some subsequent Earthquakes, have since been thrown up to the top of a Hill, where those parts with which it was by the former means covered, may in tract of time by the fall and washing of Waters, be again uncovered and laid open to the Air, and all those Substances which had been buried for so many Ages before, and which the devouring Teeth of Time had not consumed, may be then exposed to the Light of the Day.

Two other Causes of the changes on the superficial parts of the Earth: first from overflowing of the Streams and Inundations of the Sea.   There are yet two other Causes of the mutation of the superficial Parts of the Earth, which have wrought many great changes in the World, and those are either the Sea's overflowing of a Country or Place, when forced on it with some violent Storms or Hurricans of Wind, or from the over-flowing of Rivers from great falls of Rain, or from something stopping their Course, of these we have many Instances in Voyages, and we have very often times here at *London* felt the effects of the Wind driving in the Tide with such great force, as that it has oft times overflow'd the Banks, fill'd the Streets and Cellers to the no small damage of the Inhabitants. ' At *Chatmoss* in *Lanka-*
' *shire* (saith *Childery*) is a low mossy Ground very large, a great part of which
' (saith *Cambden*) not long ago, the Brooks swelling high carry'd quite away
' with them, whereby the Rivers were corrupted, and a number of fresh Fish
' perished. In which place now lies a low Vale watered with a little Brook,
' where Trees have been digg'd up lying along, which are suppos'd by some
' to have come thus. The Channel of the Brooks being not scower'd, the
' Brooks have risen, and made all the Land moorish that lay lower than o-
' thers, whereby the Roots of the Trees being loosned by reason of the bog-
' giness of the Ground, or by the Water finding a passage under Ground,
' the Trees have either by their own weight, or by some Storm, been blown
' down, and so sunk into that soft Earth and been swallowed up: For 'tis ob-
' servable, that Trees are no where digg'd out of the Earth but where the
' Earth is boggy; and even upon Hills such moorish and moist Grounds are
' commonly found, the Wood of these Trees burning very bright like Touch-
' wood (which perhaps is by reason of the bituminous Earth in which they
' have been so long) so as some think them to be Fir-Trees. Such mighty
' Trees are often found in *Holland,* which are thought to be undermin'd by the
' Waves working into the Shore, or by Winds driven forwards and brought
' to those lower places where they settled and sunk. *Brit. Bac.* Page 167,
' 168.'
' The Sea (as is said before) has eaten a great part of the Land away of
' these Western Shires. · There are on the Shore of this Shire (*Cumberland*)
' Trees discovered by the Winds sometimes at low Water, which are else co-
' vered over with Sand ; and it is reported by the People dwelling there-
' abouts, that they dig up Trees without Boughs out of the Ground in the
' places

' places of the Shire. *Child.* p. 171. Many Trees are found and digged out
' of the Earth of the Isle of *Man. Ide.* p. 178.'

' In divers places of the Low Grounds and Champian Fields of *Anglesy,* the
' Inhabitants every Day find and dig out of the Earth the Bodies of huge
' Trees with their Roots, and Fir-Trees of a wonderful bigness and length.
' Page 150.

' At the time when *Henry* II. made his abode in *Ireland* were extraordina-
' ry violent and lasting Storms of Wind and Weather, so that the Sandy Shore
' on the Coasts of the *Pembrockshire,* was laid bare to the very hard Ground,
' which had lain hid for many Ages, and by further search the People found
' great Trunks of Trees, which when they had digged up, they were ap-
' parently Lopped, so that one might see the strokes of the Ax upon them,
' as if they had been given but the Day before; the Earth look'd very black,
' and the Wood of these Trunks was altogether. like Ebony. At the first
' discovery made by these Storms, the Trees we speak of lay so thick, that
' the whole Shore seem'd nothing but a lopped Grove. Whence may be ga-
' ther'd, saith *Childry,* that the Sea hath overflow'd much Land on this
' Coast, as it has indeed many Countries bordering upon the Sea, which is
' to be imputed to the ignorance of the *Britans* and other barbarous Nations,
' which understood not those ways to repress the fury of the Sea which we
' now do. p. 142. 143.

' In the low Places on the South side of *Cheshire,* by the River *Wever,* Trees
' are oft times found by digging under Ground, which People think have lain
' buried there ever since *Noah*'s Flood. p. 129. ' St. *Bennets* in the *Holme* hath
' such fenny and rotten Ground, that (saith *Cambden*) if a Man cut up the
' Roots or Strings of Trees it flotes on the Water. Hereabout also are
' Cockles and Periwinkles sometimes digged up out of the Earth, which makes
' some think that it was formerly overflowed by the Sea.' Divers of these
Effects do seem to be caused by Inundations of the Sea, tho' there are o-
thers of them that do rather seem ascribable to Earthquakes, than to Inundations caus'd by Storms; for that Earthquakes have produced such Effects as the burying of Trees and Plants, divers of the formerly mention'd
Histories do sufficiently manifest.

The *Lignum Fossile* which is found in *Italy,* of which we have a good ac- *An Account of*
count given by *Francesco Stelluti* (tho' by that Author it be supposed to be ge- *Lignum Fos-*
nerated out of the subterraneous Parts of the place where it has been found; *file* and other
yet) from many remarkable circumstances in this History, it seems very probable *Subterraneous*
to me to have been first buried by some Earthquakes, and afterwards to be *Matters.*
variously metamorphosed and changed by the Symptoms which usually follow
Earthquakes, and which this place is much vexed with, as is indeed almost all
the Country of *Italy,* to wit, the emitting of hot Steams and Smoaks proceeding
from subterraneous Fires, which do their often shift their places, burn the
parts of some of those Trunks into black and brittle Coles; melt a kind of
Ore into the Pores of others; petrify the Substance of another sort; bake
the Dirt and Clayish Substances which have soaked into the Pores of a
fourth sort into a kind of Brick; rot the Parts of others, and convert them
into a kind of Dirt or Muddy Earth; and so act variously and produce differing Effects upon those buried Substances, according to the Nature of the
Earths, Minerals, Waters, Salts, Heats, Smoaks, Steams, and other active
Instruments casually applied to the parts of the buried Trunks, by the confusion of the Earthquakes, and by immediate application, and long continuance and digestion, as I may call it, in this Laboratory of Nature, transformed
into other Substances, and exhibit all those admirable Phænomena mentioned
by that Author, whereby the bury'd Bodies are transformed. Nor is it so
much to be wondered at, that such Substances as Vegetables (which being
exposed to the Vicissitudes of the Air and Water, are quickly corrupted and
consumed, and many of them much sooner if buried in the Earth) should after so many Ages perhaps, remain intire, and rather more substantial sound
and permanent than if they were newly cut down. Since if we consider the *Whence the de-*
Nature of the decaying and corruption in all kind of Animal and Vegetable *cay of Bodies.*
Substances

Substances, we shall find that the chief cause of it seems to be from the Action of the fluid Parts upon the solid for the dissolving of them: and wheresoever the Internal Fluid is either first changed or altered by the mixture of some other heterogenous Substance, so as to loose that dissolving property as by the intermixture of Salt, Spirit of Wine, &c. or by incorporating with it and hardning it into a solid Substance, as in Petrifactions, &c. Or, secondly, exhaled by a gradual and gentle degree of heat, and so the solid Parts only left alone, and kept either dry, or fill'd with a fluid of an heterogeneous Nature, such as unctuous and spicy Juices with watery Substances. Or, Thirdly, Congealed and hardened either by cold or the peculiar Nature of the Juice itself ; such is freezing and the hardning of Coralline Plants, or Submarine Vegetables, Horns, Gums, Bones, Hair, Feathers, &c. wheresoever, I say, Bodies are by these means put into such a Constitution, that the Parts act not upon one another, and continue in that state by being preserved by adventitious Moisture or soft'ning by homogeneous Fluids, they are, as it were, perpetual, unless by extraordinary Heat, many of those otherwise solid and unactive Substances are made fluid by such active Disolvents; and unless they be immersed in such Liquors or Menstruums as do of themselves dissolve and work on them ; we shall not, I say, wonder at the lastingness of these buried Substances, if we consider also the various Juices with which several parts of the Earth are Furnish'd, Unctuous, Watery, Styptick, Saline, Petrifactive, Corrosive, and what not. There are some Juices of the Earth which do, as it were, perpetuate them by turning them into Stone. Others do so deeply pierce and intimately mix with their parts, that they wholly, as it were, change the Nature of those Substances, and destroy that property of Congruity which all Bodies generated in the Air and Water seem to have, which are very apt to be dissolved and corrupted by innate aerial and aquous Substances. Such are all kinds almost of oleaginous and sulphureous Substances, and divers saline and mineral Juices. Others indeed do not preserve the very Substance of those Vegetables, but insinuating into the Pores, and there, as it were, fixing, they retain and perpetuate the Shape and Figure, but corrupt and dissolve the interpos'd part of the Vegetable ; of all which kinds I have seen some Specimina, as I have also of divers other Substances Pickled, Dried, Candyed, Conserv'd, preserv'd, or Mummify'd by Nature : where therefore the Substances have happen'd to be bury'd with preservative Juices, they have withstood the injury of Time ; but where those Juices have been wanting, there we find no Footsteps of these Monuments of Antiquity.

A 2d Cause of alterations on the Earth beside Earthquakes, is violent motions of the Air. But to return to what I was prosecuting, another cause which may make alterations on the Surface of the Earth, is any violent motions of the Air, whereby the parts of the Earth, in dry Weather, are transported from place to place in the Form of Dust. Of this kind Travellers tell us very strange Stories of the removal of the Sands in the Deserts of *Arabia*, and other Deserts in *Africa* ; and we have some instances of it here in *England*, to wit, in *Norfolk* and *Devonshire* (in the former of which there are often found natural Mummies which have been buried alive by those removing Sands, and by their driness preserv'd) But these greater and more suddain removals of Sand and Dust are not so universal, and therefore not so much to my present purpose; tho' possibly they may have been more frequent heretofore, which the Layers of Sands to be found in digging Pitts and Wells seem to hint : But that which is most universal, is very slow, and almost inperceptible, and that is the removing of the Dust from the higher Parts, and settling in the lower by the Wind or motion of the Air. This tho' its effects be almost insensible, yet being constant, must needs, in length of time, much promote the levelling and smoothing of the Surface of the Earth.

3dly, A gradual sinking of heavy Bodies into the Surface. I might name also another cause of the transposition of the superficial Parts of the Earth ; and that is from the gradual subsiding or sinking into the Earth of the more heavy, and the Ebullition or respective rising of the more light Parts upwards. Hence we may observe, that many old and vast Buildings and

and Towers have funk into the Earth. And the like we judge of thofe vaft Stones in *Salisbury* Plain, and we find conftantly almoft in all Stone Monuments placed in Church-yards, and in all old Churches unlefs placed on a very high place, and founded on fome Rock. The Caufe may poffibly have great Influence where the Earth is very foft, fpungy, or boggy ; and poffibly many of thofe Trees which are found in boggy Grounds, may have been buried, by having been either fell'd, or blown down by Wind, or wafh'd down by fome Inundation well impregnated with mineral Juices, and fo made heavier than the fubjacent Earth, and fwallowed into it. Several of the former Relations do indeed pretty well agree with this Hypothefis ; and I am very apt to think that where the Surface of the Earth has not been much alter'd fince the Creation, if any fuch there be, if it were fearch'd into it would be found that the lighteft Parts, lye next the Surface, and fo heavier in lower Parts, which makes me imagine that the natural place of Minerals is very deep under the Surface of the Earth, and (poffibly) to be found under every ftep of Ground, were fearch made under it to a fufficient depth ; and that the reafon why we find it fometimes near the Surface of the Earth, as in Mountains, is not becaufe it was there generated, but becaufe it has been by fome former Subterraneous Eruption (by which thofe Hills and Mountains have been made) thrown up towards the Surface of the Earth. And as Gold is the heavieft, fo it is the fcarceft of all Mettals. And I do not at all queftion but that there may be other Bodies or Mettals as much heavier than Gold, as Gold is then common Earth. To make thefe Conjectures the more probable, fee what Sir *Philiberto Vernatti* writes from *Batavia* in the *Eaft-Indies,* in anfwer to fome Queries fent him by the Royal Society. ' I ' have often (fays he) felt Earthquakes here, but they do not continue long. ' In the Year 1656, or 57, (I do not remember well the time) *Batavia* was ' covered in one Afternoon about two of the Clock, with a black Duft, which ' being gathered together, was fo ponderous, that it exceeded the weight ' in Gold. It is here thought that it came out of a Hill that burneth in *Sumatra* ' near *Endrapeor.*

Thefe fiery Eruptions in all probability come from a very great depth and with a great violence ; and poffible even that golden Powder that is fometimes thrown up may have fomewhat conduced to the caufe of the violence of it. We know not what Method Nature may have to prepare an *Aurum Fulminans* of her own, great quantities of which, being any ways heated and fo fired, may have produced the Powder. However, whether fo or not, it were very well worth trial to examine, whether the Flower that may be catch'd in a Glafs Body, upon fulminating a quantity of fuch Powder gradually by fmall parcels, would, by being ordered as common Gold, make again an *Aurum Fulminans* : Or whether this Fulmination, which is a kind of Inflaming of the Body of the Gold, does not make fome very confiderable alteration in the Nature and Texture of it. Since we find that kind of Operation, to wit, inflaming or burning does confiderably alter the Texture of all other Bodies fo wrought on. This only by the way.

But to proceed to the laft Argument to confirm the 6th Propofition I at firft undertook to prove, namely, that very many parts of the Surface of the Earth (not now to take notice of others) have been transform'd tranfpos'd and many ways alter'd fince the firft Creation of it.) And that which to me feems the ftrongeft and moft cogent Argument of all is this, That at the tops of fome of the higheft Hills, and in the bottom of fome of the deepeft Mines, in the midft of Mountains and Quarries of Stone, *&c.* divers Bodies have been and daily are found, that if we thoroughly examine we fhall find to be real fhells of Fifhes, which for thefe following Reafons we conclude to have been at firft generated by the Plaftick faculty of the Soul or Life-principle of fome animal, and not from the imaginary influence of the Stars, or from any Plaftick faculty inherent in the Earth itfelf fo form'd ; the ftrefs of which Argument lies in thefe Particulars.

The laft Argument to prove the fixth Propofition from the Shells, &c. found on, and in the Earth.

1ſt. *Proof that they are true Shells.* Firſt, That the Bodies there found have exactly the Form and Matter, that is, are of the ſame kind of Subſtance for all its ſenſible Properties, and have the ſame External and Internal Figure or Shape with the Shells of Animals.

2d. *Proof.* Next, That it is contrary to all the other acts of Nature, that does nothing in vain, but always aims at an end, to make two Bodies exactly of the ſame Subſtance and Figure, and one of them to be wholly uſeleſs, or at leaſt without any deſign that we can with any plauſibility imagine. The Shells of Animals, to our Reaſon, manifeſtly appear to be done with the greateſt Councel and Deſign, and with the moſt excellent contrivance, both for the Convenience and Ornament of that Animal to which it belongs, that the particular Structure and Fabrick of that Animal was capable of: Whereas theſe if they were not the Shells of Fiſhes, will be nothing but the ſportings of Nature, as ſome do finely fancy, or the effects of Nature idely mocking herſelf, which ſeems contrary to her Gravity. But this perhaps may not ſeem ſo cogent, tho', if it be thoroughly conſider'd, there is much weight in it.

3d. *Proof.* Next therefore, Wherever Nature does work by peculiar Forms and Subſtances, we find that ſhe always joins the Body ſo fram'd with ſome other peculiar Subſtance. Thus the Shells of Animals, whilſt they are forming are join'd with the Fleſh of the Animal to which they belong. Peculiar Flowers, Leaves, and Fruit are appropriated to peculiar Roots, whereas theſe on the contrary are found mixt with all kind of Subſtances, in Stones of all kinds, in all kinds of Earth, ſometimes expos'd to the open Air without any coherence to any thing. This is at leaſt an Argument that they were not generated in that poſture they are found ; that very probably they have been heretofore diſtinct and diſunited from the Bodies with which they are now mixt, and that they were not formed out of theſe very Stones or Earth, as ſome imagine, but deriv'd their Beings from ſome preceding Principle.

4th. *Proof.* Fourthly, Wherever elſe Nature works by peculiar Forms, we find her always to compleat that form, and not break off abruptly. But theſe Shells that are found in the middle of Stones are moſt of them broken, very few compleat, nay, I have ſeen many bruiſed and flaw'd, and the parts at a pretty diſtance one from another, which is an Argument that they were not generated in the place where they are found, and in that poſture, but that they have been ſometimes diſtinct and diſtant from thoſe Subſtances, and then only placed, broken and disfigured by chance, but had a preceeding and more noble Principle to which they ow'd their Form, and by ſome hand of Providence, were caſt into ſuch places where they were filled with ſuch Subſtances, as in tract of Time have condenſed and hardened into Stone: This I think, any impartial Examiner of theſe Bodies will eaſily grant to be very probable, eſpecially if he take notice of the Circumſtances I have already mention'd. Now, if it be granted, that there have been preceding Moulds, and that theſe curiouſly figured Stones do not owe their form to a plaſtick or forming Principle inherent in their Subſtances; why might not theſe be ſuppoſed Shells, as well as other Bodies of the ſame Shape and Subſtance, generated none knows how, nor can imagine for what.

5th. *Proof.* Further, if theſe be the apiſh Tricks of Nature, Why does it not imitate ſeveral other of its own Works? Why do we not dig out of Mines everlaſting Vegetables, as Graſs for inſtance, or Roſes of the ſame Subſtance, Figure, Colour, Smell? &c. Were it not that the Shells of Fiſhes are made of a kind of ſtony Subſtance which is not apt to corrupt and decay. Whereas, Plants and other animal Subſtances, even Bones, Horns, Teeth and Claws are more liable to the univerſal Menſtruum of Time. 'Tis probable therefore, that the fixedneſs of their Subſtance has preſerved them in their priſtine Form, and not that a new plaſtick Principle has newly generated

them

them. Besides, why should we, not then doubt of all the Shells taken up by the Sea-shore, or out of the Sea (if they had none when we found them) whether they ever had any Fish in them or not? Why should we not here conceipt also a plastick Faculty distinct from that of the Life-principle of some Animal; is it because this is more like a Shell than the other? That I am sure it cannot be. Is it because 'tis more obvious how a Shell should be placed there? If so, 'twould be as good Reason to doubt if an Anchor should be found at the top of a Hill, as the Poet affirms, or an Urn or Coins buried under Ground, or in the bottom of a Mine, whether it were ever an Anchor, or an Urne, or a coined Face, or made by the plastick Faculty of the Earth, than which what could be more absurd: And those Persons that will needs be so over confident of their Omniscience of all that has been done in the World, or that could be, may, if they will vouchsafe, suffer themselves to be asked a Question, Who in form'd them? Who told them where *England* was before the Flood; nay, even where it was before the *Roman* Conquest, for about four or five thousand Years, and perhaps much longer; much more where did they ever read or hear of what *Changes* and *Transpositions* there have been of the parts of it before that? What History informs us of the burying of those Trees in *Cheshire* and *Anglesy?* Who can tell when *Tenariff* was made? And yet we find that most judicious Men that have been there and well considered the form and posture of it, conclude it to have been at first that way produced. But I suppose the most confident will quickly upon examination, find that there is a defect of Natural History, if therefore we are left to conjecture, then that must certainly be the best that is backed with most Reason, that Clay, and Sand, and common Shells can be changed and incorporated together into Stones very hard. I have already given many instances, and can produce hundreds of others, but that I think it needless, that several parts of the bottom of the Sea have been thrown up into Islands and Mountains. I have also given divers Instances, and those some of them within the Memory of Man, where 'tis not in the least to be doubted but that there may be found some Ages hence several Shells at the tops of those Hills there generated; and as little, that if Quarries of Stone should be hereafter digged in those places, there would be found Shells incorporated with them; and were they not beholding to this inquisitive and learned Age for the History of that Eruption, they might as much wonder how these Shells should come there, and ascribe them to a plastick Faculty, or some imaginary Influence, as plausibly as some now do. I have also shewed, that Water and divers other fluid Substances, may be, in tract of Time, converted into Stone and stony Substances; and so such Liquors penetrating the Pores of these Shells, and especially if they be assisted by the benumming Steams that sometimes issue from Subterraneous Erruptions, may very much contribute to the preservation of those Shells from Corruption and crumbling to Dust under the crushing Foot of Time. Besides, that the Shells themselves are so near the Nature and Substance of Stone, that they are little subject to the injuries of the Air or Weather; so that these small pyramidal Houses of Shell-Fishes seem not less lasting Monuments than those vast piles of Stones erected by the antient Inhabitants of *Egypt*, which outvye all the more curious Fabricks of *Grecian* and *Roman* Architecture both for their Antiquity and present Continuance. Nor do they exceed the Works of Architects for lasting only, but for Ornament, for Strength, and for Convenience.

Now if all these Bodies have been really such Shells of Fishes as they most resemble, and that these are found at the tops of the most considerable Mountains in the World as *Caucasus*, the *Alps*, the *Andes*, the *Appennine*, and *Pyrenean* Mountains, to omit other Hills nearer and of less note, and that tis not very probable that they were carried thither by Mens Hands, or by the Deluge of *Noah*, or by any other more probable way than that of Earthquakes; 'tis a very cogent Argument that the superficial Parts of the Earth have been very much chang'd since the beginning, that the tops of Mountains have been under the Water, and consequently also, that divers parts of the bottom of the Sea have been heretofore Mountains: For tho' I confefs I have but few Inftances to prove it, befides that of *Plato's Atlantis,* and fome others that I have already mention'd; yet 'tis very probable, that whenfoever an Earthquake raifes up a great part of the Earth in one place, it fuffers another to fink in another place; for Gravity is a Principle that will not long fuffer a fpace to remain unfill'd under fo vaft a pile of Earth as a Mountain, unlefs the Subftances, fo thrown up, be of very hard, clofe and vaft Stones that may, as it were, vault it: In which cafes 'tis very probable (and *Kircher* and divers other Authors that write of Mines and Quarries, gives us many inftances to confirm it) that thefe Cracks and Cliffs fo left, are fill'd up with fuch Petrifying or Mineral Waters as do make great varieties of Stones, Marbles, Sparrs, Caulks, and Ores, and fo there is made a tranfpofition as well as a transformation. Which fuppofition (by the way) I think will furnifh a very probable Reafon of the fhape of the Veins and Cracks of fpeckled Marbles and other Stones, of the form alfo of the Veins of Ores, Stones, Clays, &c. of the Earth, and of their fo mixing together; of the lying of Mettals in Mountains and other Mines, &c. but of thefe only here by the Bye, becaufe I refer what I have to fay of that to another Subject, *viz.* A Hiftory of the Forms and Proprieties of Minerals and Metals. To proceed then.

The feventh Propofition con- firmed.   The Seventh Propofition that I undertook to make probable, was, That 'tis very probable that divers of thefe Tranfpofitions and Metamorphofes have been wrought even here in *England*: Many of its Hills have probably been heretofore under the Sea, and divers other parts that were heretofore high Land and Hills, have fince been covered with the Sea. Of the latter of thefe I have given many Inftances already, and that which makes the firft probable, is the great quantities of Shells that are found in the moft Inand Parts of this Ifland; in the Hills, in the Plains, in the bottoms of Mines and in the middle of Mountains and Quarries of Stones. Of this kind are thofe Shells, which any inquifitive Man may find great quantities of in *Portland*-ftone, *Purbeck*-ftone, *Burford*-ftone, *Northamptonfhire*-ftone, out of which I have often pick'd Mufcles, Cockles, Periwinkles, Oyfters, Scallop, and divers other Shells that are buried in the very Body and Subftance of the Stone; and indeed they may be found of fome kind or other in almoft all kinds of Stone. That the *Kainfham* Snail Stones, and thofe found in feveral onher parts of *England*, have been the Shells of Fifhes, I hope the Arguments I have already urged may fuffice to evince. As alfo, that thofe Helmet Stones (of which fort I my felf have found in many places of *England*, and others have fur- nifh'd me with many more found in other parts of it) are nothing but the fillings of the Shells of a fort of Echini or Egg Fifhes.

Now 'tis not probable that other Mens Hands, or the general Deluge which lafted but a little while, fhould bring them there; nor can I imagine a- ny more likely and fufficient way than an Earthquake, which might hereto- fore raife all thefe Iflands of Great *Britain* and *Ireland* out of the Sea, as it did heretofore, of which I have already mention'd the Hiftories; or as it lately did that Ifland in the *Canarys* and *Azores,* in the fight of divers who are yet alive to teftifie the Truth and Manner of it: And poffibly *England* and *Ireland* might be rais'd by the fame Earthquake, by which the *Atlantis,* if we will believe *Plato,* was funk. And I doubt not but any inquifitive Man that has opportunity of traveling and examining feveral of the Mountianous Parts and Cliffs, and of the Mines, Quarries, and other fubterraneous Parts of *England,* will meet with a great many other Arguments to confirm this Sup- pofition, befides thofe I have already alledg'd: But thofe I hope may fuffice for the prefent to excite Men to this Curiofity, which was the chief reafon of this prefent exercife. And this makes way for the Eighth Propofition, which is

The eighth Pro- pofition con- firmed.   Eighthly, That moft of thefe Mountains and Inland places whereon thefe kind of Petrify'd Bodies and Shells are found at prefent or have been heretofore, were formerly under the Water, and that either by the defcending of the Waters to another part of the Earth by the alteration of the Center of Gravity of the

the whole bulk, or rather by the Eruption of fome kind of Subterraneous Fires or Earthquakes, great quantities of Earth have been deferted by the Water and laid bare and dry. That divers places have been thus raifed by Earthquakes has been already proved from many Hiftories; and then why may not all of them have the fame Original, efpecially fince there is no other more probable Caufe that we know of, that fhould convey and place thofe Shells on the tops of Mountains? That they really are Shells, and have been the receptacle of Fifhes, I hope the Arguments I have already alledg'd may fuffice to perfuade: If then they have been Shells, and have been there placed, why fhould we not conclude that That part hath been under the Water with as much reafon as feeing Towers, &c. under the Water near------ -------we do that thofe parts have been heretofore above Water, which Hiftories inform us of, or as we might have done if we had had none even from what the thing itfelf fpeaks. I think we may with as much reafon doubt if an Urn fhould be digg'd up full with old Coins, ftamped with the fame impreffion, made of the fame Subftance and Magnitude of thofe ufed by the ancient *Romans*, or any other Nation, of which we have good Hiftory; Firft, Whether ever thofe Coins were made by Mens Hands, or by a plaftick Faculty of Nature; for it is certainly no more difficult a task for Nature to imitate the one than the other. And, Secondly, Whether ever that Urn were made and thofe Coins were put into it and fhaped by Mens Hands, or that they were fhap'd and thrown into it meerly by Nature; perhaps thofe fuppofitions might not be impoffible, but fure all Men will judge them very improbable: And I think the Cafe in this particular I am fpeaking of very much the fame. Firft, That there is much greater reafon to imagine the Shells fo found to have been the *Exuviæ* of fome living Creature, and next, that they have been placed there where they are found when that part was under Water, and that part to have fince been rais'd up to that height above the Sea by fome preceding Earthquake. There is no Coin can fo well inform an Antiquary that there has been fuch or fuch a place fubject to fuch a Prince, as thefe will certify a Natural Antiquary, that fuch and fuch places have been under the Water, that there have been fuch kind of Animals, that there have been fuch and fuch preceding Alterations and Changes of the fuperficial Parts of the Earth: And methinks Providence does feem to have defign'd thefe permanent fhapes, as Monuments and Records to inftruct fucceeding Ages of what paft in preceding. And thefe written in a more legible Character than the Hieroglyphicks of the ancient *Egyptians*, and on more lafting Monuments than thofe of their vaft Pyramids and Obelisks. And I find that thofe that have well confider'd and ftudy'd all the remarkable Circumftances to be met with at *Teneriffe* and *Fayale*, do no more doubt that thofe vaft Pikes have been raifed up by the Eruption of Fire out of their tops, than others that have furvey'd the Pyramids of *Egypt*, or the Stones on *Salisbury* Plain do doubt that they have been the effects of Man's Labours. And they do it with as much reafon; for all Conclufions that are not immediately grounded on Senfe, or the refult of it are but Hypothetical and from a Similitude; for fince it has been heretofore and lately feen, that fuch Eruptions have produc'd fuch kind of Hills and Iflands, and that the tops of thefe Hills do as yet burn, and that there are all about the fides of them huge Stones and Rocks, and even Mountains lying in Poftures as if they had been tumbled down from the top; 'tis a rational Conclufion to fay, that 'tis very probable thefe have had the fame Original with thofe.

But as to thofe vaft tracts of Ground that lye very far from the Sea, it may perhaps to fome feem not impoffible, that the Center of Gravity or Method of the attraction of the Globe of the Earth may change and fhift places, and if fo, then certainly all the fluid parts of the Earth will conform thereto, and then 'twill follow that one part will be cover'd and overflow'd by the Sea that was before dry, and another part be difcover'd and laid dry that was before overwhelm'd. Now, tho' this Conjecture may at firft reading feem a little extravagant, yet if we confider, that as great alterations have been really obferv'd, we may a little moderate a two fevere Cen- *Change of the Earths Center of Gravity hinted.*

sure ; That the Magnetical Poles and Meridians of the Earth have been alter'd, and that they do at this present continue to do so is granted almost
by all, and confirmed by a multitude of Observations made in divers Parts of
the World, and by collecting and comparing the Observations I have met
with : I suppose the Pole of the Magnetism to be at a certain distance from
the Pole of its daily Motion, and that it does move round that Pole at a certain distance in a certain number of Years, and that it does annually proceed in this Circle some parts of a Degree: So that whereas the Magnetical
Pole was formerly North-East of *Russia*, it is now grown North-West of it,
and a little to the Westward even of *England*'s Meridian. Monsieur *Petit*
Engenier to the *French* King, is of Opinion, That the Pole of the diurnal
motion of the Earth alters, but I confess I cannot in the least assent to it
from any of those Arguments that he alledges, but I do rather think that
divers of them do make against his Hypothesis; yet 'tis not impossible but
that a very great Earthquake altering the Center of Gravity, may also alter
the Pole of Rotation; for we find by experience, that if any thing be laid
upon one side of a large *Lignum Vitæ* Ball suspended by a String, and that Ball
be turned round upon the String, it shall not turn exactly about the Point
by which 'tis suspended, but about some other Point. Besides this, we know
that the direction of these Poles, as to the Heavens, doth vary, for whereas,
it pointed at a part of the Heavens many degrees distant from the Star in
the top of the tail of the little Bear, now it points almost directly towards
it. Besides this, we find that the Points of the Intersection of the Æquinoctial
and Ecliptick varies, and possibly even the motions of all may vary. A diurnal
Revolution of the Earth may perhaps have been made in a much shorter time
than now ; possibly there may have been the same alterations in the Annual,
and then a Year, or a Day at the beginning of the World would not be of so
long a duration as now when those motions are grown slower ; for if the
motions of the Heavens be analogous to the motion of a Wheel or Top, as
I think I can by very many Arguments make probable, then if the Earth
were (as it were) at first set up or put into a rapid circular Motion, like
that of a Top, 'tis probable that the fluid Medium in which it moves, may
after a thousand Revolutions, a little retard and slaken that motion, and
if so, then a longer space of time will pass while it makes its Revolution
now than it did at first.

Possibly the old Patriarchs lived no longer in some sense than Men do now.   Hence possibly the long Lives of the Posterity of *Adam* before the Flood,
might be of no greater duration then Mens Lives are ordinarily now ; for
though perhaps they might number more Revolutions of the Sun, or more
Years than we can now, yet our few Years may comprehend as great a space
of time ; this perhaps might deserve to be inquired into had we a certain
measure of time, such as some would have a standing Pendulum of a certain
length ; but since we are upon suspecting, we may even doubt whether the
power of Gravity itself may not alter in time ; we find that the Poles of the
Loadstone may be changed, that it does take up more at one time than another ; that its virtue may be wholly destroyed by Fire, and some other
ways ; and besides that, one of these changes is really wrought in the Earth,
and therefore 'tis not impossible but that even the attractive Power of the
Earth (tho' I confess I think it quite differing from that of the Loadstone)
may be intended or remitted ; if so then the Pendulum will be no certain Standard for the examination of the length of Time by; for the more
the gravitating Power is increas'd, the quicker will be the Vibrations of a-
ny Pendulum and the more weak it is, the slower are the Vibrations : But
this Digression only by the bye. To return then, I say, tho' somewhat may
be said for this Supposition I have started, yet I confess I do more incline to
believe that what Mutations there have been of the Superficial Parts , have
been rather caus'd by Earthquakes and Eruptions, which ushers in my Ninth
Proposition. Namely,

That

That it feems very probable, that the tops of the moſt conſiderable Moun-*The ninth Pro-* tains of the World have been under Water, and that moſt probably they *poſition con-* feem to have been raiſed to that height by ſome Eruption: So that thoſe pro-*firmed.* digious piles of Mountains are nothing but the effects of ſome great Earthquakes. This the Poets feem'd to vail under the feign'd Story of the Giants, thoſe Earth-born Brothers waging War with the Gods, where they are ſaid to heap up Mountains upon Mountains, *Oſſa* and *Olympus* upon *Peleon*, and to caſt up huge Stones and Fire at Heaven, but that at laſt overcome by *Jove* with his Thunder, they were buried under Mountains, the chiefeſt of them, namely, *Typhæus* under *Sicily*, according to *Ovid Metamorph.* Lib. 5.

Vaſta Giganteis imjecta eſt Inſula membris
Trinacris, &c.--------
Thus Engliſh'd by *Sandys.*

Trinacria was on wicked Typhon thrown,
Who underneath the Iſlands weight doth groan;
That durſt attempt the Empire of the Skies:
Oft he attempteth, but in vain to riſe.
Auſonian Pelorus his right Hand
Down weighs; Pachyne on the left doth ſtand;
His Legs are under Lilybæus ſpread;
And Ætna's baſes charge his horid Head:
Where, lying on his Back, his Jaws expire
Thick Clouds of Duſt, and vomit flakes of Fire.
Oft times he ſtruggles with the weight below,
And Towns and Mountains labours to overthrow.
Earthquakes therewith: The King of Shadows dreads
For fear the Ground ſhould ſplit above their Heads, &c.

And that nothing elſe but an Earthquake is underſtood by that Gigantomachia of the Poets ſeems yet plainer from what *Virgil* in the Third Book of his *Æneis*, ſpeaks in his Deſcription of the Shores of *Sicily.*

Portus ab acceſſu ventorum immotus, & ingens
Ipſe, ſed horrificis juxta tonat Ætna Ruinis,
Interdumq; Atram prorumpit ad Æthera nubem
Turbine fumantem piceo & candente favilla,
Attollitq; globos flammarum & ſidera Lambit
Interdum ſcopulos Avulſaq; viſcera montis
Eiicit eructans, liquefactaq; ſaxa ſub auras
Cum gemitu glomerat fundoque exæſtuat imo.
Fama eſt Enceladi ſemiuſtum fulmine Corpus
Urgeri mole hac, Ingentemq; inſuper Ætnam
Impoſitam, ruptis flammam expirare caminis:
Et feſſum quoties motat Latus,intremere omnem
Murmure Trinacriam & cæco Subtexere fumo.

Thus Engliſh'd by *Ogilby.*

The Port was great and calm with ſhelt'ring Shores,
But near from horrid Ruins Ætna roars;
There in black Whirlwinds pitchy Clouds aſpire,
With ſparkling Cinders mixt with blazing Fire,
And Globes of Flame high as the Stars are born;
Out are the Mountains Marble Entrails torn,
Then upwards vomited, and melted Stones
Belcht from his Stomach, hot with horrid Groans.

Enceladus with Thunder ſtruck, they tell,
Under the weight of this huge Burthen fell,
Above him was the mighty Ætna laid,
Who now breaths Fire, through broken Trunks (convey'd
And as he weary turns, a Thunder crack
Sicilia ſhakes, and Heav'n is hung with black.

And as the Poets above-mention'd had particular Stories and Giants for *Sicily* and *Ætna*, ſo had they alſo for other Vulcans, and from the frequency of them in former Ages, about *Greece* and the other Parts of the Mediterranean, *Sophocles* calls them ὁ γηγενὴς ςρατός, γιγάντων the Earth-born Army of the Giants; and that nothing but Earthquakes were deciphered by theſe Giants may be further collected from the place where they were ſaid to be bred, namely, the *Phlegrean* Fields in *Campania*, a part of which is now called the Court of *Vulcan*, a place that is the vent of many Subterraneous Fires. ' 'Tis (ſays *Sandys*) a naked Level, in form Oval 1246 Foot long, and 1000 ' broad, environ'd with high cliffy Hills that fume on each ſide and have their
ſulphureous

' sulphureous Savour transported by the Winds to places far distant ; you
' would think the hungry Fire had made this Valley with continual feeding,
' which breaks out in a number of places.   Here the Fire and Water make a
' horrible rumbling, conjoining together as if one were Fuel to the other,
' here and there bubling up, as if in a Cauldron over a Furnace, and spouting
' aloft into the Air at such time as the Sea is inrag'd with Tempests, &c.
Besides, how well do their Actions agree with the Effects of Earthquakes,
for, they are said to throw up burning Trees against Heaven, and huge Rocks
and vast Hills, which falling into the Sea became Islands, and lighting on the
Land became Mountains.   Nor does the manner of their Generation
speak less, for they are said to be generated by the Blood of Heaven falling down on the Earth, that is, by the heat or influence of the Celestial Bodies operating within the Bowels of the Earth, and brought forth
of her Womb in revenge to the Gods, or that they break forth with such horror and violence as if they threatned the Heavens.   And he that shall read
the Description of the most notable of them *Typheus*, and compare it with
the natural Description of an Earthquake, will easily explicate the several
parts of the Poets mystical Descriptions.

This Theory which I have endeavoured hitherto to evince, tho' indeed it
be very hard positively to prove, we being, as I instanced before, very deficient in Natural History, yet if we consider what has been already said, and
compare it with the late Observations of divers Travailers over them, we
may find it altogether more than probable.   I have been inform'd by several
worthy Persons, that there are great store of Shells found at the tops of the
Alps, *Appenine* and *Pyrenean* Hills, which are by much the highest of *Europe*. And
I have now by me several of those Shells which have been dug out of them
and brought into *England*.   If therefore these have been real Oyster-Shells
and Scallop-Shells as upon viewing the Substance and Make of them, I see
not the least cause to doubt ; and that there are great quantities of them
to be found in divers Parts which lye buried in the Cliffs and incorporated with
the Stones ; and if that these Mountains have been infested with Earthquakes both formerly and lately, as we have several Histories that testifie ;
and if that other Eruptions and Earthquakes have raised Mountains even
out of the bottom of the Sea, and that the power of included Fire is sufficient to move and raise even a whole Country all at once for some hundreds
of Miles, as Historians assure us: If to this we add the universal silence in
History of any part of *Europe*, or any of other certain places of the World
before the Flood, or indeed for almost two hundred Years after the Flood, I
think there will be much less scruple to grant it propable that the *Alps*, and
divers other high Mountains, on whose tops are found such numbers and varieties of Sea-Shells, may have been heretofore raised np from under the Sea,
and now sustain'd by the sinking of other Parts into the places from whence
they were raised.   This the very form of them will also very much argue for ;
for I have been inform'd by several that took diligent notice of it, that the
parts are continually tumbling down from the higher parts to the lower, and
that some of them do seem to overhang very strangely, which cannot in any
probability be imagin'd to be the form of the first Creation, it being contrary to that implanted Power of Gravity, whereby all the parts of it are
held together and equally drawn towards the Center of it, and so all the
parts of it ought to have been placed in their natural position which must
have constituted an exact Sphere, the heaviest lowest, and lighter at the top
and the Water must have covered the whole Surface of the Earth, which
seems to have been indeed their first position, according to the Description
of *Moses* in *Genesis*, besides all those Hills that have been made by subterraneous Eruptions are of the like Structure ; such as the *Pike* of *Tenariffe*, the
Pike of *Fayale*, the new Mountain in *Italy*, *Ætna* and *Vesuvius*, all which
seem to have been made up of great Stones thrown up out of the Mouth of
their several Vulcans, many of which lie in such tottering postures that oft
times they tumble down to the bottom, and make great destruction of the
parts beneath ; of this we have lately had several memorable Examples.   To
mention only two or three, we are inform'd by Historians, that among the

Alps

Alps in the *Grisons* Country, a Town named *Plura*, seated in a Plain at the Foot of the *Alps* near the River *Maira*, and continuing by estimation at the time of its fatal Catastrophy, at least fifteen hundred People was, by the falling down of a great part of a huge high Mountain that hung over the said place upon the twenty sixth of *August* 1617, together with the Inhabitants, in a moment crusht and buried deep in the Earth, and that there is nothing now left in the place thereof but a vast abyss or bottomless Gulf. And we are now newly inform'd by Letters brought out of *Italy* that a great part of the City of *Ragusa* has been this Year destroyed by the like falling down of some part of the Mountain above it.

The Tenth and last Conjecture which I shall at present mention (as reserving some others which will seem at first sight much more strange and extravagant, till I can by a sufficient number of Observations make them more plausible) is, that it seems not improbable but that the greatest part of the inequality of the Earths Surface may have proceeded from the subversions and overturnings of some preceeding Earthquakes. *The tenth Proposition confirmed.*

And for making this Conjecture probable, I might repeat all the Arguments I have already urged to make probable the Generations of Islands, Mountains, Abysses, &c. but that I suppose will be needless, they having been so lately mention'd. I could also instance in a multitude of other smaller effects produced by Earthquakes, of making the Surface of the Earth irregular; but those are so numerous, and so very well known in those places where Earthquakes are more frequent, as in *Italy*, *Turky*, the East and West *Indies*, &c. that I shall not insist on them. To this I might add the universality of Earthquakes, there being no part of the World of which we have any good account, but we find to have been some time or other shaken by Earthquakes ; and 'tis very probable had we receiv'd any certain account of the State and Constitution, and being of the Earth in its Infancy (as I may say) or first Being of the Earth after its Creation, when 'tis not improbable but the parts of it that lay uppermost and next the other were more fluid and soft, we might have had a thousand otherobservables. Of which I shall say more hereafter when I mention some other Conjectures.

Thus much only I shall add at present, that from what I have instanced about Petrifactions and the hardning of several Substances, it seems very probable, that in the beginning the Earth consisted for the most part of fluid Substances, which by degrees have setled, congealed, and concreted, and turn'd into Stones, Minerals, Mettals, Clays, Earth, &c. And that in process of time the parts of it have by degrees concreted and lost their Fluidity, and that the Earth itself doth wax old almost in the same manner as Animals and Vegetables do; that is, that the moisture of it doth by degrees decay and wast either into Air, and from thence into the Æther; or else by degrees the Parts communicating their motion to the Fluidether either grow moveless and hard, almost in the same manner as we find the Bodies of Animals and Vegetables when they grow old in their several proportinate times, all the Parts tend and end in solidity and fixtness, the Gelly becomes Gristles, and the Gristles a Bone, and the Bone at length a Stone, the Skin from smooth and soft grows rough and hard, the motions grow slow, and the moveable Parts and Joints grow stiff, and all the Juices decay and are deficient. The same thing happens in Trees and other Vegetables. If therefore the Parts of the Earth have formerly, in all probability, been softer, how much more powerful might Earthquakes be then in breaking, raising, overturning, and otherwise changing the superficial Parts of the Earth ? Besides, 'tis not unlikely but Earthquakes might then be much more frequent before the Fuels of those subterraneous Fires were much spent. That the Parts of the Earth do continually grow harder and fixt and concrete into Stone, I think no one will deny that has consider'd the Constitution of Mountains, the Layers and Veins of them, the Substances mixt with them, the Layers of the several Earths, Sands, Clays, Stones, Minerals, &c. that are met with in diging Mines and Wells, The Nature of Petrifying Waters, the shapes of Crystals, Ores, Talks, Sparrs, and most kind of precious Stones, Marbles, Flint,

Chalk,

Chalk, and the like, every of which are by their forms sufficiently discover'd to have been formerly fluid Bodies, and whilst fluid, shaped into those forms: One or two undeniable Instances I shall add of the fluidity of Flints, and that shall be that I have now by me, a Flint that has so perfectly filled the Shell of an *Ecknius*, and inclosed it also that it has received all the impressions of the cracks of the Shells both on the Concave and Convex Part thereof, and has exactly filled all the Holes and Pores thereof, and has so perfectly received all the shape thereof as if it were nothing but Plaister of *Paris* tempered, Wax, or Sulphur that had been melted and cast on it; notwithstanding which it is a Flint so hard as to cut Glass very readily, and is of a very singular and uniform Texture; to this I might add many others of the like kind, which have the impressions of these and other Shells, and yet are some Marble, some Pebbles, some Agats, some Marchasites, some Ores, some Crystals, &c. Some Flints I have marked with impressions as exactly as if they had been soft Wax stamp'd with a Seal.

Further, That the Subterraneous Fuels do also wast and decay, is as evident from the extinction and ceasing of several Vulcans that have heretofore raged; which Considerations may afford us sufficient Arguments to believe that Earthquakes have heretofore, not only been much more frequent and universal, but much more powerful. If to this we do add what I formerly mention'd, that there seems to be no other more probable and intelligible Cause in Nature of the inequality of the Earths Surface, the natural Principle of Gravity reducing the Parts of it as near to an exact spherical Figure as their Solidity and forc'd Postures will permit, and consequently (as I mention'd before) the natural form produc'd by Gravity would be a multitude of Spherical Shells concreted of the several Substances of which it consists, incompassing each other, not unlike the Orbits or Shells (for we have no proper name for that kind of hollow Spherical Figure) of an Onion, or as the *Ptolemaiick* Astronomers do fancy the solid Orbs of the Heavens, ranged every one in its distinct Order according to its Density and Gravity; that is, that which hath been heaviest would have approach'd nearest the Center, or at least nearest to that part which is attractive and the cause of Gravitation, if such a Body there be in the middle of the Earth, and the next lighter in the second place, and so on to the third, fourth, fifth, &c. according to their several degrees of Gravity and Density, they would have taken their several Quarters, and so Water would always have covered the Face of the Earth, and the lightest Liquor would always have been at the top, and the Air above that, and Æther above that; and as in Fluids so also in Solids, the Shells of Gold would have been the lowest of any Body we yet know, that of Quicksilver next, that of Lead next, and so the rest in their order, which seems also really to have been the form of the Earth, till disturbed by Earthquakes, which I conceive to be the reason of the scarcity of those heavy Bodies of Metal near the Surface, and of the greatest scarcity of Gold which is the most heavy, and that it is not to be found but in such places where there have in probability been great subversions by Earthquakes, as in Mountains, or in Rivers running out of Mountains, or in Earth washt and tumbled down from Mountains, and such like places, as by many Circumstances may be guest to have been formerly deeper under the Surface of the Earth.

There is yet one Argument more that to me seems very good, and that is fetcht from no less distance than the Moon and the Sun by the help of Telescopes. These Bodies, as I have formerly hinted in the latter end of my Micrography, seem to have the same Principle of Gravity as the Earth, which, as I have there argued, seems probable from their Spherical Figure in general, and the several inequalities in particular, visible by the help of Telescopes on the Surface of the Moon, and the several Smoaks, and Clouds, and Spots that appear on the Surface of the Sun; and as they have that Principle in common with the Earth, so it seems to me that they are not free from the like motions with those of an Earthquake: For as to the Moon 'tis easily to be perceiv'd through a Telescope, that the whole Surface of it is covered over with a multitude of small Pits or Cavities which are incompassed round with a kind of protuberant Brim, much like the Cavities

or

or small Pits, which are left in a Pot of Alabaster Dust boyled dry by the Vapours which break out of the Body of it by the heat of the Fire ; and all the inequalities that appear on the Surface of that Body, seem, by their form, to have been caus'd by an Eruption of the Moon, somewhat Analogous to our Earthquakes; all those Pits in the Moon being much like the Caldera or Vent at the top of Vulcans here on the Earth, or like those little Pits left at the top or surface of the Alabaster Dust by the natural subsiding of that Dust in the place where the Vapours generated within the Body of it break out. I need not, I think, spend time in urging Arguments to prove the sufficient powerfulness of the Cause to produce Effects as great as any I have ascribed to it, as being able to raise as great and high Mountains as those of the *Alps, Andes, Caucasus, Montes Lunæ,* &c. especially since even of late we are often informed of as great effects elsewhere, and even of the shaking and moving those vast Mountains by our latter and more debilitated Earthquakes, tho' those Mountains are now in probability much more compacted and tenacious by the since acquired Petrifaction, than they were before their first accumulation; and tho' 'tis not unlikely but the Fuel or Cause of the Subterraneous Fire may be much wasted and spent by preceding Conflagarations; Yet possibly there may be yet left in other Parts sufficient Mines to produce very great effects if they shall by any accident take Fire; and 'tis not impossible but that there may be some Causes that generate and renew the Fuel, as there are others that spend and consume it.

From all which Propositions, if at least they are true, will follow many others meer Corollaries which may be deduced from them.

First, That there may have been in preceding Ages, whole Countries either swallowed up into the Earth, or sunk so low as to be drown'd by the coming in of the Sea, or divers other ways quite destroyed; as *Plato's Atlantis,* &c. *The Corollairs from the foregoing Propositions.*

Secondly, That there, many have been as many Countries new made and produced by being raised from under the Water, or from the inward or hidden Parts of the Body of the Earth, as *England.* 2.

Thirdly, That there may have been divers Species of things wholly destroyed and annihilated, and divers others changed and varied, for since we find that there are some kinds of Animals and Vegetables peculiar to certain places, and not to be found elsewhere; if such a place have been swallowed up, 'tis not improbable but that those Animal Beings may have been destroyed with them; and this may be true both of aerial and aquatick Animals: For those animated Bodies, whether Vegetables or Animals which were naturally nourished or refresh'd by the Air would be destroy'd by the Water. And this I imagine to be the reason why we now find the Shells of divers Fishes Petrify'd in Stone, of which we have now none of the same kind. As divers of those Snake or Snail Stones, as they call them, whereof great varieties are found about *England,* and some in *Portland,* dug out of the very midst of the Quary of a prodigious bigness, one of which I have weighing near   Pound weight, being in Diameter about   Inches, which I obtain'd from the Honourable *Henry Howard* of *Norfolk:* We have Stories that there have been Giants in former Ages of the World, and 'tis not impossible but that such there may have been, and that they may have been all destroyed, both they and their Country by an Earthquake, and the Poets seem to hint as much by their *Gigantomachia.* 3.

Fourthly, That there may have been divers new varieties generated of the same Species, and that by the change of the Soil on which it was produced; for since we find that the alteration of the Climate, Soil and Nourishment doth often produce a very great alteration in those Bodies that suffer it; 'tis not to be doubted but that alterations also of this Nature may cause a very great change in the shape, and other accidents of an animated Body. And this I imagine to be the reason of that great variety of Creatures that do properly belong to 4.

to one Species ; as for inftance, in Dogs, Sheep, Goats Deer, Hawks, Pigeons, *&c.* for fince it is found that they generate upon each other, and that variety of Climate and Nourifhment doth vary feveral accidents in their fhape, if thefe or any other animated Body be thus tranfplanted, 'tis not unlikely but that the like variation may follow ; and hence I fuppofe 'tis that I find divers kinds of Petrify'd Shells, of which kind we have none now naturally produced ; of this fort are many of thofe Helmet Stones which have been made by the Petrifactions of Subftances in the Shells of feveral forts of *Echini,* whofe forts have been deftroyed by the alteration of the Nature of that part of the Sea where they were produced ; and hence 'tis we find fcarce any Shell-Fifh in our *Englifh* Sea that has a Shell like thofe forts of *Nautili* ; from whence our *Keinfham* and other forts of Snake-Stones are produced.

5. Fifthly, 'Tis not impoffible but that there may have been a preceding learned Age wherein poffibly as many things may have been known as are now, and perhaps many more, all the Arts cultivated and brought to the greateft Perfection, Mathematicks, Mechanicks, Literature, Mufick, Opticks, *&c.* reduced to their higheft pitch, and all thofe annihilated, deftroyed and loft by fucceeding Devaftations. Atomical Philofophy feems to have been better underftood in fome preceding time, as alfo the Aftronomy evinc'd by *Copernicus,* the *Ægyptian,* and *Chinefe* Hiftories tell us of many thoufand Years more than ever we in Europe heard of by our Writings, if their Chronology may be granted, which indeed there is great reafon to queftion.

6. Sixthly, 'Tis not impoffible but that this may have been the caufe of a total Deluge, which may have caufed a deftruction of all things then living in the Air : For if Earthquakes can raife the Surface of the Earth in one place and fink it in another fo as to make it uneven and rugged with Hills and Pits, it may on the contrary level thofe Mountains again, and fill thofe Pits, and reduce the Body of the Earth to its primitive roundnefs, and then the Waters muft neceffarily cover all the Face of the Earth as well as it did in the beginning of the World, and by this means not only a learned Age may be wholly annihilated, and no relicks of it left, but alfo a great number of the Species of Animals and Plants. And 'tis not improbable but in the Flood of *Noah,* the Omnipotent might make ufe of this means to produce that great effect which deftroyed all Flefh, and every living thing, fave what was faved alive in the Ark.

7. Seventhly, 'Tis not impoffible but that fome of thefe great alterations may have alter'd alfo the magnetical Directions of the Earth ; fo that what is now under the Pole or Æquator, or any other Degree of Latitude may have formerly been under another ; for fince 'tis probable that divers of thefe parts that have fuch a Quality may have been tranfpos'd, 'tis not unlikely but that the magnetick Axis of the whole may be alter'd by it, after the fame manner as we may find by experiment on a Loadftone, that the breaking off and tranfpofing the parts of it, do caufe a variation of the magnetick Axis.

I could proceed to fet down a great many other Corollarys that would naturally follow from thefe Principles if certainly proved. But this Effay I intended only as a hint or memorandum to fuch Gentlemen as travel or any other inquifitive Perfons, who for the future may have better opportunities of making Obfervations of this kind, that they may be hereby excited, or at leaft intreated to take notice of fuch Phænomena as may clear this Inquiry tho' never fo feemingly mean and trivial, fince it feems not improbable but that they may difcover more of the preceding duration and alterations of the World than any other Obfervations whatfoever, and that thence may flow fuch inftructions as may be of fome of the moft confiderable ufes to humane Life and Society, to which end all our Philofophical Studies and Inquiries tend. Ended *Sep.* 15. 1668.

THE preceeding *Discourse of Earthquakes* was wrote, Anno. 1668, as appears by the Date at the end thereof, and lay by the Author for a considerable time, till afterwards he took the Subject into consideration again, and read several Lectures in confirmation of his former Hypothesis, and in them produced several Observations and Collections quoted from divers Authors Ancient and Modern, and answered many Objections, which I shall in the next place present the Reader with as near as I can in the order they were read to the Royal Society, not doubting but the Curious will find Entertainment and Satisfaction in them. The first that I find to this purpose, is a Lecture which was among his other Papers, tho' I know not the exact time when it was read, yet since it contains several Arguments to prove that the figured Stones found in many parts of the World are real Petrifactions, I shall here give it in the first place.

R. W

I Am not, I suppose, the only Person who hath heard some Persons (with what Reason I dispute not) ask what the *Royal Society hath done for so many Years* as they have met. And other Persons as confidently affirm that they have done *just nothing*. Nor am I ignorant that the same Reflections have been made upon me in particular with more severe Aggravations. As to what concerns my self I shall not now spend time in answering, designing to do it by another way. But as to what concerns this Honourable Society, I conceive it might be a satisfactory Answer to assure such Objectours that this *Society* have been imployed in collecting such *Observations*, and making such *Experiments* and *Trials* as being fitly apply'd and judiciously made use of, will very much tend to the advancement of *Natural Knowledge*: And tho' the things so collected may of themselves seem but like a rude heap of unpolish'd and unshap'd Materials, yet for the most part they are so qualified as that they may be fit for the beginning, at least of a solid, firm and lasting Structure of Philosophy. *[marginal note: A Vindication of the Royal Society.]*

But because some of those may doubt whether really there be any such Collection made, and more of the practicableness of making such a Use and Application of them, and will not acquiesce and be satisfied with the effects hereof that future times may produce, but are desirous to see some *Specimen* of what may be hoped for, by seeing the Ground designed and set out, the Foundation laid, and the Workmen beginning to raise the Walls, and make use of the Materials that are said to be got in readiness for such a Fabrick.

I conceive, it may not be altogether unseasonable this following Year nor improper for this *Honourable Society's Care* to make some attempt of that kind by shewing some *Specimen* of such a Structure raised from Observations and Collections of their own, that it may appear that they have not disquieted themselves in vain, in heaping up such a Treasure which they know not who shall enjoy or make use of; that is, to see whether any of these things they have been collecting, will afford sufficient Evidence to ground a deduction of a higher Nature upon, such as is more obscure to be seen, or more difficult to be ascertained of, to see whether, when a weight comes to be laid open the Stones or the Bricks, the natural Observations, or the Artificial Trials and Experiments, they will not crush under it, and fail of sufficient Solidity; and if they do, whether such may not be fit for other places, and whether it will not be necessary to seek out for some others that may be more firm and solid, and such as are of a closer and better concocted qualification, which may be more powerful to sustaine a higher Superstructure, and a greater weight of Argument to be laid upon them.

In order to this it is necessary (for the Architects at least) to know, 1*st.* What are the particular qualifications necessary for the several Materials of their designed Fabrick. 2*dly.* The Methods by which these qualifications may be examin'd. 3*dly.* The place where, and the means how Materials so qualified may be proved, without which præmeditated Design, Knowledge, *[marginal note: What makes a Collection of Experiments Observations useful.]*

and

and Care ; a Collection, tho' very great, made at a venture muſt needs contain abundance of ſuch as will be of little uſe for the end aimed at, and not only ſo, but will alſo prove a great Obſtruction and Confuſion in finding out ſuch as are proper, and in ſeparating the Good from the Bad.

The Structure aimed at, is a true and certain knowledge of the Works of Nature, and this is deſigned to be attained as faſt as may be, and to be perfected as far as may be ; or the end of the Inquiſition is the promotion and increaſing of Natural Knowledge.

The Analytick Method.

The methods of attaining this end may be two, either the Analytick, or the Synthetick. The firſt is the proceeding from the Cauſes to the Effects. The ſecond from the Effects to the Cauſes : The former is the more difficult, and ſuppoſes the thing to be already done and known, which is the thing ſought and to be found out ; this begins from the higheſt, moſt general and univerſal Principles or Cauſes of Things, and branches itſelf out into the more particular and ſubordinate.

The Synthetick Method.

The ſecond is the more proper for experimental Inquiry, which from a true information of the Effect by a due proceſs, finds not the immediate Cauſe thereof, and ſo proceeds gradually to higher and more remote Cauſes and Powers effective, founding its Steps upon the loweſt and more immediate Concluſions.

An Inquiſition by the former Method is reſembled fitly enough by that Example of an Architect, who hath a full comprehenſion of what he deſigns to do and acts accordingly : But the latter is more properly reſembled to that of a Husbandman or Gardener, who prepares his Ground and ſows his Seed, and diligently cheriſhes the growing Vegetable, ſupplying it continually with fitting Moiſture, Food, Shelter, &c. obſerving and cheriſhing its continual Progreſſion, till it comes to its perfect Ripeneſs and Maturity, and yields him the Fruit of his Labour. Nor is it to be expected that a Production of ſuch Perfection as this is deſigned, ſhould in an inſtant be brought to its compleat Ripeneſs and Perfection ; but as all the Works of Nature if it be naturally proceeded with, it muſt have its due time to acquire its due form and full maturity, by gradual Growth and a natural Progreſſion ; not but that the other method is alſo of excellent and neceſſary uſe, and will very often facilitate and haſten the progreſs to Perfection. An Inſtance of which kind I deſigned ſome Years ſince to have given this Honourable Society in ſome of my Lectures upon the motions and influences of the Cæleſtial Bodies, if it had been then thought fit ; but I underſtand the ſame thing will now be ſhortly done by Mr. *Newton* in a Treatiſe of his now in the Preſs : But that will not be the only Inſtance of that kind which I deſign here to produce, for that I have divers Inſtances of the like Nature wherein from an *Hypotheſis* being ſuppoſed or a premeditated Deſign, all the *Phænomena* of the Subject will be *a Priori* foretold, and the Effects naturally follow as proceeding from a Cauſe ſo and ſo qualified and limited. And in truth the *Synthetick* way by Experiments Obſervations, &c. will be very ſlow if it be not often aſſiſted by the *Analytick*, which proves of excellent uſe, even tho' it proceed by a falſe poſition : for that the diſcovery of a *Negative* is one way of reſtraining and limiting an *Affirmative*.

But not to ſpend more time at preſent upon the more particular explications of Theſe Methods, which would make of it ſelf a very large Diſcourſe, I ſhall proceed to the Subject which I began to diſcourſe upon the laſt meeting, premiſing only in general what I think neceſſary thereunto, an Explication of what I underſtand by natural Knowledge, or the Knowledge of Nature.

What Knowledge is and how acquired.

By *Knowledge* then in the higheſt *Idea* of it, I underſtand a certainty of information of the Mind and Underſtanding founded upon true and undeniable Evidence.

True

True and undeniable Evidence is afforded either immediately by *Senfe* without Fallacy, or mediately by a true Ratiocination from such Senfe.

I call that *Senfe* without Fallacy, where the *fallacies* of Senfe being detected and known, the Evidence produced thereby is examined and found to be free and clear of all such *Fallacies*.

I call that true *Ratiocination* from such Senfe, where being sure of the Premifes, the Conclufion neceffarily follows from them ; which is the method of Reafoning made ufe of i *Geomotry*, and by which we arrive at as great a certainty of things unfeen as feen. Thus *Ovid* defcribes the method of *Pythagoras*, in fcaling the Heavens. *The true Method of Reafoning.*

> ———*Ifq; licet cæli Regione Remotus*
> *Mente Deos adiit, & quæ natura negabat*
> *Vifibus humanis, oculis ea pectoris haufit.*

Now tho' in Phyfical Inquiries, by reafon of the abftrufenefs of Caufes, and the limited Power of the Senfes we cannot thus reafon, and without many Inductions from a multitude of Particulars come to raife exact Definitions of things and general Propofitions; yet by comparing of varieties of fuch Inductions we may arrive to fo great an affurance and limitation of Propofitions as will at leaft be fufficient to ground Conjectures upon, which may ferve for making *Hypothefes* fit to be enquired into by the *Analytick* method, and thence to find out what other Experiments or Obfervations are neceffary to be procured for the further progrefs in the *Synthetick*, which will queftionlefs fo far inform us of the general and univerfal progrefs of the Operations of Nature, that nothing but what is really the truth fhall be propofed but the abfurdity and infufficiency thereof will prefently be detected and proved. *The difficulty thereof in Natural Philofophy.*

So that tho' poffibly we may not be able to produce a *Pofitive* Proof, yet we may attain to that of a *Negative*, which in many cafes is as cogent and undeniable, and none but a willful or fenfelefs Perfon will refufe his affent unto it. Thus much I thought was neceffary to premife in order to what I have further to propound to the Confideration of this noble Society upon the Subject I have difcourfed of formerly only by way of Queries; it being my aim at prefent to fee what *Pofitive* or *Negative* certainty at leaft may be attained concerning the fame, either from the information of Senfe freed from Fallacies or from the fuperftructures of Reafoning. *A Negative many times as cogent as an Affirmative.*

I propounded then two Hypothefes for the folution of the *Phænomena*, obferv'd in *Petrified Bodies*, of the refemblance of Animal and Vegetable Bodies; fuch as the Shells and Bodies of Fifhes, the Bones, Teeth, Hornes, &c. of Fifh, and alfo of Terreftrial Animals, the Wood, Leaves, Bark, Roots, and Fruits of Plants and Vegetables; which refembling Bodies are found to be of variety of Subftances, fometimes of Stone, as Flint, Marble, Black, White, Gray, and of various other Colours, of Free-ftone, *Portland*-ftone, Chalk, and an infinite variety of other Stone, fome harder, fome fofter : Of various kinds of Clay, Earth, Sand, &c they have been found near the tops of the higheft Hills, and the bottom of the loweft Wells and Mines, in the middle of the folid Quarries of Stone and other Minerals, and thofe the moft remote, or at leaft very far diftant from the Sea. Some of thefe have the perfect reprefentation of the Figure of fuch Creatures and other Subftances as are now well known, others of fuch as have fome analogy and likenefs to them, yet different from what are known of thofe Species to which they feem to belong, either in Magnitude, Figure, Colour, &c. yet retain fuch characteriftick marks as feem to indicate them to belong to this or that Species of Animals or Vegetables. Some of thefe are nothing but perfect Stones of feveral kinds, others are inclofed with a Subftance feeming to be the fame, with that of the very Animal or Vegetable they refemble. Add to this, that in as many varieties of places there have been found others of thefe Figured Bodies, *Of Petrified Subftances.*

dies,

dies, which have as to Senfe the very fame Subftance and Figures with thofe of the correfponding Species of Animals or Vegetables, and do not feem to be at all of a petrify'd and ftony Subftance, but rather of an Animal or Vegetable ; of every of which Particulars I have viewd and examined Inftances. And if it were not for detaining you too long, could have here produced a more particular Account and Defcription. But they being fo generally known at leaft fo univerfally almoft fpread over the whole Earth, fo that no Country almoft but doth afford them, I thought it would be needlefs.

How to come to a certain knowledge of them. The Queftion now is how we fhall come to a certainty of Knowledge concerning them, by which we may be able to underftand what they really are : And Secondly, What was the Caufe of them. Thirdly, How they came to be difpofed, placed, or made in thofe parts where they are, or have been found. Fourthly, Thefe Difcoveries being made to fatisfaction, of what ufe or benefit will it be to Mankind, or how fhall we be the wifer, or how will this Knowledge be an improvement of Natural Knowledge ? Which is the aim of this Society.

For Anfwer then to thefe feveral Queries I fhall propound thefe following Confiderations.

To know what Subftance they are of. *Firft,* As to the way of knowing of what Subftance they are, I conceive there can be no better way than what we generally ufe when we inquire into the true Nature or Subftance of any other Body when it is delivered to us to be examined or denominated ; for inftance, if a peice of Metal be delivered to be examined, it will firft be viewed to fee what Metal it refembles in Colour and Confiftence, or in fuch other obvious and fenfible Qualifications as may enable one to judge or guefs what kind of Metal it is ; as fuppofe it refembles Gold for clofenefs and ponderoufnefs, thefe give intimation enough of examining it yet a little more curioufly, fince all is not Gold that glifters, and it may be that fome Counterfeit in thofe more obvious Qualifications has mimicked that noble Metal, to do this, it is tried further by being put into good *Aqua Fortis,* to fee whether that will diffolve it, for if it doth, it cannot be Gold. Secondly, The Specifick Gravity thereof is more curioufly and exactly found by the help of Scales and Weights, by which it is weighed in and out of Water, becaufe if thereby it be found to be lighter than Gold it cannot be Gold. Thirdly, By Hammering and a Gold Beater, 'tis found to be Malleable, and by looking through the Leaf, 'tis found of a tranfparent Greenefs and reflects a true Golden Colour, then 'tis tried by copelling and found fixed in the Fire, then it tarnifhes not in the Air, and Amalgams Readily with *Mercury,* then its Solution in ARtinges, the Skin and Nails red, and a further trial fhews it to tinge Glafs of a Ruby Colour. Now if it bear all thefe feveral ways of Examination, and anfwers to the properties of Gold, it may fafely be concluded to be true Gold, and whoever fhall deny it to be fuch muft be looked upon as one that doth it without Reafon, unlefs he can produce a further Criterion by which it fhall be found to be very differing from it. Now, tho' this Metal were found at the bottom of a Mine a hundred Foot under Ground, or at the top of a Hill a hundred Foot above the Level of the Plain ; or in the Pores of a growing Vegetable; or in the Tooth or Thigh of an Animal, tho' poffibly it may be difficult to affign the Reafon or Caufe how it came to be placed there ; yet the Examiner hath the Evidence of Senfe to affure him that this Metal is Gold, and he ought to conclude and acquiefce in it, that fuch it is ; otherwife there can be nothing at all known that it is this or that Body, and then there is an end of all further Inquiry or Experiment.

Now though there may not be known fo many various ways of examining every other kind of Body, as, by reafon of the value of it, there have been found out for Gold ; yet in many Bodies at leaft a much lefs number will ferve the turn to give affurance, that the Body fo examined is of this or that kind and in many the very outward form as vifible to the naked Eye, but efpecially if the inward vifible appearance of the Subftance be joined with it, will

be

be affurance fufficient to force an Affent or Conclufion of what kind the Body is that is fo examined, and it ought not to be denied to be fuch without as evident a manifeftation to the contrary.

This Difcourfe I have been the larger in premifing, becaufe, till it be agreed what is fufficient evidence to prove a natural Body of this or that kind there can be nothing done. If Experimental Philofophy, and if Poofs of this kind will not fuffice, I cannot expect that all that I fhall bring to prove the *Hypothefis* will be of any validity. That then which I fhall indeavour to prove is;

Firft, That there have been, and daily are found, the real Shells of Fifhes in fuch parts of the Earth as are much above the prefent Level of the Sea, and others buried at a very great depth under the Surface of the Earth, where notwithftanding, 'tis evident that they were not there placed by any humane Power or Defign. *A Recapitulation of the Heads mention'd Pag. 288. Supra.*

Secondly, That many of thefe Shells are of a form differing from any of thofe Shells of that Species to which they feem to belong, which are commonly known at this Day.

Thirdly, That there are others of them which to all appearance are of the very fame Species now known and to be found living.

Fourthly, That there are many of thefe Shells which are and have been in procefs of time, fill'd within and inclofed without with divers forts of Earth, fuch as, Clay, Lome, Sea Sand, and divers other kinds of Sand, Mud, Chalk, &c.

Fifthly, That thofe filling and inclofing Bodies have been, and are by degrees, in procefs of time, petrify'd and hardn'd into Stones of differing Natures, Hardnefs and Contextures retaining the Impreffion, Form, or Signature of thofe Shells, fo inclofed.

Sixthly, That thofe Shells fo filled and inclofed, as above faid, are according to the differing Nature of the Petrifactive Liquor or Juice: fometimes alfo Petrify'd retaining ftill the fame Figure they were of when the Petrifactive Juice began to operate upon them.

Seventhly, That others of them remain yet perfect Shells without Petrifaction or Alteration, when as yet both the Subftance that fills them, and that which enclofes them is converted into Stone of differing Natures and Textures.

Eighthly, That many of thefe Shells are either by length of Time, or by the Nature of the Petrifactive Juice perfectly rotted and decayed fo as to be eafily frangible between one's Finger and Thumb into a very fine Powder and yet ferve to give a perfect Mould or Shape to the inclofed and inclofing-Stone.

Ninthly, That in many cafes the Shell is not only Petrify'd by the faid Juice, but fometimes after the impreffion hath been made as aforefaid, the Shell hath been clearly diffolved and carried away from the inclofing and inclofed Subftances, leaving only the Space empty where the faid Shell hath been placed.

Tenthly, That it fometimes happens that the Subftance that filled the Shell hath been Petrify'd, and after the Shell hath been rotted away, the Petrify'd Body that was inclofed and had received that Impreffion, hath been afterwards inclofed with a Subftance which hath afterwards Petrify'd and fo inclofed it in Stone.

Eleventhly, That thefe kinds of Shells or the Petrify'd Subftances that have been formed by them, have been for all Antiquity, and are at this Day to be found in moft parts of the known World.

Twelvethly, That they are moft of them differing from one another, tho' all referable to fome Species of Shell-Fifhes now to be found; yet in many particulars each of them alfo differing from them; that is, thofe that are found in one Country or Region, are very differing from thofe of another Country or Region, and that not only as to the Nature of the Petrify'd Subftance inclofed and inclofing, but alfo as to the Figure and Make of the Shells themfelves; and many of thofe alfo differing from the fhape even of

P p p p

thofe

thofe Shell-Fifhes which are now to be found in fuch parts of the Seas which are fituated near to the places that they are found in.

Concurring to this Head I fhall prove that Shell-Fifhes of the fame Species in differing Countries now to be found, have many differences one from another, as much as any one of thofe Petrify'd Bodies have from any of the prefent Shells.

The end of the Author's Difcourfes.　I have in my former Difcourfes explain'd the end and aim of thefe my Inquifitions, namely, to make fome Ufe and Application of feveral Obfervations and Experiments that have been Collected in order to deduce fome Doctrine from them, which may ferve to direct fuch further Inquifitions as fhall be neceffary for the perfecting of the fame, or at leaft to find whether fuch are wanting, and of what Kind and Nature they are.

The Doctrine aimed at, is, the Caufe and Reafon of the prefent Figure, Shape and Conftitution of the Surface of this Body of the Earth, whether Sea or Land, as we now find it prefented unto us under various and very irregular Forms and Fafhions and conftituted of very differing Subftances.

Hiftories deficient, and why.　Now, becaufe when we look into Natural Hiftories of paft Times, we find very few, if any, Footfteps of what alterations or tranfactions of this Nature have been performed, we muft be fain to make ufe of other helps than what Natural Hiftorians will furnifh us with, to make out an account of the Hiftory thereof: Nor are there any Monuments or Medals with Literal, Graphical, or Hieroglyphical Infcriptions that will help us out in this our Inquiry, by which the Writers of Civil Hiftories have of late Years been much affifted from the great curiofity of modern Travellers and Collectors of fuch Curiofities.

The great tranfactions of the Alterations, Formations, or Difpofitions of the Superficial Parts of the Earth into that Conftitution and Shape which we now find them to have, preceded the Invention of Writing, and what was preferved till the times of that Invention were more dark and confufed, that they feem to be altogether Romantick, Fabulous, and Fictious, and cannot be much relied on or heeded, and at beft will only afford us occafions of Conjecture.

Proofs of the foregoing Propofitions mentioned Pag. 333.　For Proof then of the firft Propofition that, &c. I could produce a multitude of Authorities fetched out of printed Authors, and as many others that I have received from the Relations of very credible Perfons that have found them themfelves, but it would be too long, I fhall therefore only name one who was formerly a worthy Member of this Society, and well known to divers here prefent, and that was Dr. *Peter Ball*, he paffing over the *Alps* to go into *Italy* by a narrow Paffage, where there was on the one hand a prodigious high Cliff above him, and on the other hand, as prodigious deep Precipice below him, obferved in the Cliff a Layer of Sea Sand and Shells for a very great length buried under that high Mountain above ; he had the curiofity to take up and bring home with him into *England* divers of them which he dug out of the faid Layer of Sand which he fhewed me, and I found them to be true Oyfter-fhells, not Petrified but remaining perfect Shells, one of which he gave me, and had divers others which he kept ; he obferved alfo, that there were divers other Subftances among the Sand as if it had been upon the Sea-fhoar. To this I fhall add an Obfervation of my own nearer Home, which others poffibly may have the opportunity of feeing, and that was at the Weft end of the Ifle of *Wight*, in a Cliff lying within the *Needles* almoft oppofite to *Hurft-Caftle*, it is an Earthy fort of Cliff made up of feveral forts of Layers, of Clays, Sands, Gravels and Loames one upon the other Somewhat above the middle of this Cliff, which I judge in fome parts may be about two Foot high, I found one of the faid Layers to be of a perfect Sea Sand filled with a great variety of Shells, fuch as Oyfters, Limpits, and feveral forts of Periwinkles, of which kind I dug out many and brought them with me, and found them to be of the fame kind with thofe which were very plentifully to be found upon the Shore beneath, now caft out of the Sea.

This

This Layer is extended along this Cliff I conceive near half a Mile, and may be about sixty Foot or more above the high Water mark.

Another Instance I observed nearer this place, and that was in St. *James's Fields*, where St. *James's* Square is now built, in which place when they were making Bricks of the Brick Earth there dug, they had sunk several Wells, which I judge might be near twenty Foot in depth, to procure Water for that purpose; going down into several of those, I found, at the bottom, a Layer of perfect Sea Sand, with variety of Shells, and several Bones, and other Substances, of which kind I dug out enough to fill a small Box and shewed them to Mr. *Boyl*, and also to this *Society*. And I was informed also, that the same kind of Substances were found in digging of a Snow Well in St. *James's Park*; and I doubt not but whoever shall sink any where thereabout to that depth will find the same things. Now whoever will consider the Positions and Circumstances of the said places, will easily grant, I suppose, that they could not be there placed by the Industry of *Man*, but must be ascribed to some other cause to be fetched from *Nature*.

As to the second Head, That, &c. I shall produce several Oyster and Cockle Shells which have been and are to be found in many Parts of *England*, which *See* p. 333. in many particulars of their shape, do differ from those of the Oysters and Cockles now to be found; yet upon examination of them they may be found to be true and perfect Shells by all sensible Qualities, except only their exact shape, and therefore I conceive that to be sufficient Evidence to prove them to be really such, because it is all the Evidence the Matter is capable of. If in digging a Mine, or the like, an artificial Coin or Urne, or the like Substance be found, no one scruples to affirm it to be of this or that Metal or Earth he finds them by trial to be of: Nor that they are *Roman*, *Saxon*, *Norman*, or the like, according to the Relievo, Impression, Characters, or Form they find them of. Now these Shells and other Bodies are the Medals, Urnes, or Monuments of Nature, whose Relievoes, Impressions, Characters, Forms, Substances, &c. are much more plain and discoverable to any unbiassed Person, and therefore he has no reason to scruple his assent: nor to desist from making his Observations to correct his natural Chronology, and to conjecture how, and when, and upon what occasion they came to be placed in those Repositories. These are the greatest and most lasting Monuments of Antiquity, which, in all probability, will far antidate all the most ancient Monuments of the World, even the very Pyramids, Obelisks, Mummys, Hieroglyphicks, and Coins, and will afford more information in Natural History, than those other put altogether will in Civil. Nor will there be wanting *Media* or *Criteria* of Chronology, which may give us some account even of the time when, as I shall afterwards mention.

As to the Proof of the third Proposition, *viz.* That, &c, All those Instances I have named are of sufficient evidence, for that those which I found in both those places I mentioned were of the same kinds with those that are now to be found near those places, as whoever shall examine will find.

And the fourth will also from the same, and hundreds of others be as evident, and therefore I suppose none will scruple to assent to this Proposition, *viz.* That, &c. Page 333, especially if the truth of the former be granted, which I conceive cannot be denied.

For Proof of the fifth Proposition, namely, That, &c. The place I mentioned before near the *Needles* in the Isle of *Wight* afforded a most evident and convincing one as could well be desired, which was from the following Observation. I took notice that the aforesaid Earthy Cliff did founder down and fall upon the Sea-shoar underneath, which was smooth and Sandy, and bare at low Water so as to be walked on, but at high Water a great part of it was covered by the Sea. I observed several great lumps of the said Founderings lying below, some whereof, which lay next the Cliff, tho' they were somewhat harden'd together more than they were above in the Cliff, were yet not

hard

hard enough to be accounted Stone; others of them that lay further into the Sea were yet more hard, and fome of the furtheft I could not come at for the Water, were as hard I conceived as *Purbeck* Paving (which is taken up from the Shore of *Purbeck*, lying juft oppofite to it on the Weft fide of this Channel or Paffage) divers of thefe Stones I obferv'd to be made up of the peices of Earth that had foundred down from the Cliff, which I was affured of by carefully obferving and finding divers of them to confift of the feveral Layers, and in the fame order as I faw them in the Cliff; among the reft I found divers that had the Layer of Sea Sand and Shells which I had obferved in the Cliff inferted in the Stone with the adjoyning Layers all petrify'd together into a hard Stone. Here I found multitudes of the faid Shells I before mention'd to have obferv'd in the Cliff, mix'd loofely with a Sea Sand ; now together with the faid Sand both fill'd, inclos'd, and petrify'd altogether, and I broke off many peices of the faid Rocks, where I found the faid Petrifactions, and found them much like other Stones I had feen from other Inland Quarries here of *England*, wherein I had obferv'd alfo fuch kind of petrify'd Shells, tho' how they came there to be fo Petrify'd I could not be fo well inform'd. For that which I conceive was the caufe of this fuddain Petrifaction (for I conceive thofe that I examin'd had not been Stones for very many Years, which I judged by their diftance from the prefent Cliff, and from the quantity thereof, which *Communibus Annis* did founder down) was that clofe by this Cliff, there is a vitriolate or aluminous Spring or Rill which runs into the Sea, where formerly thofe Salts have been made of it by boyling, but has been now omitted for many Years. Thefe faline Springs or Rills I conjecture mixing with the Sea-Water, may be the caufe of the faid Petrifaction, and the want of it is the caufe why other founderings in other parts of the faid Cliff are not at all fo Petrify'd. Now from the affur'd Obfervation of thefe Petrifactions, I cannot but judge that the truth of this Propofition will moft evidently appear, and needs no other to confirm it. However I doubt not but that any one who fhould there lay a part of the faid Cliff fhaped and marked as he pleas'd for his own affurance, would find the fame very hard Petrify'd in two or three Years, which may not be unworthy of farther Inquiry and Trial for fuch as have opportunity.

As to the Proof of the fixth Propofition, it will not be difficult, the preceding being once granted for that there may be thoufands of Inftances of that Nature found in the Stones dug out of divers of our *English* Quarries; fome of which Stones are found full of fuch Petrifactions.

Upon this occafion I think it not improper to mention an Obfervation which I have often taken notice of, which is of the Flints which are generally found intermix'd with Chalk in Quarries of that kind of Stone. I have obferv'd then that thefe Flints are nothing elfe but the Body of the Chalk united together, and, as it were, firft diluted by a petrifick Juice, and by that diffolved into it, and fo make a uniform clofe Body which by degrees doth all petrify and harden together into that folid hard Body of the Flint. This I found by taking notice of the Nature of thofe Flints when broken, and how the Grain, Colour and Hardnefs of them was fituated efpecially towards the edges ; for there where the Juice feem'd to be almoft fpent, the Flinty Body appears of a midling Nature between Chalk and Flint, befides I have obferv'd fometimes other Bodies inclofed, and fometimes lumps of Chalk alfo, toward which the Limb-parts of the Flint were colour'd and terminated juft as towards the incompaffing Chalk. And from the curious and fharp running and mouldings which I have obferved in Flints, I conceive that the firft Liquid Subftance of it was altogether as fluid as Water, tho' it were imbu'd with a Saline Sulphureous or other petrifactive Tincture. Thefe Indications may be much more plainly manifefted by fuch a peice of Flint than 'tis poffible for any one to defcribe by words; and therefore I fhall omit the farther mention of them till I can meet with a Flint to fhew them. I mention this here only to fhew that the petrifactive Juice is often found to infinuate itfelf into the clofeft Pores of Body, by reafon of its great fluidity which inables it oft to petrify even the very Bodies and Subftances of the Shells themfelves.

But

But tho' some of these Petrifactive Liquors be thus fluid, yet they are not all ; and thence it comes that many Shells remain unpetrify'd, tho' the Substances that fill'd them and enclos'd them be so wrote upon, which was the seventh Proposition I undertook to prove. This I can make evident by divers of the Petrifactions that are kept in this Repository, and by thousands of others which I have seen: And any one that will but diligently examine them will find the very Shells themselves preserved Shells, tho' inclosed in the middle of a Stone, as of *Portland*, *Purbeck*, and divers other Inland Stones here dug in *England*. And I am promised to have sent me a flake of a Stone which is very hard, which notwithstanding is all over full of Shells. I say Shells, for that I cannot call them any thing else, since to all sensible trials they are so, both as to Figure and Substance.

As to the Proof of the Eighth, I cannot produce a more pregnant one than the *Echinus* or Helmet-Stone, found by Mr. *William Ball* upon the Shore of *Devonshire*, near *Exeter*, which he presented to the Society, and I suppose may yet be seen in the Repository, for by that alone it will plainly appear, that there had been formerly a Shell that had caused both the formations of the containing and contained Flint, there being just the due thickness of such a Shell vacant between them, but there may be hundreds of others produced of the like kinds if it were needful.

A Proof of the Ninth and Tenth, *viz.* I think the large *Cornu Ammonis* may afford ; for here it seems plain, that a great part of the Shell was wasted away before the perfect Petrifaction of both the inclosing and inclosed Stone, tho' part of the Shell be yet remaining sticking between them.

Tis a hard matter to make a positive Proof of the Eleventh, *viz.* Because of the infinity of them that would be necessary, yet I think it would not be difficult to bring credible Testimonies enough to supply one for each Country, and that I suppose may suffice to make it probable that they may be found in all others, since, as I shall afterwards prove, they have been produced all by the same cause.

As to the Twelfth Proposition which I undertook to prove, *viz.* That most of those Shells or other Substances found as above, whether Petrify'd or not Petrify'd, are in the first place differing from one another in many particulars both of Figure and Substance, tho' yet they retain such particular Characteristicks as are sufficient to denote and show to what Species they belong, either of Vegetables or Animals, whether of Fishes or terrestrial Creatures, such as are now to be met with alive ; that is, not only that such as are thus found in one Country, are differing from those which are found in another : And in Petrify'd ones this is not only remarkable in the Substance inclosing and inclosed, but also in the magnitude, Figure and Make of the things themselves ; and in the second place many of them do considerably differ from the shape of those Shell-Fishes, and other Substances which are now to be found alive in such parts of the Seas as are nearest situated to the places where these Fossil or Land Shells are now to be found. For the proof of which I have no better means than to have recourse to the Substances themselves, which have been so found, of which there is an excellent Collection in the Repository of this Society, though I have also seen divers other instances in other Collections and Observations which I have elsewhere met with, which I cannot now produce. Yet one Instance for all I suppose may be this great Volnta which I have here produced, that was taken out of a Quarry in *Portland* (and I believe that those two other great ones in the Repository which I begg'd of the late Duke of *Norfolk* for the Repository are of the same kind and from the same place) for by these I think it plainly enough appears, that they are very differing from all the other Substances or particular Petrifactions that are in the Repository, both in Magnitude, Colour, Shape and Substance including and included, and even in the very Substance of that which I call, and shall prove the Shell; and not only do they thus differ from the Petri-

faction

factions Foffile or Land found Shells, but they differ alfo from all the known forts of Shells of that Species of Fifhes, to which I would refer them, which are now to be found any where near that place alive, nay, in any part of the World that I yet knew of; notwithftanding all which, they do retain, I conceive, certain Characterifticks of their Form, which fhow them to have belong'd to that Species of Shell-Fifhes which are call'd *Nautili*. Thefe *Nautili* are defcrib'd by *Gefner, Aldrovand, Johnfton*, and others, where you have their Names and a Picture or two of the Shells, and fome Stones alfo tending to a Defcription of the Creature and two Species of them; but he that fhall think to find any fuch Characterifticks by reading their Defcriptions and feeing their Pictures of them, will be much miftaken. And indeed it is not

The Defect of Natural Hiftory.

only in the defcription of this Species of Shells and Fifhes, that a very great Defect or Imperfection may be found among Natural Hiftorians, but in the Defcription of moft other things; fo that without infpection of the things themfelves, a Man is but a very little wifer or more inftructed by the Hiftory, Picture, and Relations concerning Natural Bodys; for the Obfervations for the moft part are fo fuperficial, and the Defcriptions fo ambiguous, that they create a very imperfect Idea of the true Nature and Characteriftick of the thing defcribed, and fuch as will be but of very little ufe without an ocular Infpection and a manual handling, and other fenfible examinations of the very things themfelves; for there are fo many confiderable Inftances that may by that means be taken notice of, which may be ufeful to this or that purpofe for which they may be inftructive, that 'tis almoft impoffible for any one Examiner or Defcriber to take notice of them, or fo much as to have any imagination of them. It were therefore much to be wifhht for and indeavoured that there might be made and kept in fome Repofitory as full and compleat a Collection of all varieties of Natural Bodies as could be obtain'd, where an Inquirer might be able to have recourfe, where he might perufe, and turn over, and fpell, and read the Book of Nature, and obferve the *Orthoography, Etymologia, Syntaxis*, and *Profodia* of Natures Grammar, and by which, as with a *Dictionary*, he might readily turn to and find the true Figure, Compofition, Derivation and Ufe of the Characters, Words, Phrafes and Sentences of Nature written with indelible, and moft exact, and moft expreffive Letters, without which Books it will be very difficult to be thoroughly a *Literatus* in the Language and Senfe of Nature. The ufe of fuch a Collection is not for Divertifement, and Wonder, and Gazing, as 'tis for the moft part thought and efteemed, and like Pictures for Children to admire and be pleafed with, but for the moft ferious and diligent ftudy of the moft able Proficient in Natural Philofophy. And upon this occafion tho' it be a digreffion, I could heartily wifh that a Collection were made in this Repofitory of as many varieties as could be procured of thefe kinds of Foffile-Shells and Petrifactions, which would be no very difficult matter to be done if any one made it his care: For *England* alone would afford fome hundreds of varieties, fome Petrify'd, fome not. There are few Quarries of Stone here in *England* I believe, but if they were look'd into fome kind or other of thefe Petrifactions might be found in them: I have obferv'd them in Marbles almoft of all varieties of Colours, as Black, White, Red, and otherwife Speckled: I have feen them in great varieties of Flints and Pebbles, in various forts of hard Stones, as *Purbeck, Portland, Yorkfhire, Kentifh, Northamptonfhire*, &c. I have feen many of them of Coperofe or Vitriol Stone, or *Pyrites*, and *John Bauhine*, and others have defcribed many of them of that Nature. Others of thefe are found above Ground, and others alfo under Ground very deep. fometimes unpetrify'd and remaining perfect Shells, Bones, Woods, Roots, &c. and have been found by feveral forts of trials to be truly fo, not only in External Figure, but alfo in the Internal and Subftantial Parts of them; fo that in truth there is no manner of Reafon to doubt them to be of thofe very Subftances they fo perfectly and fully refemble.

But if yet there fhould be fome one that fhould make a doubt of their identity or famenefs with fuch Subftances as they feem to refemble, I would willingly know what kind of Proof will fatisfie fuch his doubt, and by what Indications or Characterifticks he will know a Shell of an unknown Species (for

such

such may be shewn him) when it shall be presented to him, or a peice of Wood of some strange Tree brought from an unknown place; if he will say by the relation of the bringer, that I conceive is not becoming a good Naturalist; and so one might have been impos'd on by the Relation of the incombustible Linnen which was here examin'd; but if he will say by its Properties, which he finds the same with that of Shells, or Vegetables, or other resembling Substances, then I answer, that the same will in these be manifestly shewn. Now, the more of these certain Characteristicks of the several Species of Bodies there are known, the greater certainties and assurances will be afforded by the artificial and strict Examination of them. As for instance, the knowing the Existence and Form of the microscopical Pores of Wood, is a better Characteristick to know that a Substance is Wood than the outward Figure and Appearance thereof, which may be artificially or accidentally imitated, by which means I found that a peice of Lignum Fossile sent from *Italy* by Cavalier *Pozzo* to Sir *George Eut.* and by him supposed to be only Earth shaped into that form and not to be real Wood, as *Stelluti* also indeavours to prove. By the examination, I say, and discovery of the microscopical Pores thereof with a Magnifying-Glass to be like those of Firr, I produced a better Argument that it was really Firr than any *Francisco Stelluti* has argued to prove it Earth. Another was, that it burnt as Wood, and made Coles like those of Wood, with microscopical Pores; had I had enough of it I could have examin'd it by Distillation, and various other Chymical Probations; for the more of Testimonies and Confessions are fetch'd from these Examinations and Wracking, the greater will be the Evidence of the true Nature of those Substances so examin'd, tho' oftimes the Evidence afforded by some one, may be sufficient clearness to save all further Enquiries: Such as these the Lord *Verulam* call'd *Experimenta Crucis,* which serve to direct the Inquierer to proceed the right way in making his Judgment. These are such marks as I call Characteristicks, which expresly determine and limit the Nature and Species of the Body under Consideration. For Instance, I conceive that all those Petrify'd Substances which are call'd Snake-stones in *English,* from some resemblance imagin'd of a Snake coyled up; and in Latin (*Cornu Ammonis,* or Sand Horns possibly from their being found in those Sandy Deserts.

These Petrifactions, I say, I conceive to be nothing else but the Petrifactions of several sorts of Substances that the Shells of some sorts of *Nantili* happened to be mix'd with, whilst those Substances were yet very soft and Liquid, and before they came to be hardned into Stone by the Petrifactive Agent. This Conception I grounded upon these Characteristicks, which in examining a great many of them I have found. First, That in very many of them I have manifestly seen the the real moulding Shell there preserved, together with the moulded Substance.

Next I conceive, that this Shell did belong to the Species of the *Nautili,* or sailing Fish, from these Characteristicks. First, That the Shell is of a true Conical Figure from the *Base* to the *Apex.* Secondly, That this Cone is turned into a *Voluta* or Spiral Cone, so that the *Azis* thereof doth perfectly lye in the same Plaine. Thirdly, That this Spiral being a true proportional Spiral, is continually at certain distances intercepted by Diaphragmes; so that those Diaphragmes being taken as Bases of several Cones, the Cones shall be found to diminish in a series Geometrically Proportional. Fourthly, That every one of these Diaphragmes is perforated with a hole similar and proportional also according to a Geometical Series.

To these I might add other accidental Proprieties of the flating, crenating, depressing, ridging, stringing, and the like, ornamenting, as it were, of the outward sides of this voluted conical Body, and the undulation and foliation, as I may call it, of the Diaphnagme, and the Fringing and Ruffling thereof; all which are found of great variety in this or that Subalternate Species, as is also the Section of the Base, or that of the Diaphragme; but these are not to be looked upon as Characteristicks or Differences to denominate a new Species.

And

And here by the bye I cannot but take notice of the imperfect and inaccurate Description of this so curious a Fish as the *Nautilus* must needs be, if one may guess at the curiosity thereof from those descriptions, which I find in *Johnston* out of *Aristotle*, *Pliny*, *Bellonius*, *Piso*, *Cardan*, *Fauconerius*, and others, and from the curious make of the Shell, for by all those descriptions I cannot imagine any one can get any tolerable Idea or Notion, what the make of so wonderful a Fish must be that has such an admirable quality as to buoy himself as *Pliny* says, *ex alto mari* from the bottom of the Sea, and make himself to swim and sail upon the top of the Water, and at pleasure, or for fear presently to sink himself down again to the bottom. This will appear so much the more wonderful to one that shall consider the great pressure of the Water at the bottom of the Sea, and in how differing a state of compression this Animal must be at those two places, and by what power it becometh able to make itself so light at the bottom to rise and seem half out of the Water, and yet presently so heavy as to sink down to the bottom, and this without Finns or Tail to move itself. Now as this Property is peculiar to this Fish only, so is the make of the Shell differing from all the Species of Nature besides, and as I conceive is the Engine by which he performeth this admirable Exploit; for the whole Shell is divided into a multitude of Cells or Cabins separated and distinguished one from another by several Diaphragmes or Partitions without any other perforation, save one small one, through which passeth a small Pipe, which I take to be the Gut of the Animal; this Gut doth not fill a two hundred part of the Cavity through which it passeth, and the remaining part must either be filled with Air or Water. Now if it be filled with Water, as probably 'tis, when he sinketh himself to the bottom, 'tis prety hard to conceive how he filleth it with Air under so great a pressure and at such a distance from it as to buoy himself up, unless it be caus'd with such a fermentation of the Excrements of the Gut, or other Juices of the Body as doth produce an artificial Air, which serves for that purpose; which seems to me to be the true Cause, especially since I find *Gulielmus Piso* to add this Remark to his History and Description of it. *Cum damno meo Plinii Discriptionem verissimam esse compertus sum namdum talem pisciculum* (speaking of the *Nautilus* of China) *in mari captum imprudentius manibus meis contrettassem, tantus ardor manum invasit, tanquam si aqua serventi suffusa esset, & nisi apposito statim allio conraso cum aqua mihi ipse subvenissem, procul dubio præ dolore in febrim incidissem: Unde ego ipsum piscem de Holothuriorum esse genere contenderim, ut quæ omnia in maria fluctuantia, eam aerem calorem attrettantibus inurunt quod & fallacissimi omnium mortalium* Chinenses *noverunt, qui illa Orjzæ miscent, ut liquorem suum Destillatitium* (quem Arac hos hic vocamus) *tanto callidius reddant, perniciose invento, quod hinc miseri nostri Socii navales, sanguinis sputam, phthisin, marasmum deniq & ipsam tandem mortem incurrant.* By which it plainly appears, that the Juices or Excrements of this Fish are of a strange fermenting or burning Nature which may be the cause of so singular and wonderful an Indowment, which whether it be so or not, I could heartily wish that some Person curious in Anatony that has the opportunity of meeting with them alive would give us a more accurate Description of its external and internal Formations and Qualifications.

But to leave this Digression, which I have the longer insisted upon to shew the great imperfections of the Descriptions of the Species of Nature and their Qualifications and of the varieties of them (for that I have seen two Species of this sort not described or mentioned in any Author) and of how great use a good Collection and Description of them would be, as particularly concerning this very Fish I shall have occasion shortly to mention. To leave, I say, this Digression, we may from this perceive how little able we are from the want of this Knowledge and Collection, to conclude, that because we do not already know a Fish or Shell exactly of the shape of this or that *Cornu Ammonis*, therefore that it could never have been any such Shell, since it then cannot presently be proved that there is at present, or ever was any such Fish in being, which some possibly too confident of their Omnisciency may Object, because they know none such themselves, or have read of them; and therefore that there is more reason that such Arguments as are drawn from the examina-

tions

tions of the Substances, and the Characteristicks of the Form should be of sufficient evidence to evince that these Bodies that have these Qualifications could not be formed but for such purposes, as those Animals which we are informed of, we know have all parts fitted for each singular and surprizing use designed; for it is certain that Nature doth nothing *frustra*, but manifestly with an admirable and wise design, the truth of which Maxim will more and more evidently appear, the more the Works thereof are curiously examined and searched into; and no unprejudiced person that thoroughly examins them can fail of being convinc'd of the Truth and Certainty thereof, there being such a Harmony, Consent and Uniformity, as I may so speak, in all its Operations, and a gradual transition from one to another, that it is evident that all these kinds of Petrifactions have been moulded by some Animal or Vegetable Substance, as by Shells, Bones, Teeth, Fruits, Woods, &c. and that many of them are the Substances themselves, yet unaltered.

Now this being proved or granted, which I conceive the inspection and examination of the things themselves will most powerfully effect; it must follow as a Consequence of that Phænomenon, that all parts almost of the present Earth extant and appearing above the Sea, have been for some considerable time under it, and covered therewith. Since I conceive there is scarce any Country in the World where these Monuments of Antiquity, these Medals of Nature, or these Sea Marks and Evidences are not to be found either above, or at some depth under Ground, and some not very deep; particular Testimonies of which Truth I have collected many out of the few Natural Historians I have had the opportunity to peruse since I have had this Notion; and I doubt not but that abundantly more may be collected even out of Books. But inquisitive Natuarlists, if it were made an Head of Inquiry, would questionless meet with multitudes of other Instances almost every where not as yet handed by any Historian, of which truth I have been assur'd by many Testimonies from other Persons; but of this I have spoken already sufficiently.

From the comparing of which Evidences with several other pertinent Circumstances that may be observ'd may be deduced Conclusions very instructive as to the preceding and subsequent State also of this World. *Nam Res accendunt lumina Rebus*, and the understanding the History of the Course and Progress of Nature preceding will afford sufficient information of the Method of proceding, which in most things we may find to be very constant, uniform and regular. By such means we have arriv'd to the present Knowledge of Cæleftial Motions, and by the like, to that we have of the Motions of the Seas and Winds, and tho' none of these are yet come to their highest perfection, yet Inquiry, and Ratiocination, and Comparison will carry us much further towards that end, which the comparison of the present state thereof with what it was two or three hundred Years since, will give us good reason to hope.

It remains then to inquire by what means these prominent Parts of the Earth which at present are dry Land, came to be so, since by these Testimonies it is, I conceive, evident that they have been for some time under the Water.

And here in the first place I think it will be evident, that it could not be *This could not be from Noah's Flood.* from the Flood of *Noah*, since the duration of that which was but about two hundred Natural Days, or half an Year could not afford time enough for the production and perfection of so many and so great and full grown Shells, as these which are so found do testify; besides the quantity and thickness of the Beds of Sand with which they are many times found mixed, do argue that there must needs be a much longer time of the Seas Residence above the same, than so short a space can afford.

Nor could they proceed from a gradual swelling of the Earth, from a Sub- *Nor from a gradual swelling of the Earth.* terraneous fermentation, which by degrees should raise the parts of the Sea above the Surface thereof; since if it had been that way, these Shells would have been found only at the top of the Earth or very near it, and not buried at so great a depth under it as the Inſtances I mentioned of the Layer of Shells in the *Alps* buried under ſo vaſt a Mountain, and that near the *Needles* in the *Iſle of Wight* found in the middle of an Hill, could not rationally be ſo cauſed.

Nor from the waſhing away by the Water.

Nor could it proceed wholly from a waſhing of the Water from off the Face of thoſe parts of the Earth, for the ſame Reaſon, for how ſhould the Mountain come to be placed on the top of them.

Now, if after all theſe topicks of Proofs, there ſhall yet remain ſome who will not allow any of them to have been Shells, becauſe they are found in the middle of Stone; I have, as a ſuppliment, added my Obſervation of the Place where, and the Manner how they may be obſerv'd to be ſo incloſed into the Body of a ſolid Stone, namely, at a place near the *Needles*, at the Weſt end of the *Iſle of Wight.*

With ſuch now as ſhall not think all, or any of theſe convincing Arguments to prove them Shells, I cannot, I confeſs, conceive what kind of Arguments will prevail, ſince theſe ſenſible Marks are, in all other things, the Characteriickſts and Proofs by which to determine of their Nature and Relation, and why they ſhould not be allow'd to be ſo in this particular Caſe I cannot well conceive.

The chief Objections.

The great ſcruples I find are theſe; Firſt, That they know not how they could come to be placed where they are and have been found; ſome Conjectures at which I ſhall after ſhew.

And, Secondly, That many, nay moſt, of them are of ſomewhat a differing Shape, and of a much greater Magnitude than are tne Shell-Fiſhes of the like Animals to be found upon the Coaſt of *Portland*, or near the places where they have been found; and indeed againſt this my Hypotheſis or Aſſertion I find none more preſſingly urged than this, that there is not one to be found either in the Seas near thoſe Parts where ſuch are found, nor in any part of the known World, any ſuch Animals or Vegetables as thoſe which are ſuppoſed to have afforded the Subſtances of ſome of them, or the Moulds of ſome other; and particularly it has very much been urged upon the Conſideration of the Petrifaction or *Cornu Ammonis* taken out of the Quarry of Stone in the Iſle *Portland*, whether it could be reaſonably ſuppoſed that ever there were in the the World a Species of the *Nautilus* of this ſhape, and of ſo vaſt a bigneſs, of which it is ſuppoſed the World has not afforded an equal in a living Species. And I perceive that the very ſuppoſition is looked upon as very extravagant and ridiculous. However, it may be poſſibly worthy ſome Mens Conſiderations to inquire, Firſt, Whether there may not yet be found in the World many Species of Shell-Fiſh they have not hitherto heard of, or ſeen in the Writings of Natural Hiſtorians, or in relations of Voyages, or by their own Experience.

Secondly, Whether the exceeding greatneſs of this Shell be a ſufficient Argument to conclude it ridiculous to ſuppoſe, that there could be a living Fiſh that might fill ſo great a Shell, ſince I ſhew'd the laſt Day out of *Maudelſlo* and *Olearius*'s Travels, an inſtance of Oyſters found in *Java*, that ſeem'd much to exceed this Magnitude: And poſſibly ſome here preſent may have ſeen, as well as my ſelf, the great pair of Shells in the *Muſæum Harveanum* before the Fire in 1666. And that the Shells of a *Pinna Marina* are now to be ſeen in this Repoſitory, which exceed the common bigneſs of a Muſcle as much as this *Cornu Ammonis* doth the ſmaller ſorts of *Nautili*, and varieth alſo as much from them in Shape: And that hotter Countries, ſuch as are in the *Torrid Zone*, produce Turtles or Sea Tortoiſes, abundantly more exceeding the ſmaller ſorts of theſe of colder Regions, of which there are Teſtimonies enough to be had both from Natural Hiſtorians and Travellers, which it were neceſſary I could produce.

But becaufe it may be upon this Head further Objected, That all thofe extraordinary great Species are the productions of the *Torrid Zone*, or the hotter Climates, and not of the colder, and fuch as lie fo far remov'd towards the Poles as *Portland* or *England* do, about which there are now no living Fifhes to be found that any wife come near to that Magnitude, but are of much fmaller fize and of different fhapes.

Therefore before the Opinion be wholly rejected, I would defire them to confider, whether it may not have been poffible, that this very Land of *England* and *Portland*, did, at a certain time for fome Ages paft, lie within the *Torrid Zone* ; and whilft it there refided, or during its Journying or Paffage through it, whether it might not be covered with the Sea to a certain height above the tops of the higheft Mountains. And further, how deep this may have lain below the Surface of the Sea, when it might have been in that Paffage, and how long time it may have fpent in fuch a ftate, and how long fince it may have been emerged. Such as are better verfed in ancient Hiftorians than I ever have been or hope to be, may poffibly refolve fome of thefe Doubts, or at leaft may prove the impoffibility thereof, which may fave further trouble of inquiry : But if after inquiry it fhould be found that Natural Hiftory is defective in that particular, then I will indeavour to fee what Helps and Hiftories will be pertinent towards the determination of thefe Queries.

That England lay formerly in the Torrid Zone, *and was there cover'd with the Sea.*

And in order to determine the Poffibility or Impoffibility of this Matter, I could wifh it were well confidered further, whether the Superficies of the Ocean be equally diftant from a Central Point in the Bowels of the Earth, and whether any other perpendiculars to the Surface thereof, befides thofe of every fingle Parallel, and its Poles, do tend to any other Point of its Axis ; and if there fhould be found more than one Point, then what are the limiting or terminating Points of a Line of fuch Points ; that is, at what diftance they muft be from one another, or from a Central Point ? This I mention'd in two of my preceding Lectures, the one read about ten or twelve Years fince, and in the other about two Years fince ; in both which I indeavour'd to fhew that the form of the Earth was probably fomewhat flatter towards the Poles than towards the Equinoctial, fince which I have met with fome Obfervations that do feem to make a probability in my Conjecture and Hypothefis.

Q. Whether the Ocean be every where equally diftant from the Center.

The *Antipodes* were once thought a Chimera, length of time hath made that notion more reconcileable to Senfe and Reafon ; thefe may poffibly at firft hearing appear much more extavagant, and Time that brings all to Light, may poffibly evidence them to be nothing but *Chimæra*'s ; I will not prejudge, nor pre-poffefs, but leave them to their Fortune. However it were defirable by the Experience and Inquiry of a fhort time to difpatch and haften the Growth and Ripenings of the Productions of Nature, fince the Experience and Duration of a Man, whether he looks forward or backward, is very fhort in comparifon of what feems requifite for this Determination ; his Sight is weak and dim, his Power and Reach much fhorter, yet may it be worth confidering (tho' he cannot lengthen or prolong his limited time either paft or to come), whether by Telefcopes or Microfcopes he may not fee fome hundreds of Years backwards and forward, and diftinguifh by fuch Microfcopes and Telefcopes Events fo far diftant both before and behind himfelf in time, as if clofe by, and now prefent ? And whether by Inftruments he may not extend his Power, and reach things far above his Head, and far beneath his Feet, in the higheft parts of the Heavens, and the loweft parts of the Earth ; for could he perform things of this Nature and Quality as they ought to be, he would lengthen his Life and increafe the injoyments thereof by a multiply'd and condens'd knowledge of times paft, and of times alfo yet to come.

But before we come to this laft Expedient, I could wifh we had a good Account and Collection of what Hiftories pertinent to this, or any other Natural Inquiry are to be found in Printed or Written Authors, which I conceive is yet a *Defideratum* ; and that this is poffible to be fo I fhall mention one Obfervation, tho' not pertinent to this prefent Enquiry, yet to another which I have read formerly before this Society, *viz.* about the Chinefs Character and about the Chinefe Printing. Inquiring then about *Tartary*

and

and *China*, upon occafion of the Difcourfe that was here lately made, I found that in *Purchas* his Pilgrims there is a part of the Works of *Roger Bacon* pub-lifh'd, whereby I find that he fo long fince knew they had a way of Printing, *Page 58. Part* and had a better account of their Character than any one, or all we have *3.* fince that time.   *Sciendum quod a principio Cataiæ Magnæ Nigræ ufq; ad finem o-rientis Sunt principaliter Idololatræ fed mixti Sunt inter eos Saraceni & Tartari & Neftoriani, qui funt Chriftiani imperfecti, habentes Patriarcham fuum in oriente.* This *Cataia magna nigra* is one of the North Provinces of *China*, and the *Patri-archa* is the *Lamos* mention'd in the Voyage of *Verbieft*.

Jugres qui habitant in terra ubi Impertor moratur,----Sunt optimi Scriptores, un-de Tartari acceperant Litteras eorum & illi Sunt magni Scriptores Tartarorum & Scribunt a furfum in deorfum & a Siniftra in dextram, multiplicant Lineas & legunt. Zebeth Scribunt ficut nos & habent figuras Similes Noftris. Tanguæ Scribant a Dex-tra in Siniftram ficut Arabes & multiplicant Lineas afcendendo. Cataii orientales Scribunt cnmpunctorio, quo pingunt Pictores, & faciunt in una figura plures literas comprehendentes unam Dictionem, & ex hoc veniunt Charactteres qui habent multas Literas fimul. Vnde veri Charactteres & Philofophici funt, compofiti ex literis & habent fenfum Dictionum.   Thus much concerning the Character, where I fhall note only by the bye, that both the *Jugres* and *Cataians*, thofe of *Tebet* and *Tangut*, may be faid to write all the fame way with us, for that they differ only in the Pofition of the Page as to the Eye when read or writ.   Next, as to the ufe of Printing, he fays in the fame Page, fpeaking of the Money of the *Cataians*. *Iftorum Cataiarum moneta vulgaris eft charta de bombafio in qua im-primunt quafdam Lineas.*   This I fuppofe he took in part out of the Voyage of *Gulielmus de Rubriques*, a *French* Frier, who wrote an account of his Travels into thofe Eaftern Parts to the King of *France*, and for divers Reafons I believe it to be a very true Relation, for I find in the thirty fixth Chapter of his Book as follows. ' The common Money of *Cataia* is Paper made of Bombaft the ' length of an Hand, upon which they imprint Lines, like the Seale of *Man-* ' *gu*, they write with a Penfil wherewith Painters Paint, and in one Figure ' they make many Letters comprehending one word.   The People of *Thebet* ' write as we do, and they have Charactters very like ours.   They of *Tangu* ' write from the right Hand unto the Left, as the *Arabians*, and multiply ' the Lines afcending upwards.   *Jugur*, as aforefaid from above downwards. This is very much the fame with *Roger Bacon*, whereby we had above four hundred Years fince a hint of the Chinefe Printing ; as alfo that the Chinefe Charactters were compounded of certain Elements, which expreffed both a literal and philofophical Word.   I have one Obfervation more to add before I leave this Digreffion, and that is in anfwer to another Objection which was made againft my Conjecture of the deducing the Name of *Cornu Ammonis*, or Sand Horns from a probability that they might poffibly be found in thofe Sandy Deferts of *Pentapolitana* in *Africa*, now call'd *Barca*, which lieth Weft of *Egypt*, between that and *Africa Minor*, almoft oppofite to the *Morea* of *Greece*, a large and barren fandy Defert, troublefome to be travailed in, by reafon of the inftability of the Footing, and for that the Sand is thrown to and fro by the Wind, in the midft of which ftood the Temple of *Jupiter Ammon* whofe Effigies was adorn'd with Horns fuppofed to be Rams Horns, but I conjectur'd they might poffibly be the refemblance of thofe petrify'd *Nautili*, found in that Sand.   To this Conjecture I have only this to add, Firft, That *Lucan* in the defcribing this Idol, calls him *Corniger*, which feems to argue, that the Statue had Horns.   But which feems more to agree with my Con-jecture, is what is related of the form of this Idol by *Curtius*, that it was without the form of any Creature, but like a round Bofs or Navel, (*Vmbilicus* is the word) befet with Jewels ; this was carried in Proceffion by the Priefts in a guilded Ship hung with Bells on both fides, *&c.* by which it fhould feem that the very Idol itfelf was nothing but fuch a *Nautilus* Petrify'd, as I have produced, befet round with Jewels for ornament, and carry'd in a Ship pof-fibly as a Hieroglyphick, to fignifie the manner of fome eminent Deliverance of that Country from a former Flood, or the ufe of Ships in that place, whilft an Ifland and that Defert was cover'd with Water.   But this is only Conjectural, which I fubmit to further examination.

But

But to leave this Digreſſion and proceed. I ſay, it were very deſirable in *Searching of* order to the ſolution of this and divers other Inquiries in Natural Philoſophy; *Natural Hiſto-* that we had a Collection of ſuch Obſervations as are to be found, already *ries uſeful.* made and recorded in Natural Hiſtories, to ſee what Light ſuch Hiſtories would afford, which may be perform'd by the joint Labour of many Perſons who would peruſe and collect ſuch Matters ; but poſſibly it may be believ'd that little can be found pertinent to this Inquiry, as indeed I fear there will be no great matter ; yet *Pliny* in the tenth Chapter of his thirty ſixth Book takes notice of a matter which is not altogether impertinent, affirming, that an Obelisk ſet up by *Auguſtus* for ſhewing the length of the Day, was found af- ter ſome time to go falſe.

But upon this I build no great matter, and I fear the ancient Obſervations will in general help us no great matter, though they may give us cauſe of ſuſpicion, as particularly concerning the Latitudes of Places, of which Mr. *Vernon* takes notice that the preſent Latitude of *Athens* is near two degrees differing from that aſſign'd it by *Ptolomy*, which is remarkable, it being of a Place ſo eminently known in former Ages. But upon neither of theſe can much be built as to the accuracy of determining ſuch a motion ; tho' they may ſerve well enough for hints for Inquiry farther concerning them. Mon- ſieur *Pettit* has alſo written a Treatiſe to prove that the Latitude of *Paris* is differing from what it was formerly. *Scaliger* alſo had a notion of ſome ſuch matter, but I connot tell what he would have, nor do I believe he well knew himſelf. The place is quoted in *Chilmedes* Engliſh Edition of *Hues de Globis* ; others alſo have mention'd it, but none have determin'd it or brought it to a certainty. I did therefore upon this occaſion, where I am diſcourſing con- cerning the general Form and the proprieties or Motions of this great Body of the Earth, think fit to inſert it as a thing worthy of determination ; ſince 'tis not improbable but that there may be ſome ſuch motion of the Earths *Axis* as may alter both the Latitudes of Places, and alſo the poſition of the Meridional Line. And that this may not ſeem ſo abſurd, we may conſider the alteration of the *Axis* of the Earth in reſpect of the fixt Stars long ſince diſ- cover'd, and the variation of the magnetical *Axis* diſcover'd firſt about fifty Years ſince by ſome of the Profeſſors of this Colledge.

But now the Queſtion is how theſe general Queries can be determin'd ; *Some General* that is, Firſt, *Whether there be any alteration of the gravitating Center of the Earth.* *Queries.*

Secondly, *Whether the Body of the Earth be of a true Spherical or Oval Figure, and thence whether it hath one or infinite Centers of Gravitation.* 2.

Thirdly, *Whether the Axis of its Rotation do change its Situation or Poſition in reſpect of the Parts of the Earth* ; and thence, *Whether the Latitudes and Meri- dional Lines of places do differ in proceſs of time,* and if ſo in the 3.

Fourth place to determine *What is the particular motion that cauſeth it, and by what ſteps it hath devolved for the time paſt, and will proceed for the time to come.* 4.

The CONTENTS.

THE beginning of this Lecture being loft I cannot certainly find when it was read, but judge it preceeded that which I have here placed after it. It contains several Positions to solve the Phænomena before-mention'd relating to the great alterations of the Figure and Motion of the Earth: Of these there are enumerated fifteen; tho' this be proposed only as an Hypothesis, yet the Author thinks it deserves examination before it be wholly rejected, the discovery of Truth being his only aim: And adds, That 1st. 'Tis not impossible for three Reasons. 2dly. 'Tis no more Folly to invent this Hypothesis, than 'twas to invent several others. 3dly. 'Tis not only possible but probable. He inlarges upon the Proof of two of them, viz. The prolated Sphæroidical Figure of the Earth and Sea, and the variation of the Axis of Rotation.

R. W

1. MY First Proposition then is this, That we should suppose First, That this Globe or Ball of the Earth was carried round the Sun in the plain of the Ecliptick, making an entire Revolution in that Plain once in a twelvemonth, and thereby making the Sun to appear to pass continually in the Ecliptick Line, as *Pythagorus*, *Ariftarchus Samius*, *Copernicus*, &c, have supposed.

2. Secondly, That this Globe or Ball whilst it maketh one such Revolution, is likewise whirled round three hundred sixty and five times, and about $\frac{1}{4}$ upon an *Axis*, or imaginary Line passing through, or near the Center thereof, which *Axis*, is all the while kept in an Inclination to the said Plain of $23\frac{1}{2}$.

3. Thirdly, That this *Axis* doth continually keep a Parallelism to itself very near ; all which *Axes* at present respect a Point in the Heavens, not far distant from the last Star of the Tail of the little Bear call'd the *Pole-ftar*, but heretofore 'twas at a greater distance from it.

4. Fourthly, That this *Axis* doth, in process of time, vary its respect to that Star or Point of the Heavens, and by degrees proceed nearer towards it, not directly, but in a Circle parallel to the Ecliptick, or whose Center is the Pole of the Ecliptick. Thus far I take the same with the Hypothesis of *Copernicus* and his Followers. But

5. Fifthly, I suppose yet further, that the *Axis* of the *Diurnal Rotation* of the Earth hath also had a progressive motion, and hath, in process of time, been chang'd in position within the Body of the Earth, and consequently that the Poler points upon the Surface of the Earth, have alter'd their Situation ; so that the present Polar Points have formerly been distant from those Poles that were then ; and consequently that those former Polar Points are now remov'd to a certain distance from the present, and ·move in Circles about the present.

6. Sixthly, I suppose that the Form of the Surface of the Water at least, is, and hath been, ever since the duration of the Earth, of an *Oval Form*, whose longeft Diameters lye in the Plain of the Equinoctial, and whose shortest is the *Axis* itself of the said Rotation.

7. Seventhly, As a Consequent of this I suppose the Center of *Gravity* of the Earth to be drawn out into a Line into the *Axis* thereof, and consequently into infinite Centers, there being one for every Parallel Line upon the Surface of the Earth, and that no Perpendiculars but those of the Poles and Æquinoctial, respect or tend directly to the Central Point, but that all the Perpendiculars from the other Parallels respect certain Points in the opposite Parts of the *Axis* which are so much the further remov'd from the Center, by

how

how much the nearer the Parallels approach the Polar Points ; which Points of Gravitations and Pofition of Perpendiculars in refpect of the *Axis*, may be determin'd both *a Priori* by Theory, and alfo *a Pofteriori* by Experiments or Obfervations.

Eighthly, As a Confequent of thefe, I fuppofe, that in procefs of time there will be caufed an alteration of the gravitating Power and Tendency of the Parts of the Earth, both Solid and Fluid, and that according as the Pofitions of them are alter'd in refpect of the Polar Points, either prefent Precedent or Subfequent, there will be caufed in the   8.

Ninth Place, an indeavour of fliding, fubfiding, finking and changing of the Internal Parts of the Earth, as well as External, tho' the latter will be more powerful, as being more affected by the Rotation thereof; and this may caufe in the   9.

Tenth Place, an alteration in the Magnetical Power and Vertue of the Body of the Earth, efpecially of fuch Parts as are more loofe and of a more fluid Nature. And   10.

In the Eleventh Place, may be a caufe alfo of fome of thofe *Tremores Terræ*, or Earthquakes. which have in all Ages been in the Earth, tho' we have no Hiftories or Records that have preferved the Memory of them, but only fuch Signs and Monuments as they have left by the unequal ragged and torn Face of the Surface of the Land and the Bodies that are difcovered ; which proves that they had fome time an other Pofition than they are found to have at the prefent.   11.

Thefe two laft notwithftanding I do not fuppofe the only caufes of thefe Effects of Earthquakes, no nor the Principal, but only as concurring and adjuvant Caufes which may have their Effects in fome meafure, but how far and how powerful they may be fuppofed, will be proper to be refolved under the Heads of Magnetifms and Earthquakes , and more efpecially under that of the Air. The fame Principles or Suppofitions will alfo produce in the

Twelfth Place ; a more than ordinary fwelling or rifing of the Sea in thofe Parts which are near the Æquinoctial, and a finking and receeding of the Sea from thofe which are near the Poles ; fo that as any Parts do increafe in their Latitudes, fo will the Sea grow fhallower, and as their Latitudes decreafe, fo muft the Sea fwell and grow high ; by which means many fubmarine Regions muft become dry Land, and many other Lands will be overflown by the Sea, and thefe variations being flow, and by degrees will leave very lafting Remarks of fuch States and Pofitions, in the fuperfieial Subftances of the Earth.   12.

And hence alfo will follow in the Thirteenth Place, a great alteration and variety of the Productions of thofe Parts which are thus alter'd in their Pofition, whether they are parts of the Sea or parts of the Land ; for as there feems to be fomewhat which is peculiar to this or that Soyl or Spot of Land whereby this or that Animal or Vegetable doth grow and thrive and increafe both in Quantity and Quality, and the contrary : So is there alfo fomewhat in the Climate and Pofition to the Sun and Heavens, which doth as powerfully at leaft, if not much more, affect the Productions, Propagations, *&c.* of Plants and Animals. And as 'tis a known Obfervation, that in the fame Country, this or that Field, or Soil is more effective for this or that ufe ; fo 'tis as well known that the tranfplanting of animate Subjects to differing Climates, tho' the Soil feems of the fame Nature, doth as effectually co-operate in the changing or alteration of them. And hereby a fruitful Land may be turned into Barrennefs, and be made unfit for Production as well as Barren and Ufelefs may be made Fruitful ; for that the Temper and Conftitution of a Soil may be fuch as to be fit for many purpofes in fome Climates, which in others is fit for nothing.   13.

From

14.   From hence also will follow in the Fourteenth Place, That many places which by degrees are made Submarine, will be cover'd with various Coats or Layers of Earth; so that the former Surface of it, when Land will not only be drown'd with Water, but buried under Earth; for that, as the parts of the Land, are continually washed down, and by the Rivers carried into the Sea, and there deposited in the Submarine Regions, so much more powerfully and plentifully are the higher parts of the Submarine Regions by Tides, Currents, and other Agitations of the Water, removed and transported into the lower, partly by sinking out of the muddy Water, but principally by tumbling and rowling down from the higher, which sorts of covering or burying Earth must be posited in certain Layers or Stratifications of divers kinds of Substances according to the nature of those which are this or that way brought thither, and there deposited. Hence also it will follow, that the Earth itself doth, as it were, wash and smooth its own Face, and by degrees to remove all the Warts, Furrows, Wrinckles and Holes of her Skin, which Age and Distempers have produced.

15.   And hence in the Fifteenth Place will follow, That such Regions as have for a time been Submarine, and produced Substances of Animals or Vegetables proper for them, when they come to be dry Land and to lye above the Waters, must produce Animals and Vegetables proper and peculiar to that Soil, Element and Climate they are then furnish'd with; preserving in the mean time the Characteristicks and Marks of the former Qualifications, when in another Condition.

But some possibly may be ready to say before a thorough examination, that this is only a supposition, and that there are no such Phænomena as here are put for the Supposition: Others, that 'tis foolish to make an Hypothesis for the solving of any one Phænomenon. Others may possibly demand how comes this to be now discover'd, which none hath hitherto known? Or how is this to be proved? By what History? By what Signs and Tokens? I must leave every one to his own freedom to judge as he sees cause, and censure as he pleases; however, I conceive it ρᾷον μωμᾶϑαι ἢ μεμεῖϑαι easy to play the Momus or the Mimick. *Sed siquis quid rectius istus noscat, candidus impertiat.* But if he know better let him not, hold his Tongue but tell us. I shall not impose on any; I propound it only as an Hypothesis, and have shewed what will be the Consequences of it, whether there be Phænomena answerable to be observ'd let it be examin'd; and let there be produc'd another Hypothesis that will solve the various Phænomena that are to be every where met with better; for that I have no farther design in propounding it than to have it strictly examin'd, and in order thereunto to have such Observations made and taken notice of for the future as may ascertain the Truth whether for or against it.

Yet give me leave to add a word or two, before I wholly leave it to its Fortune.

The supposition 1st. not impossible.   First then, I say, That what is here supposed is not impossible. First, 'Tis not impossible from the Natural History now to be met with of the things supposed; for that all things may be the same as they now appear, and yet this may be true; for no one Phænomenon, that I can think of, is contradicted by it, either fetch'd out of ancient Histories, or yet Collected by present Observation. As there are no Observations of Latitudes, or fixed, accurate meridian Lines, or Eclipses for the Oval Shadow of the Earth, or Mensuration of Degrees to find their difference in differing Latitudes. Nor Secondly, Is it impossible from the Nature of the things supposed, for that there is as yet no certain Cause assigned, why the Earth doth move upon the *Axis*, it now doth, and not upon another, nor why it should always continue and remain the same without change, contrary to all other motions in Nature. Nor is it impossible because not discover'd before, which yet is more than can be positively proved; for if so, then would Magnetical Motions fall under the same Censure, as also, Optick-glasses, Guns, Printing, and other new discoveries.

coveries. And by the fame Argument the Motion of the Sun, and *Jupiter* upon their Axes, the Reality and Revolution of the Satellites of *Jupiter* and *Saturn*, the Ring of *Saturn* and the Belts of *Jupiter*, and the like might be condemned.

Secondly, I fay for it, that 'tis no more folly to invent new Hypothefes to folve Phænomena in the Earth, than it was in *Pythagoras, Ptolomy, Copernicus, Ticho, Kepler,* and others in the Heavens; for that each of them conceiv'd by fuch Hypothefes to folve the Phænomena more agreeably to the other appearances of Nature; whereas yet no one of them has hit the right I conceive, and I fhall, I hope, in due time demonftrate. *2dly, Not ridiculous.*

But in the Third Place, for Affirmative, I fay, 'tis not only poffible, but probable, and altogether confonant and agreeable to the reft of the Works of Nature, and even to the very Conftitution and Phænomena to be obferv'd upon the Earth itfelf. *3dly, 'Tis probable.*

And Firft for the *Oval Figure of the Sea and Body of the Earth in fome meafure.* If the gravitating Power of the Earth be every where equal, as I know no reafon to fuppofe the contrary, then muft this Power be compounded with a contrary indeavour of heavy Bodies to recede from the Axis of its Motion, if it be fuppofed to be mov'd with a diurnal Revolution upon its Axis, and confequently a part of the gravity of fuch Bodies towards the Center muft be taken off by this *Conatus*, which is every where oblique, but only under the Æquinoctial, which muft therefore moft diminifh its Gravitation, and confequently the gravity will act the moft freely and powerfully under the Poles, and the more powerfully the nearer the Bodies are plac'd to thofe Poles; and that Phænomena do anfwer to this Theory, has been verify'd, firft by Mr. *Hally* at St. *Helena,* and fince by the *French* in *Cayen,* and now lately in *Siam,* in all which places it is affirmed, that 'twas neceffary to fhorten the Pendulum to make it keep its due Time. *Of the Oval Figure of the Earth.*

In the Second Place for the *variation of the Axis of Rotation* in the Body of the Earth. I fay it is confonant to all the other motions of Nature : For firft it is found that the *Axes* of the *Ellipfes* of the Planets do vary a little, I fay a little (tho' Mr. *Street* only will have them not to vary at all) becaufe all Aftronomers have hitherto affirmed, that they do, and from my own Mathematical Hypothefis I collect the fame, tho' it be but a little, yet it is fomewhat, fince there is fome impediment in the Medium. Next there is alfo a motion in the Nodes, all which are very eminent in the Moon. And again, the direction of the *Axis* in the Earth is varied as to its refpect to the Heavens, which the preceffion of the Æquinoxes do manifeft. Nay yet further, the *Axis* of the Magnetical Motions which is within the very Body of the Earth, and feems even to go through its very Center, hath, about fifty Years fince, been prov'd to vary alfo fomewhat analogous to this which I have fuppofed, whereby both the Magnetical Latitudes, and Magnetical Meridians have moft certainly been varied ; which feems abundantly more difficult to be granted than this which I propound, did not certain Obfervations both here at home and all over the World confirm the truth of Matter of Fact, and that becaufe this doth feem to prove a motion of a Magnetical Core or Magnetical Globe of the Earth, within this outward earthy and watery Shell; whereas this which I fuppofe is nothing but a progreffion of the *Axis* of Rotation, which may be caus'd by the vifible accidental Mutations of the outward and fuperficial Parts, as well as by other unknown alterations which may fucceed within the Bowels of the Earth. So that 'tis very probable that there is fome fuch motion of the faid *Axis,* fince we are certain both of outward and inward changes. *Of the variation of the Axis.*

It only remains then Pofitively and Experimentally, or Hiftorically to prove the Reality thereof. Now the motion of the Mutation thereof being but flow, as I conceive, and the Obfervations of the Antients Recorded in Hiftories neceffary for this purpofe, being fo unaccurate and uncertain for fuch a determination as this, I fear they cannot be rely'd upon ; but whatever fhall be alledg'd as a proof of this Theory, will be attributed to a fault in the Antient Obfervation, as that *Ptolomy* puts the Latitude of *London* 52 10 and the longeft Day 17 Hours. Nor will I infift on the Latitude of *Athens* found by Mr. *Vernon*, to differ near a Degree : Nor on the Latitude of the *Herculean Streights*, which varies as much from the prefent, as that of *London*, tho' all these were remarkable places, as was also *Conftantinople* ; but rather rely upon Obfervations to be made for the future ; the way of performing which I fhall treat of hereafter, whereby I fhall fhew, how, in a fhort time, the fame thing may be determin'd as well as by fo long a time.

The CONTENTS.

THIS Lecture was read Feb. 2. 168$\frac{6}{7}$, and contains the Confirmation of what was offer'd in the preceding. 1ft. As to the fuperficial Figure of the Sea ; and for this purpofe he propofes fome Experiments, the fuccefs of which was fhewn to the Royal Society ; and next feveral Obfervations are brought to the fame purpofe, which are ranged under two Heads, 1ft. Confequential Proofs. 2dly. More immediate Proofs. 2dly. As to the alteration of the Axis of the Earth's Rotation.

R. W.

Suppofitions as extravagaut have been made.

WHat I propounded the laft Day by way of an Hypothefis, may poffibly be look'd upon not not only as very extravagant, but very improbable ; from the laft of which I hope I did then clear it ; and as to its extravagancy, I hope I may be able to fhew, that there have been fuppofitions altogether as extravagant, which yet have not only been made, but accepted and imbraced, and for many Ages as ftifly defended as the moft probable. My Inftance fhall be in the *Ptolomaick* Hypothefis of the Heavens, which, that you may the better judge of, I have here a Book to fhew the whole Defign and Intrigue of it, in which the fame and all its parts are moft curioufly delineated, whereby all the Wheel-work may be at once difcover'd ; and if it be defir'd to be made in Clock-work, I have another Author that fhall give the bignefs of the Wheels, and the number of the Teeth and Pinions neceffary to accomplifh the fame in Clock-work : And yet when all is done, there will want as many more to make out all the irregularities of appearances exact ; the reafon of which proceeded from one falfe Principle, that one Body was capable of no more than one fimple motion, whereas in truth there is no body mov'd but is capable of, nay, actually mov'd by thoufands.

But it may poffibly be faid that this *Hypothefis* was the Product of an Age not fo inquifitive and able to judge as the prefent, which will hardly be impos'd on with fuch improbabilities ; nor was all this clutter thought neceffary at firft, but the maintainers of that Opinion, to make out the appearances, as well as they could, have fince found it neceffary to help out the firft Invention by additional Expedients ; and if thefe were fufficient, I conceive it might yet be an acceptable *Hypothefis*, tho' we have no *Medium* to prove that there is any fuch thing in Nature as a *Solid Orbe*, or a moving *Genius*.

The like favour I hope may be allow'd to what I propound, if upon due examination the *Phænomena* are anfwerable to what the *Hypothefis* does hint.

Now what would be confequential to what I have propounded, I fhew'd the laft Day ; it only now remains to examine whether Phænomena do anfwer.

1ft. Of the Figure of theSea.

Firft then to determine whether the Figure of the Sea from North to South be Oval, fwelling towards the Æquinoctial and deprefs'd towards the Poles, it will be neceffary to make fome few Trials, Obfervations and Experiments.

Experiments to prove it.

And Firft for Experiments that may be made here. Let a Bowl or Bubble of Glafs be made and melted in a Lamp, and when fo melted let it be blown into a hollow Ball or Bubble, which will naturally form and Shape itfelf into a round and fpherical Body, efpecially if the Subftance be of an equal thicknefs and equal heat, which let be examin'd ; then let the fame be melted again as before, and as it is blowing, let it be mov'd round upon the Pipe, by

which

which it is blown, by a pretty quick Circular Motion, and you will find that instead of the Spherical Figure it will receive an Oval one, such as I suppose the Surface of the Sea to have. This Experiment I shall by and by shew here (which was accordingly done).

Now in this Experiment here are evidently two kinds of Powers that cooperate in the production of this Form: The first is that of the Congruity of the Matter, which, as I have many Years since in a small Treatise, Printed in the Year 1660, proved, doth shape the Glass into a true Spherical Figure, and so maketh every part to indeavour towards the Center of the whole. The next is that of the vertiginous Motion, which giveth to every part, an indeavour to recede from the *Axis* of the vertiginous Motion; this driveth the shape of the whole into that Oval Form it receiveth and retaineth.

The same Experiment may be much better made at the Glass-house, where a greater quantity of Glass may be melted, and that more equally and a quicker Motion may be given, which will make the Experiment the more sensible, the Glass retaining its melted heat much longer. Besides, it may be there tried with a solid lump of Glass which will receive the same Figure from a vertiginous Motion about the Puntilion. And again, to make the Glass Oval the other way, the same is whirled round with a motion wherein the Puntilion is made the Radius of the vertiginous Motion.

A second Experiment to shew that the Water doth naturally recede from the Poles towards the Æquinoctial is this. Take a round Dish of Water, and let it be set upon a Stand where it may be gently mov'd round upon an an Axis passing through the Center of the Dish perpendicularly; first observe the Surface of the Water when it stands still without motion, there you find it smooth and horizontal; then move the stand gently round by degrees, till you find the Water begins to receive the motion of the Dish; then examine the Surface thereof and you will perceive the Water to sink in the middle, and to recede and swell towards the Circumference of the Dish: And the better to satisfie you I have prepared the Experiment which I will by and by shew. The Experiments are plain and common, yet I humbly conceive not less instructive to the present Controversy, than the most pompous and more chargeable Experiments.

This last Experiment doth hint, that the Convexity of the Sea near the Poles of the Earth must necessarily be much flatter than elsewhere, and not only less Spherical than the rest of the Sea, but possibly plain, nay, beyond a plain, possibly Concave, for that the Water cannot but have or receive from the vertiginous Motion, an endeavour to recede from the Center of that Motion, and the Gravity of the Earth working there more powerfully and freely. But this only by the bye. But which seems more material, I conceive that a Degree of Latitude, if there measured would be very much longer than a Degree of Latitude under the Æquinoctial, of which I shall speak more by and by. *The Superficies of the Sea next the Poles possibly Concave.*

In the next place then we are to consider what other Observations and Trials will serve to the direct and positive proof of this *Hypothesis, That the Figure of the Earth is that of a prolated Sphæroide, not of an oblong Sphæroide, nor of a Sphære.* And those may be ranged under two Heads, First, Such as are consequential Proofs drawn from the similitude in Nature's Operations, on other Bodies similarily affected. And Secondly, Those which more immediately and positively prove the Effects thereof upon the very Body of the Earth itself. *Observations to prove the Theory.*

The first sort of Observations are to be fetch'd from the Cælestial Bodies, such as we are assur'd by Observation have a vertiginous Motion about their Axis, as Hypothetically only we suppose the Earth to have; such are the Body of the Sun Primarily and Principally, which was discover'd by *Galileo,* and prov'd and perfected by *Scheiner*; next the Body of *Jupiter,* which was first found to move about its own Axis, in the Year 1664, and which has since been perfected by *Cassini.* Now, if by exactly examining the true Diameters of the Sun when we are in the plain of its Æquinoctial (which is in the beginning of *June* and of *December*), if I say by Trial, we find that the Diameter *per Axin* of the Sun is shorter than the Diameter of its Æquator, then there will be a

further

further probability that the like may be in the Earth if it be fo mov'd, as is now generally fuppofed: The liketrial may be made of the like Axis of *Jupiter* though the Trials will be therein more difficult, as being much lefs fenfible, from the fmallnefs of the Difference; however 'tis worth examining, as it will be to examine alfo the Diameters of *Mercury* and *Venus* when they pafs under the Sun, tho' we are not yet affur'd of their vertiginous Motion, and if Monf. *Gallets* Obfervation may be credited, fuch a *Phænomenon* was taken notice of by him in the late tranfit of ☿ *Sub Sole*, as appears by his account of the Paffage of ☿ *Sub Sole*, Printed in a Treatife by itfelf, and in the Journal *des Scavans.* Now, if this Obfervation do anfwer in the Diameters of the Sun, it will afford us alfo a further information of the Nature of that Glorious Body, and will, I conceive, prove it to be of a fluid and yielding Subftance, efpecially the fhining and fuperficial parts thereof. Trial alfo may be made of the like Diameters of the *Moon*, tho' her vertiginous Motion in comparifon of her bulk, be the floweft of all we yet know as turning round on her Axis but once in a Month. The like may be made of the Body of *Saturn*, when the Ring is fo pofited as that the Diameters that lye in the longer and fhorter Diameters of the Ring may be plainly difcover'd; what the reafon of that Ring may be I fhall difcourfe of elfewhere. Thefe I fuppofe will be the eafieft and fooneft made, and if judicioufly and accurately perform'd, with a due regard of Refraction, and the true pofition of the Axis, will give a great probability or improbability to this fuppofal, but ftill I confefs it will afford no more than a probable Argument either for or againft it: However, that probability being very great, and the trial not very difficult; it will be well to make the Obfervations, efpecially thofe of the Suns Diameter, with all imaginable accuratenefs, which may be done to a very great one, if there be fit Inftruments and fufficient Care ufed therein, fo as very many times to out ftrip all that I have hitherto met with of that kind, the whole method of which will be too long and tedious now to explain; however, if I can procure Affiftance, I refolve to try it this following *June*, which is much the beft time of the whole Year to avoid the inconveniency of Refractions, and the true Phænomena thereof I will produce here, without being biaffed for this Hypothefis, for which I have no further concern than as it fhall be found agreable to the truth of Appearances. Now, tho' I confefs alfo, that I cannot expect that the difference of the longer Diameter in the Sun from the fhorter will be very much in regard of the very ftrong power of Gravity in that Glorious Body whereby it is able to detain all the planetary Bodies in their Orbs from running from him, and even that of *Saturn* fo vaftly remov'd; yet when I compare that with the Magnitude of its Body, and the time of its Rotation, I am apt to think that accurate Trials may difcover fome fenfible difference, which I muft leave to Trial.

The fecond fort of Obfervations or Trials neceffary to prove this Hypothefis, which are direct and pofitive, and may be truly call'd *Experimenta Crucis*, according to the Lord *Verulam* are principally two, which are fufficient to prove it thoroughly, tho' the other fhould fail; the firft is to procure an exact trial to be made of the Time that a Pendulum Clock will keep under or near the Æquinoctial, which is adjufted exactly to the time by the Sun or Stars in a much greater Latitude; or the trial of fuch a Clock in two places very much differing in Latitude after the Clock hath been exactly adjufted in time, to one of thofe places; becaufe fuch a difference if it be found and determin'd will be of fufficiency to determine the proportional co-operation of thefe two Powers. As for inftance, this may be fufficiently examin'd by a Clock adjufted in *England*, and tried in the *Barbadoes*; if Care and Accuratenefs be ufed in both thefe places, which I conceive might be eafily procur'd by the Favour and Affiftance of this Honourable Society. The fecond which is a much more difficult Experiment, but yet much more pofitive and convincing than any other, is the meafuring of the quantity of a Degree of Latitude upon the Earth, in two places very much differing in Latitude; the one as near as might be towards the Pole, as upon the Ice in the *Finniek Gulf*, as Monfieur *Thevenot* propofeth, which might be procur'd by Mr. *Hevelius* at *Dantzick*, or Dr. *Rudbeck* at *Stockholm* in *Sweedeland*, who might do it himfelf or

procure

procure it to be done at the North end of that Gulf, which would be yet better, and by some Persons in *Jamaica*, or other parts nearer the *Æquator.* These last trials, if accurately made, would be undeniable Proofs of this supposition, if it should be certainly found that a Degree in the more Northern Countries were more large than a Degree in the more Southern Climate, and the Experiment with the Pendulum Clocks would likewise more exactly adjust the true Gravity of the Earth consider'd simply without the composition of the vertiginous Motion. And thus much for the first part of the Hypothesis, that the Figure of the Water above the Earth is that of a prolated Sphæroeid whose shortest Diameter is that of the Axis of its Rotation.

Next for the examination of the second Part thereof (namely, whether the Axis of its Rotation hath and doth continually by a slow progression, vary its Position with respect to the Parts of the Earth ; and if so, how much, and which way, which must vary both the Meridian Lines of Places, and also their particular Latitudes) it had been very desireable, if from some Monuments or Records of Antiquity, somewhat could have been discover'd of certainty and exactness, that by comparing that or them with accurate Observations now made, or to be made, somewhat of certainty of information could have been procur'd : But I fear we shall find them all insufficient in accurateness to be any ways relied upon ; however, if there can be found any thing certain and accurately done, either as to the fixing of a Meridian Line on some Building or Structure now in being, or to the positive or certain Latitude of any known place, tho' possibly those Observations or Constructions were made without any Regard or Notion of such an Hypothesis, yet some of them compared with the present state of things might give much Light to this Inquiry. Upon this account I perus'd Mr. *Graves* his Description of the great Pyramid in *Ægypt*, that being Fabl'd to have been built for an Astronomical Observation, as Mr. *Graves* also takes notice. I perus'd his Book I say, hoping I should have found, among many other curious Observations he there gives us concerning them, some Observations perfectly made, to find whether it stands East, West, North and South, or whether it varies from that respect of its sides to any other part or quarter of the World, as likewise how much, and which way they now stand ; but to my wonder, he being Astronomical Professor, I do not find that he had any regard at all to the same, but seems to be wholly taken up with one Inquiry, which was about the measure or bigness of the whole and its parts, and the other matters mention'd, are only by the bye and accidental, which shews how useful Theories may be for the future to such as shall make Observations ; nay, tho' they should not be true, for that it will hint many Inquiries to be taken notice of which would otherwise be not thought of at all, or at least but little regarded, and but superficially and negligently taken notice of. I find indeed, that he mentions the South and North sides thereof, but not as if he had taken any notice whether they were exactly facing the South or North, which he might easily have done. Nor do I find that he hath taken the exact Latitude of them, which methinks had been very proper to have been retain'd upon Record with their other Description. [Here by the bye because it agrees with a former Conjecture, I here proposed, concerning those stupendious Works, namely, that the Core of them was probably some natural Rock cut and shaped fit to be cased or cover'd with another sort of Stone, which was at that time much contradicted, by Affirmations, that the whole Country and Place of their Station was nothing but Sand. Give me me leave to take notice that Mr. *Graves* doth affirm, That the great Pyramid is founded upon a natural Rock which riseth above the rest of the Sand, and that the Rooms about the second Pyramid are hewen and shapen out of the natural Rock ; and I doubt not but that if they were all examin'd, they would be found to be so and nothing else, which would much alleviate the stupendious Labour and Work of Men that must otherwise have been supposed to be made use of; but this only by the bye.] To proceed then where I left, I say that I conceive it were very desirable for the future, that those I have mention'd, and several other particular Observations, were purposely

2dly, Of the alteration of the Axis of the Earths Rotation.

U u u u   made

made for that such would give a great light to judge and make a true valu-ation of the State and Nature of places and things, which in most Descrip-tions we find altogether wanting. As among many other things I could hint, I should be very glad to find such a Description of the Nature of the Sand of those Parts as would inform me whether it have not been all a Sea-Sand: I say, not only of this Country of *Ægypt*, which is so exceeding plain, and so exceeding Sandy, with many cragged Rocks rising out of it ; but of *Arabia Deserta*, and *Arabia Petræa*, and all the parts near the *Tigris* and *Euphrates*, and all the parts on this side of *Egypt*, as the Region of *Barca* and *Pentapoli-tana*, and many other which are said to be all smooth and cover'd with Sand ; for Observations designedly made, would easily discover whether such Sands had been owing to the Sea, or to some other Cause, which, by some curious Observations I have met with in the Travels of *Peter de la Valle* and *Belloni-us*, and others, I judge they have. I shall here present you with one of them. *Pietro della Valle parte terza Lettera 11da d'Aleppo* Aug. 5. 1625. *Vidi per terra molte Conchiglie marine, lustre dentro comme Madre Perle, parte in-tere, e parte spezzate, che in Luogo tanto lontano dal mare mi marvigliai come potessero trovarsi, vidi anco sparsi per tutto molti pezzi di Bitume, che in quell terre-no salmastro, e che in qualche tempo dell anno per allagarsi d' acqua si genera, del quali ne presi e tengo mostra appresso di me.* NB. This Place is betwixt *Bassora* and *Aleppo*, in the Deserts of *Arabia*, fourteen Days Journey from the Sea.

In *English* thus, ' I Saw on the Ground many Sea-Shells shining within like
' Mother of Pearl, some whole, some broken, I much wonder'd how they
' could be found in a place so far distant from the Sea ; I saw also scattered
' every where many bits of Bitumen, which in this salt Earth and Soil is ge-
' nerated and rises upon the Water at some times of the Year, of which I
' took some, and keep the Specimens by me to shew. Moreover, I hoped to have found something remarkable to my purpose in the Voyages of Sir *George Wheeler*, where he hath describ'd *Greece* and *Athens* in particular, and all the remarkable places about it, which are Places the best described of any thing of Antiquity, and more especially in his Description of the Temple of the Eight Winds, which is said by *Vitruvius* to be given to the City of *Athens* by *Andronicus Cyrrhastes*, and is remaining intire to this Day, all except the Vane or Weather-Cock at the top. I expected, I say, I should have met with some very exact and curious Observations, which methinks the very design of the place should have hinted, of the true Position of it as to those eight parts or *Plagæ mundi* ; but I find nothing more to this purpose but that each Wind ans-wer'd exactly to the compass, in the mean time not telling what was the va-riation of that compass at that time or place ; however, he doth shew that the Position and Latitudes of places do much differ from what they had been described to us, but then how far we may relie upon antient Observations, will be a further doubt.

I should be glad that such as are better read in ancient Records would for the future at least take notice of any Observations they meet with which may afford some light to this Inquiry ; and so for that Matter I must there leave it ; for tho' I could accumulate many Observations which do seem to make for it, yet the uncertainty and unaccurateness of the Observations of the Anci-ents in this particular make me omit them.

And so I am reduced at last to such Observations as have been made in latter times, and with more accurateness and diligence, and with better In-struments, and to what may be purposely made with Instruments a hundred times more axact, and with designed and pertinent Observations for this ve-ry end ; and such Observations will be principally of two kinds, First, Such as examine and state the exact Position of the Meridian Line of places even to a single second, or to a greater accurateness if required. And Secondly, Such as examine and state the true Latitude for that from some few such Observati-ons accurately made, as they ought, more may be proved by seven Years Ob-servations than by seven hunder'd Years Observation of the Antients, nay tho' they were again multiplied by seven. But of this I shall discourse in my next.

The

The CONTENTS.

THis Lecture was read Feb. 9th. 168⁶/₇, the design of which is to prove that the diurnal Motion of the Earth must cause a recession of the Æquinoctial Parts thereof, and an accession of the Polar, and so make it of the suppos'd prolated Figure, and this is performed by a short and plain demonstration deduced from the Earths diurnal Motion: A principal of Motion premised, viz. That a Body moved will persevere to move with that velocity received in a strait Line; from hence some deductions are made, and a short and plain demonstration that the Figure of the Terraqueous Superficies is a prolated Spheroid, and that gravity tends no where to the Center but at the Poles and under the Æquator; and then the Author desires that Experiments may be made for that purpose. Next follows the proposal of a way to determine by accurate Observation, whether the Axis of the Earths Rotation changes or not.

R. W.

I Hoped I had by my Discourse at the last meeting evidenced the first part of my Position which I deduced as a Corollary from the diurnal Motion of the Earth, namely, that such a motion must cause a recession of the Sea from the Polar parts towards the Æquinoctial, which must necessarily make the Surface thereof of a prolated Sphæroidical Figure. But I perceive some notwithstanding the Experiment, which shewed of the recess of the Water from the Center, do yet doubt of the Consequences thence deduced with reference to the Earth, and seem'd not to be satisfied that the two Methods which I propounded for the examination and determination thereof were sufficient.

Now that I might not leave any rub behind which might be a stumbling Block at the entrance, I have now prepared a short demonstration of the necessity and infallible certainty thereof, as it is a deduction from an Hypothesis which is now by most Philosophers and Astronomers granted, namely, the diurnal Motion of the Body of the Earth upon its Axis.

In order to which Demonstration I must premise this principle of Motion, *A Body moved* That *every Body that hath received, or is moved with any degree of motion if it re-* *will persevere* *ceives no other motion from any other Body whatsoever, will constantly persevere or* *in that motion.* *continue moved with the same velocity in the streight Line of its tendency infinitely produced.* The reason of which is this, that no Reason can be assigned why its Motion should cease where there can be no impediment. Nor is there any reason why it should deflect to any side out of its direct way, since from the supposition there can be no new motion added to it from any other Body. Now this being a Principle will not admit of any other Demonstration than that of Induction from particular Observations in Natural Motions, by which all such Principles are made; for whosoever shall strictly and accurately examine and analyse all local Motions, will find hundreds of instances that after a due analysis is made do sufficiently evidence the universality and certainty of this Principle in all local Motions.

From which Principle it will follow, that any Body moved Circularly with any degree of velocity (whilst some way continu'd to move about that Center) will at the instant that containing Power is remov'd, proceed to move directly forward in the straight Line of its tendency, which straight Line is a tangent to that Circle in which it aquired, or had its imprest velocity; for the conteining Power, which by a continual atraction or otherwise towards the Center, kept it in that Circulation, ceasing, and no other Body whatsoever impressing any new motion upon it (as is supposed in the first Proposition) the Body must continue to move in the streight Line of its Direction without any Deflection, Retardation, or Acceleration.

From hence it will follow, that the farther it is moved in that Line, the more and more will it recede from that Center of Motion to which it was detained, and that for a short time with Spaces in a duplicate proportion of the times it spendeth, or of the Spaces it passes in that tangent Line, namely, in the proportion of the smaller Secants. This, as shewn by *Gelileo* and others, I pass over without farther proof.

From

Tab. 8. *Fig.* 1. From hence it will follow, that in all Circular Motions that make their Revolutions in equal times about the same Center, but in Circles of differing Radii, the recess in equal times will always be in the same proportion as the Radii of those Circles, or as the Tangents or Secants of the same Angle at the Center ; this will be plain by the Scheme, where a represents the Center of the Motion, *eg, di, cl, &c.* Similar Arches of different Circles on the same Center *a,* the Bodies placed in *b, c, d, e,* are put to pass their respective Arches *bn, cl, di, eg,* all in the same time ; now the Tangents *ef, dh, ck, bm* being in the same proportion with their respective Radii, and their respective Secants, their respective receding from the Center *a,* will be in proportion to their Radii.

Hence it follows, that the recess of the Parts of the Earth from the Axis of the diurnal Rotation will be in the same proportion as the Sines complement of the Latitude of those places, which recess is no where directly from the Center of Gravity, but under the Æquinoctial it being every where perpendicular to the Axis of Rotation.

Now the simple Gravity of the Earth as a Globous Body at rest can be no other than to the Center of that Globe, it being consider'd only as a Globe without any Circular Motion, as I shall prove when I speak of Gravity. And this Gravity every way equal, it will thence necessarily follow, that by the composition of those two Powers acting on Bodies, there will necessarily follow these Consequences, First, That every Meridian Line upon the Surface of the Sea, is of an Elliptical Figure, whose shortest Diameter is in the Pole, and whose longest is in the Plain of the Æquinoctial. Secondly, That the Gravitation of the Earth, as moved on an Axis, is in every Latitude different, the least under the Æquator and the greatest under the Poles.

Demonstration of the Figure of the Earth. *Tab.* 8. *Fig.* 2. Thirdly, That the Perpendiculars or Lines of Gravity or Descent do no where, except under the Poles and Æquinoctial respect the Center of the Earth ; but other Centers in the Axis of its Rotation, let *Abc,* represent a quarter of the terrestial Globe Orthographically projected upon the plain of a Meridian, where let a, represent the Center, *b,* the Pole, *ab,* the Axis, *ac,* the Æquinoctial, let *ae βg γi* represent the Radii of certain parallels of Latitude, whose Rotation about the Axis *ab,* gives each of them a proportion of velocity corresponding to their length or distance from their Axis of Motion *ab,* that is in proportion to the Sine complement of the Latitude of the place or parallel. Let *c, g, b, r, n, y,* represent a very thin Superficies of the Globe of the Earth or Sea ; let *ac, ae, ag, ci, ab,* represent the natural Lines or Rays of Gravity tending to the Center of the Earth all of equal length and equal power as to Gravity. The parts then in the Figure being understood, I proceed to the Exposition of the Doctrine, let *g,* then represent a Body somewhere placed upon the Superficies of the Earth ; I say, this Body will be affected or moved with a double Power : First, By a Power gravitating towards the Center *a,* which is the same where ever the Body be placed ; this gives it a power of descending from *g,* to *n,* in a certain space of time. Secondly, by a levitating power in the Line *βg,* whereby in the same space of time it would ascend from the Center of its motion *β,* from *g,* to *h.* Now draw, *no,* parallel and equal to, *gh,* and draw, *og,* and *oh.* Now because in both these Motions the acceleration is in duplicate proportion of the times it spendeth in passing them, it follows, that the Motion composed of both those Motions shall be made in a straight Line, namely, in the Diagonal Line *go,* for *g,* being by Gravity carried to *n,* and by Levity, as aforesaid, removed from *n,* to *o,* the place of the Body *g,* at the end of that time, shall be found *o.* The same Demonstration will serve for *c, e, i,* and *b, Mutatis Mutandis ;* whence it follows necessarily, that the Lines of Descent of such a Body are not to the Center of the Earth at *a,* but to some other point of the Axis of Motion, as *t, v, &c.* Secondly, The Figure of the Water will be Oval, or truly Elliptical, as *x m, o, q, r,* because *xy, ml, on, qp, &c.* are all proportioned to their respective Radii. Thirdly, The power of this compounded Motion will affect all Bodies in differing Latitudes with differing Gravity, which were the proprieties to be proved.

From

From which demonſtration it plainly appears, that the Conſequences I have deduc'd from the Hypotheſis of the diurnal Rotation of the Earth are neceſſary, and cannot, according to the Laws of Motion, be otherwiſe than what I have deduc'd, not frivolous Suppoſitions taken up at random to ſolve one Phænomenon, but ſuch as will give light to many other conſiderable effects of Nature, as I ſhall demonſtrate in explaining ſeveral other Phænomena both of the Earth and of the Heavens.

It further appears alſo, that the Experiments or *Criteria* I have propounded, are both pertinent and ſufficient to determine and ſtate this Enquiry without any other, and that they are neither impoſſible nor very difficult to be procur'd to be try'd with accurateneſs enough.

Now as theſe may eaſily enough be procur'd by the mediation of this Honourable Society ; ſo I doubt not but they may, with little more trouble, procure ſuch Obſervations and Experiments to be made as would afford great Light towards the perfecting ſeveral other parts of uſeful Knowledge, ſome few of which, if judiciouſly and pertinently contriv'd ſo as to be plain and eaſy, would give us the determination of many old, yea, and many new Theories poſſibly not hitherto thought of, ſome of which I ſhall hereafter have occaſion to mention. Such Obſervations will be worthy the Care of this Society, and will be better than accidental and caſual Trials, which, tho' ſurpriſing and pleaſant, are at beſt but like thoſe of the ſeekers of the Philoſophers Stone and perpetual Motion, who generally make trials at a venture, to ſee if there good Genius or Fortune will direct them to meet with what they ſeek ; whereas indeed all Experiments ought to be directed to ſome end for the examination of ſome ſuppoſed Truth, and for that end to take notice of all ſuch Circumſtances as may give any information concerning it, whether it be for Confirmation, or Confutation of ſuch a Doctrine, and if ſo, the plainer and the more obvious the Experiments are, the better.

If yet there ſhall remain any doubt either in the deduction of this Concluſion, or the ſufficiency of the Experiments to determine and ſtate the truth thereof, I would very willingly explain any part thereof.

The next part of my Hypotheſis is, that by many Obſervations I conceive that there may be in the Rotation of the Body of the Earth, a change of the Axis of that Rotation, by a certain ſlow Progreſſive Motion thereof, whereby the Poles of the ſaid Motion appear to be in ſuperficial parts of the Earth, which heretofore were at ſome diſtance from the then polar Points or Parts. *A Method of determining whether the Axis of the Earths Rotation alters.* I have waved all the Obſervations that I have hitherto met with in Hiſtories which might ſeem to favour this Hypotheſis, as having found them irregular and unaccurate enough in Obſervations of this kind, and have put the whole ſtreſs of its Proof, or rather Examination, upon trials to be made for the future. But becauſe this Motion, if any, ſeems to be very ſmall and ſlow, and therefore ſince the Age of Man, which is very ſhort comparatively, ſeems inſufficient for ſuch a purpoſe ; I have therefore indeavour'd to carry Mahomet to the Mountain, ſince I cannot bring the Mountain to Mahomet, and that is by contriving ſuch ways as may perform that in a ſhort time, which, by the Methods of the Antients, could not be perform'd in leſs than ſome Ages. This Contrivance conſiſts only in the exactneſs of Inſtruments, and the accurateneſs of making Obſervations ; for if for inſtance we are not ſure of the truth of the Latitudes of places recorded by *Ptolomy* and *Strabo* to a degree or two, as I can ſhew hundreds of places that differ more than that from the Truth ; and if by any new Method we may be able to make Obſervations either of the Latitude of a Place, or of the true Meridian of any ſuch place to a ſingle ſecond Minute, than we may by ſuch a means arrive to a certainty in a three thouſand ſix hundred part of the time that could be arriv'd at by ſuch Obſervations as theirs are ; wherein their Defects lay whether in their Inſtruments, or their way of uſing them, or their negligence in computing, or the want of our preſent arithmetical Art, and of proper and accurate Tables, or in the Doctrine and Practiſe of plain and Sphærical Trigonometry, I do not inquire ; but certain it is, we have at preſent a great advantage of them in all theſe particulars, but above all, moſt eminently by the Knowledge and Uſe of Optick Glaſſes, eſpecially as they are

X x x x

applied

applied to Mathematical Inftruments, for by them only we are truly made Gygantick, and our Eye from the little Ball of lefs than an Inch in Diameter is grown to be of fifty, fixty, nay a hundred Foot and more in Diameter, and may be made able to do fome thoufands of times more than what our bare Eye alone without the ufe of fuch helps can perform; and therefore tho' *Hevelius* might have fome reafon to be uneafy, and fo to rail at me for afferting of this Truth to the World after he had publifh'd his *Machina Cælefis* to fhew he had made ufe of the beft Inftruments in the World for his Obfervation; yet why Dr. *Wallis* and his Adherents, fome of which have made ufe of the very Contrivances which I Publifh'd, fhould with fo much Gall write againft me for it, I cannot but wonder: But I doubt not but to prove to all the World in my own Vindication, that neither the one nor the other had any reafon but ill Will for what they did, and at the fame time to prove the truth of every particular which I have afferted in that Book to any that will believe his own Eyes; but not to trouble you any further with this Controverfy at prefent, defigning fuddainly to publifh my Anfwers to them where they may be feen more at large, I fhall proceed to the Methods of making Obfervations both of the Meridian Line of any place, and alfo of its true Latitude in refpect of the Heavens to the accuratenefs of a fingle Second.

And here only I have one or two Poftulata to premife, which I fuppofe every one that hears it will readily grant; it is no more but thefe; Firft, That it is poffible, nay, practicable, to find a Point below perpendicular, to a Point above, tho' the diftance between them be a hundred Foot, and to be certain of the truth thereof to the exactnefs of a Second Minute.

Secondly, That the Refraction of the Air at fixty Degrees Altitude above the Horizon does not at vary the Azymuth of a Body a fingle Second Minute.

A Third Truth I will put by way of a Poftalutum, that 'tis poffible, nay, eafily practicable to diftinguifh the parts of a far remov'd Object by the help of Telefcopes long enough, tho' they really appear to the Object Glafs of that Telefcope lefs than that of a fingle Second Minute.

Thefe I conceive fo eafy and certain, that I have put them as *Poftulata*; but yet if any doubt of their certainty, I do undertake to prove the Truth of either of them both by Experiment or Demonftration, which of the two fhall be judg'd moft convincing.

The next thing to be fhewn is how to order a Telefcope fo that it may be made a fight, that the true Line in which the Object appears may be certainly determin'd, and this, be the Telefcope fixty or a hundred Foot or more in length, and how to make by this, an Inftrument as large as the faid Telefcope is a fight.

For the performance of thefe Qualifications there will be no greater difficulty, than the making a Tube for fuch a Telefcope, or, if that be thought too much, it may be done by two fmall Scaffold Poles joyned together in the middle with convenient Lines to keep them ftreight, or if this be ftill thought too difficult, it may be done by fitting the Object Glafs in one Cell, and the Eye Glafs and Thread-fights in another, with Lines ftrained between them to keep them directly parallel to each other; but the beft way is by a Telefcope Tube of a due length and bignefs for the Object-glafs made ufe of.

Inftruments for that purpofe.   Suppofing then a Telefcope of fixty, eighty, or a hundred Foot in length thus fitted with a Tube, to find the true Line of Direction, I faften to the Cell that holds the Object Glafs a Needle with the point outwards againft the middle of the Glafs. And the like I alfo fix in a fmall fliding Plate, that lieth upon the Cell, that holdeth the Thread-fight together with the Eye-glafs: This Plate, by a very fine Screw, I can caufe to flip out or in at pleafure, till it be adjufted to a Line from the point of the Needle faften'd to the Cell of the Object-glafs: To adjuft this Telefcope then for a fight, I direct it to fome very remote Object in the Horizon, and fix a Pin or Wire juft touching the point of the Needle at the Object-glafs; then having found and remarked fome convenient Point of the Object in the Horizon, I move the Tube till the Thread of the fight exactly lie upon it; then inverting or turning the Tube, making the under fide upermoft, and the uper fide undermoft, the right the left,

left and the left the right; I cause the point of the Object-glass Needle, as also, that of the Cell of the Threads to touch the same Points as before inversion, then looking at the point of the Horizontal Object, I see whether the a-fore-said Line of it do cover the same part of the Object as it did before in-version. If it happen so to do, then I am certain that the Telescope is al-ready adjusted; but if it do not, it will be adjusted by moving the sliding Plate with the Needle at the Eye-cell: When thus adjusted, these two Needles points become the Indexes to my Instrument, for exactly taking the visual Line of the Object, I observe to as great accurateness as is desired. Having thus prepar'd the sight for my Instrument, I make choice of some Tower of a convenient height for the resting the end of the Tube that holdeth the Object-glass, and order it so that the Needles point may touch a fixed point upon the same; then I make a Board below upon the Ground lying Horizontal, whereupon the other end of the Tube may be slid Horizontal and easily remov'd at pleasure. The Object I make choice of is the Pole-star, or the Star in the tail of the lesser bear. I by this means observe its most Eastern and Western Excursion the same Night; or if it happen that one is in the Night and the other in the Day, by means of this Telescope I can plainly see it, tho' the Sun shine. Now the Needles point at the Object-glass touching in both Excursions, and the Needles point at the Eye-sight shewing the two Azymuthes of the said Excursions, wherein the Refractions can have no effect to make the Ray bent, it will be easy enough accurately to divide the space between the two Excursions into half, and as easy to fine the Point below perpendicular under the Point above marked by the Needles Point of the Object-glass, or which for this purpose will be better to find a point above upon some building of equal height with that of the Object-glass, by which two Points I direct my Telescope to the Horizon either North-wards or Southwards, and find what Object lies directly in the Meridian Line, which I diligently note and draw the Landscape of that part of the Horizon which appears through the Glass when so posited with the very point of the same cover'd by the Thread-sight; which done, I continue the said Landscape by the help of the Telescope till I bring in some remarkable known Object, by means of which I shall be able a Year or two after to find the same again, when the same trial is again to be repeated with the same care. In order to determine this Question, whether the Meridian Line up-on the Surface of the Earth do change; by which means if it be alter'd but a Second or two, I shall be able to distinguish it in the Horizontal Landscape. Now tho' this Experiment upon the whole Matter may seem troublesome and difficult to be perform'd duely as it ought, yet if we consider the Impor-tance thereof in this Matter, and how much can be done by the Care of one Man in a short space, which by the Method of the Antients was to not be ex-pected from the performances of any one or many under the expectation of some Ages, I conceive the Experiment may be look'd upon in the whole as compendious, cheap and easy; there being nothing therein so difficult but that two Men may every day, for some days together, repeat the Observati-ons and Trials after the apparatus is made ready and put in order, and need not spend above four Hours in twenty four to make them sufficiently accurate.

Nor will it be very difficult in this City to find a convenient Building or Tower for the resting the end of the Telescope of a hundred Foot long if it be made use of; or of finding a good prospect of a far distant Meridional Ob-ject in the Horizon, whether towards the North or South, they being both or either equally sufficient for this Observation: And if a fifty or sixty Foot Te-lescope be made use of, which will be able to perform the Observation accu-rately enough, with a little more Care and Circumspection, tho' with less Labour, and Pains, and Charge, there are Houses enough to be found of suf-ficient height.

Now this Experiment I conceive sufficient to perform what is design'd, or to be expected from it, as to this Inquiry, and all things consider'd, I con-ceive the best, tho' I could produce some others if there be occasion; and further, I conceive the same to be free from all material Objections: As

First,

First, If it be Objected, that the Refraction of the Air doth make the Cælestial Objects to appear out of their true places. I say, that in this Experiment it can have no effect, because the Azymuth and Circle of Position only are sought and those the Refraction of the Air alters not; for the Star being only to be obferv'd when it it is either ascending in its most Eastern Azymuth, or descending in its most Western Azymuth, the effect of any would be the same, since they are so found and obferv'd at the same Altitude both ascending and descending; and tho' the Refraction should raife them, and the whole Circle, and the said Star to a sensible higher Position than the Truth, yet the Points to be obferv'd being both of equal Altitude, the effect will be the same, which will no way disturb this Observation.

Next if it be Objected, that this Star doth alter its distance from the Polestar every Year, and that will make the Excursions less in the succeeding Year. I say, as to this Inquiry, it would have no effect, tho' it should alter ten times more, because the middle between the Excursions in the same day, is that which is sought in this Experiment.

If the parallax of the Earths Orb be Objected, which is the most material, I Answer, That the succeeding Experiments are to be try'd again when the Earth is in the same part of the Ecliptick, which will fully answer any Scruple thence.

And, upon the whole, I cannot think of any other, ; but if any of this Honourable Society can think of any Material, I would desire to be inform'd of them, that I may think of some means of remedying them; or if they think of any other more convenient and certain, that I may put them in practise. Some other of my own I shall propound the next Day and leave them to the Judgment of the Society to chuse the most fit.

This, I hope, may save the Labour of searching into Records of Antiquity, of all which if I may be allow'd to judge by those I have met with, I believe they will at best afford us but uncertain and unaccurate Observations, and I do very much doubt whether ever there were above two thousand Years since, any Meridian truly set to the certainty of less than one Degree; so that tho' we had found by the great Pyramid, that there was either some confiderable variety from the present Meridian, or that it were now in the very Meridian Line, the Conclusions drawn from either of them would have been but conjectural, since it might have been placed true, and have since varied, as it is found, or it might have been placed wrong, and since have mov'd to a Truth, or the contrary.

Whereas, since by this Experiment, we may be able to find the Meridian true to the three thousand six hundred part of a Degree, and these Observations may be made by one and the same Man, and with the same Instrument in the same place, and at the same time of the Year, and of the Day; I conceive that one Years Observation will more ascertain us in this particular, than if we had Records of Observations made, as those I have met with 3600 Years since, which is the Expedient I have thought of for redeeming or expanding the power of the short Line of the Life of a Man.

Other Methods of determining the same Question, read Feb. 16. 168⅚.

In order to determine whether the Meridional Line of Places did alter, I did in my last Discourse wave all antient Observations, as fearing there might be wanting in them that certainty and accurateness of Observations that might be sufficient to assure us of the Matter of Fact, and that might be convincing as to the Reality or Nullity of such an alteration, as I suppos'd.

1ft. *By ancient Buildings.* But because possibly there may be some Observations of a latter date which have been here made within our present reach, which are of more accurateness, I would propound it a thing not unfit to be examin'd, whether the Position of several of the most eminent Cathedrals built by the *Gothick* Architecture, wherein great regard, if not Religion, seems to have been had of the Position of them, according to the four quarters of the Horizon, viz. E, W, N, and S. And to this end, because nearest this place, I could wish

it

it were tried at *Weftminfter Abby*, which is intirely built after that Mode ; whether that be truly fo plac'd that the four Ends or Fronts thereof do exactly face thofe Quarters, and if not, which way the variation may be, and how much it really is at this prefent. The fame Obfervation may be procur'd to be made at feveral other Cathedrals, as at *Salisbury, Winchefter, Chichefter, York,* &c. where there are fuch Buildings, which will be with no great difficulty procur'd by the Mediation of this Society.

Among other places worth examining, I could wifh that the great Dialftone in the Privy Garden at *White-Hall,* were one, for that I conceive there was very great Care and Accuratenefs ufed in the placing thereof; and tho' this may feem, if compar'd with others of a very fhort continuance fince its firft placing, yet it may be with probability enough fuppos'd to have been fo much more accurately plac'd, that That alone may poffibly make it preferable to any other whether Ancient or Modern.

Now becaufe the ways publifh'd for finding the true Meridian Line have really much of difficulty in them, and require both a great Apparatus and a confiderable time to make the Obfervations neceffary for this purpofe, without which the Informations and Examinations will be very unaccurate and fcarce to be rely'd upon, therefore I have contriv'd an Inftrument by which, in a few Minutes of Time, the exact Meridian Line, at any place, may be eafily and with accuratenefs enough, that is, to ten Seconds, if need require ; and this free from Exceptions of Refraction, Declination, &c. by which the true Pofition of any Building, Monument, &c. may be prefently difcover'd and computed.

The firft Inftrument from this purpofe, is a Telefcope of what length fhall be thought convenient to be eafily ufed and manag'd ; as fuppofe one of fix, *2dly. By fit Inftruments.* twelve, or fifteen Foot, this muft in the firft place be fitted with Eye-fights, plac'd upon a thin piece of Looking-glafs Plate, on which muft be drawn with a very fine Diamant, fuch Lines and Circles as I fhall direct, the Center of all which Circles is to reprefent the true Polar Point in the Heavens, at the time of the Obfervation of which more by and by.

This Sight-glafs being fix'd in the Tube, the next thing to be done is to fix two pieces of Brafs, or fome other convenient Metal, which may have each of them a fmall hole to hold a fmall clew of Silk fit to bear a Plumbet or fuch other Inftrument as I fhall direct ; thefe holes muft be fo place'd as that an imaginary Line drawn over the ends of them may be exactly parallel to the Axis of the Telefcope which paffeth through the Center of the Sightglafs.

Thirdly, Into thefe holes muft be fitted fmall Silken Lines with Plumbets hanging at them, which two Plumb-Lines will (when the Axis of the Telefcope paffing through the Center of the Sight-plate is directed to the Polar Point) hang in the plain of the Meridian.

Fourthly, The Axis of the Telefcope may be eafily directed to the Polar Point, by bringing three or more Stars of the *Englifh* Rofe into their proper Circles and there fixing it.

Fifthly, The *Englifh* Rofe is a Conftellation in the Heavens difcoverable only by a Telefcope, confifting of fix Stars in the Rofe itfelf, and feveral other in the Leaves and Branches, one of thefe is in the Center of the Rofe, and five in the five green Leaves of the Knob: This I have fomewhere defcrib'd about ten Years fince, but have miflaid them at prefent ; the way of finding them I then fhew'd to Sir *Chr. Wren,* and fome others of this Society at the time when my Inftrument was fixed for that purpofe.

The Inftrument or Telefcope being fix'd in this Pofition, the two Plumbholes reprefent the true Axis of the Earth, and accordingly will ferve to determine both the plain of the Meridian, and alfo the inclination of the Axis to the plain of the Horizon ; fo that by the fame Obfervation both the Meridian Line may be determin'd, and alfo the elevation of the Polar Point,

which

which may be various ways moſt exactly meaſur'd and determin'd.   Now this is a ſecond way of determining the true Meridian Line to what accurateneſs ſhall be deſir'd, for that the length of the Teleſcope is not limited, but may be us'd of what length ſoever may be made, tho' it may be three hundred or four hundred Foot, for that the Object-glaſs may be fix'd at the top of ſome Tower or Steeple, and the Sights and Eye-glaſs at the Ground.   But on this I ſhall not at preſent inlarge, becauſe, whenever there ſhall be occaſion of trial, I can eaſily direct the whole Apparatus.

As to the ſecond Uſe thereof, which is for taking the Altitude of the Po-lar Point above the Horizon ; this way is far beyond any I have met with, and is liable to one only Objection (as I conceive) and that is the Refraction of the Air, which elevates the ſame ſomewhat beyond its due Limits, but then if compar'd with the beſt yet propos'd, I conceive it to be leſs ſubject than any other, and to come nearer to a certainty and exactneſs : How-ever I grant it to have that Objection good againſt it ; but if we conſider the uſe of this Obſervation as it is deſign'd to examine the Latitude of one and the ſame place after the interval of ſome few Years, the Objection is of no validity, for that the Refraction of the Air at the height proper for *London*, viz. 51, 32, is hardly ſenſible ; but then the difference between the Refraction of the firſt and ſecond Obſervation is yet much leſs diſcoverable, ſo that for this purpoſe 'tis as effectual as the beſt.

But becauſe ſome may yet further deſire to free the Obſervation from Re-fraction, I have contriv'd another way, much leſs ſubject to it ; which way will alſo find the true Meridian Line to great exactneſs : Not to make any long preamble to it 'tis this, Make choice of ſome notable fix'd Star that paſſeth over or near the Zenith of the place, as here, for *London* the *Lucida Dra-conis*, or the laſt Star in the tail of the great Bear ; 'tis eaſy, by the way I have already publiſh'd in Print to find the Zenith, and the Meridian Line paſſing through it.

Having fix'd all things requiſite for this, about an Hour or two before the Star comes to the Zenith or Meridian near it, find and obſerve exactly its bearing, which may be done with a Teleſcope of fifty, ſixty, or more Feet in length, then by an exact Pendulum Clock number how many Seconds or half Seconds of Time paſs before it arrive at the Meridian, which note and remember, then prepare to obſerve the place of the ſame Star after ſo many Minutes, Seconds, and half Seconds have paſs'd, after the Star hath paſs'd the Meri-dian, note the Point alſo.   There are then given three Points, which, with the help of Calculation, the time being taken, it will give the Latitude of the place to a great exactneſs ; and if a Line be drawn from the moſt Eaſtern to the moſt Weſtern Obſervation, this will give the true E, and W, line ; and if the ſame be divided in half and through the ſame, and the Meridional place of the ſaid Star, a ſtraight Line be drawn, this will give the true Me-ridian Line.

So much for the methods of obſerving the Latitudes and Meridian Lines of places for the time to come.

But becauſe there have been ſome of our later Obſervations of the Lati-tudes of ſome places which have been with very great Care and Accurate-neſs made ; I could likewiſe wiſh that the Latitudes of thoſe places where they have been ſo made, might be a new examin'd, to ſee whether any conſi-derable difference can be found which cannot well be aſcrib'd to the defect of the preceding Obſervations.   As the Latitude of *Uraniburg, London, Paris, Rome, Bolonia*, &c. tho' yet I fear we ſhall be apt to aſcribe what difference ſhall be found to the faileur of the preceding Obſervations.

This is all I have at preſent to propound concerning the external Figure of the Water and Earth.   As to the motions thereof I ſhall propound ſome Conjectures after I have conſider'd the Figure and Conſtitution of the next great Fluid in compaſſing the Earth, which is the Air ; after which I ſhall propound ſome Conjectures at the various internal motions of thoſe great Fluids, which concern the Currents and Tides in the one, and the Winds in the other.

The

The CONTENTS.

THis Lecture was read March the 9th. 168⁹⁄₅, and treats of the Figure of the Air or Atmosphere; and first three known Properties thereof are premis'd, from whence, and the tendency of the Lines of Gravity before proved, is demonstrated, that the Figure of Air is more prolatedly Spheroidical than that of the Earth, which, the Lecture being short, I forbear to Epitomise, and only observe that the Author concludes this Lecture with naming the two great internal Motions of the Earth, Gravitation and Magnetism; of the first he had before treated at the end of his Discourse of Comets, of the later he only gives here his Hypothesis in short.

R. W.

I Have in my former Lectures propounded my Thoughts, and the Reasons of them concerning the Figure of the Body of the Earth, and the tendency of the Perpendicular Lines of Gravitation; as also concerning the probability of a variation of the Axis of Rotation in the Body of the Earth. I have likewise shew'd the influence of those Principles upon which I grounded those Thoughts, upon the Body of the Waters incompassing this Earthly Body.

I come in the next place to consider the Figure of the next great fluid Body, incompassing both the one and the other, and that is the Atmosphere or Mass of Air. *Three known properties of the Air premised.*

And here for the present I shall only consider so much of the Nature and Constitution of this Body, as seems necessary to the explication of the Figure thereof.

It is now very well known, that this Body is of such a Constitution, that a greater degree of Heat, or a lesser degree of Pressure will effect a greater degree of Expansion, that is, will cause the same parcel of Air to occupy or fill a larger space of rome; next that the same parcel of Air, when rarify'd, will weigh no more than when condens'd, tho' it fill a greater space, because the real quantity of the parts that compose this Air, are still the same, tho' there may be a greater quantity of other matter that fill the Interstitia or Spaces between them.

Thirdly, That the Atmosphere is compos'd of three kinds of Substances, one more fluid than the other, two of which, namely, the less fluid Cause considerable effects upon the subjacent parts of themselves, and upon other Aqueous and Terrestial Bodies by their Weight or Gravitation. These I only name at present, designing more fully to explain them and their Causes when I discourse of the Substance and Constitution of the Air.

These three things then for the present being taken as Suppositions, and the tendency of the Lines of Gravitation, being, as I have prov'd, to differing and various Centers, it follows that the Figure of the two lower parts of the Air must be of a prolated Sphæroidical Figure, and that much more considerably differing from that of a Sphærical Form than that of the Earth or Water. *The Atmosphere under the Æquator higher.*

For First, It is very evident, that the more gross Parts thereof are carry'd along with the subjacent Parts of the Earth, with an almost equal swiftness; say almost, because in the wide and open Ocean there is some kind of loss of swiftness and lagging behind, which, as I conceive, (as *Galileo* and many others have done) is the Cause and Original of the Eastwardly Winds within or near the Tropicks; from this Rotation then will follow a considerable levitation of such parts of the Air as are whirl'd round from West to East with such a Rotation; that is, those parts which are mov'd swiftest will have the greatest indeavour of Recess from the Axis of Motion; and those which are mov'd slower will have a less, as I shew'd before in my Explication of the Figure of the Water. *1st. From its swifter motion*

Next

2ly. From its springy Nature. Next it is evident from the fpringy Nature of the Air, that the lefs the preffing is upon the Body thereof, the more will it expand and ftretch it felf and poffefs a greater fpace. Now the quantity of Air towards the Æquinoctial, having a greater Levitation upwards, or lefs Gravitation towards the Earth, a greater quantity of the Air muft go to make up the Cylinder that gives an equal Preffure, and confequently the Surface or Extent of the Air towards the Æquinoctial muft upon this account be much higher than towards the Poles.

3dly. From its greater heat there. But in the Third place this Oval Figure of the Air muft neceffarily be increas'd by the differing Degrees of Heat and Cold; for that a greater Degree of Heat doth expand, and of Cold doth condenfe the Body thereof. Now it is evident that the Degrees of Heat near the Æquinoctial are very great in comparifon to what they are near the Poles.

And confequently, upon this account, alfo the Body of the Air towards the Æquator, muft be very high and rarify'd, and the Body of it towards the Poles muft be very low and condens'd; from which two Caufes it will neceffarily follow, that the Figure of the Body or Mafs of Air, incompaffing the Body of the Earth and Water, muft be of a prolated Sphæroidical Figure, much more prolated towards the Æquator than that of the Water.

Reafons of different Phænomena in different Climates. From which Confiderations, I conceive, fome Reafons may be drawn of feveral Phænomena taken notice of by Travellers; fuch as the frequency of Foggs and Mifts and various forts of *Parhelia* and *Parafelenæ*, in and near the Polar Regions; all which argue a denfe and heavy Air. And of the Hurricanes, Tornadoes and the Storm call'd the *Bulls Eye*, which defcends from a great height with great precipitation into the lower Regions of the Air, and of the frequent and violent Rains in the *Torrid Zone*; all which *Phænomena* are indications of an Atmofphere much more extended upwards, and of the vaporous Parts carry'd to a much greater height than elfewhere.

A Circulation of the lower & upper parts of the Air. From thefe Confiderations alfo will follow a neceffary motion or tendency of the lower Parts of the Air near the Earth, from the Polar Parts towards the Æquinoctial, and confequently of the higher Parts of the Air from the Æquinoctial Parts towards the Polar, and confequently a kind of Circulation of the Body of the Air, which I conceive to be the caufe of many confiderable *Phænomena* of the Air, Winds and Waters, which I fhall more fully explain when I come to confider the Conftitution and Motion of the Body of this great Mafs, whofe Figure and external Form only at the prefent I am confidering.

Nor fhall I at prefent explain any thing farther concerning the two more fluid Subftances that help to compofe or fill the fpace which is taken up by the Atmofphere, becaufe my prefent Subject leads me only to confider that part of the Air which is call'd the Atmofphere, and to fpeak only of the Figure thereof, of which I have no more to add at prefent, but fhall return to confider the Nature and Motions of each of thefe three great Maffes, *viz.* the Earth, the Water and the Air.

Firft then for the Internal motions of the Earth; there are two principally taken notice of; the firft is that of Gravitation, the fecond is that of Magnetifm.

Of the firft of thefe I have fome Years fince difcours'd more particularly, and therefore fhall omit it at prefent.

Of the fecond of thefe, namely, Magnetifm, I fhall only propound my *Hypothefis of Magnetifm.* Hypothefis now and explain it more particularly in my next Difcourfes.

My Hypothefis then is this, Firft, That all magnetical Bodies have the conftituent Parts of them of equal Magnitude and equal Tone.

Secondly, That the Motion or Tone of one Magnetical Body is convey'd to that of another by means of a Denfe Medium.

Thirdly, That the motion of the Denfe Medium is Circular and Vibrating.

From which three Suppofitions all the *Phænomena* of Magneticks will be moft evidently and clearly, even *a Priori*, deduc'd.

SInce the following Difcourfe treats of that furprifing Experiment of the Mercuries ftanding fo much above the ufual ftandard, and gives our Authors Explication of that Phænomenon, I thought fit to join it to the foregoing of the Figure
of the Atmofphere, and the rather becaufe it alfo gives feveral very good hints of
the Nature of that fluid, as likewife concerning the Æther. This Difcourfe was
firft read in one Thoufand fix hundred feventy odd to my Lord Brouncher, and with
fome fmall alteration in the firft Page produced again to the Royal Society 1684,
as it is here Printed.

R. W.

Of the ftanding of the Mercury in the Tube to the height of 75 Inches, read May the 28th. 1684.

THat *Theories* are not altogether ufelefs, we may perceive by the happy
invention of the ingenious *Galileo*, and the addition of the acute *Torricellius*, which two compleated the Experiment of the *Æthereal Vacuum*; the
further Improvement and Obfervation of which hath produc'd the *Barometer*,
now ufeful for predicting the variation of the Weather, and the *Pneumatick*
Engine much more prolifick of difcoveries; the caufes of moft of whofe
Phænomena are fufficiently obvious, and certainly known to be the Gravitation and Spring of that part of the *Atmofphere*, which is call'd *Air*, and
agreed to by the moft accurate of the Modern Philofophers. But Mr. *Hugens* about twenty Years fince having tried Mr *Boyle's* Experiment of making
Water defcend in a Tube, the Orifice of which was inclofed in an exhaufted
Receiver, found that if the Water were firft well freed from the Air that is
ufually latent in it, and then inclofed, the Water would not defcend in the
Pipe, tho' the preffure of the Air were wholly taken off; this occafion'd the
trial to be made here with *Quickfilver* inftead of Water, and by many Experiments it was at laft found by Mr. *Boyle* the Lord *Broucher*, and feveral o-
thers, that the *Quickfilver* alfo when the Tube was very well freed from
the latent Particles of Air, would not part from the top of a Tube, tho' it
were twice as high as the ufual height the *Quickfilver* ufed to ftand at; and
tho' there were no more preffure upon the ftagnant Veffel than was ufual,
and that the bottom of the Tube were as open and free for the *Mercury* to
run out, as was ufual for Experiments of the Mercurial Standard. This
feem'd at firft to overthrow the Theory of the Gravity of the Air, and was
made ufe of by fome *Antagonifts* to that purpofe, but with little reafon; for
it was obferv'd, that in the making this Experiment if a little Jog were
given to the Tube in which the *Mercury* thus remain'd fufpended, the
Mercury would immediately leave the top and fall down in the Tube to the
ufual height of about thirty Inches, and there exhibit all the fame Phænomena as the common Mercurial Standard or Torricellian Experiment had
been obferv'd to do. However it could not but affect the inquifitive after the
caufes of things, with a defire of fatisfying themfelves with fome probable
Conjectures at the caufes of this fo ftrange an Effect, fome fuppofing one
thing, fome another; what my Conjectures were, and ftill are, I fhall in
brief declare and leave them to be confider'd by fuch as have better Abilities,
and fhall pleafe to trouble themfelves with fuch inquiries.

Since I firft made the Experiment, I faw an abfolute neceffity of a preffing *Proof of the*
Fluid very much more fubtile than the Air, and yet confifting of parts of a deter- *Æther.*
minate bulk, which would eafily ftrain through and pervade the Pores of Glafs,
Water and other Bodies impervious to the Air, but could be kept out by the
nearer Conjunction of fome of the conftituent parts of thofe Bodies which confti-
tute Pores of a much lefs Magnitude or Capacity, which fluid I fuppos'd might
be fomewhat of the Nature of the fecond Element of *Defcartes*, tho' for
many Reafons drawn from Experiments, I fuppos'd it to have many differing
Proprieties from thofe which he afcribes to his, and I faw alfo a neceffity of
fuppofing a third Element confifting of a matter yet more fubtile and fluid,

Z z z z

as

as he supposes, and more then that, of several other fluid Matters, some more subtile than others, each of which have their proprieties distinct, and are the causes of this or that Phænomenon in the World, of which there hath as yet been no intelligible reason given of their Power and Original, as I may hereafter shew in the Explication of some of them. And I do believe, from that little insight I have had of the Operations of Nature, that all the sensible part of the World is almost infinitely the least part of the Body thereof, and but, as it were, the *Cuticula*, or outward Filme of things; whereas that which fills up and compleats the space incompass'd by that Filme consists of a multitude of insensible Bodies, each of them as distinct in their Natures and Operations, as Air and Quicksilver, or any other two sensible Bodies we can name; for so many, so curious, and so minute are the insensible workings of Nature, that without supposing some such Instruments as these we shall quickly find a *non plus* in the explication of any one appearance in Nature. But for the finding out the Number and Nature, of these Elements we can proceed but by slow and single steps, and 'tis not to be expected but from a long and close prosecution of Nature as we see that the pressure of the Air was not detected till *Galileo* and *Torricellius* happily light upon that Notion, and this second Element was not experimentally manifested till the making of this Experiment of the *Mercury*'s standing much above the height discover'd by *Torricellius*. The matter on which the Loadstone works will perhaps be found another, and that which causeth Gravity a Fourth. But this by the bye.

My Notion and Explication of this Phænomenon is this, That there is another fluid Body; this Fluid is the Menstruum or Liquor into which the Air is dissolv'd like a Tincture of Cocheneel into Water, which, as I have explain'd in the 15th Observation Microscopical, *Page* 96, and 97, doth penetrate the Pores of the Glass Water, and several other terraqueous Bodies (possibly all such as are transparent, for that I have not a sufficient supellex as yet to determine positively; nor is it material for the Explication of this Phænomenon, as other more curious and critical Experiments shall be found out, it will be time enough to determine it.)

Next that this fluid, as all other sensible fluids we meet with, hath a greater Congruity or Incongruity to this or that Body it is contiguous to, and therefore doth more readily join to this Homogeneous than to that Heterogeneous Body, whether Solid or Fluid, and doth more easily penetrate the small Pores of the Homogeneous, and not without some difficulty the Pores of the Heterogeneous Bodies. And in short, that this Congruity or Incongruity of it to other Bodies doth make it perform the same kinds of Effects with those we find perform'd by sensible Fluids and Solids, such as I have explicated in my sixth Mycroscopical Observation.

Thirdly, That this Fluid doth not at all penetrate the Body of *Quicksilver*, tho' *Quicksilver* may be penetrated by a great number of other more subtile Fluids, such as those which cause Gravity, Magnetism, Fluidity, &c. if at least it shall be found necessary by future Experiments to ascribe those three Properties to more than one fluid.

Fourthly, That several other Liquours whose greater Pores are penetrated by this Fluid, may yet be sustain'd by it above the level equivalent to twenty nine Inches of *Quicksilver*, so long as the Pores are not so far seperated as to admit the parts of this Fluid between them where they are more neerly contiguous, and have some more subtile fluid Body only between them. Of this kind Water well purged of Air may be one, as the Experiment of the not subsiding of Water purg'd of Air doth maaifest.

Fifthly, That this Fluid hath a pressure every way analogous to the pressure of the Air, and that this pressure is much greater than that of the Air.

Sixthly, That there is no need (for the explicating any Experiment I have yet heard of) of supposing it to have a springy Nature like that of the Air, since all the Phænomena may be solved without it.

For the more intelligibe Explication of this Solution, I shall indeavour to shew an Experiment very much like it, in sensible Bodies. I took then a small Glass Cane *a, b, c,* open at both ends, then having procur'd a long small Glass

Pipe

Pipe in a Lamp almoſt as ſmall as a Hair, I brake it into a great many ſhort ones and made of them a Stopple by binding them together Fagot-wiſe with thread, and melting Wax or Cement about them, ſo as that none of their Perforations were ſtopt, I put them into the end *a, b*, for a Stopple, then I had another Cane of Glaſs big enough to contain the former wholly as Def. *Tab.* 8. *Fig.* 3. which was fill'd with Water; then the firſt Tube with the open end down-wards was immers'd into the ſaid Tube Def. till the Water had fill'd the whole, and the ends of the ſmall Pipes *iiiii*, then gently raiſing up the Tube *a, b, c,* out of the Water, I found I could raiſe it ſo high as that the Water in the Tube *a, b, c,* did ſtand above the Surface of *g, h,* the Water in the Glaſs Def. ſome Inches. Wherein 'tis obſervable, that tho' all the ends of the Pipes *iiii* were pervious to the Air, yet by reaſon of a greater Congruity of the Water to Glaſs than of Air, the Air was not able to force its way thorough without the help of the Gravity of the Cylinder of Water *a, g, h, b*; the ſame Experi-ment I tried alſo with *Quickſilver*, by making the Stopple *k,* of Braſs, and inſtead of the ſmall Pipes cauſ'd to be drill'd, thro' the ſame a great number of ſmall holes, then by the help of *Aqua Fortis* I cauſ'd all thoſe holes to be whited with *Quickſilver* then holding my Finger againſt thoſe holes, and filling it with *Mercury*, and ſtopping the other end, and immerging it under other *Mer-cury* in a Diſh, by degrees I rais'd the ſame, and found that the Air would not force its way in at the above-ſaid drill'd holes, till the end *A, b,* was rais'd above the level of the *Mercury* in the Diſh ſome Inches.

From both which Experiments 'twill not be difficult to underſtand my ex-plication of this Phænomenon of the extraordinary hight of the *Mercury* in a Tube, well fill'd, and perfectly cleans'd of Air: For if we ſuppoſe in the for-mer Experiment, that the Ambient Air doth repreſent the Ambient Fluid, whoſe preſſure we do ſuppoſe, and that the Perforations of the ſmall Pipes do repreſent the imaginary Pores of Glaſs, and that the Water with which it is fill'd doth repreſent the *Quickſilver* in the new Experiment, and that we ſuppoſe that *Quickſilver* hath a greater Congruity to Glaſs than the other, and that conſequently it keeps the other from getting a Body within the hol-low of the Tube by ſtopping it at its firſt entry, 'twill be eaſie to imagine how, tho' the Glaſs can be ſuppoſed all over Porous, through which the Æ-ther can paſs, the Ambient new Fluid can by its more free preſſure on the Surface of the bottom, keep the *Mercury* ſuſpended forty five Inches above the former Standard of thirty Inches.

Nor doth the ſecond Experiment explicate it leſs naturally; for the Air repreſents the Æther, or what other name ſoever it be call'd by: The *Quick-ſilver* in the one repreſents the *Quickſilver* in the other. Immerſe that Diſh in a Bucket of Water, and you ſhall find that the top of the Tube will be rais'd conſiderably higher above the Surface of the *Mercury* in the Diſh be-fore the *Mercury* will leave the top; Then the Water, under which the *Mer-cury* is immers'd, will repreſent the Air or Atmoſphere, and the holes in the Braſs Stopper, the Pores of the Glaſs, the additional raiſing of the height of the *Mercury*, after 'tis put under Water will ſhew how part of the ſeventy five Inches is aſcribable to the preſſure of the Air, and the other height will ſhew how another part of it is aſcribable to the preſſure of the Æther. I think I need not explain it farther, only 'tis obſervable, that tho' the Air finds a difficul-ty to make its firſt entry into the ſmall holes of the Glaſs Pipes, or of the Braſs Stopper, yet after it hath got through, and that there is Air within the Tube as well as without, it very readily and freely maintains its Paſſage, and the ſame *Phænomenon* alſo happens in the *Quickſilver* Experiment, for as ſoon as ever the *Mercury* begins to ſeperate from the top of the Tube, and the Æther hath a Body within the Tube, it readily falls down to the height ſupport-ed by the preſſure of the Air. The Reaſon of the two preceding Experi-ments, to wit, of the ſuſpenſion of Water in the Tube whoſe end is ſtop-ped with a bundle of ſmall Glaſs Pipes, as alſo of the ſuſpenſion of the *Mercury* in the Tube whoſe end is ſtopp'd with the perforated peice of Braſs, *of Congruity &* will be, I think, ſufficiently manifeſt to him that ſhall thoroughly conſider *Incongruity.* the Nature of the Congruity and Incongruity of Bodies to one another; ſome-what of my Thoughts concerning the ſame I have formerly deliver'd in the sixth Obfervation of my Micrography, which was indeed but a curfory Meditation for the folving of the Phænomenon then mention'd ; but whofoever fhall thoroughly examine the Nature and Power of it, will, I dobut not, find it much more univerfal. To me indeed it feems to be not only the caufe of this extraordinary *Phænomenon*, but of the Conglobation and Tenacity of moft Liquors of the Tenacity Springynefs, Sonoroufnefs, Malleability, *&c.* of all folid and hard Bodies : But of this elfewhere when I have occafin to examine what is the caufe of Congruity itfelf, which I do not fuppofe a firft Principle, but rather of a fecond, third, or fourth Rank, which being more univerfal, muft be afcended to by degrees, after the Synthetick method. To proceed then, I did heretofore propound in the twentieth Page of my Micrography as a thing worthy trial to examine what Power was requifite to force a Liquor through holes of feveral bignefes made in a Heterogeneous folid, and fill'd with fome Liquor Homogeneous to that folid ; for were that accurately done I judge this Experiment of the extraordinary height of the *Mercury* above the ufual Standard would give us a demonftration of the bignefs of the Pores of Glafs ; for fince we find that a hole of------of an Inch will make the *Mercury* ftand fufpended one Inch in height a hole of-----of an Inch will make it ftand fufpended two Inches ; a hole of-----of an Inch will make it ftand three Inches, it will follow that a hole of-----of an Inch will make it ftand forty five Inches, and a hole of-----of an Inch will make it ftand a hundred Inches, which minds me of feveral other Experiments worth trial, for determining this controverfy ; fuch as thefe ;

Several Experiments hinted

Firft, Whether fome Glaffes are not more porous than others, and confequently whether the *Mercury* will not ftand to a much greater height in Tubes made of Glafs of a more opacous or more refracting Subftance than in Tubes of a more tranfparent or lefs refracting Subftance.

2.

Secondly, Whether in a Tube made of Lead very intire from holes and perfectly cleans'd of Air and rubb'd with *Mercury* that doth every where ftick to the fame ; if the faid Tube be fill'd with very well cleans'd *Mercury*, the *Quickfilver* will not ftand fufpended to a much greater height than it doth in Tubes of Glafs, for if Lead, Silver, *&c.* be impervious to this fluid Subftance that fo freely penetrates Glafs, it feems not improbable, but that the *Mercury* may ftand fufpended to a very much greater height, and if fo it will be a certain way of finding out the force or preffure of this fluid ; from the determination of which will follow probably the reafon of the Strength, Weight, Sonoroufnefs and Springynefs of Metals. And I am the more inclin'd to believe that this Experiment will fucceed, becaufe I judge that the fame fluid that conveieth height, is the caufe of this Phænomenon ; and whatfoever Body is perfectly impervious to Light, is alfo impervious to this fluid. But herein I would be underftood not to mean fuch Bodies, as by the thicknefs of their bulk and fome degree of opacoufnefs, do intercept the direct paffage of this fluid Matter, and fo by confequence caufe a kind of opacoufnefs, as a thick Body of Red and Blew, *&c.* Glafs which notwithftanding are not perfectly opacous Bodies, becaufe, when made very thin, they are tranfparent of a Red or Blew Colour : For fuch Bodies tho' they may intercept the direct paffage of the Light, yet may they admit the fluid freely to pafs through their winding Pores, and fo may not perhaps keep the *Mercury* fufpended much higher than a Tube of Cryftal-glafs ; whereas I am very apt to think, that if there could be a Tube made of a Subftance perfectly impervious to this fluid Matter, the *Mercury* may poffibly remain fufpended as many Feet as it doth now Inches ; but this trial will more fully inform. Now

A way to difcover the Microfcopical Pores of Bodies.

that a Body may be pervious to fome Liquors and yet not pervious to Light, is evident by the Experiment of forcing *Mercury* through the Pores of Wood, for if you take a Pipe of Beech, Elm, Oak, Firr, Afh, or the like, of four, five, fix, eight, or ten Foot long, and ftopping one end thereof, you erect it with the open upwards and fill it with *Quickfilver*, you fhall find that the *Quickfilver* will as freely and plentifully pafs through the Microfcopical or Imperceptible Pores of the fame, almoft as it will be ftrain'd through the
Pores

Pores of Cloath, Linnen or Leather, and will thereby fo fill the Pores of the Wood as to make it feel almoft as heavy as Lead ; by this way I have been a-ble to force *Mercury* into the Pores of Charcole, and divers other Vegetable Subftances, whereby the Pores of the fame are made very confpucious, by placing fmall peices of thofe Subftances at the bottom of a Glafs Tube of four, fix, eight, or ten Foot long, and filling the Tube with *Mercury* over them, for thofe and moft other Vegetable Subftances, will, by the preffure of fuch a Cylinder of *Mercury*, be fill'd with *Quickfilver*, and thereby plainly dif-cover the Shape and Texture of their Pores. I have not had the opportunity to try Bones, Horns, Teeth, Hair, Quills, and the like animal Subftances this way, tho' it feems to me very probable, that their Pores may be difco-ver'd this way, at leaft by lengthing the Cylinder, and making the preffure yet greater, or by a condenfing Engine : Nay, I am inclin'd to believe, that *Mercury* may be forc'd even through the Pores of Glafs itfelf if the Cylinder preffing be fufficiently lengthned ; for by this Experiment of the fufpenfion of *Mercury* at feventy five Inches high, it feems that *Mercury* has a greater Con-gruity to Glafs then the preffing Fluid or Æther hath to the fame, and there-fore 'tis not improbable but that a force as great in proportion to the bulk of *Mercury*, as the force of the Æther is to the bulk of the Æther, may force it through the Pores of Glafs, that it may be fubtile enough to do it, feems probable from this, that it doth fo readily penetrate the Pores of Gold, Tin, Lead, Silver, &c. thofe Bodies with whom it hath a perfect Congruity even with meer appofition and contiguity ; and therefore 'tis not improbable but that a degree of force may make it penetrate the Pores of Glafs, which in probability are much greater than thofe of the congruous Metals, efpecially fince we find it can be forc'd into the Pores of Wood, Cork, Pith, Coles, &c. fo as to drive out the Juices contain'd in them ; whereas thofe Juices having a greater Congruity, do penetrate them by meer appofition. Now that this penetrancy of *Mercury* into Glafs is not meerly conjectural, I fhall fhew you by taking notice of certain Spots or Stains which I have found in polifh'd Looking-glafs-Plates after they have remain'd a long while foil'd, and then being unfoil'd, for I have very plainly feen with a Microfcope that there hath been in the place, where fpots appear, an infinite number of exceeding minute Parts of *Mercury* which feem to be gotten into the very Pores of Glafs, and can by no kind of rubbing be fetcht out without wearing away fo much of the very Subftance of the Glafs itfelf: What therefore is thus done acciden-tally by duration, might in probability be much better done by preffure, if we were able to make it confiderable enough, as by letting down Glafs in *Mercury* to a very great depth under Water, where that can be done ; or to a confiderable depth under the preffure of *Mercury*. It may poffibly be Ob-jected, that if *Mercury* hath a greater Congruity to Glafs than this fuppos'd Fluid, why doth not the *Mercury* without much force penetrate the Pores of Glafs at firft, and fo running through it, make it appear opacous. To which I Anfwer, That tho' I fuppofe *Mercury* to have a greater Congruity to Glafs than this Subtile Fluid, yet that it hath not a perfect Congruity, but rather an Incongruity in refpect of other Fluids that are more Congruous, as Air. Nor hath that a perfect Congruity, but rather an Incongruity in refpect of Water ; for there may be infinite degrees of Congruity, as Water falt hath more Congruity to Glafs than Water frefh, Waters than Vinous Spirits, Vi-nous Spirits more than Oils, Oils more than Airs and Fumes, and they more than *Mercury*, and *Mercury* than this fluid Æther, or what other Name fo-ever we call it by ; and in every one of thefe degrees of Congruity or In-congruity there may be a multitude of other Subdivifions ; as for inftance, un-der the firft Head there may be a very great variety ; I know fome, acid Li-quours that will of themfelves, without any force, penetrate the Pores of Glafs fo as to diffolve it into a Powder, whereas others will not at all penetrate or diffolve it by any means I have yet found: But this part of Congruity and Incongruity by which folid Bodies become diffoluble by Fluids, and where-by Fluids readily penetrate each other, and unite with one part of a Fluid, and feparate or precipitate another, belonging to another Subject, I fhall pre-

A a a a a   termit

termit at prefent, and only take notice of fome things that may be pertinent to the Inquiry under Confideration ; and thofe may be thefe ;

Variety of fluids in the fame Liquor.

Firft, That there is no difficulty at all in admitting, that within the fame Liquor, which to the fight appears uniform, there may be a greater variety of Fluids of differing penetrancy, for we find in *Aqua Regis* for inftance, that there are the *Sal Armoniack* parts that help to penetrate Gold ; the *Nitrous* that penetrate Silver, Copper, &c. the *Flegme* that will penetrate neither : There have been few Experiments made of the penetrating of one Fluid by an other, befide that I formerly fhew'd of Water and Oil of *Vitriol*, 'tis a copious Head, and contains much of information ; Copper and Tin melted are an example of it. From which Obfervation we may without difficulty fuppofe the Air (as it is commonly taken) to be a Body confifting of a great variety of Fluids, of which this Æther we fupppfe may be one ; and poffibly the principal which takes up the greateft fpace, and whofe Effects are the fufpenfion of *Mercury* above the height fufpended by the preffure of the Air and the like ; tho' yet I fuppofe it not the fubtileft, there being many Experiments that do feem to require a much more fubtile and penetrant Fluid, of which more elfewhere. The Elaftical Part of the Air that caufes the Phænomena of Springing a Second, the Steams of Bodies a Third, the Nitrous part a Fourth, each of which have feveral degrees of penetrancy, and may poffibly be feveral diftinct Fluids, tho' when blended altogether they make that compound Body, which we call the Element of Air. Now as the Air confifts of a variety of Fluids, fo 'tis not unlikely but that each of thefe may differ in their proportionate quantity, and in their refpective Gravity ; fo that if we fhould take the whole bulk of the Air or Atmofphere we might poffibly find

Tab. 8. Fig. 4.

it made up of divers Fluids, as of the Fluids *A, B, C, D, E, F, G, H,* &c. and each of thefe of differing proprieties, both as to penetrations, Quantities and Gravity, Congruity, and the like ; and that That part of it which is next the Earth might be a compound of the Fluids *A, B, C, D,* and *G, H,* extending to a certain number of Yards above the level of the Sea, the next part of the Atmofphere immediately above it may confift of *B, C, D, E,* and *G, H,* and have nothing of *A,* or *F.* The third Region may confift of *C, D, E, F, G, H,* and have nothing of *A,* or *B :* And this feems probable, Frft, becaufe we find that there are feveral diftinct Surfaces of the Air, upon which the feveral Regions of the Clouds feem to fwim like Froth upon the Surface of Water ; for tis obvious to any that fhall obferve it, to fee the under Surface of the Clouds fmooth and level, and the upper in confus'd heaps, and further, that all the under Surfaces of Clouds appearing at the fame time lye as near as one can judge by the Eye in the very fame Level. Next that the make of the Clouds in a higher Region are quite differing. Thirdly, that the parts of the Air in feveral heights from the Earth, have differing proprieties, as it hath been found in very deep Wells, that the lower twenty Fathoms were all poffefs'd by a Damp, or an Air in which no Fire would burn, or Animal live. We are inform'd alfo, that the Air at the top of fome exceeding high Mountains is of fuch a Nature as will not ferve for Refpiration. Poffibly the prefence of *A,* in the loweft, may be the caufe of the firft Effects and the want of *B,* at the tops of Mountains may be there the caufe of thofe other Effects.

IN the following Lectures the Reader will find a Confirmation of the foregoing Treatise of Earthquakes and their several Effects or Consequences, as likewise of the Corrollaries raised from them, and tho' they are not all here Printed in the order of time they were read, I think that is excusable, since I thought it more proper to joyn those Tracts together that related to the same Subject than interpose others of far different Matters. In these our Author endeavours to confirm his former Hypothesis by Histories; and in the first place by two very remarkable ones, the first that related by Plato in his Timæus, the other that of the Circumnavigation of Hanno the Carthaginian. The next Discourses contain the interpretation of several of the Fables of Ovid's Metamorphosis; how the Learned will receive them I know not, but in my Opinion they are at least very plausibly explain'd.

R. W.

I Have indeavour'd to discover and prove the true Figure of this Body of the Earth upon which we Inhabit, and likewise to give some Conjectures concerning the *Form* and *Shape* of the *Superficial* Parts thereof. This I have done in order to comply as near as I could with a Natural Method of Natural History: This great Body being the Mother of all Terrestial Productions, which make up the greatest part of *Natural History*; and the Foundation, as it were, upon which, not only all that History, but all the other Parts and Superstructures almost do rest; for from the Productions of this we take our Principles, we raise our Axioms and Maxims, we form our Similitudes, we make our Observations, Experiments and Trials, and by Analogy from Comparison and Similitude we deduce our Conclusions. I thought it therefore not improper, since Natural History will carry us into forein Parts of the World, very far remov'd from this our Country of the Earth, to be first of all a little acquainted, at least, with what we have at home, that thereby we may the better be able to observe and judge of what those far remote Parts may present us with, whether they be like our own or not, in what they agree, and in what they differ, that these we know at home may be the Standards and Touch-stones of all the rest we meet withal Abroad.

In prosecution of this Method, I began first to shew what seem'd to me to be the most likely Figure of the whole Body, which I shew'd for several Reasons seem'd to be of a prolated Sphæroidical Figure, not of a perfectly Globular, as most Authors suppose and affirm, much less of an Oblong Oval, as the ingenious Author of the sacred Theory of the Earth, and some others, have indeavour'd to make probable. *Of the Figure of the Earth, &c.*

From this I deduc'd the prolated Sphæroidical Figure of the Waters also, and more eminently of the Air or Atmosphere, and from that deduc'd these Conclusions, That the Lines of Gravitation or Perpendicularity did not tend to one single point, as all hitherto have asserted, but to infinite points in the middle parts of the Axis.

And that a Degree, or a 360th part of the *Æquinoctial* did not agree exactly with any one Degree in a *Meridian*, and thence that the Magnitudes of the respective Parallels were not to be estimated as if the Body were truly Globular.

From this I deduc'd a necessity of a differing Gravitation of the same Body in differing parts of the Earth, and thence a necessity of a differing length of Pendulums to measure by their Vibrations the same quantity of time, by which the universal Standard of Measure, by some suppos'd from the length of a Pendulum, became questionable and dubious.

I have likewise shewn what Observations of Celestial Bodies were likely to be assistant to the perfecting and confirming of these Matters, at least of discovering the Truth whether really so or not.

I have also inquir'd concerning the fixedness and instability of the Terrestial Axis, and shewn some Arguments to induce us to believe that it may have and suffer a mutation, and not be always fixt in the same parts of the Earth, and by what methods that may be ascertain'd in a short time with more exactness than

than many Ages of Observations made with less accurateness would have done.

And from thence I have deduc'd what would be some of the necessary Consequences of such a mutation; such as the differing Latitude of places in differing Ages. The differing Azymuth of Places as to one anothers Position; the differing Altitudes of Places with respect to the Superficies of the Sea, as the Emerging of some places from below that Surface and the sinking under, and the being overwhelm'd by that Surface in others, and consequently of changing the Nature, Soil, Climate, &c. of the superficial Parts of the Surface; to which, as I conceiv'd, some alterations might be ascribed.

But Lastly, I shew'd that the ruggedness and inequalities of Hills and Dales, Mountains and Lakes, and also the alterations of these superficial Parts of the Earth, as to the seeming Irregularities thereof at present, seem'd to me to be most probably ascribable to another Cause, which was Earthquakes and Subterraneous Eruptions of Fire. That there had been many such alterations I indeavour'd to prove from the almost universal Disposition of those curious Medals of former Ages now found in the petrify'd Monuments of the parts of several both Terrestial and Aquatick Animals and Vegetables, but especially by those Productions of the watery Element found in places now far remov'd from the Sea, and far above its Level; of which I have produc'd several Instances, some of which, and those very considerable, were procur'd by the inquisitiveness of a Person here present.

I have made some Excursions out of this Method; as First, in order to answer the Doubts and Scruples of some, and the Obloquies of some other Persons, who, I hope, are now, or will be somewhat better satisfy'd, which I wish all might be, for I have no desire to impose Conjectures and Inquiries as Demonstrations, but only to shew what Arguments have inclin'd me to be of these Opinions, which, whether sufficient, I must leave to their better Judgments and Examinations, hoping at least that no prepossession will hinder them from examining them with Candor and Indifference, as I indeavour to do in all my Inquiries. Next by some Experiments made for the clearing some accidental Discourses at the meeting, as those about the best ways of communicating force at a distance, and of making a Pendulum to observe by Trials the Velocities of the parts of Pendulous Vibration, and to make a Pendulum that shall, without Clock-work, continue moving twelve Hours or longer. And Thirdly, By accidental Observations made of the growth of Trees and some others; nor will it, I hope, be taken amiss that I indeavour to produce such Arguments as occur to me, that seem to favour these Conjectures, tho' possibly much better may be shewn by others eithers for or against them; however give me leave to alledge what I can to answer such as I conceive are not sufficiently cogent Arguments against what I have supposed.

One of the most considerable Objections I have yet heard, is, that History has not furnish'd us with Relations of any such considerable changes as I suppos'd to have happen'd in former Ages of the World; I do confess our Natural History as to these and many other matters of the first Ages is very thin and barren, but yet I conceive not wholly devoyd of Instances, nay, possibly if they be look'd into with a little more attention than hitherto has been used, they may be found to contain many more than has of late Ages been imagin'd. Some things of this kind, I fancy I have detected, of which I shall produce some, together with some Remarks upon them, which I have added, they are, I conceive, related as true Histories; but whether so or not I must leave others to judge who are better Antiquaries and Criticks.

An Account of the Atlantis out of Plato's Timæus. What Learning and Accounts of Ancient Times the *Ægyptians* might have in their Histories, who are said by *Plato* in his *Timæus*, to have had accounts of great alterations in the World for nine thousand Years before *Solon*, which is now above two thousand Years since, it is very hard to guess from that short account that is there given of it; yet since of all the Records that are to be met within the Ancient Historians to this purpose, this is the most considerable, I thought it would not be improper to relate it on this occasion, by reason that tho' it should be accounted *fabulous*, as some have thought, and

to

to be only a Fiction in *Plato* in order to lay a Scene for his Republick; yet there is fo much of Probability in it (bating only his number of Years) and fo much of Reafon and Agreement with the State of things, that if it be not a true Hiftory, it will at leaft fhew that *Plato* himfelf had, at that time, fome fuch Notion or Imagination of the *Preceding State of the Earth*, and that he faw, or found at leaft, fome very good Arguments for his being fo ; *Plato* then in his Dialogue maketh *Critias* thus fpeak, ' Hear, O *Socrates*, a won-
' derful indeed, but yet a true Hiftory, which *Solon*, the wifeft of the feven
' Wife Men, related to my Grandfather *Critias*, as the old Man hath fince
' told me ; among other things he told me of the memorable Actions of this
' City *(Athens)* by length of Time, and Death of many, quite obliterated.
' But among the reft he related one remarkable Paffage, which I think now
' proper to acquaint you with, and it was an old Hiftory, which he being
' then about ninty Years old, told to me when I was about Ten, upon a folemn
' Day, when I, with divers other Boys, as the Cuftom was, were wont to re-
' cite divers Verfes by Heart to fee which could excel, among which were
' divers Verfes of *Solon :* And I remember I heard my Grandfather then fay,
' that if *Solon* had but committed to Verfe, not what he did for refrefhing
' of his Mind, but ferioufly, and like other Poets, the Hiftory, which he,
' returning out of *Egypt*, refolv'd to have written (from which, by difturbances
' which he met with at home, he was interrupted in perfecting) neither *Ho-*
' *mer, Hefiod*, nor any other Poet, would have been comparable to him. This
' was of the greateft Affair that had been tranfacted by this City, of which
' we have no remains at prefent, by reafon of the length and injury of Time.
' The fumm of what I remember was, That *Solon* going into *Egypt* to *Saim*, at the
' Mouth of the *Nile*, when *Amafis* was King, was there receiv'd honourably.
' There he inquiring of thofe Priefts which were moft fkilful in thofe Matters
' concerning the Memorials of great Antiquity, found, as he related, that
' neither himfelf nor any other Greek knew any thing of Antiquity; and
' when he to provoke the Priefts to tell him fome of their Knowledge, had, in
' there prefence, fpoken concerning the moft antient Actions of the *Athenians*
' of *Phoroneus* and *Niobe*, and of *Pyrrha* and *Deucalion*, after the inundation of
' the World, and of the times when thofe had happen'd ; one of the Seniors
' of the Priefts cried, O *Solon, Solon*, you Greeks are all Boys, not one Old
' Man among you. *Solon* afking him why fo? The Prieft anfwer'd, beeaufe
' you have young Heads always that contain nothing of ancient Hiftory,
' of ancient Opinion, or of Old Mens Science, which has happen'd to you by
' reafon that there have been already, and fhall be many and various De-
' ftructions of Men : But the greateft of all will be caus'd neceffarily, either
' by a Conflagation of Fire, or an Inundation of Water ; but the leffer by
' innumerable other Calamities : For what you tell of *Phaeton*, the Son of the
' Sun to have got into his Father's Chariot, and not knowing how to Drive
' like his Father, had fired the Earth, and with that Flame had almoft fet
' Fire to the Heavens, tho' it may feem fabulous, yet 'tis not without its
' truth in fome fenfe. For in long procefs of time there is a certain *permuta-*
' *tion of the Cæleftial Motions which a vaft Inflammation muft neceffarily follow.*
' Whence fuch as inhabit high and dry Places will fuffer more than fuch as are
' nearer the Sea and Rivers. Now our *Nile*, as it is in moft other things ve-
' ry wholefome for us, fo will it preferve us from fuch a Deftruction. But
' when the Gods of the Waters fhall wafh away the Filth of the Earth by a
' Flood, thofe which feed Sheep and other Cattle at the tops of the Moun-
' tains will fcape the danger; but your Cities that are fituated in the Plains,
' by the impetuofity of fuch Floods will be fwept into the Sea. But in our
' Region we have no Water defcends from above, but all ours fprings out of
' the very Bowels of the Earth ; which is the reafon that with us the Re-
' cords and Monuments of the moft antient things are fafely preferved.
' Whence it comes to pafs, that where neither too great a Storm of Rain
' nor any extraordinary Fire happens, tho' fometimes more, fometimes fewer,
' yet ftill fome Men always efcape. Now whatever we hear that is worthy
' notice, either acted by our felves, you, or any other Nation we keep defcrib-
' ed in our Temples : With you indeed, and other Nations things lately

' done have been committed to Writing, and preserved by other Monu-
' ments. But in certain periods of Time there come from the Heavens cer-
' tainDestructions which depopulate all; whence the followingGenerations are
' depriv'd both of Letters and Learning. Whence you are all again made
' Boys, rude, and altogether ignorant of preceding Matters. Hence 'tis that
' what but now you speak of, O *Solon*, differs very little from Childish Fa-
' bles. First, In that you make mention but of one Inundation, whereas
' many have preceeded. Next, That the stock of your Ancestors which was
' most Eminent, and of the best, you know nothing of; whence both thy self
' and the other *Atheneans* had your Birth, which was a small Remnant that
' scaped the publick Destruction: Which becomes unknown to you; for that
' this Remnant and their Posterity for many Years wanted the use of Let-
' ters; whereas your City before that had excelled both in the Arts of War
' and Peace, of which we had a full account. [So he proceeds to tell how
they had Records of their own City for nine Thousand Years, and of the
Laws, *&c.* as also, of long times for *Athens*, which I pass over, and only
mention what seems to relate to Natural History.] He proceeds then,
' Many wonderful Actions of your City are preserved in our Monuments;
' but one above the rest for Greatness and Virtue exceeds; for 'tis said, that
' your City resisted a numberless company of Enemies, which coming out of
' the Country where the *Atlantick-Sea* now is, had conquer'd almost all *Eu-*
' *rope* and *Asia*; for at that time was that navigable Streight which is call'd
' that of *Hercules Pillers* which had near the Mouth, and as it were in the
' very entrance of it, an Island then said to be bigger than *Lybia* and *Asia*,
' through which was a Passage to other Neighbouring Islands, and from the
' Islands was a prospect to the main Lands lying near the Shoar, but the
' Mouth of the Streights was very narrow. This Sea was truly the Ocean,
' and the Land was truly a Continent. In this *Atlantick Island* was a most
' great and wonderful Power of Kings, who Rul'd over, not only that whole
' Isle and many others, but over the greatest part of the Continent, and e-
' ven over those which were near us, for they Reigned over a third part of the
' World, which is call'd *Lybia* even unto *Ægypt*, and over *Europe* even to the
' *Tyrrhene* Sea; the whole power of these collected together, invaded both
' ours and your Country, and even all the Lands within the *Herculean*
' Streights, but both your and our Country repell'd them; the manner I o-
' mit. Afterwards by a prodigious Earthquake and Inundation which hap-
' pened in a Day and a Night, the Earth cleaving swallow'd up all those War-
' like Men, and this Island of *Atlantis* was drown'd by a vast Inundation of
' the Sea, by which means that Sea became unnavigable, by reason of the Mud
' of that sunken Island which was left. the rest I omit.' Now,

Whether this Relation be a Fiction or Romance invented by *Plato*, or a
true History, I shall not now dispute, only by all the Circumstances of *Plato*'s
relating of it, I conceive he design'd to have it to be reputed a true History
and not a Romance, for that his design for laying a Scheme for his imaginary
Government, needed no such Fiction, and accordingly he made very little, if
any, use of the Circumstances of it that relate to Natural History. However, be it what it will, it evidently shews that *Plato* did suppose and believe
that there had been in many preceding Ages of the World, very great changes
of the superficial Parts of the Earth by Floods, Deluges, Earthquakes, *&c.*
for as much as he could suppose a Continent or Island as big as the third part
of the known Earth, to be by one Earthquake sunk into the Sea and overwhelmed by it.

I think therefore I may at least conclude, that divers of the Antients, and
particularly *Plato*, had some knowledge of past Catastrophys of some parts of
the World. And those to have been caus'd by Earthquakes and fiery Eruptions, such as had sunk some places into the Sea and rais'd other places out of
it, of great Floods also and Inundations by Rains and Eruptions of the Sea:
And that some of those had happened in *Greece*, others without the Streights
Mouth, and others elsewhere, and at another opportunity I shall produce a
Cloud of Witnesses to this effect which, I conceive, will put it past dispute.
but because this Relation has been possibly too long, I shall only add one Relation

lation more, becaufe it feems to relate to the remainders of the Ifland of *Atlantis*, and it feems to be of a later date much than the *Egyptian* Stories.

That which I mean is the Hiftory of the *Periplus* of *Hanno* the *Carthaginian*. When it was writ I know not, but fure it was very ancient, 'tis lately in the Year 1674, Publifh'd by *Abrahamus Berkelius*, with fome fragments of *Stephanus Byzantinus*, with the Commentaries of *Gefnerus* and *Bochart*, being but fhort I have put it into Englifh.

It pleas'd the *Carthaginians* that *Hanno* fhould fail beyond the Columns of *Hercules* and build *Lybyphenician* Cities, he went then with fixty fail of Ships each rowed with fifty Oars, in thefe were tranfported to the number of 30 Thoufand Men and Women with neceffary Provifion and Stores. After we had failed two Days without the Columns; the firft City we built we call'd *Thymiaterium*; under this lay a large Plain, thence carried Weftward we made *Solunte* a Cape of *Lybia* cover'd with Wood, where having built a Fane to *Neptune*, we tacked about and failed ϖρὸς ἥλιον towards the South, half a Days fail into a Lake not far from the Sea; filled with many and large Canes, where were fed Elephants and various other wild Beafts; having paffed this Lake in one Days fail, we built thofe Maritime Cities, *viz. Caricus, Gytte, Acra, Meliffa* and *Aranibys*; failing thence we arriv'd at the great River *Lixus* which falls out of *Libya*. Near this the *Nomades* (a fort of Grafiers or Cattle-herds) and *Lixitæ* feed their Cattle, with thefe having made Friendfhip we ftay'd fometime. Beyond this the favage *Æthiopians* live, whofe Country is full of wild Beafts, and intercepted with great Mountains from which the *Lixus* flows. Thofe Mountains the *Trogloditæ* inhabit a ftrong fort of People fwifter in Running than Horfes, as the *Lixitæ* told us. From hence we coafted two Days Southwards, and then one Day more Περὸς ἥλιον and in a Bay found a fmall Ifland five Stadia in Compafs, where we left fome Planters and called it *Cerne*; this, by the Journal of our Voyage, we judged to be in the fame parallel with *Carthage*, and as far without the Columns as *Carthage* was within. Hence we enter'd a great Lake, through which paft a great River, which we called *Chrefes*. There we found three Iflands bigger than *Cerne*. From thefe in a Days Voyage we reach'd the inermoft parts of the Lake: It was incompaffed with vaft Mountains, inhabited by Savages, who threw Stones at us. Thence failing we paft a large River full of Crocodiles and Hippopotams, and return'd to *Cerne*. From hence we paft twelve Days by the Coaft towards the South, all inhabited by *Æthiopians*, much afraid of us, and not underftood by our Interpreters; the laft day we difcover'd great Mountains covered with Woods, which were of various Kinds and Odoriferous. Coafting round thefe Mountains we found an immenfe opening of the Sea, that fide which was next the Continent was a plain Country, from whence by Night we perceived Fires from all places, fome greater fome leffer Watering here we Coafted along for five Days till we came to a great Bay, which they called Ἑόϖέρν κεϱς Here we found Lakes and Iflands, where landing we found nothing by Day but Woods, but in the Night we faw many Fires, and heard an innumerable noife of Drums, Trumpets, Cymbals, and the like; wherefore being afrighted, and our South-fayers commanding us alfo to leave it, we Coafted χωϱαν διάϖοϱον θυμιαμάϭων the burning Coaft of ftinking Vulcano's, from whence there run out into the Sea Rivers of Fire, and the Earth was fo burning hot that our Feet could not indure it. Hence therefore we hafted and for a Days fail we faw all the Land full of Fires in the Night; but in the middle of thefe was one vaftly bigger than the reft, fo that it feem'd to touch the Stars; this, in the Daytime, we found to be a prodigious high Mountain call'd θεῶν ὄχημα or the Chariot of the Gods, in three Days fail more we paft all the fiery Rivers, *&c*.

The reafon why I have been fo particular in tranflating the whole Story, is becaufe I conceive it is an inftance in Hiftory fo confiderable, efpecially as to the preceding Relation of *Plato*, that I can hardly believe there is a better Inftance to be found. *Plato* tells us of the Ifland of the *Atlantis* that it was by an Earthquake fome Thoufands of Years before him funk into the Sea, but yet fo that it left many Lakes and unnavigable Places. This gives us a

The Hiftory of Hanno's Circumnavigation

Re-

Relation of a Navigation (over the very place where the *Atlantis* was placed and sunk by the former Relation) in the times of *Philip* of *Macedon*, or sooner, as some suppose; these Navigators find the Coast of *Africa* without the Mouth of the Streights to trend Westward almost πρὸς ἑσπέραν *ad Occasum*. *Gesner*, in his Notes upon this place, seems a little startled, and says, *Atqui mihi videtur ambientibus Africam omnis post columnas Navigatio converti vel ad Meridiem vel ad Orientem & postremo ad aquilonem*; not thinking, I suppose, of this Supposition. He seems also to be as much to seek about the situation of *Cerne*, but at last he thinks it may be the *Maderas* (p. 85.) which I conceive to have lain North-westward from it, but with divers Gulphs and Bays in which were divers great Lakes and Islands, divers Mountains likewise and some Rivers. But which is most considerable, a great part of this Island to the South was then all on Fire. Now comparing this Relation to the present State of those parts, we find all that Continent which they passed by between the Columns and *Cerne*, to be wanting, for 'twill be hard to reconcile the Relation with the present State of that Country, so in probability sunk and cover'd with the Sea; for *Cerne* by this Description, lying in the same Latitude with *Carthage*, and as far from the Pillars without as *Carthage* was within, it must have lain to the North or North-west of the *Maderas*, from which place the Coast of the main Land seemed then to trend South for twelve Days Voyage as far as the *Canary Islands* are now found, or somewhat farther, from whence it turned away to the Eastward. About these Islands, I conceive, was the Land that was all on Fire, multitudes of which they saw in the Night, and heard the noise of the Vulcanes, and Rivers of Fire running into the Sea, and in some places found the Earth so hot as to burn their Feet. That which directs me the better in this Conjecture, is the prodigious *Vulcano* mention'd, called θεῶν ὄχημα the Chariot of the Gods, by reason of its prodigious height, seeming to touch the Stars. This, in all probability, seems to have been the same with the present *Pike* of *Tenarif*, which tho' it burns not now, yet, yet there are present Evidences enough, as I have been told by those who have been at the top of it, to prove it to have formerly been a *Vulcano*. And if they had now been wanting, yet no longer since than *Sebastian Munster*'s time it was known to be so, and in his Geography he has so described it. Besides, this by late Example, as in 1639, and by a latter in *Ferro*, which I have Printed, it appears, that those Vulcanoes are not Strangers to those Parts even in this Age: But I have detained you too long with those Conjectures, yet if all Circumstances be examined in the Relation of *Plato*'s *Atlantis*, and in that of *Hanno*'s *Periplus* and compar'd with the present Condition of those Parts, I conceive there will appear many Reasons to make us conclude that there have been in those parts prodigious alterations somewhat like those I have supposed in my Hypothesis, which may serve as an instance of History for such Mutations. The next opportunity I shall produce many other, which, I conceive, will as plainly speak the same thing, according to the Mind and Intention of most of the Ancients, and this is to take off the odium of Novelty.

After the foregoing Passages quoted out of *Plato*'s *Timaus* and the *Periplus* of *Hanno*, I shall adventure to present this illustrious Assembly with some of my Conjectures at the meaning of the Fables of the Poets, but first to say something as to that of *Plato* and of the *Periplus*, which last is suppos'd by several Authors to be very Ancient. From both those Relations compar'd together, there seems at least to result a probability, that there has been some great changes of the superficial Parts of the Earth, where the now *Atlantick* Ocean without the Streights of *Gibraltar*, as they are now call'd, is; and then we have certain Histories now to prove that the main of *Africa* or *Libya* hath extended Westward beyond the *Maderas*, and Southward as far as somewhat farther than the *Canaries*. I have given the Reasons why I entertain'd those Conjectures, which I submit to the Judgment of such as are more knowing and better read in Historical Matters.

Varro

Varro has distributed the Ages of the World into three, *viz.* the ἄδηλον, μυθικον, and ἱσοριμὸν of the ἄδηλὸν we know nothing from Heathen Writers; of the μυθικὸν we must look for an account from the Fables of the Poets, *Homer, Hesiod, Ovid,* &c. *Ovid,* to pass by *Hesiod* and *Homer,* is said to have imitated the Greek Poet *Parthenius,* and has left us a very large History of the changes that had anciently happened in the World, his whole Metamorphosis, being, as I take it, written for that purpose: We are extreamly obliged to *Pliny* and some few others, as all well know, for what they had collected out of others, or wrote from their own Observation and Knowledge.

Now, that *Ovid's* Metamorphosis was penned for this end we may find by the 4 first Verses.

In nova fert animus mutatas dicereformas
Corpora, Dii cæptis (nam vos mutastis & illas)
Aspirate meis, primaq; ab origine mundi
In mea perpetuum deducite tempora carmen.

I sing of Beings in new shapes array'd,
Assist ye Gods (for you the Changes made,)
That from the Worlds Beginning to these Times
I may comprize their Series in my Rimes.

That is the time of *Augustus Cæsar* in which he Lived.

The Hypothesis in *Ovid* (for I conceive it only an Hypothesis in him) is this, that the præ-existent Matter of the World was first, a quantity of Matter without any particular form, *Rudis indigestaq; moles,* a rude disorder'd Mass, and yet it had the property in it which (when directed afterwards to some Center) was weight, which as yet he calls *Pondus iners* unactive weight. Secondly, It had in it the seminal Principles, which were afterwards to effect the Productions, these he calls *discordia semina rerum,* the jarring Seeds of things, as being then *non bene junctarum,* not well conjoined, no not to form the Sun, Moon, or the Earth, the primary or secundary Planets, *Nec cirsumfuso pendebat in aere Tellus, ponderibus librata suis,* nor did the self-poiz'd Earth encompast round hang in soft Air; these Verses do seem to glance at an *Hypothesis* I have formerly acquainted this Society with, somewhat of which Mr. *Newton* hath Printed. *Tellus, Pontus & Aer,* Earth, Water, and Air were yet all confounded with each other, like Mortar or Mud. *Instabilis Tellus innabilis unda.* The Earth unstable, Waves for Keels unfit, which it comes to attain afterwards, and remains so for sometime, till by degrees again it lost it when *Astræa* left it, which was just before the Gygantomachia; for *Astræa,* as I shall by and by make appear, is the Virgin and primitive Smoothness and Stability of the superficial Parts of the Earth, from (α) the first or Primitive, as (α and ω) *Alpha* and *Omega,* and σερνα stability, *Et Virgo cæde madentes ultima Cælicolum terras Astræa reliquit.* The last of Deities from Blood polluted Earth *Astræa* flies; for like moist Pap or Mud, by degrees the watery and Aerial exhaleing, it settled into a smooth, tender, and uniform Substance, like the Youthful and Virgine Constitution, but a farther separation of the Fluid Parts makes the Earthy, Dry, Rough, Rincled and Chopt; inclining to the Countenance and Constitution of Age, and the Virgin Beauty is fled: For a while there was a jumble, *Corpore in uno, frigida pugnabant Calidis, humentia siccis, mollia cum duris,* the Cold, the Hot; the Moist, the Dry ones fight; the Soft, the Hard, all incorporated strove together, *Sine pondere habentia pondus* with weight, yet weightless, that is, they all being Bodies had a capacity of being weighty, but a gravitating or attracting Center not yet being existent, they had no actual Gravity any way; but so soon as *hanc Deus & melior litem Natura diremit,* God and the better Nature ends this War; that is, God and Nature had made the gravitating Center, presently the heavier descend towards it, the lighter rise from it

Et Cælo tærras & terris abscidit Undas
Et liquidum sprisso secrevit ab aere cælum.

From Sky the Earth, thence Floods divided were,
And liquid Æther from the thicker Air.

The Atmosphere inclosed the Ball, and was distinct from the Æther; 'tis remarkable that he makes the Water the lowest in this and the following Account.

Ignea convexi vis & sine pondere Cœli
Emicuit.

Of the convex and weightless Heav'n the bright
And fiery Power shin'd forth.

He seems to make it by the word *Emicuit* to be at the first encompassed with a shining Fire like a Star or Sun, for its place was *in arce*, above all; within this was Air.

Proximus est aer illi levitate locoque.

The next to this in weight and place is Air.

The Earth is assigned next.

Densior his Tellus Element aq; grandia traxit,
Et pressa est gravitate sui.

Prest by its weight Earth sinks, to which repair
The heavier Elements.

And the Water lowest.

————Circumfluus humor
Ultima possedit solidumq; coercuit orbem.
The Floods at last sink in
From every side, yet leave a spherick Skin.

So that it seems there was a notion that the middle part of the Ball of the Earth was filled with Water as well as the outside covered with it: To which also agrees *Des Cartes* Theory and that of the ingenious Dr. *Burnet* in his *Theoria Sacra.* Thus far, I suppose, it will easily be granted that the Poet gives us a short History of the formation of the Earth, and 'tis as plain that the twenty eight Verses following are to the same effect, wherein he describes the cutting and forming the Face of the Earth into Lakes, Seas, Rivers, Hills, Dales, &c. the dividing the whole into Zones, and assigning the use of Air, for Clouds, Rain, &c. nor has he yet Personated or Mithologized any thing, but in the twenty ninth Verse following, *viz.* The sixtieth Verse of this first Book he begins calling the Winds Brothers, *Tanta est discordia fratrum,* &c. the Sense of all the rest is plain till the eighty second Verse, where he begins again to personate Actions Mythologically; for speaking of the formation of Man,

————Natus homo est, &c.
Sive recens tellus seductaq; nuper ab alto
Æthere cognati retinebat semina Cœli;
Quam satus Japeto, mistam fluvialibus undis,
Finxit in effigiem moderantum cuncta Deorum.

Man's Born, *&c.*

> --------*Or th' Earth new gain'd*
> *From nobler Æther, some Seeds still retain'd*
> *To Heav'n ally'd, which Earth* Prometheus *took*
> *And mixt with Waters of a living Brook*
> *Made Man like th' all-commanding Deities.*

From this place onwards he seems to Mythologize the most part of his History, of which he gives notice in the eighty sixth and eighty seventh Verses.

> *Sic modo quæ fuerat rudis & sine imagine Tellus*
> *Induit ignotas hominum conversa Figuras.*

> *So what was rude and shapeless Earth, puts on*
> *When chang'd, the unknown Character of Man.*

Hitherto he had spoken of things as Dead and Unactive Earth, but from hence forth he will describe the Earth as changed and clothed with the various shapes of Men and Persons, and so having described the Formation or first Generation of all things Physically and plainly, he comes next to tell the Age or Ages of the World, and what Periods of Life or Being it hath had, and the States it hath been in during those several Periods.

The first Age or Chilhood of the World he calls the Golden Age : Gold is soft, flexible the most ductile of Metals, it has the best Lustre, and has always had the greatest Esteem. This state of the Earth he represents to be like that of Childhood, wherein all things are gay and pleasant, all things flow plentifully and smoothly; the Skin or Shell is yet smooth, succulent and soft, moisture and heat abound; so that things sprouted forth and flourish : There is a continued Spring, all things are Budding, Blossoming, and bearing Fruit at the same time, no need of Art as yet to help the progress of Nature forwards; or to regulate it, no one part of Nature intrenched, invaded, or hindred the free progress of another; there was plenty and enough, for all Rivers flowed with Milk and Nectar, and Honey drop'd from the Leaves of Trees.

All these Poetical Expressions, which the Author seemeth to speak, as of Men, and their Actions, and Enjoyments, I take to be significative of all acting Powers of the Earth whether Vegetative or Animal, *Per se dabat omnia tellus, Ver erat æternum. Sponte sua sine lege fidem Rectumq; colebant.* The Earth gave all things of itself, Spring was Eternal, and Justice observ'd without Law, *&c.*

Now, tho' all that happened in those times of the World, fell within the Age which *Varro* calls the *Adelon Tempus*; that is unknown as to the Heathen Writers, yet I look upon this Account almost as considerable, if not more, than those things which fall within the Mythologick ; for I take this to be the Summe and Epitomy of the Thoughts and Theories of the most ancient and most knowing Philosophers among the *Ægyptians* and *Greeks* ; and howmuchsoever there may be some who slight and neglect and villify the Knowledge, Doctrines and Theories of the Ancients, which Humor I am apt to think proceeds from their ignorance of what they were, and the difficulty of attaining the knowledge of them : Yet certainly former times wanted not for Men altogether as eminent for Knowledge, Invention, and Reasoning as any this present Age affords, if not far before them ; for if we do believe a time of the Creation or Production of this Earth (as we have somewhat more of Argument to persuade us than possibly the Heathens had from the History thereof written by *Moses*) then 'tis very rational to conclude, that in the more Youthful Ages of the World, there was a much greater Perfection of the Productions of it, and that before those many and great Alterations and Catastrophies that have since happened, and before the senile Iron and decaying Ages of the same, wherein every thing by degrees grew more Stiff,

Rocky,

Rocky, Unactive and Barren, and fo a degeneration of the Productions there-by feems a neceffary Confequent. In the times, I fay, that preceded all or many of thefe, it feems very rational to conclude, that it might produce Men of much longer Life, bigger Stature, and with greater accomplifhments of Mind (of all which we have very good Teftimonies without the Argumen-tations, Hiftories, Traditions or Theories of the Heathen Writers) upon which account tho' this Defcription of the Genefis of the Earth, and the firft Age of the World fhould be fuppofed to be but the Theory or Philofophy of fome of the moft eminent Men, as *Orpheus*, *Pythagoras*, &c. in Ages fo much nearer to thofe more active Ages of the Earth, yet, upon that ac-count, they may, I conceive, be well worth our inquiring into, to fee, at leaft, how Confonant thofe things are which they thought Reafon, to that of ours at this prefent. Some poffibly may be of *Ariftotle*'s Opinion that the Earth was eternal: But I am apt to think that fuch as are fo, have not fo fully confulted their own Reafon and Experience, nor much troubled them-felves with that Speculation. We found that the *Ægyptian* Priefts by that Paf-fage I quoted out of *Plato*, had the notion of the *Genefis* Mutations, Cata-ftrophies, by Fire and Water, and the like of the Earth, if we will not allow them to have the Hiftory of them, or the Accounts of fo many 1000 Years as *Plato* mentions. But it will by fome be required perhaps, by what means can we judge of any fuch preceding Age? I anfwer, That poffibly the petrified Shells that lye in the Repofitory, and the prodigious Bones and Teeth that have been found buried in the Earth, of which the Repofitory affords fome inftances, and more might be fetched elfewhere: Thefe, I fay, might to fome unprejudiced Men prove Arguments, but for others 'tis beft to let them enjoy their own Thoughts. But to return to the Subject I was indeavouring to prove, namely, That the Metamorphofis of *Ovid* was a continued account of the Ages and Times of the duration of the Earth. I fay, fo far as I have gone, namely, to the end of the Golden Age, none will doubt but that this was the defign of it, to relate what were the moft celebrated Opinions con-cerning its Formation and firft Ages, and as I conceive more particularly that of *Pythagaros*, who had fpread and left his Doctrines in *Italy* long before *Ovid*'s time.

We come next to the 313 Verfe where he begins to give an account, tho' very fhort, of the Youthful time of the Earth, which he calls the Silver Age. *Poftquam Saturno tenebrofa in Tartara miffo, Sub Jove Mundus erat, Subiitq; ar-gentea proles.* After a long time was paft and buried in Obfcurity, the World had got a new Face and was under the Regiment of *Jupiter*, which fignified the *Æther* and *Celeftial Fire*; before this 'tis faid in the Golden or Infant Age of the World, *Ver erat æternum; placidiq; repentibus auris, mulcebant Zephiri natos fine femine flores.* The Air and Earth was moift and tepid, which made a continual Spring, but now that moifture is dried up, and fervour, heat and drinefs is got into the Air. *Subiit argentea proles*, now *Jupiter antiqui contraxit tempora veris, perq; hiemes æftufq; & inæquales Autumnos, & brene Ver, Spatiis exegit quatuor annum.* This ingrefs of *Jupiter* caufed thofe ftrange changes in the Air, that we in part now feel; for 'tis not immediately the heat of the Sun that makes that difference in the heat of the Air, tho' that be alfo a Caufe. But as I fhall have occafion to treat in an other place 'tis the Confti-tution of the Air, nor is it the oblique Radiation (as all which one confent af-firme) nor the nearnefs to, or diftance from the Sun, but it is the ingrefs of *Jupiter* that makes the Air fufceptible of thefe Mutations. *Tunc primum fiecis aer fervoribus uftus canduit*, &c. then entered Lightening and extraordinary Heats; and fo he proceeds in the defcription of the other Seafons and Con-ftitutions of Air, *Semina tum primnm longis cereolia Sulcis, obrnta funt*, &c. The Earth being now dried having loft much of its Infant foftnefs and moi-fture, needed fome helps to make the Seeds grow. After this iuvenile Age was paft over, then *Tertia poft illem fucceffit a henea proles, Sævior Ingenio & ad hor-rida prompior arma, non Sclerata tamen.* All the aforefaid Qualities increafed, the Earth growing drier and drier, and the Air more intmperate, but yet it pro-duced no direful Effects of terraneous or aerial Cataftrophies. But *De Duro eft ultima ferro.* Now the Shell of the Earth is Petrified, and the Iron Con-

ftitution

ftitution is introduced, all its Rocks and Iron Mines. *Protinus Erupit venæ pejoris in ævum omne Nefas.* Then followed all the difmal effects of Subterraneous and Superterraneous Diffentions, Conflagrations, Floods, Earthquakes, the Sea overwhelming the Lands, and the Lands getting out from under the Seas, here Iflands, there Lakes, here Mountains, there Voragoes and Abyffes, and multitudes of other Confufions which rafed and mangled the fuperficial Parts of the Earth, fo that no place was free from the effects of thefe difcordant Principles. *Aftrea*, as I faid before, which fignified the Virgin, *Juvenile* fmooth, foft, and even Face and Conftitution of the Earth which it firft received from the gentle Influence of the Heavens, and preferved in the Infant, *Juvenile* and pretty well in the Virile or brazen Ages. Now, that the Earth was arrived to its old Age, Wrinkles, Chops, Furrows, Scarrs, and the like, had not left one fpot of *Aftrea* unblemifh'd, then fhe is faid to have left it. This is a fhort account of this Iron or old Age of the World, of which I fuppofe the whole following Metamorphofis is written; this in good part falling within the Mythologick Hiftory of the Poets, but the Genefis and three preceding Ages, I look upon to belong to *Varroe's* Ἄδηλον *tempus*, and to be the Epitome of the Theories of the moft antient and moft approv'd Philofophers. This I could in part prove, as I could alfo many other Paffages of this Difcourfe, by Quotations out of other Authors among the Antient, and alfo by the confent of many more Modern Writers. But that poffibly might feem too tedious, and I doubt not but there are others who having more applied their Studies that way will do it more fully. The firft of the memorable events of the Iron or old Age of the World is defcribed in the next following Verfes.

Neve foret terris fecurior arduus Æther,
Affectaffe ferunt Regnum cælefte Gigantes
Altaq; congeftos ftruxiffe ad fydera montes.

But leaft high Heav'n fhould unattempted reft,
Afpiring Thoughts the Giants Minds poffeft,
Mountains they rais'd 'gainft the ætherial Throne.

Now the difmal effects of the old Age of the Earth appear, the outward *Of the Fable of* Shell of the Earth being now hardned and petrified, and the Pores of Ema- *the Giants.* nation ftoped fo that the fiery and watery Vapours and Rarefactions below the fame, could not now find their ufual tranfits; thefe are faid to confpire againft Heaven to break out of that Prifon of *Tartarus*, where *Jupiter* had lately thruft down and inclofed *Saturn, Saturno tenebrofa in tartara miffo*, and to force their Paffage into the open Heaven, where *Jupiter* now prevails; thefe therefore fermenting together had raifed the fubterraneous Parts into many Cavities and *Cryptæ*, and therefore were faid to have a thoufand Hands, being fo many Caverns and far extending *Cryptæ*, wherein thefe fubterraneous Sprits convened, in which lay their ftrength; and becaufe fuch *Cryptæ* are winding and not ftreight, they were called *Anguipedes* like Snakes; thefe at laft break forth and make Mountains, lay *Pelion* upon *Offa, Altaq; congeftos ftruxere ad fidera montes.* Then *Jupiter* is faid to have rent the Heavens with his Lightning and to have buried them at laft with Mountains heaped on them; that is, thefe Vapours having made Eruptions and thereby carried the Earth up with them, fo as to make Mountains one of the top of the other, the Vapour got into the Air where it produced hideous Lightning and fo fpent it felf in the Air, and the Mountains being left, and the Vapours that raifed them fpent, *Jupiter* is faid to have deftroyed them and buried them under thofe Mountains: One of thefe is faid to be buried under *Sicily*, and to breath through the Mountain *Ætna*. But I muft not ftay too long upon the particular Explication of every thing concerning it, it may be fufficient for me at prefent to hint the meaning in general; only 'tis to be noted, that the Blood of thefe produced a generation that was of the fame kind; that is, that the remainders in the Earth were of the fame kind.

Thefe

These remainders of the firft Effects were fo prodigious that they made *Jupiter* groan and grow white hot with Anger, that is, made Thunder and Lightning, and call a Council of the Gods,

> *Terrificam Capitis concuſſit terq; quaterq;*
> *Cæſariem, cum qua terram, Mare, ſydera movit,*
> *Talibus inde modis, ora indignantia ſolvit.*
> *Non Ego, pro mundi Regno magis anxius illa*
> *Tempeſtate fui, qua centum quiſq parabat*
> *Injicere anguipedum captivo brachia Cælo.*

> *The Thund'rer oft this dreadful Treſſes ſhakes,*
> *At which the Heaven, the Earth, and Ocean quakes,*
> *And thus he his affronted Mind expreſt.*
> *Not a more anxious thought my Mind poſſeſt*
> *For the Worlds Empire, when the captive Skies*
> *With hundred Hands the Snake-feet did ſurprize.*

It ſeems this was as great a Conflagration, or Collection of ſubterraneous Spirits, and like to be as dreadful as the preceding, nay greater, for that was but one ſingle Enemy, but one ſmall part to be deſtroyed; but now there is an univerſal defection, all muſt be deſtroy'd; for ſpeaking of the laſt Eruption,

> *Nam quanquam ferus hoſtis erat, tamen illud ab uno*
> *Corpore, & ex una pendebat Origine Bellum.*
> *Nunc mihi, qua totum Nereus circumſonat orbem,*
> *Perdendum eſt mortale genus,* &c.

> *For tho' the firſt was a fierce raging Foe,*
> *From one Original the whole did flow,*
> *And all the War depended on one Head.*
> *Now whereſo'ere the ſilver Waves are ſpread,*
> *I muſt deſtroy Mankind.*

The Fable of the Lycaon *explain'd.* And why muſt all this be? Why *Jupiter* being informed of this deſigned Conſpiracy, coming down found *Lycaon* had laid a deſign to deſtroy not only the *Semidei, Fauni, Nymphæ, Satyri,* and *Sylvni,* that were the terreſtrial Deities of the Plains, Rivers, Woods and Hills; but even *Jupiter* himſelf, who ruled the celeſtial Deities, the Æther, Air and Meteors, all which he had call'd together, who

> *Confremuere omnes ſtudiis ardentibus.*
> *A Murmur rais'd with an inflam'd deſire.*

But who is this *Lycaon?* Λυκάων, as the Word ſignifies, is Diſſolution, the general Congregation of the Sulphureous, Subterraneous Vapours being every where pent in, threaten'd a general Diſſolution and Cataſtrophy of the whole World at once, and ſo would not only overturn Hills, Plains, Rivers and Woods, but ſet on Fire and deſtroy the Air; for, as in another place he expreſſes it,

> *Vis fera Ventorum cæcis incluſa cavernis*
> *Expirare aliqua cupiens, luctataq; fruſtra*
> *Liberiore frui Cælo, cum Carcere Rima.*
> *Nulla foret toto, nec pervia flatibus eſſet,*
> *Extentam tumeſcit humum: Seu Spiritus oris*
> *Tendere Veſicam ſolet.------*

> *Winds raging force within close Caverns pent*
> *Desirous to break out at any Vent,*
> *Long strives in vain t'injoy a freer Field*
> *Of Air, the well-clos'd Pris'ns no Crannys yield;*
> *At last it stretches out Earths hide-bound Shell,*
> *As with strong Breath blown up tight Bladders swell.*

The whole Earth was big with these collected, subterraneous, fiery Spirits and watery Exhalations.

> *--------Partim ferventibus artus*
> *Mollit aquis, partim subjecto torruit igne.*

> *-------Part soft with the boyling Waters, part*
> *He roasts with Flames beneath.*

Jupiter therefore descending destroys him *vindice flamma,* that is, fires into Lightning such as had broken out,

> *Territus ipse fugit, nactusq; silentia Ruris*
> *Exululat.*

> *Frighted, to dark and silent Groves he flies*
> *In these he howles aloud.*

This made the subterraneous Vapours fly to other places and make a noise under Ground, and in some places where it broak out, it had

> *-------Veteris vestigia formæ:*
> *Canities eadem est, eadem violentia vultus,*
> *Iidem Oculi lucent, eadem feritatis Imago*

> *He still the marks of his old Form retains:*
> *The same gray Hair, the same stern Look remains,*
> *The same Eyes stare with wildness still the same.*

The same white tops of Mountains, the same gaping devouring Mouth, the same flaming Eyes, the *Caldera* at the top yielding Fire, the same frightful and terrible Aspect, like that of a devouring Wolf; and that this is the meaning of the shape of a Wolf which *Lycaon* is said to be transformed into, is more plain by what is said in the eleventh Book, Verse 365, of *Psamathes* being turned into a Wolf, where *Antenor* is introduced telling a story to *Peleus* of a devouring Wolf destroying Men and Cattle which had come out of the Sea: It will be plain to any that shall read it, that an Earthquake is there meant by the description of the Wolf, but I must not now insist upon it.

But to proceed, there was yet but a stop put to some small *Vulcano* or Eruption which had destroyed but some small Country *de Gente Molossa,* some of which it had overflowed with Water, and destroy'd some other parts with Fire.

> *---------Sed non Domus una perire*
> *Digna fuit, qua terra patet fera regnat Erynnis.*
> *In facinus jurasse putes.*

> *Thus one House perish'd by revenging Flame*
> *Deserv'd by all, the Furies all possess;*
> *You'd think the World conspir'd in Wickedness.*

But this was not sufficient to vent these subterraneous imprison'd Spirits; but an universal Catastrophy was necessary, because *Erynnis* ruled over the whole Globe ; *Jupiter* therefore is said to have considered which way to effect it, whether by an universal Conflagration by fiery Eruptions

Jamq; erat in totas sparsurus fulmina terras,
Sed timuit ne forte sacer tot ab ignibus Æther
Conciperet flammas, totusq; ardesceret Axis.

And now he just was ready to let fly
His Light'ning, but he fear'd the sacred Sky
Should catch the Flame, and Heav'ns whole Axis blaze.

He concludes at last to do it by an Inundation.

But I must not dwell too long upon the Explication, which with this notion will plainly appear to him that reads the Poet's Description. Next this follows the Story of *Python,* which is nothing but the Corruption and ill effects of it from the Mud and Stagnations left by the Flood, which the Sun by its Rays by degrees destroys, drying it up. And the next of *Daphne* turned into a Laurel by *Apollo,* is nothing but the pleasant verdures the Sun produced upon the Earth, inriched by the Inundation after it was dried. I could proceed, but I fear I have already wearied you with this Recital, which was only designed as a Specimen to shew what I hinted the last Day, namely, That this Mythologick History was a History of the Production, Ages, States and Changes that have formerly happened to the Earth, partly from the Theory of the best Philosophy; partly from Tradition, whether Oral or Written, and partly from undoubted History, for towards the latter end we find accounts of many things our Histories reach, as *Orpheus,* the *Trojan* War, *Pythagoras, Romulus, Rome, Numa,* and it comes down even to the Death of *Julius Cæsar,* and the Reign of *Augustus,* under whom he lived.

IN Confirmation of what is said in the foregoing Page concerning the Giants, I shall here insert a loose Paper as I found it among Dr. Hook's Manuscripts, inscribed, A Copy of Dr. Thomas Gale's Paper concerning Giants.

R. W.

S I R,

IN Answer to your Question about the word Rephaim *and* Gigantes, *I make this short return.*

1. *There is no rudical word in the Hebrew Language whose signification doth at all lead us to understand* Gigantes *by the word* Rephaim, *so that the Radix of* Rephaim *is either lost as to the present Hebrew Language (as many others are) or else that word* Rephaim *is a foreign word to that Language, as many more such are now found in the Bible.*

2. *The Septuagint Translators do often render Hebrew words not according to their Natural Sense, but with respect to some History or Tradition, or general belief prevailing at that time: The reason was because those Translators lived among Greeks at* Alexandria: *And they were desirous to shew that the Bible was not unaquainted with the Greek Stories, where the thing could be done without injury to their Books.*

3. *In their rendring of the word* Rephaim *by* Gigantes *and* Mortui, *and the Verb———they plainly point at the Story of the* Titanes, *who in the Greek Mythologies are said* Ταρτηρωθῆναι. *St.* Jude *uses the same word when he speaketh of the Hellish Angels,* ἐξαρτηρωθησα. *Another Greek Translator rendereth the same word* Rephaim *by* Titanes.

4. *As to the suspicion that the* Gigantomachia *was an Earthquake, or perhaps several Earthquakes, but by the Poets put altogether, the true notation of the word* Gigas *seems to make for you. In Hebrew the Radix* Gagash, *is* terra commota fuit. *And the Substantive* Gigas, *tho' commonly taken for a Greek word, is indeed of Hebrew or Phænician Original. In that place of* Isaiah *where the 70 use* Gigantes, Symmachus *uses* θεομάχοι, *both alluding to the Poetical Fable, but the 70 do it more warily,* Symmachus *more plainly.*

But

But to me I confess it seems rather to allude to the fourth Verse of the sixth Chapter of *Genesis*, where it is said, that there were Giants in the Earth in those Days, because the word γιγαντες is made use of by the Septuagint δι δε γιγαντες ησαν επι της γης εν ταις ημεραις εκειναις, and it seems to be a full Period, besides we find that God immediately after this Passage, is said to be very highly displeased with the wickedness of Mankind at that time upon the Earth, and to resolve their Destruction and Extirpation, which shews that there is a great agreement of the Poets Mythology with this History of *Moses*: For *Ovid* makes this *Gigantomachia* to precede the Flood of *Deucalion*, as the Scripture doth make this to precede that of *Noah*. And besides joins the Fable of *Lycaon* to that of his Giants, which seems plainly to allude to the wickedness of Men mentioned by *Moses* upon this occasion. Further, I do not know whether the word may not sometime have been used to denominate Earthquakes, or subterraneous Powers; for in the ninth Verse of the fourteenth of *Isaiah* where the same word is used by the seventy. It seems plainly to signify some such thing; but this is besides my Province, and I shall rather leave it to the Divines to determine: For *Gigas* is the same word with the Greek word γιγας, which *Eustachius* derives from γη and γαω that is an Off-spring or Progeny of the Earth, *i. e.* somewhat generated in the Bowels or Womb of the Earth and thence Born, brought forth or protruded, which is a very proper Appellation and Description of that production of Nature, wherewith the Earth seems to be first impregnated and made tame, then to be in great Agony and Pangs, and to have many pangs and throws before it is delivered of it; and last of all to produce Islands, Mountains, or the like Monsters, which seem to threaten or aspire at the Celestial Mansions.

When I gave an account the preceding Meeting, *July* the thirteenth, of what I conceived the Poets meant by the Mythology of the Giants warring with the Gods, some of the Society then present were very Inquisitive to be informed what should be meant by the History of *Python* which was destroy'd by *Apollo*, of which though I had made some mention in a former Discourse concerning the Mythology mention'd by *Ovid*, yet being then only mention'd *in transitu*, I have now somewhat more particularly drawn up my Sentiment concerning it. I mention'd before then *Ovid* by this Mythology (as I conceived) did design to describe the state of the Earth from its first beginning and formation out of a *Chaos*, through all the various Alterations, Changes and Metamorphoses it had undergon even to that time in which he lived. And therein to comprise the Traditions and Opinions of the Antients, and possibly also some of the Moderns of his Times, and some also of his own, thereby to give some Account and some Reasons of the then present Phænomena of the World. I need not repeat what I have formerly instanced in, about the *Chaos* and the Ages succeeding, nor what I said concerning the Fable of the *Giants*: But to make the probability of my Conjectures the more manifest, I would observe to you the Co-hærence and Connexion of the Mythologies, as they are ranged in this first Book. After the War of the *Giants* which had raised up Mountains that seemed to threaten the very Heavens by their height, and the disturbances that had thereby been caused in the Air by Lightning and Storms which he makes to be the means by which the Gods destroy'd their fury, he comes to consider the Face of the Earth as it was left, which he Mythologizes by the Story of *Lycaon*, whereby he describes the confusion there was left by the subversion, sinking, overwhelming and destructions that had been made, the *Rustica Numina* as the *Fauni, Nymphæ, Satyri,* and the *Sylvani* of the Mountains, were all likely to be destroyed for the future; that is, the fine Plains, the Woods, the Rivers and Rivulets, the Woods on the Hills were all deformed, confounded, and put into confusion, and not only so but the Air itself was from the Clefts and Chasms poisoned and continually filled with noxious Expirations out of the Earth, the People remaining were distracted and grown barbarous, preying upon and destroying one another; it was thought therefore by *Jupiter*, i. e. Divine Power, necessary, that all must be set to rights again by a general Deluge, whereupon the Poet brings in *Jupiter* Swearing,

Nunc mihi qua totum Nereus circumſonat orbem
Perdendum eſt mortale Genus: Per flumina juro
Infera, ſubterras Stygio labentia Luco.
Cunƈta prius tentanda, ſed immedicabile Vulnus
Enſe recidendum eſt, ne pars ſincera trahatur.

Now whereſo'ere reſounding Waves are ſpread,
All mortal Beings muſt die ; by Streams that run
Beneath, I ſwear, Streams that ne'er ſee the Sun.
All ways firſt try ; But th' incurable Wound
Muſt be cut off, leſt it infeƈt the Sound.

The Fable of Deucalion and the Flood explained.

The Flood then follows that was to reduce this torn aud confounded Face of things into ſome better Form and Order, by which the Caverns left ſhould be filled, the ruggedneſſes plain'd, the ſuperficial Parts, now Rocks and Stones, and the Recrements of the Eruptions ſhould be cover'd by a more ſoft, and fine, and fatter Skin of Earth, which ſhould be fit to produce and nouriſh Vegetables and Animals as before. The Poet then deſcribes the Flood, and thereby makes all Men and other Creatures to periſh by it, except only *Deucalion* and *Pyrrha*, who were to be the reſtorers of Mankind, whom he ſuppoſed to have ſomewhat more Divine than all the reſt of the Creatures, which he conceived to be generable out of Corruption, as you will ſee by and by ; but Man only by propagation, yet his method of Propagation looks at firſt glance but very extravagant, namely, from Stones caſt behind them by *Deucalion*, and *Pyrrha*, *Deucalion*'s being generated into Men, and *Pyrrha*'s transformed to Women *(quis hoc credat niſi ſit pro teſte Vetuſtas)* ſays *Ovid* ; and I am very apt to think that *Ovid* himſelf was one of the Unbelievers, notwithſtanding the Teſtimony of the old Traditions, that is, that he did not take it to be a truth in the plain Senſe of the Words, tho' he ſeems to draw a Conſequence from them. [*Inde genus durum ſumus experienſq; Laborum.*] But that he underſtood what was meant or intended to be ſignified by this MythologickDeſcription [*Et Documenta damus qua ſumus origine nati.*] But to proceed. After he has told us how Mankind was preſerved and propagated after the Deluge, he next comes to the other Creatures.

Cætera diverſis, Tellus animalia, formis
Sponte ſua peperit ; poſtquam vetus humor ab igne
Percaluit Solis, Cænumque udæq, Paludes
Intumuere æſtu, fæcundaq ſemina rerum
Vivaci nutrita ſolo, ſeu Matris in alvo
Creverunt, faciem aliquam cepere morando.

All other Creatures took their numerous Birth
And Figures voluntary, from the Earth,
When ſlimy Marſhes from the Suns vaſt heat ;
And with his Power impregnated grow great
With Child, and Seeds, as from the Mothers Womb,
By Steps and Time both Growth and Shape aſſume.

And here he is for *Æquivocal* Generation to the height, if you underſtand him literally, or according to the words, *Quippe ubi temperiem Sumpſere Humorq; calorq; concipiunt & ab his oriuntur cunƈta duobus.* All came from two Principles ; for he ſeems to make all things to ariſe or be generated out of a temperature of Heat and Moiſture, and by that means the Earth, when left by the Deluge, abounding with muddy and boggy Places the heat of the Sun working thereupon produced, according to him, not only all the ſeveral Creatures anew which had been loſt and deſtroyed by the Deluge, but divers others of ſtrange, and before unknown, and monſtrous Forms, which were terrible and deſtruƈtive to Mankind, and amongſt the reſt he mentions a ſtrange, venomous and prodigious *Serpent*, which he calls *Python*, which he

The Fables of Python explained.

relates

relates to be killed or deſtroyed by the Darts of *Apollo*. By which I conceive no more is meant, but that thoſe boggy Places after a time corrupted and produced peſtilential, dark, Clouds and Vapours, which frighted and was noxious both to Men and Beaſts.

But that in ſome time after the Rays of the Sun and Lightning having prevailed, did thereby burn off and diſcharge the poiſonous Exhalations, and put an end to that monſtrous off-ſpring, nor need we be much concerned for what the *Dæmonologers* had thereupon ſuperſtructed for the promoting and carrying on of their *Theourgy*. After this drying of the boggy places of the Earth by the Sun ; we have the account of the production of Woods and Trees by the Power of the Sun in the Story of *Daphne:* And then the deſcription of the Rain, Dew and the Foggs that moiſtened the Air, and made Rivulets and Streams producing Graſs in the Fields, and greenneſs on Trees and Plants by *Io* then *Juno*, the Air finding theſe Vapours to be drawn up into her Bed or Reſidence by the *Sun* or *Jupiter*, is ſaid out of jealouſy to ſet *Argus*, that is, the Stars to watch it by Night and cauſe it to fall: But *Mercury*, or the light of the Morning cuts off the head of *Argus*, that is, makes the Stars diſappear and the Sun return to raiſe them, and *Io* is then reſtored to her former Shape, or the Dew or Moiſture on the Ground is raiſed into Vapours. By the bye he inſerts the Generation of Water, and River-plants by *Syrinx*, and the production of the *Rain-bow* by the Head of *Argus*, placed by *Juno* or the power of the Air in the Feathers of *Juno*'s Bird, which are the Clouds of the Air. By theſe Mythologies having deſcribed the poſtdiluvian ſtate of the Waters, and the Air and watery Meteors, he ends the Book with the Pedigree of *Phaeton* which he compleats in the beginning of the next, of which hereafter.

Daphne.

Io
Argus.

Syrinx.

But as to *Python*, which gaye the occaſion of my preſent Diſcourſe, 'tis plain that its Name ſignifies Corruption, and by the manner of its Generation, 'tis evident that he ſuppoſes this Corruption to be cauſed by the Bogginess or Floods that remained in the Plains, Lakes, or Holes, lower Grounds or Vales incompaſſed with higher Grounds that the Water could not run off: From the fermentation of the ſoftned Earth he ſuppoſes the Animals to be formed that were of the ſame form with the *Antediluvian* ; but from a longer ſtay of the Waters this fermentation turned to Corruption, and then produced not only Monſtrous Creatures, but noxious and dreadful Exhalations , whence proceeded Diſtempers and Diſeaſes, becauſe theſe Waters by ſeveral Streams moved (as moſt commonly they do) to lower Places and Cavities and there made a great Body which poſſeſſed a conſiderable part of the incompaſſing Hills or Mountains: *Apollo* or *Jupiter*, that is, the Sun by many Days and Years irradiating with its Darts, Rays or Beams, doth partly dry by Exhalations, partly by flaſhes of Lightning, diſſipate, and diſpel, and laſt of all it cauſeth Clefts and openings of the Earth which ſwallow it up, and leave thoſe Cavities like the black Wounds which the Poet affirms to remain for a witneſs to Poſterity.

Python.

--------*Sed te quoq; maxime Python*
Tum genuit : Populiſq; novis, incognite ſerpens
Terror eras ; tantum ſpatii de monte tenebas.
Hunc Deus arcitenens, & nunquam talibus armis
Ante, niſi in damis Capriſq; fugacibus uſus,
Mille gravem telis, exhauſta pæne Pharetra
Perditit effuſo per vulnera nigra veneno.
Neve operis famam poſſet delere vetuſtas,
Inſtituit ſacros celebri certamine Ludos,
Pythia perdomiti ſerpentis nomine dictos.

Huge

Huge Python th' Earth against her will then bred,
A serpent whom the new-born People dread:
Whose bulk o're so much of the Mountain spread.
The dazling God that bears the silver Bow,
(Inured before to strike the flying Doe)
That Terror with a thousand Arrows slew,
His Quiver empty'd, and the Poison drew
Thro' the black Wounds : Then least the Memory
Of such a work in after times should die,
He instituted celebrated Games
Which from this Serpent he the Pythian *names.*

The Earth produced various Creatures some monstrously shaped, these were *invita terra* contrary to its proper teeming Vertue brought forth : Of these one was more corrupt than the rest, and more contrary to Nature ; this possessing so much room of the Mountains, wrigling on all sides by the Rills that ran into its vast Body or Lake, by its Poison became dreadful to the new produced Creatures : This Celestial Power that kept the Tower of Heaven (so I English *Arcitenens*) that is, the Sun, Fire, or Heat, by its Rays and by thousands of flashes of Lightnings (insomuch that one would have thought they had been all spent and the whold stock fired off and whereas those Rays before had been only used to dispel and scatter small Clouds or Foggs) did hereby at last destroy or disperse this stagnant and corrupted Body of Water, by causing it to rise into Thunder Clouds discharging by Lightning its poisonous Vapours with which it swelled ; besides the heat of the Sun and the Lightning also kindling the Subterraneous Spirits, caused Clefts and Chasms in the Earth, which swallowed up most of the remaining stagnant Waters, and so destroy'd the Cause or Original of those Evils, leaving in several places divers of those Chasms or black Wounds which the Poet describes.

To this purpose there is a notable Passage in *Lucian*, which, among others, to another intent, is quoted by Dr. *Burnet, Theor. Sacr.* Part 2. Chap. 4. 'These 'are the Matters (says *Lucian*) which the Greeks have related concerning 'the Flood of *Deucalion*. But among the things that have happened soon af- 'ter it, there is a certain relation of the Inhabitants of *Hierapolis*, which is 'justly looked upon with great admiration, namely, that in their Country 'there had happened to be made a great Chasme in the Earth, which had 'swallowed up all the remaining Waters ; whereupon *Deucalion* had built Al- 'tars and a Temple dedicated to *Juno* over the same. Now for a sign that 'this Relation is so, they do thus twice every Year, Water is brought from the 'Sea to this Temple, and not only the Priests bring it, but all *Syria* and *A-* '*rabia*, and many which dwell beyond the *Euphrates*, go to the Sea and fetch- 'ing the Water from thence bring it to this place : And first indeed they 'pour it out into the Temple, and then it runs into the Chasm, and tho' 'this Chasm be but small, yet it swallows an immense quantity of Water. 'When they perform this Ceremony, they say that *Deucalion* instituted this 'Rite and Law of this Temple, that it might be a Memorial as well of the 'Destruction by as of the Deliverance and Safety procured against the Flood. 'This (says *Lucian*) is the old Story concerning this Temple. This Tradi- tion, 'tis very probable, *Ovid* was not ignorant of and might therefore add to his Relation *Fuso per vulnera nigra veneno. Neve operis famam posset delere vetustas.* And 'tis very probable also that the Mythology of *Argus* has a respect to the Generation of the Rainbow soon after the Flood as it is mentioned by *Moses.* For 'tis plain that their Signs or Hieroglyphical Representations and Notions, were many of them abundantly more incongruous with the things signified than this is ; for Clouds may by an easy Figure be fancied the Fowls or Birds of the Air, as we usually say when great flakes of Snow fall, the Winter is plucking its Geese or Fowls : And which among all Fowls, or indeed Crea- tures, does better represent the Rainbow then the Peacock when it spreads its Tail, whereby it represents such a glorious Arching of a most stupendious Variety

riety of Colours as numerous and as refplendent as the very Rainbow. And to make the coherence the greater thofe Rings being made up of a Circular Order of beautiful Spots, what could he better Metamorphofe it from than from a Head adorned with abundance of Eyes, which he makes to be of one *Argus?* I fuppofe for want of Microfcopes he knew not that the Eyes of Flies were planted in fo curious an order, otherwife poffibly that might have ferved for a Hieroglyphick for the Star-light-Night as well as *Argus.*

I have formerly difcourfed concerning the great and ftrange Effects that *The occafion of this Lecture.* have been produced on the fuperficial Parts of the Earth by means of Earth-quakes, the raifing of Hills, the finking of Vallies and Lakes, the fwallow-ing and new producing of Rivers, the raifing and finking of Iflands, the cleaving of Hills and Rocks, and the tumbling and difordering of the fuper-ficial Parts of the Earth, by which means have been produced the Veins and various mixtures in Marbles and other kinds of Stone, and moft of the pe-trifactive Productions, befides the Production of Mines and Metalline Bodies, as well as of other Saline, Sulphureous and divers other mineral Subftances. And in fhort I conceive that the whole Surface of the Earth, as it is at pre-fent, has been fome ways or other influenced and fhaped by them : I have on feveral occafions alledged feveral Arguments and Obfervations to make thefe Conceptions probable , and have produced feveral Hiftories that feem to be that way conducing. But moft of the greateft Mutations having in probability been performed in the "Αδ'ηλον or μυθικὸν the uncertain or fabulous Times, as they are termed by *Varro,* there is not to be found in the *That the Egyp-tians had Re-cords of Phae-ton in their Hiftories.* Hiftorical time very many that do make much for it ; the greateft Inftance I conceive to be had of it, is the Hiftory of *Phaeton,* which, tho' among the Greeks it be included within the fabulous times, yet it feems by that Paffage of *Plato* which he relates concerning what *Solon* had learned from the Ægypti-an *Preiſt* that the Ægyptians had Records thereof in their Hiftory, as in probability they had of many others, of which the *Grecians* were wholly igno-rant, as may in part appear by the Relation of the *Atlantis* ; for the *Greeks* had nothing of Hiftory elder than the Flood of *Oygges,* which, as *Eufebius* fays, happened about the times of *Jacob,* which was long after that of *Noah,* and long before that of *Deucalion,* which was about the latter end of *Mofes's* Life. All which time according to *Varro,* and many hundred Years after e-ven to the beginning of the *Olympiads* (which was but 776 Years before Chriſt) was included in the Fabulous Age, which was likewife 776 Years after *Mofes* his Death, he dying in the 1552 Year before Chriſt's Nativity; within *At what time that happened.* which fpace of time the Cataftrophy Mythologifed by the Story of *Phaeton* feems to have happened ; for *Orofius* relates it to have been much about the time of the *Ifraelites* departure out of Ægypt ; as he doth alfo affert that of *Deucalion's* Flood, in which the greateft part of the People of *Theffaly* were loft, only fome few efcaping who fled to the Mountains, efpecially *Parnaffus,* near the Foot of which *Deucalion* then reigned. Now if we confider the Story as it is related by *Ovid* in the fecond Book of his *Metamorphofis,* making al-lowance for what is Poetically fpoken, one may plainly enough from the whole drift of the Fable conjecture at the Hiftory or Tradition that is couch-ed under it, as well as fomewhat alfo of the Philofophy ; as for the morality thereof enough have taken notice of and writ concerning it. As for the time of it, *Ovid* places it foon after the Fable of *Deucalion* which is the feventh Fable of his firft Book, and the eighth, ninth, tenth, eleventh, twelvth, are of Matters confequential of that Flood which muft have followed it in a very fhort time (as I may on fome other occafion make more probable) or rather prævious to this, as being indeed part of it. But to let that pafs for the pre-fent, I fhall only take notice now of the Phyfical or Philofophical part thereof, which to me feems to contain a Defcription of fome very great Earthquake or fiery Eruption which affected a great part of the World then known.

Firft then we find *Phaeton* to be termed a Son or production of the Sun, *An Explication of the Fable of Phaeton.* which is the biggeft and moft powerful Fire of the World, that we who live upon the Earth do know, but by the Mothers Side, to be the Son of *Clymene* which is an epithite of *Pluto* and denotes *Phaeton,* or this afpiring Fire to be generated by the Sun in the Bowels of the Earth ; all the proeme of the

F ffff   Story

Story is Poetical and of a moral Signification to denote a Genius aspiring and undertaking more than what it was able or fit to perform and manage, yet it is so ordered as to comprise the main Design and Physical meaning of the Poet, *viz.* that by some extraordinary or universal influence of the Suns Beams the Subterraneous Vapours had been kindled, and that a fore-runner of this was Lightning and Thunderings in the Air, which seems to be expressed by the description of the Horses that drew the Chariot of the Sun.

> *Interea volucres Pyroeis, Eous & Æthon*
> *Solis equi, quartusq; Phlegon, hinnitibus auras*
> *Flammiferis implent, pedibusq; repagula pulsant.*

> *Mean while the Suns swift Horses, hot Pyroeis,*
> *Light Æthon, fiery Phlegon, bright Eous,*
> *Neighing aloud inflame the Air with heat,*
> *And with their Thundring Hoofs the Barriers beat.*
> Metam. Lib. 2. v. 153, &c.

The Managery and Course of the Horses and Chariots through the Heavens is all poetical, accommodated to shew the Constellations of *Aratus*, and to the Cosmography of the Poets, to signify the concurrence of the other Celestial Bodies and Powers: But the effects it produced on the Earth as the flaming and burning of Mountains, the cleaving and chopping of the Earth, the swallowing up of Rivers, the rising of Lands out of the Sea, as especially that about *Ægypt*, and the Sandy Deserts on the West side of it, seem to be Historical as well as Poetical.

But I confess the whole is so Poetical that much certainty of History cannot be fetched out of it ; yet for the present let me add thus much that I conceive may be deduced therefrom, and that is this, That there was an ancient Tradition among the *Greeks*, and that there was an ancient History among the *Ægyptians* of some very great and almost general Conflagration or Eruption of fiery Streams which made very great Devastations on the Earth, especially of those parts mentioned by the Poet in this Relation ; such as *Athos, Ida, Oete, Tmolus, Taurus, Helicon, Æmus, Ætna, Parnassus, Othrys, Cynthus, Erix, Mimas, Rhodope, Dindyma, Caucasus, Mycale, Cytheron, Pindus* and *Ossa, Olympus,* the *Alpes* and *Appenine,* all which Mountains are said to have been on Fire, and to have cast up Smoak, Ashes, and burning Coles, and to have thickned and darkned the Air.

> *Tum facta est Libye raptis humoribus æstu*
> *Arida, tum Nymphæ passis, fontesq; lacusque*
> *Deflevere comis,* &c. v. 237.

> *Then a dry Desert Libya became,*
> *Her full Veins empty'd by the thirsty Flame ;*
> *With their scorcht Hair the Nymphs the dry'd up Streams*
> *And Lakes, their ancient seats, bewail.*

Then were cast up the *Libyan* Desarts and many Lakes and Rivers swallowed up and perverted, the names of which the Poet mentions, which are too many now to repeat ; then the other parts of the Earth were cleft and tumbled to and fro.

> *Dissilit omne Solum penetratq; in Tartara Rimis*
> *Lumen & Infernum terret cum Conjuge Regem.*
> *Et mare Contrahitur Siccaq; est Campus arenæ,*
> *Quod modo pontus erat ; quosq; altum texerat æquor*
> *Existunt montes, & Sparsas Cycladas augent.* V. 260.

Earth cracks, to Hell the hated Light descends
And frighted Pluto *with his Queen offends;*
The Ocean shrinks and leaves a Field of Sand,
Where new discovered Rocks and Mountains stand,
Which multiply the scatter'd Cyclades.

Then was the Sea contracted into a narrower but deeper Cestern, the Hills and Lands on each side of it raised from under the former Sea and made dry Lands and Mountains, the Islands that are now dispersed in it were thrust up out of its bottom, and stand in that Position to this time : In short not to detain you at present too long upon this Mythologick Story, I conceive it to contain the History or *Cabala* of the Production or Birth of the present *Mediterranean, Ægean* and *Euxine* Seas, and of all the bordering Shores and Countries near adjacent to them, together with all the Islands, Peninsula's, Cliffs, Promontories, Mountains, Hills, Lakes, Rivers and Countries which had been before that time all covered with the Sea, but by a prodigious Catastrophy which Divine Providence then caused to be effected, the former Face of those Parts was transformed and metamorphosed into much what it is now found, in General, tho' not in all Particulars ; for that there may have since been by the same Divine Providence produced other particular Catastrophies and Mutations, of which there are many Instances mythologically Recorded in this our Author, some of which I have already mentioned, and divers others which I may have occasion to mention some other time, besides divers others of which we have plain and not hitherto doubted or disputed Histories. Now, tho' I confess what I have here asserted to be seemingly very Extravagant and Heterodox from the general Conceptions of most that have had occasion to mention this Fable ; and tho' it had been less improbable, I should not have expected any Concurrence of Opinion : Yet possibly when the Matter has beeen more sedately and without prejudice thought of and examined, it may, as well as some of my former Extravagancies, receive at least a more mild Censure, tho' it should not be wholly accommodated to the Gusto of every such Examinant. In these Matters Geometrical Cogency has not yet been applied, and where that is wanting, Opinion, which is always various and unstable, prevails. However, I may on some other occasion shew that there is to be found in Physick, as well as Geometry, unanswerable Probation.

And when the Extravagancy and Novelty of the Doctrine has run the Gauntlet of Censures, I shall indeavour to add somewhat to cover and cure its Scars.

I did the last day indeavour to shew what I conceived was veiled by the Poet under the Story of *Phaeton*, and that was this, That by this Mythology the *Grecian* and *Latin* Poets did preserve the memory of some extraordinary great Catastrophy, which all the parts of the Earth or Countries not far removed from the *Mediterranean, Ægean, Euxine,* and *Caspian* Seas had suffered by fiery Eruptions or Meteors, effecting Earthquakes.

This to me seems probable from the Order and from the Manner of the whole Relation.

For the Order of it ; we find it placed by *Ovid* soon after the Flood of *Deucalion,* and so we find it is related by *Paulus Orosius* (which I hinted the last day) for in the ninth and tenth Chap. of his first Book of Historys he makes the Flood of *Deucalion* to have happened much about the time of the Plagues of *Ægypt,* and the Passage of the *Israelites* through the Red Sea, by which Flood the greatest part of the People of *Thessaly* were destroyed. *Quo* (says *Orosius,* speaking of that Flood) *Major pars populorum Thessaliæ absumpta est, paucis perfugio Montium Liberatis. Maxime in monte Parnasso, in Cujus Circuitu Deucalion tunc Regnabat ; qui ad se confugientes Ratibus Suscepit & per gemina*

Parnassi

Parnaſſi Juga fovit aluitq; ob idq; locum fecit Fabulæ ut ab eo Reparatum Genus humanum diceretur. His *etiam temporibus adeo jugis & gravis æſtus incanduit ut Sol per Devia tranſvectus, univerſum orbem non calore affeciſſe, ſed igne torruiſſe* Dicatur. *Impreſſnmq; Fervorem & Æthiops plus Solito, & inſolitum Scytha non tulerit. Ex quo etiam quidam, dum non concedunt Deo ineffabilem potentiam ſuam, Inanes Ratiunculas conquirentes Ridiculam Phaetontis Fabulam texuerunt.* Thus far he, by which it ſeems that *Oroſius* did, in the Stories of *Deucalion* and *Phaeton* for the main, believe the Matters of Fact to be true, but he was not for giving a Philoſophical Conjecture at the Cauſes of it, or the aſcribing them to the Pagan Deities, but for aſcribing it immediately to the ineffable Power of God.

Now I do not conceive it doth any ways detract from the Omnipotency and Power of God, to explain the Cauſes that he was pleaſed to make prævious to thoſe Effects : For the Power of God is not leſs wonderful, in producing and diſpoſing the Cauſes of things, than in producing the things more immediately. But ſuch a Story as this Fable of *Phaeton* is, and to give ſuch an account of its Cauſes, as the Poets have there given, if underſtood literally, ſeems ſufficiently ridiculous, and impious. But it is eaſy enough to be ſeen that thoſe who made this Fable knew better things, and only made uſe of Mythology to conceale their knowledge from the Vulgar, and yet communicate it to ſuch as had the Key to unfold the Myſtery contained therein.

And this appears plain enough from the whole ſeries alſo of the Hiſtory ; for as I noted before, *Phaeton* is ſaid to be produced or generated by the Sun in the Womb of *Clymene,* an Epithite of *Pluto,* that is, in the Subterraneous Regions; and that it is ſo underſtood, appears plainly by the behaviour of *Clymene,* who is ſaid, after the Death of her Son, to have been *Lugubris & amens, & Laniata Sinus totum percenſuit orbem, exanimeſq; Artus primo, mox oſſa requirens.* Which ſeems to denote the murmuring and tumbling in the Earth that continued after the Conflagration was over, and the Story of the Siſters of *Phaeton* ſeems very conſonant alſo thereunto if I had time now to conſider them.

Phaeton being grown to maturity, is ſaid to have a great deſire to know his Father, whom *Clymene* directs to go to the Palace of the Sun ; that is, the Vapours being copiouſly generated in the Earth are expelled into the Air aſcending towards the Sun. *Phaeton* is ſaid to have come at length to the Palace of the Sun, and there to have been much pleaſed with the glorious work thereof, and more eſpecially with the Workmanſhip of *Vulcan* in the Gates. *Nam Mulciber illic Æquora cœlarat medias cingentia terras, terrarumq; orbem Cælumq; quod imminet orbi. Cæruleos habet unda Deos, Tritona Canorum, Proteaq; ambiguum Balenarumq; prementem, Ægeona Suis immania terga lacertis,* &c. *Terra Viros, Urbeſq; Gerit, Sylvaſq; Feraſq; Fluminaq; & Nymphas & Cætera numina Ruris. Hæc Super impoſita eſt Cœli fulgentis Imago Signaq; ſex foribus dextris totidemq; ſiniſtris,* &c. Then approaching the Sun——. *Sedebat, in Solio Phœbus claris Lucente Smaragdis, a Dextra Lævaq; Dies & Menſis & Annus, Sæculaq; & poſitæ Spatiis æqualibus Horæ. Verq; Novum Stabat Cinctum florente Corona : Stabat nuda Æſtas & Spicea certa gerebat. Stabat & Autumnus calcatis ſordidus uvis, Et Glacialis Hyems Canos hirſuta Capillos.* The meaning of all which ſeems to be this, That the ſtate of the World before this Cataſtrophy was much the ſame *(facies non omnibus una, nec diverſa tamen)* with the State of it afterwards ; that is, the Courſe of the Sun was through the twelve Signs ; there was a Spring, Summer, Autumn, and Winter, as there has been ſince ; no alteration of the Axis or obliquity of the Ecliptick : But there were Ages, and Years, and Months, and Days, and Hours as now ; and *Phœbus* deſcribing the way to drive his Chariot through, doth name the ſame Conſtellations : So that the Philoſophers who made the Theory, or the Poets that made the Fable, did not underſtand or ſuppoſe the obliquity of the Ecliptick to be made by that Deviation of the Chariot, or that this Cataſtrophy had altered the Axis of the Earth, with reſpect to the Heavens. But neither did they deſign to ſignify, even by this Story, the Deviation of the Sun it ſelf at that time, as if that had deſcended and fired the Earth : For *Phœbus* did not accompany the Chariot, *Occupat ille levem juvenili corpore currum,* v. 150. But
they

they rather seem to make *Phaeton* a fiery Meteor proceeding from the East, and moving Westward by another way and course than the Sun usually took, and differing from the Direction that *Phæbus* had given to *Phaeton* to observe: But his Horses now mounted upwards towards the fixt Stars, now downwards towards the Earth, now far to the North, then as much to the South, and last of all he was broak all to peices by Lightning, and fell down like a Meteor upon the Earth, and like some such Meteors as have of late Years been observed, but much greater. *At Phaeton, Rutilos flamma populante capillos, volvitur in præceps, Longoq; per aera tractu Fertur, ut interdum de cælo Stella Sereno, quæ si non cecidit potuit cecidisse videri.* Whether there might ever have been any such Comet as in its Course might come so near the Earth as to set the superficial part on Fire, and to kindle or excite the Subterraneous, Sulphureous and Nitrous Minerals, or whether it were some Exhalation collected into a great Body in the upper Regions of the Air, and being kindled might seem to pass near those Constellations, through which *Phaeton* is said to be hurried and to come so near the Mediterranean parts as to burn the superficial Parts, and to inkindle the Subterraneous Mines of combustible and inflammable Substances; or whether it were some prodigious quantity of inflammable Steams collected in the Air, and so burnt off by continual Lightning, it is hard positively to determine, because that part of the Story I conceive to be Hypothetical, and Conjectural, or Philosophical, and not meerly Historical. But the Effects produced, those I conceive to be Historical; that is, that there were divers parts, which were before covered by the Sea, that by this Eruption, were raised from under it and left dry. *Tum facta est Libye, raptis humoribus, æstu arida: Tum Nymphæ passis fontesq; lacusq; Deflevere comis.* 237, 238. *Et Mare contrahitur, Siccæq; est campus arenæ, quod modo pontus erat.* 262 263. Then also were raised from under the Sea both Islands and Mountains. *Quosq; altum texerat æquor Existunt montes, & Sparsas Cycladas augent.* 263, 264. Then also did other parts sink under the Water. *Ipsum quoq; Nerea fama est, Doridaq; & Natas, tepedis latuisse sub undis.* Other parts were overflowed by the Sea and again deserted. *Ter Neptunus aquis cum torvo brachia Vultu, Exerere ausus erat, ter non tulit aeris ignes.* 272. Then were also caused great Earthquakes, and overturning and tumblings of the Earth. *Alma tamen Tellus, ut erat circumdata ponto, inter aquas Pelagi, contractosq; undiq; fontes, Qui se condiderant in opacæ viscera Matris, Sustulit Omniferos Collo tenus arida Vultus: Opposuitq; manum fronti,* Magnoq; tremore omnia Concutiens *paulum Subsedit; & infra, quam Solet esse fuit.* Then also was the Air filled with Fumes and Smokes, and the Surface of the Earth covered with Ashes and Cinders. 231, 232. *Et neque jam Cineres ejectamq; favillam ferre potest, calido involvitur undiq; fumo.* And again, 283, 284, speaking of the Earth, (*Presserat ora vapor*) *tostos en aspice crines, inq; oculis fumum; volitant Super ora favillæ.* The superficial parts of the Earth, Vegetable and Animal, were destroyed. 210, *&c. Corripitur flammis quæq; a'tissima tellus, fissaq; agit Rimas, & Succis aret ademptis, pabula canescunt; tum frondibus uritur arbor, Materiamq; Suo præbet Seges arida Damno: Fluminea volucres medio caluere Caystro.* The Earth was rent and cleft, and all the high Hills on Fire like *Ætna* or *Vesuvius:* Those I named the last day. By this means many Rivers were swallowed up into the Earth; others dried up by evaporation and boyling Heat. *Mediis Tanais fumavit in undis.* 243, &c. *Nili Ostia septem Pulverulenta vacant, Septem sine flumine Valles.* And, to be short, all the effects that have ever been observed in Earthquakes, are here eminently expressed. So that there can be no manner of doubt of the design of the Story, *viz.* That it was designed to denote or describe a Catastrophy of the Mediterranean parts of the Earth by Earthquakes; since all things are so properly delineated and represented for that end, as if the Poet or Maker thereof had been spectator or Eyewitness of it, or at least a Contemporary with it. And we may here find the whole Progress or Phænomena of an Earthquake from its very first beginning to its very last end, and the effects also that precede it, and those that are subsequent to it, as I could plainly shew if it were not too much for this present Discourse, by explaining the Mythologick Histories immediately prefixt and following it. Nay, there has not been in this late Earthquake in *Sicily*

(which

which feems to be the greateft mentioned in Hiftory) any one Phænomenon which cannot be fhewn in this of *Phaeton*, and indeed moft of the Phænomena mentioned in this of *Phaeton* have been exhibited or exemplified in this laft of *Sicily*; which I could eafily manifeft by comparing *Ovid's* Defcription with that of the *Italian* Frier; but I fhall pafs it by for the prefent.

Part of another *Lecture to the* *fame purpofe.* I have, in fome of my former Difcourfes, indeavoured to fhew fome Probabilities, that the Mythologick Stories of the Poets did couch under thofe monftrous and feemingly impoffible reprefentations of Actions performed by humane Powers, fome real and actual Cataftrophies that had been caufed by the Body or Face of the Earth by other Natural Powers, of which the *Ægyptians, Chaldeans, Greeks*, or fome other learned Nations had preferved fome Hiftories or Traditions among the more learned part of them; which, that they might the better conceale their Knowledge, and keep it to themfelves, and abfcond it from the Vulgar, and fuch as were not initiated and admitted into their Fraternities, they had contrived and digefted into fabulous Stories, which, as they might ferve to amufe and awe the Vulgar by the Dæmonology they had thereupon fuperftructed, fo they might ferve to inftruct and inform the Adepti, or fuch as were admitted to the true interpretation and underftanding of what they knew, of the real Hiftory that was concealed thereby, as alfo of their Philofophical or Phyfical Hypothefis for the Explication and Solution thereof. I think it cannot be doubted that the Theogonia of *Hefiod* was of this nature, which if it was *Hefiod's* (of which, yet I confefs their are fome Moderns make a doubt) it feems to have been fome of the firft Notions which the *Greeks* had obtained of thefe Matters from the *Ægyptians* or *Phænicians*, or fome other of the Eaftern Nations; except we fuppofe that *Orpheus*, who preceded both *Hefiod* and *Homer* near five 100 Years, might in thofe times have known and communicated fome what of what they had by the fame Methods procured. The Hiftories of thofe times are very dark and uncertain, and nothing convincing can be built upon them. It will be therefore but loft Labour to indeavour to prove my Conjectures from Hiftories, or hints to be fought among thofe few Fragments which are now to be met withal among the Relicks of written Antiquities. Thofe, if fuch there were, (as being committed to fmall and perifhable Subftances) have been more eafily drowned and fwallowed by time, or buried and overwhelmed with the Duft of Oblivion: And the Copy or Counterfeits of fome of them, which have been made by fome of thofe we now call the Ancients (though with refpect to them they are to be accounted Modern) feem to have been but very imperfect, and to have been like Structures made up and peiced of the Rubbifh, Ruins and Fragments of thofe Antiquities which they in thofe times could rake together; fo that though fome great Buildings have been by thefe fecundary Ancients erected; yet being made up of fuch Fragments or Parts of thofe more ancient facred Piles by the new Difpofition and Order of them they now appear a prepofterous *Moles*, yet we cannot but conceive that they had fome better and more certain informations of thofe more ancient Hiftories or Traditions than what we now can find; and we cannot think fo mean of them as not to believe they did in fome meafure comprehend the Intention, Meaning, and Drift, or Defign of thofe that preceded them; and tho' they wanted a compleat knowledge, yet from the knowledge they had of the then Ruins, they were better inabled to Judge and Conjecture concerning them, than we now can. And tho' their Conjectures might not be all right, yet we cannot but think they might be tollerably near the matter, and that they did acquaint Pofterity by their Writings what thofe their Conjectures were. And of this Nature I take the Metamorphofis of *Ovid* to be, who, I conceive, had made it his ftudy to inform himfelf as fully as he was able of what was then to be found concerning that knowledge, and out of thofe informations he compiled that Book which was to comprife all the Records of Antiquity concerning the Changes and Cataftrophies that had happened to the Earth from the Creation unto his own time, which his four firft prefactory Verfes do plainly enough declare. *In Nova fert animus mutatas dicere formas, Corpora dii captis nam vos mutafti & illas, Afpirate meis, Primaq; ab Origine mundi, In mea perpetuum deducite tempora Carmen.* Which is as much as to fay, My defign in

this

this Book is to ſpeak concerning the various alterations and transformations which the Bodies or ſuperficial Parts of the Earth have, by the Divine Powers, undergone ; for to thoſe he doth aſcribe them, *Nam vos mutaſtis & illas,* and therein to comprize all the knowledge I have been able to procure from the very firſt Creation or Original of it, even to theſe very times in which I live. And accordingly we find him to begin this his Hiſtory, even with the beginning of the Creation of the Earth itſelf, and therein to have followed the Traditions, Opinions, and Doctrines of the moſt Ancient Sages concerning its manner of Formation out of a preceeding Chaos; which Doctrine that it was very ancient, and indeed the moſt ancient of all others concerning the Origination of it, I think the Learned and Ingenious Dr. *Burnet* in his *Archæologia* has ſufficiently proved, and therefore I ſhall not need to ſay any thing concerning it; only I would make this one occaſional Remark, That how ancient ſoever it was, it did not favour of an unlearned or ignorant Age or of a firſt beginning of real Knowledge, for that we find by *Ovid's* Copy of it, that it contained a more refined Conception concerning the Figure, and Shape, and Properties of the Earth, than many of the Greek Philoſophers (who in probability were many hundreds of Years after thoſe firſt Sages) had concerning it. Some of thoſe Greek Philoſophers making the Earth to be of the form of a Drum or Cylinder, others of an infinite Column, others of a Skiff or Boat, or of a floating Iſland in the midſt of an infinitely extended plain Ocean, and others of other extravagant Shapes; whereas we find that the Doctrine of the Chaos made it to be of a Sphærical Form, *Solidumq; coercuit orbem,* to conſiſt of Land and Water, to have a proper Gravity that kept all its parts in that ſhape, or his *Tellus (Elementaq; grandia traxit & preſſa eſtgravitate ſua)* to be Involved with the Air, and that again with the Æther. *Hæc Super impoſuit liquidum & gravitate carentem Æthera nec quicquam terræna fæcis habentem,* to be ſuſpended in the Air, or Æther, or ſpace of Heaven without being ſupported by any imaginary Foundation, as thoſe Greeks fancied. *Circumfuſo pendebat in aere tellus, Ponderibus librata ſuis.* Nay, and by ſeveral other Paſſages and Expreſſions of this Book, it is clear, that in thoſe very ancient times, whenever they were, for 'tis hard certainly to limit them; the Learned Men that then lived, had arrived to a very great height of Natural Knowledge, eſpecially of that part which concerned the Coſmography or Conſtitution of the Univerſe; and by that Expreſſion, *Ignea convexi vis & ſine pondere Cæli emicuit, ſummaq; Locum ſibi legit in Arce.* It ſeems plain that they placed the Sun in the Center of the univerſe, and made the Earth to move about it. *Principio terram, ne non æqualis ab omni Parte foret, magni Speciem glomeravit in orbis.* But this only by the bye; for I know the common interpretation of theſe places, is altogether differing from what I now give, yet were it now my buſineſs, I think I can ſhew ſufficient Reaſons to perſuade any unprejudiced Perſon that what I have given is the deſigned meaning of them; but I proceed to ſhew the general deſign of *Ovid* in this Book. After the Deſcription of the formation of the Earth, he comes to deſcribe the firſt times of its continuance; that is, the ᾿αδηλον, or unknown Ages of the World, of which he makes four, the Golden, Silver, Brazen and Iron, in the laſt of which comes in the Mythologick and Hiſtorick, for that he himſelf hath Mythologized alſo ſome of the Hiſtorical Times and Events. What ſpace of Time he allows to each of theſe Ages it doth not ſo readily appear, but it is certain that the *Chaldeans, Ægyptians, Brachmans,* and ſome Heathen Hiſtorians have aſſigned ſpaces large enough and even beyond belief almoſt; and Mr. *Graves* tells us, that the Chineſe do make the World 88640000 Years old. He begins the Mythologick Times with the Gygantomachia, which to me ſeems to be nothing elſe but a Deſcription of ſome prodigious Earthquakes or Eruptions. And that by the Giants he plainly means nothing elſe but the Subterraneous Fires or Accenſions which break out, and throwing up before them the Earth, ſeemed to threaten the very Heavens by piling Mountain upon Mountain (*Affectaſſe ferunt Regnum Cæleſte Gygantes Altaq; congeſtos Struxiſſe ad Sidera montes*) I ſhewed before in the interpretation of the Rape of *Proſerpine,* where it plainly appears what was meant by *Typheus* one of thoſe Giants, who is ſaid to lie buried under the Iſland of *Sicily,*

cily, and therefore shall not need to say more upon that Subject. After the breaking forth of these Subterraneous Streams and Flames, we find *Ovid* describing them to be burnt off with Lightning. *Tum Pater omnipotens misso perfregit Olympum Fulmine & excussit Subjectam Pelion Ossa. Obruta mole Sua cum corpora dira jacerent, perfusam multo Natorum Sanguine terram immaduisse ferunt, Calidumq; animasse cruorem.* This we find to be a general Concomitant or Subsequent of such Eruptions, and it were easy to produce many Examples of it in our late Eruptions ; and 'tis also as usual for many of those places that have been thrown or raised up into Hills to be sunk or tumbled down again, *Excussit subjectam Pelion Ossa.* So we are told of a Hill that lately rose up by *Catanea*, which soon sunk again. [*Obruta*] by this, I think, is plainly signified the Eruption of fiery Streams or Rivers of melted Minerals out of those Orifices or fiery Vents, such as in the two last Earthquakes in *Sicily* have broke out of *Ætna*, and overflowed and burnt up and destroyed several Towns, Villages, Fields, *&c.* for what can better express the moving, raging and devouring Qualities of such a stream of Liquid Fire, than to call it an animated, or living scalding Gore from its red and fiery Colour, its scalding and burning Heat, its fluidity and rapid Motion, and its devouring and consuming Power; but it would be too tedious to insist on all the remarkable Circumstances and Expressions, which, I conceive, makes it plainly enough appear what was the Design and Scope of the Story ; nor need I mention the Description of it by other Mythologers, as *Claudian, Hygynus, Antoninus, Liberalis.* Nor will it, I hope, be needful to answer any thing to those who would interpret it another way : Some making it to be only a Description of a Rebellion ; others a disguising of the History of the Tower *Babylon.* I shall rather leave it to the Judgment of every one to make choice of which interpretation he shall, upon duly considering the relation, think to be most aggreeable to the whole drift of the Book. And what I now deliver I would not have to be taken otherwise than only as my Reasonings and Conjectures upon the like Considerations : For as I observed before, the Poet has so couched all his Relations and Expressions as to comprize a Physical, a Moral, and an Historical Meaning in them. And it may be so interpreted as if it were designed to describe some particular Earthquakes, or some particular Rebellion, or the general Rebellion of wicked Men against Heaven, and the Divine Powers, or the attempt of those at *Babel*, and at the same time it may also be found designedly to contain in brief the Theory of Opinions of the most antient Physiologers which they held concerning the Causes and Effects of Earthquakes upon the uper Face of the Earth ; which to me, I confess, seems to be the principal aim and design of this Story of *Ovid*, as well as of the most part of the rest of the Book, which I design, God willing, to prove more expresly and particularly in a Treatise upon this Subject, so soon as I have settled some Affairs, which have hitherto hindred me from perfecting that and many other Subjects.

I shall not need here to say any thing concerning the Custom of the *Greeks* in those former Ages of turning all their Histories into Mythologick Poetry ; 'tis plainly enough proved by that Relation I read the last day out of *Plato*'s *Timæus* ; and it was not only used by them but by divers other Nations, as the *English* and *Germans*, as you will know. I suppose the reason was for the better fixing it into the Minds of the Youth by a kind of indelible Character, as *Plato* expresses it : Which could not be forgotten ; for extravagant Marks we know are the great helps of Artificial Memory, for that they raise extraordinary Attention; and that extraordinary Attention and Wonder does stigmatise or burn in as twere indelible Ideas in the Memory. Pleasure also is another help to fix Ideas, and that Poetry and Songs contribute to, and the activity of the Spirits in Youth work the Effects more powerfully, and make them more durable. These, I imagine were the Reasons why the *Ægyptians, Greeks* and other Nations converted their true Histories into these Romantick Fables : Not that I do here undertake for the truth of History in every Fable, for I conceive that there are as various kinds of Fables as there are of Histories. Some are repeated and believed Fables which are true Histories, others are believed true, but are really Fables : Some are believed Fables

and

and are really fo., and others are believed true and really are fo. But of this fourth Head I fear is the fmalleft number; but we muft take the beft Evidence we can to confirm our Belief of thofe that are generally fo reputed: Among which none has been more looked after of late than Medalls, Infcriptions, and real Monuments, yet remaining of the preceding Perfons and Actions, thefe are by all looked upon as a moft undeniable Proof to confirm a written Hiftory, and yet we know that many things of this kind have been counterfeited, yet that cannot be faid of all: Now, if thefe that may be counterfeited be yet looked upon as more Authentick than Written Hiftory, then certainly thefe Medals, Infcriptions, or Monuments of Natures own ftamping, (which I alledged to prove an Hypothefis) which 'tis impoffible for Art to counterfeit, might in reafon be looked upon as Proof fufficient tho' no Hiftory could be produced. If I faw a perfect Medal, tho' I could not be affertained whether it were Antique or Couhterfeit, yet I could certainly conclude it had been made by Art from the fenfible Characterifticks of it; now it feems very ftrange to me that fo many evident Characterifticks as may be plainly difcovered in thofe figured Bodies fhould not force an affent; but truth will in time prevail; but to give as much fatisfaction as I can to all Doubts, I will pitch upon one or two of the Fables of the Metamorphofis for inftances, to fhew that they were defigned to convey a certain Hiftory very much differing from the firft appearance of the Fable. I will begin with thofe of *Ferfeus*, *Atlas*, *Andromeda* and *Medufa*, becaufe, as I conceive, they have relation to the *Herculean Columns*, and to the *Atlantis*, or thofe parts of *Libya* which were near it; they are fomewhat long, however I muft beg your Patience to explain them a little more fully, and I will be fhorter in the reft.

Perfeus from περιζέω *circumferveo*, I take to fignifie hot inflamed Air or *of Perfeus*. Lightning which is the Earthy Exhalations fet on fire by the Air diffolving them; he is faid to be the Son of *Jove*, that is of Ætherial or Elementary Fire begotten in a fhower of Gold or Fire from Heaven, that is Lightning. He carries with him the *Gorgons* Head haired with Vipers, the Picture of Lightning.

> *Viperei referens fpolium mirabile Monftri*
> *Aera carpebat tenerum ftridentibus alis.*

> *Bearing the fpoil adorn'd with fnakey Hair*
> *With clafhing Wings he rends the yielding Air.*

This I take a proper Defcription of Thunder and Lightning, fiery Serpents reprefenting the Emanations of Lightning, or the wrigling flafhes of it darting out fometimes: 'Tis reprefented as held in the Hand of *Jupiter*, fometimes in the Mouth, fometimes in the Claws of his Eagle, and we fhall find afterwards in the Fable, that the Actions of *Perfeus* againft the Sea Monfter or the Flood are compared to thofe of *Jupiter*'s Eagle.

> *Cumq; fuper Libycas Victor penderet arenas*
> *Gorgonei capitis, guttæ cæcidere cruentæ,*
> *Quas humus acceptas varios animavit in angues.*

> *And while the Victor hover'd in the Air,*
> *The drops that fell from* Gorgon's *Bloody Hair,*
> *By Earth receiv'd, were turn'd to various Snakes.*

Thefe are the effects of Heat in thofe fandy, hot, burning Countries, and I conceive this alludes to the Snake-Stones, or Thunder-bolt-ftones, as well as the living Serpents; for the vertue of the *Gorgon*'s Head, which is Subterraneous Eructations or Damps, was the petrifying Quality converting all things to Stone.

Hhhhh

Inde per immensum ventis discordibus actus,
Nunc huc, nunc illuc, exemplo Nubis aquosæ
Fertur, & ex alto, seductas æthere longe
Despectat Terras, totumq; supervolat Orbem :
Ter gelidos Arctos, ter Cancri brachia vidit,
Sæpe sub Occasus, sæpe est sublatus in Ortus.

Thence carry'd by discordant Winds he's hurl'd,
As watery Clouds through the expanded World ;
Now here, now there, on the far distant Plains
He casts a glance, then Heav'nly Arches gains ;
Thrice the cold Bear, thrice the hot Crab his Eyes
Survey, as oft to West or East he flies.

This I conceive very properly apply'd to Lightning, which is now here, now there, all over the World.

Jamq; cadente die veritus se credere Nocti,
Constitit Hesperio, regnis Atlantis in Orbe
Exiguamq; petit requiem, dum Lucifer ignes
Evocet Auroræ, Cursusq; Aurora diurnos.

And now not trusting to approaching Night,
Doth on th' Hesperian Realms of Atlas Light,
And craves some Rest, 'till Lucifer displays
Auroras blush, and she Apollo's Rays.

This describes the settling of this fiery Vapour about the Westermost parts of *Africa* ; where

Hominum cunctis ingenti corpore præstans
Japitionides Atlas fuit : Ultima Tellus
Rege sub hoc & Pontus erat, qui solis anhelis
Æquora subdit equis, & fessos excipit axes.

Gigantick Atlas Empire here possest
O're Lands extended to the farthest West ;
Where Titans panting steeds his Chariot steep,
And bath their fiery Fet-locks in the Deep.

It was a Country that lay farthest Westward where the Sun seemed to set in the Sea.

Mille greges illi, totidemq; armenta per herbas
Errabant-------

A thousand Flocks, a thousand Herds there Graz'd
On verdant plains------.

It was a delicate Country for Pasture and Cattle.

Et Humum vicinia nulla premebat.

No Neighbouring Lands offended this.

It was an Island not joined to any Continent.

Arboreæ

Arboreæ frondes auro Radiante nitentes
Ex auro Ramos, ex auro poma ferebant.

The dazling Trees there glitter in the Air,
Which golden Fruit and gilded Branches bear.

Its Rivers and Rivulets all abounded with Gold or golden Sand.

Rivers are very properly Mythologifed by Trees, the greater Body of Wa=
ter refembling the Trunk, the leffer Rivers the Branches, the Rivulets, Foun=
tains, Springs and Sources, the Twigs and Leaves; and the Hills and Mountains the Fruit: For as I have already, upon another occafion, hinted, Trees
receive the greateft part of the Sap from the Air and little from the Earth:
And they diftribute more moifture to the Earth from their Bodies by their
defcending Sap than they draw from it by their Veffels, and as the Sea Returns the Water it receives out of the Rivers into the Air, whence it circu-
lates again into the Fountains and Rivulets by condenfation and Rain, fo
doth the procefs of Nature alfo operate in the manner of returning the moifture into the Leaves, as I fhall upon another occafion more particularly ex=
plain, having mentioned it only upon this occafion to fhew how properly the
Rivers are Mythologifed by the Trees, Branches, Leaves and Fruit.

The next Verfes expreffing *Perfeus*'s Addreffes to *Atlas* is Poetical, as alfo of
Atlas's Refentiment, upon remembrance of an old Prophefy that *Parnaffian*
Themis; or all knowing Predeftination had fore-fhewn, *viz.* That time fhould
come when an Off-fpring of Celeftial Fire fhould deftroy that golden Coun=
try; for fear of which it is faid,

Id Mentvens folidis Pomaria clauferat Atlas
Mænibus, & vafto dedit fervanda Draconi,
Arcebatq; fuis externos finibus------.

This fearing, he his Orchard had inclos'd
With folid Cliffs : A Dragon too oppos'd
All Entrance------,

This *Hefperian* Garden was incircled with high Cliffs and encompaffed round
by the Sea.

Huic quoq; vade procul, ne longe gloria rerum
Quas mentiris, ait, longe tibi Jupiter abfit
Vimq; minis addit, manibufq; expellere tentat
Cunctantem, & placidis mifcentem fortia dictis.

Begon, faid he, for fear thy Glories prove
But Counterfeit, and thou no Son of Jove.
Then adds uncivil Violence to Threats ;
With ftrength the other feconds his intreats.

This Ifland had not been troubled with Thunder, Lightning, Earthquakes,
or Eruptions, poetically thus defcribed ; and how thefe came on by degrees,
and Barrennefs with Drouth increafed, and how the Inhabitants endeavoured to prevent it by their Labours ; but at laft becaufe they ftrove againft the
Courfe of Nature, the Poet makes *Perfeus* fay,

Accipe Munus, ait, Lævaq; a parte Medufæ
Ipfe retro verfus fquallentia protulit ora.

Take then, faid he, thy due Reward, to's view
Shewing Medufa's Head, his own withdrew.

That

That is, the subterraneous Eruption, and therewith the petrifactive quality exerted itself, upon that Country, and as a Consequence thereof,

> *Quantus erat ; Mons factus erat nam barba comæque*
> *In Sylvas abeunt, juga sunt humeriq; manusq;*
> *Quod caput ante fuit, summo est in monte Cacumen :*
> *Ossa Lapis fiunt, tum partes Atlas in omnes*
> *Crevit in immensum-----.*

> Atlas *to a Mountain, equal to the Man,*
> *Was turn'd, where Hair and Beard was, Trees began*
> *To grow, his Shoulders into ridges spread,*
> *And what was his, is now the Mountains Head :*
> *Bones turn to Stones, and vastly all increase-----.*

A prodigious Mountain is raised, and the *Hesperian* Garden or Country lost, this Mountain being the only remains thereof. Now before this Metamorphosis of the Country of *Atlas* into that Mountain, *Perseus* had destroyed the *Gorgons,* and cut off the head of *Medusa.* These *Gorgons* were said to inhabit certain Islands lying near *Atlas,* they were called the *Phorcidæ,* of which there were two which were said to have but one Eye between them ; possibly a *Vulcano.*

> *------Gelido sub Atlante jacentem*
> *Esse locum solida tutum molimine molis,*
> *Cujus in introitu, geminas habitasse sorores*
> *Phorcidas, unius sortitas Luminis usum.*

> *------Under frosty* Atlas *side*
> *There lay a Plain with Mountains fortify'd,*
> *In whose access the* Phorcidæ *did lye*
> *Two Sisters, both of them had but one Eye.*

This he takes with him ; that is, I suppose there began the Earthquake or the Subterraneous Vapour kindled, and thence extended to the farthest extreamity of those Islands, possibly the *Atlantick.*

> *Id se solerti, furtim dum traditur, astu*
> *Supposita cepisse manu ; perq; abdita longe,*
> *Deviaq; & Sylvis horrentia fana fragosis*
> *Gorgoneas tetigisse domos, passimq; per agros*
> *Perq; vias vidisse hominum simulacra ferarumq;*
> *In silicem ex ipsis, visa conversa medusa.*

> *How cunningly thereon his Hands he laid,*
> *As they from one another it convey'd ;*
> *Then thro' blind Wasts and rocky Forrests came*
> *To Gorgon's House ; the way unto the same*
> *Beset with forms of Men and Beasts, alone*
> *By seeing of* Medusa, *turn'd to stone.*

By which it seems to have extended a great way and to have been very Rocky, Cragged and Uninhabitable, where Men and other things had been before that time petrified. Being there arrived, he finds *Medusa* asleep ; that is, I suppose, the *Vulcano* not burning : But by this new Eruption the Head of *Medusa* is taken off, and the Vapour or Eructation riseth into the Air, partly in Flames and Lightning and fiery Vapours, which is *Perseus* ; partly in watery Vapours and Wind, which is,

Dumq;

Dumq; gravis somnus Colubros ipsamq; tenebat
Eripuisse Caput collo ; pennisq; fugacem
Pegason & fratrem, matris de sanguine natos.

And how her Head he from her Shoulders took,
E're heavy sleep her Snakes and her forsook ;
Then told of Pegasus, *and of his Brother,*
Sprung from the Blood of their new slaughter'd Mother.

This may represent the mounting of fiery Eruptions, which rise as swift as *Pegasus*, and shine like his Brother, who was supposed to brandish a golden flaming Sword. But I must hasten, *Perseus* having performed those Exploits of sinking the *Atlantick*, and raising Mount *Atlas*.

------Pennis ligat ille resumptis,
Parte ab utraq; pedes, teloq; accingitur unco,
Et liquidum motis talaribus aera findit:
Gentibus innumeris circumq; infraq; relictis
Æthiopum propulos Cephæaq; conspicit arva.

His Wings at's Feet, his Faulcion at his Side
He sprung in th' Air : Below, on either Hand,
Innumerable Nations left, the Land
Of Æthiope, and the Cephean *Fields survey'd.*

The fiery Vapours flies over several Countries till it comes to the Country of the *Æthiopians*, and the Plains of *Cepheus* or the *Drones*. Here he finds *Andromeda* chained to a Rock expecting to be devoured by a Sea Monster. *Andromeda*'s Name and Description agrees with that of an half drowned and *The Fable of* Rocky Country, by turns overflowed with the Sea at High Water and cover- *Andromeda* ed with Sand (*Jusserat Ammon*) and seems to be that part of *Africa* where *Jupiter Ammon*'s Temple was built ; which since raised, is all Sandy, and therefore is called *Ammon* or Sandy. *Perseus*, its said would have thought her Marble, but that he saw the waving of her Hair by the Wind, which may signifie that some Reeds, or such Water-plants, might grow among the Sand and Rocks sometimes overflowed by the Sea. Here (to make it short) *Perseus*, or the fiery Eruption, raiseth the frontier Parts to the Sea, and repelleth the Tide of Flood from overflowing and drowning the Land. And so *Andromeda* becomes Ἀναδρόμη, raised and freed from the Inundation ; this is so very plainly specified in the Description, that bating a little poetical Expression about Love; which *Ovid* had well studied, having a gust for it. It seems plainly to design the History of such a Metamorphosis, and very probably of that very Country I before-mentioned ; and were it worth while, I am apt to believe, that the Histories designed by all the other Fables may be discovered; for that they have all such Histories couched under them, I do no ways doubt ; not only for the Arguments I at first mentioned, but for several others. Moreover I do conceive, that there is a Chronologœ of the preceding times to be discovered out of them, and that they are written, not fortuitously, but with great Care, and according to the due Order in which they happened. And tho' possibly this do not at first view so plainly appear, nor can be so undeniably demonstrated without a more perfect knowledge of the *Hieroglyphick* and *Mythologick* Characters, yet I am almost certain that some such Chronogick Account is couched in the Fable, and may, if well examined, be detected; and to conclude, I am apt to believe, that in this Mythology is contained the greatest part of the *Ægyptian* and *Grecian* History of the preceding Ages of the World ; the truth of which I do not undertake to defend, we must take that as we do all other Histories, upon trust till we can have better

Proof either for or againft them. And if thefe be fo admitted, this Book will furnifh a fufficient number of fuch Cataftrophies that have happened in former Ages to make the Hypothefis, I have indeavoured to explain, to feem at leaft probable, if not neceffary, and neither fo abfurd or impoffible as fome have afferted.

The Fable of the Rape of Proferpina.

Read *March* 8, 169⅔. I have fome Years fince propounded in this place my Conjectures for the explication of the Mythology delivered by *Ovid* in his *Metamorphofis,* namely, That he thereby defigned to comprife a Hiftory of the changes which had happened to the World from the beginning thereof to the times wherein he lived, which he fignifies Ænigmatically by the firft four Verfes. The method of which is by perfonating Things and Powers: The one by Mortals, namely, material Things, the other by Immortals, namely, Powers, or Energies and comprifing therein a three fold *Cabala* or Tradition, namely, A *Phyfical,* comprehending the Caufes, Effects and Reafons; an *Hiftorical,* comprehending the Times, Ages, Perfons and Places, And a *Moral,* to make them Inftructive and Ufeful for the Regiment, and moralifing the more vulgar part of Mankind. In which he has indeavoured to follow the method of the Greek Poets, who, as I have formerly exemplified in *Homer, Hefiod,* and the reft of the Mythologers, did profecute the fame defign. By the interpretation of which Mythology, if we could difcover and find out the true Key, I conceive it would open and make manifeft much of the Hiftory of the Cataftrophies that have happened in the World, and of the places and Ages wherein they were produced.

That which makes me repeat this Notion at this time, is the dreadful Effects of the late Earthquake in *Sicily,* which put me in mind of what I had here formerly inftanced, on the Story as it is delivered by *Ovid* in his fifth Book concerning the Rape of *Proferpina* by *Pluto,* which I then conceived and am ftill of the fame Opinion (however others were of a contrary) was defigned by the Poet to reprefent fome dreadful Earthquake that had formerly happened in *Sicily,* not far, nor much differing from the Place and Effects of this late dreadful Cataftrophy: Save only that we do not yet hear of the fwallowing up, or the finking down into, or under the Water of any confiderable Country or Town, which I conceive is plainly fpecified by the Poet to have been effected by that which he defigns to delineate: For *Proferpina* or *Abreptà,* as the Name fignifies, is plainly defcribed to have been feated in that place of the Ifland where the Lake *Pergufa* was in *Ovid*'s Time, and where it remains, I fuppofe, to this Day: It is defcribed to be the Daughter or Off-fpring of *Ceres,* that is, a City or Place flourifhing in a much civilifed and well cultivated Country; for that *Ceres* doth plainly denote, and is fo fignified by the Poet.

> *Prima Ceres Unco Glebam Dimovit aratro,*
> *Prima dedit Fruges alimentaq; mitia terris;*
> *Prima dedit Leges: Cereris funt Omnia Munus.*

> *Ceres with crooked Plough Gleabes firft did turn,*
> *And firft taught Men to feed on Fruits and Corn:*
> *She firft gave Laws Ceres did all adorn.*

This Place or Country was alfo very pleafant and flourifhing with Fruits, Flowers, Fountains, efpecially Woods, in which *Proferpina* is faid to be difporting and innocently gathering Flowers, when *Pluto* fuddainly feifed her and carried her into the Earth; that is, whatever the place were, whether Town, Village or City before the Rape, it feems to have the fame fate with St. *Euphæmia* mentioned by *Kircher* in his *Mundus Subterraneus*; that is, to have been by an Earthquake fwallowed up into the Earth, and to have funk fo low, as to have left a Bafon for a Lake for after Ages to this Day. Now, that this is plainly the Phyfical meaning of the Poet will appear plain if the whole Story be taken in. Firft, The Poet tells you the place to be *Trinacria* or *Sicily.* This Country, tho' moft Delicious, Pleafant, rich in Soil, well Cultivated and Tilled, and

very

very much Civilifed and Governed by good Laws, as is figured by *Ceres*, as I have mentioned, was yet feated on a Sulphureous, and Fiery, Cavernous Foundation, fubject to Heavings, Tremblings and Earthquakes, expreffed by the Giant *Typhæus*, who had endeavour'd to invade Heaven, that is, to belch up Flames, and throw Stones and Rocks againft it, but at length came to be covered with this Ifland. Verfe 346, to 356. Hereupon *Dis* or *Pluto* , that is, the Spirit of the Earth is fained by the Poet to be roufed up to fee leaft the Vault of the Earth over his place of Refidence, fhould be broken by the fury of the Giant *Typhæus* ; that is, by the working of the Sulphureous Vapours and Fulminations, Ver. 356----*Et Rex pavet ipfe filentum*, Ver. 362. That is, the Earth rofe and fwelled, and there were Eruptions of Smoke fignified by the Black Horfes his Chariot was drawn by, and there was a general Earthquake over all the Ifland, but the great Eruption was at the place where the Lake *Pargufa* is. Here the Poet fains that *Pluto*, or the Subterraneous Powers were in Love with the Beauty of this Goodly Place perfonated by *Proferpina*. *Venus*, or Youthful Beauty or Thoughts doth excite *Cupid* or Love and Defire in this Terreftrial or Subterraneal Power to take away this pleafant Place, *Proferpina* from its curious Situation, and fwallow it up, or hurry it away on a fudden into his own, or the Subterraneous Regions. Ver. 363, to 385. All Poetical to exprefs how *Dis* was thus enamored of *Proferpina*, from 385, to 395. The pleafant Situation of *Proferpina* is defcribed. from 395, to 408. The Cataftophy is defcribed, which manifefts, that this terrible Earthquake extended from the place where the Lake *Pergufa* now is to the Place where the City of *Syracufe* ftood, now called *Saragofa*, where the River *Anapis* runs into the Sea : By this the Lake *Anapis* was broken open and made a Bay to the Sea, and no remainder of *Cyane*, but fome fmall Brooks that run into that Bay. This I take to be the meaning of the Poet from 409, to the end of 437. The remaining part of the Story feems to be a defcription of the Devaftations made in the Country, being made unfit for Tillage, and therefore *Ceres* is faid to feek her Daughter *Proferpina* all over the World, the remaining Husbandman feeking for other places fit for Tillage, but returns to *Sicily*, at Verfe 463.

It would be too long to interpret all which I think I could eafily do, and fhew plainly the meaning of the Phyfical *Cabala*. But I defigned to mention this only at prefent as an example pertinent to this prefent time, when we yet have the noife of the *Sicilian* Earthquake, and fome others, yet founding in our Ears : As to the Moral *Cabala* many have handled it ; and for the Hiftorical, I fhall take fome other time to Difcourfe of it, and to give my Conjectures.

A Lecture read Feb. 15, 168⅔. *confirming what the Author had before faid as to Earthquakes and their Effects.*

I need not repeat what I have formerly faid as to the feveral curioufly figured Stones found in many parts, nay, I may fay, all parts of the Earth, that they are really the feveral Bodies they reprefent, or the mouldings of them Petrified, and not, as fome have imagined, *a Lufus Naturæ* fporting her felf in the needlefs formation of ufelefs Beings.

I fhall only add fome Confirmations of the Conclufions I then deduced from an *Hypothefis*, which I took the liberty to propofe. And Firft,

As to the Sphæriodical Figure of the Earth, and thence of the Decreafe of Gravity towards the Æquator inftead of the Increafe, as moft of the followers of *Des Cartes*, Mr. *Hobbs*, and divers others of the Modern Naturalifts affert; tho' it were at firft much oppofed, yet I find that it is now by divers not thought fo improbable but that it may be fuppofed ; and tho' I find the confequent Suppofition as yet oppofed, yet I queftion not but in time to make that appear to be neceffary alfo ; but every thing muft have its time. As to that alfo which I have Publifhed, how unlikely foever it may appear, I hope

alfo

also to be able to produce very good Arguments for it, and that it was not an Hypothesis proposed at random, as some may imagine.

But because these in themselves, tho' fully proved, were not sufficient to solve all the *Phænomena* of Nature as to the Disposition of those figured Bodies, whether Shells or other Substances; therefore in the fourth place I laid down as a Supposition, that the superficial Parts of the Earth had been very much altered by *Subterraneous Eruptions*, whereby divers Parts that had before such Eruptions or Earthquakes been under the Sea, had been raised out of it and been made Islands; and that other parts that had been dry Land had been sunk into and covered by the Sea; that Vallies had been turned to Cliffs, and Hills to Vallies or Lakes, and the like.

Confirmation of the Atlantis. This was likewise opposed and thought very improbable, because for so long time as our History will reach backwards, it was affirmed there had happened no such change; and therefore, because it was supposed no such History could be produced, this also was to be rejected, and we must again have recourse to the *Lusus Naturæ* as the only expedient to give satisfaction; only some kind of Subterraneous Passages were thought of, by which Oysters and other Fish might be conveyed to the middle of the *Alps*, going along with the Stream of the Water from the Sea to supply the Springs and Fountains at the top of the Hills.

I confess it seemed to me a little hard, because I could not give the Pedigree of the Fish, therefore I should not be allowed to believe it a Fish, when I saw all the sensible marks of a Fish; and that, because I could not tell who it was, or upon what occasion that caused the Stones on *Salisbury* Plain to be dispersed in that irregular Regularity, that therefore I must allow them to be a *Lusus Naturæ*, or placed there by *Merlin* or, some such unknown way, and not by the Hands, Labour or Workmanship of some such Men as are now living. Nevertheless that I might, as far as I was able, satisfy these Objections also, I produced the History of *Plato* as brought out of *Ægypt* by *Solon*, concerning the Island of the *Atlantis*. But this tho' related by *Plato*, with all the Circumstances, as if he believed it a true History, was yet supposed to be only a Fiction of *Plato* to lay the Scene of his Common-wealth, or at best a Fable of the *Ægyptian* Priest to magnify the knowledge of the *Ægyptians* as to the History of preceding Ages. I confess the account of the nine thousand Years is Argument enough to make the whole History to be suspected as a Fiction; but yet till we are certain what space of Time is there signified by a Year it will be a little hard to reject the whole for that Circumstance, since most of the other Circumstances of it are more probable.

And that they were thought so by divers of the Ancients, is plain from several Testimonies that might be alledged; I shall only mention what *Strabo* says of it in his second Book, where examining whether *Eratosthenes* had duly amended the τῆς οἰκȣμενης πίνακα of the Antients he adds, that τὸ ϳε εξαίρεɔϑαι τlω γὴν ποτὲ, &c. *Eratosthenes* (says he) has done well in expounding the manner how the Surface of the Earth may be changed, by relating how the same may sometimes be raised, and sometimes be sunk by Earthquakes, and various otherways changed, as we also have in many particulars Enumerated, by which also he hath properly shown how the History, which *Plato* relates concerning the Island of *Atlantis*, as it was brought out of *Ægypt* from the Priests there, by *Solon*, may be well believed not to be a Fiction, but a true History. From which Passage it is plain, that both *Strabo* and *Eratosthenes* did look upon this History of *Plato*, or rather of the *Ægyptians*, as very probable; *Pliny* also was of the like Opinion, as appears, not only by his mentioning the History of *Plato*, but by the several other Mutations, which he relates to have been made by the means of Earthquakes.

But because the Scene of this Tragedy of *Atlantis* was placed very far backwards in times remote, and that we have no other History of this change but what *Plato* is pleased to relate, I did therefore indeavour to produce some History concerning the changes that had happened since that time, namely, within the reach of the Greek Histories, in the same place where this *Atlantis*

was

was said to be sunk down into the Sea. For this I produced the History of the *Periplus* of *Hanno*, the *Carthaginian*, as it is set forth by *Berkelius* ; from which I collected that at the time when this Expedition was made, the place where the *Atlantis* was said to be sunk, was found to be partly Sea and partly Islands, and that the same extended, as I conceive, as far to the Westwards almost as the *Madera* Island, about which place was then found a small Island called *Cerne* ; from which Coasting Southwards for twelve Days, they found the Land all on Fire, and one prodigious high Mountain flaming out at the top, called *Theon Ochema*, or the Chariot of the Gods ; which, by all Circumstances, I conceived to be the same with the now Pike of *Teneriff*. Supposing which Relation true, I deduced thence that there must needs have happened great changes in those Parts between the time of this Expedition and the present ; for that all those places which seem to be described by that History are not now to be found in the places where they are by that Relation placed. But this Relation was also looked upon as fabulous, because I produced no other Authority for it besides the Relation itself and the Testimony of *Pliny*. But those who are better read in Ancient History, may find that it was by most of the Ancients supposed real ; and all agree that the *Phænicians*, of whom the *Carthaginians* were a Colony, were very skillful in Astronomy, Navigation, Arithmetick and Traffick, and that they were the first introducers of these among the Greeks, together with the Knowledge and Use of Letters. And from those Particulars I noted in the said Relation, it seems to me very evident, that they understood what Longitude and Latitude was, and knew how to keep account of their Course and Distance ; and tho' the Interpretation thereof which I produced, be differing from all the other I have yet known : Some supposing it to relate wholly to the Coast of *Africa* as it is shaped, at present, and others in other Situations , yet whoever (taking this Notion of their skill in Astronomy and Navigation along with them) shall strictly examine the Relation itself, he will, I conceive, be persuaded to be somewhat of my Mind. *Strabo* therefore says of them. *The* Sidonians *were reported to be good Artists in various things, as it is also manifest by their Actions ; as also, good Philosophers, Astronomers and Arithmeticians, and such as well knew the secret of Numbers and of Sailing in the Night also.* From which consideration I conceive, that χαὶ εὐθυ in the Relation can signify nothing else but the same Parallel of Latitude, or the same straight Line with that from *Carthage* to the Mouth of the *Streights*.

I was not then able to quote the place in *Aristotle* which relates to this discovery of the *Carthaginians*, tho' I was well assured I had met with such a Relation ; 'Tis in his Book, περὶ θαυμασιῶν ἀκυσμάτων, in these Words, εν τῇ θαλασσῇ τῇ εξω Ηρακλείων ϛηλῶν φασὶν ὑπο καρχηδενίων νῆσον ευρεθῆναι ερ ἡμιν ἐχϙσαν ὕλϙω τε παντοδαπλω ῇ ποταμϙς πλωτϙς ῇ τοῖς λοιποῖς καρποῖς θαυμαϛλω ἀπέχϙσαν ἢ πλεῖονων ἡμερῶν, &c. ' In the Sea that lies without the Pillars of ' *Hercules*, they say, that, by the *Carthaginians*, there has been discovered an ' Island deserted, but abounding with variety of Woods, and rich Rivers fit ' for Navigation, abounding also with variety of Fruits, distant from the ' Continent several Days Sail. *Pomponius Mela* also mentions the extream *Atlantick* to be inhabited by a wild sort of People, which he calls *Ægypanes*, *Blemmeæ* and *Gamphasentes*, and a kind of *Satyrs*. And in his Third Book and tenth Chapter, he says, *Ultra hunc sinum mons altus ut Græci vocant* Θεῶν ὄχϙυα *vehiculum Deorum perpetuis ignibus flagrat*, &c. *Diodorus Siculus* also mentions some such Island in his Fifth Book τὴν λιϐυϙω χεῖται μὲν πελαγία νησος, &c. That is, ' Against *Libya* there is situated an Island in the Ocean, considerable ' for Magnitude, several Days Sail distant towards the West, *&c.* I could cite several other Authors who mention some such Place, which may have relation to the discoveries of the *Carthaginians* in *Hanno*'s Expedition ; all which do plainly make it appear, that his discoveries were towards the West, and not towards the South ; and therefore it seems very probable, that at that time there were Islands both greater and smaller to the Westwards of the Streights Mouth, which are not now to be found, and consequently they must have suffered a Submersion by some intervening Catastrophies, which was the thing I indeavoured to deduce from it. Nor will it seem so unlikely if we will

K k k k k   but

but confider the alterations by Eruptions out of the Sea near the Iſlands of the *Canarys*, and in one of the Iſlands alſo within theſe few Years ; the for-mer was the Eruption out of the Sea, in the Year 1639, which *Athanatius Kircher* has given a deſcription of, and I have received a relation of it by Word of Mouth from two Perſons who were both upon the *Tenariff* Iſland at the ſame time, and had each of them often obſerved it tho' at a conſiderable diſtance: The latter Eruption happened within a few Years ſince in one of the ſame Iſlands, of which I have Printed the Relation in one of my Collections.

And thus, I hope, I have given ſome ground to believe that the Antient Hiſtorians knew and gave ſome Credit alſo to both theſe Relations, namely, that of *Solon* and that of *Hanno*, which, by that Paſſage of *Ariſtotle*, appears to have been made either before or in his time.

I came in the next place to ſhew that the *Metamorphoſis* of *Ovid* contained many Hiſtories of great Changes and Cataſtrophies that had happened long before his time to the parts of the Earth ; which, tho' rapped up in Mytho-logy and Maſcarade, yet thoſe diſguiſes being removed, it will not, I con-ceive, be very difficult to make appear what the true Hiſtories are, which now paſs Incognito. To this purpoſe I did obſerve that *Ovid* has in ſome part or other of his Fable, given Marks or Characteriſticks by which it may be found what the Hiſtory is which he doth there Mythologize; this he doth very often in that part which ſerves as a Link to join the Story into a con-tinued Chain or in the Etymology of the Names, tho' often times alſo in the proceſs of the Poem. And 'tis uſual with him all along to have and mix a treble Deſign in each of them, namely, an Hiſtorical, a Phyſical, and a Mo-ral; and this he hath done with great Judgment and Subtilty of Invention, and upon ſeveral occaſions, he makes Excurſions into this or that Deſign, and proſecuting it for a time, as if he had no reſpect to the other two ; but yet, if well examined, it will be found, I conceive, in moſt that he influenc-eth, even there alſo, that deſign by the other two. If I had leiſure to pro-ſecute this Speculation, I conceive I could trace moſt of theſe his Deſigns, but it would be too long a Work ; however, I hope in a ſhort time to be able to give ſeveral Inſtances and Examples out of thoſe I have more attentively ex-amined, which may ſuffice to ſhew that there is a probability in this Con-jecture how differing ſoever it be from other Commentators.

But thoſe perhaps may not be thought ſufficient for the preſent Diſpute to ſatisfy ſuch as demand poſitive and direct Hiſtories, and undoubted Records of ſuch Changes, as I have ſuppoſed neceſſary to make out the Hypotheſis of the figured Bodies, which are found to be real Shells, *&c.* and to have been by them diſpoſed and ſituated in the places where they are now found : For ſuch therefore I ſhall prepare a Cloud of Witneſſes, which, unleſs they will deny all Hiſtory, will ſtand the Proof.

I confeſs I cannot ſee any Circumſtance in the Story of *Hanno* that ſhould render it ſuſpected, ſince 'tis granted by all, that the *Phænicians*, of whom the *Carthaginians* were a Colony, were ſo early eminent in Arts, eſpecially in that of Navigation and Traffick ; ſo that we find *Solon* made uſe of them ; and that *Sanchoniathon Beritius* before the time of the *Trojan* War, did write the Theology of the *Phænicians* (as *Porphyrius* relates) in the *Phænician* Language : And that the Philoſophy of the Greeks was derived principally from them ; as alſo Aſtronomy, and even the knowledge and uſe of Letters. For *Thales* was a *Phænician*, and *Pherecides* who was the Maſter of *Pythagoras*, and the founder of the Italick Phyloſophy, and co-equal with *Thales* learned it out of the occult Books of the *Phænicians*. And from *Pythagoras* his Philoſophy ſprang and flowed both the *Platonick* Philoſophy, and alſo the Philoſophy of his Scholar *Ariſtotle*, tho' ſomewhat altered by the Pipes it ran through. So that tho' we have but very little of the Hiſtory of thoſe Times, yet by thoſe few Fragments diſperſed here and there, we may be ſufficiently ſatisfied they were able, and actually did make as great Voyages and Diſcoveries, as that of *Hanno* ; of which there are divers Relations mentioned by *Herodotus* in his ſecond Book.

But

But tho' (notwithſtanding what I have alledged) all theſe Hiſtories ſhall be looked upon as Fictions and Romantick without any real Ground, yet what I have indeavoured to ſhew by Experiment and Inſpection, and the deductions made therefrom, will not be found deſtitute of good Authority, proved from very eminent Authors both Antient and Modern, to make out the Truth and Certainty thereof.   As firſt to prove, that thoſe Bodies were found at the tops of Mountains, and that they were notwithſtanding aſſerted to be Shells ; we have the Teſtimony of *Herodotus* in his *Euterpe* or ſecond Book, and twelveth Section, where ſpeaking of the Country of *Ægypt*, as having been moſtly raiſed by the Mud and Sand of the *Nile*, he ſays, the whole Country was of ſuch a Soil, only the Mountain above *Memphis* was Sandy, and had *Conchilia* or Fiſhes Shells upon it, and abounded with Salt, ſo that it corrupted the *Pyramids*.   Which Paſſage is very pertinent to my preſent purpoſe, and is alſo fully confirmed by *Ariſtotle :* For it ſeems all the lower *Ægypt* was a Plain, which had roſe by the ſettlement of Mud of the *Nile*, which he ſays, in the ſpace of nine hundred Years, had been raiſed eight Cubits, or twelve Foot ; for that eight Foot riſe of the *Nile*, in the time of *Myris*, overflowed all *Ægypt*, and in his time there was neceſſary ſixteen Cubits, or twenty four Foot ſwelling to overflow it.   So that he ſeems to underſtand, that all the lower *Ægypt* had been at firſt Sea, and that the *Nile*, by degrees, had filled it up to the height of the Plain, and ſo had covered all the bottom or Sand of the Sea, only the Mountainous part above *Memphis* was above that level, and ſo that kept its old bottom or covering of Sand and Shells.   This ſeems to be the meaning of what he argues for ; but yet I muſt needs ſay, that does not ſolve all the Difficulty ; for how comes this Mountain to be ſo much higher than the Plain, as it was then raiſed by the *Nile*, and thence that Plain to be much above the Sea that was thereby excluded, unleſs we do ſuppoſe alſo that ſome Subterraneous Power did raiſe that Mountain above the level it was of when covered by the Sea, or that the Sea had ſometimes been ſo high as to cover that Mountain, which, tho' *Herodotus* takes no notice of, yet *Ariſtotle* does fully ſolve it ; but be it which way ſoever, 'tis Teſtimony enough of the matter of Fact, that *Herodotus* himſelf calleth them κογχυλια, and obſerved the exudation of the Salt.   But this Place is alſo obſervable for another Paſſage, and that is to confirm Conjectures I formerly acquainted the Society with, concerning the *Pyramids of Ægypt*, namely, that I conceived them to be *founded on and Aſhler'd, as it weere about a Core of Rock,* and by this Diſcourſe it is plain, that the place where they ſtand is ſo qualified ; for by this Deſcription 'tis plain, that it is deſcribed as Rocky, and covered with Sea Sand ; for that *Herodotus* takes notice it had both Sea-ſhells, and Salt mixed with it ; but this here only by the bye.   Before I leave *Herodotus* his Teſtimony, I cannot but take notice of another Paſſage in the ſame Book, in the 74th. and 75th Paragraphs ; the tranſlate runs thus, *Circa Thebas ſunt Sacri Serpentes Nihil omnino hominibus noxii, puſillo corpore, binis prædti cornibus e ſummo vertice enatis, quos defunctos in Jovis Æde ſepeliunt, huic enim Deo Sacros illos eſſe prædicant* ; thus far is the ſtory he is told by the *Ægyptians. Eſt autem Arabiæ Locus, ad Butum urbem fere poſitus ad quem Locum ego me contuli quod audirem volucres eſſe Serpentes. Eo cum perveni, Oſſa Serpentum aſpexi & Spinas multitudine Supra ſidem ad Enarrandum quarum acervi erant magni, & his alii atq; alii minores ingenti Numero. Eſt autem hic Locus ubi Spinæ projectæ Jacebant hujuſcemodi, ex Arctis montibus exporrigitur in vaſtam planitiem Ægyptiæ Contiguam. Fertur ex Arabia Serpentes alatos, ineunte ſtatim vere, in Ægyptum volare, ſed eis ad ingreſſum planities occurrentes aves Ibides, non permittere ſed ipos interimere, & ob id opus Ibin magno in honore ab Ægyptiis haberi, Arabes aiunt.*

Part of this ſtory is what he was told, part what he ſaw ; he was told of flying Serpents, which the Bird *Ibis* met over that Valley, and ſo devoured them leaving only the Back-bone.   I have heard many ſtories told of our Snake-ſtones or *Cornua Ammonis*, and I have ſeen ſome to confirm the ſtory with a very formal Head carved on them ; I think not long ſince here was one ſhewed in this place ; I am apt to think the Spines of the Serpents *Herodotus* there found in ſuch plenty and ſuch variety of bigneſſes, were no other than thoſe *Cornua Ammonis*, and thence, I conceive, proceeded the ſuperſtitious

Cuſtom

Tho' Hiſtory ſhould fail Experiments are Cogent.

Proofs out of Herodotus.

The Pyramids are founded on a Rock.

Cuftom when they found any of thefe Stones or Spinæ they carried and buried them in the Temple of *Jupiter Ammon*, and it feems to me a farther confirmation of what I formerly hinted concerning the Stone adorned with Jewels, and carried in proceffions by the Priefts of that Temple, mentioned by *Pliny* and feveral others. But to proceed, to this Teftimony and Opinion of *Herodotus*, I fhall add that of *Pythagoras*, as related by *Ovid* in his 15th Book of the Metamorphofis, *ver.* 262, and fo onwards. *Vidi ego quod fuerat quondam Solidiffima tellus, effe fretum. Vidi factas ex æquore terras : Et procul a pelago conchæ Jacuere Marinæ. Et vetus inventa eft in montibus anchora fummis.* From which Teftimonies 'tis plain that this Phænomenon of Shells was taken notice of by the Antient Hiftorians and Philofophers : And I am apt to think that this might, in fome meafure, fpread among them, the Notion of general Deluges that in preceding Ages had happened, as *Pythagoras* feems to hint in this place, by fuppofing them to happen after a certain long Revolution of time ; and that *Thales*, and many others, fuppofed that the Principle, from which all things fprung, was Water : And that the Paffage in the Fragment of *Sanchoniathon*, where he fpeaks of the firft Original of all things, fays, That in the *Phænician* Language it was called μὰτ, which poffibly may be much of the fignification of ‎מוט‎ in the Hebrew, which fignifies Motion ; that is, Fluidity, for fo the interpretation of *Sanchoniathon* feems to make it τѢτο πινές φαςιν ἰλον οἱ ἢ ὑδατάδης μίξεως σήψιν ἢ, ἐκ ταύτης ἐγένѢτο πᾶσα απορά κτίσεως ἢ γένεσις ὅλων. Which fome will have to be Mud, others the Corruptions of watery mixtures (as if μὰτ were derived from ‎מות‎, *Mors* Death or Corruption) from which fprung the Seeds of all living Creatures, and the Generation of all things. That the *Ægyptians* threw the Hiftory of the Flood fo far backwards, and make it fo differing from the Chronology of the Bible, I take it to be for no other Caufe but to make the World believe they were preceding to all others in Antiquity of Hiftory and Chronology : To which purpofe *Herodotus* tells a pleafant Relation of *Pfammiticus*, that the *Ægyptians* before his time had vaunted themfelves to be the firft People upon the Face of the Earth, but he having a mind to be informed of this by Experiment, caufed two Children to be bred up in a Defert Place by a Shepherd, fo that they fhould not hear any Language at all fpoken, to the end to fee what Language they would naturally fpeak of themfelves ; from hence he fuppofed they would fpeak the firft and moft Natural Language. This having been done, and the Children grown two Years old, the Shepherd opening the Door of the place where they were fo kept and fed with Milk, they both reached out their Hands to him crying *Beccos*, which the Shepherd taking notice of acquainted *Pfammiticus* with, who inquiring what that word might fignify in any Language, was informed that *Beccos* fignified Bread in the *Phrygian* Language ; from which time *Herodotus* fays, the *Ægyptians* loft their feniority, and granted the *Phrygians* to be the firft and themfelves the fecond People for Antiquity. So that tho' their account of Years may be hence fuppofed to be uncertain, yet their Learning and their lafting Monuments of their former greatnefs, namely, the *Pyramids*, *Obelisks*, *Coloffi*, *Labyrinths*, and the like, fhewed them to have been long before *Herodotus* his time very confiderable for Arts and Literature. And that they had fome Records of a preceding Flood, I have before mentioned, whether the fame with that of *Noah*, or fome more particular Flood, which thofe of *Deucalion* and *Ogyges* feem to have been, I leave to the learned Antiquaries to determine. I could produce feveral other Teftimonies to fhew they had the notion of a Deluge.

of Noah's *Flood.*   But it feems to me very improbable, that thefe Shells fhould have been the effect of *Noah*'s Flood by reafon of its fhort duration ; which was not long enough of continuance to produce and perfect thofe Creatures in fo fhort a fpace to the bignefs and perfection they feem to have had. It muft therefore have been either fome particular Floods of a longer duration ; or elfe the places where they are found, muft have been fome times or other the bottom of the Sea, and afterwards raifed by Subterraneous Motions, Swellings, or Eruptions : Which, whither thofe juft immediately preceded the end of the general Deluge in the time of *Noah*, and that That part which before the Flood was Land, did fink, and became covered by the Sea, and thofe

parts

parts which were before under the Sea, did, by degrees, towards the determination of that Cataftrophy, rife and fwell up into Land, Hills and Mountains, I leave to the Learned to determine. Certain it is, that there were fome very great changes of the fuperficial Parts of the Earth at that time; fince it is faid, that all the Fountains of the Deep, or Abyffe, were broken up; the Scripture renders ἐῤῥάγνσαν πᾶσαι ἀι πηγὰι τῆς ἀβύσσε κὶ οἱ καταῤῥάκται τῶ ϗρανῶ ἠνεῴχϑησαν. There feems by the Expreffion to be a twofold fupply of Water to caufe this Flood, the one by the opening of the *Stereoma* or Firmament in the middle of the Waters, *viz.* that of the ϛερέωμα ἐν μέσω τῶ ὕδατος, and of the ϛερέωμα τῶ ϗρανῶ, the gathering together of the Waters above the former ϛερέωμα ; but ὑποκάτω τῶ ϗρανῶ, thefe God called the Sea, and the parts of the Earth that were uncovered thereby he called dry Land. The *Stereoma* τῶ ϗρανῶ is affigned for the place of the Stars, Sun and Moon, *&c.* and has always the Epithet of τῶ ϗρανῶ joined with it. *Ovid* likewife who feems to allude in fome meafure to this Hiftory of the Creation delivered by *Mofes* in the firft Chapter of *Genefis*, fays, *Circumfluus humor ultima poffedit folidumq; coercuit orbem.* I think, were it proper to the prefent Subject, I could give a very plaufible account concerning the manner of that Deluge, as it is expreffed by *Mofes*; tho' it differ from all that I have yet met with, yet I can prove it warranted both by the Text and by genuine Phyfical Principles ; but it would be too long a digreffion for the prefent Subject, and I fhall fhortly have a more proper opportunity to demonftrate the inner Parts and Conftitution of this Globe, my prefent Bufinefs being to explicate the Phænomena of the outward and fuperficial Parts, and to prove that the Bodies, which I have afferted to be Shells, have been fo reputed by the Antient as well as the Modern Hiftorians : Next to fhew that they are, or have been, found in moft Parts of the World. And if thofe two be proved, then will neceffarily follow that there muft have been fome time or other fuch Cataftrophies, Metamorphofes, or Mutations as muft haue caufed thofe parts, which were once the bottom of the Sea, to be now, or at the time when they were fo obferved, to be dry Land.

That they were fo efteemed by divers of the Antients I have in part fhewn and could inlarge upon that Head, but that I would likewife fhew that they have been fo efteemed by the moft eminent of our Modern Naturalifts, and for this I could produce the Teftimonies of *Georgius Agricola, Cardan, Gefner, Aldrovandus, Ferranti Imperatus, Wormius, Calceolarius, Bauhinus, Belonius, Fracaftorius, Cifalpinus, Fabius Columba, Stevinus,* and a great many others yet more Modern, befides the Teftimony and Opinion of divers others, who have themfelves declared their Judgment by word of Mouth ; but this would be too great a wafting of Time to prove that which carries in itfelf the true *Medium* of its Proof and Demonftration, which is by fenfible examination. I fhall therefore only give one Inftance or two for all, and that is, Firft, That of *Fabius Columba,* who has writ a Treatife on purpofe to evidence this Truth by many Arguments; 'tis at the end of his Treatife *De Purpura. Nituntur* *Proofs out of Modern Writers.* *quidam* (fays he) *acanis Naturæ in medium adductis, omni Refponfione Seclufa, Linguas Serpentinas aut Gloffo-petras ; quia non Solum mari, proximis & infulis, fed etiam Longe diffitis, copiofe Reperiri traduntur, ab ipfa formatrice natura, fic genitas atq; Lapideas effe : Vel qui dentes effe dicunt, non Carchariæ, Lamiæ, Malthæ aut ejusdem generis Cætaceorum, fed illis fimiles fponte fic ortos Quin etiam id tantum Naturam produxiffe eo loci, quod ratione materiei aptum erat ad formam illam Recipiendam affirmant. Hoc Argumento in dubium Revocare videntur, an unquam Locis illis mare fuerit,* Quod probatiffimi antiquiores Philofophi & Hiftorici affirmarunt. Nos *quidem dicimus hujusmodi concretionem* non effe lapideam, *ex ipfo* afpectu, Effigie *rei,* ac tota fubftantia : *Ac neminem cenfemus tam Craffa Minerva Natum, qui ftatim primo* intuitu *non affirmarit* Dentes effe Offeos *non* lapideos, *Sed præter* afpectum *omnia quæ Ligneam, offeam, & Carneam Naturam habent,* Uftione *in* Carbonem *prius abeunt, quam in* Calcem, *aut* Cinerem. *Ea vero quæ tophace vel Saxea Sunt Natura, non in Carbonem fed in Calcem abire, nifi liquuntur propter vitream ant Metallicam mixtionem. Cum igitur hi dentes ftatim* affati tranfeant *in* Carbonem & *tophum adhærentem minime,* clarum crit offeas effe *dentes non Lapilleas.* He hath many other Arguments to confirm this Truth, which would be too long to trouble you with at this time, and I only proceeded so far that I might give an occasion to have the Experiment now tried in the presence of this Society, there being several of that kind in the Repository, and the trial being very easy will not be long in making, all things being in a readiness for it. I shall only add one more Testimony, which is of *Andreas Cisalpinus* in his first Book *de Re Metallica* and second Chapter. *In fodinis metallorum seu Marmorum* (says he) *aliorumq; Saxorum Nunquam vivens Corpus Reperitur. Etsi enim aliquando in eorum Cæsura ostrearum testæ aut cætera Conchilia Reperta sunt; hæc recedente Mari & Lapidescente Solo inibi derelicta in Lapides concreverunt. Ubiq; enim vbi nunc est arida aliquando affuisse Mare testatur Aristoteles. Hoc enim modo Censere magis Consonum est rationi, quam putare vim animalem, intra Lapides, rudimenta animalium ac plantarum Gignere ut quidam putant.* He hath not told where *Aristotle* hath maintained this Doctrine; but whosoever shall examine his Writings, shall, by many Passages in them find, that he was fully of this Judgment: And more fully in the fourteenth Chapter of the first Book of *Meteors*, where also he confirms the same Sentiments of *Herodotus*, which I have newly quoted; and concurs likewise with the Doctrine of the alterations that are caused by slow degrees of Progress, which I have Hypothetically explained by the Oval Figure of the Earth, and the alteration of that shorter Axis to differing parts of the Earth: But this only by the bye to shew how much soever that Hypothesis were exploded by a learned Dr., by reason of the Consequences that would follow from it; yet *Aristotle* (though he hath not explained by what means and in what manner) hath asserted Mutations as great and much after the same method of Progression, as those which are alledged to be the *extravagant Consequences of that Hypothesis*, some of which I shall have occasion to mention at another time. So that to conclude for this time I hope I have shewn good grounds to evince. First, That these kind of Bodies are either Animal or Vegetable Substances. Secondly, That the places where these are found must have sometimes been covered with the Sea. Thirdly, That the general Deluge of *Noah* was not of duration enough to effect it, unless the manner of its effecting were after that which I proposed, by changing that part which was before dry Land into Sea, by sinking; and that which was Sea into dry Land, by rising underneath it. Fourthly, That the universality of the *Phænomena* over the whole Earth seem to argue for this manner. Fifthly, That there have been several particular Floods, as that of *Deucalion*, the *Atlantick*, &c. which being caused, for the most part, by Earthquakes, may have been the causes of divers particular *Phænomena*, such as the raising of some parts from under the Sea, and the sinking of others into it, or into Lakes.

The former Lecture was read *Feb.* 15*th.* 1688.

Feb. 29. 1688. I have, in my former Lecture, proved how early and how generally the Phænomena of Shells were taken notice of by the most antient Historians and Philosophers, and I could have given many other Instances to confirm it, if it had been thought necessary. And thence, I conceived, might be continually revived the Traditions and Theories concerning preceding Floods and other Catastrophies that had happened to the Earth in Ages long preceding. But because, among the Philosophers, I only quoted that place in *Plato* about the *Atlantis*, which was thought to be a Fiction (however that shewed he had such a notion) and the Doctrine of *Pythagoras* as reported by

Proofs out of Aristotle.

Ovid, which was thought Poetical (tho' as I conceive all those Mythologies have certain Historical and real Truths thereby represented) I shall therefore add one out of *Aristotle* which I hinted the last Day out of his first Book of Meteors. ' The same parts of the Earth (says he) are not always dry or
' moist, but they receive a change from the increase or defect of Rivers;
' therefore parts bounding Sea and Land change often, nor is the same part
' always Sea or always Land, but is changed in time, and that which was Sea
' is Land, and that which was Land is Sea; but this is in a long process:
' This arrives from interior changes of the Earth, which from a long Consti-
' tution grows old, as the Bodies of Plants and Animals, and that not singly the
' Parts

' Parts but the whole. It may therefore for a time be moiſt, and by degrees
' grow dry and old: This may happen both by the decreaſing of Rivers and alſo
' of the Sea ; but theſe happen not, but in a long time, in compariſon of our
' ſhort Life, which is the cauſe they are not noted, the change being ſo little
' in the ſpace of one Life, and ſo ſeveral Ages paſs before they are finiſhed ;
' whence the memory of them is loſt. (He adds much more to the ſame effect
' to explain his Notion) Exemplifying his Doctrine by *Ægypt,* which (ſays
' he) has been all made by Mud of Rivers, and is obſerved continually to
' grow drier, and the Lakes filling up by degrees have been inhabited, and
' length of time has obliterated the memory of ſuch changes ; for all the pre-
' ſent Mouths of *Nile,* except the *Canobic,* have been cut by Art ; for old
' *Ægypt* was that only about *Thebes,* as *Homer* teſtifies, who lived not long
' after theſe Changes ; for he mentions *Thebes* only as if *Memphis* had not yet
' then been, ſo he proceeds in explicating, and inſtances again in ſaying, ſo
' marſhy places grow better by draining, but dry grow worſe and barren, as
' it has happened to the Country about the *Argives,* and the *Mycenæans,* and
' what has happened to theſe parts, the ſame may be conceived of the whole.
' So many parts which have been Sea have been added to the Continent ; and
' the contrary, thoſe that do *reſpicere ad pauca,* aſcribe theſe changes to the
' Heavens, but they are miſtaken ; but they are to be aſcribed to Cauſes that
' happen after a long proceſs of time, as that of *Deucalion*'s Flood, which hap-
' pened only to *Greece* about that part which is called old *Hellas,* which is
' that about the preſent *Dodon* and *Achelous* ; this happened from great abun-
' dance of Rains which are generated by the Mountains, which are by de-
' grees changed and ſo produce differing effects. He exemplifies his Doctrine
further by *Ægypt,* and the Country where the Oracles of *Jupiter Ammon*
was, ſaying, ' 'Twas formerly Marſhy, but by degrees dried and grew parched ;
' ſo not only the preſent moſt famous Rivers will come in long proceſs of time
' to be dried and changed, but the Sea alſo ; and that which was Sea will be
' Land, and the Land will be Sea. I have here given the ſum of his Doctrine
which he doth much inlarge upon to explain it ; but to ſave time, I have only
abſtracted the meaning, and given you the Epitomy of it that may eaſily e-
nough be more fully explained or read at large in the fourthteenth Chapter of
his firſt Book of *Meteors.* By the whole it plainly appears, that *Ariſtotle* was
of the Opinion that all the dry Land of the Earth had been ſometimes covered with the Sea, which he ſeems to be informed of by the then preſent *Phænomena,* as he plainly expreſſes in his deſcription of *Ægypt,* and of the Country about the Oracle of *Jupiter Ammon* ; and 'tis not to be doubted but one
of thoſe *Phænomena* and poſſibly not the leaſt conſiderable was that of the Sea-
ſand and Shells, which I ſhewed the laſt Day *Herodotus* had taken notice of. I
do therefore humbly conceive (tho' ſome poſſibly may think there is too much
notice taken of ſuch a trivial thing as a rotten Shell, yet) that Men do generally too much ſlight and paſs over without regard theſe Records of Antiquity which Nature have left as Monuments and Hieroglyphick Characters of
preceding Tranſactions in the like duration or Tranſactions of the Body of the
Earth, which are infinitely more evident and certain tokens than any thing of
Antiquity that can be fetched out of Coins or Medals, or any other way yet
known, ſince the beſt of thoſe ways may be counterfeited or made by Art and
Deſign, as may alſo Books, Manuſcripts and Inſcriptions, as all the Learned
are now ſufficiently ſatisfied, has often been actually practiſed ; but thoſe
Characters are not to be counterfeited by all the Craft in the World, nor can
they be doubted to be, what they appear, by any one that will impartially examine the true appearances of them : And tho' it muſt be granted, that it is
very difficult to read them, and to raiſe a *Chronology* out of them, and to ſtate
the intervalls of the Times wherein ſuch, or ſuch Cataſtrophies and Mutations have happened ; yet 'tis not impoſſible, but that, by the help of thoſe
joined to other means and aſſiſtances of Information, much may be done even
in that part of Information alſo. And tho' poſſibly ſome may ſay, I have
turned the World upſide down for the ſake of a Shell, yet, as I think, there
is no one has reaſon for any ſuch aſſertion from any action I have hitherto
done ; yet if by means of ſo ſlight and trivial Signs and Tokens as theſe are,
there

there can be Discoveries made and certain Conclusions drawn of infinitely more important Subjects; I hope the attempts of that kind do no ways deserve reproach, since possibly 'tis not every one that takes notice of them, nor one of a hundred that does, that will think of a reason; besides, much greater conclusions have been deduced from less evident and more inconsiderable Marks, if we respect Bulk, Magnitude, or Number, and much more weighty Consequences may, and will in time, be drawn from seemingly more trivial, and much lighter and slighter Indications, yet where the Testimonies are clear, certain and self-evident, they are not to be rejected for their bulk, tho' it be so small as no Eye or Sense can reach it unless assisted by Engines, as the Sight by a Microscope, Telescope, and the like: In how few Letters, Words, or Characters is the History of the World before *Noah*'s Flood? Is it therefore not to be believed because we have not as many Volumes of its History as there are now to be found words? In how little room will the History of the Flood be contained if *Homer*'s Iliads could be boxed in a Nutshell? But to leave every one to the freedom of his own Thoughts, I shall proceed to what I thought was further necessary to be added to what I hinted the last Day, which was concerning the Flood of *Noah*, because I find the generality of those who indeavour to give a solution of these *Phænomena*, are inclined to ascribe them to the effects of that Flood, and because what I then said was but in brief, and so possibly what I design might not be so plainly apprehended, or it may be misconstrued, I thought it might be necessary to explain it a little more fully. I said then, that I conceived that those universal *Phænomena* of the remainders of the Sea which are found in all parts almost of the present superficial Parts of the Earth, could not be caused by the general Flood of *Noah*, if the manner of performance and executing thereof were such as is for the generality supposed and explained by Commentators by reason that they make the time of the continuance of the present superficial Parts of the Earth under the Waters to be no longer than the time of the duration of the Flood, as it is recorded in Holy Writ. Supposing that the present Earth and Sea is in the same places with respect to the Body of the Earth as they were before the Flood; nor will the Hypothesis or Explication of the ingenious Author that has lately writ of that Subject, reach it, he supposing there was no apparent Sea before the Flood, but that the Sea was all covered by the Earth, if at least I do rightly comprehend his intentions; for that space of time will not be found of duration long enough to produce *de novo* such multitudes of those Creatures, and to such Magnitudes and Ages of growth as many of them seem to have had, and it will be difficult to be imagined, that such Creatures as do not swim in the Water, should, by the Effects of that Deluge, be taken from their Residences in the bottom of the Sea and carried to the top of the Mountains, or to places so far remote from those Residences. So then, if we will ascribe those Phænomena to that Flood, it will be necessary to consider which way that Catastrophy might be effected that it might be the occasion of such effects. I therefore said, that unless we supposed that there were thereby a change wrought of the superficial Parts of the Globe, and that those Parts which before the Flood were dry Land became Sea, and the Parts which were before covered by the Sea after the said Deluge, became the dry Land, it seems to me, that these appearances cannot be solved by *Noah*'s Flood.

Tho' possibly this may seem a little improbable upon the first mentioning of it, yet possibly also upon a little further examination, it may be thought to have somewhat more of liklyhood than is yet imagined, at least I hope the manner will be conceivable.

We have no other means of being informed of the true History of it, but what is to be found recorded in the sacred Writings of *Moses*; and therefore those are to be consulted, and the true meaning of them, as far as can be, must be obtained; for whatever else may be scattered here and there in other Authors that seem to relate thereunto in all probability, were some way or other fetched from his Informations.

A further explication of Noah's Flood and the formation of the World.

I conceive then, that considering the Descriptions of *Moses* both of the Generation of the Earth and manner of the Flood, the History of both may be thus explained.

First, For the Fabrick of the Earth, the Description is but short in the first Chapter of *Genesis* and 2d Verse. *Et terra erat Solitudo & Inanitas, & Caligo Super facies abyssi, & Spiritus Dei manabat Super facies aquarum, & dixit Deus sit lux & fuit lux.* This doth seem to represent the order of the four Gradations, Earth in the middle, Water next, then Spiritus, then Light; the Central Earth is described only as a *Vacuum*, and called the *Abysse*, and Darkness inclosing it; that is, the Water follows next above it, which covered it all round: Above this the Air, and lastly the Fire, Æther, or Light in the fourth Verse, according to the Hebrew, *Et divisit Deus inter Lucem & inter tenebras:* The Septuagint renders it, καὶ διεχώρισεν ὁ θεὸς ἀνὰ μέσον τῶ φωτῷ καὶ ἀνὰ μέσον τῶ σκότῳς. That is, God caused a twofold Seperation, one in the middle of the Light or Æther, and another in the middle of the Darkness, which covered the Face of the Abysse or Central Earth; which covering of Darkness was the Water, which is often called the Abysse or great Deep; the former of these is afterwards always called the σερέωμα τῶ ὀρανῶ, the Firmament of Heaven, to distinguish it from the latter, called the σερέωμα ἐν μέσω τῶ ὕδαλος, the Firmament in the middle of the Waters; for in the sixth Verse it is so exprest, καὶ εἶπεν ὁ θεός γενηθέτω σερέωμα ἐν μέσω τῶ ὕδατῷ. Let there be a Firmament in the middle of the Waters, and let it be a division between the Waters and the Waters: And in the seventh Verse; and God made the Firmament, and God made a separation of the Waters that were below the Firmament, from the Waters that were above the Firmament. And in the eighth Verse, καὶ ἐκάλεσε ὁ θεὸς τὸ σερέωμα ὀρανὸν; it is generally rendered, and God called the Firmament Heaven; I conceive it may be rendered, Also God called the Heaven the Firmament, for to shew that there was also a Firmament of the Heavens; for so it is afterward every where called, σερέωμα τῶ ὀρανῶ. But this I submit to Divines.

This first Firmament then, ἐν μέσω τῶ ὕδαλῷ, seems to have been a solid and hard Sphærical Shell, as it were, which incompassed the Ball of the Earth Central, not clear without the Liquid Water, as the hard Shell of the Egg is without the White, and so the Egg-shell doth inclose the whole White of the Egg, as well as the White incloseth the Yolk: But it was, as I conceive, meant, that this Firmament or Sphærical hard Shell was placed, as it were, in the middle of all the White, or of the incompassing Water; the Circumferential half of it being without the Shell, and the Central half of it within the Shell. So then at its first Creation, the order was first the Central Earth or great Abysse; this was in the middle as the Yolk of the Egg round or Sphærical; this was inclosed in Darkness by the Shell of Water underneath the Firmament, being half the whole Body of the Water which was inclosed perfectly within this Firmament, as the White of the Egg by the Egg-shell; and by that hard Shell it was perfectly seperated from the other half of the Water which was above the Firmament, and as it were a second White of the Egg without the Shell, and was the Water upon the Face of which the Spirit was said to move; so that the whole Globe, for that time, was all covered with Water. This *Ovid* seems to allude to, when he saith, *Circumfluus humor ultima possedit, Solidumq; coercuit orbem*; which I took notice of in my Lecture about the History of the World, as expressed by that ingenious Mythologick Poet; for he seems to make the Water to be both below the Shell of the Earth and to encompass it.

Plato also was of that Opinion in making *Tartarus* the place of the Waters, *of Tartarus.* that is, the middle and Central parts of the Ball or Globe of the Earth; and so the hard part of the Earth to be nothing but this Shell near the Superficies, and it seems also, that *Pythagoras*, yea, and the *Ægyptians* and *Chaldeans* likewise were of the same Sentiment, and divers are of Opinion that *Moses* also understood the same by the great Abysse which he mentions in the Description of *Noah*'s Flood. But by this Description of the Creation he seems to be understood otherwise, when he says, *Et terra erat Solitudo & Inanitas & Caligo super facies Abyssi.* For by this he seems to make the form of the Terraqueous

M m m m m   Globe

Globe to be no other than that of a Bubble, such as Children blow into the Air, that is, only a Sphærical Film or Orb of Water, which within it had nothing but *Solitudo & Inanitas* תהו ובהו , *Vacuum & Jnane,* ἀόρατος ὴ ἀκαλα-σκεύαςτς, and only that this Film of Water was divided in the middle by the solid hard Shell of the Firmament which inclosed half the Film; that is, the inner side; and excluded the other half of the Film; that is, the outward superficial Parts: And hence 'tis possible that *Virgil* in the eighth Book of his *Æneids,* says, *Spiritus Intus alit, totamq; infusa per Artus men agitat molem & magno se Corpore miscet. Inde hominum pecudumq; genus vitæq; volantum & quæ marmoreo fert monstra sub æquore pontus,* &c. He seeming there to make the place for the Soul of the World; others there are who would have it to be Fire, and thence to proceed the Causes of the Vulcanos and fiery Eruption; but *Aristotle* there places the pure Element of the Earth; some of the Modern Philosophers would have it to be all one great Load-stone. I could produce various other Opinions, but they are all but Opinions; and it matters not much what the Substance be that fills it, as to the present inquiery; I shall therefore proceed.

This Firmament then in the middle of the Waters, I take to be that which in many places of the Bible is said to be the Foundation of the Earth, as in *Psal.* 24. 2. *The Earth is the Lords and the fullness thereof, for he hath founded it upon the Seas.* (Prov. 3. 19.) *The Lord by wisdom hath founded the Earth, by understanding hath he established the Heavens,* (this seems to refer to the two Firmaments) and in the following Verse, *By his knowledge the depths are broken up, and the Clouds drop down their Dew.* (This seems to refer to the Causes of the general Deluge by opening of those two Firmaments, as I shall by and by shew.) So *Job* 38. 6. *Whereupon are the Foundations of the Earth fastned?*

This Sphærical Firmament or Shell then in the middle of the Waters, we may suppose, was in some places raised or forced outwards, and some other parts were pressed downwards or inwards, and sunk lower, when in the ninth Verse, God commanded the Waters under the Heaven to be gathered together to one place, and the dry Land to appear; for by depressing in of some parts of that Sphærical Shell (to make room to receive all the Waters that had before covered the whole) other parts must be thrust out, the Contents within being the same, and so requiring equal Space or Extension; so that what went below the former Sphærical Surface, must be equalled by other parts ascending without that Surface, and so the quantities of the Waters both within it, and those without it, remained each the same, and still distinct and separated by this Firmament in the middle of the Waters, tho' altered from its Sphærical Figure; and the outward Surface of the outward Water, as well as the inward Surface of the inward Water, must remain Sphærical, because of the Power of Gravity from without a Central Earth, or Yolk within, formed of a Sphærical Figure.

In this State the Earth seems to remain till the time of the Flood, which is accounted between sixteen and seventeen Hundred Years according to the Hebrew. When *God looked upon the Earth, and behold it was corrupt, for all flesh had corrupted their way upon the Earth,* as Chap. VI. v. 12. And in the thirteenth told *Noah,* that he would destroy all living Creatures with the Flood. This Destruction began in the six Hundred Year of *Noah's* Life, Chap. VII. v. 11. The manner of which was expressed thus in the Septugint ἐῤῥάγησαν πᾶσαι ἀι πηγαὶ τῆς ἀβύσσα ὴ ὁι καταραρράκλαι τᾶ ὀρανᾶ ἀνεώχθησαν. *The fountains of the great deep were drawn up, and the windows of Heaven were opened.* This refers again to the twofold Firmament, that ἐν μέσω τᾶ ὑδαλ⊙,and that τᾶ ὀρανᾶ. As for that of the Heavens the effects of the opening of them was, that it Rained 40 Days and 40 Nights; but the Consequents of the other are not expressed any otherwise, but that the Flood was upon the Earth forty Days, that is, the Sea continued to flow in upon it. *And the Waters increased, and bare up the Ark, and it was lifted up above the Earth,* v. 17. *And the Waters prevailed exceedingly upon the Earth, and all the high Hills, that were under the whole Heaven, were covered,* v. 19. *Fifteen Cubits upwards did the Waters prevail, and the Mountains were covered,* v. 20. *Every living substance was destroyed which was upon the Face of the ground,* Noah *only, and those with him in the Ark, remained alive.*

live,v.23. By which it appears, that not only all Men, Beasts, Cattle, Fowls, Insects, Worms, &c. perished by the Flood, but every living Substance; that is, all Vegetables also; for all Animals were enumerated before: We see therefore that here was a double Cause of the Waters. First, The Rain from above. And, Secondly, The pulling up of the Fountains of the great Deep: What I understand by the great Deep, I shewed before; that is, the sinkings inward of the Firmament in the middle of the Waters; and the forcing up of the Fountains of the great Deep, I conceive to signify the raising again of those parts that were before sunk to receive the Sea; and a Consequent of that would necessarily be a sinking of that which was the dry Land, and a Consequent of that, flowing and increasing of the Sea from out of that which was the great Deep, and a prevailing and increasing upon that which was a sinking Earth; and this motion being forty Days in progression before the rising Surface of the Sea, and the sinking Surface of the highest Land met. So long the Waters were said to be flowing and increasing before it was wholly covered; nay, the History goes on with the Journal of its progress, till the Waters were gotten fifteen Cubits above the highest Mountains; but then the account ceaseth, and adds only, that the Waters prevailed on the Earth a hundred and fifty Days, and so long the whole Firmament was covered with Water. So that in probability the progress of the alteration of the Firmament proceeded so far till it recovered its perfect Sphærical Figure truly in the middle of the Waters, as it was at its first Creation placed at about seventy five Days after the forty; but as I conceive it staid not there, but the progression of both the parts went onwards; that is, the sinking parts went as much below the Level, as before they were above, and the rising parts by degrees ascended as much above as they had been below, and that which had been the bottom of the Sea under the Water, became the dry Land, and that which had been before the dry Land, now became the bottom of the Sea, whether the Waters retreated from off these parts which were raised when the Flood was finished; for it is said in the eighth Chap. That God remembred *Noah*, and what was with him in the Ark, to prepare them another Habitation, by making dry Land for them again; and, First, The Heavens were cleared from Raining. And, Secondly, By turning of the Water that had fallen, into Vapours, and by turning all those Vapours, which such a Commotion of the Earth and Sea had caused, into Wind, and by causing the Waters to return from those parts which it had covered into the Deeps that were appointed for their Reception; so that at the end of the hundred and fifty Days the new Earth began to appear. *Ver. 3. And the Waters returned from off the Earth continually, and after the end of the hundred and fifty Days the Waters were abated.* And, *v. 4. And the Ark rested in the seventh Month, on the seventeenth day of the Month, upon the Mountains of* Ararat, which probably was the Name of the Mountain after the Flood in the time of *Moses.* Ver. 5. *And the Waters decreased continually until the tenth month, when the tops of the Mountains were seen. Forty days after this* Noah *opened the Windows of his Ark and sent out a Raven.* So that it seems that as the old was forty Days in being covered, so the new was forty Days in being discovered; but *Noah* staid yet many Days longer before the Surface of the Ground was dried. This Explication, I think, doth fully answer to the words of the History of the Flood as they are written by *Moses*, and will likewise shew a probable Cause how those Phænomena of Sea-sand and Shells are become so universal over the Face of the whole Earth, as it is at present, which were the two things which I now indeavoured to make intelligible. I have not, I hope, given any Explication, or made any Supposition, how differing soever it be, from all the Explications I have yet met with, that will any ways distort the plain words of the Text; for I have in this, as near as may be, guided my progress by that Direction, and I hope I have hereby shewed a very plain and intelligible way how the Flood became so perfectly universal, and the Earth returned perfectly to its primitive and first Created Figure, without any extravagant supposition of new Created Waters, or bringing them down from above the highest Heavens; nor is here any great need of Calculation to know how great a quantity of Water would need to be new Created and afterwards Annihilated, or first fetcht down from the

Heavens,

Heavens, and then sent back again; nor is there any need of supposing the Earth to be broken to pieces since the Flood, and the Antediluvian World without any visible Sea. And if it were much to the purpose, I could shew how all this, that I have supposed, may be Physically explained, and the Æquilibrium maintained : And, in short, to shew how consonant this Hypothesis may be both to several Expressions in the most antient Authors, and, in a word, with the Rules of Nature itself, of which I have formerly given divers hints to this Society, and may some other time more fully explain, but I fear I have detained you too long at this time.

THE following Treatises were Lectures read at several times relating to the Authors Theory of Earthquakes, and their Effects, and contain several very remarkable Histories of the Alterations that have been caused by them in the several parts of the World; the first is an account of an Earthquake in the Leeward *Islands. These are backt by a Citation out of* Aristotle, *and several deductions from it, are made by the Author. The next is a Discourse explaining some Effects of Earthquakes by the Phænomena of Thunder and Lightning, and relates to the Causes of Earthquakes. That Nature is always changing. That Earthquakes were formerly more frequent,* &c.

R. W.

July 23. 1690. *A Discourse of Earthquakes in the* Leeward *Islands.*

THE greatest Objection that has hitherto been made against a Theory which I have several times discoursed of, to give a rational and probable account of the Reasons of the varieties observable in the present superficial Parts of the Globe of the Earth; which was, that all those inequalities of its Surface had been caused by the Power of Earthquakes, or Eruptions of fiery Conflagrations inkindled in the Subterraneous Regions, which by that means did sometimes raise Mountains, Hills, Islands, &c. and sometimes produce the quite contrary Effects, by levelling of Eminences or sinking of Places, swallowing up Rivers, and making Lakes of Land, or sinking Lands under the Sea, and the like.

The greatest Objection, I say, against this, I find hath been, that there were wanting Instances to confirm it from History. For that, all Places, Countries, Seas, Rivers, Islands, &c. have all continued the same for so long time as we can reach backwards with any History : All *Greece* and the *Greecian Islands*, *Italy*, *Ægypt*, &c. are all the same as they were above two Thousand Years since, and therefore they were so from the Creation, and will be so to the general Conflagration ; and as to the effects of Earthquakes, First, They have happened but seldom : And, Secondly, They have not produced any notable Change, such as I have supposed them to be the Authors and Efficients of ; so that it seems but a bare Conjecture and without Ground or Foundation sufficient to found and raise such a Superstructure of Conclusions as I have thereupon raised.

For Answer to which I shall not now repeat what I have formerly produced here, and alledged to that purpose, such as were the Instances that were to be met with here and there dispersed in antient Writings ; since many of those Occurencies having been long since produced, and the relations of them made by such as were not Eye-witnesses, many of the particular matters of Fact have been doubted or disputed ; I shall therefore take notice of some particular Instances which have happened within our own Memory, and more particularly of this late instance which hath happened in the *Antilles*, of which we have an account but this last Month in the *Gazet*, namely, in that of *June* the 30th., and another in that of *June* the 16th. preceding ; both which Relations, tho' they are but short and imperfect, as to what I could have wished and shall indeavour to obtain, yet as they are, they will be found to contain

many

many Particulars, which do very much illuftrate and confirm my Conjectures. And tho' the particular effects were not fo great as to equalize thofe which I have fuppofed to have been the productions of former Eruptions, fuch as the raifing of the *Alpes, Pyreneans, Appennines, Andes,* and the like Mountains, or the making of new Lands, Iflands, *&c.* or the finking of Countries, and drowning of Iflands as the *Platonick Atlantis* and contiguous Iflands, yet if they be confidered they will be found to be of the fame Nature, and to differ only in Magnitude, *Secundum Magis & Minus,* but not in Effence.

The firft Account is dated from *Nevis, April* the thirtieth, in thefe words, *Of Earthquakes in the Leeward Iflands.* [' On *Sunday* the fixth Inftant, about five a Clock in the Evening, was, for ' fome few Minutes, heard a ftrange hollow noife, which was thouht to pro- ' ceed from the great Mountain in the middle of this Ifland, to the admira- ' tion of all People ; but immediately after, to their greater Amazement, be- ' gan a mighty Earthquake, with that violence, that almoft all the Houfes ' in *Charles* Town, that were built of Brick or Stone, were in an inftance le- ' velled with the Ground, and thofe built of Timber fhook, that every Body ' made what haft they could to get out of them. In the Streets the Ground ' in feveral places clove about two Foot afunder, and hot ftinking Water ' fpouted out of the Earth a great height. The Sea left its ufual Bounds more ' than a third of a Mile, fo that very large Fifh lay bare upon the Shoar, ' but the Water prefently returned again. And afterwards the fame ftrange ' motion happened feveral times, but the Water retired not fo far as at firft. ' The Earth, in many places, was thrown up in great quantities, and thouf- ' ands of large Trees went with it, which were buried and no more feen. ' 'Tis ufual almoft at every Houfe to have a large Ciftern, to contain the Rain- ' water of above nine or ten Foot deep, and fifteen or twenty Foot Diameter, ' feveral of which, with the violence of the Earthquake, threw out the Wa- ' ter eight or ten Foot high ; and the motion of the Earth all over the Ifland ' was fuch, that nothing could be more terrible. ' In the Ifland of St. *Chri- ftophers* (as fome *French* Gentlemen, who are come hither to treat about the exchange of Prifoners, do Report) there has likewife been an Earthquake, ' the Earth opening in many places nine Foot, and burying folid Timber, Su- ' gar-mills, *&c.* and throwing down the Jefuits Colledge, and all other Stone ' Buildings. It was alfo in a manner as violent at *Antego* and *Montferrat* ; ' and they had fome feeling of it at *Barbadoes.* Several fmall Earthquakes ' have happened fince, three or four in twenty four Hours ; fome of which ' made the biggeft Rocks have a great motion, but we are now in great hopes ' there will be no more.]

This is the whole of the Relation from *Nevis.* But the other Account from *Barbadoes,* of the 23d. of *April,* taketh notice of other particulars than what are mentioned in this Letter ; the Printed Account is this that follows. [' About three Weeks fince there were felt moft violent Earthquakes in the ' *Leeward Iflands* of *Montferrat, Nevis* and *Antego* ; in the two firft no confi- ' derable hurt was done, moft of their Buldings being of Timber ; but where ' there were Stone Buildings they were generally thrown down, which fell ve- ' ry hard in *Antego,* moft of their Houfes, Sugar-mills and Wind-mills being ' of Stone. This Earthquake was felt in fome places of this Ifland, but did ' no manner of hurt to Men or Cattle ; nor was any loft in the *Leeward Iflands,* ' it happening in the Day-time. It is reported to have been yet more violent ' in *Martinico,* and other *French* Iflands. And feveral Sloops who came from ' *Nevis* and *Antego* paffing between St. *Lucia* and *Martinico* felt it at Sea : The ' agitation of the Water being fo violent, that they thought themfelves on ' Rocks and Shelves, the Veffels fhaking as if they would break in pieces. ' And others paffing by a Rock and unhabited Ifland, called *Rodunda,* found ' the Earthquake fo violent there, that a great part of that Rocky Ifland fplit ' and tumbled into the Sea, and was there funk, making a noife as of many ' Cannon, and a very great Cloud of Duft afcending into the Air at the fall.] [' Two very great Comets have lately appeared in thefe parts of the World, ' and in an Hour and a quarters time the Sea Ebbed and Flowed to an unufual ' degree three times.'] In thefe Relations are many confiderable Effects produced, which will much confirm my former Doctrine about the Effects of

Earthquakes.

Earthquakes. And First, It is very remarkable, that this Earthquake was not confined to a small spot or place of the Earth, such as the Eruption of *Ætna* or *Vesuvius* out of one Mouth, but it extended above five Degrees, or three hundred and fifty Miles in length; namely, from *Barbadoes* to St. *Christophers*, and possibly, upon inquiry, it may be found to have gone a great deal further, and to have produced Effects in *Statia* St. *Martin, Anguilla, Porco Rico*, or some other of those Islands in the North-west of St. *Christophers*, where, by the Relation, it seems to have been the most violent: And tho' possibly there might not be opportunities of feeling or taking notice of the effects in all places of the Sea where it might have been felt; yet by those few Instances which are related, we may probably conjecture, that its effects might be very considerable, and sensible a great way in breadth under the Sea; for we find that the Strokes or Succusions thereof were felt by the Vessels sayling over some parts of the Sea so affected; and those so violent as if the Vessels had struck upon Rocks, which could be from nothing else but the suddain rising of the bottom of the Sea, which raised the Sea also with it, like Water in a Tub or Dish: And that this was of that Nature does further appear by the unusual Tides at the *Barbadoes* mentioned in the last Relation, *viz.* That in an Hour and $\frac{1}{4}$ the Sea Ebbed and Flowed three times in an unusual Degree; which, in probability, were nothing else but Waves propagated from the places where the Ground underneath, and the Sea above, had been by the Concussions of the Earthquake raised upwards. This appears also farther by the recess of the Sea from the Shore at *Nevis* ; of a Mile; for the whole Island being raised by the Swelling or Eruption of the Vapour or Fire underneath, made the Sea run off from the Shores, till it settled down again into its place after the Vapour had broken its way out through the Clefts that were made by those Swellings: From all which Particulars, and several others, 'tis manifest, that the space of Earth raised or struck upwards by the impetuosity of the Subterraneous Powers that caused it, was of great Extent, and might far exceed the length of the *Alps*, or the *Pyreneans*, &c. But there may be other Instances also produced of the great extent of the Powers or Effects of Earthquakes, as those I have formerly mentioned to have happened in *Norway* about thirty Years since; and those which happened in the Northern parts of *America* of a later date.

Another particular notable in this, is the Recess of the Sea from the Shore, and the leaving the Fish upon the so raised bottom; and tho' this part soon after sunk again, so that the Sea returned to its former bounds, yet if some other parts of the Subterraneous Ground had filled up the made Cavity, or that they had so tumbled as to support the so raised parts, Instances of which kinds of Accidents may be produced from other Earthquakes, then it would have left some such kind of Tract as it is now in *Virginia*, where, for many Miles in length, the Low-land is nothing but Sea-sand and Shells, which have been, in probability, so raised into the Air, and there supported and continued from sinking again and being covered with the Sea: Of Shells taken up from this Tract, there can be no doubt that they have belonged to Fish of their kind, they remaining hitherto perfect Scallop Shells; of which kind there are some in the Repository.

A Third particular Remarkable, is the overturning and burying of thousands of Trees which were no more seen, being covered by the Earth which was thrown up by the Eruption. This gives us a very plain Instance of the manner how Trees that are now found in divers parts of *England* buried under the Ground, may have come to have been there so disposed and deposited; for tho' possibly in those places there may be no such Trees now growing; and tho' we have no History when there were, or of any such Eruption that might have so overturned and buried them; yet the Records that we have of the antient or former State of those Parts, are not so full and particular, but that we may well enough suppose that such Catastrophies may have happened long since we have begun to have Writings and Records in *England*; that is, since the time that the *Romans* first conquered this Isle; and yet not find any mention thereof there made; since possibly those that might be in or near those Parts might have perish'd with it, and those which were at a

distance

distance took little notice or regard of what they had little concern for: Besides, in those Days very small were the number that could Write and Read, and fewer were those that minded any thing the effects produced by Nature: What was written was either somewhat relating to Religion or Civil History, very few and rare are the Instances that can be met with of Natural History; and it has not been a Defect peculiar to these parts of the World only, but was taken notice of two Thousand Years since by *Aristotle* upon this very account, as we find in the fourteenth Chapter of his first Book of *Meteors*; ' Moreover (says he in the beginning of this Chapter) the same Parts of the ' Earth are not always dry Land, or always covered with Water, but they ' suffer a change from the rising of new Rivers, or decay and drying of old; ' therefore also in places near the Sea there are wont to happen these changes. ' So that those which are Land, or those which are Sea do not always re- ' main so; but where was Land there is Sea, and where was Sea there is Land; ' and we are to conclude these changes to happen according to some order. ' Now (says he) because many of these changes happen but slowly in com- ' parison to the quickness and shortness of the Life of Man, therefore they ' are hardly taken notice of, a whole Generation having passed away before ' such changes have come to perfection. Other Catastrophies that have been ' more quick, have been forgotten, by reason that such as escaped them were ' removed to some other parts, and there the Memory of them was soon lost; ' at least a longer tract of Time did quite obliterate the remembrance of ' them, and the transplanting and transmigration of People from place to ' place much contributed thereunto. This is made plain enough by the little remembrance was found in *America* of their preceding Estate, when they were first visited by the *Spaniards* and other *Europeans*.

A fourth particular Remarkable in these Relations, is the Chapping and *Of the Veins in* cleaving of the Earth and Rocks, and the spouting out of them of stinking *Marble.* Water to a great height; as also of Smoke or Dust, which serves to explain the Reason and Causes of the Flaws and Veins in Marbles and other Stones; for by the Power and Violence of the Subterraneous Heavings or Succussions the stony Quarries become broken, flawed and cleft, and Subterraneous Mineral Waters impregnated with Saline, Metalline, Sulphureous, or other Substances are driven into them and fill them up, which having petrified Qualities in them, do, in process of time, petrify in those Clefts, and thereby form a sort of stony Veins of different Colour, Hardness, and other Qualifications, than what the parts of the broken Quarry had before, and oft time inclose divers other Substances by their petrifying Quality, which have happened to fall into those Clefts, and thence sometimes there are found Shells petrified in the middle of the Vein, as I have seen, and other Substances. These Clifts or Chaps hapening not only upon the Land, but even under the Sea; so that not only the Sea-water may descend and fill up those Clefts, but it may carry with it Sands, Shells, Mud, and divers other Substances from the bottom of the Sea, that then lay above it, there to be, in process of time, changed into Stone somewhat of the Nature of that which hath been so cleft.

Fifthly, 'Tis worth noting, that this Earthquake happened at so great a distance from the main Land and great Continent, and that the noise of the same was first observed to begin at the great Mountain in the middle of the Island of *Nevis*, not but that it might in other parts have begun sooner or at other times; from which I draw these deductions. First, That it seems probable, that this great Mountain may have been formerly visited with Eruptions; and possibly might have been first produced by some such Power, and so have great Cavities within its Bowels produced by such a preceding Eruption, the dislocated Parts not returning each to its own place. And next, that it may hence seem probable, that some such preceding Earthquake (tho' then possibly more violent before the foment of the Fire was by inkindling exhausted) might, not only be the cause of raising this Mountain, but of lifting up from the bottom the whole Isle, nay, possibly of all the Islands of the *Antilles*, since one seems as possible as the other, and the Northern of them all seems to hint as much, if considered, in the Map; besides, there seems to be be many Inftances of a like Nature, as in the *Canaries, Tenariff* feems to be a moft remarkable Character of fuch a Suppofition ; to this may be added *Del Fuogo* among the *Azores* and the Ifland of *Madera, Sicily, Strombulo,* and *Lipary* in the *Mediterranean, Ifeland* in the North Sea, *Mafcarenos* near *Madagafcar* ; to this I may alfo add the many Iflands of the *Archipelago,* which, tho' they have now no great figns of burning Mountains, yet to this Day Earthquakes are very frequent, and antient Traditions do preferve fomewhat of the memory of very great alterations that have happened in thofe Parts by fuch forts of Caufes ; but I will not now meddle with that kind of Hiftory, nor of Mythology, having faid more concerning it in a more proper place ; but I fhall rather on this occafion take notice of thofe Iflands that have *Vulcanoes* in or near them, which to me feem to proceed from the fame Caufe and Principle. And I do not queftion, but that all thofe Iflands which lie fo far in the Sea, if they were thoroughly examined, would plainly manifeft whence they have proceeded by Characters of Nature's Writing, which to me feems far beyond any other Record whatfoever. Here I conceive it Lawful and Philofophical to *Jurare in Verba,* when Nature fpeaks or dictates; however, I fhall leave it free to every one to judge, as he thinks moft reafonable.

Sixthly, 'Tis very remarkable that the Ifle of *Rodunda,* which it feems is all an uninhabited Rock, was fplit, and a part of it tumbled down and funk into the Sea; upon which occafion it feems it made a prodigious noife as of many Cannon, and fending up at the fame time a great Cloud of Duft, as they term it, which, in probability, was alfo mingled with Smoak. Which puts me in mind of the Phænomena I obferved lately, when the Pouder-mill and Magazine at *Hackny* blew up; for befides the very great noife of the Blow which I heard, being within a Mile of it, in the Fields, I obferved immediately, a great white Cloud of Smoke to rife in a Body to a great height in the Air, and to be carried by the Wind for two Miles and better without difperfing or falling down, but perfectly refembling the white Summer Clouds : But this only by the bye. From thefe Phænomena of the Earthquake it feems very probable, that it proceeded from fuch Subterraneous inkindling as refembles Gun-powder, both by the noife it yielded, and in the fuddennefs of its firing, and its powerful Expanfion when fired; for the noife was as of many Cannon; this alone proves it to be very fuddain. Next the fplitting of the Rocky Ifland proves its Power to be very great ; this is proved yet farther by the Blow and Strokes it communicated to the Sea, and fo to the Ships that failed upon it ; for no flow motion whatever could have communicated fuch a Concuffion through the Water to the Veffels upon it ; but it muft be as fuddain as that of Pouder, otherwife the ftroke of the Earth upon the incumbent Seas, would never have had the like fuccefs ; for if it had been a gradual rifing of the bottom, the Sea would gradually have run off from it, and upon its finking again have gradually returned, and the Veffels on it would only have been fenfible at moft but of a Current or Running of the Water to or from the place finking or rifing, fomewhat like the effect that happened at *Nevis* ; which doth plainly fhew, that, befides the fuddain Strokes or Concuffions, there was alfo a confiderable rifing and finking of the whole Ifland as to the level of the Sea. But that which I principally note under this Head is, that a good part of the faid Ifland tumbled down and was funk into the Sea, which gives an account how many parts of the Earth come to be buried under Ground and difplaced from their former Situations, and thence how Ships, Ankers, Bones, Teeth, &c. that have fometimes been digged up from great depths, may have come to be there buried.

Seventhly, 'Tis remarkable alfo, that this Eruption fent up into the Air great Clouds of Duft and Smoke, which for the moft part muft foon fall down again into the Sea, or contiguous parts of the Ifland. This will give a probable account how the Layers of the Superficial Parts of the Earth may come to be made ; for the bigger part of this Duft muft come down to the bottom firft and fettle to a certain thicknefs and make a Bed of Gravel, then will follow Beds of coarfe Sand, then Beds of finer and finer Sand, and laft of Clays or Moulds of feveral forts ; again much of that which fell upon the

higher

higher parts of the Iſland, will, by the Rivers, be waſhed down into the Vales, and there produce the like Beds or Layers of ſeveral kinds, and ſo bury many of the parts that were before on the Surface. Thus Plants and Vegetable Subſtances may come to be buried, and the Bones and Teeth of the Carcaſſes of Dead Animals: Theſe may alſo ſometimes be buried under Beds or Cruſts of Stone, when the parts that thus make the Layers chance to be mixed with ſuch Subterraneous Subſtances as carry with them a petrifying Quality. But I ſhall not detain you any longer with farther Deductions from theſe few Remarks we find in theſe two caſual Relations of this Earthquake; I ſhall only add, that I could heartily wiſh that ſome care were taken that a more particular account might be procured of it whilſt the effects thereof are freſh in Memory, that they might be Recorded and added to the Collections of Natural Hiſtory. And for the ſame end it were deſireable to know what former Earthquakes have been taken notice of in theſe, or any other of theſe Iſlands, as *Jamaica, Cuba, Hiſpaniola, Porto Rico,* &c. for that the Memory of ſuch Accidents, if they be not Collected and Recorded whilſt the Spectators are in being, are ſoon forgotten and loſt or not regarded by the ſucceding Generations, as *Ariſtotle* has taken notice of alſo in the Chapter I before quoted.

What is moſt remarkable in theſe Earthquakes in the *Leeward* Iſlands, is, that they have all happened to places not far diſtant from the Sea, or even under the Sea itſelf, though the Eruptions have been, for the moſt part on the Land. So that there doth ſeem to be ſomewhat of Reaſon to Conjecture as *Signior Bottoni* in his *Pyrologia Topographica,* that the ſaline Quality of the Sea-water may conduce to the producing of the Subterraneous Fermentation with the Sulphureous Minerals there placed, which the Experiment lately here exhibited at a Meeting of this Society, does yet make more probable; for by that it was evident, that the mixing of Spirit of Salt with Iron, did produce ſuch a Fermentation as did produce a Vapour or Steem, which by an actual Flame was immediately fired like Gun-pouder, and if incloſed, would, in all probability, have had a like effect of raiſing and diſperſing of thoſe parts that bounded and impriſoned it. Now, 'tis evident that the melted Matter which was vomited out of *Ætna* in the Year ſixty nine (of which we have a part now in the Repoſitory) was very much like to melted or caſt Iron, and I doubt not but that there may be much of that mineral in it; beſides, the Foot of that Mountain does extend even to the very Sea, and in all probability may have Caverns under the Sea itſelf, which is argued alſo from the Concurrency of the Conflagration of *Strombolo* and *Lipary,* Iſlands conſiderably diſtant from it by Sea, at the ſame time, where it is generally believed that there may be Subterraneous Cavernous Paſſages between them, by which they communicate to one another; ſo that ſometimes it begins in *Ætna,* and is communicated to *Strombolo,* and reciprocally communicated to *Mongibel.*

Why Iſlands & Sea-Coaſts are moſt ſubject to Earthquakes.

This poſſibly may afford a probable Reaſon why Iſlands are now more ſubject to Earthquakes than Continents and inland Parts; and indeed how ſo many Iſlands came to be diſperſed up and down in the Sea, namely, for that theſe Fermentations may have been cauſed in the parts of the Earth ſubjacent to the Sea, which being brought to a Head of Ripeneſs, may have taken Fire, and ſo have had force enough to raiſe a ſufficient quantity of the Earth above it, to make its way through the Sea, and there make itſelf a vent, as that of the *Canaries* did in the Year 39, which, if ſufficiently copious, may produce an Iſland as that did alſo for a time, though it hath ſince that time again ſunk under the Surface of the Sea. But the Iſland of *Aſcenſion,* which, by all appearances, doth ſeem to have been the ſame way produced, doth ſtill remain as a witneſs to prove this Hypotheſis. A like Teſtimony to this, of the Cauſe and Manner of their Production, I take the Iſland and Pike of *Tenariff* to be, ſo *Hecla* of *Iceland,* ſo *Bearenberg* of *John Mayens* or *Trinity Iſland,* ſo *del Fuego* of the Icelnds of *Cape Verd,* ſo *Ternate* of the *Moluccas,* and the Iſland of *Maſcarenas,* of the Iſlands about *Madagaſcar* among the *Antillas* or *Caribes,* all which do ſeem to me to be remaining Teſtimonies how, and in what manner, and by what means thoſe other Iſlands which have now worn out the marks of their firſt Origination, were at firſt

O o o o o produced.

produced. And tho' the Fires be extinct in many of the other Islands, yet 'tis observable, that the prodigious high Mountains or Sugar-lofe Pikes or Hills do yet remain as marks of what they had been heretofore ; so the Pike of *Fayal* among the *Terceras*, and the whole Island of St. *Helena*, and several others of those about *Madagascar* and of the *East-Indies*, and of those of the *Antilles*, and that of St. *Martha* mentioned by *Dampire*, do seem to me to be plain evidences of the former and Original Causes of them all.

Nor do I in the least doubt but that an inquisitive Person who should purposely survey all other Islands that wanted these Marks or Tokens of such Eruptions, might find enough of other Indications to manifest by what means they so came to be placed in the Sea, so far from any part of the Continents they are opposite to. Nor do I conceive they were all thus formed at once, but rather successively, some in one, some in other Ages of the World, which may probably be in some measure collected from the quantity or thickness of the Soil or Mould upon them fit for Vegetation ; whence the Island of *Ascension* may be rationally concluded to have been a Production of not many Ages, and the *Bermoodas* also of not very many more, because of the thinness of such a Soil. So also the Island of *Barbadoes*, and some others, whose Mould is yet but thin in respect of what it is in some others, and especially in those of greater Magnitude and in the greater Continents.

Hereupon possibly it may be inquired why those greater Islands and Continents should be of greater Antiquity than the smaller Islands. To which I answer, that in the first Ages of the World there were much greater Magazines, or Stores of the Materials fitted for this purpose, which being first kindled threw up from under the Sea, with which they were covered, vast quantities of it all at once, and thereupon those Magazines became in a manner exhausted, yet not so totally as not to leave some smaller parcells of those Substances so disposed, as not to be ready for inkindling together with those greater ; besides there remained other smaller parcels of it disposed and placed in other parts of the Globe sufficiently distant from them, not to be affected or inkindled at the same time, as those I have mentioned to have been the causes of the Islands far distant from the Continents. Nor do I conceive that all those Clusters were all thrown up at once, as the *Greecian* Islands in the *Archipelago* the *East-Indian* in that part called the *South-Sea*, the *Maldivia Islands* near the Coast of *Malabar*, the Islands scattered at the North of *Madagascar*, the Islands to the South-west of St. *Helena* in the *Atlantick* Ocean, *Finidnda dos picos*, the Isles of *Cape Verd*, *Canaries*, *Terceras*, *Orcades*, &c. also the *Gallopegas* and others in the *Pacifick* Sea or *Mar del Zur* ; but rather that some were made in one Age, some in other Ages of the World. And this was timed as the several Magazines came to be ripened and then fired ; they only indicating, as I conceive, that in those places of the Terrestrial Globe, there were placed the proper mineral Foments or Seeds as it were of them, which, when the convenient times were come and accomplished, then they were put into Act, and then they produced their Effects, which are the Islands that now remain the lasting Monuments of them. Nor can I suppose that all the Magazines of the Earth of this kind are blown up and spent, but that there may be many other yet remaining for future Ages to be made sensible of their Effects. Nor can I be fully satisfied that all the main Continents were thrown up or made Land all at once. Nor have we any proof that the Continent of *America* was in the time of *Noah's* Flood, nor indeed how large the habitable World then was, but certain we are, that what was then in being was all overflowed and drowned by it, and all living Creatures, except those preserved in the Ark with *Noah*, perished by it. But whether the dry Land that appeared after the Flood, were the same with that before the Flood, is a question not easily determinable ; to me it seems that the preceding Earth was wholly changed and destroyed, and that there was produced a new Earth which before that had not appeared ; and this Doctrine seems to be indicated by that Text in *Genesis* vi. 13. *And God said unto* Noah, *the end of all Flesh is come before me ; for the Earth is filled with violence through them, and behold I will destroy them with the Earth.* And again *Chap.* viii. 21. *I will not again curse the ground any more for Man's sake.* And 2 *Pet.* iii. 5. *By the*

the word of God the Heavens were of old, and the Earth standing in the Water and out of the Water. (ver. 6.) *Whereby the world that then was, being overflowed with Water, perished.* But the clearing this Doctrine by the Expressions in Scripture I shall leave to the Divines; nor shall I in the least interfere with them: However, it seems to me, that the Expression of *Breaking up the Fountains of the great Deep,* might signify the raising up of the bottom of the Sea; and the *Water prevailing so as to cover the top of the highest Mountains,* might denote to us the sinking or subsiding of the former part of the dry Ground: So as *the former was wholly drowned and destroyed,* which was *Cursed* for Man's sake, so a new one was raised, which God promised should not *be Cursed for Man's sake,* as the former had been; but this only by the bye. Certain I am that I have never yet met with my self, or heard of any other that hath any Records of the Age of *America,* which, for any thing appears, may have been much younger than the Flood of *Noah:* Nay, I believe it will be pretty difficult to prove even these Islands of *England, Scotland* and *Ireland* to have been in being ever since that Flood, and much more that there were such before it. And tho' some may Conjecture that they have been so (which is the most that any one can do) yet others may Conjecture that they have not (which is every deal as valid). The same may be said of a very great part of the Earth, without any trespassing upon our Faith or Religion; nay, it was we know, not long since, that a Bishop was condemned of Heresy because he asserted Antipodes. So skillful were some of our Fore-fathers in the Geography of the Habitable Parts of the World, or of the Figure of the Earth; and I do very much question, whether any Inhabitant of *Europe, Asia,* or *Africa* had ever any knowledge of *America* till within these last three hundred Years. But my present subject is not so properly to search and inquire into the History, as to find out what have been the Natural or Physical Causes of their Productions, Situations and Forms, and that, I think, I have shewn to have been in probability some preceding Earthquakes, which Earthquakes may have been caused by Subterraneous Fermentations and Accensions.

But some perhaps may except against this Doctrine as supposing it Derogatory to Divine Providence to assert any other Cause but the immediate Hand of God. To which I Answer, That 'tis not denying of Providence to inquire into, or to assign the Proximate Causes of Phænomena in Physical Subjects. For that we have Instances in the sacred Scriptures of such Explications, as in the case of the *Israelites* through the Red Sea; where 'tis said, *The Lord caused an East Wind to blow, which made the Sea to go back and to leave the bottom dry Ground.* And at the Waters of *Marah* God shewed *Moses* a Tree, which, when he had cast into the Waters, the Waters were made sweet. So in the Description of the Deluge, we find that God caused it to Rain forty Days and forty Nights, and the Foundations of the great Deep to be broken up, and the Windows of Heaven to be opened; which denote by what Natural Means God was pleased to effect and Collect the great quantity of Water that was to drown and overflow the then Habitable Earth; and many other such Instances there are to be met with in Holy Writ, where the Physical Causes are explained, for it is the same Omnipotent Power which does influence the remote Causes as well as the proximate and the universal Providence that ordereth all the effects, doth also determine and appoint all the Causes and Means conducing thereunto; nor is there a necessity of supposing new created Causes for all the effects that we are ignorant how they are brought to pass, or to believe every thing effected supernaturally, of which we cannot find out the Natural Cause; the Divine Providence is not less Conspicuous in every Production that we call Natural, and think we know the Causes of it, than in those we are less skillful and knowing in: 'Tis the Contemplation of the wonderful Order, Law and Power of that, we call Nature, that does most magnify the Beauty and Excellency of the Divine Providence, which has so disposed, ordered, adapted and impowered each part so to operate, as to produce the wonderful Effects which we see; I say wonderful, because every natural Production may be truly said to be a Wonder or Miracle, if duly considered; for who can tell the Cause of the Growth, Form, Figure, and all the Qualifications and peculiar Proprieties

of

of each, or any one Vegetable or Animal Species or individual ?   An obferving Naturalift may perhaps tell the Steps or Degrees he has taken notice of
in its Progrefs from the Seed to the Seed : Again, how he has obferved the
Seed to fprout, how that Sprout increafeth and forms itfelf of this or that
Magnitude, Shape, Colour, &c. and how it produceth fuch a Flower, and
after that Flower fuch other Seeds as that from which it fprung : He may alfo
tell the Times and Seafons in which thefe Progreffes have been or will be performed ; but if it be inquired how the Progreffes come to be acted, what is
the moving Power, or what is the inlivening Principle that orders, difpofes,
governs and performs all thefe wonderful Effects, there he finds the *Ne
plus ultra*, there is the Miracle that he may truly admire but cannot underftand ; however, *Eft aliquid prodire tenus fi non datur ultra*, let us firft find the
proximate Caufes, and then proceed to the more remote ; I think no one
ought to be blamed or difcouraged from fearching after thefe Caufes and Reafons of Natural Productions fo far as the Powers he is endowed with will enable him ; for this will more powerfully convince him of a Divine Providence
that Rules and Regulates the things of this World, than all the other methods of Contemplation or Argumentation whatfoever.

July 30. 1699. *A Difcourfe of the Caufes of Earthqnakes.*

I mentioned in fome Lectures that the Earth did feem to grow old and to
have loft many of thofe Parts, which, in the younger times of the World, it
feemed to me to have more abounded with ; that which I inftanced in, was
the Foment or Materials that ferve to produce and effect Conflagrations, E-
ruptions, or Earthquakes.   Thefe Materials I conceive to be fomewhat analogous to the Materials of Gun-pouder, not that they muft be neceffarily the
very fame, either as to the Parts or as to the Manner and Order of Compofition, or as to the way of Inkindling and Accenfion ; for that as much the
fame Effect may be produced by differing Agents, fo the Methods and Order
of proceeding may be altogether as differing : A clear Inftance of this we may
find in the Phænomena of Lightning, wherein we may obferve, that the Effects
are very like to the Effects of Gun-pouder.

Of Lightning and Thunder.   For we have firft the flafh of Light, which is very fuddain, very bright,
and of very fhort continuance, being almoft momentaneous, at leaft every
fingle flafh is fo, tho' the kindling of feveral parts at fome diftance from one
another does fometimes continue a fucceffion or longer duration of the
Light.

Next we may obferve the violence of the Crack or Noife which is likewife
as momentaneous as the Fire, if it be fingle, but if there be many particular
flafhes that contribute to this effect, and thofe made at feveral diftances, then
the duration of the Thunder heard is longer than the duration of the flafhes
of Lightning, which proceeds, as I conceive, from two Caufes ; Firft, For
that thofe flafhes that are farther diftant, have their Thunder a longer time
in paffing to the Ear, than thofe which are nearer, by reafon, that tho' the
Paffage or Motion of Light be almoft inftantaneous, yet the progreffion or
motion of found is temporaneous, and requires a certain fenfible time to
pafs a fenfible fpace, and the times are proportionably longer as the fpaces
paffed are greater.   But a fecond Caufe of the duration of the Thunder, I
conceive, proceeds from Echoes that are rebounded both from parts of the
Earth, and likewife parts of the Air, as from charged Clouds ; of both
which I am fenfibly affured both by natural Reafoning and from fenfible Obfervations, and I have obferved much the fame Effects produced by the Echoe-
ing and Rebounding of the found of a peice of Ordnance, from places at
feveral diftances adapted for the production of fuch Repercuffions.

But, Thirdly, We have alfo the Power and Violence of the force of the
Fire and Expanfion, in fireing feveral things that are Combuftible, in fuddenly melting of Metals and other Materials, which are difficult and flow
enough otherwife to be made to flow, in rending, taring, throwing down and
deftroying whatever ftands in its way, and the like ; and yet after all, that
which

which causeth these and many other strange Effects resembling those of Gun-pouder, seems to be nothing but a Vapour or Steem mixed with the Body of the Air, which is inkindled, not by any actual Fire, but by a kind of Fermentation or inward working of the said Vapour. Again, we find that the *Pulvis Fulminans* as 'tis called, which hath some of its materials differing from that of common Pouder; as also *Aurum Fulminans*, which is yet more differing both as to its materials and as to its way of kindling, have yet most of the same effects with Gun-pouder, both as to the flashing and thundring Noise, and as to the Force or Violence. So that as these are differing in many particulars, and yet produce much the same effects; so 'tis probable, that what is the cause of Earthquakes and Subterraneous Thundring, Lightning and violent Expansion, as I may so call those Phænomena observable in those *Crises* of Nature, may be in divers particulars differing from every one of these, both as to the materials, and as to the form and manner of Accension, and yet as to the Effects they may be very Analogous and Similar. So that tho' I cannot possibly prove what the materials are, yet the Effects speak them to be somewhat Analogous to those of Gun-pouder, or *Pulvis Fulminans*, *Aurum Fulminans* or Lightning, which, tho' they seem very differing in many particulars, yet when I come to shew the Causes and Reasons of those Effects, I shall manifest, that 'tis but one Operation in Nature, and that which causes the effect in one causes the effect in all the rest, and the outward appearances of the differing materials, and the differing way of Operating, are nothing but the Habits, and Dresses, and Vizards of the Actors, and the differing Modes and Dances by which they Act their several Parts, which, when they have done, they are at an end, and have exerted their whole Power, and there must be a new set of Actors to do the same thing again; the Oil of the Lamp will be turned all into Flame, but you must have fresh Oil, if you will have the Flame continued. So the Materials that make the Subterraneous Flame or Fire, or Expansion, call it by which name you please, is consumed and converted to another Substance, not fit to produce any more the same Effect ; and if the Conflagration be so great as to consume all the present *All things are* Store, you might safely conclude that place would no more be troubled with *in a perpetual* such Effects; but if there be remainders left, either already fit and prepared, *change.* but sheltered from Accension by other interposing incombustible Materials ; Or that there be other parts not thoroughly Ripe, and sufficiently prepared for such Accension, then a concurrence of after Causes may repeat the same Effects, and that *toties quoties* 'till all the Mine be exhausted, which I look upon as a thing not only possible, but probable, nay, necessary, for that I find it to be the general method of Nature, which is always going forward, and continually making a progress of changing all things from the State in which it finds them in at the present; all things as they proceed to their Perfection, so they proceed also to their Dissolution and Corruption, as to their preceding Estate ; and where Nature repeats the process, 'tis always on a new Individual.

Now, tho' it may be Objected, of the material that produceth Lightning, tho' it seemeth to be all kindled and so burnt off by the flash, yet we find that after some time the same is again renewed, and so from time to time, and therefore as one Operation doth destroy and consume it, so another doth generate and produce it anew, and therefore it doth seem probable that the same may be done in the Subterraneous Regions, and thence, tho' there were many Accensions and Consumings of the foment of Earthquakes in former Ages, yet if Nature did thus again repair it, there would be little reason to suppose, that former Earthquakes should be greater than those which have in later, or in this present Age, been observed ; to which I Answer, That tho' it seem plain, that the foment of Lightning is renewed, yet I conceive that to be only by new Emanations from the proper Minerals in the Body of the Earth, and not for that the same Substance which is burnt off in the Lightning, is again restored into its former State and made fit for a second Accension; for tho' there may be necessary a prævious Digestion of the Steams, which is performed by the Air and heat of the Weather, yet that does only prepare it with a proper fitness, but it must be some proper Mine-

Ppppp
ral

ral that muſt furniſh the Materials : And the ſame thing is more evident in *Vulcanoes* and burning Mountaiñs, which are there only oberved to break forth and burn where there is plenty of Brimſtone and other proper Subſtances for ſuch Conflagrations ; for if the ſame were only a continual new Generation of Combuſtible Materials for the Fire, then I ſee no Reaſon why thoſe *Incendiums* ſhould not be equally frequent and equally great in all places, as well as in thoſe where they are now frequently obſerved ; for why ſhould it not as frequently happen in our Hills and Mountains, as it does in *Sicily,* or *Iſland,* in *Ætna,* or *Hecla,* the one being as much colder then we, as we are then the other ? It follows therefore, that it muſt be cauſed, not by the Renovation of the Foment, but from the Duration of the Mines or Minerals that ſupply fit Materials, and conſequently, that when thoſe ſhall be quite conſumed, then, and not 'till then will the Fire go quite out. Nay that there are ſome ſuch Inſtances of preceding *Vulcanoes,* which have heretofore burned and are now almoſt quite ſpent, may be concluded from the *Pike* of *Tenariff,* which, by all Circumſtances, ſeems to have been formerly a burning Mountain, but is now quite extinct, and the Iſland of *Aſcenſion* ſeems to be another ſuch an Inſtance. All which Conflagrations are the ſeveral Symptoms of the progreſs of Nature in the determined Courſe and Method, which, tho' it be differing from that of Life or Vegetation in leſſer Bodies, yet it may be poſſibly as Natural and Neceſſary in the greater.

I cannot therefore ſee any Abſurdity in thinking or aſſerting that this Globe of the Earth on which we inhabit is in a ſtate of Progreſſion from one degree of Perfection to that of another degree, which may be termed of Perfection, for as much as it is the Progreſs and Operation of Nature ; and at the ſame time it may be conceived in a progreſs to Corruption and Diſſolution in as much as it continually changed from its preceding State, and acquires a new and differing one from what it had before, which new Eſtate may be upon ſome accounts conſidered as more perfect, tho' upon other accounts it may be accounted corrupting and tending to its final Diſſolution ; and as 'tis certain that it is continually older in reſpect of Time and Duration, ſo I conceive alſo that it grows older as to its Conſtitution and Powers, and that there have been many moreEffects produced by it in its more Juvenile Eſtate,than it doth or it can now produce in its more Senile, as more particularly to Earthquakes and Eruptions ; for to me it ſeems moſt evident and paſt doubting, that there have been in ſome preceding Ages of the World Eruptions and Conflagrations which have infinitely ſurpaſſed any that have happened of later Years, or indeed any that we have any certain account of in Hiſtory. Some kind of Memory of ſome antient Traditions concerning a very great one that ſometimes happened, ſeems to be preſerved by the Poetical or Mythological Hiſtory of *Phaeton,* of which *Plato* alſo tells us, that the *Ægyptians* had a more perfect knowledge and account, than ever the *Greeks* were Maſters of, who, at beſt, as to Hiſtories of preceding Ages, were, by the *Ægyptian* Prieſts, accounted but Boys and Children ; however, *Ovid,* by his wording of that Fable, does ſeem plainly to have had ſome knowledge of what was meant or underſtood thereby ; and tho' he ſeems to aſcribe the Cauſe thereof to ſome extraordinary heat of the Sun, yet that might be nothing elſe but the relating the Opinion of the Antients preſerved by the ſame Tradition, by which the Memory of the prodigious effects that had been wrought had been retained.

In which caſe we are to diſtinguiſh between Hiſtories of Matters of Fact, and thoſe of Opinion ; and *Plato* takes notice of as much when he mentions the Relation. The Matters of Fact ſeem to have been the Conflagration of many parts of the Earth at once, and thoſe the moſt eminent, ſuch as the Mountains, which, whether they were in being before the Conflagration, or made by that Eruption, does not appear by the Story, but it ſeems moſt probable, that that was the time of their Production ; and the calling of them by ſeveral Names, yet retained, does ſignify no more, but that thoſe Mountains, which are now called ſo or ſo, were then on Fire and burning.

But

But having before explain'd this Fable of *Phaeton,* and several others of *that* ingenious Mythologick Poet *Ovid,* I shall forbear the repetition of them here, and for the present would only infer, that in former and younger Ages of the World those kind of effects, produced by Eruptions and Earthquakes, have been much more considerable than those which are now produced, or which have been produc'd since we have had any Records kept of such Events; and therefore we are not to conclude that such huge Mountains, as the *Alpes,* the *Andes, Caucasus, Atlas,* or the like, could never be produced by means of Earthquakes or Eruptions, because we do not now find Instances of Effects of the same Grandure produced in our present Age, or in the Ages of which we have some more perfect account; for that in the former Ages there have been a much greater plenty of those kinds of Minerals which have been consumed, and for that the Relicts which are now left are but very small, and in probability not so apt for Conflagration, nor so strong and efficacious in their Operations; besides many of their Substances that were left may have since been petrify'd and converted into Substances, wholly unfit for the Foment or Fuell of such kinds of Fire; for that such Mutations have been effected by length of Time, I think no one that has observ'd and consider'd the Nature of Petrifaction can at all doubt, any more than he can whether there be any such Substance as Stone; for that all Places and Quarries especially will furnish him with Evidences enough to convince any that will not be wilfully ignorant. *Earthquakes formerly more frequent, and why.*

This effect of Petrifaction is a Symptom of old Age; for as plenty of *Spirituous, Unctuous* andCombustible or Inflammable Juices and Moisture is a sign of Youth: So the want of them, and of the Effects produced by them, is a sign of old Age, in which those unctuous Juices are consumed and the Spirituous Fluids wasted, and the Parts become dry, and hard, and Stiff, and unactive; neither fit to inkindle the active Flame or to maintain it; neither fit to make other Substances fluid, nor to be made fluid themselves; which Fluidity is an inseparable Concomitant of that we call Spirituous Substances: And 'tis the plenty of those kind of Substances that maketh the Youthful Ages both of Plants and Animals to flourish, and the Consumption and want of them, that makes both Plants and Animals to decay and grow old, as we call them, to grow stiff, and dry, and rough, and shrivelled; all which Marks or Sypmtoms may plainly be discovered also in the Body of the Earth, and I am apt to believe would be very much more if we could be truly inform'd of the former and younger Condition thereof; for I have very good Reason to believe, that there has been times of the Earth wherein it hath had a much smoother and softer, and more succous Skin than now it hath, when it more abounded with Spirituous Substances, when all its Powers were more strong and vegete, and when those Scars, Roughness and Stiffness were not in being; and tho' possibly some may think all these Conceptions to be groundless and meerly Conjectural, yet I may in good time manifest, that there are other ways of coming to the discovery of many Truths than what have been to this purpose hitherto made use of, which yet are not less capable of Proof and Confirmation, than Histories or Records are by Coins, Inscriptions or Monuments. And tho' it may seem difficult to understand or be informed of the State of the subterraneous and inaccessible Regions, and of the Ages before History, yet I do not look upon either as an impossibility, no, nor as insuperable by the Industry of a few, nay, of a single Person. And possibly I may some other time shew divers other ways of Inquiry, and other Methods of Demonstration of Causes than what have been yet applied to those purposes. *The Earth grows old and less fruitful.*

Nor is this Assertion of the growing old of the Earth to be looked on as so great a Paradox, or as Heterodoxical, or Scismatical, for we find in Scripture that the Kingly Prophet *David* in the 102 *Psalm* has an Expression that doth plainly assert it, not only of the Earth but even of the Heaven. *Of old hast thou laid the foundations of the Earth, and the Heavens are the works of thy hands, they shall perish, but thou shalt indure; yea all of them shall wax old like a garment, as a vesture shalt thou change them, and they shall be changed.* Which Expression is almost verbatim repeated by the Prophet *Isaiah,* Chap. 51. v. 6. *Lift up your eyes to the heavens and look upon the earth beneath, for the heavens shall vanish away*

away like Smoke, and the Earth shall wax old like a Garment. Nay, this Expreſſion of the *Pſalmiſt* is verbatim repeated by St. *Paul* in the 10. 11. and 12. Verſes of the Epiſtle to the *Hebrews.* By all which it is evident at leaſt, that *David, Iſaiah* and St. *Paul* were all of that belief. I could produce many Expreſſions to the like purpoſe both in Sacred and Prophane Hiſtories, both of Chriſtian and Heathen Writers, but thoſe I have quoted I ſuppoſe may be ſufficient to anſwer Objeƈtors of that kind.

As for any other Objeƈtions that may be brought againſt this Doƈtrine, ſuch as the equal Stature and Ages of Men for ſo long time as we have had any Hiſtory; from the want of Hiſtories of ſuch Juvenil Eſtates, from the Permanency and Duration of all the Species of Plants and Animals in the ſame Eſtate, from the Incorruptibity of the Heavens and Cæleſtial Bodies, and ſo of their Influences, Cauſations, and many other of the like Nature; I doubt not to be able to give a ſatisfaƈtory Anſwer if any of them ſhall be preſſed or inſiſted upon, tho' at the ſame time I cannot hope that all will be convinced, much leſs, that all will confeſs themſelves to be ſo, tho' really they are. All I can ſay, is *Valeat quantum valere poteſt,* let every one enjoy his own freedom.

AN *Extraƈt of a Leƈture read* July 18. 1688. *relating to the Conſequences and Concomitants of Earthquakes, and the alterations cauſed by them in the Conſtitution of the Air as to Sickneſs,* &c. *Next follows an account of an Earthquake in* China, *and another in* Spain.

R. W.

THE Aim of my preſent Diſcourſe is rather a Progreſſion in the Theory of the Nature of the Air, than of any of the formerly mention'd Effeƈts of Earthquakes, and the rather by the way of Query and Inquiſition, than of poſſitive Theory and Affirmation.

Of the Conſtitution of the Air after Earthquakes.

As Firſt, Whether the late Feaveriſh Diſtemper that was here ſo frequent, ſuppoſed by ſome to be inclined to Peſtilential, tho' not ſo Mortal, might not be cauſed by ſome Infeƈtions or poiſenous Vapours caſt into it by thoſe late Eruptions in *Italy* or *America* ?

Secondly, Whether the coldneſs, unſeaſonableneſs of the Spring, the ſtrange Rains, Storms and Tempeſts, and other ſuch unuſual Accidents, that have lately happened in the Weather, may not have been cauſed by the ſame Efficients that cauſed the Eruptions ?

Thirdly, Whether it may be reaſonable to conceive, that there could be any Communication Subterraneous between theſe places of thoſe Eruptions in *Naples* and *Lima* ; or whether it were Superterraneous through the Air and Æther ?

Fourthly, Whether it may be rationally conceived, that Steems raiſed into the Body of the Air in *Lima* or in *Naples* could be continued ſo long in it as to be conveyed from either of thoſe places to *England, London,* &c. ?

Fifthly, How long time may be judged neceſſary for ſuch a Conveyance ?

Sixthly, Whether ſuch Diſtempers of the Air may be precedent to the Diſtempers within the Earth, and ſo be of the Nature of a Procatarƈtick cauſe of the Earthquakes, and if ſo, whether thoſe Diſtempers may ariſe from the Nature of the Air itſelf, or from ſome external and influential Cauſe, either from the Æther, Comets, or ſome of the more Conſpicuous Cæleſtial Bodies ?

Seventhly, Whether there may be not ſome general, tho' yet unknown, Cauſe, that may produce both thoſe effeƈts in the Earth and thoſe in the Air, nay, and thoſe in the Æther alſo, ſuch as Comets and ſome kinds of Meteors alſo ? becauſe of the uſual Concomitance of them; as will in part appear by ſubſequent Relations.

Theſe

These possibly may be looked upon as not very easily solvable, and therefore not so proper to be propounded as Queries, unless they could also be as satisfactoraly answered. I must leave every one to Censure as he thinks meet, only this I must add, that the first step towards Knowledge is Inquisition.

And that I may manifest that these Queries are not altogether at random, I shall add some Natural Histories, that may possibly give some hints of their Solution; and those shall be the Accounts of some Accidents or Effects similar to those, which have lately happened at other Times, and in other Places; from whose Congruities one would be apt to conjecture a similitude of Causes, and if not a necessary, yet somewhat more than an accidental Concurrency of Effects, and a kind of Periodick Revolution of them.

In the Year 1672, in the Islands of the *Archipelago*, that is, the Islands of *Greece*, this Winter was so Stormy and Tempestuous, that not only the Trees and Plantations, but the Houses also were destroyed by the Lightning and Hail; so that both the Towns and Villages became almost unknowable, being reduced to Ruins.

In the *Barbadoes* also was a most violent Hurricane, in which many of our Nation Perished.

Near *Ancona*, *Fauno* and *Rimini*, there were this Year, in *April*, many Houses overturned by an Earthquake; and more especially in *Romania* and St. *Marc*, there were above six hundred People killed, and above quaruple that number hurt: At *Rimini* the Cathedral Church was overthrowed, the Bells shaken out of the Tower, and many People lost their Lives. At *Fauno* twenty eight Persons were killed by the fall of a Bell. The Churches of the *Theatines*, St. *Agnie*, St. *Apollonce*, St. *Mary de la Gomia*, St. *Innocent*, St. *Bernard*, St. *Mary della Colonolla*, and all the others except only those of the *Capuchines*, and of *Maria de Mari*, were endamaged. A great number of Palaces and Houses were ruined: This happened whilst People were at Church; so that above fifteen Hundred were killed, and many more were hurt. At *Pesaro* and *Senegallo* the Walls of the City and many Chimnies were thrown down. *Ancona* and *Rimini* were abandoned by their Inhabitants, who were constrained to lie under the open Canopy of Heaven.

September the 30th., of the same Year, there was a Hurricane passed trough all *Spain*, but it was most furious about *Madrid*, insomuch that it blew down the Roofs, Chimnies, nay, and the Houses too; as also the Towers and Churches; insomuch that the Damage was exceeding great along the *Prado* and at *Buon Retiro*. But all this was nothing in comparison of what happened the same Day in almost all the Countries of *Spain*; for this furious Tempest caused such Ravages in *Andalusia*, *Gallicia*, *Castil*, *Grenada*, *Valencia* and *Biscay*, as were truly Amazing: But what was most remarkable was this, that three Days after the Gallions of the Plate-Fleet, which came from the *West-Indies*, being arrived at the Islands of *Terceras*, felt not the least of it.

In this Year were also seen two Comets,----one in *January* another in *April*.

Eight Years before this, namely, in 1664, were two Comets also; but all the other Natural Histories, or Physical Accidents of that Year I have not yet procured.----

But eight Years after this, *viz.* 1680, which is now also eight Years since; First, For the Comets they are yet in most Mens Memories, and besides there are Histories enough extant; but next for the Earthquakes: First, By a Letter from *Botavia* we have an account of a great Earthquake that happened in *China* about *Peking* the preceding *August*, viz. That the $\frac{1}{3}$ of *August* 79, about ten in the Morning, there happened a most terrible Earthquake, which overturned almost all the Houses of that great City and the parts thereabout, whereby a World of People were destroyed in a most dreadful manner, besides multitudes that were hurt, whose number we cannot yet learn to this Hour: Two Heads of certain Beasts, which were Carved and fixed over the Imperial Palace Gate, were beaten off and thrown down to the Ground by the force of the shake. All the Palaces of the *Mandarines*, and their Families, and the Courts of Justice round the Palace were tumbled down; the Emperor commanded the principle *Mandarines*, that had command over the five parts of

the

the City of *Peking*, to examine themselves in their proper Persons, and to give him an account of all the damages that had happened, that he might the better advise of ways to help the Poor People that had suffered. This they did, and advised, that if his Majesty would distribute to each two or three Crowns of Silver at twenty five Frecks the Crown, it might be a sufficient supply: But he thinking this was too little, commanded ten Thousand Crowns to be taken out of his Treasury and distributed for the present Necessity. The first, second, and following Days that it lasted, the Earth was shaken five, six, or seven times a Day, but not with so much violence as by the first; so that the Inhabitants were in such Consternation as to forsake their Houses; the Soldiers and their Wives were most afflicted having nothing left to subsist; by Day they were exposed to the Sun, and by Night to the cold Heaven, which much incommoded them. The Emperor also was in great Pain to know the Damages that had happened in the Neighbouring Parts by this Earthquake, and commanded one of his great *Mandarines*, named *Samolio*, to inquire and inform him of them, who returned this Report, That the $\frac{13}{23}$ of *August*, whilst the Heaven was covered all over with dark Clouds, the Earthquake shocked extraordinarily the City of *Tongfu* about a Days Journey from *Peking*, that all the Imperial Magazines there had been overturned, as likewise the old Walls of the City; so that of ten Parts of the City scarce one remained which had not been indamaged, whose pitiful Condition was deplored by every one. The Commissioners of the Magasines Emperial who had escaped, render'd themselves presently to His Imperial Majesty to give him an account of the flying of the under Officers for the Consternation, and of their fear of the Robbing of the remaining Rice and Provisions by Thieves, which caused him to send them sixteen Hundred Soldiers for their Guard. The *Primier Intendant* of the Navy was killed by the overturning of his House. The Emperor had also reported to him, how the Robbers had wasted much of his Treasury in the Magazines that had been overturned; and upon the consideration of the general Calamity, the Emperor makes a most Pious Speech to the principle *Mandarines*, which I shall not trouble you with, only my Author adds, What Christian could have spoke better? Will not such as he rise up in Judgment against many Christians? This is a short Account of what happened to two Cities of *China*: I say Cities; for tho' generally we have only an account of the Damages caused to Cities, Towns and Men, yet we are not to conceive, as if the shaking and disorders of an Earthquake were only aimed at Cities like Marks and Goales to be shot at; no, certainly, there may, in all such Concussions and Devastations have happened much greater and different Effects from those which come to our knowledge; for that the most part of the World have little concern for what may happen in the Mountains, Hills, Plains, Forrests, Seas, &c. which make not any great or publick Calamity to the more considerable sort of Men; wherefore questionless, tho' many strange Effects of this kind may also have happened, and may have been seen and observed by some Men, yet they are but as it were *In transitu*, and quickly forgotten, since there is none to Record them. So that many thousands of such Effects have been swallowed up by the Oblivion of Time, where one has chanced to get by some accidental hint to lie Recorded by chance among the heap of other Histories. Comets indeed, as glaring in every ones Eyes, have found, among the multitude of Observers, some that have Recorded somewhat of them to Posterity, but even among them also, I doubt we shall not find that one of ten has obtained a History. But this Earthquake in *China* was not the only Accident of this time which I would mention; for upon the Coast of *Coromandal*, the Sea so overflowed the Country, that infinities of Men and Cattle were destroyed, many Cities and Villages were drowned. This overflowing was also found at *Jafnapatnam*, where it did much mischief to the Fortification, and to the Country, and the Cattle, but not so much to the Men.

Nor were these kind of Accidents only felt in *India*, but the same Year there happened a considerable Earthquake in *Spain*, and particularly at *Malaga*.

All *Spain* was this Year so perished with Drouth, that not only the Pits, Fountains and Rivers were dried, but the Harvest was spoiled, and many perish'd by this means : On the other side in the *Autumn* arose such horrible Tempests and Earthquakes as were felt long after. After the beginning of *September* they had continual Thunder and Lightning, by which divers perished. The Hail fell so on *Pardo*, a Pleasure-house of the Kings of *Spain*, that it rooted up the greatest Trees, and kill'd so many Beast and Foul, that not only the Fields were almost cover'd, but the River *Mancanarez* ; it much indamaged the Village *Foncarral* ; the old Bridge *de Aranda de Duerro* was born down by the Waters of the River *Tagus*, which run under, and did much damage to *Aranivez*, sweeping away divers People, Cattle, Trees, Bridges, and Houses : The like Ruins were caused almost over all the Kingdom, insomuch that in one Village, only, forty People were lost. The greatest violence was at *Madrid* the twenty sixth of *September*, where the Water overflowed so as to mount into the Garden of the *Augustines* and throw down the Wall ; also into the fair Parterres of the Countess *Ognate*, and run into her House, ruin'd the rich Furniture of Pictures, *&c.* of the lower Story ; ruin'd the Stables and razed one House. The River also bore away fifty Foot of a strong Stone-Wall made to stop the Passage into the River *Prado :* This River one of the least in *Spain*, so swelled as to carry away almost all before it, as four Iron Gates, and the Cross of the *Via Sacra.* It beat down the Bridge before *Buon Retiro*, and broke through the middle of the Stone Bank. It rush'd into the Gardens of *Nostre Dame de Arocha* after it had beat down the Wall ; it run into the general Hospital carrying with it an Arch of Stones. The twenty seventh the overflowing continued with constant Thunder and Lightning, when the River *Mancanarez* bore down the fair Bridge of *Toledo* of sixty Arches. The twenty eighth the Streams of *Prado* so swelled by the Torrents from the Mountains, that all the Champain near it was drowned, the King and Queen of *Spain* were like to be lost in their return from *Nostre Dame de Arocha* ; *Malaga*, a City of the Kingdom of *Granada*, situated on the *Mediterranean*, twenty five Miles from the Streights, a Place Great, Rich and well Peopled, had, the ninth of this Month, such violent Shocks of an Earthquake, that all were frighted, the Sea was so disturbed, that the Fish leaped out of the Water, and the Ships in the Harbour were cast above twenty Foot from their places, which the Mariners believed to be sunk ; the Harbours and Walls were sunk, together with the Bulwarks, Towers and Fortifications of four Parishes, of which the City consisted, having 4284 Houses, 1057 were ruined to their Foundations ; 1259 so decay'd, that they must be Rebuilt to be Habitable. Divers Churches and Palaces felt the effects also ; five Cloysters of Religious with the People were utterly ruined, and above all, that of St. *Francis*, where Stone was not left on Stone, where fourteen Persons Perish'd, four Hospitals, one Colledge, the Bishops Palace, the Palaces of *d Diego de Argote, de Jo. de Torrez, de Diego de Cordua*, and a fair House joining to the Cathedral was thrown down, yet the Church which had been Repairing and Beautifying ever since 1521 scaped, tho' divers times shaken. In the Suburbs *Los Perchelez* two hundred and twenty five Houses were thrown down, so that in all 1282 Houses were destroy'd. Many Houses in the Confines of *Malaga* were overturned ; besides the Earth opened in divers places and disgorged Waters in great abundance, which swelled the Rivers and made them overflow. Many Houses in the Villages were destroyed, as at *Pizaria* four Miles from *Malaga*, fifteen of twenty four Houses were overturned ; some Mountains were displaced, and divers Persons and Cattle lost : The Wall of *Alhaurin de la torte*, two Miles from *Malaga*, opened four Foot, but closed again : The Jasper Columns of the Church were lifted up and setled down again on their Pedestals. At *Competa*, six Leagues from the City, nothing but the Tabernacle and the Cross of the Church remained whole. At *Aloizana* forty Houses were tumbled down, as many at *Cartama*, and thereabout also at *Coin*, and a great number of People perish'd. At great *Alhaurin* two hundred and forty Houses and the Church were destroy'd, of which only fifty three were somewhat Habitable. In the City of *Minorz* five Leagues from *Malaga*, thirty seven Houses were tumbl'd down, and fifteen

teen Perfons crufh'd. The Church at the City *Binal-Madera* fell on a heap, and all the Houfes render'd unhabitable. The Earth opened at *Veles Malaga,* and fo fwelled a River, which run fome fpace from thence, that it rofe ten Pikes above the tops of the Houfes, which it fquafh'd in running. Many Houfes were ruin'd at *Aloro,* others much endamag'd, with the Cloifter of St. *Francis.* All the Churches of *Granada* were fhaken, and a Chappel in the Church of *Mercy* ruin'd : All which were fad Spectacles.

I have given the Particulars of the whole Relation, moft of which concern Buildings, Men and Cattle, thofe being the Particulars moft People are affected with and fo obferve, and you find only two hints, as it were, of other Effects, the one is of the removing feveral Mountains, the other of the Earths opening and difgorging a Flood. But 'tis not to be thought but that an inquifitive Naturalift might have found ten times more remarkable Effects in the Country than the fhaking down a few Houfes in the Towns and Villages, all which, if taken notice of, are foon forgot and loft, and fo have been in former Ages, and therefore no wonder if we hear nothing of them in Books : But Nature itfelf has preferved fomewhat of the memory of them by the Medals or indelible Characters of Shells or other Petrify'd, or otherwife preferved Subftances, which any, that have Senfes and Underftanding, may read. But this is not the aim of my prefent relating thefe Hiftories, but to give an example of a Contemporarinefs of Earthquakes at great diftances upon the Earth, and a fimilitude of Effects with thofe we have this Year heard of from *Italy* and *America* ; nay, and let me add what we have had in *London* and *England, viz.* a kind of Agueifh Diftemper, yet not Peftilential, which, 'tis well known, has been very general ; for I find that in *October* Agues were as frequent this Year in *France,* as the late Cold or Diftemper was here : It was then that Dr. *Tabour* cured the Prince of *Conde,* and many other Perfons of great Quality, among the reft the *Dauphinefs* firft, and afterwards the *Dauphin* himfelf, by a Medicine he had invented ; tho' *Tabours* demanding five Thoufand Crowns for difcovering his Receipt, made the *Dauphin* firft make ufe of other means, but without effect. (I will not like an Aftrologer name to you the Occurrences that then happened at *Cologne,* nor make comparifon with the prefent, but leave thofe to the Aftrologians, *&c.*) The Plague alfo this Year 1689, was very much at *Prague,* fo that fome judged there died in that City thirty Thoufand, at *Drefden* above four Thoufand, at *Leipfick* about three Thoufand ; I cannot fay there hath been a Comet this Year, but I have been confidently told, that there appear'd one in the Mornings about a Month fince, but I could not have the luck to fee it, tho' I looked for it divers Mornings after I heard of it, but 'tis more likely it may appear in *October,* or later ; but that belongs to another Head, the Affected Earth and Infected Air being thofe I defigned at prefent to compare ; and in thefe we find the effects in *China* and *Coromandel* eight Years fince to anfwer thofe of *America* this prefent Year, and that then of *Spain* to this now of *Italy* ; and thofe then of *France* and *Germany* to the late here in *England,* tho' in all particulars thofe of the Year eighty feem to exceed thofe of the prefent Year. But as the Relations of that are but fhort and imperfect, fo are thofe of the prefent as yet much more ; but 'twere to be wifh'd fome more full might be obtained and Recorded before they be forgotten, which a little fpace of time will otherwife effect, and 'tis not to be doubted but we might hear of much ftranger effects of the *Lima* Earthquake, than yet have arrived, if care were taken to procure a fuller account of them. And by the Yefterdays *Bruffells* we are informed of a Cleft in a Mountain belonging to the *Marquis de Tarracufa,* of four Spans broad and two Miles long, of which they can find no bottom, and of a Fire fhot into the Heavens like a great Beam, of which they loft the fight, not knowing whether it went.

But in the mean time poffibly it may not feem altogether unreafonable to fuppofe, that fuch an Eruption may emit poifenous Vapours, as well as fometimes poifenous Waters ; as appears by that of *France* which I have Printed in one of my Collections. Nor may it feem fo ftrange to fuppofe its effect may operate at fuch diftances, and not at the very place ; when we confider how fiery and volatile fuch Steams may be, how violently fhot into the Air,

and

and blow far off the Dust and Ashes of *Hecla*, *Ætna*, the *Palma*, and many others have been carried in the Air before they have fallen, of which Instances may be produced. And that, in probability, the less active or dead Earthy Materials are those, which fall near the place, whose Qualifications may be of differing Natures. Nor will any very long time bethought requisite for their transport to far distant Countries imbody'd in the Air, when I have proved the velocities of its motions. Nor will it seem strange to one that shall well confider the known Effects of the several Winds, to suppose such kind of transports: But of these Particulars I shall say more upon some other occasion.

THis Lecture was read May the 29th. 1689, and Answers two Objections against the Athor's Theory of Earthquakes, particularly as to Petrifactions.

R. W.

I Delivered in my last Lecture in this place, the Methods I had made use of for the founding and establishing the Doctrines or Conclusions I had made concerning the Causes and Reasons of the present State and Phænomena of the Surface of the Earth, which was by a methodical Induction from the Phænomena themselves of the most remote, as well as the more approximate and immediate Causes thereof. But notwithstanding all the Arguments I have alledged, and the Proofs I have produced in the delivery of this *Theory*, I still find that there remain upon the Minds of some such Doubts and contrary Persuasions, that they cannot forsake their former Opinions; and therefore (tho' I think I have already fully proved every part, so that the Confutations of such Objections would be but the necessary Corollaries from the said Doctrine, yet since I find they are still insisted on as material Objections that will need a more particular Discussion and Examination) I thought it not impertinent to examine them more strictly, to find the Power and Efficacy, or to discover the Weakness and Insufficiency of them for the purpose they are designed. That thereby the *Idola* (as my Lord *Verulam* says) which pre-possess the Minds of some Men, and molest them in the discovery and imbracing of Sciences may be detected, and, as much as may be, removed and dissolved, thereby to leave the Mind more free to Discourse and Reason aright, without the prejudices of any unsound, unaccountable and unwarrantable Doctrines formerly imbrac'd.

The Objections I shall at present examine are only two, *viz.*

First, That if these large Petrified Bodies, such as the *Ophiomorphite* Stone which I did formerly shew to this Society in the place, be supposed to have been the Production of this Shell of a certain kind of *Nautilus* of that bigness and shape, which, in preceding Ages of the World, had been produced and perfected to that Magnitude in the bottom of the Sea, which then was near the place where they are now found, as I have argued for; then it will necessarily follow, say they, that there have been, in former times, certain Species of Animals in Nature, which in succeeding and in the present Age have been and are wholly lost; for neither have we in Authors any mention made of such Creatures, nor are there any such found at present, either near the places of their position (as on the Shores or Sea about this Island) nor in any other part of the World for ought we yet know. Now, to suppose such a Doctrine as doth necessarily infer such a Consequence, is looked upon by such as absurd and extravagant; for that it would argue an imperfection of the first Creation, which should produce any one Species more than what was absolutely necessary to its present and future State, and so would be a great derogation from the Wisdom and Power of the Omnipotent Creator.

Obj. 1st. As to a Species being lost.

To this first Objection I Answer, First, That tho' it may possibly be true, that there is at present no such *Nautili* to be found upon the Coast or Shores

1st. Answer.

of the Lands where thefe forts of figured Stones are found, yet no one is affured that there are not fome of the fame Species, and as big in fome other
parts of the World, as poffibly at the bottoms of fome of the great Oceans.
Of fuch Productions and thofe Multifarious both Vegetable and Animal, no
one can doubt that has found in foundable Depths fuch variety of teftaceous
and cruftaceous Animals there refiding, as in their proper and Natural Regions; which would by no means poffibly be produced or kept alive in parts of
the Sea where they fhould want their natural Accommodations; one of which
may poffibly be a fufficient degree of Preffure from the incumbent Column of
Water, which, if fuch be neceffary to their Life and well Being, we are
no more to wonder that they fhould not be found in fhallower Waters, than
that Men fhould not be found inhabiting the tops of the *Andes*, of the *Atlas, Alps*,
or *Caucafus*, which from the thinnefs and coldnefs of the Air at thofe heights,
are no ways fit for Refpiration and fuftaining Life. Now, that the prefent
Land of *England* may have in former Ages had fome fuch Pofition with refpect to
an incumbent Sea, I could produce feveral Arguments were they now material to the anfwering the prefent Objection, but I will not now infift upon it.

2d. *Anfwer.*   But in the fecond place I anfwer, That tho' poffibly there may be no fuch
Nautilus to be found defcribed in any Natural Hiftorian at this Day, yet 'tis
poffible there may be many of the fame Species, and of as great Magnitudes
in divers parts of the World, fuch as have been either not yet difcovered by
the *Europeans* or but of late, or but little frequented; and fo tho' they may
be there frequent and plentiful enough, yet none may have been brought
thence into *Europe* as yet, or poffibly fo much as feen there; 'tis not to be
doubted that there really are great multitudes of differing Species of Vegetables, Infects, Beafts and Fifhes yet in places lefs frequented, of which we
in *Europe* have hitherto had no knowledge or information; and tho' many
ftrange things have been of late Years brought to our view, yet we may with
Reafon enough affert, there are many more yet latent, which Time may make
manifeft: For if we confider the fmall knowledge of things of this Nature
that we yet have acquired, of places remote, even the moft frequented, we
need not much wonder at the leffer information of fuch, as are not known or
lefs frequented; for not to infift upon the multitudes of Vegetables that have
been newly fhewn to us by the Authors of the *Hortus Malabaricus*, and by
Brennius, and others, we are put in hope, to fee the Defcriptions of as many
more yet by the fame Authors, from the fame places, which yet are but two
fmall fpots in refpect of the vaft Spaces, and variety of Soils and Climates
yet unfurvey'd; and 'tis not to be doubted but that the Earth, and Air, and
much more yet, the Seas of feveral Countries and Climates would afford as
great varieties of Birds, Beafts, Infects and Fifhes, if there were found knowing and diligent fearchers and defcribers of them: And that this is fo, I fhall
mention only one Inftance, becaufe 'tis pertinent to the prefent Subject, namely, that I have had a peculiar kind of *Nautilus* brought from the *Caribys*,
where they are in great plenty, and yet I do not find any Author has taken
notice of them, nor could I ever meet with more than one Man that had taken notice or knew any thing of them, tho' the Ifland has been long inhabited and planted by the *Englifh*; which Shell I have formerly fhewn to this Society, who were fatisfy'd by the Characteriftick that it is a Species of the
Nautili.

And as we yet want a *Hortus Sinenfis, Japonenfis, Tartaricus, Canadenfis, Vir-
ginianus, Brafilianus, Peruvianus, Americanus*, &c. fo we want the Natural Hiftories of the Animals of moft kinds, of thofe places, and even of the Fifhes
which are frequently enough met with by Navigators, tho' not further taken
notice of than as they may be ufeful for their prefent Food, or the like. We
are therefore two hafty in our Computations and fumming up all we have,
and concluding that muft be the fumme of all that can be had; for that there
are yet many particulars behind, that muft come into the fame account before
the inclofure be fully made and the Books be fhut, if at leaft a full Account
be expected. We are informed by Mr.-----*Cole*, and divers other late inquifitive Men, how many new things have been difcover'd here at home, where

yet

yet there have not formerly been wanting inquifitive Men; what then may we not expect from other places where none fuch have ever come, at leaft, that we know of?

Again, how apt fhould we have been, if there had been found a Petrify'd *Stella arborefcens Rondeletii*, before we had been certify'd of the exiftence of fuch a ftrange fhaped Fifh of the Species of the *Stellæ*, to have concluded there had never been fuch a Fifh, becaufe it differs fo very much from the Star-fifhes or five Fingers, as they term them, commonly taken on our Coafts? The like may be infer'd concerning the ftrange variety I have feen of the *E-chini* brought from feveral parts; for they differ much more from one another than the Helmet Stones, which I have hitherto feen, do from feveral forts of them: The like may be faid of the varieties of Sharks Teeth, as to one another, and as to the *Gloffopetræ* found upon the Land.

So that upon the whole we may conclude, that it does not necefarily follow, that thofe *Species* of *Nautili*, muft be now wholly loft that produced the moulding Shells of thefe *Ophiomorphite* Stones, we find here in *England*, becaufe they are not now found upon our Shores, nor becaufe we cannot now certainly affirm where they are to be found, and therefore that the induction or inference is made from too few Particulars, and may, nay, ought to be ex-amined a-new, when we can procure a more full Account of the Productions of the Shores and Oceans, which Time and Induftry may poffibly effect.

But not further to infift upon this way of Defence, we will, for the prefent, take this Suppofition to be real and true, that there have been in former times of the Word, divers *Species* of Creatures, that are now quite loft, and no more of them furviving upon any part of the Earth. Again, That there are now divers *Species* of Creatures which never exceed at prefent a certain Magnitude, which yet, in former Ages of the World, were ufually of a much greater and Gygantick Standard; fuppofe ten times as big as at prefent; we will grant alfo a fuppofition that feveral *Species* may really not have been created of the very Shapes they now are of, but that they have changed in great part their Shape, as well as dwindled and degenerated into a dwar-fifh Progeny; that this may have been fo confiderable, as that if we could have feen both together, we fhould not have judged them of the fame Species. We will further grant there may have been, by mixture of Creatures, produced a fort differing in Shape, both from the Created Forms of the one and other Compounders, and from the true Created Shapes of both of them. And yet I do not fee how this doth in the leaft derogate from the Power, Wifdom and Providence of God, as is alledged, or that it doth any ways contradict any part of the Scripture, or any Conclufion of the moft eminent Philofophers, or any rational Argument that may be drawn from the Phænomena of Nature; nay, I think the quite contrary Inferences may, nay, muft, and ought to be made.

For firft we do find that all individuals are made of fuch a Conftitution, as that beginning from an Atom, as it were, they are for a certain period of Time increafing and growing, and from thence begin to decay, and at laft Die and Corrupt. And in every part of their Life they are in a continual change or progrefs, from more perfect to more imperfect, there being a continual growth of Death and Decay to the final Diffolution; yet this is not Argument againft the Omnipotence, Providence and Wifdom of the Creator, who thought fit fo to Create them. Again, we find that the Powers and Faculties of the animated Bodies do continually exert a fucceffion of differing Effects, and continually change the Figures and Shapes from one degree to another. As we fee that there are many changings both within and without the Body, and every ftate produces a new appearance, why then may there not be the fame progreffion of the Species from its firft Creation to its final termination? Or why fhould the fuppofition of this be any more a derogation to the Perfection of the Creator, than the other; befides, we find nothing in Holy Writ that feems to argue fuch a conftancy of Nature; but on the contrary many Expreffions that denote a continual decay, and a tendency to a final Diffolution; and this not only of Terreftial Beings. but of Celeftial, even of the Sun, Moon and Stars and of the Heavens themfelves. Nor have

I hitherto

I hitherto met with any Doctrine among the Philosophers, that is repugnant to this Doctrine, but many that agree with it, and suppose the like States to happen to all the Celestial Bodies, that is, to the Stars and Planets that happen to the Individuals of any Species; and consequently if the Body of the Earth be accounted one of the number of the Planets, then that also is subject to such Changes and final Dissolution, and then at least it must be granted, that all the Species will be lost; and therefore, why not some at one time and some at another? This Objection therefore, I conceive, is of little validity against the Doctrine I have delivered, and therefore I shall proceed to the second Objection, and examine the Validity thereof.

2d. *Obj. As to figured Spars and Chryftals.* It is Objected then in the Second place, That since it is manifest, that there are many curiously figured Bodies found in the Earth, which cannot be imagin'd to be produc'd by the Causes and Means that I have alledg'd, as the Shapes of Salts, Sparrs, Ores, Chryftals, and divers other kinds of regular mineral Bodies, also, Agates Mochufes, curiously speckled Marbles, and the like. Now, since it must be granted, that they are made by a Plastick Faculty, why may not that Faculty extend also so far as to be the cause of those other Figured Stones, which resemble Shells or other Animal or Vegetable Substances?

To this I answer, That tho' it be manifest, that Salts, Chryftals, Sparrs, &c. do plainly receive their regular Figures from the Texture or Nature of their own Parts, as is evident, most especially in the Chryftallization of Salts, and the Petrifactions of the like Figur'd Substances, yet the Figures, and painted and stained Shapes, as it were of *Agates, Mochus's* and the like, are not to be ascribed to the Designs of Nature, but to the Productions of Chance; for instance, the Pictures that in *Mochus's* seem to represent Trees, Hills, Houses, and other perspective Representations, they are no otherwise caused than by some Clefts, or Flaws in the said Stones, into which some colour'd Juices have insinuated themselves, and by that means formed those Representations which appear in the Body of the Stone, and that this is so, and may be Artificially produc'd by several Bodies and Liquors, which have no affinity, either with *Agate, Mochus,* or Marble, I can make it plainly appear by Experiment, which, if it be thought fit, I shall produce either now, or the next Meeting.

THe Experiment here mention'd, was by taking two flat Marbles or Glass-plates, and laying upon one of them several drops of a dark Oil-colour, such as Painters use, and pressing the other flat Stone or Glass upon it, by that compressure several curious Representations, like the branchings of Vegetables, and the like, were exhibited; which explain'd the Representations in Agates, *&c. a different colour'd mineral Juice insinuating itself into the Clefts or Interstices of the Stone, and afterwards petrify'd to an equal hardness with the rest of the Stone; tho' many times there is a different hardness in the Veins, or Representations from the other parts of the Stone, as is seen in Marbles and other veined Stones.*

R. W.

We have lately had an Account from Mr. *Tentzelius* Historiographer of the Duke of *Saxony,* of the Skeleton of an Elephant found buried in *Germany,* at the Foot of a Hill or Mountain at fourteen Foot deep, and cover'd with several Layers of Earth, but buried in a Sand, which the whole adjacent Mountain is found to consist of, being at a place call'd *Tonna* near *Erfond* in *Germany.* [I take notice of these Particulars, because they may be found to give some light as to the explication of an other Phænomenon which I shall by and by relate.] Now, tho' *Tentzelius* really judged and pronounced it to be the Skeleton of an Elephant, yet it was not without the Contradiction of many others of divers differing Opinions; the greatest number of which were for asserting it to be a *Lusus Naturæ,* as it seems the whole Colledge of *Gottha,* and divers other Learned Professors; but their Arguments are prov'd insignificant, and his own Doctrine sufficiently Establish'd in the Epistles which he wrote to Snr. *Magliabechi* and Publish'd in Print, and this Honourable Society

ciety were yet farther convinc'd of the certainty of it, by the Fragments and Specimens of the trials he had made of several of those Bones: But, after all, great Difficulties arose concerning the Means and Cause of the burying of it at such a place, and at such a depth and the covering of it, to be the natural Layer of the Earth, and not the Artificial filling up of a Grave or Pit dug by Art to bury it: Some attributed it to the effect of *Noah*'s Flood, as 'tis usual for most to do in the like Cases, where they can think of no other Cause; to me, I confess, it seem'd rather to be the effect of some preceding Earthquakes, as I formerly here deliver'd in a Discourse on that Subject, when I first met with a Relation of it, as I have in other Discourses also about *Lignum Fossile* or Subterraneous Trees, and other Substances found buried, and now dug out from under the Ground, not only in *Italy, Germany* and *France,* &c. but even in *England, Scotland* and *Ireland.* Now, because by our forreign Gazets, and also by our own from them of a late Phænomenon in the *East-Indies,* we have the History of a late Earthquake that happened there this present Year, whose effects do give an evident Proof of the Doctrine which I supposed, and indeavour'd to maintain, I thought it would not be improper to mention it here, and to add it as a further addition to the History of Nature. I shall indeavour to get the full Account of it Printed at *Batavia* in *Java,* an Abstract of which was Printed in the *Harlem* Currant in *October* last, and an Epitomy of that in our Weekly News-papers, which was this. Transcrib'd out of the *London* Post for *Sep.* 30. 1699. Printed for *Ben. Harris.*

' *Amsterdam October* 2. Our Letters from *Batavia* in the *East-Indies* of the
' 8th of *February,* say, That on the fifth of *January,* about two in the Morn-
' ing, a most terrible Earthquake happen'd, which was so violent, that one
' and twenty Brick Houses, and twenty others were overturn'd, so that if it
' had lasted a little longer they must have been all thrown down. About 40
' or 50 Persons were Buried alive under the Ruins of the Houses that fell, and
' near the same number were Lamed. Some small time before the Earth-
' quake, the Blew Mountain, otherwise call'd Mount *Sales,* burst with such
' a terrible Flame and Noise, that it was both seen and heard there, tho' six
' Days Journey distant. Next Morning the River which falls into the Sea
' here, and has its Rise from that Mountain, became very high and Muddy,
' and brought down abundance of Bushes and Trees half Burnt; and the
' Passage being stopt, the Water overflow'd the Country round, all the
' Gardens about the Town, and some of our Streets; so that the Fishes lay
' Dead in them: It was a whole Month before the River could be clear'd,
' altho' 3000 *Indians* were daily imploy'd to clear the same, during which
' time we were oblig'd to fetch fresh Water from *Bantam,* which is forty Miles.
' All the Fish in the River, except the Carps, were kill'd by the Mud and dirty
' Water: A great number of drown'd Buffaloes, Tigers, Rhinocero's, Deer,
' Apes, and other Wild Beasts, were brought down by the Current; and
' notwithstanding a Crocadile is Amphibious, several of them were found
' Dead among the rest.

The Phænomena of this Earthquake, tho' they afford a probable solution of the more common Phænomena of fossile Trees, Wood, Nutts, Leaves, &c. of Vegetables, and of the fossile parts of Animals, &c. such as Teeth, Hornes, Bones; yet there are some other strange Phænomena, which I conjecture to have been effected by the same efficient Cause. If it be inquir'd what those strange Phænomena are, that I may give you an Instance, I shall acquaint you with one I late met with and receiv'd from a curious Person, who made the Observations himself, of which I have since been confirm'd by another curious Person who had seen and observ'd all the same Particulars. The Relation, in short, is this.

A Description of the Ridge of Mary Burrow *in the Queens County in* Ireland.

' This Ridge runs North and South, from *Tymohoe* to *Mary-burrow,* about
' seven Miles, from thence towards *Montmelick,* four Miles further, and as
' this Author was inform'd through the King's County of *Westmeath,* towards

'*Athlone*, but in these last mention'd Countries is much lower than in the
' Queens County.

'From the said *Tymohoe* to *Montmelick*, being both in the Queens County,
' it is about fourteen or fifteen Foot high, where highest, as near as this Au-
' thor can conjecture, being laid as irregular as the Sands are usually laid by
' the Waves on the Sea-shoar, with several bendings in and out, high
' and low ; the Sides so steep, that in most places not easy to ride up, and in
' many places Trees growing on the Sides, and a little thin Skin of Grass,
' apt to be burnt or scorch'd with the least dry Weather.

' It is so broad on the top as to afford room enough for four Horse-men to
' ride a Breast, the Road, in many places, lying on the top thereof.

'It is compos'd altogether of small rough Pebble grayish Stones about the
' bigness of a Mans Fist, and other smaller ones mix'd with Sand or Gravel,
' but no mixture of Clay or Loam, as this Author ever observ'd, which several
' times he sought after as he travell'd that way.

'None of the Lands adjacent to this Ridge have any of the materials where-
' of it is compos'd, mix'd with their Soils ; in most places there are Boggs to
' within a very few Yards of its Foot, and where any Arrable lies near it, there
' is no mixture of the above Pebble or Sand therewith.

' So that it should seem probable that this Ridge of Pebble and Sand was
' brought from some remote places by some violent motion of Waters, and
' dispos'd into the form it now remains in, which induc'd the Author se-
' veral times to say, he believ'd it to be the effects of *Noah*'s Flood, the Con-
' sideration whereof he refers to better Judgments.

' If any farther Particulars relating to this Ridge are desir'd, and a few
' Lines sent by the Post directed to the Author at *Rathdowney* near *Burris*, in
' *Ossory, Ireland*, they shall be carefully inquir'd into and answer'd by

Nov. the 14th   *Your most humble Servant*
1699.   Ric. Prior.
          This Ridge is distant from the Sea about thirty Miles.

The same curious Person who is now return'd to his Estate, which lies in
the Queens County not far from it, has promised me to make many other Observations about it, which I desir'd, and has promis'd to send me an account
of his success, by which I hope I shall be better enabl'd to explain the Cause
and Reasons thereof ; 'till when I shall forbear for the present to make any
further Reflections on it.

THis Lecture treats of *Animal Substances found buried in the Ground in several
parts of the World, and of a Ship found in* Switzerland *with the Bodies of
forty Men in it at a considerable depth under ground.* Secondly, *An account of a Ship
found in the bottom of a Lake in* Italy, *supposed to be ever since* Tiberius's *Time,
with several Deductions and Queries thereupon.*

                                                                    R. W.

Of Animal   MAY 26. 1697. We have lately had several Accounts of Animal Sub-
Substances   stances of various kinds, that have been found buried in the superficial
found buried. Parts of the Earth, that is not very far below the present Surface ; as particularly the parts of the Head of an *Hippopotamus* at *Chartham* in *Kent*, that of
the Bones of the *Mammatoroykost*, or of a strange Subterraneous Animal, as the
Siberians fancy, which is commonly dug up in *Siberia*, which Mr. *Ludolphus* judges
to be the Teeth and Bones of Elephants ; and indeed that peice which I saw of it
was much like Ivory in its Texture, only the out side of it seem'd to have
been cover'd by a kind of Skin, which I never heard of or saw any Elephants
Tooth so cover'd with ; then the Bones and Teeth of a large Elephant lately
dug up in *Pomerania*, of which I some while since transcrib'd the Relation out
of one of the late Monthly Mercuries, and read it at one of the Meetings of
                                                                         this

this Society; also the great Bone in the Repository presented to the Society by Sir *Tho' Brown,* which was found upon the foundering or calving of some Cliff in *Norfolk,* which seems to have been the Leg-bone of some Elephant, if it be not some Bone of the fore Fin of some Whale; 'tis equally admirable which soever it may be found to be by one skill'd in the Osteology of those Creatures; and lastly the great Hornes that have been often found and dug up in *Ireland,* of which the account is Printed in the last Transaction; all which, and divers others which I could mention, do shew that the present superficial Parts of the Earth have suffer'd very great Alterations, which I in my Lectures in 1664. indeavour'd to prove to have been the effects of some preceding Earthquakes, without which Supposition I cannot conceive any probable Cause can be assigned, much less can there be any such rational Cause assigned for the Position of many other Phænomena which have been observ'd of such like Substances found and dug up at much greater depths, that is, of more than two or three Fathoms below the present Surface, at which depth those I have mention'd are said to be found. I conceive it will be very improbable to assign the Cause to the universal Deluge of *Noah,* and much more so to ascribe it to any particular Deluge, as to that of *Deucalion,* &c. for how could the Flood bury the Shells of Fishes in the middle of some of the highest *Alps,* and cover them with a prodigious height or thickness of Rocky Mountains? Or how should the bottom of the Sea come to be raised to such a prodigious height above the present bottom of the Sea at the Shore next such places? To me, I confess, it seems a most improbable, and groundless supposition: Improbable, for that 'tis hardly conceivable how the Water should heap up these Substancess, such prodigious masses of Stony or Earthy Concretions; and groundless, for that we have no mention in Sacred or Prophane History of any such effects produced by a Flood. However, tho' we should grant that Elephants might be carry'd by the Waters of the universal Deluge from the more Southern or Æquinoctial Parts to those Northern of *Siberia* or *Pomerania,* yet how shall we conceive by what means the universal Deluge should bury a Ship and forty Men at a hundred Fathom under Ground, and that at so great a distance from the Sea, as *Switzerland* now is, of which nevertheless we have an undoubted History? I say undoubted, because I have not found any Author that has question'd the truth of this Relation. Now, tho' I confess I did not know 'till lately (upon perusing Dr. *Wagners* curious Natural History of *Switzerland*) who inform'd me who was the first Historian that had acquainted the World with this discovery; tho' I had met with the account in several other Historians, yet none of them speaking of it with any doubting Expression I conceiv'd it must be related by some Historian of good Repute. This Enquiry then Dr. *Wagner* answer'd by telling me the first relater of it, which was *Baptista Fulgosi* Duke of *Genoua,* which Author's Book I have since procur'd, and have read his Account of it, which I will presently give you as I find it expres'd by *Camillus Gilnus* in Elegant Latine, being by himself, and his Father translated from the Original, Publish'd by the Author in the Year 1483, but the Book translated into Latin was Printed 1565. In this Book I find an account of the Author, and the Esteem he had, and the occasion of the writing of it, which was partly to drive away melancholy Reflections on his past Misfortunes, having lost his Dukedome, and partly for Instruction to his own Son. In which Relation 'tis remarkable, that this Ship and Men should be buried so deep in the Earth as a hundred Fathom or six hundred Foot. Next, that the Bodies of forty Men should be found in the Ship itself. 3*dly.* That this should be a Ship of the Ocean, and not of some River, because of the great distance of it from the Sea. 4*thly.* That the Anchors and Sails, tho' torn, should yet remain and be plainly discoverable. 5*thly.* That he did not take this Story from uncertain Report, but from divers grave Men, who had been Eye-witnesses of it, who had inform'd him themselves. 6*thly.* That it was so remarkable in that time, that the Learned Men had meditated and reason'd on it to assign the Cause of it; that is, to give a rational Hypothesis, by which to shew how it might come to pass, they having it seems pitch'd upon two especially, which do both of them to me seem very insufficient, not to say very absurd. So that upon the whole Matter, there seems to me no Reason or Cause to doubt the matter of

Of a ship found buried deep in the Ground.

Fact

Fact or the ὅτι, but all the difficulty lies in the διότι that then shall be the next thing to be examin'd, and that the rather, becauſe this ſeems to be a true *Experimentum Crucis* to diſtinguiſh between my Hypotheſis and thoſe of ſome other Authors.   As firſt, concerning the two Solutions ſpecify'd by the Author, not as his own, but as of ſome other Philoſophical Men, who then lived, and who were ſatisfy'd, it ſeems, of the truth of the diſcovery, and 'tis not unlikely it might be ſome of thoſe. *Plurimi Graves viri qui rem perſpexerunt & qui in Re preſenti fuere a quibus ipſe accepit.* For as for himſelf he ventures not at any Solution, but ſays only *Cæterum utcunq; res fuerit admirationis non Mediocres relinquit Cauſas.*

That it could not be from Noah's time.First then, for the Hypotheſis of *Noah*'s Flood, 'tis not ſaid in any Hiſtory, that Navigation, eſpecially on the Ocean, was grown to ſuch a perfection in *Noah*'s time as to make Ships of that bigneſs and perfection of Anchors, Sail and Rigging, as this by this ſhort Deſcription ſeems to have been; and 'tis very likely if any ſuch Navigation had been, it would have been taken notice of in the Hiſtory of the Bible; for it cannot be ſuppos'd that *Noah* ſhould not be inform'd of it, if any ſuch Art had been then practiced in any part of the World how remote ſoever from the place of his Abode. Next, if ſuch ſhould have been, it might have happen'd that ſome other Men or Creatures might have eſcap'd with Life beſides thoſe in the Ark. Next, ſuppoſing that there had been ſuch a perfection of Navigation at the time of the Flood, I cannot conceive how a Ship of that bigneſs, as this ſeems to have been, ſhould be carry'd down ſo deep under the Surface of the Earth as 600 Foot: Certainly a twelve Month ſoaking of the Earth, much leſs forty Days, could not reduce the ſuperficial Parts to ſuch a haſty pudding Conſiſtence as this Phænomenon does ſeem to require, ſince I doubt whether there can be found in the World any part of the bottom of the Sea, that has been ſoaked for ſome thouſands of Years, that is ſo ſoftned.

Next for the ſecond Hypotheſis of a Subterraneous Navigation, to me, I confeſs it ſeems a ridiculous Suppoſition, tho' I know a late Author has imbrac'd ſuch an Hypotheſis to ſolve the Phænomena of Sea-ſhells, and the like Subſtances found in Mountains and Mines; tho' Mr. *Purchas* has Publiſh'd a like Story of *Andrew Knivet*, but I am apt to think that moſt Readers will look upon it as told by a Seaman and a Traveller.

But the Matter of Fact being ſo well atteſted, it muſt at leaſt be ſuppos'd to be there plac'd by ſome Natural Cauſe, as muſt alſo all thoſe other Phænomena I have ment'on'd.

Now for aſſigning a Cauſe ſufficient, I conceive there cannot be a more probable one, than the effect of Earthquakes, which have, and do ſtill produce as conſiderable Effects as any of theſe; the late Relations we have had of the effects wrought by them in *Lima*, *Jamaica*, among the *Cariby* Iſlands, among the *Eaſt-India* Iſlands, about *Veſuvius*, in *Norway*, and in the Iſland of *Sicily*, will furniſh us with Phænomena almoſt as ſtrange; beſides it ſeems rational to believe, that Earthquakes in former Ages before we had Hiſtory, were not only more frequent, but much greater and more powerful.

Theſe, I conceive, have not only produc'd wonderful Effects in this or that part of the Earth at one time, but at many times ſucceſſively, poſſibly at the diſtance of many Ages; ſo that at one time they may have raiſed the bottom of the Sea to make a dry Land, and ſunk other parts ſo as to be overflow'd by the Sea, which were before far above the Surface of the Water, or to make Inland Seas or Lakes, as that of *Geneva* and divers others thereabouts: But by ſucceeding Earthquakes thoſe effects may have been quite differing, ſo as to ſink again thoſe parts it had raiſed, and raiſe again and fill up with other Earthy or Stony Matter, thoſe it had formerly ſunk, and ſo alſo by various Efforts at various Times it may have overturn'd and turn'd upſide down, or otherwiſe tumbl'd and confounded the parts of the Earth, which ſeems plainly to be hinted to us by the Mythologick Story of the Giants fighting with the Cæleſtial Powers, and heaping Mountains upon Mountains; and (I do confeſs) I conceive there can be nothing more reaſonable and conformable to the proceeding of Nature in theſe Times, than to ſuppoſe there have been the like and much greater, in former Ages of the World.

I con-

I conceive then, that whenever that part of *Switzerland* was the bottom of the Sea, this Veſſel (which the Author calls *Navis* or a Ship) was upon that Sea over this very place, when there happen'd an Earthquake juſt underneath it, which did raiſe the ſame above the level of the Water, as much as it now is ; and that by this there having happen'd to be an Opening, Cleaving, or Chaſm in the Ground under it which ſwallow'd up ſome of the Sea, and with it this Veſſel, and afterwards cloſed again, and incloſed what it had ſwallowed ; or elſe that this part had been ſome very deep Inland Lake, as that of *Geneva*, and divers others there about, that this Veſſel was Navigating in this place when ſome Earthquake happen'd, which overthrew ſome Neighbouring Mountain, Hill or Lands, which, falling into this Water, did not only ſink the Ship, but fill'd up and levell'd the Lake with the Contiguous Lands or Shoars of it ; neither of which ways of explicating it do need any other effect, but ſuch as we are by antient and much more later Obſervations aſcertain'd, are the uſual effects of Earthquakes.

I have conſider'd the Paſſage mention'd by *Leo. Bapt. Alberti* in the fifth Book and Twelfth Chapter, concerning *Trajan*'s Ship found in his time in *Italy*. Now, I find that this *Alberti* was a *Florentine* Gentleman, who flouriſh'd about the Year 1483, and was accounted the *Vitruvius* of his Time : He being a Scholar, an excellent Painter, Sculptor and Mechaniſt, and an excellent Architect, he was the firſt that indeavour'd the Explication of *Vitruvius*, in which he made great progreſs, much to the improvement of that Age ; in order to which he ſurvey'd and meaſur'd the remainders of Antiquity ; he underſtood Perſpective alſo, and writ a Book on that Subject, which was not well underſtood by the Antients, nor much by the Moderns in his Time. But my preſent Inquiry is chiefly about this Paſſage mention'd in his Book *De Re Ædificatoria*, produc'd the laſt Day by Mr. *Bridgman* concerning *Trajans* Ship diſcover'd in *Alberti*'s Time, which had lain ſunk in a Lake of *Italy*, which he calls *Nemorenſis*, ever ſince the time of *Trajan*, which was near one hundred Years after Chriſt, for he died in the Year ninty eight, which is now full ſixteen Hundred Years ſince, and ſo was more than thirteen Hundred in the time of *Alberti*. The Paſſage is as follows. *Leo Baptiſta Albertus De Re Ædificatoria. Pariſiis,* 1512 8°. *Libro* V. *Capite* XII. *Materiam omnem reprobant quæ fiſſilis, fragilis, ſindens, putricoſaque ſit, clavoſq; & ligulas æneas præferunt ferreis, ex Navi Trajani, per hos dies dum quæ ſcripſimus commentarer, ex lacu nemorenſi eruta, quo loci annos plus mille trecentos demerſa & deſtituta jacuerat, adverti pinum, materiam, & cupreſſum egregie duraſſe, in ea tabulis extrinſecus duplicem ſuperextenſam & pice atra perfuſam, tela ex lino adglutinarant, ſupraque id chartam plumbeam claviculis æneis coadfirmarant. (Lacus Nemorenſis) a dix huit Milles de Rome vers l'Orient, il s'appelle aujourd' huy Lago di Nemi.* What this Ship was, and the Hiſtory of it, I have not met with, nor can I find any ſuch Lake as is call'd *Lacus Nemorenſis,* or *Nenorenſi Lago,* as *Petrus Laurus,* in his Tranſlation of this Book into the Vulgar *Italian* renders it. *Bartoli,* who Tranſlated this Book into *Italian* after *Caius* renders it *Lago della Riccia. Pliny* indeed mentions a Ship of *Layus,* which was purpoſely ſunk at *Oſtia* to found the Mole upon ; but he could not ſay any thing of this, he dying almoſt 20 Years before *Trajans* time ; nor do I treat upon what occaſion it was that caus'd them to dig it out, nor at what depth it was found, nor whether it were buried in the Ground, or were only ſunk into the Mud : If any have met with any further information concerning it in their Reading, I ſhould be glad to be inform'd concerning it. *Fulgoſus* having writ his Book much about the ſame time that *Alberti* writ this, I thought I might have met with ſome account of it in him, it being ſomewhat Analogous with his Relation of the Ship found in *Switzerland,* about the ſame time ; but I do not find he hath any mention of it. It ſeems pretty ſtrange how either of theſe Ships ſhould come to be tranſported into the places where they are ſaid to be found ; but 'till we know the Hiſtory we can at beſt but conjecture concerning them. There are many other particulars I ſhould have deſir'd information of beſides thoſe which he has mention'd, and 'tis very likely ſome of them may have been taken notice of in the Relation of its diſcovery, which I am inclin'd to believe muſt be ſomewhat more at large and more fully related than we find it here, which only hints two Remarkables proper to the purpose, for which it is mention'd, *viz.* About the durableness of Timber fit for building of Ships in its own Nature : And, Secondly, Of the way of securing it against the Corrosion of Worms, which it seems was so long since taken notice of and provided against by the Shipwrites of *Trajan's* Time ; which they perform'd by a double Sheathing; the first, next the double Planking, (*Tabulis extrinsecus duplicem Superextensam & pice atra perfusam tela ex lino adglutinarant*) was a kind of Tarpollin, they covering the Planks with Pitch, and that Pitch with Linnen-cloth sticking to it ; the second was a thin sheet of Lead fastn'd by Brass Nails to the Plank; that it was very thin, I think is denoted by *Charta Plumbea*, that is, such kind of thin Lead as they formerly us'd for Writing on, much like the thinnest sort of Mill'd-Lead now made by the new Engine ; which how they made is not known, nor do we certainly know how they make the like Sheets of Lead in *China*, of which kind I have seen a great variety, and all of it very even and regular: The Plumber will tell you 'tis done by Casting the Lead on Ticking, but that I conceive will not make it so thin and even as I have seen it ; we have a way of beating it after the manner of Gold-beating, which doth foliate it very thin and even, 'tis commonly call'd *Tin Foile*, and 'tis us'd for foiling Looking-glasses ; 'tis a mixture of Lead and Tin, as is also the *Tootenag* of *China*, and possibly theirs may be done the same way ; but the Rowlers in the Mill I take to be much the better way ; 'tis by somesuch Engine they foliate Brass and Copper in *Germany*, tho' they do some sorts also with the Hammer, as Kettles, and the thin Iron Plates for Latton by beating many of them together at once, as they do also Leaf-gold, Silver and Brass ; but Asidue somewhat thicker, is done by an Engine with Rowlers, as they flatten Wire for Threads ; and so also is a sort of Sheet Brass somewhat thicker : Possibly both ways may be known and made use of in *China*, where they have many other curious Inventions which we have not yet attain'd, and 'tis not unlikely but that the Antient *Romans* might for this foliating of Lead, have somewhat the same.

Sheathing Ships with Lead known to the Romans. Now as to the use of it for Sheathing of Ships, I find the *Spaniards* make use of it at this time, and have done so for a long time. This I find Sir *Rich. Hawkins* takes notice of in the account of his Voyage to the South Sea, Page 87, which see.

Here we have an account of all the ways of Sheathing of Ships he knew, and his Judgment or Censure of them, which how just they are must be left to Experienc'd Men ; however, I have been lately inform'd that the *Spaniards* make use of the same way still for their Gallions, which 'tis not likely they would if they knew any way better ; they had indeed another help to keep out the Water in case of any failure in the outward Plank, and that is the filling all the Space between the Ribbs and Planks with a certain sort of Plaister which may be a security to the innermost Plank, but not at all to the outermost against the Worm or Springing of them ; however, 'tis of good use to keep off a suddain overflow or entrance of the Water in case of either Defect. But the best way of all seems to be the *Chinese*, by the Varnish, which neither Worms nor Water, nor Heat will damnify ; nor in their way of building their Junks, do they leave any vacuity in the thickness of the sides to need Plaister, but what is fill'd with Damar, which is in itself lighter than Water, and will swim on it. But that way is not practicable here in *Europe* where we want the Varnish, whereas the others are, especially that of Sheet Lead, of which Metal this Nation affords us great plenty, and the late invented Mill doth certainly out do all other for giving it a proper Form ; besides, if Plaister were necessary, we have as good as the World affords, or which possibly may be better, we can have Pitch enough (much of the same Nature and Use with Damar) to prevent any suddain gushing in of the Water : But this only by the bye.

The strangeness of the Relation or History of the Ship found sunk in a Lake, some where in *Italy*, mention'd by *Leo. Bapt. Alberti*, and the shortness and imperfection thereof as deliver'd by him, made me very desirious to get a more full and perfect Relation thereof. I thought *Bayfius* in his Treatise *De Re Navali* might have taken notice of it, he having Written since that time ; but he has never a word concerning it as I can find, nor do I find any
mention

mention of it in *Daßie's* Book *de L' Architecture Navale* ; but *Pere Fournier* in his Hydrography (Book the Fourth, Chap. the Firſt) treating of the Navigation which was before the univerſal Deluge of *Noah*, ſays, it ſeems rational to think that (conſidering the long Life of Men before the Flood, and the populouſneſs of thoſe Times) there was no part of the World uninhabited, tho' we have no Hiſtory of them but the Bible, and tho' that has not one word concerning it ; and that not only the great Continents of Land, but there being Iſlands both in the Seas and Rivers, thoſe alſo were inhabited which could not be ſuppos'd without the uſe of ſome kind of Navigation. Add to this in the third place, that 'tis reaſonable to think that the *Antediluvians* were as ingenious, if not much more, than the *Poſtdiluvians*, for the inventing of Ships, and for the uſe of them, for the tranſplanting of Colonies, for Trading and for War. Moreover (ſays he) in the Year 1462, as is Recorded by *Fulgoſus*, at *Bern* in *Switzerland*, as they were working in the Mines, at above a hundred Fathom deep in the Earth, there was found an old Wooden Ship built as ours are, whoſe Anchors were of Iron and the Sails of Linnen, with the Carkaſſes of forty Men. *Peirre Naxis* Relates a like Hiſtory of another, ſuch a one as was found under a very high Mountain. In like manner the Jeſuite *Euſebius Neurembergius*, in the Second Chapter of the Fifth Book of his Natural Hiſtory, ſays, ' That near the Port of *Lima* in *Peru*, as ' they were working a Mine for Gold, thoſe which follow'd the Vein in the ' Mountain found an old Ship, which had many old Characters very differing ' from ours, which all People believed to have been there buried by the uni- ' verſal Deluge.————*Namq*; *Juxta portum Limæ in Peru cum eviſcerarat avaritia terram, inſecuta auri venam, Navigium inventum eſt ſub ipſo monte, quod a noſtris, & hactenus ſama & Scriptis antiquorum notis plurimum diſſidebat. Creditumq; ab univerſis illuvie fuiſſe humatum.* There was found alſo in a very high Mountain of *Mexico* a prodigiouſly large Elephants Tooth, tho' in all *America* there was never yet found any Elephant. ' Without doubt (ſays he) all ' theſe things have been thus buried by the tumbling and overturnings of a ' univerſal Deluge, as well as the Wreeks of other Veſſels which have been ' found at three Thouſand Stadiums or Furlongs from the Sea, as *Strabo* re- ' lates in his Firſt Book. Thus far Father *Fournier* to this purpoſe. Nor do I find that he hath taken any notice or made the leaſt mention of this Veſſel, mention'd by *Alberti*, which, methinks, he ſhould not have been ignorant of, eſpecially conſidering the great Pains he has taken, and great Learning he hath ſhewn concerning the Subject of Shipping.

The *Heer Witſen* in his Book intitled, *Ael Oude en Heden dueyſche Scheeps Bouven· Baſtier*, in the Fourth Chapter of his Firſt Book, hath given us a ſomewhat larger account and more particular than *Alberti*, but quotes not the Authors from whom he receiv'd it ; ſo that we muſt rely on his Reputation 'till we can be better inform'd. His Relation in *Dutch* is to this effect. ' In ' the time that the Pope, *Pius* the Second, poſſeſt the Chair (which I find was ' from *Auguſt* 1458, to *Auguſt* 1464) Men found in the *Numidiſche* Lake twelve ' Fathom under Water, in the Mud, a Ship, in length thirty Foot, and in ' breadth proportionable ; built of *Cypreſs* and *Larix* Wood (which is a Species ' of Pine-Tree Wood) which was become of ſuch an hardneſs, that it could ' neither be burnt nor broken, if it were needful. This Ship had lain under ' the Water for fourteen Hundred Years without the leaſt perceivable Rotting ' to decay it : It was on the Deck done over with Pitch, and that cover'd with ' a Coat or Cruſt of a certain Pap or Morter made of Clay and Iron well tem- ' per'd or beaten together, which art of mixture is now conceil'd ; tho' others ' are of Opinion that this mixture was not made of Clay and Iron, but of Clay ' and Pitch well kneaded together. The Deck was cover'd with Paper, Lin- ' nen Cloth, and Plates of Lead, which were nailed to the Planks with Cop- ' per Nails guilded. This Ship (a wonder) was found ſo ſtanch, that not the ' leaſt drop of Water was found to have ſoaked into its Hold ; it had the length ' of an old *Trireme* Veſſel, and the breadth of a Hulk. In the Hold was ' found the Hangings of fine Velvet of an Orange Green, and in the mid- ' dle of the Floor a Copper Coffer faſtned by four black Strings, which being ' open'd there appear'd an Earthen Urne or Veſſel, which was ornamented
with

' with a Gold Plate, and fill'd with Afhes ; and becaufe Men faw the Name
' *Tiberius* feveral times engraven upon fome Leaden Plates about the Border
' of it, they conceiv'd this might be the place of his Sepulture.

This Account, tho' in divers Particulars different from that of *Alberti*, yet
feems to be tranflated from the fame Original Hiftory, which neither for them
having mention'd by what Author it was written, we are yet to feek of the
true account, which probably may be much more particular than either of
thefe, or both of them put together ; for that it is ufual in fecond Hand Relations, to take notice of fuch Paffages of the Original, as concern the prefent Subject they are treating of, and to omit many other Particulars, tho' in
themfelves much more remarkable ; this therefore I further fought for in divers other Authors; and in *Riccioli*'s *Hydrography*, I found a further account
of it, which alfo gave me a hint of the true Author : *Riccioli*'s Account is
this, Chapter the thirty ninth of the Tenth Book, which whole Chapter
treats of Ships that have been much celebrated for their Magnitude, Splen-
dor, Voyages, or other very remarkable Conditions; among which, Page
340, he brings in the Ship of *Tiberius* as one very remarkable inftance, whofe
Hiftory he thus defcribes, *Narrat Æneas Sylvius, fuo tempore repertum in
lacu Numicio Cubitis* 12 *Sub aquam, navem ex Larice Cubitorum* 20 *Bitumine &
mixtura ferri terræque; nefcio cujus incruftatam, quæ per annos* 1400. *non computru-
erat. Siquidem in multis canalibus, ac fiftulis incifum erat Tiberii Nomen ; Exifti-
matumq; in ea Cineres illius Tyranni inclufos fuiffe.*

Thus we have found at length the Bufh where this Game is feated, and
whence it is to be ftarted if we will have it, and I have follow'd it by its fcent
and Foot-fteps to its Seat ; but in what part of the Volume of the Works of
Æneas Sylvius it is to be found I cannot yet difcover, for his Tracts are many
and make a bulky Volume together, which, whether it contain all that he
writ I am not yet well inform'd ; for he wrote very many particular Tracts,
and left fome imperfect and not ready for the Prefs, as *Conrad Gefner* informs
us. This was the Man that, in *Auguft* 1458, was made Pope, and who died in
Auguft 1464, fo that he poffeft the Chair fix Year; within which time it
feems both thefe difcoveries were made, (if at leaft they were two differing
Difcoveries, for poffibly they may be only two differing Relations of the fame
Difcovery) the one noting one fort of Circumftances, and the other, another.
I cannot fo well judge of the matter, 'till I find this Relation of *Sylvius*; however, 'tis obvious that what *Riccioli* makes to be only twelve Cubits, Mr.
Witfen makes twelve Fathom, which is four times as much ; and poffibly this
twelve Fathom or feventy two Foot *Fulgofus* might make one hundred Cubits,
and yet all of them innocently without a defign of impofing on their Readers,
they writing from the Relations of others, and poffibly from the failing of
their own Memory to boot ; for we find how rare a thing it is to find out the
truth of a Fact, tho' 'twas done but Yefterday and almoft at next Door, if
allowances are not made for the Circumftances of the Relators, and the defects of every one's Memory and Comprehenfion ; upon which account it is
*Vide Philof.
Tranfact. No.
234, p. 757.* that I could wifh that Relation concerning the Elephant lately found in *Germany* and made by the Colledge of *Gothan* might be inferted into a Tranfaction as well as that of *Tentzelius*, that Men might fee how much the Humour and Inclinations of the Relators will diverfify the Relation, and confound
the Apprehenfion and Judgment of the Reader ; and therefore I conceive it
would not be amifs alfo to add to this laft account the Sentiments of this Society, or at leaft of fome of their Members, concerning the Subftances fent
by *Tentzelius* to be perus'd and examin'd by them ; for there is no better way,
I conceive, in the World to give a fatisfactory account to Pofterity of this
Fact than this Courfe ; for there cannot be made a good Hiftory, either of
things Natural or Artificial, without curious judicious and accurate Obfervations, and Pertinent and Critical Experiments, that may be as thoroughly examin'd and verify'd, as a Geometrical Propofition by Perfons fufficiently accomplifh'd for fuch a Task. 'Tis not one poffibly of a hundred is fit for fuch a Bufinefs, and yet fuch are neceffary, and hence I conceive it is, that we have
fuch a multitude of medicinal Obfervations made or pretended to be made by
young Phyficians, and poffibly not one of five Hundred of any manner of real

Ufe

Ufe or Benefit; for that the moft of fuch Writers are two much biaffed by precarious Hypothefes, and many likewife Compofe and Publifh them only for Intereft, that is, as Advertifements to make themfelves the more known, and fo to get Practice; and tho' this or that Symptom may be true and matter of Fact, yet the true Caufe of the Diftemper, and the reafon of the Cure or Mifcarriage of the Patient poffibly was really quite differing from thofe affign'd by them; and tho' fome of them may have been truly defcrib'd, yet thofe that know how fmall and inconfiderable Circumftances in themfelves will yet make great and moft confiderable alterations in the Effects, will be more cautious than to take them all for true which are in reality quite otherwife; thofe therefore that relate an Experiment or Obfervation, fhould be both very underftanding in the Subject, and very diligent in taking notice of, and relating the Circumftances of it; for that all that can be done in this way will be little enough of information to him, that is to make ufe of it for making Deductions and Inferrences therefrom, and indeed it will be hazardous to build any thing upon Foundations fo uncertain; for even in the moft perfect Accounts of this Nature, a Writer or Applier of it for the founding or examining a Theory thereby will find a neceffity of ocular infpection and examination proper and fitted to his prefent Subject, either to obviate fome Objection, or to give fome further Light; for oft times the moft confiderable part of the whole Experiment may lie in fome one trivial Circumftance, which not one of a thoufand would otherwife have thought worth taking notice of, yet to him that knows what that Circumftance is that makes for or againft his Theory which he is inquiring into, will judge it very confiderable, and be fure not to omit the Scrutiny and Teft thereof; and 'tis prepofterous for any one to write an Experimental Natural Hiftory without making and examining the Experiments needful to the perfecting thereof, without making the Experiments himfelf, nay, and without the repeating of them, as Doubts may arife after the firft Trial, or as he may need further information upon them; nay, without making them whilft he is writing, that he may truft, as little as may be, to his own Memory and Judgment. Thus in Anatomical Experiments and Obfervations, how many confiderable Difcoveries do we owe to fuch repeated Trials omitted wholly, or fcarce hinted at in many preceding; For every difcovery gives a new fet of Doubts and Inquiries, as well as a new Light, not only δὶς κ, τρὶς *Sed etiam decies repetita placebunt*, as I have very often experimented my felf; nay, I have found it abfolutely neceffary, and even that not enough to make fome Spectator to apprehend the Confequences thereof: But this only by the bye. Before I leave this Subject I cannot but take notice of a Doubt that arifes from the variety of thefe Relations, and that is, whether the Sheet Lead were ufed for the Sheathing of the outfides of the Ship under Water, or only for the Covering and Houfing of the Deck, as the *Heer Witfen* makes it; nor know I how to folve it without feeing the Original Relation, only I muft not omit one Paffage of *Riccioli*, which feems to hint the ufe of Sheet Lead fomewhat Analogous to Sheathing, and that is this, defcribing the Ship of *Hieron*, whofe Architect was *Archimedes.----Dimedia Pars navis per* 300 *operarios fex menfibus abfoluta, rimæ afferum laminis plumbeis tectæ*, &c. My doubt on this Paffage is, whether the Veffel were Caulked and Pitched in the Joints of the Planks under the Sheet Lead, or whether the Plates of Lead were only made ufe of inftead of Caulking and Pitching, the defcription is at large in *Athenæus*, which I have not by me, and he, it feems, had it from --------, who writ a whole Book of the Defcription of it: It was in this Ship where *Archimedes* made ufe of his admirable Invention of his helical Pump, which he himfelf hath no where defcrib'd.

The fmall number of Authors that have recorded fo remarkable a Phænomenon as this, informs us how little curious the World have been in the matter of Philofophical Hiftory, and thence how vain a thing it is to expect to find every fuch accident as this to be Recorded, tho' very remarkable in its felf; for if thefe Ships were differing, then they have each but one Original Hiftorian; for all the other Authors that have fince mention'd them, feem to have borrow'd the Accounts from thefe two; but if the Relations were

only

only of one and the same Veſſel (as methinks the Circumſtances of the time and the being ſunk deep into the Earth ſeem to intimate) then we have but two Hiſtorians that take notice of ſo remarkable a Fact ; and thoſe ſo diſcordant in their Stories, that one knows not which of them to give Credit to ; the one making it to be found in the *Lago de Nemi*, about twenty Miles from *Rome* towards the Weſt ; the other making it to be found near *Berne* in *Switzerland*, when 'tis not known that ever there was any Lake there, as *Fulgoſus* mentions and Objects. It is therefore unreaſonable to reject all Hypotheſes that ſuppoſe other Accidents to have been the occaſions of producing Petrify'd Subſtances, than thoſe Recorded in Hiſtory, eſpecially if they happen'd before Printing was in uſe, or poſſibly Writing commonly known ; for even ſince that time many conſiderable Phænomena have been very ſlightly hinted only, and ſcarce taken any notice of ; as for inſtance, the Comet that appear'd in 1580, which produc'd but one diligent Obſerver and Hiſtorian, which was *Mich. Maſtlin*, and the great Earthquakes and Cataſtrophies in *China*, which are Recorded in the *Mercurie Hollandois*, and no where elſe that I know : So 'tis probable this newly happening Earthquake at *Conſtantinople* would have been quickly forgotten, and probably never recorded to Poſterity, if the *Gazett* and News Papers had not taken notice of it : But this only by the way.

As to this accident of the Ship, I conceive it to have afforded ſo many particular Informations worthy to have been Recorded, that I could wiſh it had happen'd in a more curious Age ; at leaſt I conceive it very deſirable, that the Original Hiſtory of it, ſuch as it is, might be ſifted out and inſerted in a more proper place to be found, than where it is ſaid to be at preſent.

The misfortune of Inventors. The Memoires of the *Pariſian Academy* have furniſh'd many curious Diſcoveries both Mathematical and Phyſical, yet divers of them or of the ſame kind have been firſt diſcover'd in this Society, tho' not entertain'd with that approbation, which they have there met withal ; nor are the *Engliſh* ſo nimble in Publiſhing what they diſcover themſelves, nor ſo ſharping to arrogate to themſelves what they know to have been firſt diſcover'd by others ; (as I do find divers to be) who will leave no means unattempted to make all their own, tho' there be never ſo evident Arguments againſt their Cauſe. But tho' this be a Practice to be abhor'd by every ingenious Man, and the baſhfulneſs of the other be blameable, yet there is ſomewhat to be ſaid both for the one and the other Party, that may ſeem to countenance theſe proceedings of them. As firſt, 'tis a diſcouragement to any one to Publiſh that which he finds by Diſcourſe is generally diſapproved. A Man may rationally enough diſtruſt his own Thoughts and Reaſons, nay, and even his Senſes too, if he finds thoſe he converſes with to be of another Opinion, tho' acquainted with the Arguments that prevail'd with him, at leaſt 'till he finds, that it was done for ſome Siniſter Deſigns to defraud him of his Diſcovery. Next, when by publiſhing, more Opponents or Emulators (which are both Enemies) are produced, than approvers or indifferent Perſons, who at beſt will do him no good ; 'tis thought better to abſtain with quietneſs, than with Labour and Induſtry, to create new Troubles. But on the other ſide 'tis certain, however, that ambitious Minds will try all means to obtain their Deſigns ; they find that ſuch Practiſes often prevail, and therefore *Quid tentare Nocebit* ; they find that the generallity of Men are not much concern'd for the firſt Diſcoverer, and that they uſually take him for ſuch, who firſt acquainted them with it ; and for one Reader that can diſprove them, or detect them of Plagiary, there are a thouſand that can not, and for thoſe that can, they find ways to evade and by Confidence carry the point, and even with a general Approbation and Advantage : 'Tis, I confeſs, a general Obſervation, that ſeldom the firſt Inventer reaps either Honour or Advantage by his Invention, but on the contrary, thoſe that come in at a ſecond Hand acquire them both. *Several Matters mention'd in the Works, of the French Academy were firſt found out here.* But be it as it will, certain it is, that many Diſcoveries pretended to in the Works, of the *French Academy*, were firſt made here and elſewhere, nay, and many of them publiſh'd too in Print, and ſome of them alſo in the *French* Language, which yet they will not own, or mention to have ſeen. I ſhall inſtance but in two or three things : The Firſt is that of *Torricellius* about

bout his Invention and Demonſtration of the *Solidum Acutum Hyperbolicum*, which was Publiſh'd by him, together with his other Works at *Florence* in the Year 1644, and that without Contradiction by *Roberval* ever ſince; yet now a Letter is trumpt up, and ſome Papers found that muſt needs perſuade us that *Torricellius* ſtole it from *Roberval*. The like ſlur is caſt upon the Works of Mr. *James Gregory*; both which Perſons have given ſufficient Proofs by their other Works, that they had very little need of ſtealing from *Roberval*, who has not yet made it evident, nor any other for him, that he was Maſter of either of their Problems, 'till ſince the publication of them by the ſaid Authors.

The Second is the diſcovery of the Glade of Light obſervable in the Evenings in *Febr.* and *March* each Year, which was firſt made by our Dr. *Childrey*, and an Advertiſement of it Publiſh'd in his *Britannia Baconica*, in the Year 1660; which Book was Tranſlated into *French*, and Publiſh'd at *Paris* ſoon after, which was long enough before it is pretended to be diſcover'd there. However, the ſecond Perſon has the Title of the diſcovery, and the firſt is defrauded of his due Praiſe. I could add a hundred other Inſtances to prove this Aſſertion; but I ſhall not at preſent ſpend time thereon, tho' it may poſſibly not paſs without ſome Reflections on another Occaſion, that every one, as near as may be, may have his due Praiſe. For my own part, I think it ingenuous to mention any thing of theirs, which I have occaſion to make uſe of, and to own all ſuch things as theirs, as I find to be new or ingenious; and that Firſt, Becauſe I would give every one that which is due to him. But, Secondly, Becauſe I find it neceſſary to back a Doctrine with a *French Approbation*. I know there are many things will not be regarded, 'till they have that Stamp to make them current, and then they will readily paſs with the preſent Age and Humor.

In the Memoir of the 31ſt. of *June* 1692, (ſo 'tis marked) I find an Obſervation concerning a Petrify'd Subſtance produc'd and examin'd by the *Royal Academy*, with ſome Reflections on it made by Mr. *De la Hire*, which becauſe conſonant to ſome Diſcourſes I have formerly made in this place, I thought might countenance ſomewhat the Doctrine I then deliver'd, I have alſo render'd the ſame in *Engliſh* before I make Reflections upon the ſame. *A Remark out of the French Memoires.*

' The Cabinets (ſays he) of the curious are fill'd with all ſorts of Bodies
' Petrify'd, as of Plants, Fruits, Woods, and of divers parts of Animals,
' but Naturaliſts are not yet agreed about the cauſe of their Production; ſome
' ſuppoſing them to be Stones ſo ſhaped by accident, but others ſuppoſe them
' produced by a Water that has a power of converting thoſe ſeveral Subſtances into Stone, after it has long pickled them; probable Reaſons are
' alledg'd for each Opinion.

' Mr. *L' Abbe de Louvoys* ſent to the *Academy*; a Petrifaction, which may
' ſerve to decide this Controverſy, namely, two peices of the Trunk of a
' Palm converted into Stone, they were brought from *Africa*, with two other
' pieces of a Palm juſt like them, but not Petrify'd, the better to compare
' them together; the Petrifactions are *true Flints*, as appears by their hardneſs, by their Colour, and ſomewhat of Tranſparency, by their Sound,
' which is clear and ſonorous, and by their Gravity, which is more than ten
' times that of the unpetrify'd; yet theſe two Flints are ſo like to the two
' pieces of Wood, that there is no ſhew of Reaſon to conceive, they ſhould
' be ſo formed by chance.

' One of theſe Flints which is two Foot long, and about four or five Inches
' Diameter, is a piece of the Trunk of a Palm Barked of its Rind; in this
' may be ſeen all the Fibres of the Wood of the bigneſs of $\frac{2}{3}$ of a Line, ſome
' of which are forked; they run the length of the Trunk and are hollow like
' Pipes. The Pulp, which is between the Fibres, which ſerves to join them
' together, is chang'd into a kind of *Gluten*, but very hard.

' Mr. *De la Hire* gives a Reaſon of the hollowneſs of the Pipe, *i. e.* that
' the outward Parts being dry'd before the middle, when they are dry, they
' are by the outward Parts kept from ſhrinking, and ſo the Pipes become
' ſtretched from the Center outward *(which is the ſame Reaſon with that I have
' given for the blebbs that appear in the Glaſs drops.)*

Now,

'Now, tho' some might fancy (yet without the least probability) that this
'with streight Fibres might thus be formed by chance, yet 'tis impossible to
'conceive so of the other piece, which is a part of the bottom of the Trunk;
'for this is not only compos'd of streight Fibres as the other, but its Bark is
'all garnish'd with small Roots as big as one's little Finger, and about three
'Inches long, which is cover'd with a thin Skin, which contains an infinite of
'small Fibres like Hairs; in the middle of each of these Fibres is a ligneous
'Chord, that one may call its *Nuel* or Pith, about ½ of the bigness of one's
'Finger, whose hollow was fill'd with a Pithy extended Substance. All which
'Parts are also exactly shaped in the Flint, where are visible not only the
'long streight Fibers, but the Roots and all the small Fibres of a blackish
'transparent Substance, but the Pith in the middle is of a whitish opaque
'Substance, and in the most of the small Roots it is hollow; which Mr. *De la*
'*Hire* conceives to proceed from the same Cause that he before assigned.

'It is evident therefore (says the Author) that this was no *Lusus Naturæ*,
'but that these two Flints were originally two pieces of the Trunk of a Palm
'afterwards chang'd into the Substance of a Flint; and what *Father Duchatz*
'reports in his Physical and Mathematical Observations, doth decide the
'Controversy, and leaves it without doubt.

'This Father there says, that the River that passes by *Bakan* in the King-
'dom of *Ava*, has, for the space of ten Leagues, or twenty eight Miles,
'the vertue of Petrifying Wood, and that he had seen great Trees Petrify'd
'thereby so high as the Surface of the Water reached, but that the other
'parts of them remained still dry Wood. He adds, that those Petrify'd
'Woods were as hard as the Flints of a Fire-lock; and such indeed was the
'hardness of the two pieces of which we have been speaking.

'This Account of *Duchatz* is to be found in the Second Volume of Obser-
'vations made in the *Indies* by the *Jesuits*, sent thither by the King of *France*,
'but Corrected and Printed by the care of *P. Gouye*; I have not yet seen the
'Book, but by the Account of it I find in these Memoires, I conceive it will
'be well worth the procuring, as containing many other curious Observations,
'and Histories of Matter of Fact.

Remarks & De-
ductions from
the former Ac-
count.
This Memoire of Monsieur *De la Hire is much the same with what I have former-*
ly presented to this Honourable Society, and have Printed among some other Observations made with *Microscopes*; wherein I examin'd the Shape, the Colour,
the Hardness, the Weight, the Brittleness, the Incumbustibleness, the Solidity, &c. of it; for I found it to be for its appearance to the naked Eye, perfectly like a piece of Wood, and to have the visible Grain of Wood, and
farther by a Microscope, I found it to have all the Microscopical Pores like
Wood; I found it of the colour of Wood, but of the hardness of a Flint,
and that it would cut Glass: I found its Weight to be to Water as 3¼, which
seems to be much the same with this of Mr. *De la Hire*; only he compares
its weight to that of the Palm Wood, which, by his description, must be
much lighter than Water, and mine was only comparative to Water. I found
it incumbustible in the Fire, tho' dissolvable by corrosive Liquors. I found it
Brittle and Friable like a Flint, and to feel cold to the touch, as a Stone, or
Mineral Body usually doth; from all which I concluded it to have, at first,
been a piece of Wood, and afterwards, by some Petrifying Water or Vapour, converted into the Substance of a Stone or Flint. And I find that
from the very same Arguments, the *French Academy* draw the same Conclusions
as to this Substance, and they confirm it by the Observation of *P. Duchatz*;
this therefore passing there for a good Argument, I see no reason why it may
not also be a good Argument here, and why the same will not also pass for the
Petrifactions of other Bodies both Vegetable, as Leaves, Fruits, Roots, and
also Animal, as Shells, Bones, Teeth, Scales, &c. which are found to have
the same Qualifications, that is, the Shapes, Colours, Textures, &c. of
those animate Substances, nay, and often times the very Bodies themselves
not Petrify'd, tho' included in Petrify'd Bodies, as Stones or Minerals; must
these be questioned or rejected, only because such Substances are found in
places where we cannot give particular Histories of their pristine Estate, and
how they come to be there placed and transformed, or so inclosed; or because
possibly

poſſibly we are not able to produce patterns of Creatures now at hand, and in being, which are exactly of the ſame Shape and Magnitude as the Academy did produce, to Authorize, or at leaſt incline them to be of that Sentiment ; certainly the ſame Argument that is cogent for the one, ought not to be leſs valid for the other ; for if the finding of Coines, Medals, Urnes, and other 'Monuments of famous Perſons, or Towns, or Utenſils, be admitted for unqueſtionable Proofs, that ſuch Perſons or things have, in former Times, had a being, certainly thoſe Petrifactions may be allowed to be of equal Validity and Evidence, that there have been formerly ſuch Vegetables or Animals. Theſe are truly Authentick Antiquity not to be counterfeited, the Stamps, and Impreſſions, and Characters of Nature that are beyond the Reach and Power of Humane Wit and Invention, and are true univerſal Characters legible to all rational Men.

Now, if theſe are ſuch (as to me they ſeem to be, notwithſtanding I cannot tell the time when, or the certain Hiſtory how, they came to be there diſpoſed and ordered as they are now found) then certainly it cannot be irrational to conclude at leaſt, that there have been ſome precedent means that have produced theſe Effects; and that thoſe means have been ſuch, as we have from Hiſtories and Relations within the times of our own Memory, Experience and Information, that they have produced much the like, which tho' they are not exactly the ſame, nor poſſibly by much ſo great and powerful as they muſt neceſſarily be granted, that did effect thoſe we now diſcover ; yet I think it not unreaſonable to conceive, that there may have been much greater and more powerful Agents than thoſe we now have had, yet ſtill of the ſame kind, and acted by the ſame Powers ; for if there are now newly ſuch as have raiſed,removed,cleft and torn Mountains,have made Lakes, fill'd and levelled Plains, ſtopped and turned Rivers, ſpouted out Sea-water at a great diſtance from the Sea ; raiſed the Sea-ſhore above the Surface of the Sea and left it dry, with the Fiſh, and the remainders of them to cover the Surface of it ; at other places to raiſe the bottom of theSea,which was manyFathoms under Water, and place it above the Surface, and many ſuch other wonderful Effects ; then certainly it cannot be unreaſonable to ſuppoſe, that there may have been much greater in former Times, whilſt the matter was yet unconſumed and diſpers'd up and down in more places, and more Copiouſly, and that more Powerful and Effective.

. But it is Objected by ſome, That for ſuch Perſons, Places, or Things, of which we find now the Relicks ; we have Hiſtories that tell us what, who, and when they were ; whereas for the other we have no ſuch Hiſtories in being, nor during the times whereof we have any Hiſtories, can we find any parallel Inſtances that can countenance ſuch Mutations, Changes, and Cataſtrophies as are, and muſt be ſuppoſed to ſolve the Phænomena. *Greece,* *Ægyt, Italy, Spain* and *France* have continued the ſame ; no new Lands have been raiſed out of the Sea, much leſs Hills or Mountains. Beſides, there are many of thoſe Bodies that we now find, both Animal and Vegetable Subſtances, that are as perfectly like the Species of thoſe ſuppoſed Creatures now in being ; and therefore we are not to ſuppoſe, that any Species could be utterly deſtroyed, which yet that Suppoſition ſeems to make neceſſary, if well conſider'd, and the Conſequences thereof produced.

To which I Anſwer, Firſt, That tho' we have no true Hiſtory, when, or by whom, or by what means the *Pyramids* of *Ægypt* were built; yet all that have ſeen them do conclude that they were built by Men, and that thoſe Men were good Maſons and Architects and Engineers ; and that they were not produced of that Shape or Magnitude, by a *Vegetative Power,* or by a *Plaſtick Faculty, or by meer chance, or the accidental concurrence of Petrifactive Atoms.* Nor can I ſee any reaſon to conclude, that the vaſt *Obelisks* that have been tranſported from place to place, and erected, were ſo ordered by Conjureing or Diabolical Magick, tho' I may not be able to tell by what means they become ſo ordered ; I ſhould rather be inclin'd to believe that they were ſo made and placed by the Induſtry, and Invention, of ſome knowing and ingenious Mechanick, who had ſome Contrivances to perform his undertaking that I am ignorant of. Nor do we make it an Argument that theſe

Pyramids

Pyramids were never made by Men, becaufe no Hiftory does tell us when the like have been made fince. Befides, I conceive it would have been a very abfurd Conclufion, if any one fhould have afferted that thofe Horns, I lately mention'd here, were a *Lufus Naturæ*, and not the parts of any living Animal, becaufe he could not tell of what Creature they were; or if he fhould have concluded that the Species of the Creature that produced them were loft, becaufe he knew not where to find it. Certainly there are many *Species* of Nature that we have never feen, and there may have been alfo many fuch *Species* in former Ages of the World that may not be in being at prefent, and many variations of thofe *Species* now, which may not have had a Being in former Times : We fee what variety of *Species*, variety of Soils and Climates, and other Circumftantial Accidents do produce; and a *Species* tranfplanted and habituated to a new Soil, doth feem to be of another kind, tho' poffibly it might return again to its firft Conftitution, if reftored to its firft former Soil.

The Conclufion.   But I fay again, that we have, fince the times wherein Hiftories have been Written, many Inftances of the like Changes and Cataftrophies, as I have fuppos'd to be the neceffary Confequences of this Theory of Petrifaction, and feveral fo lately, that the found of them is hardly out of our Ears; fo that we need not be beholding to antient Hiftorians, to tell us when and where they have actually been produced; for firft there is no place in the Earth that we do know, nor can we indeed know any fuch, that is now and ever has been exempt and free from fuch Mutations, as I have fuppofed; who can tell what part of it hath ever been and ever will be exempt and free from Earthquakes? And tho' Hiftories fhould inform us that during the times of which they writ, there had been no fuch Crifis of Nature (which yet would be a very improbable Affertion as being a Negative) yet it were impoffible to be affured by them, that there had never been any before that time, nor never would be for the future.

And, Secondly, There is no impoffibility in the Suppofition that every part hath, at fome time or other, been fhaken, overturned, or fome way or other fubject to Earthquakes, and transformed by them; and when we confider how great a part of the preceding Time has been *adelon*, or unknown, and unrecorded, one may eafily believe that many Changes may have happened to the Earth, of which we can have no written Hiftory or Accounts. And to me it feems very abfurd to conclude, that from the beginning things have continued in the fame ftate that we now find them, fince we find every thing to change and vary in our own remembrance; certainly 'tis a vain thing to make Experiments and collect Obfervations, if when we have them, we may not make ufe of them; if we muft not believe our Senfes, if we may not judge of things by Trials and fenfible Proofs, if we may not be allowed to take notice of and to make neceffary Confectaries and Corollaries, but muft remain tied up to the Opinions we have received from others, and disbelieve every thing, tho' never fo rational, if our received Hiftories doth not confirm them; this will be truly *Jurare in verba Magiftri*, and we fhould have no more to do but to learn what they have thought fit to leave us : But this is contrary to the *Nullius in verba* of this Society, and I hope that fenfible Evidence and Reafon may at length prevail againft Prejudice, and that *Libertas Philofophandi* may at laft produce a true and real Philofophy.

This was read in the Royal Society *July* the 25th. 1694.

LECTURES

CONCERNING

Navigation and Aſtronomy.

Several Lectures relating to the improvement of NAVIGATION, *read in the Year* 1683.

IN theſe the Author at firſt gives an account of his Deſign, viz. to treat of the Theorical part, two things neceſſary to be known, viz. 1ſt. The Situation of places, in reſpect to each other, and the diſtance between them. 2dly. The ſafeſt and neareſt Courſe to be kept to attain the Port deſired. Sea Charts falſe. The uſe of Journals. Of the ſituation of the places. Of the Figure of the Earth. Of an Antient Learned Age. Arguments for the Round and Oval Figure of the Earth: An Objection againſt the Oval Figure anſwered. The Earth pretty nearly of a Sphærical Figure. Of the Meaſure of a Degree by the Antients and Moderns; that they differ. Of an univerſal Standard for Meaſure. The Pendulum propo'd, with Objections againſt that way. A Degree propoſed for a Standard. The uſe of an univerſal Standard. That the Earth ſhrinks. The ways of meaſuring a Degree. 1ſt. The Aſtronomical ways. Methods to find the Latitude. The inconvenience of Refraction. Stars near the Zenith beſt for this end. 2dly. The Geographical or Mechanical ways of meaſuring a Degree. The uſe of the Inflective property of the Air. A way to diſcover a Ships diſtance off at Sea. Of the ways yet known of diſcovering the place of a Ship on the Sea. 1. Celeſtial. 2. Geographical. Of the true notion of the Horizon. Whence the Looming of the Sea. A Propoſal for a Natural Univerſal Standard for Meaſure.

R. W.

NAVIGATION is a paſſing from place to place upon the Sea, by the help of ſome Veſſel; ſo that to *Navigation*, the firſt thing neceſſary is the Veſſel or Engine to Float or Swim upon the Water, to the end that it may be moved to the Place, and by the way we deſign. *What Navigation is.*

For this there are requiſite two helps; Firſt, Somewhat to move it: And, Secondly, Somewhat to guide or direct that Motion; in the ſupply of which two in all particulars to the beſt advantage, conſiſts the Art of *Navigation*.

Of the firſt of the Three, namely, of the *Ship*, or of the Form, Structure, or Make of the Veſſel, much more may be ſaid and done than has been hitherto, but I ſhall ſay nothing at this time, it being a particular Mechanical Art, and ſo more proper for another Occaſion, where I may have Reaſon to treat more largely and more particularly of it. Nor ſhall I at all meddle now with the Second Head, namely, concerning the ways of giving Motion to the Veſſel, which may be by various means performed, either by Animate or Inanimate Movers; but the moſt commonly uſed are either Sails by the help of the Wind, or Oares, by the ſtrength of Men. Tho' there may be other Ways and Means (much more Advantageous and Commodious than what are at preſent) made uſe of for the ſame purpoſe, as poſſibly I may afterwards manifeſt.

The

The principal Matter I here defign to treat of, is concerning the Third thing requifite to the Art of *Navigation*, and that is the way of guiding or directing a Ship or Veffel, fo as to pafs from Place to Place, of from Port to *The Author's chief defign in this Treatife, viz. The Theorical part.* Port the neareft, fureft, fafeft, and fpeedieft way : In doing of which I fhall not meddle with the Mechanical Part, or the Bufinefs of the Mariner or Steers-man, or he that guides and moves the Rudder to Run or Steer the Ship in this or that Courfe or Rumb, that being more properly taught and learnt at Sea by Practice ; but fhall confine my felf only to the *Theorical* part, which is proper to the *Pilot* or *Mafter*, who directs the Steers-man, what Courfe to take, and which way to Steer the Veffel.

Two things to be known. Things neceffary to be known in this part of *Navigation* are principally two ; Firft, The true Situation of places in refpect of one another, and of the interjacent Seas, both as to the *Longitude* and *Latitude*, and thence the *Rumb* and *Diftance*.

And, Secondly, The fafeft and neareft Courfe (all things confidered) that is to be kept for attaining the defired Port ; for the moft direct Courfe and fhorteft diftance is not always the beft way, but that way which is fafeft, that has the beft and fureft helps of Winds and Currents, is leaft endangered by Rocks, Shoals and Storms.

For both thofe in part, but for the firft wholly we muft at prefent be beholding to the Difcovery and Obfervations that have been made by diligent and inquifitive Navigators, and other Artifts, who have been affiftant to the making and rectifying our Maps and Charts, which tho' they may labour under many Errors and Imperfections, yet 'tis to be hoped that the Induftry of ingenious and fkillful Artifts may much amend and rectify thofe Failings, and reduce the Defcriptions to a much greater certainty and exactnefs ; and in time give us fuch Maps, as may be a true Picture or Reprefentation of the Surface of the Earth and Sea, which is the firft principal thing. I need not *Errors in the prefent Sea Chartes.* inftance in the great Errors that are to be found in our prefent Maps, nor in the Difcrepancy they have one with another ; fince none that has been any way converfant in them can be ignorant thereof: However fuch as they are we muft be content to make ufe of them, 'till by the collected Obfervations of fome that have already communicated their Knowledge, and others that may for the future labour in this Work, there be a compleater fet of Mapps and Charts Graved and Publifhed a-new for the Benefit of Mankind. For the doing of which I could fuggeft many things that would very much improve their ufefulnefs, both as to *Geography*, and *Hydrography*, or *Navigation* ; of which I fhall fay more hereafter upon another occafion.

Secondly, The other part is partly Theorical, and party Hiftorical.

The Hiftorical Part confifts in the Relations of Voyages that have been or are now made to any known Part, wherein we may find an account of what Courfe they have hitherto obferved to be the beft to be kept from place to place, what Seafons of the Year, what Currents are to be met with, and at what times ; what Winds blow at certain Places and Seafons, what fafe and convenient Harbours lie in the way for Victualling, Watering, Careening, and the like: What Sands, Rocks, Shoals, &c. are to be avoided ; what variation they have found of the Compafs at this or that part of their Courfe, or Ports they have touched at, and at what times they were obferved becaufe of the continual Variation of the Variation ; what figns they have of enfuing Storms, and what methods they have ufed to fecure themfelves ; and many other of the like Nature----. And it were much to be defired that the *The ufe of Journals* Journals and Obfervations of all Navigators were in fome certain place retained and preferved, that Recourfe might thereto be had for extracting and methodizing all fuch Obfervations into a compleat Hiftory of fuch particular Voyages, and for the compleating a general Theory. For tho' many confiderable things are known to divers fkillful Navigators to thofe parts, partly from their own Obfervations, and partly from the informations they have had from others, yet a very great number of Obfervations and Methods, that have been formerly and lately known and obferved by divers others, have been loft and forgotten, and are not now to be found. And to fpeak of Artifts now living, 'tis to be feared that even thofe things which they themfelves

felves know, when they Die, will be loft, and others that fhall follow them, will be fain to begin upon a new fcore with their own Obfervations; feveral of thofe may poffibly be handed from one to another by Difcourfe and oral Tradition; but that at beft muft needs be very imperfect, fince we find that Men themfelves forget in a little time their own Obfervations, and this or that particular Circumftance will flip out of their Memory, efpecially in matters of number; and certainly there could be no better way to preferve them for future Ufe, than by treafuring them up in fome one certain place, where they might be fafely preferved: And it were as much for the obfervers Intereft fo to do, fince it would put him upon obferving as well as upon writing his Obfervations, and 'twould prompt him to recollect things taken notice of, whilft the impreffions of them are yet frefh in his Memory, by which means he would not only fix them more laftingly in his own Memory; but it would be an occafion to him of making his Obfervations much more certain and determinate, and of minding many other confiderable Circumftances, which he would otherwife not at all have regarded; as any one that makes trial will eafily be convinced of; this therefore, we hope, Time may produce.

The Theorical Part, which is that I aim principally to Difcourfe of, is a *The Theorical* knowledge or Art, by which Directions are obtained for Guiding and Steer- *part.* ing a Veffel from any one place to any other, whereof we have the Situation given and all the material Circumftances, that have been taken notice of to be ufually met with in Voyages made to thofe Parts; for 'tis with Voyages at Sea oftentimes as it is in Journies upon the Land, that the fartheft way about is oft times the neareft way thither: The caufe of which, in Sea Voyages, is to be afcribed either to the Winds or to the Currents and Tides; of which I fhall fay more hereafter. And tho' the general Theory would direct you to Sail or Steer by the fhorteft and ftraighteft way through the open and free Sea from one place to another, yet the intervening of thefe and fome other Circumftances do make you take a very differing Courfe, and go fometimes this way, and fometimes that way, for the better attaining your end. As when they Sail to the *Barbadoes,* they do not Steer on the direct Rumb that leads thither, but Sail a-way more towards the South, that they may get into the Trade or Eafterly Winds, which may carry them from thence more directly and fpeedily towards their Port; whereas in the direct Rumb they meet with Calms or contrary Winds and Currents, which would take up much more Time, and caufe much greater inconvenience; 'tis plain therefore, that both thefe parts are neceffary, *viz.* Firft, True Charts of the Situation of Places: And, Secondly, A true Hiftory of the Conveniences and Inconveniences of paffing by this or that Courfe.

For the firft of thefe, namely, for the knowing of the true Situation of *For knowing* Places to one another, it is requifite to underftand, Firft, the Figure of the *the Situation* Body of the Earth: And, Secondly, The Magnitude. Concerning the Fi- *of places.* gure of the Earth; there have been very many, and thofe very differing Opinions among the ancient Philofophers, but whether their Opinions are truly related to us, or whether they had any Grounds or Reafons for thofe Opinions we are uncertain, becaufe little is faid concerning them. *Anaximan- Of the Terra- der* is faid to have fuppofed it like a Column; tho' yet confidering his skill in *queous Figure,* Aftronomy, 'tis hardly to be believed. *Leucippus* like a Cylinder or Drum. *the Opinions of* *Cleanthes* like a top or double Cone, whofe Points were at the Poles, as fome *the Antients.* fay; but others, that he fuppofed it like a Difh, hollowed in the middle, but rifing towards the Edges, that the Sea might not run over, of which Opinion *Heraclitus* is alfo faid to bee *Anaximenes* and *Empedocles* are faid to have fuppofed it like a round Table, or a round Plain, being the top, as it were, of a mighty Cylinder or Column, for the bottom of which they affigned no bounds; of which *Ariftotle* in his Book *De Cælo,* and *Plutarch De Placitis Philofophorum* give an account. Of this Opinion are moft Men who are ignorant in Aftronomy and Geography, and that becaufe the vifible appearance, they always have of the Earth, is a very large Plain covered with the Heavens as with a Hemifphere, and becaufe the Land was always bounded by the Sea, and that the Limits or Bounds of that Sea was not known, it was fuppofed

that

that the Sea was bounded by the hollow Hemifphere of Heaven, and thence that the Sun, Moon and Stars that Rofe and Set, did rife out of the Sea, and fet or defcend again into the Sea, which was the occafion and ground of thofe Expreffions and Fables of the antient Poets; and even to this day ignorant People, that have been no better informed, are from the fame Caufe, as I have already mention'd of the fame Opinion ; for this caufe alfo it was, that fome were of Opinion, that τὸ πᾶν, or the whole of the World was Water, and that there was a kind of Arch or Firmament of Heaven, which kept off the Waters that were above this Arch from coming to the Waters which were beneath the Arch, upon which the Earth floated, as it were a Difh ; and that beneath the Earth that kept up the Waters above, was the fpace, wherein the Air and Meteors were placed-----. This alfo was much countenanced by the vifible appearances both of the Earth and the Heavens, and fo needs not much of Arguments to make it pafs with the Vulgar and Illiterate, and fuch as have not been ufed to confider and reafon about thefe Matters. Hence comes it, that even to this Day, we may every where find People who retain as abfurd Imaginations, and who ftill look upon Antipodes as impoffible Fictions, and the Product only of the Authority of Seamen and Travellers to tell ftrange things ; nor has it been only the Opinion of the Vulgar and Illiterate, but even of many otherwife very Learned and Excellent Men, fuch as were feveral Fathers of the Church, who, from their want of this fort of Knowledge, and from their mifunderftanding fome Texts of the Scripture, have zealoufly oppofed the Opinion of the roundnefs of the Earth and of Antipodes.

Parmenides, among the Antients, is faid by *Diogenes Laertius*, to be the firft that ever afferted the Earth to be a round Ball or Globe, and feated in the middle of the World, and the firft, that fet out or limited the habitable Parts of the World, and bounded them by the Frozen *Zone* on the óne fide, and the Torrid or Burning *Zone* one the other fide, as is related of him by *Plutarch* in his Treatife *De placitis Philofophorum* : This Man flourifhed in the fixty nineth *Olympiad*, that is, about five Hundred Years before *Chrift*. But tho' this Perfon were an extraordinary Philofopher and great difcoverer of Nature, and fo might poffibly receive this Opinion, yet we find by the fore-mentioned Book of *Plutarch*, that this Opinion is afcribed to *Thales*, who lived above a Hundred Years fooner ; and if we had not been defective in the Hiftory of antient Times, without doubt we fhould have been informed that Aftronomy and the Theory of the World, revived by *Copernicus*, was, long before *Thales*, well known, and if fo, then the roundnefs of the Body of the Earth could not be a thing unknown to fo learned an Age ; of which learned Age, beyond all the Hiftories now to be met with, *Hugo Grotius* has given us a Collection of Teftimonies.

Of an antient learned Age.

Simplicius in his Notes upon *Ariftotle*, mentions, that *Califthenes* (who upon the taking of *Babylon* was prefented by *Ariftotle* to *Alexander* the Great) had feveral very antient Writings of Aftronomers very long before that time, namely, of 1903 Years, which, according to the common Account, muft fall about threefcore Years after the Flood, and confequently, if Aftronomy were fo early fo well known, the Figure of the Earth could not be unknown ; for whatever ftrange Opinions fome of the Phiiofophers might have, who had only contemplated fome of the leffer Bodies and Productions of Nature which were within their reach, yet moft certainly thofe that were skillful in Aftronomy could not be ignorant of its Form, which we may plainly enough prove from their affigning the Eclipfes of the Moon to be from the fhadow of the Earth ; but efpecially if the Syftem of *Ariftarchus* were fo very antient, wherein the Earth is fuppofed a Planet.

Of the Sphærical Figurr of the Earth.

But to omit any further mention of the Opinions or Theories of the Antients concerning the Figure of the Earth, it is now fuppofed or granted by all Philofophers, Aftronomers, and Geographers, that the Figure of the Body of the Earth is Globular, or every way equally round, or of a Sphærical Figure, and accordingly the Model of it is commonly made of that Figure, a Globe, and the Parts or places of it are fet down and defcribed upon the Superficies of a perfect Globe and fo the diftances from place to place are

computed

computed as upon such a Sphærical or bending Surface; and many Arguments are commonly brought to prove this Opinion, which, because they are to be met with in almost every Geographical Writer, I shall pass by at present; some only I would here take notice of, that tho' it be so generally assented to, and concluded by all, yet I conceive there is no one positive and undeniable Proof to evince it against some I have lately met with, who would have it to be somewhat of an Oval or Egg-like Figure, the Axis of its motion being *of the Oval Figure thereof.* supposed the longest Diameter; or of another, who supposes it may be of an Oval Figure the contrary way, and that the longest Diameter of it is the Æquinoctial, and the shortest the Axis; the reason of the first was alledged to be, for that the Sun does exhale and draw up into the Air from the parts of the *Torrid Zone* a great quantity of Water and other volatile Materials from it into the Air, and drive them towards the two Polar Parts, where they again præcipitate and fall down in Rain, Snows, Hails, &c. and so turn to Ice, and so raise the parts thereof towards the Pole, and diminish the parts about the *Torrid Zone :* But the Answer to this Argument is very easy, that if the Water be most raised within the *Torrid Zone* and rain'd down again in the Frigid, then it would follow, that there must be a continual passage of Water from the Frigid towards the Torrid, and possibly it must carry more parts along with it in its return towards the Æquinoctial in the Form of Water, than from the *Torrid Zone* back to the Frigid in the form of Air : This therefore will be a better Argument for the second Hypothesis than for the first, but *What the Author mentions here of the Oval Figure, is* 'tis judged no positive and certain Argument for either, since what it carries back towards the Æquinoctial, serves only to fill up the Caverns in the bottom of the Sea : The Argument alledged for the second Opinion, was, that *more largely treated of and* the Globe of the Earth being whirled round upon its Axis, the parts near the Æquinoctial have less Gravity than the Parts near the Poles; but tho' *demonstrated Page 355. Supra.* this be more significant than the former, yet it may be said that the Body of the Sun, tho' it be moved upon its Axis as well as the Body of the Earth, yet the Figure thereof, as far as we can discover by the Telescope, is still perfectly round. Now the proportion of the Diameter of the Sun to the Diameter of the Earth being greater than the period of the Sun's Revolution to the Period of the Earth's; it follows that the parts of the Sun move swifter than the respective parts of the Body of the Earth. Now, tho' it be alledged that the Body of *Mercury* passing through the Body of the Sun in the last Conjunction observed by Monsieur *Gallet,* was by him said to appear of this Figure, yet no such appearance was taken notice of by others that observed the same; and if it had, 'tis not yet known whether *Mercury* be moved round upon its Axis or not, and therefore no certain conclusion can thence be deduced. But as neither of these Assertions is sufficiently proved, so I must needs say that the absolute roundness of the Ball of the Earth does yet want a positive Proof; for no one of the Arguments or Experiments, yet brought to prove that Figure, are sufficiently exact and positive to prove it; for tho' they do most of them prove it to have a Figure which is near a round, yet they do not prove it absolutely; for First, It cannot certainly enough be discovered by the Eclipses of the Moon; for the shadow may be somewhat Elliptical either way, and yet the appearances not sufficient to determine the difference; for we find that no Observation hitherto made doth exactly agree with any Calculation yet made; and to what to ascribe the difference is not hitherto agreed. Next, none of the measures of a Degree, tho' some of them, as particularly that of the *French* lately Published by the *Royal Academy,* are made with great exactness, for each of them only shew what measure was found of a Degree of the Meridian in that Latitude; but they differ enough one from another to shew that no two of them compared together will be sufficient for this purpose. Further, tho' two of them should pretty near agree, as that of Mr. *Norwood* here in *England,* and that of Mr. *Picart,* yet to make them significant for this purpose, the same examinations should have been made Eastward and Westwards, to see whether the Parallels would have answered to the respective Latitudes; and therefore if these Proofs be not sufficient, much less will the Observation of Seamen, whose computations of Leagues failed, are by no means accurate enough to determine this matter,

ter; for there may be a confiderable difference, and yet they unable to detect it.

Objection against the Elliptical Figure. Againft this the moft material Objection is, that if the Body of the Earth fhould be Elliptical, as there is fome probability that it is fo, not with the longeft Diameter in the Axis, which would make it of an Egg form, but with the longeft Diameter, in the plain of the Æquinoctial, which would make it of a Turnep or Bowl Form, and that becaufe the Rotation thereof muft neceffarily make the parts of the Earth, which are carried the fwifteft with that motion, have an indeavour outwards, or from the Axis of Rotation, as we find in all Bodies moved with fuch a motion; which indeavour muft neceffarily take off from the Gavitation of thofe Bodies towards the Center, and thence if the power of Gravitation be every ways from the Center equally forcing towards the Center, the parts of the Earth towards the Æquinoctial muft have lefs Gravity than the parts of the Earth that are nearer the Poles; and confequently there muft be a longer Cone or Cylinder near the Æquinoctial to counterpoife a fhorter near the Poles, and confequently to keep the Water of the Sea in a Counterpoife, there muft be a rifing of the Sea above the Sphærical Surface near the Æquinoctial, and a depreffion of the Sea below *From the pointing of the Perpendicular.* that Sphærical Surface near the Poles, which makes it of this Turnep or Bowl fhape. Againft this, I fay, the greateft Objection is this, either the Perpendicular doth point directly to the Center of the Earth, or it doth not: If it be afferted that it points directly to the Center of the Earth, then the Surface or the vifible Horizon would difcover fuch a variation from perfect Sphæricalnefs by an obliquity of its plain to the Plumb Line, which then would *Anfwered.* not be Perpendicular to it. To which I Anfwer, that this Obliquity being but little, it would not eafily be difcovered by reafon of the Refraction of the Air near the Horizon, yet if it really be fo, I grant it may with great care be found, if a place convenient for fuch an Obfervation, and the Experiment be purpofely and with great care made, as at fome promontory of Land running Eaftward or Weftward into the Sea, where the Surface of the Sea or the Horizon thereof may be feen both to the North and to the South. But this I do not find has ever yet been obferved as it ought to be, and therefore there may be fuch an appearance, and yet not hitherto detected. But, Secondly, If it be afferted that if the Plumb-Line do not point to the Center, then this would be difcovered by the different account of Leagues failed Eaft and Weft, from the Leagues failed North and South, to anfwer to a Degree, or by the differing length of a Degree in differing Latitudes; to which I Anfwer, that I do confefs that there would be really fuch a difference, but yet I *Accurate Obfervations are yet wanting.* fay no Obfervation hitherto made could detect it; there are wanting therefore many Obfervations neceffary for the verifying and pofitively demonftrating this Queftion, which, tho' it has fcare been ever yet mentioned by any Writer, yet I judge it may be well worth the while to have it exactly tried and examined; for tho' it hath been generally believed and afferted, that the Figure of the Earth is exactly Sphærical or Globular, yet I affert that there is not one, that I have ever yet met with, that has proved or demonftrated it fo to be; and to me it feems very probable from fome Phyfical Confiderations, that it may be confiderably otherwife; of which I have difcourfed much more largely on another Subject, wherein I have fhewn the neceffary Confequences, and the feveral Proprieties thereof, which are much differing from the Notions hitherto commonly received.

The Earth pretty nearly of a Sphærical Figure. However probable it is, that 'tis pretty near the Sphærical Figure, and therefore, 'till it be fome ways found to be otherwife, the computation of diftances may be fo made as if it had been pofitively proved fo to be, and the meafures of diftances made accordingly; which brings me to the fecond neceffary to be known, and that is the true Magnitude of the Body of the Earth compared to the common known meafures, as that of a Foot, Pace, Fathom, Stadium, Mile, League, or the like.

The meafure of a Degree attapted by feveral of the antients and moderns. For this then we have an account of very many Experiments and Trials that have been made both heretofore, and of later Days; but if we compare them together, one would be apt to imagine, either that they were very imperfectly made, or elfe that we are very ignorant of their feveral particular

measures,

measures, or else that there may be a real difference of the measure of a Degree taken at several Latitudes of the Earth; for *Aristotle* makes it 1111 Stadia, *Eratosthenes* 700, *Possidonius* 666, and *Ptolomy* 500, and the *Arabians* yet less; but in truth we know not what ways they took for exactness, nor what measure any of them made use of compared with those in use at present among us; and therefore it will be much less difficult not to err our selves, than to know whether the Antients err'd or no.

If we consider the Modern Experiments for this purpose, we may find that Mr. *Norwood* in the Year 1635, did find the Meridian Altitude of the Sun on the eleventh of *June* to be 59, 33', and that two Years before that, *viz.* on the eleventh of *June* 1633, he had found the Meridian Altitude of the Sun at *London* 62° 01', whence he concludes (not making any allowance for declination, Refraction, or Parallax) that *York* was more *North* than *London* 2. 28. Now by measuring the distance by Chains of ninety nine Foot long, or six Rod of 16½ to a Rod, he found it to be 9149 Chains, or 905751 Feet; whence he concludes in a Degree there are 367196 or 367200 Feet, which is sixty nine Miles and an half and 236 Feet, whence there will be 6120 Feet in one Minute or a gradual Mile, which is 840 Foot more than our Statute Mile which is 5280 Foot.

The last Experiment that has been made for determining this measure, is that of Monsieur *Picart*, and the Gentlemen of the *Royal Academy of Paris*, who with great exactness of Instruments and great Skill and Care in performing, examin'd the measure of a Degree and found the same to be 57060 Toises or Fathoms of the Castle of *Paris*, each Fathom or Toise containing six Parisian Feet, and thence a Degree contains 342360 Parisian Feet; and the Parisian Foot being to that of *London* as 16 to 15, a Degree will contain 365184 *English* Feet, or 69 Miles and 864 Feet; which is almost ⅞ part of a Mile, a sixth part of a Mile being 880 Feet, so that by this Account a Degree is less than what Mr. *Norwood* makes it by 2012 Feet, and consequently a Minute or gradual Mile will contain 6086⅗ Feet, which is longer than a Statute Mile 806⅗ Foot, which is almost a Sixth, *viz.* 880. Now having the measure of one Degree, it will be easy to find the measure of the Circumference of the whole Earth, there being 360 such Degrees in a great Circle of it. 360 times 365184 gives 131566240 Feet in the Circumference of the Earth, or 24915 Miles and 504 Feet.

These two last Mensurations are less than that which was made by the *Arabians* about the Year of our Lord 827 by several skilful Mathematicians at the command of *Almaiman* an *Arabian* Prince, in the Plains of *Mesopotamia*, they finding a measure of a Degree, which, reduced to our *English* Measure, amounted to 370222 Feet; so that That of Mr. *Norwood* is less by 3022 Feet, and that of Mr. *Picart* 5038; so that *Norwood* is less by about 1¦0 part of a Degree, or about half a Minute, and *Picart* is less by a 72½ part of a Degree, or almost an *English* Mile.

What to ascribe the Reason of these differences one from another to, is pretty hard to say, but most probably it is partly the differing method each of them took, and partly also the uncertainty of the comparative Magnitude of the measures they each of them made use of; for to go no farther back than Mr. *Norwood*, we are not well assured but that the Foot he made use of was less than the Foot we now make use of by 181½ part by which he differs from *Picart*, which is about half a Centesm; for the Standard Foot we now use was since that time agreed upon by a Club of our Mathematical Instrument-makers, of whom Mr. *Elias Allen* was the chief; we will not now mention any other cause, tho' possibly there may be another more considerable than either But not to trouble our selves with what the measure of a Degree has been, 'tis only necessary for our present Enquiry to know what really it is now, reduced to a known and certain and invariable measure, in which all Nations may agree; for 'till that be done, our measuring the Course at Sea by the Logline is false and leads into great Errors and Mistakes; for if with the Logline we measure a League, or the 60th part of a Degree, and account it to hold but 15840 Foot, or 2640 Fathom, and it really contains 18259⅗ Feet, or 3043 Fathoms, then the Course measured by such an erroneous measure must needs very much confound our reckoning

To what the Discrepancy may be ascrib and of the difference of measures.

The Logline at present leads into errors.

It will be neceffary therefore in the firft place to rectify our meafure and the length of our Line.

Many have been the attempts and defigns both of Antient and Moderns to perform this neceffary *Præcognitum* to Geography and Mechanicks, but to this Day it remains a thing to be fought after. The laft and beft way hitherto thought of is, that by the length of a *Pendulum* vibrating Seconds of Time meafured by the Sun's middle motion in the Ecliptick, reduced to the Æquinoctial or right afcenfum, which, for ought I know, was firft invented by the *Royal Society,* tho' it has been fince publifhed by Monfieur *Hugens,* Monfieur *Picart,* and divers others. Or which were yet more eafy to be found and more certain, by reafon that the Sun's true *Anomaly* is not yet afcertained by the length of a *Pendulum* vibrating a Second of Time, by the diurnal Revolution of fome notable fixt Star; becaufe, in all probability, that is always equal and the fame at any time of the Year, and in any Year, either paft or to come. And tho' the ingenious *Kepler* has from his Hypothefis of the turbinating Power of Light fuppofed that the turbinating or diurnal Motion of the Earth upon its Axis is accelerated and retarded in that diurnal Rotation, according as it moves nearer to, or further off from the Sun; yet there is no one certain and pofitive Experiment or Obfervation yet brought to prove any fuch inequality; and from another Hypothefis which I have of the caufes of that motion, which is very differing from that of *Kepler,* I fuppofe there can be none fuch, and therefore 'till by fome certain Obfervation, it be found to be otherwife, we may, with great Reafon, fuppofe it to be at all times of the Year, the fame; fo that if a *Pendulum* be made of fuch a length as to make 86400 fingle vibrations in the time that any fixt Star paffes from the Meridian, 'till it return to the fame the next Night, that length may be taken for a perpetual meafure of length or a Standard Yard, to which all other meafures of Length, Breadth, Solidity, Capacity, Weight, or Power, may be reduc'd; and ⅓ of that may be taken for the univerfal Foot, and two of thofe for an univerfal Fathom, and five of thofe may make a Rod or Pole; or which were yet better, to divide this length into ten, for Decimals or Hands, and each of thofe into Decimals which may be called Digits or Fingers, and each of thefe into Decimals which may be called Threads, and each of thefe into Decimals which may be called Clews or Hairs, and fo onward by Decimal-fubdivifion, to continue downwards, fo as you have occafion, of a fmaller or fmaller meafure, which may be call'd Tenths, Hundreds, Thoufands, ten Thoufands, hundred Thoufands, *&c.* and for greater meafures to compute only by the number of fuch Yards, Arms, or Paces.

Monfieur *Hugens* has determined the length of a *Pendulum* vibrating Seconds by the Sun, to be three Foot 8⅗ Lines of the *Parifian* meafure, accounting the Limits of his meafure fo taken, to be from the Center of Sufpenfion, to the Center of Ofcillation or Vibration, which is a Point to be found by a proportion which he affigns, depending on the length of the Diameter of the Ball to the length of the String by which it is fufpended.

The Toife or Fathom of the Obfervations of *Paris,* which Monfieur *Picart* made ufe of for the meafure of a Degree, was, according to the laft eftablifhment at *Paris,* compared with the Standard of the length of a *Pendulum* vibrating Seconds of Time conformable to the mean motion of the Sun.

The Toife contains fix Parifian Feet, and the Parifian Foot to the *London* Foot is in proportion as 16 to 15.----Each of thefe Parifian Feet is divided into Duodecimals or Inches, and each Inch into Duodecimals or Lines.

Now, by many trials, he found the length of fuch a *Pendulum* to be thirty fix Inches, and eight Lines and an half.

The *Pendulum* he ufed, as he himfelf declares, was made of a Ball of Copper of one Inch in Diameter exactly turned, and the firft String, he ufed to fufpend it by, was of a flat Silk. The length of the *Pendulum* he reckons to be from the Center of Motion to the Center of the Ball, omitting the part proportional taken notice of by Monfieur *Hugens,* the Ball being but a thirty fixth part of the length of the Thread; otherwife if the Ball be bigger, the proportional part muft be taken notice of as making a confiderable variation, the Vibrations

ons

ons also obferv'd were very fhort, otherwife there would have been a confiderable variation in their Duration or Time, but afterwards finding that the Silk was apt to fhrink and ftretch by the leaft drinefs and moifture of the Air, it was found much better for that purpofe to make ufe of a flake of Silk Grafs, which is a fort of long and very fine Flax brought out of *America,* which is very flexible and yet very ftrong, and not fubject to fhrink or ftretch. The upper end of this Flake was put between the Chops of a fmall Vice which held it very firm when pinched by the Screw, and the length was meafured by a fmall Rod of Iron made exactly of the length of the String, when the Ball hung Perpendicular between the Head of the faid Vice and the Ball.

This *Pendulum* was adjufted by two large *Pendulum-Clocks,* whofe *Pendulum* had been by trials adjufted to move Second Minutes by the mean motion of the Sun, and which were found flower by three Minutes and fifty fix Seconds, at every return of the fame Star to the Meridian; and that to fuch an exactnefs, that they differed not one from another, one fingle Second during many Days; the fingle *Pendulum* was fo fufpended and put into motion, that it vibrated the fame way as the *Pendulum* of the Clock; and if it were of 36 Inches eight and an half Lines, it continued its Vibrations the fame with thofe of the Clock, but if it were never fo little either longer or fhorter than that meafure, it became, in lefs than an Hours time, fenfibly differing; however he acknowledged that this length was not always found fo precife, but that it feemed it ought to have been a little fhortned in Winter and lengthned in Summer; but that, he conceives, ought to have been but the tenth part of a Line, and the excefs on both fides being pretty near equal, he therefore made choice of the length of 36 Inches, eight and an half Lines, as the medium or middle length between that of the Summer and that of the Winter.

Now, if this were made the general Standard for the meafures of all Countries, or that there particular meafures, whatever they be, were reduced to this, then the knowing the proportion they bear to the Standard would manifeft the proportions they have to one another, and fo the meafures given of a Degree in one place, by the meafures of that Country might eafily be reduced to the meafures of any other; and fo Experiments truly made might be as accurately examin'd and compar'd together.

But againft this way of finding a natural, univerfal, and perpetual Standard meafure of length there may be divers Objections not inconfiderable; as, Firft, That if the Gravitating Power of the Earth be greater in one place than in the other, as towards the Poles more than towards the Æquator, then the length of a *Pendulum* to vibrate Seconds, muft alfo be confiderably longer towards the Poles than towards the Æquinoctial, otherwife the *Pendulum* of the fame length with what is determin'd in *France,* which is about the middle between the North Pole and the Æquinoctial, will go too quick near the Poles, and too flow near the Æquinoctial. Now, what I many Years fince difcover'd in this place, reading about Penduls for Longitude, and what I have now before mention'd concerning a probability, if not a neceffity of fuch an inequality of Gravitation, and confequently of a Boul-like form of the Earth, does at leaft hint that fome Experiment of that kind ought to be try'd at fome place near the Æquator, to fee whether it be fo or not, and 'till that be done there can be no certain Conclufion made thereupon. *Objections against this Standard.*

Next, 'tis not impoffible but that the Gravity or attractive Power of the Earth may be at fome times greater than at others; for we fee that there is hardly any thing in Nature that ftands at a certain ftay, but does fometimes increafe and fometimes diminifh; and if fo, then that Iron Rod, that is the exact meafure of the length of the String of the *Pendulum* this Year, will be differing from the length of the fame, which was three or four Years fince, and may be three or four Years hence; this therefore ought to be firft examin'd by Experience, before any certain Conclufion can be made thereupon. *Gravity may differ in the fame place.*

Thirdly, It is not yet certainly known, but that the Gravitating Power of the Earth may be different at various Seafons of the Year, as when the Earth is in its *Apholion* and *Perihelion;* for which poffibly there may be a plaufible Reafon affign'd; and if fo, it will then be neceffary to mention at what time *And at different Seasons.*

of

of the Year the measure is taken; for if the gravitating Power should be found to be lesser when the Earth is in its *Perihelion* in our Winter, than when in its *Aphelion* in the Summer, then the *Pendulum* must be accordingly proportion'd to the time of the Year.

Fourthly, If the Rotation or Diurnal Motion of the Earth should be accelerated in its *Perihelion* in our Winter, and retarded in its *Aphelion* in our Summer, as the ingenious *Kepler* supposes, and seems to assert from Experiments, then the quite contrary will follow, and the *Pendulum* must be shorter for the Winter than for the Summer; which will be necessary to be prov'd by trials, before any thing can be built thereupon.

Fifthly, If both these two last mention'd Effects are produc'd, and that they keep in some proportion one to another, then a *Pendulum* of the same length may serve at all Seasons of the Year; but if either exceed the other in that proportion, then must the length of the *Pendulum* be accordingly lengthen'd or shortn'd.

Sixthly, If the differing Density of the Air have an influence upon the Motion and Velocity of the *Pendulum* made in it, as most certainly it has, and that a Body in a dense Air moves not so quick, *Cæteris paribus*, as in a rarify'd Air, then the *Pendulum* must be shorten'd in the Winter, and lengthen'd in the Summer; and so the same measure will not last round the Year.

Seventhly, If the *Pendulum* be made of a Brass, Silver, or Iron Rod, then the length of the same Rod will be greater in Summer than in Winter, and consequently the space measur'd therewith will be found shorter in Summer than in Winter; for those and the other Metals, when hot, will have larger Dimensions than when cold, and so cannot make an exact Standard for the measure of length.

Eighthly, If the *Pendulum* be made with twisted Threads, then the Threads will be found to be longer in dry Weather than in moist, and so 'twill be necessary to take an account of the Seasons when the Experiments are made, and to reduce to exactness the limits of such shrinking and stretching.

I could mention divers other Objections against this way, tho' notwithstanding I conceive it to be the best and easiest that has been yet Publish'd; and with finding out the true limitations to all those Qualifications, it may possibly prove the best for use.

A Degree proposed for an universal Standard. There have been others who have thought the best way for the making an universal Standard for the measuring of length, to be the finding the exact length of a Degree upon the Earth; and to do that by most exactly determining two places upon the Earth that are both in the same *Meridian*, and differ from each other exactly one Degree of Latitude, observ'd by a very large and curious Instrument; which places being so found out, their true distance is to be exactly measur'd and found some one certain measure; then this length, to be divided into sixty equal Parts, which may be called Geographical Miles or Minutes, and each sixtieth part being subdivided into a thousand parts, may denote Geographical Paces, and each thousanth part, being again subdivided into five parts, may denote a Geographical Foot, and each of these fifth parts being again subdivided into twelve, may denote Geographical Inches; and these again subdivided into twelve parts, may denote Geographical Lines; and so subdividing onward by Duodecimals the least sensible length may be determin'd in proportion to the Circumference or Diameter of the Earth.

Objections against this way But against this way of making a Standard for the measure of length there may be these things Objected; First, The great difficulty that there will be, First, To determine exactly by Astronomical Observation two such places to the certainty of five Hundred Foot. Secondly, In measuring their true distance.

Secondly, If the Body of the Earth be not exactly Sphærical, then the measure of a Degree, taken in one Latitude, will be differing from what it is in another, and so it must be determin'd, First, By trials exactly made in differing Latitudes, whether any such difference be or not, before any Conclusion can be made thereupon.

Thirdly,

Thirdly, 'Tis not improbable but that the Body of the Earth itself may shrink and grow closer together, and so grow lesser, that the Gravity thereof does continually press the parts thereof harder, and possibly closer together; and so 'tis possible the irregular Surface of the Earth may have been, in part, caus'd by the puckering of the Cortical Parts thereof; and if so, then the measures, this way found, will every Age grow shorter and shorter; which, possibly, may have been the Reason why the measures of a Degree, which have been taken in several Ages, have always been found shorter and shorter, the later they have been taken, as I before-mention'd.

Fourthly, The same Objections do lie about the shrinking and swelling of the last Substance that preserves the Standard, as in the former way. I could instance in some other Objections, but that I conceive these will be sufficient to shew the difficulty of procuring such a measure.

I have been more particular upon this Inquiry, for that this seems to be the very *Basis* and Foundation of Geography and Navigation; and, 'till this be well determin'd, all the Superstructure will be but infirm.

June 21. 168 3. I did the last Day explain to you the necessity there was of a certain and determinate Measure or Standard of length; that might be so, not only to all the World at present, but that it be and remain to all Posterity for the future; that so, by means of that, all things that could be reduc'd to a certain Weight, Measure, Capacity, Power, &c. might, by that means, be compar'd, First, To that common Standard-measure, and afterwards one with another; because without such a natural and perpetual Standard, neither could the present quantities of things be compar'd with those of preceding Ages, nor indeed one with another at present; nor could future Ages have the true Use and Benefit in this Particular of the Obversations and Inventions of this present; for to instance in no other Particular at present, I shew'd you how every one of the measures of the Earth taken by any of the Antients differ'd both one from another, and all of them from the measures now last of all found; and how those quantities, which they took of a Degree, thereby seem'd to have diminish'd ever since the first that was taken this way. So that it doth necessarily follow, either that the Standard-measure, made use of by them, did continually increase or grow bigger, the longer it remain'd in the World, or that the very Body of the Earth itself, did really, from time to time, as it grew older and older, shrink into less and less Dimensions, much after the same way as we find divers animated Bodies, as Plants and Animals, upon growing old, really to do; whence, as I hinted, the Mountains and Vallies, and the like inequalities of the Earth's Surface might seem to be nothing else but the wrinkles and puckering of the Skin of the old *Vesta*. There is no impossibility nor absurdity in either of these Solutions or Suppositions. Nor will I determine or prepossess any with a positive assertion of my Opinion, which is the most likely; only this I may say, that there seems a kind of necessity to admit either the one or the other, if at least we will give any credit to the truth of the Relations, or to the certainty and exactness of their Observations (for it may lie also in either of those) but that seems not so probable; for my part I am inclin'd to believe that the Body of the Earth doth really shrink and grow less, by reason that the Gravity of the Earth doth seem to press and ram the parts thereof continually closer and closer together, and for that it seemeth not so natural to conceive that the common measure should continually grow bigger and bigger, especially, since it is believ'd rather that the size of Men grows less and less, and consequently it seems less probable, that the Foot, Fathom, Pace, and the like, which are deduc'd from the size of Mens Feet, fathoming and going, should grow bigger; but be that what it will, it seems at least to shew the great Use and Conveniency of a natural, universal, and perpetual Standard of length: I have already mention'd two ways that have been thought of and attempted for the making this universal Standard, and those were; First, The length of a single free *Pendulum* vibrating Seconds of Time.

The use of an universal Standard for measure.

That the Earth shrinks.

Secondly, The length of one Thousanth part of a Minute or Mile found upon the Earth by accurate Astronomical and Geometrical Mensuration to be for a Geometrical Pace, and a fifth part of that for a Foot.

I told you also what Objections there lay both against the one and the other way, and I shew'd you also how those uncertainties might be ascertain'd, and the difficulties remov'd ; but neither of them could be perfectly regulated and ascertain'd without a great deal of Care, Pains and Skill, which yet (for all accurate Observations) is necessary to be done. I could have shew'd some other ways of making a universal, natural and perpetual Measure ; but for the purpose of Geography and Navigation, these possibly, when rectify'd as they ought, may prove the best. I explain'd the last time how one of those measures might be found or made by Observation ; I shall now a little more particularly discourse of the second way, namely, That, by the true length of a Degree upon the level Surface of the Earth, found by accurate Observations. Now there are many ways to find out and determine the Magnitude of a Degree that are mention'd by Authors, and there may be many more ; but they may be all reduc'd to two general Heads.

The ways of measuring a Degree.

First, Such as require some Cælestial Observations to determine the Degree, or other certain part of a great Circle imagin'd upon the Surface of the Earth.

And, Secondly, Such as only require Observations made upon the Earth to determine the same. The First, for brevity's sake, may be call'd the Astronomical ; the Second Geographical.

The Astronomical ways.

The Astronomical ways are two, *viz.* First, The finding the difference of Latitude between two places lying due North and South of each other, or under the same Meridian, by accurate Observations of some Cælestial Bodies, whether Sun or Stars.

And the Second, The finding the said difference of Latitude between two places lying in some other Position to each other, whose true Positions are known, and not in or very near the East and West of each other, and so finding the proportional length of the part of the Azymuthal Circle, then finding by exact Mensuration upon the Earth, or otherwise with some known measure, the true distance between them in a straight Line.

To find the Latitude of a place.

The Astronomical Observations necessary for the finding the true *Latitude* of any place may be either made in the Day or in the Night ; by the Sun whose Altitude, Azymuth and Declination for any time of the Day being known, the *Latitude* may easily be found, but the best of all Azimuths is the true South and Meridian : For that First, The labour of Calculation to reduce it to the Meridian is sav'd : But, Secondly, Because the Body of the Sun is there mov'd with a horizontal or level motion, and so does not so suddainly change its Altitude, but remain sensibly the same for some time. Thirdly, Because the Body of the Sun is there most remov'd from the Horizon, and so will there have the least Refraction, which, in this Case is very considerable, and must be avoided as far as may be. In the Night the Latitude of a Place may be found by the observation of the Altitude of any one known Star, whose Azymuth and Declination is known ; but here also the best Position of any such Star for this purpose is, when it is in the Meridian, and if it pass the Meridian both Northwards and Southwards, the Zenith ; the best is that to the Southwards ; and of all Stars for this purpose,

Stars near the Zenith best for this purpose.

those are best for such Observations as pass the nearest the Zenith of the place. (Because, as I shew'd before, the great incumbrance of all Astronomical Observations is thereby remov'd, namely, Refraction.) Now, the Refractions are always so much the greater, the nearer the Body observ'd is to the Horizon, but the nearer the Zenith the less ; but the quantity of proportions of such Refractions is not so certainly found, because, neither is the Refraction the same at all places, nor the same at one and the same place at differing Seasons of the Year, nor in differing times of the Day and Night,

tho'

tho' the Sun or Star be in both thofe times in the fame Altitude, and is not yet reduc'd to any certain Rule or Calculation: And therefore the beft way of all, is that which doth wholly avoid that Inconvenience, which is the way that I above twenty Years fince, for this very end and intention, explain'd to the *Royal Society*, and which, about fourteen Years fince, I made ufe of in making my Obfervations for the finding the parallax of the Orb of the Earth among the fix'd Stars, which had hardly been poffible any other way, efpecially to avoid all manner of Doubt or Objection ; and that was the Obfervation of fome Star which pafs'd very near the Zenith of the place ; where in a very clear Night there is no Refraction at all ; and this was the way which Monfieur *Picart*, and the Gentlemen of the Royal *Academy* of *France*, have, fince that time, made ufe of in their Obfervation for the finding the difference of Latitude between *Paris* and *Amiens*, which, upon this account, is much more accurate than any of the other ways which before that time had been taken by any, either of the Antients or Moderns who had made this Obfervation : For tho' I confefs we do not certainly know what ways fome of the Antients made ufe of, yet by confidering of the ways they might make ufe of, we may with probability enough conceive, that it was not this way, by obferving the Stars in the Zenith, efpecially fince we do not find that they had any notion of Refraction at all, and therefore 'twas not very probable that they fhould provide againft it, the notion or invention of Refraction being not much before *Ticho Brahe*, and he feems to be the firft that reduc'd it to Rule ; for tho' *Ptolomy* and fome of the Antients did take fome notice of the alterations of the Air, and of fome alterations they caus'd in the appearances of Cæleftial Bodies through them, yet it feem'd to be no more than this, That they conceiv'd that the groffer Air and Vapours near the Horizon did caufe the Cæleftial Bodies to appear greater near the Horizon than near the Zenith, which was a miftake likewife ; for neither does the Refraction of the Air any ways caufe fuch an appearance, but rather the contrary ; nor is there indeed really any fuch appearance, if it be more curioufly inquir'd into, it being only Optical, and rifing from the imaginary greater diftance of the Sun and Moon near the Horizon, where the known diftances upon the Earth can be compar'd with them ; for otherwife the Bodies of the Sun and Moon would appear lefs, as is very evident in the vertical *Diameter*, which is fometime a quarter lefs than it ought to be, as any one that will examine the Rifing or Setting Sun, will plainly perceive, by the help of a Telefcope fitted with a Micrometer. Again, The Refraction of the Air elevating the two extream Points of the Horizontal Diameter pretty near perpendicularly in the two Vertical Circles that pafs through thofe Points ; and all thofe Vertical Circles meeting in the Zenith, it follows, that the greater the Refraction of the Atmofphere is, the fhorter will appear the Horizontal Diameter of the Sun or Moon, nor was this Propriety, whether known or not, made ufe of by any before *Ticho Brahe*, tho' ever fince that time it hath been acknowledg'd and verify'd by all Aftronomers, and yet 'tis not agreed upon, what the Proportions of it are ; but a fort of randum Numbers are fet down, of which the true ground is not affign'd, that I know, any where ; and poffibly the thing itfelf in ftrictnefs may be almoft impoffible, being uncertain even in itfelf, and being in a continual ftate of change.

Refraction does not make Bodies to appear bigger near the Horizon.

I need not, I fuppofe, mention the way how to come by the Latitude of a place where the Declination, Altitude and Azymuth is given, that being common and eafily enough known. Nor fhall I need to mention any other difficulties in this Aftronomical way, but rather proceed to the fecond way how to find two places in any Pofition whatfoever, which are diftant from each other a Degree of a great Circle of the Earth, or any other lefs affignable part without making any Obfervation of any Cæleftial Body ; which is that which I call the Geographical or Mechanical way.

This Mechanical or Geographical Probleme then may, by various Means and Inftruments, be perform'd according to the particular way that is made ufe of for effecting thereof ; the thing that is to be found being the inclination of the Perpendiculars of two diftinct places one to another. This, as I told you, was moft certainly found by finding where thofe Perpendiculars pointed

The Geographical way of meafuring a Degree.

in

in the Heavens, by seeing how far the Zenith of the place was distant from this or that Star which pass'd the Meridian, the Zenith of the place being the continuation or upper end of the Perpendicular or Plumb-line of the place. This also may be found by Calculation from the height of the Sun or fix'd Stars taken in any known Azymuth. But the Geographical ways are by the level Lines of any two distant places, which level Lines are Lines at right Angles, to the Perpendiculars of those places; and in this way the Query is to find what Angle the two level Lines make with one another, or with the Perpendiculars of the distant places. This way, were the Ray of Vision from place to place a true straight Line, might, by convenient Instruments, be made the easiest and the most exact; and it were possible this way to determine the quantity of a Degree even to a single Third, which would come within two Foot by measure, according to the quantity of a Degree collected from the best Observations which have yet been made. So that could the Mensuration of the distance be made as exact as the Observation of the level Line, or the certainty of the magnitude of the Body of the Earth, or of the quantity of a Degree, it might be adjusted to all imaginable exactness; and since there are some places upon the Earth which may be seen more than a Degree, nay, more than two Degrees distant, it were possible to determine it within one single Foot: For, First, By means of the level of Water, an Instrument to take the level Line may be made of any length desir'd, so as to be able to distinguish Thirds of a Degree; and since by the help of Telescopes, which may be made and easily used in a Horizontal Posture almost to any length, the sight can distinguish the parts of the Object to as great a certainty, there need to be no deficiency in the exactness of such Observations, were the Rays of Vision true right Lines. And by the same means of long Telescope Sights, the distances between such two Stations might as accurately be measur'd, as I shall mention by and by. There are various ways of performing it this way, mention'd in several Authors, but I think none more plain and easy than these I shall instance in.

As, First, From a very high Cliff adjoining to the Sea, the Altitude of the same above the level of the Sea being exactly measur'd, the Angle that the Perpendicular makes with the visual Ray, that touches the Horizon of the Sea, must be exactly observ'd; or else the Angle that the visual Ray makes with the Horiozantal or level Line; for in both those Cases the Effect or Consequence is the same; for the level Line being at right Angles with the Perpendicular of the aforesaid Angles so found, must be the complement of *Table* IX. *Fig.* 4. the other to a right Angle. As for instance, let CD represent the Surface of the Sea, A the Center of the Earth, BC the Cliff, the height of whose highest Point B above the level of the Sea is exactly known by measure, the Angle ABD is found by the Plumb-line BC, and the Telescope BG directed at the Horizon of the Sea D, or the complement thereof the Angle FBG is found by the level EF, and Telescope BG, having therefore the Angle ABD by Observation, the complement there of ABD is likewise given and in the same manner, if FBG be given by Observation, BAD equal to it is also given. Now by the common Tables of Secants you may from the length of BC and the Angle DBF or DAB easily deduce the Diameter of the Earth; for as the difference between the Radius and the Secant of the Angle at A is to the Radius, so is the height of the Cliff BC, to the Semidiameter of the Earth. I could have instanc'd in several other ways of finding the Diameter of the Earth from the knowledge of these two, of which *Cassati* in his *Terra Machinis Mota*, gives a great many, some of them complicated enough, but I mention this as being the most facile and simple way that can be thought upon, there being hardly any difficulty at all, either in the Instruments necessary either for the observing the Angle, or of measuring the height above the level of the Sea, or in computing the Consequence when the Experiment is made, or of finding the Meridian Line or Azymuth or Distance or Latitude, Longitude, or the like; which are necessary to be observ'd in other ways, and that with great accurateness, I thought the best to mention. So that one would imagine there could not possibly be any other way to equalize it for this purpose.

But

But what I mention'd to you heretofore to be the incumbrance and per-plexity of all Astronomical Observations, *viz.* the Refraction, or rather In-flection of the Air, is abundantly more considerable, and perplexing here in-somuch that how plausible soever this may seem, yet this inconvenience in-terferring makes it almost wholly impossible: For the Rays of Vision which run as Tangents to the Surface of the Sea, are by the Refractiveness or ra-ther Inflectiveness of the vaporous Air near the Horizon rais'd much higher than they ought to be, if they proceeded in direct Lines from the Eye or Sight of the Instrument at the top of the Cliff to the Horizontal Point D of the Surface: Which Refraction or Inflection, were it also certain, might, by some trials, be remedied and reduced to a Rule, but that being so extreamly uncertain, and various, and differing almost with every blast of Wind, and every several Degree of Heat and Cold, Driness, or Moisture, Gravity, or Levity of the Air, the Effects thereby produc'd are so various and uncertain, that 'tis impossible to reduce them to any certain Rule.

However, for variety, I shall mention a second Geographical way which may be made use of for this purpose, *viz.* from two very high Hills which are very far remov'd from each other, as suppose 60, 80, 100, or more Miles, which yet are so situated, as that by means of a great Plain between, or else of an interjacent Sea, they are visible each to other, whereof there are many in-stances to be found in the World, and even in *England, Scotland,* and *Wales.* Let the inclination of the common visual Ray between them be exactly ob-serv'd with the Perpendiculars or level Lines of both those Places, and thence deduce the true inclinations of the two Perpendiculars, or the two level Lines of those places to one another, whereby you will certainly have the quantity of the Angle of the Perpendiculars at the Center of the Earth, or the quantity of the Arch of a great Circle of the Earth that is interjacent between those places; then if the distance be over a Plain upon the Land by measuring the interjacent Space by Chains, Rods, Wheels, or Triangles of observation made from place to place, you will obtain the distance between those Stations, and consequently the Magnitude or Semidiameter of the Globe of the Earth. Or if the space interjacent be over the Sea, then by measuring a certain length of Ground at right Angles with the visual Ray, if it may be upon either of the said Hills, which is visible from the other of those Hills, and by exact Observation finding all the Angles of such a Tri-angle, you will easily and very exactly, and much truer than by any Mensu-ration made between them, obtain the same thing as the other way, namely, the true distance between them, and consequently the Magnitude or Semi-diameter of the Globe of the Earth; for instance, in the Figure, let B and C represent the tops of two very high Hills distant from each other, by com-pute about threescore common *English* Miles, which are notwithstanding by means of a large Vale or Sea between them, visible to each other. By In-struments as before, find at B the Angle ABC of the Perpendicular AB with the visual Ray BC, and by Observations at C find the said inclination of the Perpendicular AC, and visual Ray CB, namely the Angle ACB; then either by an actual Mensuration of the Space or Distance BC, or by Triangles of Observation in *Snellius* his way, or else by measuring a certain length, as BD on the top of one of the Hills, as B, whose extreams B a D are visible to each other, and to the Point C of the other Hill, find any two of the Angles at B C and D, and from thence find the side BC, and having before all the Angles A, B, and C, you will easily find the Sides AB and AC which are the distances of those places from the Center of the Earth, and if the space in-terjacent be Sea, you will easily obtain the side AE, which is the Semidiame-ter of the Globe, or Sphærical Surface of the Sea, and consequently the true length of a Degree of a great Circle on the Sea, which, for Navigation, is the principal thing sought, and thence also collaterally may easily be found the several heights of those Hills B and C above that level, and the like. But this way, as the former, is also incumbr'd with the Refraction, or ra-ther Inflection of the Air; so that the Line BC is not really a straight Line, but a crooked or bended Line, and so those places B and C are visible to each other much farther than they really could be, were there no inflection in the

The inconve-niences of this and the like ways from Re-fraction.

A second Geo-graphical way.

Table IX. Fig. 5.

This way has its inconveni-ences.

Air,

Air, but that the Ray that touch'd the Sea interjacent, did always proceed straight.

Micrography.
p. 217.

We need not therefore trouble our selves either with those, or with any other of the like ways, tho' there are divers to be found dispers'd here and there in Authors, and more of that kind might be thought of, but they will be all in vain, since the Refraction or Inflection of the Ray near the Horizon, upon the exact observation of which so much is built, do so confound the truth of the Angle, that since great things are to be calculated from little, 'twill be in vain to think of coming at any possible certainty by the ways of Observation. Now, that this is not *Gratis dictum*, besides what I my self have observ'd, and Publish'd at large in the Year 1664, let me acquaint you with what the *French* have lately taken notice of in their way of trying by a Level: They observ'd then, that an Object which at break of Day appear'd in the Horizon, or Level-line, or a little above it, a little after Sun-rising appear'd below it; and the same appearance they found in the Evening, for the Object before Sun-set appear'd below the Level, which soon after Sun-set would appear in it or above it; insomuch, that in half an Hours time the difference has been observ'd to be no less than three Minutes, which must needs cause a very great Error in the computation of the Magnitude of a Degree, and consequently the Magnitude of the Earth; for if there be three or four Miles Error in the space of less than a quarter of a Degree, it will amount to an Error of a fifth or sixth part of a Degree in a whole Degree, and so a vast Error in the Compass of the Earth. The cause of which appearances they

*The cause of
this Inflection.*

conceive to be the Cold of the Night condensing the Vapours, and so making them to descend towards the Earth, leaving the higher parts of the Air more pure, thin and serene, which makes an Inflection of the Ray which is to pass obliquely through Media of such differing density, and so the Refraction or Inflection is the less. But yet, even then the Ray doth not pass without a considerable Refraction or Inflection; for which they give us Experiments of two Observations both made at Noon Day, by which the same Persons not only found there was a Refraction, but that there was a considerable difference between one Day and another Day at Noon as to their Refractions. To this purpose in the Summer time, at Noon, in a clear Day, they observ'd the Tower of *Montlehery* from the top of the Tower of *Nostre Dame* at *Paris*, and found the Foot of the said Tower of *Montlehery* to appear exactly in the Level or Horizontal Line; but some Days after, at Noon also, observing the top of *Nostre Dame* Tower from the Foot of the Tower of *Montlehery*, they found it to be 11′. 30″. below the level; but comparing the measur'd distance of those two places, and examining from the measure of a Degree, found the other way nameless by the Perpendicular Stars, they found that the Angle ought to have been 13′. 30″. which is two whole Minutes difference in the distance of 81894 *English* Feet, or about fifteen Miles and an half; by which we may plainly see what exactness is to be expected from any Mensuration of the Earth that should be this way made; and therefore there can be no more certain way of determining the Magnitude of the Earth by measure, than the way I first of all propos'd, and that was by observing the Stars near the Zenith.

*The Use and
Benefit of Re-
fraction or In-
flection.*

Now, tho' this inflective quality of the Air be a great incumbrance and confusion of Astronomical Observations made both at Sea and Land, yet is it not without some considerable benefit to Navigation; and indeed in some cases the benefit thereby attain'd is much greater than would be the benefit of of having the Ray proceed in an exact straight Line. I shall not need to instance in the Observation made by the *Hollanders* that wintered upon *Nova Zembla*, who, by means hereof, found that the Night in that place shortned no less than a whole Month, which must needs be a very great Comfort to all such places as lie very far towards the North or South Poles, where the length of the Night, and want of seeing the Sun, cannot chuse but be very tedious and irksome. But then it may be said, that this benefit is only to a very small part of the World, and that the most inconsiderable and least frequented of all, by reason of the extremity of the Cold, and want of other necessary accommodations for the use of Man. But yet we find that some of those Northern Parts have, of late Years, been frequented by Navigation not without very confiderable benefit and advantage in the returns, and may, in time, be very much more, when the Induftry and Skill of future Undertakers fhall difcover Paffages that way to the *Indies* or South Sea, which for feveral Reafons, I conceive, may in time be effected, and with very great advantage frequented: But this only by the bye. The great advantage I confider therein, is the firft difcovery of Land upon the Sea ; for by means hereof the tops of Hills and high Lands are raifed up into the Air fo as to be difcoverable feveral Leagues farther off on the Sea than they would be, were there no fuch Refraction ; which is of great benefit to Navigators for fteering their Courfe in the Night when they approach near Land, and likewife for directing them in the Day-time much more certainly than the moft exact Cæleftial Obfervations could do by the help of an uninflected Ray, efpecially in fuch places as they have no foundings.

And I doubt not but that by fome Obfervations carefully made; the Inflections of the Air may be reduc'd to exactnefs enough, for feveral forts of Terreftrial Obfervations which may be of great ufe in the practice of Navigation, tho' I very much doubt whether it will ever be exact enough for determining the meafure of a Degree, and confequently that of the Earth ; the ufe that I chiefly intend of this difcovery may be for determining the diftance of a Ship at Sea by means hereof from a Land fo raifed : The way how I conceive this may be effected is thus. Firft, The defcent of the true Level-line below the apparent Level-line, for feveral diftances, muft be known by Calculation, the true Level being a Circular Line upon a Sphærical Superficies of the Earth, and the apparent Level-line being a tangent Line, it will be eafy enough from the knowledge of the Earths Semidiameter to find this Defcent.

To difcover a Ships diftance at Sea.

Now the Semidiameter of the Earth from the moft accurate Obfervations that have been yet made being 20923500$\frac{4}{3}$ Feet, or 3962$\frac{3}{4}$ Miles, and 180 Feet of 5280, which is our Statute *Englifh* Mile, it will follow that the true Level-line will be eafily found by the help of a Table of Secants ; the Defcent below the Horizontal Line for any determinate diftance being always to the Semidiameter of the Earth, as the excefs of the Secant of the diftance above the Radius is to the Radius. But becaufe this Statute Mile is of no ufe in Navigation, Navigation always accounting the fixtieth part of a Degree to be a Mile, and three of thofe Miles to be a League, it will be neceffary to reduce the Mile, we account by, to the meafure of a Degree found, accounting it to be a full fixtieth part of the length thereof which is found, and accordingly ought to be the Meafures and Divifions of the Log-line. Now, by the aforefaid Obfervations there being no lefs than 365184 *Englifh* Feet in a whole Degree, there will be 6086$\frac{4}{10}$ Feet in a fixtieth part thereof, and therefore the meafure of every fuch Mile ought to be accounted 1014 Fathom two Foot and $\frac{4}{10}$, and confequently a League will be 18259, or 18260 Feet, or 3043 Fathom and two Foot; the Defcent then for fuch Leagues will be as follows, for one fuch League, 7, 976688 Feet, or to make ufe of round numbers eight Feet, at two Leagues diftance thirty two Foot, at three Leagues feventy two Foot, at four Leagues one hundred and thirty Foot ; or if you will reckon by Minute Miles, then the defcent of one Mile is 10$\frac{3}{4}$ Inches almoft, at two Miles will be three Foot and an half, at three Miles eight Foot, at four Miles fourteen Feet, or thereabout; at five twenty two Foot and an half, at fix Miles thirty two Foot, at feven Miles forty four Foot, at eight Miles fifty fix Foot, at nine Miles feventy two Foot. Now the ufe that may be made of this knowledge I conceive to be this, that when a Land is approach'd by afcending the Shore or Maft with a fmall Perfpective Glafs, 'till the Surf of the Sea upon the Shore be difcover'd by knowing the height of the Eye, that fo difcovers it from the Surface of the Water by the Ship, a much nearer and truer compute of the diftance thereof can be made than by any other way yet practis'd : But this only here by the bye, becaufe hereafter when I come to fpeak of that Subject, I fhall mention feveral other feafable ways of doing it. I here only mention it upon the account of the Refractivenefs of the Air, which tho' it fpoil the accuracy of Obfervations for the meafure of a Degree, yet in fuch Obfervations as thefe it may ferve well enough, at leaft 'till better and more accurate be made ufe of.

Of reduceing the meafure of a Mile.

Thefe

These two Fundamentals concerning the true Figure and Shape of the Earth, and likewise of its Magnitude being acquir'd, it remains in the next place to find out some means to distinguish every Point or Part of the Surface of this Globular Body in respect of any other ; we are therefore to inquire what helps are to be found that are useful for this purpose : For upon the Surface of a perfect Sphærical Body, there is no one point but has the very same Respect to the whole Surface thereof, that any other Point hath ; as suppose the Sphærical Body were of Chrystal or Glass perfectly Polish'd and Uniform, no one Point has any Mark or Characteristick to distinguish from any other, and a Point being once lost, 'tis impossible to find the same again, tho' it be turn'd a thousand times ; because there is suppos'd to be no one Point of it that differs from any other, and they cannot be distinguish'd or measur'd from, and every point may be said to be the middle of the whole Circumference ; and thence it is that the People of every Country and Place have thought themselves to be in the middle of the Earth, and all the Neighbouring Ambient Countries to lie towards the Extremities. Which Opinion always hath and always will possess the Minds of ignorant People, 'till by Learning and Art they are better inform'd ; for seeing an extension of Land or Seas round about them on every side, and seeing the Sky whelm'd over them like a Dish or Hemisphere, the middle of which seems to be just over their Heads, and the Brims to touch the Earth and Seas at a great distance, they cannot without much thinking and considering (which few People care to do, especially in matters which they think not of immediate concern) they cannot chuse but be impos'd on by the appearance to their Sense, which seems so to represent it ; and if so at Land, much more does it appear so on the Sea where there is no sight of Land, when the Superficial Parts of the Sphærical Surface have no remaining visible marks more than the Chrystal Ball. On the Land indeed, and in sight of Land there are many obvious helps to find and distinguish one place from another, and the Positions of one from all the other that are visible and accessible, as Hills, Vales, Mountains, Woods, &c. But the Surface of the Sea wants all those, and has nothing but a fluctuating changing Surface, which way soever you look 'tis all alike, you know not which way you go forwards or backwards, whether the Wind blows for you or against you, or the Current sets you near to or further from your Port ; which was the cause why the Antients never durst venture out of the sight of Land but went along the Shores, they being not then able to distinguish, especially in cloudy or close Weather, which way lay the Quarters of the Earth or Azymuth. And indeed before Astronomy was known, the very Quarters of the Wind were not distinguish'd with respect to the Heavens, but only with respect to the Countries from whence they seem'd to come. Thence we find that they call'd one *Vulturnus*, another *Phænicius*, a third *Africus*, *Olympius*, *Thracius*, *Hellespontius*, and the like, which were the Names of the Countries from whence they seem'd to come.

But the Diligence and Inquisitiveness of succeeding Ages has furnish'd us with better and more universal ways of distinguishing and naming the Quarters of the Winds, or the Azymuthes, or Divisions of the Horizon, and Positions of the Parts of the Surface of the Earth, and not only so, but of determining the distance of any place from the Points certainly fix'd upon this Globe of the Earth.

Of the ways yet known to discover the place of a Ship at Sea. I shall therefore in the next place consider what means there are hitherto found and made use of for dividing, and distinguishing, and defining of the Superficial Parts of this Globe of the Earth, so as certainly to know any one Point of the Surface of it, from any other determin'd, whether upon Land or Sea ; for that there are no two Points of the whole Surface but that have some ways or other their distinct Characteristiks.

There have been various ways invented of performing this Effect ; those that are thought of the best, and so apply'd at present to use, may be reduc'd into two Heads, and these are Cælestial or Terrestial, namely, some Respects or Aspects of Cælestial Bodies, or Situation, Substance, Qualification, Form, &c. of some Terestrial Bodies.

The

The Cæleſtial are ſuch as are afforded by the Motion or Poſition of the Cæleſtial Bodies, *viz.* the Sun, Moon and Stars.

The Terreſtrial are either, 1*ſt.* Magnetical, by the help of the Compaſs, or Magnetical Needle : Or, 2*dly*, Computatory, by keeping account of the Courſe and Diſtance, ſail'd from a known place : Or, 3*dly*, By ſounding the depth of the Sea, and examining the Subſtances that are to be found at the bottom : Or, 4*thly*, By the Sight and Proſpects of ſome high and eminent Places which may be ſeen at a great diſtance upon the Sea, and from thence collecting the Poſition bearing and diſtance from them.

The Cæleſtial, and the two former of the Terreſtrial are of uſe in all places, the two laſt are more particular, and reſtrain'd only to ſuch places where ſoundings are to be found ; for there be many places where there is no Bottom to be ſounded, and many others where no part of Land can be diſcover'd ; in which Caſes recourſes muſt be had to the more general ways, by the Heavens, the Needle, the Courſe, and Diſtance.

The helps which the Heavens afford for diſtinguiſhing of places on the Earth *The Cæleſtial* either are, 1*ſt.* Their Poſition in reſpect of the Earth : Or, 2*dly*, Their *ways.* Motion. By their Poſition they ſerve as helps to find the Latitude of a Place ; and by their Motion they may, in time, ſerve to diſcover the Longitude.

Firſt, By their Poſition they help us to diſcover, that this vaſt Globe on *By their Poſiti-* which we live, and which ſeems ſo fix'd and ſteadfaſt, is mov'd round (like a *ons.* Globe which is commonly made to repreſent it) on an *Axis*, or an imaginary Line that paſſes from ſide to ſide through the very Center thereof ; or like a two Headed Top upon two imaginary Points, which are Diametrically oppoſite to each other upon the Surface thereof ; each Revolution of which is perform'd once in twenty four Hours from Weſt to Eaſt, and thereby each part of the Earth, according to its Situation or Diſtance upon the Surface from one or other of thoſe two Points, moves or is mov'd in a Circle round the ſaid Axis greater or leſs, according to its diſtance from the neareſt of them ; ſo that all the Parts that lie at equal, and the greateſt diſtance from them both are mov'd in the greateſt Circle of all the reſt. By means hereof is diſcover'd, Firſt, The Poſitions of Places one to another, in reſpect of their Revolution ; that is, the Azymuths or Quarters of the Horizon, or uſual Limit of the Heavens ; for by means hereof the Cæleſtial Bodies firſt begin to appear at one Quarter of the Horizon, and to croſs the Heavens over us, and to Deſcend, and Set, and Diſappear on the other ; whence the former is call'd the riſing part of the Heavens, and the other the ſetting part, and the middle part between theſe two are call'd the Meridional, and the Polar, which is either North or South ; and then an imaginary ſtraight Line ſuppos'd drawn between them either upon the Earth, or in the Heavens, is call'd the Meridian of that place where this Suppoſition is made.

Now that end of this North or South Line which goes towards that Quarter of the Heaven where the Star is in the extreamity of the Tail of the little Bear, near which is the Polar Point in the Heavens, is call'd the North, and the other end is call'd the South. Now, one or the other of theſe is always viſible both at Land and Sea in all parts of the Globe in a clear Night ; but the Polar Points of the Earth, either in the North or South, have not yet been diſcover'd.

This North and South Line then is diſcoverable by means of the Heavens in every point of the Surface of the Earth, and by means of that, the Poſition of Places with reſpect to them, is eaſily known, and thence alſo all the other Quarters or Parts of the Horizon of any Place are eaſily diſcover'd ; for a Line imagin'd drawn in the Plain of the Horizon through any place, cutting the former Line at right Angles, points out in the Limb of the Horizon, the Eaſt and Weſt,

C c c c c c

Theſe

These two Lines diftinguifh the Horizon or vifible Limb of the Heavens into four equal Quarters or Quadrants, *viz.* The firft between the North and Eaft ; the fecond between the Eaft and South ; the third between the South and Weft ; and the fourth between the Weft and North.   Now each of thefe Quadrants may be, and ufually are fubdivided into leffer Divifions.   The Sea-men generally content themfelves in Steerings and taking Bearings, with a Divifion of each of thefe into eight parts, fo that the whole Horizon is di-vided into thirty two Parts, which they call Points, becaufe they are pointed out by their Compafs or Winds, becaufe of their taking notice in which of thofe Points the Winds blow ; the firft are the principal Points, *viz.* N. S. E. W., the Lines that divide thefe four Quadrants in half are the half Winds or Points, namely, NE. SE. SW. NW. ; the eight Points in the middle of thefe are the Quarter Winds, *viz.* NNE. ENE. ESE. SSE. SSW. WSW. WNW. NNW. all thefe together make fixteen, and thefe being again fub-divided into halves make fixteen more, which are the by Winds, *viz.* N. b E. N. b W. S. b E. S. b W. E. b S. E. b N. W. b S. W. b N. and N. E. b N. N. E. b E. S. W. b. S. S. W. b W.   Thefe again they do fubdivive into four Parts in their Accounts caft up, or protraction of their Courfe.   Aftronomo-ers divide the Circuit of Horizon as they do all other, into Degrees, Mi-nutes, *&c.*   And fo do Mariners in obfervations of Amplitudes and Varia-tions of the Compafs, tho' not in the Bearings of Lands and Iflands.

Now, thus far the Heavens only ferve for determining the Pofition of any Place whatfoever, with refpect to the bearing of thofe Polar Points of the Earth I but now mention'd, but fhew not at all how far they are remov'd or diftant from either of thofe Points.   This alfo the Magnetical Needle or Compafs does in part difcover, but not wholly without Rectification by the help of the Heavens, as I fhall, in its proper place, explain.   But this does little as to its determining the pofitive Point of this Place upon the Surface of this Globe, but only by the account of the Courfe Sail'd, 'tis known pretty near which way the Place lies, from whence the departure is made, and which way the Courfe lies to the Place bound to.   Some further information therefore is requifite to determine the diftance from thefe Polar Points, or from an imaginary Circle incompaffing the Globe, lying at equal diftance be-tween them, call'd the Æquinoctial-Line, or more commonly the Line ; of which I fhall fpeak more hereafter.

This then the Heavens afford an help for, namely, by their Pofition or height above the Horizon, or the vifible Limb of the Sky which feemeth to touch the Earth ; but before I fpeak of this I fhall a little further explain the true notion of the Horizon.

Of the true no-tion of the Ho-rizon.   The Horizon, or, as the Seamen call it, the Orifon, at Sea is the extream edges of the Sea which the Sky feems to touch, which, in clear Weather, is very eafy to be feen in the Day-time, like a black Line bounding the Sky, and may be alfo plainly enough difcover'd in a very clear Star-light-Night, efpe-cially when the Moon is pretty well inlighten'd, or in the time of the Twi-light, when as yet the Stars are very vifible ; but when the Air is thick and hazy, tho' the Sun, Moon, or Stars may be difcover'd when they are a pretty way above it, yet the Horizon cannot be diftinguifh'd, but the Sea and Sky gradually mix with one another, fo as no Obfervation can then be made of it, there being no diftinct vifible feparation.

This vifible edge of the Sea is nearer or further off, according as the Eye that fees it is nearer to, or higher from the level Surface of the Sea ; the pro-portions of which one to the other I hinted the laft time, but fhall now fome-what farther explain.

The fenfible Horizon Mathematically confider'd, is an imaginary Plain touching the Globe of the Earth or Sea in any Place or Point thereof, which is to be confider'd ; and this Plain is fuppos'd to be extended to the extrea-mities of the univerfe every way ; fo that when any Star or Cæleftial Body on the Eaftern fide of the Meridian appears in the Plain thereof, it is Rifing, and when they appear in the Weftern fide thereof, they are Setting ; or ac-cording to the Copernican Hypothefis, the Horizon is an imaginary indefi-nite Plain, touching the Globe of the Earth at the place defign'd, which,

together

together with the motion of the Globe, is carry'd round once in a Day, and so twice in that time passes over the Cælestial Bodies that lie in its Zone; when the Easter-most side passes them, they are said to be Rising, and when the Wester-most, they are said to be Setting, both which Hypothesis equally solve the Phænomena; and upon this speculative notion of the Horizon, there is also suppos'd a Rational Horizon, which is also an imaginary indefinite Plain passing through the Center of the Earth, and parallel to the former, namely, at the distance of the Semidiameter of the Earth; which distance being extended to the fixt Stars, becomes wholly insensible, being view'd from the Earth, and so as to them, and even to the Planets superior or farther distant from us than the Sun, they become wholly the same, and the sensible and rational Horizon are one and the same imaginary Plain or Circle in the Heavens; but in the Moon especially, and in the Planets nearer to us than the Sun, they are, by curious and nice Observation, sometimes discoverable: But those Speculations more concern Astronomy, than Geography or Navigation, and therefore I shall say no more of them at present, but rather speak of a third Horizon, which is a real and visible Circle, and that which Navigators call the Orison.

The sensible Horizon, as it concerns Navigation, is not a Plain, nor a Sphærical, nor Conical Surface, but rather an imaginary *conoeidical* Surface touching the Sphærical Surface of the Sea in a Circle, which Circle is nearer or farther off from the Eye, which is in the Apex of the Conoeid, according as the Eye is lower or higher rais'd into the Air above the Surface of the Sea, and according as the inflective quality of the Air is less or greater; and from the same causes that the distance thereof from the Eye is diminish'd or augmented, does the imaginary Limits or Base of it, which is a Circle in the Heavens, descend lower and lower below the Rational, or notionally sensible Horizontal Line, or imaginary Circle in the Heavens. This is a third Horizon differing from both the other, and below them both in the Heavens; so that to the Eastwards the Stars and Planets appear to have pass'd the Nautical or Mariners Orison some time before they arrive at the Speculative or Notional Horizons, and in the West they have pass'd the Notional Horizons some time before they touch or arrive at the Nautical and Visible Orison. So that all those Observations which are made at Sea, either for finding the Azymuths, or for discovering the variation of the Compass, or for Altitudes, or the like, are every one of them Erroneous, and there ought to be a rectifying thereof made: For, First, How much the said Line appears below the true Level or Tangent Line of the place, by so much less is the Altitude of the Cælestial Body taken from it, than what it is taken at; and the Amplitudes in an Oblique Sphere will thereby also be considerably augmented more than what they should have been by the common Theory of the Sphere, Calculating as from a true Horizon; for all the Geometrical Rules that are made concerning the Notional Horizons, are produc'd from the consideration of the Globe, and of the Proprieties and Affections thereof, and of Plains either passing through the Center, or touching the superficies, and from the Hypothesis that the Rays of Light pass in straight Lines from the Cælestial Body to any Point of the Surface of the Earth, in which they suppose the Eye of the Observer to be plac'd; but because the Eye is never known to be exactly in the Superficies of the Surface of the Sea, but at some height above it; therefore the visible Orizon of the Navigator, if the Rays of Light were straight, would be a Conical Surface, and not a plain; and the higher the Eye is rais'd the sharper will be the Cone. But because the Rays of Light are not really straight in their passage through the upper and lower parts of the Atmosphere, but are by the Inflection of the unequal Density of the parts of that Medium inflected into Curves, whose Concave side is towards the Earth, therefore the Superficies of every visible Orizon is not a Conical, but a Conoeidical Surface, in the Apex of which is plac'd the Eye and the edge of the Sea, which is a Circle upon it, the Center of which is in the Perpendicular below the Eye, and thereof is very near as much below the Surface of the Sea under the Eye, as the Eye is rais'd above it; and as this Orizon on the Earth is a lesser Circle, and not a greater Circle, so the Basis of this

Conoeidical

Conoeidical Body, in the Heavens is not a great Circle, as is the Rational Horizon, but a leffer parallel Circle below it, and that fo much the more below it, as the Eye is higher elevated above the Surfaces of the Sea, and as the inflective quality of the Air is greater.

Now, if we firft confider the Rays of Light as ftraight Lines, we fhall find the Angles of the feveral Conical Superficies adapted to the feveral heights of the Eye, as I have already mention'd, and thence the diftance of Objects may be ghefs'd where they are difcoverable; but that which I here mention it for is in order to find the true Situation of any place upon the Sea, in refpect of the two Polar Points where no Land is difcoverable, which I fhall next fhew you is difcoverable by the Heavens, by knowing the height of the Cæleftial Bodies above the true Plain of the Horizon, or as Navigators commonly above the Line, they call the Orifon. And I have been fomewhat the longer upon this Difcourfe of the Orifon, becaufe it feems to be the Foundation of all the Cæleftial Obfervations that are made at Sea, and if that be Erroneous, then all the Obfervations will be fo too. It will therefore be neceffary to have the true Theory thereof, both for Latitudes and Amplitudes, or Azymuths; I fhall therefore add one Obfervation concerning the Mariners Orifon, and fo conclude this prefent Difcourfe.

Whence the Looming or Glaring of the Sea.

The Obfervation then is this, That there are fome Conftitutions of the Air, near the Surface of the Sea, that do really elevate the Orifon above the true Horizon or Level-line, and that is at fuch times as the Sea is faid by the Sea-men to *Loom* and *Glare*, as if it were Smooth'd and Polifh'd, whereby the Surface of the Sea feems to be lifted up above its own level Surface into the Atmofphere incompaffing it: And this I have often taken notice of, and as near as I could ghefs from what Obfervations I was able to make; I judge it to proceed from a denfe, and, as it were, foggy Air which lieth equally fpread upon the Surface of the Sea, not extending above ten or twelve Foot, or there about, above the fame, and there terminating in a kind of Level, the Air above it being perfectly clear and tranfparent, but this under Air having a Fogginefs or Hazinefs in it, nothing can be feen through it but only what appears above it; fo that at a diftance (tho' nothing of it can be perceiv'd at the Ship) it appears to coalefce with the very Sea, and the Surface of this feems to be the Surface of the Water; fo that by this means the Mariners Orifon inftead of being below the true Horizon, is really rais'd above it; and confequently Altitudes taken from that will be too low, and additions ought to be made to the Altitudes found, to bring them nearer to the true Horizon. Now, how to rectify this and the other Irregularities of the Orifon, I fhall fome other time give an account.

THe *Author having mentioned in the foregoing Difcourfe feveral Methods that have been propofed for finding and fettling an univerfal Standard for Meafure, I thought it not improper to infert part of a Lecture read about* 1683 *upon that Subject, and omitting the beginning of it, which treats only of the feveral unfuccefsful ways yet attempted, the reft of the Difcourfe is as follows.* R. W.

A new Standard of Meafure propos'd.

WHat I have farther to add, as to the finding a Natural Univerfal Standard for Meafure, is a Conception of my own, of a way differing from any other way whatfoever that I have ever heard of, which, I conceive will afford a Natural Standard for Weight and Meafure at all times, and in all places, and which, I conceive, will not be very difficult to perform, if trial be made with convenient Care and Accuratenefs; not that I pretend to difcover any new Thing or Propriety which none have ever obferv'd before, no, 'tis that which all fee and all know, and as trivial as the pendulous vibrating Motion, which, in Contempt, hath been call'd Swing Swangs, tho' the Application and Ufe of it, found by *Galileo*, hath fince prov'd of fuch excellent ufe; and poffibly this alfo which I fhall mention may not be unimproveable to much better ufes than I fhall now mention.

It

It is I doubt not sufficiently known to all present, that all fluid Bodies whatsoever from the *Homogeneity* of their Texture and *Heterogeneity* to the incompassing fluid *Medium*, have a power of Conglobation or forming themselves, when in small parcels into Globular Bodies, and that the smaller they are and the less difference of weight, the nearer they approach to a perfect Globular Figure, and the bigger and more differing the contain'd, and containing Fluids are, the more doth the form of the contain'd differ from that perfect Sphærical Figure, and there is one certain quantity of every simple Fluid, which, in some certain *Medium*, will make the Conglobated Figure to be flatted or ovall'd; so that the longer Diameter to the shorter shall bear a certain assign'd proportion; for instance, to take the most remarkable, namely, 2. to 1. I conceive then, that this quantity being certainly found, and most accurately measur'd, will afford a natural and perpetual Standard of measure; for instance, let *Quicksilver* perfectly depurated, and *Rain*, or *Distill'd Water* be the two Fluids; I say, there is a certain quantity of *Quicksilver* which, in such *Water* will be form'd into an ovall'd or flatted Body, so that the Horizontal Diameter to the Perpendicular shall be as 2. to 1. This longer Diameter I make a Primitive and Natural Standard of length, and the weight of this Body of *Mercury* so ovall'd, I make the Primitive Sandard for Weight; the same may be done with any other Fluid.

This may be also done by purely refin'd *Gold* or *Silver*, whose Purity may be found by the proportion of weight it beareth to Rain-water; for if a certain quantity of Gold be melted and pour'd out upon a perfectly smooth and horizontal Surface of a Stone, this will form itself into an Oval Body, whose Horizontal Diameter to the Perpendicular, will be as 2. to 1.

The same may be done with any other Metal besides Gold, but only we cannot be so sure of the purity and unmixedness of the Metal, as we may be of Gold.

It would be too long now to mention the various ways there may be used for exactly finding, determining and measuring this Figure, but I design at some other time to entertain the Society with the Experiment and Trial thereof, which will make all things more evident and plain.

THe way mentioned at the end of this Discourse of exactly measuring the Figure and Shape of any Body, I find described in another Paper, read December *the third*, 1683. *and is as follows.*

R. W.

The knowledge of Nature and Art is advanc'd by the discovery of such things, as serve like Engins or Organs, to make such further Inquisitions in either as the Natural Faculties of Men, without such assistances, are not able to perform; and therefore how trivial and slight soever a thing may seem before the Use and Application thereof be known, especially to such as have no occasion or curiosity for such Inquiries, or who have not consider'd the Consequencies that may be drawn therefrom, yet to such as really have, I doubt not but they will find Reason to think them valuable. Of this Nature were the little Globules of Glass apply'd to the use of Microscopes, from whence have proceeded most of those curious Discoveries made by the inquisitive Mr. *Lieuwenhook.* I could instance in the Pendulum, and several other such Applications of things, in themselves inconsiderable, to proper purposes, which have produc'd admirable Discoveries, which would hardly have been done without them; but that would be too tedious for such an Assembly, who are already well acquainted with them.

That which I shall acquaint you with at present, is an Experiment or Method rather, by which several very considerable Discoveries may be made both in Nature and Art. It is, in short, a way of contracting a very considerable quantity of the Rays of the Sun into a very small Point or Space, the smaller the better, from which they issuing again with great Brightness and Radiancy may be able, by the differing Refraction and Reflection which those

The great use of the Suns Rays let into a dark Room.

D d d d d Rays

Rays suffer in their way, to describe upon a smooth, white plain the true shape of the Body interpos'd between that radiating Point, and that smooth expanded white Plain. This in itself is very plain and obvious, and is very little differing from the way now commonly known, it being no other than the fitly placing one or two Convex Glasses against an hole cut in the Shutter of the Window of a darkn'd Room, so as that the Rays of the Sun may pass in through the same directly and be collected into a Focus, and from thence again spread and diverge into the Room, so to as be cast upon the Table aforesaid. The Experiment itself, tho' I cannot now exhibit, yet there are several of this Honourable Society who have seen and been witnesses of some of its Effects. Tho' there are many more yet behind which I shall hereafter shew, so soon as the Sun comes in the Room I have fit for it.

By this then I discover various motions of the Medium or Air, not otherwise visible, as also the Emanation of Steams out of Bodies of several kinds not otherwise visible ; likewise several other Natural motions of transparent Bodies, not otherwise, that I know of, to be seen.

By this you plainly see the matter of a burning Candle or Lamp, which is dissolv'd by, and mix'd with the Air, to ascend from the same like a great Stream of Water running at the Tail of a Sluce or Bridge, which doth also plainly illustrate the appearances of the Blaze of Comets.

These are some of the uses of it for discovery of the Operations of Nature.

Next, for the uses of it in Art ; it most respects the Art of Painting and Statuary, as by this may be drawn the exact out Lines of any Body that is to be describ'd on a Plain, and these truly as they do appear to the Eye plac'd at convenient distance, as that of a Man's Head, Face, Hands, or Body, in which it is so curious, that every Hair that appears without the solid part of the Head, Hand, or Body, is truly represented in its Place and Magnitude.

By this the out-lines of Birds, Beasts, Shells, Fishes may be taken : As also the true shape of small Plants as they are whole and intire, or the Leaves, Flowers, Seeds, &c. of greater Plants.

By this the true out Lines of a Flower-pot, with all the variety of the Postures of the Flowers that compose it, may be represented and drawn ; all which are very useful for Painters, or such as would draw such Delineations.

By the help of this, and a pair of Compasses, may be truly drawn all Parabolas, Hyperbolas, and Ellipses, which are of good use in projections of the Sphære, Dialling, Perspective, and the like.

There are several other uses that may be made of this Experiment or Method, which I omit at present, 'till I can exhibit again the Experiment.

And I have contracted this Discourse that I might only summ up the Uses and Applications thereof, without spending your time in hearing the Causes and Reasons thereof.

THE following *Discourses were read the later end of the Year* 1684, *and contain several Matters relating to the former Subject of Navigation; there is in the beginning a Repitition of some things formerly treated of, which could not well be struck out, without breaking the thread of the Discourse; and the most part of the Author's Treatises in this Volume, being Lectures read at several times, it was necessary for him to make some Repetition of what had been before said for the better understanding of what was to follow; nor could they have been omitted here without a new Modelling and Epitomizing the whole, which made me rather trespass upon the Reader's Patience, than attempt to Alter or Abridge any thing of the Author's Sense; and indeed I thought it more advisable to give them as he left them, than adventure upon such an undertaking.*

This treats first of the Nature and Generation of a Globular Figure and its Proprieties. Of the Circles of the Terrestrial Globe. Of the Prime Meridian. Of the Parallels. Whether the Perpendiculars respect the Earths Center. Of the Variation, and its unfitness for finding the Longitude. Of the change of the Latitude and Longitude of Places. Why the Circles have been divided into three hundred and sixty Degrees. Of the difference between the Eastern and Western Literati. A new Duodecimal Progression propos'd. Several Maxims laid down, and several ways for finding a true Meridian and the Latitude.

R. W.

I Have, in some former Lectures in this place, explain'd in general the Art of Navigation, shewing by what Helps and Methods, and from what Principles the Navigator may be able to direct his Course through the Ocean to the place design'd, and at any time to be able to know in what part of the Sea his Vessel is Sailing.

For the performing of which I shew'd in general, that it was requisite that *The Requisites for a Navigator* our Navigator should, First, Be very well skill'd in Geography, or the true description of the Earth and Sea, upon the Surface of which he is to make and compute his Course. And, Secondly, That he should be very knowing in all those Particulars, which may serve him for Marks or Directions to know and distinguish the Parts one from another.

In order to understand the description of the Earth more effectually for this purpose, it will be requisite to determine,

First, The Figure of the Body of the Earth, and the several Proprieties *Four things to* belonging to that Figure, that so we may the better be able to comprehend *be determin'd.* the difference between a curve and a plain Superficies, and what Lines will be useful to be drawn or suppos'd on it, and from the knowledge of those be the better able to find and determine,

In the Second place, the Magnitude of this Body by known Measures, *2.* and to examine and prove the Ways and Methods of measuring the same; both such as have been already either experimented or invented, and such others as may be thought of or try'd for the future; for upon a true knowledge of these two are founded all the other Superstructures in this Art; these two cannot be truly and exactly obtain'd without a clear knowledge.

Thirdly, Of the motions of this Body, and what Effects are thereby pro-*3.* duc'd pertinent to this purpose, namely, what Circular and other Lines are thereby design'd, and ought to be understood on the Surface of the Earth.

The motions of this Body are either Total or Partial; the Total are, First, Gravitation. Secondly, Magnetisme. Thirdly, Rotation upon its own Axis. Fourthly, Circumvolution about the Sun Excentrically. Fifthly, Menstrual, Cycloeidation or Undulation. Sixthly, Libration. The Partial are either of the Water or Air; of the Water are, First, The general motion of the Seas, as, First, Currents. Secondly, The Tides, or of Rivers running into the Seas. Of the Air are either constant, or, Secondly, The

The uncertain Winds, and both of them either Moderate or Exceſſive; all which ought, as near as may be, to be brought to a Standard of Menſuration, without which all the Art we hitherto know or make uſe of, will not ſufficiently inable us to keep a true Reckoning or Account of the Ships way in paſſing or croſſing the Seas, or how we change our Situation Eaſtward or Weſtward, eſpecially in reſpect of the fix'd parts of the Earth; for 'tis one thing to meaſure our way through the Superficial Parts of the Body of the Water in which we float, and another thing to know how great a part, and upon what Point or Azymuth we have paſs'd over the Earth at the bottom of the Sea; the parts of the Earth at the bottom remaining fix'd and ſteady, but the Water of the Sea being carry'd various ways, and with differing Velocity over the ſame, in ſeveral parts of it.

4.   Fourthly, The differing Subſtances of which the Superficial Parts of this Body conſiſts, as of Earth, Water, Air, and the ſeveral Extents, Boundaries, and Qualities of each, and how poſited with reſpect to the Cæleſtial Bodies and proper Motions of the Earth; that is, as to Longitude and Latitude, &c. for without the aſſiſtance of Cæleſtial Obſervation, we have not as yet helps ſufficient to diſtinguiſh the Superficial Parts of the Earth one from another, at leaſt not upon the Sea where there are no Land-marks to be diſcover'd.

Having already treated in the foregoing Lectures of the ſeveral Opinions touching the true form of the Earth, I ſhall not now repeat any of them here, but proceed to ſhew ſeveral other Properties thereof neceſſary to be known, in order to the better underſtanding the Subject in Hand, *The Art of Navigation*; and, in the firſt place,

Suppoſing it, as 'tis believ'd by moſt, tho' prov'd by none, to be of a perfect Globular Figure, and conſequently the Surface of the Sea, as well as that of the Land, to be Sphærical, we will in the next place proceed to conſider of the Proprieties of this Body, becauſe 'tis upon the Surface of this Body that all our Voyages and Menſurations are to be made and not upon a Plain; for tho' the level of the Sea doth, to a vulgar Eye, ſeem to be a Plain, and generally moſt common People do believe or ſuppoſe it to be ſo, yet 'tis paſt diſpute that it is Sphæroeidical, and has a Curviture anſwerable to the Curvity of the Superficies of the Earth, tho' it be not ſo eaſily found by the proſpect of the naked Eye.

The properties of a Globular Figure.

And that we may the better find out and examine the Properties thereof, it will be fit to conſider how a Sphærical or Globular Figure is generated. I need not premiſe either Definition, Poſtulata or Axioms for this Explication, becauſe ſo much, as I have here occaſion to mention, will be eaſily enough underſtood without them, and common words of Expreſſion will be ſignificant and defin'd enough for this purpoſe.

A Globular Superficies how generated.

Table IX. Fig. 6.

A Sphærical or Globular Superficies may be conceiv'd to be generated by the Converſion and whole Revolution of a Semiperiphery upon its Diameter; and a Globular Body may be conceiv'd, generated by a whole Revolution of a Semicircle upon its Diameter: As, let ACB repreſent a Diameter biſected at C, and upon the Center C, and diſtance AC. Let ADB repreſent a Semiperiphery, every Point of which is equally diſtant from the Center C; ſuppoſe then this Periphery to be revolv'd round upon the Diameter AB remaining fix'd, this Periphery ſhall deſcribe a Globular or Sphærical Superficies, every Point of which Superficies ſhall be equally diſtant from the Center C; for ſince the Sphærical Superficies is deſcrib'd by the Rotation of the Periphery ADB, no one Point of it can be further from, or nearer to the Center C, than any one Point of the Semiperiphery ADB; but every Point of the Semiperiphery ADB is equally diſtant from the Center C; therefore every Point of the whole Sphærical Surface ſo generated, is equally diſtant from the Center C; this diſtance is always equal to the Semidiameter of the Periphery, *viz.* AC, or CB.

Next,

Next by this Rotation upon the Diameter AB, every Point in the Semiperiphery ADB will defcribe a Circle in the Spherical Surface: All which Circles are parallel to each other ; for fince that any two of them are defcrib'd by two Points of the Semiperiphæry, which two Points retain the fame diftance or place in the Semiperiphery for the whole Revolution, and that That diftance is the fhorteft that can be meafur'd upon the Sphærical Surface, it follows that any two of them will be parallel, and fince one of the two may always be one and the fame Circle, and any other Circle may be the other, it follows. that all thefe Circles, fo defcrib'd, will be parallel to each other **2.**

Thirdly, fuppofing from any number of Points, as E E E, how many foever Perpendiculars, let fall or drawn to the Diameter AB, as EF, EF, EF, which will therefore be parallel to each other, becaufe they are all Perpendicular to the fame Line, and in the fame plain of the Semicircle ADB : By the Rotation of the Semicircle ADB; every one of the Lines EF, EF, DC, &c. will defcribe a Circular Plain, and every one of thefe Plains will have its Center in the Line AB. Thirdly, Every one of thofe Plains will be parallel to each other, becaufe the Lines defcribing them are parallel to each other, becaufe they are at right Angles with the Axis, therefore the imaginary Superficies defcrib'd by them, is a Plain. Next, **3.**

Fourthly, The Diameter AB will be Perpendicular to each of thofe Plains and will pafs the Plain in the Center thereof. **4.**

Fifthly, Thefe Plains will be bigger and bigger the nearer the Perpendicular that defcribes them, is to the Center C ; and the biggeft of all will be that defcrib'd by DC, that being the longeft Perpendicular ; and becaufe DC is equal to AC, therefore the Circles defcrib'd by thofe as Radii, fhall be equal, that is, ADB, &c. and the Circle defcrib'd by the Rotation of DC ; therefore thefe Circles fhall be great Circles, therefore great Circles fhall divide the Sphærical Superficies into two equal Parts, becaufe AD is equal to DB, and confequently the Sphærical Surfaces defcrib'd by the Rotation of them. Therefore all great Circles upon a Globe are equal to one another ; and becaufe ADB is half a great Circle, the Points whereof A and B remain fix'd, whilft the Simiperiphery is revolv'd round ; and fo the fame will pafs through every Point of the Sphærical Surface defcrib'd by it, all which concur in the Points A and B ; therefore all thofe great Circles do bifeƈt each other in the Points A and B : Therefore all the leffer parallel Peripheries cut thefe great Circles at right Angles, and are all bifeƈted by them : therefore the Plains of the leffer Circles are at right Angles with the Plain of the great Circles that bifeƈt them ; therefore the Angles made by any two Pofitions of the Semicircle at the Axis of its motion, make equal Angles in all the parallel Circles and equal parts of Arches in all the Peripheries of them. **5.**

And becaufe the Center C may be fuppo'd to remain fix'd, and the Points A and B may be fuppos'd fix'd in any other two oppofite Points of the Sphærical Surface already defcrib'd, as X and Y and the Semiperiphery ADB may be fuppos'd revolv'd upon thofe Points or Poles as AB upon the Axis ACB, therefore this Revolution of XDY will defcribe the fame Sphærical Surface with the former, which will defcribe other great and leffer Circles in it ; all which will have the fame Refpeƈts and Proprieties to each other, as the former had among themfelves ; therefore the Plains of all great Circles pafs through the Center, the Diameters of them being always equal to the Diameter of the Sphære ; therefore all great Circles bifeƈt each other ; therefore the Plain of all leffer Circles cut or pafs through the Globe befide the Center ; therefore all Plains paffing through or cutting the Globe, cut it in Circles, and if they pafs through the Center cut it in great Circles, and if they pafs befide and not through the Center, cut it in leffer Circles ; therefore all leffer Circles are parallel to fome great Circle, which is in the middle between the Poles A and B ; therefore the fame Points that are the Poles of a great Circle, are

the

the Poles alfo of the leffer Circles that are parallel to it ; therefore all Sphæ-rical Surfaces that interfect each other, do cut each other in the Periphery of a Circle, and confequently in a Plain ; therefore the Line drawn between the Centers of two fuch interfering Globes fhall pafs the Center of that Plain at right Angles or Perpendicularly.

Thefe Proprieties of a Globular Body and Sphærical Surface, which follow as Corollaries from the way of the Generation of them, and fo need little Ex-planation for the evidencing the demonftration of them, will be fufficient at prefent for the Explanation of fuch Divifions and imaginary Circular Lines as have been made ufe of by Geographers, for the better Defcription, Limi-tation and Divifion of the Superficial parts of this great Globe of the Earth ; as for the other kinds of Lines which are not Circular but Sphærohelical, fuch as the Rhumbs or Magnetical Lines, thofe I fhall hereafter difcourfe of in their proper places, and explain all thofe Proprieties which are peculiar to them, and of ufe in Navigation.

Geographers then have reprefented this great Globous Body of the Earth by a great round Ball or Globe, whofe Surface is Sphærical and Smooth, and on the Surface of that they have defcrib'd the various parts of the Superficies of the Earth bearing fuch Form, Pofition, Magnitude and Variety one to another, as the real parts of the Earth do one with another ; and therein have taken notice of the Pofition, Shape, Magnitude and Boundaries of all Lands, and Continents, Iflands, Peninfulas, Ifthmus's, Promontories, Moun-tains, Plains, Deferts, and other remarkable differences, as are known, of the parts of the Earth which appear above the Water ; as alfo of all the Boun-daries and Extents of Oceans, Seas, Gulphs, Bays, Channels, Streights, Lakes, Rivers, and the like ; where the Water covereth the Face of the Earth ; as the beft Difcoveries hitherto made, can furnifh them with the in-formation of. Thefe, I fay, they have delineated and defcrib'd upon a Glo-bous Body with what exactnefs and skill they are able ; and tho' I conceive it to be far from that fulnefs, exactnefs and truth of Reprefentation that is to be wifh'd ; yet comparing what is now known and defcrib'd, with what was known to the Antients, we fhall find more than a new World has been of late Ages difcover'd : And indeed the very World itfelf ; for 'twas a long time before it was known what the Figure or Magnitude of the Earth was ; and there was a time, when the beleif of Antipodes was accounted and punifh'd as a Herefy. Every one then believ'd his own Country to be the middle of the Plain of the Earth, and that the utmoft Limits of it, which touch'd the Vault of Heaven, were the Sea, into which the Sun, Moon and Stars defcended when they Set, and out of which they afcended again when they Rofe ; and the utmoft extent of Land feem'd no more than what a Conqueror was, in a little time, able to over run and vanquifh.

The Earths Fi-gure firft found by the Greek Mathematici-ans. It is hard to conceive, how Men from fuch a ftate of Ignorance fhould ar-rive at fuch a degree of certainty of Knowledge, as the World has at prefent attain'd ; how they came to know that the Earth was a round or globular Bo-dy ; nor have we any Hiftories that do inform us ; but we firft met with it a-mong the Mathematical Philofophers of the Greeks, who, 'tis probable, from the curiofity of their Cæleftial Obfervations, and from the ftrictnefs of their Arguing came to find and demonftrate the truth thereof ; and then to in-deavour to find out alfo the certain Magnitude and Meafure thereof by Ob-fervations and Menfurations purpofely made. Thefe Cæleftial Obfervations, I conceive, were the firft occafions of their difcovery of the true Form of the Earth, and 'tis by means of thofe that the Magnitude of it hath been, and is to be truly difcover'd, there being fo many unanfwerable Objections againft all the other ways of attempting it, that I think it wholly impracticable to any tolerable degree of certainty.

Cæleftial Objects then, 'tis probable, were the Marks that guided them to this Difcovery, which were fufficient for this purpofe, whether they were fuppos'd to move round the Earth whilft that was fuppos'd to ftand ftill and fix'd, or whether they were look'd on as fix'd and immoveable as to the Diur-nal Motion ; and the Earth itfelf, according to *Ariftarchus Samius*, or our

late

late *Copernicus,* were fuppos'd to be whirl'd round upon an Axis once in twenty four Hours.

Before the revival of this Opinion the Body of the Earth, tho' accounted but a Point in refpect of the expanded Univerfe, yet was it fuppos'd to be of fuch a folid, Denfe and fluggifh Nature, as not to be mov'd out of its place or pofture, tho' the whole Univerfe, which was fo many Millions of Millions of times bigger and more noble, was fuppos'd to whirle about it with an incredible Velocity, and all to wait and adminifter to it ; which yet at the fame time was faid to be damn'd to the worft of places (as it was accounted) the Center of the whole Creation, where it was affirm'd to be made up of the very Dreggs and Drofs of the *Chaos,* to which all the vile and bafer parts of the Univerfe continually defcended, and was there excluded, as it were, and thrown out of the very Communication of the reft of the Creation. To maintain this Opinion the whole Creation was ftrangely Metamorphos'd, the moft glorious Cæleftial Bodies were depriv'd of their greateft Powers and the beft places of the Univerfe : Firft, For their Powers they were rarify'd almoft to be no Bodies, and fuppos'd more light and fpungy than Air itfelf ; and next they were wholly depriv'd of the Power of Motion, fo as to be fuppos'd to be carry'd about by certain Orbs, in which they were fuppos'd plac'd, and in them to be only Paffive and not Active at all ; and thus as fitting in Chariots to be whirl'd round this defpicable Point of the Earth, for the more State and Pomp. On the other fide to make this feem more probable, the whole *Expanfum* or *Æther* was confolidated into more than adamantine Hardnefs and Tranfparency, and divided into Sphæres or Orbs within Orbs Concentrical, Excentrical, Progreffive, Retrograde, and together with thefe qualities of Hardnefs and Tranfparency, there was added to this Subftance that fill'd the Æthereal fpace fo great a fmoothnefs, as that all thefe Orbs could pafs by each other without loofing any part of their motion by rubbing, and fuch an impenetrability as not to wear out or waft each other by Grinding or Fretting ; and yet to heighten the wonder they were fuppos'd to be Sonorous and Tonick, and to out-do all the Mufick befides in the World, by the harmonious Melody of the Symphonick Sphæres ; which Harmony yet was fo fublime as not to be heard or underftood by any but fuch as were gone out of themfelves and had left thofe Corporeal Senfes, which other Mortals here make ufe of, behind them, and were tranfported into an Exftacy of Contemplation and Attention. By this contrivance the Univerfe was all made folid and impenetrable, except only what fpace was left below the Concave part of the Moon's Orbe, which Concave part was the infide of the Walls of this Prifon to which the Earth was condemned, beyond which no Terreftial Matter could penetrate, nor any Earthly Power reach ; nor indeed could they reach fo far, becaufe this Concave Superficies was lin'd with a very thick Coat of the Element of Fire which had Power to confume and difperfe all that which rifing from the Earth, or inferior Regions of the Air, fhould attempt to invade and penetrate the Heavens. Thence Comets or Blazing Stars were fuppos'd Sublunary and Aereal Meteors, and to be kindl'd by this Guardian Element of the Fire, and by that to be varioufly thrown from place to place like other Meteors and falling Stars, retorting their ill influence back again to the Earth from whence they were fent ; or like Squibbs and Powder-Serpents drove to and fro by the blaze of their own Tail. Thus former Artificers contriv'd the Heavens into Wheel-work, and fuppofing themfelves to have eftablifh'd their Machinations by Suppofitions, which freed them from the fear of Difcovery or Contradiction they did a long while amufe the World with their Hypothefes. But later Aftronomers finding, by accurate Obfervations, that Comets did pervade all thofe fpaces which they had fill'd up, began to difcover their Fictions to be groundlefs, and foon after found out a much more probable Solution of all the Phænomena of the Heavens, by placing the Sun in the Center of the Planetary Syfteme, and inftead of whirling round the Heavens once in twenty four Hours, they found or believ'd at leaft, that the Body of the Earth itfelf turning round upon one of its Diameters as an Axis, caus'd all thofe appearances of change, which was formerly afcrib'd to the motions of the Heavens, fuppos'd to be caus'd

by

by the rapidity of the Sphære call'd the *Primum Mobile* ; but taking which Suppofition we will, as to what principally concerns the diftinguifhing of Longitude and Latitude in Geography, it will come much to the fame thing.

We fuppofe then that the Earth is, by all common Obfervations, found to be a round Body, and fuppos'd to be mov'd round upon two Points in its Surface or upon an imaginary Axis or Diameter of it, and that it makes a whole Revolution to the fame Pofition again in refpect of the Plain through the Sun once in twenty four Hours thereby making Night and Day ; and fuppofing an imaginary Plain paffing through the Center of the Sun and the two Polar Points of this motion, this Plain will defcribe upon the Surface of the Earth every moment that it moves a great Circle, and fo in a Revolution infinite of great Circles paffing through the Polar Points and dividing the whole Surface of the Earth into a Morning and Afternoon half ; the Morning half will be that which is moving towards the Sun, and the Evening half that which is moving from it :   Thefe great Circles are call'd Meridians, becaufe when any Point of the Surface of the Earth comes by its motion into this Plain, the Sun is in the Meridian of that place, and are ufually drawn in Lines upon the Globe which is made to reprefent the Earth ; but becaufe to draw them all would perfectly cover the Surface of the Globe, there being no moment paffing without an alteration of it in refpect of the Superficial Parts of the Earth, therefore on fmaller Globes they ufually draw but twelve of them, which divides the whole Surface into twenty four parts anfwerable to the Hours of the Day and Night, but in greater Globes they treble that number anfwerable to every third part of an Hour or twenty Minutes of time.

Of the prime Meridian.

And becaufe thefe imaginary Circles alter every moment, and all have the fame refpect to the Heavens, fo that from thence there is no reafon why they fhould not be drawn over fome places as well as others, that there might be a certainty where to begin to number them ; there hath been feveral attempts or profers by feveral Authors to place under that which they call their firft or beginning Meridian, this or that remarkable place of the Earth. *Ptolomy* accounted his firft Meridian from one Degree Weft of the Weftermoft *Fortunate Iflands* or the *Canarys*, and thence accounted his Longitude or diftance Eaftward, 'till he arriv'd to the Eafter-moft Border of *China*, fuppofing thereby to have compris'd all the Habitable part of the World.

Upon the farther difcoveries of late times of Lands more to the Weftward than thefe *Canaries* ; fome have taken the Meridian paffing through the Ifland of St. *Nicholas* one of the Iflands of *Cape Verd*.   And *Hondius* has chofen for his firft Meridian that which paffes through the Ifland of St. *Jago* ; but *Gerrardus Mercator* has plac'd his firft Meridian over the Ifland of *Corvo*, one of the *Azores*, becaufe at that time the Magnetical Needle or Compafs had no variation from the true Meridian Line in that place, which he therefore judg'd would be a very good mark to find it again in fucceeding Ages :   But as there are other Meridians in which the Compafs has no variation, fo it has been fince his time found that there is a variation of the variation of the Magnetical Needle ; and tho' the Needle then varied here at *London* to the Eaftward, yet fince that time, *viz.* about thirty Years fince, it had no variation here at *London*, and is now very confiderably gone towards the Weft. Some others have made the firft Meridian that which pafs'd by the moft Eaftwardly part of *Brafile* ; *Arnoldus*, and *Wendelinus* have chofen the Ifland of St. *Vincent* for their firft Meridian ; and *Jodocus Hondius* has taken the fame in his Globe making it pafs through *Iceland* ; *Robert Dudley* in his *Arcano del Mare* places it at the Ifland of *Pico* one of the *Azores* ; but *Gulielmus Blaw*, and moft of the *Dutch* Mapp makers, begin their reckoning from the Pike of *Teneriff.* The *French* Geographers, by order of *Lewis* the XIIIth. in the Year 1634, plac'd their firft Meridian to pafs through the Ifland of *Ferro* one of the *Canaries*, as is teftify'd by *Brietius* in his Parallel between the Antient and Modern Geography, much the fame with that of *Ptolomy*. Another prime Meridian was conftituted by Pope *Alexander* the firft, as a Boundary between the *Spanifh* and *Portuguefe* Divifion or Conqueft of the World, and that was after a long Debate, but never any final Decifion or Determination fuppos'd to pafs through the Mouth of the River of *Amazons* and that of *De la Platta*, as *Langrenus* has made it in his Mapp (which, whether they lie both under one Meridian or not, no one yet knows) And the *Spaniards* were to be proprietors of all Lands they discover'd to the Westwards of that Meridian, and the *Portuguese* all to the Eastward; but these two meeting each other in the *East-Indies* again, caus'd much Dispute. However, the *Spaniards* keep the *Philippines*, tho' it be thought to intrench upon the *Portuguese* half. Other Geographers have taken other beginnings, which has caus'd a very great Confusion, in particular Geographical Mapps, it being difficult to know from what prime Meridian they begin their Account.

Besides these, the Astronomers have made choice of other Meridians for their Astronomical Calculations, as *Ticho Brahe*, and his followers, take the Meridian of *Uranibourg*, being in *Huena* an Island in the *Sound*. *Origanus* takes that of *Frankfort*, *Maginus* that of *Venetia*, *Eichstadius* that of *Stettn*, and indeed almost every new Writer makes the Meridian of the place of his abode the first Meridian, and refers all the rest to that, which breeds a great and needless Trouble and Confusion in Geography; and it were very much to be wished that they had, or would for the future agree upon some one to which all might be refer'd. There is not yet found any very considerable ground in Nature why one should be agreed to rather than another; that of the direction of the Magnetical Needle in the true Meridian Line would have looked so much like such an indication of Nature, if the Hypothesis of *Linton* and *Nantonier* had been true; but since Time has discover'd that those were but groundless Hypotheses, that pretence is vain.

That of the prodigious high Mountain of the Pike of *Tenariff*, which *William Bleaw* and the *Dutch* take notice of in their Charts, is likely enough to be a lasting Mark, and 'tis considerable enough to distinguish it from all other Mountains yet known in the World; and lying conveniently in the way of Shipping, may, for ought I know, be as proper as any other place whatsoever, provided all agree to make their Compute from it; and the computing Eastwards may serve well enough since it is now generally us'd; but had it been to be now establish'd, I should think it had been much more according to Nature to have computed the contrary way.

Next, the Earth being suppos'd to be mov'd round upon this Axis, may be suppos'd to have infinite Circles describ'd upon the Surface of it, by the infinite Points of the great Circle that thus it moves round withal, which will therefore be parallel to one another, because all are describ'd by the same motion upon the Axis; that Point of it which is in the middle between the two Poles describeth a great Circle, which is call'd the Æquator or Æquinoctial Line, and all the other Circles will be lesser Circles, which being *Of the Parallels.* parallel to it are call'd Parallels; all these Circles cross the former Meridians at right Angles, and so every one of them are, by every one of the former, divided into two equal parts.

These parallel Circles are drawn upon the Globe that represents the Earth, but not all of them, for that would cover the whole superficies of the Globe, but only so many of them as may, together with the Meridians, serve to distinguish and divide the Surface thereof into Trapezia of a convenient bigness, and are generally proportion'd to the number of Semimeridians, *viz.* so many between the Æquinoctial, and either Pole, as there are Meridians, as at every Five, Ten, or Fifteen Degrees distance from the Æquinoctial Circle, from which they begin to be accounted.

Nov. 13th. 84. I explain'd the last Day various Opinions concerning the Figure of the Earth on which we live, and shew'd you why, tho' it has not been sufficiently prov'd by any Observations yet made, that it is positively of this or that Figure, yet by comparing all together it seems most probable that the Figure of it is Sphærical or Globular, or at least so near it as not easily to be discover'd of any other, by the shadow of it in the Eclipses of the Moon, nor by any other Observations yet made for measuring the Quantity or Magnitude of a Degree upon the Surface of it, which is the only certain and positive way of performing it: For tho' 'tis certain that the quantity of a Degree, or a three hunder'd and sixtieth part of the whole compass of it has been measur'd in several Latitudes, and some of them with care enough; yet 'tis

Ffffff   also

also certain, that moſt of them have been made by unaccurate Methods and uncertain Meaſures ; ſo that they are wholly uſeleſs in this particular, by reaſon we cannot make a pertinent compariſon between them ; nor do I know any other certain and uncontradictable way of proving it, than by either firſt actually meaſuring the quantity of a Degree upon the Earth in Latitudes very differing, as of one lying very near the Æquinoctial Line, and of another, as near as may be towards either of the Poles ; and thoſe Menſurations to be made as near as may be by the ſame Perſons, with the ſame Inſtruments, and the ſame Meaſures, and with the ſame Exactneſs and Care ; by the comparing together of which two Degrees ſo meaſur'd, it would plainly appear whether thoſe Degrees would prove equal or unequal; for if they prov'd to be unequal, then it would plainly appear that the Figure of the Earth was not of a perfect Globular Form, but ſome way or other Oval ; if

A way to determine the Earths two Diameters. the Degree near the Æquinoctial be found longer than near the Pole, then the greateſt Diameters of the Earth are in the Plain of the Æquinoctial ; if on the contrary, then the longeſt Diameter is in the Axis of its Revolution : This is ſuppoſing that the Perpendicular Lines paſs through the Center of the Earth, whence would follow a ſecond method of examining the Figure of it, and that is by examining whether the Horizontal Line be at right Angles with the Perpendicular ; for if the Perpendicular be not found at right Angles with the viſible Horizon, then will the obtuſe Angle be on that ſide of the Perpendicular which is next the longeſt Diameter of the Earth, and the Acute towards that which is the ſhorteſt ; it may therefore be eaſily try'd upon the ſame Place or Promontory where the Horizontal Line of the Sea can be ſeen both Northwards and Southwards with ſome exact Inſtrument fitted with a long Plumb-line and a large Teleſcope ſet at right Angles with it, by which the viſible Horizontal Line may be obſerv'd to what exactneſs it ſhall be deſir'd, by turning the Inſtrument in the ſame place, and viewing the level of the ſaid Line through it Northward and Southward. But if upon examining the Horizontal Line this way, it ſhall be found that the Perpendicular is at right Angles with the Horizontal, and yet by the other way of trial, by meaſuring a Degree in ſeveral Latitudes, it be found that the

Whether the Perpendiculars reſpect the Center. Degrees are differing, it will be an Argument that the Perpendiculars do not always reſpect the Center of the Earth, but that they croſs the Axis in ſome other part thereof, which is out of the middle, ſometimes towards one Pole, ſometimes towards the other; which may be true, and yet none of the Obſervers, that have hitherto been, may have found, or taken notice thereof; one Reaſon of which may have been, that they have not hitherto ſuſpected it, and therefore did not inquire after it. But tho' it be probable enough, that the Body of the Earth is nearly Globular, or rather was ſo form'd at firſt, that being the moſt perfect and regular Figure, and that, of which the other Celeſtial Bodies ſeem to be of, yet ſince we find that there are other varieties in Nature, as that of the Ring about the Body of *Saturn*, and even here upon the Earth, that of the differing Variation of the Magnetical Power thereof, I think it may not be improper to ſuſpect, that there may be ſuch an uncertainty of pointing in the Perpendicular or Plumb-line, 'till by certain Obſervations we are aſſur'd, and 'tis not ſafe in Philoſophy to leave inquiry 'till a certainty be found. It was for ſome time believ'd, that the Earth itſelf was a great Load-ſtone, and that the Poles thereof were the ſame with the Poles of its diurnal Motion ; and that the variation of the Needle from that North Point was occaſion'd only by the approximation to the ſides of great Continents, and according to that Theory, the cauſes of the ſeveral varia-

The Needle reſpects not the Poles of diurnal motion. tions of the Needle at ſeveral places were aſſign'd to be for this or that Continent, or this or that Ocean near adjoyning. But upon further Inquiry it was found that there were ſeveral Inſtances, that contradicted that Theory, and that the Needle ſeem'd to reſpect ſome Poles that were not in the Poles of the diurnal Motion, but at ſome diſtance from them : Theſe were ſaid to be ſome vaſt great Rocks or Mountains of Load-ſtone at certain diſtances from the Poles of the diurnal motion ; which Poles the Needle was ſuppos'd always to reſpect, and thereupon *William Nautonier* of *Caſtlefrank* in *Languedock*, wrote a large Book, which he Printed in the Year 1603, wherein he

describes

describes his Theory thereof, and furnishes it with Instruments and Tables fitted to find the Longitude thereby. Much about the same time one Mr. *Anthony Linton*, our own Country-man, a Minister I suppose, Publish'd a small Tract in *English*, under the Title of *News of the Complement of the Art of Navigation*, in which he pretended to shew a way for discovering the Longitude by the help of the variation of the Needle, and goes upon the same Hypothesis that the Earth was one great round Load-stone, and that the Poles thereof were at a certain distance from the Poles of the World, or those of the diurnal Motion; that there were, as it were, proper Magnetical Meridians, and a Magnetical Æquator and Parallels corresponding, all which bore the same respects to the Magnetical Poles, that the Meridians, Æquator, and Parallels of the diurnal Motion did to the Poles of the World; and thence he shews a way how to find the Longitude of any place by Sea or Land, in the Day or Night. But later Observations have found, that this Magnetical Variation varies, tho' yet the parts of the Earth do not seem at all to have alter'd their Position; this was found by Mr. *Foster* and others in the Year 1635.

Variation unfit for finding the Longitude.

Hereupon Mr. *Bond* makes a supposition, that these Magnetical Poles were in the Air, not in the Earth, and out of the Poles of the World at a certain distance from them, and that they were two, one North and another South; that the Magnetical Axis cross'd the other Axis in the Center, but that the Poles made a Revolution about the Poles of the Earth in a certain period of Time, but that at the same time all over the World the Needles respected these Poles both by variation and dipping; by this he suppos'd the Longitude might be found in the same manner as *Linton* and *Nautonnier* had before suppos'd; but by comparing several Observations together it is found that this Theory will not hold neither. And the ingenious Mr. *Halley* has examin'd and compar'd Observations so far, that he judges it reasonable to admit four Magnetical Poles in the Earth, two of which are near the South, and two others near the North Pole, by which he finds the most accurate Observations of variation will be solv'd very rationally.

Four Magnetical Poles.

These Instances I mention to shew that tho' the Supposition of Dr. *Gilbert* were very ingenious, and seem'd very rational, and in many things agreed with the Phænomena of the terrella or round Load-stone; yet was it not a sufficient Argument for all others to desist from inquiring farther, and examining whether upon trial all the Phænomena would answer to the Theory, and whether it would always remain the same that he in his time did find it; for things of this Nature being so far remov'd from common and vulgar Observation, and the very Maxims and Grounds of them being taken up upon I know not whose, Credit, I conceive, it might be worth inquiry by Experiment to examine whether they be really so or not, how generally soever they be believ'd or consented to; for 'till that be positively prov'd by certain Observations, there may be good Reason to hesitate upon the Reception of any Hypothesis how plausible soever it may appear.

This I mention on the occasion of considering the form of the Body of the Earth, and of the pointing of the Perpendiculars to the very Central and middle Point thereof; which, tho' it be generally taken for granted, and very agreeable to the general Phænomena, yet I think there are very good Arguments may be produc'd that may make the thing questionable, since I do not find that there has ever yet been made any Observations or Trials accurate enough to determine positively whether it be certainly so, or otherwise. 'Tis true, that it is certainly near enough to that Figure of a Globe, that the common Observations and accounts of Seamen cannot disprove it; and therefore as to that use, and so far as the accurateness of that Art is hitherto practis'd, it can make no sensible difference; but yet if that Art be carry'd to a much higher degree of Perfection, as 'tis not impossible but that it may, it may be very considerable in that particular also: But 'till that be done we will be contented to agree to the common receiv'd Opinion, and consider of it as of a Globe perfectly round, at least as to the Surface of the Ocean, that part which is of principal consideration in the business of Navigation.

The

THe following short Discourse relating to the *Magnetical Variation*, and the more exact way of observing that and the dipping of the Needle, I thought best to insert it in this place ; for I do not find that the Author has any where perfected this Theory of Magnetism, which it were to be wish'd he had done, as likewise that he had carry'd several other Subjects on to a greater pitch of Perfection, which indeed has been the misfortune of a great part of the Discourses publish'd in this Volume.

R. W.

A Discourse of the Magnetical Variation, read July 7th. 1686.

THe causes of Gravity and Magnetical Attraction are so far remov'd beyond the reach of our Senses, that the greatest part of Philosophers who have indeavour'd to give us an information thereof, have rather made us more sensible of their and our own Ignorance and Inability to do any thing therein, some making it Corporeal, some Spiritual; but what either of them mean either by Corpuscles or Magnetical Effluvia, or Atoms, or Magnetick Vertue, or Hylarchick Spirit, or Anima Mundi, when you come to inquire to the bottom you find, that neither they nor we know what is meant, and we do as good as say 'tis so, because it is so ; the Reason of which I conceive to be, that Men are usually very impatient of the Labour of examining and trying, and of going the long and tedious way of coming to a certainty of knowledge by Experiments, wherein the progress is very slow, and, as it were, step by step ; but affect rather to leap into a Theory at once, and make to themselves an Hypothesis upon some few Observations they have met with, or some few Experiments they have try'd, or some pretty Conception or Hypothesis they have accidently pitch'd upon that pleases them, to which with a little Shouldring they can make every cast to run, as it were, directly, though at last it miss the mark ; yet, rather than they will indure the trouble of farther search by Trials or by Examinations and strict Reasoninings, they are contented to take up with somewhat that may serve to amuse.

It was for some time believ'd, that the Magnetical Needle did always respect the North and South Poles, not of the Earth, but of the Heavens, and that the Pole-star was that wherein the vertue did lie. In process of time it comes to be discover'd, that this vertue was not in the Heavens, but in the Earth, and that the Magnetical Needle, had, in some parts of the World, a considerable variation from the Meridian of the place, the North end declining in this part towards the East, in that towards the West, in some places more, in others less ; but that this variation was fix'd and perpetual to the place, and that by reason, said some, for that there were to be found in the North certain Rocks or Mountains of Load-stones, which attracted the North end of the Needle to them from all parts of the World. But this, in a short time, also vanish'd as appearing ridiculous, and not answering to the Consequences that must have follow'd from it. Instead of which another cause is introduc'd for the variation, and that is the great Continents that lie either on this or that Hand, and the great Sea that lies on the other : Hence it was suppos'd that Variations would be found always regular, and the same in the same place at all times, as proceeding from the greater attraction from the parts of the Earth; which were more prominent and elevated, and which were not likely to be alter'd by time ; at least, not enough to make a sensible variation of the variation. This was Dr. *Gilberts,* but in process of Time this was, by Mr. *Gillibrand* of this Colledge, and some others, found to alter, and there was found a variation of the variation of the Magnetick Needle in the same place, and that not verify'd in one, but in thousands of places. This overthrew all the former Hypotheses, and we are now to seek a new one ; Mr. *Bond,* and Mr. *Philips,* and some others, have been hammering at a new Hypothesis, wherein they make the Magnetick vertue to be in the Air, and so the Magnetick Poles to be moveable in Circles round about the Poles of the Æquinoctial, and the Magnetick

netick Axis of the Earth to have a Conical motion about the Axis of the diurnal Revolution : Which Conical motion they suppose to be perform'd in a certain number of Years ; so that at length the Polar Points of the Magnetick vertue after they have revolv'd a periodick Circle, return from the same Point from which they did begin. Others have taken other Hypotheses, and rais'd other Conclusions and Consequences from them ; but still after all we are yet to seek whether this motion of the Magnetick Polar Points be in straight Line, or in a Curve as in a Circle, Ellipse, or some other more irregular Figure ; whether it move round the diurnal Pole or some other Point ; whether it move Eastward or Westward ; whether it move nearer or farther off from the Pole ; whether it move quicker at one time than another ; whether it will return or continually proceed ; whether there are only two or more Magnetical Poles ; whether the Magnetical Axis of one, or Axes, if there are more than one, pass through the Center of the Globe, or besides it, and if more, whether parallel to each other, or Oblique, and whether one only hath a motion or whether both ; whether these motions keep the same Velocities or differing ; and many other the like Queries might be made ; I could add a hundred, of which we are still to seek, and cannot give a positive answer, because there are not yet materials enough of Observations to build a certain Theory upon ; and the Observations that have been hitherto made have been so gross and imperfect, that little of certainty can be concluded from them, and therefore such Observations can only be rectify'd by Time, by reason that the Degrees and Steps of this progressive motion are so far undefin'd, that some Years must be stay'd before the alterations that are made in the interim in the motion can be made sensible, and when sensible, they are very imperfectly defin'd. Hence, I suppose, it may have proceeded, that we have lately heard of some such Magnetical Observations as have seem'd to prove a station of that motion, and some others of a differing Nature, which, in probability, have proceeded from some imperfection in the Observation.

For if we consider the Nature of such Observations, how many Requisites there are necessary to make any one as it ought to be, we shall quickly find that our store of fit materials to work upon will be exceedingly small ; and that upon examining into or querying upon such Observations as we meet with, we shall be apt to throw by and neglect as useless the greatest part : for there are but a very few in the World that are fit and able to make such Observations, or that know what is Pertinent and what Impertinent : Fewer there are that will be at the trouble of doing what they know fit, and tho' Skill, and Will be joyn'd, yet if Instruments and other assistances are wanting, they will come short of Perfection.

As tho' an Observer knows how to find the true meridian of the place, how to place his Needle, what inconveniences to look after for preventing (as the removing of all such Magnetical or Chalibeate Bodies as influence the Needle) how to observe the Angle the Needle makes with the Meridian Line, and the like ; yet if he wants fitting Instruments, whether Mathematical or Magnetical, to do these Requisites and convenient Assistances, and a sufficient stock of Perseverance and Industry to prosecute the trials to the utmost exactness, the effect will be imperfect, whatever is look'd after beyond that exactness : For instance, after all other Requisites are found, if there be wanting such a Needle as will certainly distinguish to the sixth part of a Degree, then any such Observations are wholly useless in such Inquiries where a much greater accurateness is requir'd ; and for the making them significant, there is no other way but staying a sufficient number of Years, and the courser the Observations be, the greater number of Years are requisite to make them equally useful ; and even then they are altogether useless for answering many other Queries ; as if it should be queried, whether the progress for that whole interval have been equal or unequal, and if unequal, what those Degrees have been and at what times, whether in differing Years, or differing parts of the same Year ? &c.

Now since Time is that which cannot be alter'd, and that therefore Posterity only are like to have the Fruit of our Labours and Indeavours of that kind, I thought it would be best to make such Instruments as would make that sensible in a very short time, which, by the common, could not be but in a long, by those means if possible to reduce our Observations to use within the compass of our own Lives; for if a Needle could be made that should distinguish the alterations or the variation of the Variation, as nicely to the parts of a Minute as the present Needles do to the parts of a Degree, then should we discern as sensible an operation or alteration in one Year, as by the other in threescore, and in ten Years as in six hundred; for that all other requisite accurateness can be procur'd, as to distinguish the Meridian Line, the division of the Angles, the interpos'd space of time, the removal of impeding or altering materials that may influence the Needles.

Divers have attempted to procure Instruments fit for this purpose, some by Needles of great length, others by shorter view'd with Glasses or Microscopes, others by other ways, as by one of the late Leipsick Acta may be seen; every of which I conceive to be sufficient for this purpose, and do only aim to discover the divisions of the same Angle; that which I am now describing does that indeed of Consequence, but directly and immediately it magnifies or multiplies the Angle, by making that a Degree which is really but a Minute, and so by consequence contracting of time.

'Tis then, in short, is no other but this,

A Needle is fix'd at right Angles upon a very light and straight Axis of Wood or Brass, which Axis hath at each end the point of a very fine and sharp Needle, the finer and sharper the better, which is easily enough procurable: these Needles points are to be put into two small Center holes, made fit for them in a Ring, or Frame made after the shape in the draught.

THus far the Author. The Figure of the Instrument is represented in the ninth Plate, Figure the first, which may be understood without farther Explanation, which the Author has omitted.

Nov. 20. 1684. In my last Lecture I explain'd to you these two last Lines or Circles which are usually drawn upon the Superficies of a Globe made to represent the Body of the Earth, which were, First, All great Circls passing through the two Polar Points of the Earth, or those Points upon which the Body of it, or the *Primum Mobile* is continually mov'd round once in twenty four Hours, or the time of a natural Day, which are call'd Meridians. And, Secondly, All those Circular Lines, which may be suppos'd to be describ'd by all the Points of any one such Meridian, turn'd round upon the said Globe, suppos'd to stand still; or by the conversion of the Globe upon its Poles, the Meridian being suppos'd to stand still, the effect being the same in both cases as to this particular. These Lines or Circles are call'd Parallels, either because they are all parallel to one another, or rather because all the lesser of them are parallel to the middlemost and great Circle, which is call'd the Æquinoctial, Æquator, or most commonly be Seamen, the Line.

These two sorts of Circles are the principal made use of in the Description of the Superficial Parts of the Earth, and to which all other Lines made use of either in Geography, Astronomy or Navigation are reduc'd, these alone serving to shew the Position and Situation of the several parts of the Earth to one another, and to determine the positive Point or Spot upon the Artificial Globe, every real place upon the Surface of the Earth ought to have, and *Vice Versa* any place situated on the Globe may be found upon the Earth: And being once so determin'd, 'tis suppos'd by most, that it is always the same, that is, the same place upon the Superficies of the Earth being once adjusted both as to its Longitude and Latitude, shall always remain and continue the same both in respect of the one and the other Position. As suppose this City of *London*, if the Latitude and Longitude be once certainly observ'd and determin'd, and so posited on the Globe, it is suppos'd that it shall always remain and continue to have the same in all succeeding Ages,

without

without any Variation or Deviation from the same, whatever Deviation or Variation doth happen in the Cælestial Bodies without it. This, I say, is suppos'd or believ'd by the most Geographers and Astronomers: But yet not by all; for there have been, and there now are some, as particularly Monsieur *Pierre Pettit*, who have not only suppos'd, but positively asserted, that these also have a Variation, and that after a certain time both the Latitude and Longitude of many places, upon the Surface of the Earth, hath a sensible change and difference; and to confirm this he hath compar'd many Observations Recorded by the Antients, of the Latitude of divers places, as particularly those of *Paris, Rome*, and some other eminent places with later and modern Observations of the Latitudes of the same places; whereby 'tis found, that there are very considerable differences between them, which he ascribes to the variation of the Poles of the Earth. Certain it is, that later Observations concerning the Latitudes of several very eminent places of the World do very much differ from those that were assign'd them by the Antients; as particularly that of the famous Accademy of *Greece Athens*, whose present Latitude is found to differ almost two whole Degrees from what was formerly assign'd to it, as I have been inform'd by the Ingenious and Learn'd Traveller Mr. *Francis Vernon*, who with great care made the Observation. I could instance also in *Constantinople*, and several other eminent places not mention'd by Monsieur *Pettit*, but I shall omit them at present 'till some farther and more accurate trials be made for this purpose, and upon this occasion mention only, that, I conceive, it would not be amiss that there should be some Observations purposely made to examine this Theory, and reduce it to a certainty, for 'till that be done it is but Hypothetical to suppose the Polar Points of the Earth fix'd or moveable, there being as great a possibility of their moveableness, as there was of the Magnetical Poles, before the discovery thereof made by some of this College in the Year 1635. That, I suppose, which prompt'd Monsieur *Pettit* to make this assertion, or at least gave him a hint for this Inquiry, was a kind of mistake of *Joseph Scaliger* in an Epistle of his wrote to *David Rivaltus* upon the occasion of the Explanation of the variation of the Magnetical Needle from the true Meridian, made by Dr. *Gilbert* in his Book *de Magnete*, Publish'd not long before. This Epistle was Printed with other Works of his at *Paris* in the Year 1610. but written in the Year 1604 for by his Discourse he would seem to explain the Reason of the Magnetical Variation of the Meridians themselves, which he pretends must needs follow from the Theory of the præcession of the Æquinoctial Points, and yet at the same time he says, that the *Cynosure* or Tail of the lesser Bear was never farther from the North Pole of the World than now it is. But in short (to spend no more time upon declaring and explaining this Opinion) I say, 'tis very evident he understood not what he said himself, or if he did, 'tis certain he grosly mistook the Explanation of the matter, and has been long since confuted by *Maginus*, who was then professor of Astronomy at *Padua*.

The Latitude and Longitude of places varies.

Now if there be any ground for this Opinion, then must also follow an alteration of all the Meridians and Parallels imagin'd to be made upon this Globe of the Earth; for if the Polar Points, or the Axis of the diurnal motion of the Earth does vary, those must also vary with it, and consequently the Positions and Distances of all places, in respect of them, must vary also; and consequently, as *Scaliger* says, the Positions or Meridians of Dials, will, after a certain time, be false, as will also the very Dial itself, as if it had been remov'd and plac'd in a wrong Latitude and wrong Position. However, the Position and distances of places one to another will contain the same, tho' they differ in respect of the Heavens; and therefore if those be procur'd, tho' both the Latitude and Longitude of all should be alter'd, this Description or Picture of the Earth, upon the Artificial Globe, would remain true and unalter'd, and other Meridians and Parallels might be drawn over them.

But to leave this Digression for the present, I shall proceed to consider of the Divisions usually made upon these Circles describ'd upon the Artificial Globe.

All

The divisions usually made on the Globe.

Of the reason why the Circles are divided in 360.

All these Circles then both great and lesser are divided, or suppos'd to be divided into three hundred and sixty equal parts, which are call'd Degrees, Grades, Steps, but none of them are number'd quite round, save only the Æquinoctial, which noteth the divisions of Longitude, but all the rest are first divided into four equal parts, which are call'd Quadrants, and each Quadrant into ninety ; what the reason was at first of pitching upon this number of three hundred and sixty, I know not, there being no Reason in Nature for this more than for some other Divisions, tho' the Astrologers make much thereof, and build much thereupon ; but the most likely seems to have been this, that the Radius being equal to the Subtense of a sixth part of the Circle, did very naturally prompt them to that Primary and natural Division of it into six equal Parts or Sextants ; which division also did both bisect and trisect the whole Circle, and gave them the Halfs and Trines, or Thirds ; then bisection being the easiest of all other Sections, the bisecting the Bisection gave them the Quadrisection, Quadrants, or Quartiles of the whole ; from these Quadrants setting off the Sextants either way, gave them the Duodecimals or Twelfs of the Circle, or the Thirds of the Quadrants or Quartiles. These Duodecimals in the Ecliptick, of which I shall hereafter speak, are call'd Signs, which signifies Marks, Divisions, or Sections of the Ecliptick. Thus far the cause of their Divisions seem'd reasonable enough, more especially for the New Moons being twelve in the Year ; as did also their next of subdividing each of these into halves, making four and twenties or Hours, into which number they divided the Natural Day, or one whole Revolution of the Earth. But the *Chinese* and *Tartars* contented themselves with the Duodecimal, dividing the whole Revolution only into twelve Cha. which we must call Bi-hours ; tho' on the contrary, they divided their Zodiack into twenty four parts, which we must call half Signs, being produc'd only by Bisection upon the first Sextants ; but why the Eastern and Western *Literati* differ'd afterwards, is not easy to guess.

Difference between the Eastern and Western Literati.

And whether the Western *Literati* did divide these twenty fourths into fifteenths, that they might introduce into the Circle both Trisection and Quisection, which are both necessary to this subdivision, I dare not determine. That which seems to have been the most likely occasion, I conceive to have been the nearness of this number of three hundred and sixty to the natural Division of the Zodiack, by the annual motion of the Sun, which every Day doth almost measure such a space, compleating its Circuit in three hundred sixty five Days and a quarter almost, as the Revolutions of the Moon in a Year might prompt them to make use of the Duodecimal Section for the Zodiack. But whatever were the Occasions or Reasons that prompt'd them to these Divisions, certain it is that now all do agree to make use thereof, and call this twelfth part a Sign, and the three hundred and sixtieth part a Degree ; and thence each Sign containeth thirty Degrees, each of these Degrees they again subdivide into sixty equal parts, which little parts they call Minutes or Primes, each of these Primes subdivided by sixty, give Seconds or Second Minutes ; a sixtieth part of a Second is a Third, a sixtieth of a Third a Fourth, and so onward by Sexagesimal Subdivision, to Fifths, Sixths, Sevenths, in a continu'd Geometrical Progression, as far as is needful ; for what Reason they have pitch'd upon this Sexagesimal Progression, I cannot imagine, unless it were because they had divided the Sextant (which, as I told you, was the first and most natural Division of the Circle, its Subtense being equal to the Radius) into sixty Degrees ; but certain it is, that it is much more incommodious for Calculation than the common Decimal way, and much more than a Duodecimal, which might be invented ; for that the Sexagesimal must take two places for every Ascent, whereas the Decimal takes up one place only for one Step or Ascent. So also might a Duodecimal, if rightly order'd, by making two new single Characters for ten and eleven, and making the Character of ten serve for twelve or Dozen ; then the next or third place will be Grosses, the fourth Dugrosses, the fifth Gross Grosses, the sixth Du gross Grosses, and so onward, answerable to Unites, Tens, Hundreds, Thousands, Ten Thousands, Hundred Thousands, &c. in the Decimal progression of places. And tho' possibly the Names and

Practise

Practife of it may feem at firft a little uncouth and ftrange, yet a little ufe will eafily overcome that difficulty, and make it manifeft to be a much better Progreffion than the Decimal, which is now generally ufed: But this only by the bye.

I fhall next proceed to fhew how thefe Divifions are made ufe of in thofe two forts of Circles. Firft, Then, the Æquinoctial, and all the leffer Circles, begin their Divifions from the Section of them by that half of the Meridian which is call'd the firft Meridian, which paffes through the *Atlantick* Ocean, of which I have already fpoken; and the Divifions of them are accounted from thence Eaftwardly, 'till the whole Revolution be compleated and end in this firft Meridian in three hundred and fixty. But the Divifions made upon the Meridians begin to be number'd or accounted from the Æquinoctial, and end at each Pole in ninety, which expreffes the feveral Latitudes of thofe places that lie under them, or their breadth or diftance from the Æquinoctial Line, either towards the North or South Pole.

Now, the next thing is to confider, how both thefe Lines and the divifions of them, proper and peculiar to any one place, may be actually found at that place, which is the ultimate end and refult of all that is fought for in the Art of Navigation; for thefe being truly found for any place, they prefently fhew its true Pofition and Situation in the refpect of all other known and determin'd places upon the Earth.

In order to perform which Inquiry the whole Art of Navigation is contriv'd, and all the affiftances that can be procur'd, either from Nature or Art, are fetch'd in and made ufe of; and all indeed that can be found, tho' very many and very curious and ingenious, are little enough, and too few to accomplifh the fame to that certainty and accuratenefs that is to be defir'd, and is neceffary to compleat and perfect the fame. *The end of the Art of Navigation.*

The Helps then that are made ufe of are either afforded, Firft, By the Heavens and the Cæleftial Bodies, fuch as the Sun, Moon, Planets and Stars. *Two Helps*

Or, Secondly, By the Terreftrial, or fuch things upon and in the Body of the Earth itfelf, as afford Indications and Characterfticks proper and fufficient to direct the Geographer and Hydrographer, for difcovering and determining, by known meafures, how every place is Pofited and Situated in refpect of thofe Lines I have already mention'd; and thence of determining their Pofition and Magnitude in refpect to one another in regard of other imaginary Lines, which are taken in from Art to affift the Mariner in his Computations and Accounts; fuch as are the Rhomb Lines and other great Circles which are neither Meridians nor Æquator, but fuch as are neceffary to be fuppos'd either for computing the way of the Ship, or Courfe fteer'd, or for computing and refolving Triangles, or for giving the Pofition and neareft diftance between place and place, in a great Circle or determin'd Azymuth.

Three things then may be found out by the help of the Cæleftial Bodies. *Three things to be found by the help of Cæleftial Bodies.*

Firft, The Meridian Line or North and South Line, and confequently all the other Azymuth Lines or Points of the Horizon on either fide of the Meridian.

Secondly, The Latitude of any place, or the diftance of that place from the Æquinoctial or the middlemoft of all Parallels between the two Poles.

Thirdly, The Longitude of any place, or diftance of the Meridian of the place from the Prime Meridian agreed upon.

But before I proceed to fhew how thefe three things are to be found by the help of Cæleftial Bodies, I conceive it neceffary to premife fome few Maxims which are not obvious to any, but fuch as have by diligent Obfervation found out and demonftrated the certainty thereof. The grounds and method of which Inventions would be as little to our prefent purpofe as it would be tedious here to repeat. I fhall rather chufe to acquaint you with the Refult or Conclufion which may be taken for granted, 'till fome more curious and exact Obfervers, than have hitherto been, fhall find and demonftrate the *Several Maxims premis'd.*

the contrary, some of which may be done by Land Observations, but not by such as can be made at Sea.

1. The First Maxim then (of which we are sufficiently assur'd for this purpose) is this, That the distance of the fixt Stars is so very great and immense in respect of the Magnitude of the Earth, that its whole Body is but as it were an insensible Point ; so that the Figure, Appearance, Position and Distance of all the fixt Stars, to, or from, one another, doth to the naked Eye, or assisted by the best common Instrument, appear exactly the same, whether the Eye be plac'd in the very Center of the Earth, or in any Point of the Superficies, or any other Point of the whole Body. So that not only the Center of the Earth may be taken to be the Center of the imaginary Concave Sphære wherein all the fixt Stars are plac'd, but any other Point whatsoever of its whole Extension or Corporeity.

2. A Second Maxim of the *Aristarcheans* or *Copernicans* is this, That the distance of the fixt Stars is so incomprehensibly great, that tho' the Earth be suppos'd to move round the Sun in a Circular or Elliptical Line, whose Diameter is ten thousand times the Diameter of the Earth, yet that even this whole Circle, in comparison of the imaginary Orb of the fixt Stars, is but a Point, and that therefore with the naked Eye and common Instruments no difference can be discover'd of the Distances and Positions of the fixt Stars in respect of one another, tho', as I have elsewhere shewn, there is a way to find a difference by the help of very long and good Telescopes, fixt at Land, but no Instruments at Sea can discover it ; which is enough for our present purpose.

3. A Third Maxim is, That two Points of the Earth do steadily point or direct towards two Points among the fixt Stars in the Heavens, which Points are call'd the two Polar Points, the two in the Heavens being Perpendicular over the two on the Earth ; and the Diameter of the Earth passing through these Points, is call'd the Axis of the World, and suppos'd to be continu'd to the fixt Stars : And tho' this Axis be carry'd round in the Orb of the Earth in a Parallelism, and so describes an Elliptical Cylinder, whose longest Diameter is the Diameter of the Earth's Orb about the Sun, yet so vastly are the fixt Stars distant, that this whole Ellipsis, among the fixt Stars, appears but a Point, and the Axis of the Earth seems to respect one and the same Point among the fixt Stars quite round the Year.

4. A Fourth Maxim is, That all Perpendicular Lines respect the Center of the Earth, and that the level of Water, and other Liquors is a plain and at right Angles with this Perpendicular in every Point of the Surface of the Earth.

5. Fifthly, That every one of these Perpendiculars, suppos'd continu'd to the fixt Stars, will, by the diurnal Rotation of the Earth, describe, among the fixt Stars, a Circular Line ; which Circular Line, answering to the Perpendicular or Zenith of any place, will appear the same round the Year, to any Instrument that can be us'd at Sea.

6. Sixthly, That the level of the Water, or any other Liquor suppos'd continu'd to the fixt Stars, will actually divide the whole Sphære thereof into two equal parts, tho' it be out of the Center of the Earth, and upon its Surface ; and tho' the Body of the Earth itself be suppos'd to be as far distant from the Center of that Orb, as it is distant from the Center of the Sun.

7. Seventhly, That the visible Angle of any Cælestial Body, with this Perpendicular or Zenith Line of any place, or with the plain of the level of the Water or Horizon will be the same (as to any thing that can be discover'd by Instruments at Sea) as if the Center of the Instrument were in the
Center

Center of the Earth, and that Center of the Earth were always in the Center of the Sun, and that Center of the Sun were the true Center of the Orb of the fixt Stars ; and thence

Eighthly, We are to conclude that all Obſervations of the fixt Stars, wherefoever made upon the Surface of the Earth and Sea, will give the ſame appearances, as if the Eye or Center of the Inſtrument (by which ſuch an Angle is meaſur'd) were at all times in the Center of the Orb of the fixt Stars. **8.**

Ninethly, That all Obſervations to be made of the Poſitions of the Sun in reſpect of the fixt Stars, will be the ſame, as if the Eye and Center of the Inſtrument were plac'd in the Center of the Earth ; and that whether the Sun be ſuppos'd to be mov'd about the Earth, or the Earth about the Sun, the viſible appearances of the Place, Line, or Point of the Sun among the fixt Stars, will be in both caſes the ſame. **9.**

I ſhall not now meddle with the appearances of the other Planetary Bodies, becauſe at preſent, for this purpoſe, I ſhall not have occaſion to make uſe of them, but reſerve the conſideration of their appearances to another part of this Diſcourſe, wherein I ſhall more particularly treat concerning the ways for finding the Longitude of places by Cæleſtial Helps.

First then, for finding the true Meridian, or North and South Line of any place, there are very many and very differing ways that have been invented and Publiſh'd by ſeveral Authors for this purpoſe, of which ſome are much more difficult and complicated, and præ-ſuppoſe ſeveral things to be known which require another method than this I am now diſcourſing of ; which may be very uſeful for performing other kinds of Problems, but are not ſo proper for what I here intend: Others that are more ſimple and plain, and yet ſufficient to perform this effect ; ſome of theſe are more proper to be made uſe of at Land, others are more eaſy and practicable, and can be made uſe of at Sea as well as on the Land. *Ways for finding the Meridian.*

Theſe ways are either, First, By help of the Sun in the Day-time, or by the help of the fixt Stars in the Night.

Thoſe, by the help of the Sun, are twofold ; First, By the help of an Azymuth Compaſs to obſerve the true Azymuth or Amplitude of the Body of the Sun in its Riſing in the Morning, and Setting at Night of the ſame Day in the Winter half Year, or the ſaid Amplitude of the Sun in Setting at Night, and riſing the next Morning in the Summer half Year ; for by dividing the Angle, made by thoſe two Azymuths, into two equal parts, the Meridian Line for the place where it is inquir'd and obſerv'd is given, the Meridian Line this way found, is that which is moſt commonly us'd, and will be near enough the truth for any common uſe, as for finding the variation of the Compaſs for the place where it is made, &c. But yet, it is not exactly true, nor can it in ſome more curious Inquiries, be made uſe of, and that, First, By reaſon that all the times of the Year, unleſs it be on the very ſolſtitial or longeſt and ſhorteſt Days, and even then alſo unleſs the Solſtice be exactly at Noon, the Sun is either increaſing or decreaſing its Declination ; and ſo the Sun is really in a differing parallel in the Morning from what it was at Night of the ſame Night, and in an other parallel at Night than what it was in the Morning of the ſame Day, and conſequently the Riſing and Setting Azymuths or Amplitudes do not make equal Angles with the true Meridian Line ; but the nearer the Sun is to either of the Solſtitial Points, the leſs the Error, and the nearer the Æquinoctial, the greater. *By the Sun two ways. 1ſt. Way.*

Secondly, The Meridian this way found is not exact, by reaſon of the differing Refraction of the Air in the Morning from what it is in the Evening, which I my ſelf have very often obſerv'd here at *London,* and may be much more conſiderable in more Southern Countries, where the difference between the warmth of the Air at Sun Riſing and Sun Setting is much more conſiderable than in this more temperate Climate, tho' on the other ſide that

greater

greater difference of Refraction may, I confess, make a much less difference of Azymuth or Amplitude where, the Sun's Rising and Setting is nearer to a Perpendicularity to the Horizon. However, some uncertainty is thereby caus'd, and in no case, but what I before mention'd, is exact: However, this is better than the way that is most made use of at Sea, for finding the variation of the Magnetical Needle or Compass, tho' yet it be far enough from the accurateness desirable; for the way by them generally practis'd is not by comparing the Morning and Evening Amplitude together, but either theMorning or theEvening alone esteeming the apparent Amplitude to be that which by Instruments or Calculation for that Day and Latitude they are in, the true Amplitude ought to be, allowing nothing at all for Refraction; in which case the visible Amplitude, by Refraction, makes more difference from what it truly ought to be, than two Amplitudes compar'd together, tho' suffering differing Refractions, will produce.

A Second way of finding the Meridian of any place by the Sun, is this, First, By the help of an Azymuth Compass to observe the Azymuth of the Sun about three Hours before Noon, at the same moment another Person with some convenient Instrument observing the true Altitude of it above the Horizon, then staying 'till about three Hours after Noon, and watching diligently when the Sun is descended to the same Altitude or height it was observ'd at in the Morning, and noting the true Azymuth thereof, and proceeding to divide the Angle between the two Azymuths, this way found by the Azymuth Compass, into two equal parts; this doth give the Meridian Line, and at the same time the variation of the Compass. This is abundantly more exact than the former way; for, First, The Sun is to be taken when at a considerable height above the Horizon, and so by that means is free for the most part from Refraction, whereas the Refraction in the Horizon is sometimes exceeding great. Secondly, The times between the two Observations being but short, as four, five or six Hours at most; the difference that is caus'd by the Sun's altering its Declination, is not so sensible as in a longer time; and therefore this of the two is much to be prefer'd, and is sometimes made use of at Sea also.

Now these Azymuths may be easily enough observ'd upon the Land, where a Horizontal Floor may be procur'd convenient for this purpose; but at Sea, where the Ship is roul'd and turn'd by the unsteady Surface of the Waves, it seems more difficult. But even there also Art has not left the Mariner without a convenience of a Horizontal Plain, which may be call'd fix'd, and that is the Compass Needle or Chard conveniently suspended in a Box; for by its suspension it maintains its Level, and by the Magnetical Vertue of the middle it keeps its Position in respect of the Points of the Horizon, notwithstanding all the unsteadiness of the Vessel in which it is carry'd: But of this and other Instruments, I shall hereafter discourse more at large.

There is another way of finding the Azymuth by the Sun or Stars at all times, either of the Day or Night, and that is by the help of exact Clocks, either with a Pendulum, or some other exact way of equally and exactly measuring and dividing of Time; and this method will be the most easy, the most exact, and most practicable at Sea, such a Clock at all times giving the true time of the Day or Night, if it be set with care at the Rising and Setting of the Sun, and then either by some one of the Projections (for it may be done by all the three usual Projections with ease) or by the Doctrine of Triangles; the Azymuth of the Sun or Star, for that time, is given, the Latitude being suppos'd known; but the Meridian is given, tho' the Latitude be not suppos'd known, and without either Projection or Trigonometrical Calculation, if the times of Rising and Setting be noted; for if by the said Clock the exact time when the Sun is risen just above the Horizon in the Morning, so that the under Limb of it just touch the Horizon, be taken notice of and set down; and the time when the under Limb of the Sun just touches the Horizon in the Evening be constantly observ'd, it will be easy to know what Hour and Minute by the said Clock, will denote either the

Hour

Hour of Twelve at Noon, or the Hour of Twelve at Night; that is, when the Sun shall be in the Meridian of the place; for by halfing the time interjacent between the Rising and Setting, or between the Setting and Rising, you have the time of the Sun's being in the Meridian to be shewn by the said Clock; and, if it be desir'd, the Clock may, by this way, be daily adjusted to the Meridian of the place. As suppose by the Clock (not yet adjusted to the Meridian of the place, but yet going equally and adjusted to the length of the Day) it be observ'd, that the Sun in Setting just touches the Horizon at 1h. 26'. by the Hand of the Clock, and that the next Morning, when the Sun in Rising be just got clear above the Horizon, the Hand of the Clock points at 11. 48'. it will be easy to find what Hour, by the Hand of the said Clock so continuing moving without altering or setting the Hand, shall denote the Hour of Twelve for the following Day; for halfing the time between 1h. 26'. and 11h. 48'. which is 10h. 22'. you have 6h. 37'. for the Hour of Noon the following Day; for half the difference between 1h. 26'. and 11. 48'. being 5h. 11'. this being added to 1h. 26'. the Hour of Setting will shew the time of Midnight to be by the Clock 6h. 37'. and consequently the Hour will be the same when the Sun will be in the Meridian the next Day. Against this way it may be Objected,

First, That tho' the Clock be adjusted to the middle motion of the Sun, *An Objection* yet that That will not be true for the length of any Day in the Year with-*against this* out regard to the proper Æquation of Time for the Day of Observation. *way obviated.* This I grant is so; but as the difference between the length of any one Day and any other is not very great, so will this difference be yet much less considerable, if it be made use of for to shew them, when is the time to observe the height of the Sun in the Meridian; and not much more considerable, if the knowing the time when the Sun is in the Meridian, the Line of North and South be to be found, or the variation of the Needle; but yet if it be thought necessary or considerable, it is easily provided against by a Table of Æquation of Time.

But then there may be a Second Objection made against this way, and *A second Ob-* that is, that a Ship being suppos'd under Sail doth continually alter either *jection obviat-* its Latitude, or its Longitude, or both; and so, tho' the Clock so observ'd *ed.* and adjusted, would at Land, or when the Ship lies at Anchor, serve to find the time when the Sun is in the Meridian, yet, by reason of this motion and progression of the Ship, the direction this way obtain'd cannot be just. This I grant is also a real cause of variety, and much greater than the former; yet 'tis not so great, but that it may be provided against, allowance being made for the same according as the case shall require; for by the Course Steer'd in the mean time, and the progress in that Course being taken notice of by the common way of keeping the Course, and distance Sail'd by the Logline and Compass, it will be easy to know, near enough for this purpose, what allowances are to be made, both in regard of the alterations of one and the other; and so the time of Noon (when the Sun is in the Meridian) may be accurately enough (for all uses at Sea) known and observ'd. And as this may serve to find the time, when the Sun is in the Meridian, in the Day, so may it serve to find the time when any notable Star, whose right Ascension is known, comes to the Meridian at Night; and so consequently (the declination of the Star being also known) of finding the Latitude of the place, by taking the Altitude of the said Star, when thus known, to be in the Meridian.----Which is the second way of finding the Meridian by the help of Cælestial Bodies in the Night.

Now as the Meridian may be found by Stars, with the help of such a Clock, so may it be found out by the Amplitudes of their Rising and Setting, or their Azymuths observ'd with an Azymuth Compass, when they are found to be of the same Altitude, before they come to, and after they have pass'd the Meridian; the same methods being us'd, as I have already shewn, are necessary to be observ'd in finding the Meridian by the Sun.

A fourth way of finding the Meridian by the Stars near the Pole.
A Fourth way of finding the Meridian Line by the help of Cælestial Bodies is by such of the fixt Stars near either of the Poles, as in the place where the Observation is to be made, do neither Rise nor Set, but continually appear above the Horizon ; this is done by noting their greatest Eastern and Western Digressions, by the help of an Azymuth Compass ; for by comparing those two together, and halving the difference, the Meridian Line is easily known, and at the same time the variation of the Needle for the place, where such Observations shall be made. Now the Times and Positions of these Stars, when in their greatest Eastern and Western Digression, may be easily found, if the Day of the Year be known, and the right Ascensions and Declinations of those Stars be also known, and a Mapp be at hand to shew the Situation of those Stars in respect of one another, and in respect of the Polar Point, about which they seem to move ; which is in part done in the Instrument call'd the Nocturnal. In making these Observations also, such a Clock, as I but now mention'd, will be of very good use to find the time precisely, when they are in their greatest Elongation from the Meridian.

These are (among multitudes of ways that have been proposed by Astronomers, Geographers, and Natural Writers) the most easy, plain, and obvious ways to be understood and practis'd by any one, not otherwise skill'd in Astronomy, nay, most of them even without knowing the Latitude of the place where the Observation is made, or the declination of the Sun, or place of the Planets or fixt Stars ; which I have chosen the rather, because to me they seem more simple and prævious to them all ; and therefore I chose first to discourse and explain them, after the ways of finding the Meridian, and consequently the variation of the Compass.

Of finding the Latitude.
The next thing that is to be obtain'd by Observations of Cælestial Bodies, is the Latitude of the place, or the distance of that place either Northwards or Southwards from the Æquinoctial Line. This is found various ways, both in the Day by the Sun, and in the Night by the Stars ; and that with much ease after the true Meridian by the former method, and consequently the variation of the Compass for the place of inquiry, are first known ; for by means of the Compass, so examin'd, the true Meridian Line is continually pointed out upon the Sea ; and so it will easily appear when the Sun or Stars are in that Azymuth. The same thing is also found by the aforesaid Clock ; then the declination of the Sun, or the true place of the Sun, for that time, being known for the Day, and the declination of the Star, to be observ'd, being known for the Night Observation, both which are express'd in Tables calculated for that purpose, by observing the Altitude of either, when in the Meridian, above the Horizon, and making allowance for the declination of the Body so observ'd, either by Addition or Subduction, as the Case requires, you find the height of the Æquinoctial Circle, which is the same with the distance of the Pole from the Zenith, the Complement of which is the Altitude of the Polar Point of the Heaven, or the distance of the Zenith of the place from the Æquinoctial Circle in the Heaven, or the Latitude of the place from the Line or Æquinoctial, suppos'd to be drawn upon the Earth.

THE Author having, in the foregoing Discourses treated of the Refraction or Inflection of the Air, as likewise concerning the drawing a true Meridian Line, and taking the Latitude of the place exactly at Land, I thought best to insert here the Abstracts of some Astronomical Lectures of that Subject, and give the descriptions of some Instruments contrived by him for the nice taking and dividing of Minute Angles, and some other useful Astronomical Instruments and Contrivances; especially, since I do not find them any where Published in any of his Works. When these Lectures were read, I know not, there being no date to them; but I judge by the Hand, and some other Circumstances, that they were read some Years before those of Navigation in 1683, and the following Years; however, the time not being, as to this, material, I hope the Reader will not be displeased with them : They treat of the Sun's Distance, Refraction and Inflection of Rays : Of the Moon's distance : Instruments to take the Diameters of the Planets : To take Angles : To draw a true Meridian, and several other Astronomical Matters.

R. W.

THE Perfection of Astronomy (a Science that has been cultivated in all Ages, but more highly improv'd in these last Centuries) depends very much upon the knowledge of the distance of those Cælestial Bodies, whose ways we would know, and whose motions and velocities we would calculate. Of which how certain we hitherto are, we need go no farther to be satisfy'd than to examine a few of the most famous Astronomers in their Opinions about the Distance or Parallax of the Sun. We find the noble *Ticho* to make the middle distance of the Sun 1150 Semidiameters. The ingenious *Kepler* in the *Rudolphine Tables* almost thrice as much, namely, 3381. The learned *Bullialdus* 1460; but *Vendelius* ten times more than he, and near fourteen times as much as *Ticho*, viz. 14656. with the half of which *Riccioli* is content making it only 7580. And these being deductions from their own several Parallaxes, and perhaps not any one of them from the true Parallax of the Sun, we shall not wonder to see them there also disagree as much *Ticho* making the Parallax of the Sun in its middle distance to be full 3′. 0″. *Kepler* only 1′. 0″. but *Bulliald* 2′. 21″. *Vendeline* 14″. and *Riccioli* 28″. And as *Herecules ex pede*, we may hence guess what is likely to be the Hypotheses of all the other Planets. Nor indeed shall we wonder if we consider, First, The accurateness requir'd both in their Calculations and Observations, and next the uncertainty of the Horizontal Refraction; and 'till this last be brought to a very great degree of accurateness and certainty, it is not to be expected that we shall ever certainly know the true distance of the Planets by the most accurate Calculations and Observations imaginable; for not to stay now on the consideration of what I shall by and by more largely manifest, viz. the small and suddain mutations of the internal parts of the Air from Heat and Cold, and Winds and Rains, and the like; we may from the differing Gravitation of the Atmosphere, which has been observ'd from the rising and falling of the Quicksilver in the Torricellian Experiments to be very considerable, namely, almost a fourteenth greater at some times than at others; we may, I say, from hence collect how uncertain the Refractions must be, which are caus'd by so unstable and uncertain a Medium. If therefore we that are thus plac'd this in Atmosphere, have yet a mind to know as much as could be known of those great Works of the Creator that seem to whirle about us and incompass us, we should, for that end, first consider well, and indeavour to acquaint our selves with the Nature of the Air or Medium through which we look, that lying the first Obstacle in our way towards those Bodies, we would contemplate. And therefore the examination of the Nature of this transparent Medium which thus incompasses us, and through which we are fain to see all the Cælestial Bodies as through a Glass Window, will deserve and require our indeavours in the first place; for being ignorant of the Nature of this ambient pellucid Body, it will be very difficult to determine any thing positively and exactly about the distance and true place of the Planets. And to this end I do not at all like their way of examining it, who first choose an

Of the difference between Astronomers as to the Suns distance.

The cause there of from the Refraction.

Hypothesis

Hypothesis of the Planets distance, and from that collect the height of the Air and the Refraction of it, and by that means reconcile what Parallax they please to the Planet they observe. Nor yet their way who fancying an imaginary Surface of the Air, at I know not what height, and there giving it an arbitrary refractive Quality, still make the Refraction of the Air as would reconcile all their Theories and Observations. Nor theirs who, from the Ecclipse of the Moon and shadow of the Earth, collect great matters ; for (as I shall anon shew) all those Phænomena may be explicated, tho' the Diameter of the Sun be no bigger, nay, tho' much less than that of the Earth, by means of the Refraction in the Atmosphere, we being hitherto uncertain how great it may be, and 'till we are assur'd of it nothing can be concluded as to the distance of the Sun or Moon from the Ecclipses. But I rather therefore suppose it necessary for him that will know the true Nature of the Air as to Refraction, and the true Parallax or Distance of the Cælestial Bodies, to go quite other ways to work to find each of them a part. And for the examination of the Air it will be requisite to collect and examine as many Phænomena of that kind as can be met with all. Such as these I shall now acquaint you with. It has been often observ'd, by the naked Eye, that the Sun and Moon, when near the Horizon, appear oval ; but since the Invention------

The remainder of this Lecture is lost.

I did the last Term indeavour to shew, from very many Experiments and Observations, that the Air or Atmosphere, wherewith we are incompass'd, had in it two Proprieties not taken notice of before, which, 'till they were well understood, examin'd and regulated, would so far spoil all the most accurate Horizontal Observations that were not somewhat regulated according to them, that there could be no certain deductions from them of the Distance or Parallax of any Cælestial Body ; no, not of the Moon itself, which is nearest to us, and consequently has the most sensible Parallax : For I then shew'd, that notwithstanding all the Affirmations, and Theories, and Calculations, and Observations of the best and most accurate Astronomers, it was possible to solve all the Phænomena, tho' the Moon, for instance, were *Of the Inflection of the Atmosphere.* suppos'd not above a third part of the distance, she is commonly by them suppos'd to be : For the Inflection of the Rays of Light, which is made in the several Regions and Spaces of the Air from the differing degrees of Expansion and Condensation of the parts of the Air in those places, does so uncertainly bend those Rays before they come to the Eye, that 'tis hardly possible by the most accurate and diligent Observations that can be made in any one place, to regulate one already rais'd Hypothesis, or to found and establish a new one ; and therefore I shew'd, that certainly the best way to redress this inconvenience, will be to get certain Observations made of the way of the *Two observers at a distance to observe the Moon's place among the fixt Stars.* Moon among the small or Telescopical fixt Stars, by two Persons very far remov'd from each other in Latitude, tho' as exactly as could be seated under one and the same Meridian as to Longitude ; each of which two Persons should observe exactly with an excellent Telescope fitted with a divided Ruler, the way of the Moon among the small fixt Stars ; and thereby we should (by first regulating the distance and knowing certainly her apparent Diameter at that *How to know the Moon's true distance; and thence the Inflection of the Rays.* time when she was at that distance) be able at all times by a single Observation of her Diameter, with a good Telescope, without any further Calculation, certainly to observe and know her true distance at that time, and then it would be easy very to know also what must be her Parallax in all Altitudes above the Horizon, and consequently it will be extreamly easy by the deduction of the Parallax of the Altitude of the Moon, to know, by the Observation, what is the then sensible Inflection of the Rays.

Requisites for this Observation. For the performing of which Observations, there seem to be very many things requisite, which I shall indeavour to explain. And the first is a good Telescope about some ten or twelve Foot long ; for this, if it be well fitted into a small and light Tube, is easily enough managable by any one single Person without much trouble. This Telescope is best adapted for Cælestial Observations, if it have only at that end which is next the Eye, one pretty deep

deep Convex Cryſtalline Glaſs well Poliſh'd and of clear Mettle; for thereby the Objects will appear much plainer and diſtincter, tho' there cannot be ſo much ſeen at a time, as through a Teleſcope fitted with two, or more Convex Eye-glaſſes: Then to fit this Inſtrument for the Obſervation of the Diameters of the ☉ ☾ ♄ ♃ ♂ ♀ or ☿, the moſt convenient and moſt eaſy way is to take a ſmall piece of Wire, and to place it ſo within the Tube, at ſuch a convenient diſtance from the Eye-glaſs, that the Eye indeavouring to look through the Tube may ſee it moſt diſtinctly; that is, it muſt be plac'd within the Tube juſt in the focus of that Eye-glaſs; then having by the Eye found the true diſtance of this Ruler to take it out and divide it into Inches, and Decimal parts of Inches, cutting with the edge of a Knife, or the like, very ſmall croſs Strokes or Gutters, in each of thoſe Diviſions, and every fifth or tenth Notch, to cut much deeper, ſo to make it more conſpicuous. Having thus divided and mark'd it, this Ruler or Wire ſhould be again put into its place, and the Tube directed againſt ſome Star in or near the Æquator, and in that Poſition ſo fixt, that the motion of that Star may be plainly obſerv'd paſſing along by the divided Ruler. Then having ſo adapted it, there ſhould be provided a Pendulum made with a Thread and Plummet and adjuſted to ſuch a length, as may make it vibrate once every ſecond Minute of Time; having this ready, the next thing to be done, is to place the Tube ſo, as that the Star may appear juſt coming into the Glaſs, then fixing the Tube, and obſerving 'till the Star be juſt upon one of the Diviſions, let go the Pendulum, and obſerve the paſſage of the Star along by the Ruler, 'till by the vibration of the Pendulum you find a minute of Time paſt, or any other determinate number of Seconds you ſhall think fit, obſerving exactly how many Diviſions on the Ruler the Star has paſt by in that time; for by this means it will be exceeding eaſy to obſerve how many of thoſe Decimal diviſions anſwer to the Subtenſe of a Minute of a Degree; for ſince we know that the motion of thoſe Stars which are in, or very near to the Æquinoctial, is near a Minute of Longitude in four Seconds of Time, or a Degree of Longitude in four Minutes of Time, 'twill be very eaſy by obſerving the motion of the Star along the Ruler, and comparing it with the Vibrations of a Pendulum, to find what length of the Ruler does anſwer to a Minute, or the five Thouſand four Hundredth part of a Quadrant; which having found, it will be eaſy to place ſeveral diviſions on the other ſide of the Ruler, that each Minute may be divided into Seconds.

Deſcription of the Inſtrument. *Tab.* 8. *Fig.* 5.

As in the fifth Figure of the eighth Table; ſuppoſe ABCD to repreſent the bright Area of Light appearing through the Teleſcope; let BD repreſent the Wire or Ruler, which ſeems, to one that looks through it, to divide that Area into two equal parts; let the ſmall diviſions on the under ſide be the Inches and Decimals; and let the diviſions on the upper ſide E F G H I K, *&c.* repreſent the diſtances, which, by the Vibrations of the Pendulum, have been found to anſwer to a Minute; for having, by the Pendulum, found the Star to have mov'd from K to E in twenty Seconds of Time, it is manifeſt, if that diſtance be divided into five equal parts, each of theſe muſt anſwer to a firſt Minute of a Degree; each of which firſt Minutes or Diſtances EF FG GH HI, *&c.* may be again ſubdivided into a determinate number of equal parts, each of which will anſwer to ſo many ſecond Minutes of a Degree; ſo that by this means not only the Diameters of the Sun and Moon may be found pretty exactly to Seconds, but the Diameters alſo of all the other Planets. The diſtances alſo of the ſmall Teleſcopical Stars one from another, may, by this means, be very eaſily obſerv'd.

Tho

THo' this Instrument may serve very well for many uses, especially for observing the Velocities of the Motions, yet I shall subjoin the description of a much nicer divider for a Telescope, as I found it delineated and described on a loose Paper among the rest of the Author's Manuscripts; it was intitled The divider for Hevelius.

R. W.

The description of an Instrument for measuring the Minute distances of Objects at the focus of the Telescope.

Tab. 10. *Fig.* 1. Aaaa, a Ruler or Frame of Box, or other close Wood, of the form describ'd in the Figure, into which it is let in; a small Plate of Brass bbb upon which the equal divisions are made; there may be also a bended Plate let into the Circular Limb for measuring the Angle at e; ccccc, two Arms of Wood which open on the under side of the Ruler or Frame upon a Joint, whose Center must be plac'd as near the point e, as conveniently as it can without hindring the Prospect. dd a pair of Forceps, with a Screw like a Vice, one of whose sides is fix'd to the Ruler and the other moveable; for the holding the end of the Hair or the Silk-worms-clew ef, ef at the Point e, the other ends thereof being fastned to the ends of the Arms nn. gg, a diagonal Hair or Clew upon which the Divisions are to be measur'd fix'd into the Ruler at gg. eh, the middle Hair or Clew crossing the other at right Angles; kk two Screws, by which the Instrument is fix'd to the Tube of the Telescope. ll, two Arms of Wood fasten'd to the other Arms ccccc at qq, serving for the opening of the Arms equally from the middle Line, and for fixing them in any posture by the help of a Button or Screw, the end of which is m, the said Screw slipping in a small grove or slit oooo. The Line of division bb, I have here plac'd at ten times the distance of gg from the Point e: So that the divisions are made ten times more distinct at bb than they could be at gg; but this distance may be either increas'd or diminish'd, as there is occasion, and the whole Instrument may be made either bigger or less, according to the use thereof. *Thus far the Author's Description of it, the rest of the Contrivance is plain by the Figure.*

Now, because for making a compleat Hoop or Zone of all the fix'd Stars in the Zodiack, the Angle afforded by the help of a single Telescope, is not sufficient for taking the true distance of Stars when many Degrees remov'd from each other; therefore for such kind of Observations there is an Instru-

A double Telescope for taking Angles, this is afterwards describ'd

ment which by the opening or shutting, or the moving of two six Foot Telescopes on a Joint in the manner of a Joint-Ruler, and a small diagonal Scale which measures the Angle they make with each other, when any two Stars, by two Observators, are at the same instant seen through those two Tubes; which Instrument I shall, on some other occasion, describe; for it is indeed one of the best for the observations of the distances and places of the Stars that has been yet thought on, and may serve also for measuring the Diameters of the Sun and Moon, tho' nothing near so exactly as the newly mention'd twelve Foot Telescope; for by the divided Ruler the Diameter of the Planets may be distinguish'd even to Seconds. Wherefore, if by means of Observations made at very far remov'd Stations, we can be assur'd of the distance of any of the Planets, and by this means, at the same time, we have the apparent Diameter of that Body, it will be exceeding easy at any other time, by observing the apparent Diameter with this Tube, to know the then true distance of the Planet at that time also; for the sines of the apparent Angles of the Diameter, and the respective distances will be very near reciprocal; that is, as the sine of the apparent Angle of the Body in the second Observation, to the sine of the apparent Angle in the first, so the dis-

Tab. 8. *Fig.* 6. tance of the Body in the first Observation, to the distance of the Body of second very near. As in the eighth Table, Fig. 6. Let A represent the Eye on the Earth, BC the Semidiameter of the Moon; for instance, in its

the

Perigeum; AB the true diſtance of the Moon at that time from the Eye, BAC the apparent Angle of the Moon's Semidiameter; let DE repreſent the apparent Semidimameter of the Moon in its Apogeum; EAD the Angle under which it appears. Then on A, and the diſtance AC deſcribe the Circle CFG, and from F draw FG Perpendicular to AD; I ſay, as FG the ſine of the apparent Diameter in the ſecond Obſervation to BC the ſine of the apparent Diameter in the firſt; ſo is AC to AE; that is, ſo is the Radius of the leſſer Circle of diſtance to the Radius of the greater, that is, very near as the leſſer diſtance of the Center of the Planet is to the greater diſtance of the Center of the Planet : For DE is very near equal to CB by the ſuppoſition, as being the viſible Diameter of the ſame Body; tho' why 'tis otherwiſe I ſhall by and by ſhew; and AC is equal to AF, as being the Rays of the ſame Circle; therefore by the ſecond of the ſixth Book of *Euclid*, as FG to ED, that is, to CB; ſo is AF, that is AC to AE; which AC and AE give the diſtance of the Center of the Planet from the Eye much more exactly than the Lines AB or AD; tho' neither of them are exact but both ſomewhat leſs than the truth. To demonſtrate which let DEF in the ſeventh Figure repre- *Tab.* 8. *Fig.* 7. ſent the Body of the Sun, Moon, or other Planet, A the Eye, B the Center of that Body, AB the true diſtance of that Center from the Eye, DAB half the apparent Angle of the Body, AD a tangent Ray that touches the Globe DEF in D; from D let fall the Perpendicular DC on AB. I ſay then, that the Line AD ſhall be much nearer an equality to AB than AC; for by the eighteenth of the third of *Euclid*, ADB ſhall be a right Angle, and the Angle ACD is a right Angle by the Conſtruction, and the Angle DAC is common to both Triangles; therefore as AC to AD, ſo AD to AB: AD therefore will be a mean proportional between AC and AB, and conſequently will be nearer to an equality with AB than AC will be. Nor is the viſible Diameter of a Globe exactly the ſame at a nearer and farther diſtance, as I even now hinted : Nor indeed is it at any time exactly the true, but tho' the appearing Diameter be really always leſs than the true Diameter, yet does it always ſubtend a bigger Angle at the Eye. To demonſtrate which, let us *Tab.* 9. *Fig.* 2. ſuppoſe DEH to ſignify a great Circle drawn on the Body of the Moon, or other Globular Body, A the Eye, DC the Semidiameter of the viſible part, BG the true Semidiameter of the Body. I ſay therefore firſt, that DC is really leſs, tho' it appear bigger to the Eye than BG; for drawing the Line BD in the Triangle BCD, the Angle C is a right Angle, and conſequently BD is bigger than DC, therefore DC is leſs than BG which is equal to BD. But Secondly, I ſay, that DC ſubtends a greater Angle at the Eye than BG; for AD being by the ſuppoſition a tangent to the Circle at D, a Line, as AG drawn from any other point of the Semicircle HGE to the point A, muſt neceſſarily divide the Angle DAC into two parts, DAG and GAC; therefore GAC being but a part is leſs than the whole DAC. Further, I ſay, of the apparent Diameters at ſeveral Diſtances, that the ſhorter diſtance has always really the ſhorter apparent Diameter, but that that ſhorter Diameter does ſubtend a bigger Angle at the Eye. That the ſhorter diſtance has really the ſhorter viſible Diameter, is evident, becauſe the Bodies are Globular. To demonſtrate which, ſuppoſe ADFG, in the third Figure, to be a plain paſſing through the *Tab.* 9. *Fig.* 3. Eye and the Center of the Sun. Let A be the Eye farther remov'd, and B the Eye nearer plac'd to C the Center of the Sun. DEFH therefore being the interſection of this Plain, and the Superficies of the Sun or Planet will repreſent a greater Circle on that Body. From the Points A and B draw the Lines AE and AH and BDBJ; which may touch the Circle in EH, D and I, and from theſe two points draw the Lines EH and DI. I ſay therefore firſt, that the Diameter EH of the Diſk of the Sun apparent to the Eye A, is bigger than DJ the Diameter of the Diſk apparent to the Eye B; for drawing the Lines EC and DC, HC and IC, 'tis evident DCJ is leſs than ECH, and conſequently by the fifteenth of the third of *Euclids Elem.* that DI is leſs than EH. Next, I ſay, that the apparent Diameter DJ ſubtends a bigger Angle at B than EH does; for BD and BI being tangents to the Circle DGI, whatſoever Lines are drawn from the point B to any point of the Circle, muſt neceſſarily be drawn between BD and BJ, and conſe-

quently

quently any two of them must make a lesser Angle than DBJ. But to omit these Niceties, which indeed are so inconsiderable in the observation of the Distance or Diameter of the Sun or Moon, and much more of the other smaller Planets, that with the most accurate Instruments that the Art of Man hath hitherto invented, they will hardly be discernable, as not amounting to $\frac{1}{10000}$ part of the Diameter of the Sun or Moon, when biggest, as may be seen by a Table of Natural Sines: It will be therefore sufficiently exact to make the Diameters and Distances Reciprocal. So that if by a good Telescope order'd, as I have directed, the apparent Diameters be heedfully observ'd, we may, supposing any one distance known, by means of two Observators, easily enough know the distance at any time, and consequently the present Parallax, and from that the Refraction, or rather Inflection of the Rays in the Atmosphere : We must therefore rectify our Refractions or Inflections, caus'd by the interpos'd Air, by our certain fore-knowledge of the present Parallax.

How to know the Moens Orbit exactly.

And this Method, tho' it be somewhat præposterous to the ways yet practis'd by the best Astronomers, is certainly the most Natural ; for having once the certain Parallax of the Moon, we may very easily, from Observations, collect exactly in what kind of Line or Orbits he is mov'd about the Earth, and with what Velocity in what parts of that Orbit, and consequently from some few Observations, her true motions may be known, which we are hitherto not so sure of; and thence consequently 'twill be no difficult matter to Compose and Constitute a true and real Theory of the motion of the Moon, and to calculate Tables accordingly ; which, tho' it has been hitherto pretended by very many, yet 'till some such Course as this be taken for the regulating of Observations, I fear 'twill not be in hast done. From which Tables, and a Hoop, or Zone of all the Telescopical Stars as well as visible, what could be less expected than an easy way for finding of the Longitudes of places ? For 'twould be no more difficulty to know the true Longitude of any place then by a six Foot Telescope, which is very easily manageable at Sea to make an Observation of the appulse of the Moon to some fixt Star in that Zone, and from those exact Tables to calculate at what time that should be in the place for whose Meridian they are calculated, and at the same time to what a Clock 'twere in that place where the Observation is made.

To get a true Theory of the Sun and the obliquity of the Eccliptick, &c.

Having, by this means, got the true Theory of the Moon, it will be so much the easier to find out the true Theory of the Sun ; for by that of the Moon we shall be able to know the Inflection of the Rays in the Air, and consequently the Parallax of the Sun, if sensible, will be quickly found, and having its apparent Diameter measur'd with a good Telescope at that time when the Parallax was calculated, it will be very easy from the apparent Diameter of the same at any other time, thro' the same or any other Telescope fitted accordingly, to know the true Parallax of the Sun at the time of the Observation ; and consequently both the Obliquity of the Eccliptick will be exactly known, and the place or Velocity of the Sun in that Eccliptick (or of the Earth in its Orbit which is all one) will be more easily found, which because the ways hitherto us'd of observing only the Meridian Altitudes, are not so accurate as might be desir'd, I shall propound a way which I think will be very easily practicable, and will afford most certain information of the apparent place of the Sun as to its Positions among the fix'd Stars at all times ; and consequently a Year or two's Observations, made after this manner, will very exactly instruct one how to make exact Tables of the Velocity of the Sun or Earth in the Eccliptick, and consequently to be the better enabl'd to raise a true Theory of the motion of the Sun or Earth; and so to be able more exactly to calculate the Ecclipses of both the Luminaries, and to foretel all the visible Phænomena of the Positions of those two Bodies one to another.

Ways to find the Meridian.

The way I propounded is this, First, To get in a convenient place for Observation, an exactly true Meridian Line drawn. This may be done very many ways, some more easy, others more exact : The most easy and plain way, and which is pretty exact also, if the Sun be near either of the Tropicks, is by procuring a large smooth Plain, which must be exactly level'd Horizontally and fixt in that Position ; then finding the middle part and taking

ing there a Point, describe about that Point, at several distances, several Circles one less than another ; then erecting a Perpendicular stile in the Center, and obſervihg a Morning and Afternoon ſhadow of the Sun, where the ſhadow of the top touches the ſame Circle in two diſtant places, and dividing the interpos'd Arch between thoſe two parts into two equal parts, a Line drawn through that middle Point ſo found, and the Center of the Plain will give the true Meridian or North and South Line of the place.

And this ſuppoſing the Sun near the Tropick of *Cancer* or *Capricorn* will be pretty near the true Meridian. But in this Obſervation care ſhould be had, that the Sun be pretty much elevated above the Horizon, before the ſhadow be obſerv'd, becauſe of the varying Refractions at ſeveral times of the ſame Day. The Meridian likewiſe may be found when the Sun is in either of the Æquinoxes, by obſerving any two ſhadows of the Stile, and drawing a Line through them, and then to that Line from the Center, drawing another Line at right Angles ; for this Perpendicular Line ſhall be in or very near the Meridian of the place.

A third way, but not ſo certain as either, may be, by a pretty large Magnetical Needle, ſuffer'd to play or move upon a very ſharp Point ; for in many places, as at the preſent, here in *London*, the Needle will, by the Magnetiſm of the Earth, be directed very near the North and South Line of the place. But none of all theſe being exact, the two firſt being uncertain, by reaſon of the annual motion of the Sun or Earth ; and this laſt by reaſon of the variation of the Magnetical direction of the Needle, 't will be requiſite to make uſe of ſome other that is more accurate.

And among theſe may be reckon'd the way by taking the Altitude and Azymuth of any known Star, which will require the calculation of a Triangle or two ; or to obſerve the Azymuths of any Star when it is in the ſame *The moſt exact way.* Eaſtern and Weſtern height ; or, which is beſt of all, to obſerve Azymuths of the moſt Eaſtern and Weſtern excurſions of a Star within or near the Artick Circle, which, how it may beſt be done, I ſhall ſhew in my next Diſcourſe, as likewiſe deſcribe ſome uſeful Inſtruments for Aſtronomical Obſervations.

I did, the laſt Day, propound three things that were requiſite for the Perfection of Aſtronomical Theories by Obſervations ; and they are ſuch as, without which, we ſhall have but little certainty of any Hypotheſis whatſoever. And indeed they were ſuch as ſhould never be ſeperate ; for either of them being wanting, the other would be imperfect : And therefore whenſoever any Obſervation is made of the one without taking notice of the other, that Obſervation muſt need be imperfect and inſignificant. The things to be obſerv'd, I ſhew'd, were three ; the firſt was the true diſtance of the Body, whoſe way and motion was to be obſerv'd from the Center of the Earth ; the only accurate way of doing which, I ſhew'd, was by means of two Obſervators very far remov'd from each other on the Surface of the Earth. I ſhew'd alſo, that the moſt convenient places, for ſuch ſtations, would be ſome two places as far remov'd from each other in point of Latitude, as could be conveniently found, and as near under the ſame Meridian or Degree of Longitude. That their beſt method of Obſervation would be to begin with the Moon, and to find her true diſtance ; and next with the Sun, obſerving at the ſame time their apparent Diameters ; for by that means I ſhew'd how the apparent Diameter of any one known diſtance being given, the true diſtance, at any other times, would be eaſily found from the apparent Diameters, and that therefore there needed no more trouble but only to obſerve the apparent Diameters by means of a good Teleſcope ; and the true diſtance might, by Calculation, be preſently known ; for I then ſhew'd, that the apparent Magnitude of the Diameter, and the diſtances were Reciprocal. I ſhew'd likewiſe by what means a Teleſcope might be ſo prepar'd as to be fit for ſuch Obſervations.

And therefore it were extreamly deſirable, that ſome, whoſe leiſure would permit them, would ſet upon this Work, and if they were not able to go through with the whole, to indeavour to do as much as were requiſite for

the

the Observations to be afterwards made, of the ways and motions of the Planets.

And for this end, if they did only regulate exactly all the places of the Stars within, or pretty near the Zodiack, that were either of the first, second, or third Magnitude ; it would be sufficient for any Observations that were to be made of the Planets, especially if the Observator were furnish'd with an Instrument which I the last Day mention'd, and promis'd then more fully to describe ; and that is with a double Telescope, as I may so call it, or an Instrument, which, by means only of two Telescopes, mov'd on a Joint, and a Ruler divided by a Line of Chords answerable to the length of the Telescopes, does, by the help of two Observators, easily and most exactly determine the Angle of distance of any two Objects. This Instrument was invented by Sir *Christ. Wren*, a Person so eminent in all kind of Knowledge, and most especially in Mathematical and Mechanical, that the naming him the Author will be a sufficient commendation of the Instrument itself. Omitting therefore any further Praises of it, I shall indeavour, in as few words as may be to describe the Instrument itself, and the several parts of it, the manner of rectifying it and using it for any Cælestial Observations.

The Instrument consists of two square Tubes or Boxes AB, and CD, which are each of them at B and D furnish'd with a good Object-glass of six Foot, and at the other ends A and C are likewise furnish'd with a very deep Lens or Eye-glass M N ; each of them also have a small Cell to keep the Eye at a due distance from the Glass ; and at a convenient distance within those Eyeglasses, as about O and P, are plac'd two small Plates of Brass, out of which a round hole is cut in the manner of the Figure R, only leaving a small Triangle, whose Point just comes to the Center or middle of this Circle at S ; this I call the Sight, the use of which I shall by and by describe. These two Tubes, thus fitted, are join'd together by a very firm Joint at E ; which Joint is made so strong and so exact, that the Tubes always, whether open or shut, keep in the same Plain : These Tubes, being thus join'd, are first rectify'd to an exact Parallelism one with another, by being directed so against some Star, and mov'd to and fro 'till the Star be seen through both of them at the same time to touch the Apex or Corner of the Triangle in the Sight ; at which time, by means of a contrivance at the other end, they are fix'd in that Parallelism ; so that against whatsoever Star one of them be directed, the other will, in the same manner, be directed also ; the conetrivance for fixing these Tubes at the ends A and C, is this : On the Tube CD is fasten'd a peice of Brass JK, at the end J, of which, is made a Center or Hole L, at the same distance from the Tube that the Center E is of at the other end ; and on to the Tube AB is likewise plac'd a corresponding peice of Brass FG, which is not so fixt to the Tube as the other, but is made to slide a little, as occasion shall require, between two pieces of Brass T and V, but so as by means of a small Screw H to be suddainly fix'd in any posture ; this piece of Brass has likewise a small Center or Hole L, at the same distance as near as may be, that the Center E is remov'd from the Tube AB ; these two Centers are both join'd together by means of a small Screw which passes through both of them ; which being done the Screw H is loosn'd, and the Tubes are, by being both directed against the same Star, reduc'd to an exact Parallelism ; which being done, by the turning of the Screw H, the Plate FG is firmly fixt in that posture to the Tube AB, and the Instrument is rectify'd for Observation.

This being done, the exact distance of the Centers E and L is measur'd, and by that distance as Radius a Ruler YY is divided, either into a Line of Chords, or, which is better, into such equal parts whereof ten Thousand make the whole Radius ; then the Screw being remov'd that held the two Centers together at L, and two small Sockets x z screw'd on, through which this divided Ruler may slide, the one on the Center of the Plate FG, the other on that of IK. And the one end of the Ruler being fix'd in one of these Sockets, so as the beginning of the divisions lies just over the Center of it ; and the other part sliding in the other Socket, according as the Tubes are more or less open'd from each other on the Center E ; the two Observators
are

are to direct each of them his own Tube to the Star, which they have a-
greed upon to observe; so that at the same time one directs his Tube to
one of those Stars, the other directs his to the other Star, and when each
of them has at the same instant rectify'd his Tube to the Star, he observes
so that the Apex or Point of the Triangle in the sight does just touch the
Star, then he that has the Tube through whose Socket the divided Ruler
slides by turning a small Screw YZ, fixes those Tubes in that posture, and by
the number of the equal divisions of the Ruler, which measures the distance
of the two Centers, the apparent Angle or distance of those two Stars, is
most exactly found to Minutes. And indeed, by means of a small additional
contrivance, which I shall elsewhere shew, it may not only be made to distinguish Angles to Minutes but to Seconds also. Now this Instrument, besides this great exactness, has many other conveniences which may render it
very considerable; for it may be made very light, and is also exceeding easily
manageable, and by being clos'd together takes up but a little room, and
may be easily transported from place to place, and made use of almost in any
Chamber; and indeed all Particulars consider'd, it is a worthy Product of its
excellent Inventor: By this, not only the places of the fixt Stars may be regulated, but even the places of the Planets may most exactly be found.

I Shall here add the Description of an Instrument for taking Angles at one Prospect, Tab. 11. Fig. 2.
as I found it describ'd upon a loose Paper. ee, ff, two long Rulers or Arms open-
ing upon a Joint or Center g, hh a Ruler divided into a thousand parts, measuring
the Angle at g by a Table of Chords; ab, a Telescope fixt on the Ruler ff, so as that the
middle of it may lie Perpendicular over the inner edge of the Ruler; a the place of
the Cross-sight, b the Object-glass, i the Eye-glass, cc the Reflex-glass whose edge
just touches the Center g, and whose Surface cc is in the same plain with that of the
inner edge of the Ruler ee: On the backside of which Glass is a Brass Plate with
two Ears dd, at right Angles, by which it is screwed to the Ruler ee.

R. W.

If therefore by the Instrument describ'd Page 502, all the Stars within or
near the Zodiack were regulated and assertain'd, it would then be much
more secure, taking the true distance of the Planets to be observ'd from
them, and much more easy to find their true place in the Zodiack; and consequently a much less number of such kind of Observations would suffice to
determine their true Ways, Motions and Velocities. Now, tho' that eminent Astronomer *Hevelius* has promis'd shortly to publish to the World a
perfect Catalogue, not only of all the fix'd Stars already taken notice of in
other Catalogues, but even of multitudes of others sufficiently manifest to
the naked Eye, yet we think that Expectation should no ways discourage
any from making Observations himself, since, at best, no Man can be so sure
of anothers Observations as of his own. And next, since it would not be a
labour of very great difficulty to regulate the places of all the Stars of the first,
second and third Magnitude within or near the Zodiack, because their number is not very great.

And, Thirdly, It cannot but be a great satisfaction to any such Observator to find when those others, promis'd by *Hevelius*, shall be Publish'd,
that his own Observations do concur with those of the other, or that he
is assur'd that his own are more exact than those.

But, Fourthly, And, most especially, he should not be deter'd, but much
rather excited, since without such Corrections of the places of the fixt Stars
nothing can be done in any other Cælestial Observation, and consequently *Observations*
such a part of a Man's time, as to this design, will be wholly lost. But to *in order to re-*
proceed with what I was saying concerning the Observations requisite for the *gulate the Pla-*
regulation of the Theories of the Planets; I say, supposing the true places *nets motions.*
of the fixt Stars, as to their Longitude and Latitude, were known, and supposing we had, from distant Observations, the Moons true distance from
the Center of the Earth, and her apparent Diameter at that time, we
might easily, by the Telescope, find her distance at all other times, and by
her

her appulfe to certain Stars, or diftance from them, together with the time of the Obfervation and her apparent Diameter, we might eafily know her true Pofition among the fixt Stars, in refpect of the Center of the Earth ; and if fuch Obfervations were continu'd every Day for fome Months, or rather fome Years, we might expect another kind of Theory than any we have hitherto had of the Moon. Now the beft time for making all thefe Obfervations of the Moon, fhould be when it can, with convenience, be perform'd when the Moon comes juft to the Meridian ; at that time the Moon being leaft incumbr'd with Refraction and Parallax ; and as for the reducing of her Orbit to the Eccliptick, that will be eafily enough done afterwards, when her paffage among the fixt Stars is once well known ; and, by the way, methinks it would be the beft way for any fuch Obfervator not to puzzle or prepoffefs himfelf with many Notions, Suppofitions, Theories and Hypothefes, but rather to lay afide for a while, at leaft, all thofe Opinions of determinate Orbs, and Epicycles and Excentricks, and Circles and Elipfes, or any other pre-conceiv'd Notion, and only to make and regulate the Obfervations fo (the manner of which I have already fhewn) that the true Place or Pofition of the Moon, among the fixt Stars of the Zodiack, in refpect of the Center of the Earth ; and her true diftance from the Center of the Earth in that Pofition, might be accurately found out and Regifter'd ; for by a good number of fuch Obfervations and Collections, we fhould not only be able to examine more narrowly all the already famous Hypothefes, and to overthrow them perhaps, but to raife and excogitate divers others, fuch as would at leaft reft upon a more fure Foundation, and if carefully and confiderately built be of a more found and fubftantial Structure.

Nor fhould thefe kinds of Obfervations be made of the Moon only, but of the Sun. *Mercury*, ♀, ♂, ♃, and ♄ ; for tho' indeed their true diftances from the Center of the Earth are not fo eafily known (tho' indeed we know not yet neither to how great a certainty Induftry may bring us even in this particular alfo) tho', I fay, the true diftances of thefe Bodies from us be very difficult to be found, yet their comparative diftances may much more eafily ; for, by the help of a very good Telefcope, we may at all times obferve their apparent Diameters moft exactly, and confequently fince, as I have fhew'd the laft Day, the apparent Diameters and Diftances are Reciprocal, we might have their comparative diftances, and perhaps alfo from comparing feveral Circumftances we might come by their true ones alfo. For fuppofing we had the diftance of the Sun and Earth (the moft likely way for finding which I fhall anon explain) we might poffibly find thofe of the other Planets by fome fuch way as this, namely, by the accurate Obfervation of their apparent Diameters with an excellent Telefcope of forty or rather threefcore Foot long, when they are neareft approaching their being hid by the Beams, and when they are in their oppofition to the Sun ; for by the comparing of thefe two we might be inform'd of the proportion between their diftances at thofe times, and confequently the difference of thofe two, feeming, for the moft part, to be afcribable to the great Orb of the Earth. It will not be difficult, from many of thefe Obfervations, to determine the proportion of the Diameter of the great Orb of the Earth to the Diameters of the Orb of *Saturn*, of the Orb of *Jupiter*. and of that of *Mars* ; the Diameters alfo of *Venus* in her retrograde Conjunction with the Sun, and in her direct ; that is, when fhe is in her neareft and fartheft diftance from the Earth, will very much help towards the finding the proportion of the Orb of *Mercury* about the Sun to that of the Earth.

As for the finding the true diftance of the Sun, the beft way would be by means of two Obfervators, plac'd as far afunder as they could be conveniently ; which two fhould either at certain times of the Year (namely, when the Sun is in or very near either of the Solftices) obferve by the help of a Quadrant (which I fhall another time more fully defcribe) by which the Altitude of any Cæleftial Body may be obferv'd to fecond Minutes ; they fhould, I fay, with fuch a Quadrant obferve moft exactly the Meridian heights of the Sun when in the Solftice, being each of them moft exactly affur'd of the true height of the Pole by obferving the greateft and leaft height of fome

notable

notable Star within the Artick Circle by means of this Inftrument. And 'tis not unlikely but that by this means, thefe two Obfervators, comparing their Obfervations, may be able to deduce the Parallax of the Sun. But fuppofing that be exceeding difficult and fcarce feafable, yet fome Ecclipfe of the Sun may fo fall out as to be difcernable by both; and then from the comparing of fuch Obfervations made by each, 'twill be no difficult matter, fuppofing the diftance of the Moon known, to know that of the Sun alfo: And having its true diftance once given, together with its apparent Diameter at that time, its diftance at any other time will be eafily enough found, fuppofing its Diameter only obferv'd.

Having found this, it will be eafy, by Obfervations, to find out the Orbit *of finding* of the Sun or Earth, and the Velocity of either of them in any part of it; *the Earth's Or-* and this will be by accurately obferving and comparing the Appulfe of the *bit.* Sun and any notable fixt Star, whofe Longitude and Latitude is certainly known to the Meridian; obferving likewife the exact Meridian Altitude of the Sun, together with its apparent Diameter. For performing of thefe Obfervations as they fhould be, there will be three things requifite befides *Three things* what I have already defcrib'd, which was the Telefcope; and thofe three *neceffary.* things are, Firft, An exact Meridian Line or Inftrument for Azymuths. Secondly, A moft exact and manageable Quadrant for obferving Altitudes. And, Thirdly, A moft accurate Time-keeper, Watch, or Clock, each of which I fhall defcribe in their order.

I did, the laft Day, fhew the neceffity of regulating the places of the fixt Stars before they could be made ufe of for finding the true place of any of the Planets, for I then hinted how much many of them had been found to deviate from the places affign'd them by *Ticho.* But becaufe it would be very difficult to rectify all the Conftellations I then hinted; that it would be fufficient for moft Obfervations, if only thofe Stars were regulated, which were the moft confpicuous or notable in or near the Zodiack; and for this purpofe I did likewife then delineate and defcribe a new and moft exact Inftrument, which I judg'd the moft convenient for that purpofe, of any that has yet been made ufe of, it being an Inftrument very eafily manageable, very little fubject to Error from the make, and if diligence be us'd, fuch as will eafily enough diftinguifh every four Seconds. I did indeavour likewife to fhew the manner of rectifying it, and ufing it for thofe Obfervations. And indeed, if only a Cæleftial Globe of all the fixt Stars were to be made, wherein only the Refpect and Pofition of the Stars one to another were to be noted, there needed no other Inftrument; but becaufe their particular Refpects alfo, both to the Poles of the World, and to the Poles of the Eccliptick, that is, to the Poles of the diurnal and annual motion of the Earth, or rather indeed the places of thofe Poles among them are to be taken notice of, therefore other Inftruments alfo will be requifite. Thofe I mention'd the laft Day would be three, and thofe were, Firft, An exact Meridian Line. Secondly, A moft exact Quadrant for taking Altitudes. And, Thirdly, An exact Watch or *To draw a true* Time-keeper. As for a Meridian Line the moft exact way of obtaining it *Meridian.* (to omit now feveral more common which I before hinted) is by obferving by the help of certain Perpendiculars, the moft Eaftern and Weftern Excurfions of fome Star not far remov'd from the Pole at leaft fomewhere plac'd within the Artick Circle. The manner of doing which may, in fhort, be this, Fix to fome convenient Beam a very long Perpendicular or Plumb-line, whofe fufpending String fhould be of Brafs-wire of a fmaller fize, to the end of which fhould be hung a Plummet of Lead, almoft as big as the Wire will conviniently bear; this Plummet fhould be fo inclos'd within a Box, that it may conveniently move, fo as to draw the Line Perpendicular, and yet be fheltered from the motions and difturbances of the outward Air. To the North of this, at a good diftance, the farther the better, from a convenient Beam fufpend two other Perpendicular Lines carefully prepar'd and fitted according to the directions I gave for the former, and fix them fo, that by looking by the firft, and one of thefe, you may be able to fee the moft Eaftern Excurfion, and by the firft and the other of them, the moft Weftern Excurfion of the Pole-ftar, or any other within the Artick Circle. And having thefe three Perpendiculars thus exactly regulated, it will not be difficult to suspend a fourth, so as that by looking by the first and fourth, the Angle made by the second, first and third, may be divided into two equal parts: Between the tops of these two Perpendiculars, extend also another small Wire which shall lie most exactly in the Meridian Line. And this I judge to be the most accurate way of any I have yet met with for finding the Meridian Line, and the most convenient for the uses hereafter to be mention'd. This Line will denote out the imaginary Circle which passes through the Pole of the World or of the diurnal Motion of the Earth, or the Pole of the Horizon or the Zenith of the

To find the Pole.

place: And this being found it will be exceeding easy to find the exact place of the Pole in it. Not by the Meridian Altitudes of the Sun ; which is to suppose that already most exactly known, which we shall afterward examine and find out ; but by taking most exactly the height of any Star within the Artick Circle, when by these Perpendiculars it be found to be in the Meridian ; for if by an exact Quadrant its height be observ'd when it crosses the Meridian below and above the Pole ; and half the difference of those two heights be added to the least elevation or height found, it will give the exact Point among the fixt Stars, to which the Poles of the Earth do at that time tend: I say at that time, because it has been found that the Poles of the diurnal Motion of the Earth do in time change and alter their places among the fixt Stars,

Of the Earths annual motion and Pol's of the Eccliptick.

so as to describe a kind of Circle about a Point, in or very near the Poles of the Eccliptick or Annual motion of the Earth. I say, in or very near, because it has not been yet certainly determin'd what the variation of the Poles of the Eccliptick or the annual motion of the Earth is ; and tho' various Astronomers have excogitated several Hypotheses, whereby they indeavour to make the variation of the Obliquity of the Eccliptick regular, and tho' some have ascrib'd that variation of that Obliquity to proceed from a motion of the fixt Stars, others from the variation of the very Orb of the Sun or Earth, others to the variation of the Æquinoctial ; yet I cannot find by all the Observations that have hitherto been recorded, that the matter can be accurately determin'd ; for since the places of the Stars, set down by the Antients, have been found by the noble *Ticho* to be in many particulars very false ; and since that even of those exact and diligent Observations of *Ticho*, there are lately found, by the excellent *Hevelius*, as I hinted the last Day, so many of them most egregiously differing from those Places and Positions they are plac'd in by *Ticho*, what hope is there of bringing that to any certainty where the Ground-work or Foundation of Observations on which the Theories are to be built, are so unstable and uncertain ? For either there can be no certain credit given to any Observations to be met with in Authors ; or if there be, I see, no reason why we may not affirm even the very apparent distance of the fixt Stars one from another, or their Positions or Respects among themselves to be alter'd, and this or that Star to be really in an other Position to the Circumambient fixt Stars; that is, really to appear in an other place of the Heaven at this Day, than it did in the times of the Antient Astronomers. Now if this be so, it will be yet a further dispute, whether this has been caus'd by some slow motions of those Stars one among another ; or whether by the alteration of the very Systeme of the Sun in respect of them ; and tho' the first seem the more probable, there having of late Years been observ'd very strange variations and alterations as to Magnitude even among those fixt Stars ; witness those several new Stars which have appear'd and disappear'd, and vary'd their Magnitudes to all degrees almost [witness also those Comets which have been by the latest and best Astronomers judg'd to be above the Orbs of the Planets, and to be equal'd with the Region of the fixt Stars ;] [as to instance in no other than that new Star which has so many times appear'd and disappear'd in the Neck of *Cætus* which was observ'd by *Hevelius* in the Year 1660, and does not, that I can find, appear at this time, no not through a Telescope.] Tho', I say, these particulars might make it most probable, that those transpositions have been made even in the Regions of Stars ; yet 'tis not impossible but that some variations even in the Systeme of the Sun, may make some sensible difference. And this, by the way, minds me of a thing which I have several Years since pro-

pounded

pounded as a thing worthy examination and experiment, and that is to be, by fixing a long and good Telescope directly against that Star of the Dragon, which is little more than three Degrees distant from the Pole of the Eccliptick, when in the Meridian, and to observe whether by that means there *To examine* cannot be found a manifest difference between the Elevation or Altitude of *that motion.* it at two distant times of the Year; that is, supposing those two Observations to be made at half a Years distance; for to me it seems not unlikely but that the annual Orb of the Earth (if such a motion it have) may, by this means, be perceiv'd to describe a small Circle about the Pole of the Ecclip-tick.

For since by a thirty six Foot Telescope it is exceeding easy to distinguish *This was wrote* the Seconds of a Degree, nay, almost Thirds, 'tis not improbable but that *before the Au-* the annual Orb of the Earth may describe a Circle about the Pole of the *thors attempt* Eccliptick, whose apparent Diameter may at least amount to some Seconds if *for the Earth's* not Minutes. And there seems not any more likely way in the World of *motion.* determining the Truth or Falsity of the Copernican Systeme than by this means. Now, tho' these Stars which lie nearest the Pole of the Ec\cliptick, if other particulars be answerable, were the best for this kind of Observation, yet the Observation of the Pole-star may perhaps be sufficient; for if the difference of the Meridian Altitudes of those Stars that are near the Poles of the Eccliptick be considerable, those Stars also which are very near the Poles of the World, cannot chuse but have a sensible variation; and conse-quently also the Pole of the diurnal motion of the Earth will describe a small Ellipse near the Pole-star, which 'tis not unlikely but some such way as this may, by several Circumstances, detect. But to return to what I was saying a-bout the manner of examining the places of the fixt Stars. I say, it were extreamly desirable that a Cælestial Globe were so made, that the exact Place and Positions of all the Stars, in respect of one another, were most acturate-ly determin'd and delineated, without any regard at all to the Eccliptick or Æquator; that is, that the distances of the Stars from one another might, by accurate Observations to be made with the double Telescope, be defin'd, after which, from a sufficient number of accurate Observations to be made, as I shall by and by direct, the true Eccliptick or way of the Sun or Earth a-mong these Stars should be exactly found out and delineated: For it is sufficiently evident from the various Theories and Hypotheses, and Tables of Astronomers, and by the variations of them all from Observations, how much they are all of them hitherto to seek in many particulars, not only in a great measure of the true Motion or Velocity of the Sun or Earth in the Eccliptick Line, but somewhat also of the very Position of the Ecclipticks-line itself, and consequently all the Æquations of times which are deduc'd from these, are somewhat uncertain also. Now for finding out the Ec-cliptick, the best way would be, First, To find out the true Point or Pole of the World, which may with care be most accurately done. Next the Æqua-tor or Æquinoctial Circle should be found, and for the Time and Year when the Observations are to be made, the Declination and right Ascension of some of the most notable Stars near the Æquator; that is, taking for the time the Longitude and Latitude of the Stars to be reckon'd after the same manner as the Longitude and Latitude of places on the Earth are, namely, by tak-ing a Meridian or great Circle passing through the Pole of the World, and any notable fixt Star, and for the present placing that as the first Meridian, as 'twere; then taking notice of the right ascension of the most notable Stars in respect of that Point where that great Circle cuts the Æquator, making some allowance in all the following Observation for the procession of the Æquinoxes, according as I shall by and by direct; and instead of the true Latitude of the Stars from the Eccliptick, which we will suppose yet to be sought, at least which we design hereby to examine, to take their Declina-tion *pro tempore*, from the Æquinoctial Circle. But because neither these nor the following Observations can be well made without the two other Instru-ments I formerly hinted; therefore in the next place I shall indeavour to de-scribe those and the manner of using them.

And,

The description of the Quadrant.
Tab. 10. *Fig.* 2.

And First, For a Quadrant to observe the Altitudes and Angles of the fixt Stars or Planets, which shall be exceeding light, small and easily manageable, and yet shall be adapted so as to distinguish an Angle as exactly as a Quadrant made the usual way, shall be capable of performing, tho' it be twenty times bigger in Diameter, I shall add this following Description.

Prepare a Quadrant of Brass or Wood, or any other convenient Substance, that will neither warp nor shrink, such as ABC in the Figure, whose Radius PB may be about sixteen or eighteen Inches long, more or less ; let, to one side of it, be fastned a long, square, hollow piece, as AD, of the same substance, and about a Foot longer than the Radius of the Quadrant having a perforation through the whole length of it, of about an Inch over, to serve for the Tube of a three Foot Telescope on the out side of the piece; suspended a Perpendicular or Plumb-line FE, whose Plummet F may be large and heavy ; then prepare a small long Index, shaped in the manner of that in the Figure IHG, which should be of some matter that is exceeding light and stiff, such as the outside of a Cane, or the like ; and so order'd, that the short end GH may counterpoise the longer HJ ; which longer HJ should be taper'd into a very small and slender Stem, and point towards I : Into the part H of this should be let in a small piece of Brass k, into which should be drill'd an exceeding small and fine Hole or Center, the smaller the better, so that it will indure the finest Steel Wire tho' as small as the Hair of a Man's Head to pass through it, and no more ; for the more curious and exact this contrivance be made, by so much the more exact will the Instrument itself prove : At the bigger end of this slender Index G, fix a small piece of Brass which may stand above the Plain about a quarter of an Inch, as X, and in the midst of it cut a very small slit only just big enough for the Plumb-line FE, to slide or be thrust between it. Having thus prepar'd this Index, by means of a small Steel Wire coming out of a hole in the middle Line of the Tube AD, at a convenient place of it, put on this Index, so that the small top of it, I, may reach and point to the small cross at F ; the other end of this Wire passes through the hole of a small bended Arm of Brass NH, and is there fastned. Having thus fitted on this Index and hung on the Plumb-line EF, making it pass through the small slit of the Brass X, that is erected upon the bigger end of the Index GHI, set the piece AD Perpendicular, which you will be able to do to the greatest exactness imaginable ; for by means of this small Index, if the piece AD be never so little out of its Perpendicularity, the top of the Index I, will make it most visible ; so that by this means you may come to as great an exactness as if the piece AD, and the Plumb-line, were above sixty Foot long ; for the end of the Index HI being near thirty Inches, and the Plumb-line being somewhat longer, and the shorter end of this Index being but one Inch, or the thirtieth part of the length, it will follow, that whatsoever motion is impress'd on the shorter end of the Index G, will be thirty times more sensible at the smaller end of the Index F, and consequently that the same exactness of Perpendicularity will be found, as if the length of the Perpendicular or Plumb-line were thirty times increas'd or lengthen'd, which would amount to more than threescore Foot. But thus far I have only explicated the way of setting the Quadrant most exactly Perpendicular. The next thing I am to shew is, how it will be able to determine Altitudes, not only to Minutes, but even to Seconds. The contrivance for performing which effect, for measuring, is this, Let the edge of the Quadrant BC be made of Brass, tho' the rest of the Quadrant be of Wood ; let this edge be an Inch thick at least, and rounded most exactly and truly to the Center P ; upon which Center P, make a Ruler PR to move, and on this fix a small Telescope MO of the same length with AD, namely, about three Foot long, having a very good Object-glass at M, and a very deep Eye-glass at O, and by this Glass the Position of an Object may more nicely be distinguish'd than it can be by any common sights, tho' they be plac'd more than sixty Foot asunder : And for the exact determination of the Angle that this visual Ray makes with the Perpendicular I, cause to be plac'd upon this Tube and Ruler a flat Circular Plate VXY, of about two Foot Diameter, the Limb of which I divide into three equal Parts, and each of those

those I subdivide again into sixty Parts, and each of those sixty I again subdivide into sixty more ; so that the whole Circumference, which will be about six Foot and a quarter, will be divided into ten Thousand eight Hundred parts ; for thrice sixty will be one Hundred and Eighty, and sixty times one Hundred and Eighty will make one Thousand eight Hundred ; which number of divisions it will easily enough bear, by means of Diagonals. This Circle is so fixt on the Ruler, that the Center of it Q may be distant from the edge or limb of the Quadrant BC, exactly one One Hundred and twentieth part of that Diameter ; then prepare a small Cylinder of Brass, whose Diameter may be exactly the sixtieth part of the Radius PB, and whose length may be equal to the thickness of the edge or reim of the Quadrant ; let this, by means of two small Centers or Pins, be mov'd in the hole, on the end of which Axis is put a small light Index ST ; these things being so prepar'd, by means of a small String which is stretch'd on the broad edge of the Quadrant BC, and at the same time rould about and fix'd to the Cylinder Q ; this Cylinder Q is so held by it, that, by the moving the Ruler PR three Degrees on the edge of the Quadrant, the small Cylinder Q makes a perfect Revolution, and consequently also the Index ST will make a compleat Revolution also : So that the Hand making a Revolution every three Degrees, and every of those three Degrees having a space or length of above twenty five Inches, it will not be difficult, as I shew'd before, to divide each of those Spaces into sixty Minutes, and each of those sixty Minutes into sixty Seconds. And this is that Instrument, which, if great Care and Art be us'd in the making of it, and in the manner of observing will be found as exact as a Quadrant of thirty or forty times that Radius, if not more, and for its lightness and smallness will be easily manageable and portable. I shall not now stay to shew the manner of rectifying and using it, but shall refer it to some other opportunity.

NB. *I do not find any thing more relating to this Quadrant nor the description of the Time-keeper here mention'd.*

R. W.

The CONTENTS.

THE *following Lectures were read in the Year* 1685. *and contain Discourses relating to the knowledge of the Longitude, with several Methods that have been or may be made use of for that end*; *of which seven are here enumerated, and the first and second farther enlarged upon, viz. the* Astronomical *and* Hodometrical; *by the way, some curious Subjects are touch'd upon, in relation to observing* Ecclipses *of the Moon, the Satellites of Jupiter, &c. and afterwards proceeding to treat of the* Hodometrical *method, the Author discourses of the Nature of the* Rumb-line *and its Proprieties*: *In order to which he treats of some matters relating to Practical Geometry, as of a Point, Line, Circle, &c. and of the difficulty of drawing either a strait Line or Circle, of any considerable length, or Radius true*; *and having shewn some methods of dividing a Line given into all its* aliquot *parts, he concludes with some Reflections on the Nature and Properties of the* Logarithmick *and* Rumb-line, *but leaves the Subject unfinished.*

To these are added a way of drawing Arches of great Circles, and an account out of the French *Memoires, and another of Sen*r. Cossini's, *touching the alteration of the Latitudes of Places, with the Author's Remarks thereon.*

R. W.

JUne 25. 1685. I have, in my former Lectures, explain'd those imaginary Lines upon the Surface of the Earth, which are of use in Navigation, and are found by the help of Cælestial Observations, *viz.* First, Meridians, being great Circles which pass through the two Poles of the Earth. And, Secondly, Parallels; namely, lesser Circles which are parallel to the Æquator, that great Circle which divides the Surface of the Earth into the Nothern and Southern Hemispheres: And have shewn you, that all indeavours in the Art of Navigation, is to be able to find out the proper Circle of both kinds, which is peculiar to the place of the Ship. How the Parallel Circle is found I have also shew'd, *viz.* how the Latitude of a place, or the distance of it from the Æquinoctial Line, is to be found by Cælestial Observations, either of the Sun in the Day time, or of the fix'd Stars in the Night; the methods of which are very easy, and commonly known and practis'd, tho' not without considerable defects both in the Instruments and the common practise of Observation, as I shall explain more at large when I treat concerning the Nautical Instruments, and their use at Sea.

I have likewise explain'd the ways of finding the Position of the Meridian, or the North and South Line of a place, by the help of Cælestial Observations, and of the Magnetical Needle, and at the same time of finding how much that Magnetical Needle or Compass doth vary there-from either towards the East, or towards the West. But this is only the finding of the Meridian consider'd as an Azymuth Circle, and not the finding of the Meridian peculiar to the place in respect of any other Meridian which passeth through some other place; which is that which is requir'd to the determination of the Position of a place upon the Surface of the Earth in respect of the Parallel and Meridian, which is the main end of Geography and Navigation.

What the Longitude is. The finding then of the Meridian of a place, which I here intend, is the finding which of all the infinite Meridian Circles which pass through the two Poles and cut the Æquinoctial at right Angles, is the Meridian that passes through the place where, or for which the inquiry is made; that is, what Angle that Meridian maketh at the Pole with any other known or determin'd Meridian that passes through any other known and assign'd place, or what part or parts of the Æquinoctial Circle are intercepted between the two Points where the said Meridians cut the said Circle. This is that Ploblem which

is

is call'd the finding of the Longitude of a Place, and which hath for so long a time puzzl'd all the Geographers, Astronomers, and Geometricians to find out a demonstrative and practical way to resolve ; and which, nothwith-standing the multitude of ingenious attempts that have been made for that purpose, doth hitherto remain an unsolvable Problem, especially at all times and at Sea, where the most use of it would be. Not but that much hath been done towards it, by various inventions, which, tho' not compleat and per-fect in their kind, are yet of very great use in Geography and Navigation, as I shall by and by shew. But the perfecting of this Art is, yet as a thing want-ing in the World, and very much sought for. And this the more, because Geography and Navigation are lame without it, having but one of its two Leggs good and sound, the other being but a Stilt or Prop ; however it hath hitherto serv'd to carry on the practice of Navigation, by which the greatest part of the World hath been not only discover'd but Traded to, and by means hereof every one part almost of the Earth, especially of Maritine Parts hath Communication with every other. It will therefore deserve to be inquir'd into and describ'd as to that state of Perfection and Practice which it hath now attain'd ; that from the knowledge from what state it is in at present, we may be the better able to discover its Defects, and what it further wants to make it compleat and perfect.

The helps then that have been propounded or made use of hitherto for finding the difference of Longitude between two places, or the Angle that their respective Meridians make at the Pole, may be reduc'd to these seven general Heads.

First, Astronomical, such as depend only upon Cælestial Motions and Observations. *Seven methods for finding the Longitude.*

Secondly, Hodometrical ; such as depend upon the Mensuration and Com-putation of Course and Distance.

Thirdly, Magnetical ; such a depend wholly upon Magnetical Proprieties and Instruments.

Fourthly, Chronometrical ; such as depend upon an exact Mensuration and Computation of Time.

Fifthly, Mechanical ; such as depend upon some Mechanical Inventions, and have no relation to any of the former.

Sixthly, Physical ; such as depend wholly upon some Physical Proprieties of the Body of the Earth.

Seventhly, Mixed or Compounded ways, making use of two, or more, of the former six principal Heads.

First, Then, for the Astronomical Methods, or such as depend wholy up-on Cælestial Motions and Observations ; there have been divers ways thought of, all which may be reduc'd to two Heads. *The Astrono-mical methods.*

First, Such as depend only upon some Cælestial appearance made for the effecting of this Inquiry in several parts of the same Hemisphere, without respect to Astronomical Tables. Or,

Secondly, Such as depend upon the truth of Astronomical Tables, calcu-lated for some known Meridian, to which such Observations may be referr'd, and the Longitude of any place, where such an Observation is made, may be presently deduc'd. Now, tho' no Astronomical Tables have been so perfect and compleat as to perform what is necessary, yet they have notwithstanding been founded upon a true Ground and Principle, and have failed only upon the account of the Imperfection of the Theories yet known of Cælestial mo-tions, a help for which I intend shortly to publish.

The

Six of them. The first way is by the Ecclipses of the Moon, obferv'd either at feveral places, or at one place only.

The fecond way is by obferving the place of the Moon crofling or reduc'd to the Eccliptick.

The third way is by obferving the true place of the Moon in any part of her Orb or Dragon, which is various ways perform'd, either by taking her diftance from one or more fix'd Stars, or from Altitudes taken in known Azymuths.

The fourth way is by obferving, with a good Telefcope, the progrefs of the Light and Darknefs over the fpots and marks in the Face of the Moon. Thefe four laft ways fuppofe a perfect Theory, and Tables of the Lunar motions, both which are yet wanting.

The fifth way is by the Satellites of *Jupiter*, or by the fix'd fpot in one of the Belts of *Jupiter* ; and this either obferv'd at divers places, or at one only. This laft fuppofeth a perfect Theory and Tables of the motion of *Jupiter*'s Satellites, which are yet wanted.

The fixth is by the Satellites of *Saturn*. Thefe two laft ways are to be obferv'd by the help of long Telefcopes, without which, the motions and appearances requifite for this purpofe, cannot be obferv'd ; and therefore 'till better Telefcopes be found than thofe we have at prefent (fuch as, tho' of but a fhort and manageable length, as of three or four Foot, will yet make the appearances as plain as one of thofe we now ufe of thirty or thirty fix Foot long) thefe ways will be of little or no ufe upon the Sea, tho' they may be of very confiderable ufe upon the Land in thofe Towns or parts where the Ship has occafion to ftay. Firft, Becaufe they happen very often in comparifon of Lunar Ecclipfes : And, Secondly, Becaufe by Obfervations of thefe kinds made on the Land at fuch places, compar'd with Obfervations made at any other known place, the difference of Longitude between thofe places will be rectify'd, and confequently they will much help to the rectifying Mapps or Chards, which is one very neceffary Inftrument to be made ufe of in Navigation.

Some things premifed. Now for the better underftanding of all thefe Aftronomical ways of inquiring the Longitude of a place, it is neceffary to premife fome præcognita which are neceffary to be known, in order to a better comprehenfion of them.

It is to be obferv'd then, that every place upon the Surface of the Earth hath a Cæleftial as well as a Terreftrial Meridian, that is, the imaginary plain of the Meridian of each place fuppos'd extended to the Orb of the fix'd Stars, doth defign an imaginary Line among them ; which, as the imaginary Meridians upon the Earth are fuppos'd to pas through the *Arctick* and *Autarctick* Poles or Points upon the Surface of the Earth, fo the imaginary Meridians anfwering to them in the Heavens, are fuppos'd to pafs through the two Poles of the Æquinoctial in the Heavens, upon which is made the diurnal motions of the Heavens in the Ptolomaick Hypothefis. When therefore the Sun is feen in any place to be in the Meridian of that place it is twelve of the Clock at that place, but at no other place whatfoever but fuch as lie under the fame Meridian, for to all other places it is either before or after Noon. So that as many Degrees as a place lies Eaftward of the place in which the Sun is at that prefent in the Meridian, by fo many Degrees doth the Sun there appear to have paft it, and by how many it lies more Weft, by fo many doth the Sun want of coming to its Meridian ; and becaufe the Sun paffeth three hundred and fixty Degrees in twenty four Hours, and confequently fifteen Degrees in an Hour, and fifteen Minutes in a Minute, and fifteen Seconds in a Second of Time, therefore it is eafy to reduce the Degrees and Minutes of the difference of Longitude to Hours and Minutes of Time, and contrary wife, to reduce Hours, Minutes and Seconds of Time to Degrees, Minutes and Seconds of Longitude.

This being premis'd, I come next to the Explication of the Aftronomical methods

The first method by Ecclipfes of the Moon. The Firft then, and principal, which hath been often practic'd, and which hath been of very good ufe for difcovering the Longitude of Places, is that by an Ecclipfe of the Moon, obferv'd firft in differing places at the
fame

same moments of universal time, but at different Local times: This Eclipse of the Moon being an accidental darkning of the whole or some part of the Moon's Face, by reason of the Moon's passage through some part of the conical shadow of the Body of the Earth, becomes visible to more than a Hemisphere of the Surface of the Earth. So that if the same were observ'd accurately in as many places as it could be seen at, this alone would shew the true Longitude of all those places in respect of one another, and would be *Local time* a means to rectify the Mapps for all such parts. By Local time, I mean that *what.* denomination of one and the same instant of universal time which it receives in several places, from the respect that the Cælestial Bodies have at that instant to the Horizons and Meridians of those several places; because the same instant that is call'd twelve a Clock in one place where the Sun appears in the Meridian, is in other places call'd, 1, 2, 3, 4, 5, 6, 7, 8, 9, 10, 11, a Clock, and all other denominations of Minutes, Seconds, &c. that can be in the twenty four Hours of the Day. Now the beginning and end of an Eclipse of the Moon being made in less than a Minute of time (for it is easy, by the naked Eye, to discover, within less than a Minute, when the real shadow just touches the Limb of the Moon, and by the Telescopes to discover to less than a quarter of a Minute) if those times be diligently observ'd in several places, and adjusted exactly to the Local times of those places, the different Local times being compar'd will give the different Longitude of those places in respect of one another; for every Hours difference of time gives fifteen Degrees difference, and every minute of time gives fifteen minutes of a Degree of Longitude: And by so much the sooner or earlier in the Local time of the Natural Day of each place it appears, by so much the more Westwardly is the place situated; and by so much the later the same appearances are seen in each place, by so much the more Eastwardly is the situation of that place. 'Tis true, that in such places where the Eclipse appeareth near the Horizon, respect ought to be had of the Refraction and Parallax of the Moon, in giving the visible Position of the Moon in respect of the fix'd Stars that may pass under or very near to it, when so Eclipsed; but if we only regard the Local time, that may be exactly found by the fix'd Stars, either by taking their Altitudes or observing their Transits by the Meridian, without having any regard at all to either of them.

The whole uncertainty that happens to Observations of this kind, is only *The difficulty* from the difficulty of discovering the very moments of the beginning and *in observing* end of the Ecclipse, because of a certain penumbra or lesser shadow which *Eclipses of* incompasseth this Conical shadow of the Earth; insomuch, that I have of-*how to obviate* ten observ'd this Penumbra to dusk that Limb of the Moon which is next *it.* the Cone for near half an Hour before the real shadow toucheth it, and for as long after the real shadow is gone off from it, after the end of an Eclipse. But generally the Umbra is so much differing from the Penumbra, that one may, with ease, be certain; to less than a minute of time, when it toucheth the Limb, especially in Immersions and Emersions out of the total darkness in total Eclipses. Those that have the convenience of Telescopes may have the particular intermediate times when the Umbra doth cover or pass through the middle of some remarkable spots in the Face of the Moon as the shadow comes on or goes off; because the Limb of the Umbra is much more defin'd upon the Face of the Moon, when both the light and the dark parts can be seen together; and 'twill not be difficult this way to be certain to less than fifteen Seconds of Time, and consequently to be sure of the difference of Meridians to less than four minutes of a Degree; which is as near to exactness as need be, for most Geographical or Nautical Uses. For the usefulness and practicableness of this way I could produce you multitudes of instances of the Rectification of the Longitudes of places from one another, and consequently of the true ground of making or rectifying of Mapps; but I shall only instance in one or two: The first shall be that which was made by Captain *Thomas James* at *Charlton* in *Hudson's Bay*, October the 29th 1631, and by Mr. *Henry Gellibrand* professor of Astronomy in this House, where he, with several other Friends, made the Observation of the same Eclipses. Now, after the return of the said Captain *James*, Mr. *Gellibrand* comparing

the

the two Obfervations together, found that the Meridian of *Charlton* was Weftward of the Meridian of *London* five hours eighteen minutes in Time ; or in Degrees of Latitude, 79°. 30′. This he verify'd alfo by another method, of which I fhall have occafion to fpeak hereafter, and found the difference of Meridians of thofe two places to be in time 5h. 14m. or in Degrees of Longitude 78°. 30′. which differs from the former account but four minutes of Time, or one Degree of Longitude. Now what difference did thus arife between the account of the former, and the latter way is certainly to be afcrib'd to the latter method, which was more complicated and depended upon the truth of Tables, there being no Obfervation made here at this place to correfpond with Captain *James's* made at *Charlton:* However, Mr. *Gellibrand* in his appology thinks it may be the better born withal, fince it could come fo near the truth in the finding the difference of Longitude of Places fo far remov'd ; fince very famous Authors, who have fought the Longitude of Places by other methods, have differ'd from one another, and from the truth fo much more ; for giving an inftance of the fituation of two eminent Cities here in *Europe*, not very far from one another, and which have each of them had very eminent Mathematicians and Aftronomers, *viz. Rome* and *Norimberg : Regiomontanus* makes their difference of Longitude 36 ; *Werner* 32 ; *Appian* 34 ; *Meftline* and *Origanus* 33 ; *Stofler* 18 ; *Maginus* 26 ; *Schonerus* 12 ; *Mercator* and *Hondiuso* 12. *Stadius* 13 ; *Janfonius* 10 ; *Longomontanus* 16 ; *Lausbergius* 10 ; but *Kepler* by two Obfervations of two Lunar Ecclipfes, made according to this method, deftroys them all, and proves them to be different but only four minutes of Time.

So that we may plainly perceive that this method, if it be duly obferv'd, and the Obfervations accurately and judicioufly made, is much to be preferr'd before divers others. And therefore I do very much wonder why the Learn'd Dr. *Voffius* in his late Treatife, that he hath publifh'd concerning the rectification of the Longitudes of places, fhould reject this way as fallacious and uncertain, whereas 'tis moft undeniably certain that 'tis infinitely to be preferr'd before the other ways which he there mentions : And indeed confidering the facility and obvioufnefs of it to any ones underftanding, and thence the practicablenefs of it by any of the moft ordinary Capacity, and with the leaft apparatus of Inftruments, and without a fuppofition of the perfection of Aftronomical Tables ; I think I may pronounce it the moft generally practicable way yet known ; not but that feveral of the other Aftronomical ways which I am to explain, will, with great Care and Circumfpection, and convenient Inftruments, together with intelligent Aftronomers to perform the Obfervations and Calculation, bring us to a much greater precifenefs. But fince thofe Requifites are not at all times and places to be procur'd, there is more of real good to be expected from this one method, than from any other yet known ; and to hint that only by the bye, I find that this Obfervation of Captain *James* and Mr. *Gellibrand* doth prove, that the moft part of the *Dutch* Mapps have made that place in *Hudfons-Bay* above ten Degrees of Longitude too much to the Weftward.

There are other inftances of this Nature might be produc'd to fhew that feveral parts of the Eaft Indies are, in the Mapps, plac'd too far to the Eaftward, contrary to the fuppofition of Dr. *Voffius* in his late Treatife. But I fhall not now infift upon further proof of that which will be fo eafily underftood by any one, who fhall well confider of its Principles.

The fecond method by the Satellites of Jupiter. Next to this way I fhall annex that of obferving the *Satellites* of *Jupiter*, becaufe they are of the fame Nature, and proceed upon the fame Grounds. And fuppofing the ufe of Telefcopes to be practicable at Sea, would be there of very great ufe, which I do not defpare to fee effected in a fhort time : But for determining the Longitudes of places upon the Land, Obfervations may be made twenty times more exact, if a convenient apparatus of Inftruments be procur'd, and diligent and knowing obfervers be made ufe of, and this by reafon of the almoft momentary continuance of the appearance, that is to be obferv'd, which will thence be feen by all the obfervers at the fame inftant almoft of time ; whereas there is a greater Latitude of uncertainty in Eclipfes of the Moon by reafon of the Penumbra.

This

This way then by the *Satellites* of *Jupiter* to knowing and diligent Astronomers is much to be preferr'd before that of *Eclipses of the Moon*, upon three accounts. First, By reason of the frequency of appearances sufficient for determining this Inquiry. *This way preferrable.*

Secondly, Upon the account of the distinctness, exactness and preciseness of the time of the appearance.

Thirdly, Upon the account of the easiness and facility of making the Tables, and of calculating the time; there being little else to be consider'd, but only the middle motions of them; at least, what inequalities soever it be in their Anomaly, it is hardly sensible or worth taking notice of them.

First, For the frequency of appearances sufficient for this purpose; whereas of Lunar Eclipses we seldom have above one or two in a Year, of those may be had one, two, or more almost every Night; and these for so long as *Jupiter* is more than a Sextant from the Sun, are very conspicuous by the help of a large Telescope; nay, within half that distance if the Position of the Ecliptick do favour the appearance either in the Morning before the Sun Rising, or in the Evening after the Sun Set: But the *Satellites* are most conspicuous, when *Jupiter* is more than a Quadrant from the Sun. Now, that this may be the better understood, it will be necessary to explain, in short, the *Mundus Jovialis*: We are to know then, that *Jupiter* being the highest Planet but one, namely, *Saturn*, being view'd through a Telescope, is discover'd to have a round Body in Diameter, when acronical about 50″.. This Body is observ'd to have several darker or dusky Belts which cross the Face of it parallel to the Eccliptick, and by a conspicuous spot, which I first discover'd, this Body is found to move round upon its Axis in about ten Hours time; besides this, *Galileo* first discover'd that it had four smaller Planets, which he call'd *Satellites*, which continually mov'd round about it; these, by later Observations, compar'd with former, have been reduc'd to such a Perfection, as that by Tables, made of their periodick Revolutions, the Positions and Affections of them, for any certain time, can be pretty near ascertain'd.. The first and innermost of these is distant about three Semidiameters, and performs its Revolution in about 42½ Hours: The second is distant about five Semidiameters, and performs its Revolution in eighty five hours and twenty minutes: The third is distant about 8½ Semidiameters, and performs its Revolution in about one hundred seventy two Hours. The fourth and outermost is distant about fourteen Semidiameters, and performs its Revolution in near sixteen Days, eighteen Hours and a Quarter; or 402¼ Hours. *Satellites first observ'd by Galileo.*

Tho' the distances and Revolutions of these secundary Planets differ very considerably from what the Learned Dr. Gregory *in his late accurate* Astronomiæ, Physicæ & Geometricæ, Elementa, *yet I have not presumed to alter them, but have Printed them as the Author has left them: They are placed by Dr.* Gregory *as follows. The innermost* Satellite *of* Jupiter *makes its Revolution in one Day* $\frac{3}{4}$, *and is distant* $5\frac{2}{3}$ *Semidiameters from the Center of* Jupiter. *The second surrounds him in* $3\frac{3}{5}$ *Days, and is distant nine Semidiameters. The third in the space of* $7\frac{1}{6}$ *Days, whose distance is* $14\frac{1}{3}$ *Semidiameters. The fourth and last in* $16\frac{3}{4}$ *Days, and is distant* $25\frac{1}{3}$ *Semidiameters. The distances are almost double, whence the mistake of our Author proceeded, I know not, but I thought best to give the intelligent this short Advertisement of it.*

R. W.

Every one of these four in every Revolution, have at least two remarkable Positions fit for this purpose; some have four, some may make six remarkable Signals. The Signals fit for this purpose, are, First, Their touching the Limb of the Body of *Jupiter*, either at their ingress or egress, and that is also in every Revolution double: First, When they are in their superior half of their Epicycle, and so move direct, they have their Ingress and Egress behind the Body of *Jupiter*. *The Satellites may serve for finding the Longitude in six Positions.*

Secondly,

Secondly, When they are in the lower half of their Epicycle and appear Retrograde, they have their Ingress likewise, and their Egress from the Face of *Jupiter*. Next when the outermost of them does not touch, but either move above to the Northwards, or below to the Southwards, their Orbit or Epicycle then appearing an Ellipsis, then there are at least two remarkable Positions of them which will be fit for this purpose; that is, their direct Conjunction and their Retrograde Conjunction. Besides these, there are two sorts of Eclipses; the first sort are those of the *Satellites*, that is, when the *Satillites* enter into the dark Cone of the shadow of the Body of *Jupiter*, or when they emerge or get out of it, both which may be sometimes plainly discover'd in the same Revolution of the *Satellite*, at other times only one of them, that is, either the Immersion or Emersion.

Secondly, There is an Eclipse also caus'd upon the Body of *Jupiter* by the shadow of the *Satellite*, by which means one may, with a good Glass, plainly perceive a dark spot or shadow entring the East Limb of *Jupiter*, and passing over some part of its Face, to leave the Body of *Jupiter* at its West Limb: Each of these Transits of the shadow will afford three remarkable Instants or Times fit for this purpose, namely, First, The Ingress of the Shadow or Spot into the Face. Secondly, Its Position in the middle of the Line of its Transit, which by reason of either of the Belts upon the Face of *Jupiter*, or the lateral Position of some of the other *Satellites*, may be easily discover'd. And, Thirdly, The Instant when it goes off or leaves the Limb of *Jupiter*, which are plainly enough discover'd by good Telescopes and diligent Observers. So that since there are so many remarkable Accidents observable, scarce any Night can pass without affording some one or more of those opportunities. Hence it will be sufficiently evident, that there will be above a hundred convenient times to make such Observations more than can possibly happen by means of Ecclipses of the Moon.

Besides these, there are other remarkable Conjunctions of the *Satellites* themselves one with another, which will serve for proper Remarks, especially at such times as *Jupiter* is in or very near the Eccliptick; for then the plains of the Orbs of the *Satellites* are very near in the plain of the Ecliptick, and the apparent motion of the *Satellites* is very near in a straight Line, and so the Conjunction of one of them Retrograde in the lower part of its Epicycle with another of them direct in the upper part of its Epicycle, is very short and momentary, and so becomes a fit mark for such an Observation. The like may also be observ'd when *Jupiter* having a considerable Latitude the way of the *Satellites* appears Elliptical; for then the Conjunction of two *Satellites*, may, with sufficient accurateness, be observ'd.

Now any one of these remarkable appearances being view'd and exactly observ'd by two Persons at differing places, if the times of such appearances be exactly taken at both places, they will certainly give the difference of the Longitude of those two places in the same manner, as I before shew'd, might be done by Eclipses of the Moon; and consequently if the same appearance were observ'd with the same care in a hundred places, the Longitudes of all those places would be thereby ascertain'd, and that in the next place to a much greater preciseness than 'tis possible to do by the help of Eclipses of the Moon; because some of these may be distinguish'd almost as easily to a Second of Time, as those of the Moon may be to a Minute, which appears yet farther, First, By reason of the smallness of the Body of the *Satellites*. Secondly, By reason of the great Velocity of all and much more of the innermost or first, which is next the Body of *Jupiter*. Thirdly, By reason of the small distances of them, and especially of the two innermost from the Body of *Jupiter*, and consequently of the small Penumbra the shadow of the Body there affords, which is also so much the more distinguish'd by reason of the vast distance of the Sun, and thence of the great Dimination of its Diameter, when view'd from the Body of *Jupiter*, and thence the smallness of the Angle of the Penumbra; for whereas the Angle of the Penumbra at the Earth is about half a Degree, the Angle of the Penumbra at *Jupiter* will not be more than ⅓ part of a Degree, the distance of the Earth from the Sun to that of *Jupiter* being but as 10 to 45, or as 2 to 9. All which Particulars

do

do contribute to the quickneſs and ſhort duration of the appearance : So that the Time is very preciſe and ſeen by a whole Hemiſphere of the Earth, as it were, in a moment ; and there is no regard to be had of Parallax, and nothing elſe to be taken notice of but the very preciſe time of the appearance ; for this only gives the true difference of Longitude between all thoſe places where it ſhall be ſo obſerv'd by the ſame method, as I mention'd before in Eclipſes of the Moon.

The Difficulties that occur in this method, are, Firſt, That pretty long *The difficulties* Teleſcopes are requiſite for making the Obſervations and accurate Pendulum *in this method.* Clocks, both which are as yet not practicable at Sea. But, as I ſaid before, notwithſtanding this it may be made uſeful in Harbours and on Shore in ſuch places where Ships may reſide, which will be of great uſe for rectifying the Longitudes of Charts and Mapps.

A ſecond Difficulty in this way, is the diſtinguiſhing of one of the *Satellites* from the other : But for this the Theory of them is ſo far brought to perfection, and was above twenty five Years ſince much advanc'd by my Predeceſſor the ingenious Mr. *Laurence Rook*, that the Poſitions and appearances of the *Satellites* can be certainly Predicted and Calculated for any certain time ; and 'tis not difficult to make an Automaton or piece of Watch-work which ſhall, at all times, give the Poſitions and appearances accurate enough for ſuch Obſervations, at leaſt to direct an Obſerver at what time he is to expect or watch for ſuch an Appearance ; and I have verify'd very many of Mr. *Rook's* Predictions and Ephemerides for thoſe Appearances, and found them pretty exact, even to leſs than a minute of Time. By which method if Ephemerides be made for one, two, three or more Years, and ſent abroad into the Eaſt and Weſt *Indies*, and other parts of the World, 'tis not unlikely but many ſuch Obſervations might be procur'd from ſeveral parts of the World, which would be of great uſe, eſpecially if at the ſame time there were ſome in *England* that ſhould conſtantly make the like Obſervations here with equal care. And I have good reaſon to hope, that by this means we may obtain the Longitudes of ſeveral places in the *Eaſt-Indies*, ſince I underſtand that the *French* King hath ſent ſeveral very able Aſtronomers into the *Eaſt-Indies* with an apparatus of fit Inſtruments, almoſt on purpoſe to make theſe and ſuch other curious and uſeful Obſervations.

Beſides this I am certainly inform'd, that it hath been of late much practiſed in *France*, whereby they have fix'd the Longitudes of the principal Towns in *France*, and alſo that of *Uraniburge* in *Denmark*, and of *Cayen* in *Iceland*, in the Poſſeſſion of the *French* upon the Coaſt of *Guiana* in *America*. But this only by the bye.

But to proceed, the ſame thing may be done by the *Satellites* of *Saturn* ; but they being diſcover'd but of late, and ſo not yet brought to ſo perfect a Theory, and beſides requiring much longer and better Teleſcopes to obſerve the Appearances; I ſhall forbear to diſcourſe farther of them 'till thoſe *Deſiderata* are procur'd ; but whatever Invention will ſerve to detect their Appearances, will be much more uſeful for obſerving the ſame of *Jupiter*, which are much more near, and ſo much more vivid and conſpicious.

The ſame thing may be done by obſerving the Appulſes of the Moon to any fix'd Star that lies in its way, when obſerv'd at ſeveral places of the Earth, wherein the Appearance is ſo very ſhort and preciſe, that even in the ſpace of a ſingle Second of Time, a Star is ſeen and quite diſappears behind the Body of the Moon ; but then by reaſon that both Refraction and Parallax are to be accounted for, which are differing to every place where the Obſervation ſhall be made, it is not fit for common uſe, but requires ſome better ſkill in Aſtronomy than moſt Obſervers are furniſh'd with, which I ſhall therefore pretermit for the preſent, becauſe I ſhall have occaſion to treat more largely of it when I explain thoſe ways that do neceſſarily require a knowledge of both thoſe.

But ſtill all theſe methods are uſeleſs as to the main deſign for which the knowledge of the Longitude is deſir'd ; which is from Obſervations made upon the place wherever it be, whether at Sea or on Land, and to determine preſently what is the Longitude of that place from any known Meridi-

an.

an. This is that Invention which has hitherto puzzl'd all the Learned Men, whether Mechanicks, Navigators, Geographers, Astronomers, Geometers and Philosophers; among which, tho' there have been many pretenders, yet no one has perform'd it, or shewn the way how to do it : 'Tis true, there have been enough have shewn what things are requisite to do it, but no one has produc'd those Requisites. 'Tis certain, that an exact Theory and Tables of the motion of the Moon, or of the motion of *Jupiter*, and his *Satellites* would perform it ; but those Theories and those Tables are hitherto wanting, as are also exact Clocks that will move exactly upon the Sea, and such Telescopes as tho' but of three Foot length, and so might be made use of at Sea, would yet do as much as those we now have of thirty Foot ; 'till which be procur'd, these ways, that I have hitherto nam'd, will be of little use for this purpose.

November 12. 1685. I explain'd to you the last Term, several præcognita necessary to be known, in order to the finding the Longitude of any place upon the globous Body of the Earth ; that is, of finding the Angle that the Meridian of that place maketh with any other determinate Meridian, whether it be the prime Meridian generally agreed upon, or any other particular Meridian of some notable place from which the Ship departs ; whose respect to the prime Meridian, or the Meridians in the Chart made use of, is known. In order to which I enumerated the several general ways that have

The several ways for finding the Longitude. been hitherto thought of for effecting this end, namely, Astronomical, Hodometrical, Magnetical, Chronometrical, Mechanical, Physical, and Mixt. Each of these ways I did more fully explain the last Term, and shew'd the several bounds of them, as also the several Objections, Difficulties and Imperfections each of them was subject to, and what they wanted to make them compleat and useful ; which I shall not now trouble you with the repetition thereof, but rather proceed to the second method or general way of finding the Longitude of places, or difference of Meridians. Namely, The

The Hodometrical way. Hodometrical, or by the observation or computation of the way of the Ship between place and place ; that is, of observing the several Rumbs or Lines in which the Ship saileth, and what way it hath made in every of those Rumbs ; that is, how many Leagues or parts of a League the Ship hath pass'd in every Rumb it hath sail'd upon, and how to compute the same, and thence to deduce the true place of the Ship at any time, in respect of the place from whence the departure is made, or the difference of the Meridians of the Ship, and that place, which is the Longitude desir'd. In order to the better explication of which it will be necessary to explain the several parts that are necessary Ingredients in every such Inquiry or Operation, that so it may be perform'd the more knowingly and scientifically, and not by wrote and ignorantly as it is now perform'd, for the most part, by practical Navigators ; and to that end it will be necessary to explain, First, What

What the Rumb or Line of a Ships way is. kind of Line it is a Ship describes upon the Surface of the Earth or Sea in its passing or sayling through it, when steer'd upon a certain Point of the Compass. Secondly, How that Line is found and distinguish'd from all other Lines that may be describ'd upon the Surface of the Earth, for that it is a Line not only differing from all other Lines upon the Surface, but because every one of those Lines differ from every other of the same kind ; and not only

How it differs from all other Lines. so, but every part of each Line differs from every other part thereof in many respects ; as First, In its flexure or bending : Secondly, In respect of its proportion to the Meridians and Parallels, namely, as to the mensuration of Latitude and Longitude : And, Thirdly, In respect of any other great or lesser Circles that may be drawn, or suppos'd drawn upon the Surface of the Earth ; such as lesser Circles of distance from any one Point or Place ; or greater Circles, such as Lines of Position or great Azymuthal Circles. Nor have I hitherto met with any Globe whereon the said Lines have been truly describ'd, or any other that has prescrib'd a Scientifical or practical way of describing the same.

The chief Propriety of the Rumb Line. The chief propriety then of this *Rumb-line*, upon the Surface of the Globe, is, that it always makes the same Angle with all the Meridional Lines or Circles that it cuts or crosseth, and consequently that it is a *Spherical-Spiral* or

Helix

Helix which incompasseth the same with infinite Revolutions which will never bring it to the two Polar Points which are the Centers, towards which it
tends both towards the North and towards the South; notwithstanding the
infinite Revolutions, yet it is a finite Line which beareth a certain proportion
to the length of a Meridian, and may be defin'd, determin'd and divided as
exactly as any other Line or Circle drawn upon the Face of the Globe, and
also the respect or proportion that any part of the whole Line beareth to
the Meridian or Parallel that it crosseth.

First, As to the length of any Rumb-line; I say, that it beareth the same *Of its length*
proportion to the length of a great Circle, that the Secant of that Rumb *and proportion*
Angle from the North or South, hath to the Diameter of the Globe; so *to a great Cir-*
that tho' it maketh Infinite Revolutions about each Polar Point, and will *cle.*
never arrive at it, yet are all these infinite Revolutions equal to a finite and
determinable length of a straight Line, and that to as great an exactness as
the proportion is or can be determin'd between the Radius or Diameter of a
Circle and the Circumference thereof. Both which Proprieties, and several
other tending to the mensuration and computation of the parts thereof, and
for manifesting the respect they bear to the Meridians or Parallels, or for determining of the respective Variation of the Longitude and Latitude which
it maketh in its Progress either way towards the North or South Poles, I
shall, in some following Lectures, demonstrate; whereby all such Disputes, as
have arisen about that Subject, will be remov'd, and the Nature and Proprieties thereof will be manifested by a much easier method of Demonstration than what hath been hitherto by any one us'd or produc'd for that purpose. I shall also shew some other sorts of Projections of the Sphære in *Plano*,
than have hitherto been produc'd, very apt and pertinent for this purpose,
whereby the Navigator may more easily, with his Ruler and Compasses,
measure the Rumb-line, and resolve all Questions that concern the sailing
by the said Line with as great certainty and exactness as is necessary to work
withal from any Observations or Mensurations that can be made at Sea by
the Logline and Compass.

But before I can well proceed with the explication of this Head, it will
be necessary to premise some Præcognita of practical Geometry, which will
be useful for the knowledge and more easy description of the Rumb-lines,
and for the measuring of the parts of them; especially by reason that the
Rumb-line as it is, or ought to be, describ'd upon the Globe, as it is very
difficult and almost impracticable to be made use of at Sea; so do I not find
that the said Lines are hitherto truly laid down upon any Globes yet extant,
or any certain way prescrib'd for the true drawing or laying down of the
same upon the Surface thereof, but they are set off by some Points from Tables
calculated for that purpose, and the interjacent parts of the Lines are fitted
up by hand and by guess, which is very imperfect and inartificial.

But by an Instrument that I have invented, it may be most exactly drawn,
not only upon the Surface of the Globe itself, but also upon several projections of the Globe in *Plano* or upon a Plain, whereby not only the several
Proprieties of the said Line may be express'd, but also the mensuration of it
by the help of Ruler and Compass, will be more facile, expedite and tract-
able for use, and the true Nature of this perplex'd Line more easily comprehended and conceiv'd: And this I do the rather, because I judge, that by
means of this way the true Course of the Ship may be more speedily, easily,
and with less subjection to mistake, be computed and protracted, than by resolving of Triangles or Arithmetical Calculationt; for if by the Instrument
can be discover'd as small a part as one can be assur'd by the Log-line in
Sailing one Watch, then all nicety beyond that is loss of Labour and Time.

By Practical Geometry then I understand that part of Geometry, which *What is here*
teaches an easy way of performing that by Operation, which is requir'd to *meant by practi-*
be done by Theory, in order to put it into effect and practise. The business *cal Geometry.*
then of this Practical Geometry, is principally to describe, design and lay
down all those Things or Lines exactly, according to the Theory which are
requir'd to be done, and to determine and measure the quantities of the parts
desir'd by, or from that Description.

I know

I know that into Practical Geometry, is ufually alfo taken all the Bufinefs of Obfervation, fuch as the taking or meafuring of Angles, of Altitudes of the Cæleftial Bodies or Terreftrial, as Mountains, Clouds, and the like, and the meafuring of Sides or Angles upon the Earth in furveying ; and the meafuring of the Contents of folid Bodies, as Timber, Stones, &c. and the meafuring of Liquors, or the capacity of containing Veffels, as is done in Gauging, and other practical parts of Mathematicks ; but thefe as not at all pertinent to my prefent purpofe, I fhall now omit, and only confine my felf to fpeak of fo much of Practical Geometry as ferves to teach the true defcribing and dividing of fuch Lines, Surfaces or Bodies as are, or may be ufeful for this part of Mathematicks upon which I am difcourfing, which is of the Art of Navigation ; namely, how any Probleme that is requir'd, or is neceffary for this Art, may, by the help of Ruler and Compaffes, be truly protracted and meafur'd upon a Plain, with as great exactnefs as 'tis poffible, by the help of the Inftruments and Methods that are hitherto us'd to make Obfervation on which to ground the Calculation.

In this then I have four things to be confider'd, which makes up the Pythagorick Tetractys, namely, Point, Line, Superficies and Solid ; of each of which I fhall difcourfe.

What is here meant by a Point. By Point then I do not here underftand an imaginary nothing, which, in fpeculative Geometry, is defin'd to be a Negation of Quantity, or an Entity that hath no Part or Quantity ; but I underftand fuch a Point as hath Quantity and Extention, but yet fo fmall and minute, as that the fenfe cannot diftinguifh that it hath any Parts; fuch as the Point of a very fharp Needle, or the Point of a very curious pair of Compaffes ; or fuch a mark with Ink as is made with a very fharp nibb'd Pen upon fine fmooth Paper, which tho' it may be eafily enough prov'd, either by Microfcopes and other Glaffes and by Reafons too to have breadth, and fo both Longitude and Latitude, nay, and Profundity too or thicknefs, yet as to the ufe, for which it is here defign'd, it is fufficient, and may pafs for a true Mathematical Point, if at leaft we will but fuppofe the middle of it to be that which is aimed at in our Operation.

A Point is determin'd or given or found when the refpects it hath to fome other Point or Points, Line or Lines that are alfo given and known, and are fufficient to determine its true place., as if it be defir'd to find or place a Point upon a plainSuperficies that fhall have the fame diftance from each of the two other Points given that they have one from another : The Proprieties can but agree with two Points in all that Plain, which two Points are one on the one fide, and the other on the oppofite fide of a Line drawn between the two firft Points given, and therefore the place of the Point is not determin'd unlefs the faid refpect be alfo given.

But if a Circular Line be given, and it be defir'd to find or make a Point which fhall be equally diftant from every part of that round Line, then is the Pofition of that Point truely defin'd, and can be plac'd but in one place to have that Refpect or Propriety.

But further, if two Points be given in a Plain, and it be requir'd to find or place another Point in that Plain that fhall have this Propriety, that the ftraight Lines drawn from the third Point to be found, fhall make a right Angle, or any other Angle at that third Point, then are the Data not fufficient to determine the Point, becaufe there may be infinite of fuch Points found, which will all fall in fome part of a Circle which paffes through thofe two firft Points ; and to determine fuch Point it will be neceffary either to give the determinate diftance from one of thofe two firft Points, or the Angle that is made at one of them. Again, if from two fuch Points it be requir'd to find or place a third Point, whofe diftances from the firft two fhall be to each other of any known or determin'd Proportion, as 2, to 3, or the like ; the Data are not fufficient to determine the third Point, becaufe there may be infinite of fuch Points, all which will fall either in a Circle or a ftraight Line ; and therefore there is fome other Propriety requifite to determine the third Point to a certain Pofition. In the like manner I could inftance a hundred other Cafes, to fhew the neceffity there is of giving Proprieties

prieties fufficient to determine the Pofition of any Point which is to be plac'd, otherwife the Practife or performance thereof cannot be done. But I fhall not here further infift upon it, becaufe that I fhall difcourfe of it more fully in the confideration of Lines, Superficies and Solids ; and the only thing to be obferv'd in the placing of a Point, is to fet it exactly in the croffing of two Lines which are to determine its Pofition.

The next we are to confider is Lines ; that is, not a length without bredth, *of Lines.* as in pure and fpeculative Geometry, but a length that hath the leaft fenfible bredth that can be defcrib'd, fuch as a Line drawn with the point of a very fharp Needle, or point of a Compafs, or fine nibb'd Pen, which may pafs for a length without bredth at leaft, if we confider the middle of it.

Now Lines may be either ftraight or bent ; a ftraight Line is that which is the fhorteft that can be drawn between two Points given, and confequently there can be but one fuch drawn, and therefore that Line is perfectly given, which is fo determin'd by two given Points, and therefore in fpeculative Geometry, 'tis put for a *Poftulatum*, that fuch a Line may be fuppos'd drawn, or is eafy to be drawn ; but in practical Geometry we muft confider of the means how to draw it actually, which in fome cafes is not fo eafily perform'd, if extraordinary truth and exactnefs be requir'd : For, Firft, if the Line be *The difficulty* to be drawn upon a plain, a ftraight Ruler being laid fo as that the ftraight *of drawing a* edge of it juft paffes over the two Points, then moving along by that edge a *ftrait Line.* fine pointed Needle or fharp nibb'd Pen, we draw a line from the one Point to the other, and for common ufe the thing is done ; but if any thing of Nicenefs or Curiofity be requir'd, we fhall find it very difficult to lay the Ruler fo as that it equally refpects the two Points, but that it will lie a little nearer one Point than the other. Again, 'tis difficult to carry the Needle or Pen along with the Hand, as always to keep the fame refpect to the fide of the Ruler. And, Thirdly, 'Twill be very difficult to find or provide a Ruler that is perfectly ftraight, but that it will have fome bending in it one way or other, be it fhot never fo true with a Plain ; for tho' the Plain be true that fhooteth it, yet if the Ruler be not fecur'd from warping it will bend under the Plain ; befides, there are very few Plains that are fo true, but that, if they are of Wood, will, in a fhort time, have fome little warping or bending; and I know an ingenious Workman that affur'd me he could never fhoot any thing true 'till he had made a Plain of Steel, which he had ground down to a truth of fmoothnefs and plainefs by rubbing and polifhing it upon another Plain, and to have a true Plain to rub it upon, it is no eafy matter to procure as I have been fufficiently fatisfy'd by fuch as have indeavour'd to have them for grinding of Optick or Perfpective Glaffes ; for I could never yet meet with any one but that, by a way I had to examine them, I have found them either a little Concave, or a little Convex, tho' that were fo little, as not, by the common ways of examination, to be eafily found. But it may be faid, that ftreigning a fine Wire, or Hair, or fine Silken Clew between two Points, will defcribe or draw a ftraight Line between two Points ; to which I anfwer, that if the Plain on which fuch a Line be to be drawn be exactly plain, and that plain lie exactly Horizontal, then fuch a Wire or Hair will perform it ; but if the Plain be inclin'd or ftand Perpendicular, and the two Points are not Perpendicular one over the other, then fuch a Line can never be ftreign'd ftrait whatever ftrength it be ftreign'd withal ; for its own weight fhall make it bend down in the middle, as has been fufficiently demonftrated by the ingenious *Galileo*, and *Merfennus*, and divers others ; efpecially if there be any confiderable diftance between the two Points. Thefe things I mention to fhew, that tho' it be taken for granted, that this which feems the eafieft of all things in practical Geometry to be done, yet is not performable without great difficulties where nicenefs and great exactnefs is requir'd : And poffibly this might be the reafon why Geometricians will not allow fuch Lines to be Geometrical, whofe way of defcribing requires the fliding of a point along by the ftraight fide of fuch a Ruler as the Ellipfe, and feveral other Curve Lines, whofe Proprieties are as exactly known and calculable as that of the Circle, and this only granted may be as eafily defcrib'd, and therefore may as reafonably be fuppos'd defcribable as the Circle or a ftraight Line.

Since

Since from what I have alledg'd 'tis evident, that it cannot be done exactly without considerable difficulties; but if the two Points be very far distant, it is almost impossible by any way to exhibit or draw such a Line; for not again to mention the bending of Rulers or Line, which 'tis impossible to prevent, even the sight itself, that is the Ray of Light, passing from Point to Point through the Air, is not a strait Line as to its Position, by reason of the differing Refraction which is in the *Medium* of the Air, which I my self have very often prov'd by Observation, finding the same three Points which appear at one time in a straight Line, at another time, sometime within half an hour, have appear'd out of it very considerably, which I have very often diligently remark'd.

I have been the more large and particular in shewing you the difficulties that occur in the actual or practical performance of that which seemeth, and is so suppos'd, the easiest sort of Line that can be drawn, that you may not think it strange if hereafter when I shew you the way of drawing Rhomb-lines of several sorts, and some other Curve-lines useful in Navigation, you meet with some kind of Difficulties and Obstructions in the methods and ways of describing and measuring of them, which yet I shall shew you as to the true use that is to be made of them in Navigation, will be as sufficient as the Circle or straight Line; but upon this I shall not now further insist, but proceed in the next place to shew how on a given Line about a Point given, a Circle may be describ'd; this, in Speculative Geometry, is a *Postulatum* and suppos'd as easy and obvious to be done, and in small Circles on a Plain or *The difficulty of drawing Arches of great Circles.* Table, it is so by opening the Compasses to the length of the Line having set one Point of the Compasses in the Point given, and with the other striking round the Circumference 'till it return to the place where it began, by which means a Circular Line may be describ'd much easier and more exact than a straight Line, or any other can be drawn. But for the describing greater Circles the thing to be done is not so easy, nay, so difficult, that 'tis almost impossible, especially where exactness is requir'd, as I was sufficiently satisfy'd by the difficulties that occurr'd in striking a part of the Arch of a Circle of sixty Foot Radius for the gage of a Tool for grinding Telescope Glasses of that length; whereby it was found that a Beam Compass made with all Care and Circumspection imaginable, and us'd with as great Care, would not perform the Operation nor the way by an Angular Compass, such as is describ'd by *Guido Ubaldus* in his description of the Planisphere, and also by *Blagrave* in his Mathematical Jewel, and several other Authors, there being found so great a difficulty in making the edges of Rulers exactly smooth and straight, as I did formerly mention, there being indeed no other practical way of making such edges but the gaging of three such edges all true to one another by rubbing and grinding, as there is hardly any other practical way of making the edge of a Ruler to be a part of a very large Arch fit to be a gage for a Tool for grinding Telescope Glasses, then by grinding and rubbing the edges of two such Rules together, the one whereof is Convex and the other Concave. The difficulties in this kind I do the more insist upon here, because of the use of such parts of large Arches in the drawing of the Projections of the Sphere, which the Work-men usually perform by the help of a Steel Bow, which is bent less or more, as is desir'd, by means of a Screw against the middle of it, the two ends of the said Bow being held by the frame of the Instrument in which the Screw is also mov'd. But this Instrument as it is much more easy and applicable to this purpose, so is it far less true and exact than the Angular Instruments. The true Figure of such a Steel Lath for bending Circularly being not yet known, which I affirm notwithstanding what *Marchetty* in his Treatise *de Resistentia Solidorum*, has demonstrated seemingly to the contrary; and if it were, and were exactly made, yet those that have been conversant or experienc'd in the Nature and Use of Steel for Springs or bending, will quickly be satisfy'd how difficult a matter it is to procure such a uniform peice of Steel, and how much harder it is to temper it equally. But I shall not insist further on this Matter at present, having only mention'd what I have here alledg'd, to shew, that tho' these two Lines which are the simplest and most easy to be drawn and

describ'd

describ'd are yet not of so easy performance in some Cases where great exactness is requisite, but that there is great care necessary in the preparing and using Instruments fit for that purpose ; and likewise to shew that if the same care be taken in the providing and using of Instruments for describing the Rhomb-lines, they may also be describ'd and drawn with the like certainty and exactness, and be every way as fit for use and practise in business of Navigation.

Nov. 19. 1685. I begun the last day to explain some part of Practical Geometry, in order to reduce Mathematical Theories about Navigation into Use and Practise, and explain'd the ways and the difficulties also of drawing the simplest and plainest of all Lines, *viz.* the straight and the Circular Lines whith are taken for granted in Speculative Geometry to be so easy to be done, which notwithstanding, when there is requir'd great exactness in the performance, are not so easy actually to be effected. It may therefore be inquir'd, why then are they put as *Postulata* as if performable by any ? To which I answer, That the business of Speculative Geometry being only to demonstrate the propriety of such quantities, as Lines, Superficies and Solids from their Definitions or Descriptions ; it is sufficient to have only a right Conception of what is to be understood by those Appellations, and that they are things possible to be done, or conceiv'd so to be, for grounding the Demonstrations thereupon, and that the actual drawing and delineating of them there, is only to help the Imagination to conceive the notion of them aright. But when we consider them in reference to Practical Geometry, we are to consider, not only that the things to be done are possible, but to teach the Ways, Instruments and Operations how they may be actually perform'd ; and therefore 'tis not here enough to conceive, that there may be a right Line drawn between two Points, or there may be a Circle describ'd about a Point or Center at a distance given or determin'd, and then to demonstrate by reason that those Lines must have such and such Proprieties ; but we are to draw them actually, and to shew by practise and actually doing, the thing requir'd, and thereby to exhibit the thing done to Sense, which is one of the ends and uses of Speculation. But it may be Objected by some, or at least thought so ; but what need is there of all this Curiosity, Preciseness and Care of placing Points aright, and drawing Lines so curiously straight, and of Circles so exactly round and true? To which I answer, that this is not a needless Curiosity, nor so slight and insignificant a Matter as not to be regarded, but a matter of great Use, nay, a thing of absolute Necessity ; and without which, all the real use of Practical Geometry, especially in Geography, Navigation and Astronomy, will be lame and imperfect : for all our deductions and conclusions in these Arts are founded upon proper and true Observations made ; and all our Observations are made by the help of Instruments ; and thence it will follow, that if our Instruments, us'd for such Observations, be not exactly made and divided, our Observations cannot be true, and if our Observations are not true, our Deductions from them will not be true neither, but erroneous and false, and consequently all the rest of our Labour and Care and Skill will be needless and insignificant : And that this is so any one will easily grant, when he considers, that in most Instruments that are us'd for the Sea, which seldom exceed two Foot Radius, the smallest Point almost that is sensible is the representation of a Minute; and that Minute upon the Surface of the Earth, is no less than 6086$\frac{3}{10}$ *English* Feet, there being found 365184 Feet in one Degree of the Earth, which amounteth to sixty nine Miles, and eight hundred sixty four Feet, or about $\frac{1}{6}$ part, the Statute Mile containing 1760 Yards, or 880 Fathoms ; so that in the make of an Instrument of such a Radius, the error of the bredth of a Needles Point in the placing the divisions of the Limb or the drawing the Diagonal Lines or Circles, or the other parts of it, will easily make an error of a Mile in Latitude upon the Face of the Earth, and much more in Longitude.

And indeed considering the carelessness that is at present in the make of the ordinary Sea Instruments made for Sale, and several other Imperfections, it is well if they can be certain to ten or twelve Minutes, that is, twelve or fourteen

Why speculative Geometry puts some things as Postulata that cannot be performed.

The defect of the common Sea Instruments,

fourteen Miles. Now what signifies the resolving and calculating of Triangles to single minutes or lesser parts, when you are not sure by Observations to ten. If therefore by the help of Instruments, such as a Planisphere, a Sector and Compasses all Problems may be truly protracted and resolv'd more exactly than the Observations can be made, on which they are grounded, what need will there be of more curious Calculations? But that this may be done, I shall prove by the sequel of this Discourse, if at least due care be taken in the materials making and dividing the Instruments, whereby I shall shew that it will not only be sufficiently accurate for all such uses ; but it will have this of advantage also, that whereas the other method by resolving Triangles Arithmetically is done blindly and by wrought, and without a true Conception of the reason of those Operations ; this will be done more knowingly by protracting ; since that alone will be sufficient to shew the reason of the Operation, and to prevent a World of mistakes of one thing for another very usual in the other way, since this way things are plac'd and and measured in their proper places. This I thought necessary to acquaint you with, that you might thereby see the great necessity and significant use of such Niceness and Curiosity, as I mention'd to you the last Day, in finding and making the Points and drawing both the straight and circular Lines true, and that such as may have occasion to make use of such Instruments, or to make them themselves, as I hope some here may do, would be very careful to see that they are made with sufficient exactness, and that the Materials be such as may continue and preserve their form without warping or shrinking. But on this Subject I shall say more hereafter when I treat of the several Instruments themselves : I shall therefore at present proceed to the other parts of Practical Geometry, and in the next place explain what is understood by the respects that two right Lines drawn upon the same Plain, bear to one another : This will fall under two general Heads ; First, Such as are equally distant from one another, and so call'd Parallels : Or, Secondly, Such as some ways cross each other, and so form an Angle between them ; for an Angle is nothing else but the Respect, Tendency, or Inclination of two Lines in the Point wherein they cut or cross each other.

This Inclination of two right Lines in the Point of Intersection is computed by the part of the Arch of a Circle drawn about the Point of intersection as a Center intercepted between those two Lines, and computed or compared with the whole Circumference of that Circle ; as if AB and DG cut each other *Fig.3.Tab.10.* in the Point C, and upon the Point be described the Circle FHKI ; FE measures the Angle FCE, for what part FE is of FHKIF, FCE is of four Right Angles.

If the intercepted part be one quarter of the whole Circumference, then that Angle measured by it is call'd a Right Angle, and the Lines are call'd Perpendiculars to each other ; as if AB and HI crossing each other in the Point C, FH be ¼ of the whole Circumference, then is HI Perpendicular to AB and AB to HI.

If the intercepted part be less than a quarter of the whole, 'tis call'd an Acute, as the Angle ECF or BCG, because FE or KG are each of them less than a quarter of the Circumference, FCE and ECH making one quarter of the Circle.

If the intercepted Arch be more than a quarter 'tis call'd an obtuse Angle, as ECB or FCG, which are compounded of a Right Angle and an Acute, *viz.* ECH and HCB, or FCI and ICG.

Hence 'tis obvious that Perpendiculars make four equal or right Angles about a Point as FCH, HCB, BCI, ICF.

And that all other crossing Lines make two Acute and two Obtuse, which four are equal to four right; and any two adjoining are equal to two Right Angles as FCE and ECB are equal to FCH and HCB. So,

From hence proceeds the necessity of dividing and measuring the parts of a Circle, and finding the proportion they bear to the whole Circumference ; which is various ways performed, the most usual and useful of which are perform'd by the help and measure of straight Lines, which have certain respects both as to lengths and position to some Diameter or Radius of the said Circle,

cle, of which I ſhall afterwards ſpeak ; ſuch as are Chords, Sines, Tangents, verſed Sines or Darts.

A Diameter of a Circle is any ſtraight line drawn through the Center, and terminated at each end by the Circumference, as FB, HI, or EG.

And a Semidiameter, which is alſo call'd a Radius, is equal to half the former, being any ſtraight line drawn from the Center to the Circumference, and terminated by them ; as the half of any of the former lines terminated at one end by the Center C, as FC or CB, HC, or CI, &c.

All Diameters of the ſame Circle are equal to one another, as are alſo all Semidiameters or Radij, becauſe every part of the ſame Circumference is e-qually diſtant from the Center.

If a ſtraight line be drawn within the Circle cutting the Circumference thereof in two Points, the part of the line intercepted between thoſe two Points is call'd a Chord or Subtenſe in ſimilitude to the String of a Bow, ſubtended or ſtretched from the ends thereof, as HG is the Chord of the Arch HKG being extended between the ends of it H and G, and 'tis call'd the Subtenſe or Chord of both thoſe Arches or parts of the Circumference which it divides or under which it is drawn ; as of HKG, and of HFG. So a Dia-meter is always the Chord of a Semicircle.

All Chords that are equal ſubtend equal Arches of the ſame Circle, be-cauſe a Circle is a bent or curve Line, whoſe bending or curviture is every where equal and uniform, every part thereof therefore which is equal in length muſt have the ſame curvature, and conſequently the ſame length of a ſtraight line extended or ſubtended from its ends.

Theſe Definitions or Deſcriptions will be enough for my preſent Uſe and Diſcourſe, I ſhall therefore proceed.

In Practical Geometry, as every regular line is drawn or deſcribed by ſome proper Inſtrument ; ſo every length is meaſured and every diviſion alſo made by ſome proper or known meaſure, by which the ſenſible truth thereof is ex-perimentally verify'd and exhibited ; I do not ſay demonſtrated, as ſome I perceive are very apt to do both in their Writings and Diſcourſe, who ſuppoſe the ſhewing a thing drawn upon Paper to be that which is under-ſtood by Demonſtration ; but that, I conceive, may proceed from a common, tho' falſe Acceptation of that Word, ſince the ſtrict and proper ſenſe thereof is much an other Notion, of which I formerly more largely diſcourſed : And therefore I now take it for granted, that the Principles of Speculative Geo-metry are already known, and as ſuch I ſhall refer to them where I have oc-caſion to make uſe of Demonſtration ; and ſhall not oblige my ſelf to follow the method of *Euclid*, but only treat of ſuch parts of Practical Geometry as relate to the Subject I have in hand.

Now becauſe I ſhall only diſcourſe of ſtraight Lines and Circular, I have no need at preſent to mention any other Inſtrument than a ſtraight Rule and Compaſſes, which are the moſt plain Inſtruments uſed, and ſo are ſufficient-ly known ſo as not to need any thing more to be ſaid of them than what I have already premiſed.

I need not alſo, I ſuppoſe, now mention the ſeveral ways how to draw or let fall a Perpendicular from a Point given to a line given, nor how to raiſe a Perpendicular from a Point in a line given to that line ; nor how to divide a line into two equal parts, theſe being ſufficiently obvious and commonly e-nough known. And therefore taking theſe for granted as already known, I proceed to other ways of dividing a line given into ſuch a number, or ſuch ſorts of parts as ſhall be required.

And Firſt for dividing a given Line into any number of equal parts, the way of proceeding is as followeth. Let AB be a line given to be divided in-*of dividing a* to nine equal parts, Firſt, Open your Compaſſes to the length of the line,*given Line.* and having one point of them in A, deſcribe the part of an Arch CB, then *Tab.*10.*Fig.*4. from the Center B deſcribe the Arch AD, then taking with your Com-paſſes the diſtance of any point in AD as D from the point A ; ſet off the ſame diſtance from B in the Arch BC to C : Then draw the lines ACE and BDF, through the points AC and BD : Then opening your Compaſſes as near as you can judge to the length of a ninth part of the Line AB, the

nearer

nearer you guefs the better; and beginning at A, fet off that length on AE eight times, as 1, 2, 3, 4, 5, 6, 7, 8, then with the fame opening of your Compaffes, beginning at B, fet off the fame length eight times on BF, as g, h, i, k, l, m, n, o, laftly, laying the Rule on i and o, 2 and n, draw the feveral lines j o, 2 n, 3 m, &c, Thefe parallel Lines fhall divide the line AB into nine equal parts as was defired in the Points p, q, r, s, t, &c. the demonftration of which is fo eafy that I fhall not ftay to infift upon it.

To divide a line into all its aliquot parts. Next let it be required to divide a line given into all its aliquot parts, or to give a feries of parts which fhall be reprocal to a feries in Arithmetical proportion, as, $1, \frac{1}{2}, \frac{1}{3}, \frac{1}{4}, \frac{1}{5}, \frac{1}{6}, \frac{1}{7}$, &c in infinitum. The method of doing it practically may be either of thefe three following ways.

Tab. 11. Fig. 4. Let AB be a line given to be divided into all its aliquot parts, as $\frac{1}{2}, \frac{1}{3}, \frac{1}{4}$, at one of its ends, as B; crofs it with the Perpendicular KI, and produce it towards I, as far as there fhall be occafion. Then taking any Point in the line BK at pleafure as D, draw DC equal and parallel to AB and compleat the Parallelogram AKDB. Then with your Compaffes taking the length BD fet it off from B towards I, as many times as you defire aliquot parts, as BE, EF, FG, GH, &c. then laying the Rule on the Point C, and thofe other Points E, F, G, H, fucceffively draw ftraight lines which fhall cut the line AB in the points 2, 3, 4, 5, &c. then fhall the line AB be thereby divided in as many aliquot Sections as fhall be defir'd; for A2 fhall be half of AB, A3 $\frac{1}{3}$, A4 $\frac{1}{4}$, A5 $\frac{1}{5}$, and fo onward fo far as you will proceed; for fince DC is parallel to AB, and equal to it the Triangles DEC, and BE2 fhall be fimilar, and DFC and BF3 are alfo fimilar; and DGC likewife to BG4, and fo onward in infinitum. It follows therefore that as ED, 2, is to EB, 1, fo CD = to AB,1,to B2, = to $\frac{1}{2}$, = A,2, in like manner as FD,3 to FB2; fo CD,1, to B,3, $\frac{1}{3}$, which taken from AB leaves A3 = to $\frac{1}{3}$, and fo for all the reft, which is obvious enough.

The fame might have been thus demonftrated; AC being made equal and parallel to BE, EF, FG, GH, the Angle CAB will be equal to ABE, therefore the Triangle CA2 will be fimilar to EB2; and therefore as CA is to A2 in the Triangle CA2; fo EB will be to B2 in the Triangle EB2; but CA is put equal to EB, therefore A2 is equal to B2, therefore A2 = $\frac{1}{2}$ AB. Again, for the fame Reafons, CA3 will be fimilar to FB3, and confequently CA. A3 :: FB. B3; but FB is double CA, therefore B3 is double A3, therefore A3 = $\frac{1}{3}$ AB, and the fame for all the reft.

Here in the practical performance of this Problem will appear the neceffity of that nicety and exactnefs I prefcrib'd in drawing of ftraight lines curious and true, and placing of the points precifely in the middle of the line and of laying the exactly ftraight edge of the Rule over the very middle of the points, through which the lines, are to pafs, and of carrying the Needle or Point with which you draw very equally and uniformly; for if all thefe particulars be not carefully obferv'd, and accordingly practis'd and perform'd, tho' the Problem be true in the Theory, yet the divifions made upon the line AB, will be but imperfect and lame, efpecially if the line BJ be far produced, and the repetitions of the equal parts be made fome fcores or fome hundreds of times, becaufe the lines drawn from the point C through thefe Divifions on the line BI produced, will be fo oblique that a very little error in any of thofe obfervables, will be apt to make an error of a whole divifion, and fo 'twill be difficult to diftinguifh for inftance between a 99th part and a 100th part, moreover becaufe the effecting of the Problem this way, if the Reciprocals run far, will require the line BJ, to be drawn out to a great length, and requireth as much room as the performing it by the Hyperbola, which in many occafions cannot be fo conveniently done, therefore the fame Problem may be effected by another way in a much lefs room and with fhorter Inftruments, which therefore will be the lefs fubject to warping, and may be more carefully perfected.

Tab. 11. Fig. 4. The fecond way then of effecting this Problem is this: Let AB be a line given, all whofe aliquot parts are defir'd, as its $\frac{1}{2}, \frac{1}{3}, \frac{1}{4}, \frac{1}{5}, \frac{1}{6}$, &c. which are reciprocals to a rank of numbers in Arithmetical progreffion, as 1, 2, 3, 4, 5, 6, &c. Upon the line AB make a Parallelogram Square or Rhombus ABCD, then

then draw the Diagonal AC. Now for finding the half, draw the Diagonal DB crossing AC in E ; through E draw FEG parallel to AD or CB, cutting the line AB in G : Through D and G draw DHG cutting the Diagonal AC in H; and through H draw IHK parallel to AD ; then through D and K draw DLK crossing the Diagonal AC in L ; and through the Point L draw MLN parallel to AD, and so proceeding so far as shall be needful or desir'd, you shall find as many aliquot parts of AB as you shall desire ; for as AB is the whole, so AG is the half, AK the third, AN the fourth, and so you may find the fifth, sixth, seventh, eighth, ninth, and so onward as far as you please. For First, the opposite sides of the Figure ABCD being equal and parallel, the Diagonals must intersect each other in the middle, because AED is similar to CEB, and therefore as AD is=CB, so AE=CE and DE=BE. Next because the Triangles ABC and AGE are similar, as AE is half AC, so AG=$\frac{AB}{2}$.

Secondly, AK is $\frac{1}{3}$ of AB ; for the Triangles AHG and DHC are similar, because the opposite Angles at H are equal, and the alternate Angles at A and C are equal, as also the other alternate Angles at D and G ; therefore as DC is to AG, which is as 2 to 1, so CH to AH ; AH therefore is $\frac{1}{3}$ of AC, and because ABC and AKH are similar, therefore as AH is $=\frac{AC}{3}$, so AK$=\frac{AB}{3}$

The like Demonstration will serve for all the rest how far soever continued.

This Problem I have been the more particular in explaining for that I shall have several occasions to make use of both in projections, and likewise in the contrivances of several useful Instruments for Navigation, as particularly in a way of sounding the depths of the Sea in such places as Lines will not reach, and in computing the way of a Ship through the Water, and several other inventions, of which I shall speak hereafter.

Now because the drawing of parallel Lines so often as there are Divisions made, may seem somewhat troublesome, therefore I shall shew another way how to effect this Problem without drawing parallel Lines ; which is thus. Let AB be a line given to be divided into all its aliquot parts. Through the Points A and B draw right Lines parallel to each other, as CD and FE, whether at Right Angles or not with the line AB it matters not. Set off on each side of each of the Points A and B in the lines so drawn parallel a Point, as C, D, E, F, of equal distance from the respective Points A and B. Then draw CE, which shall cut AB in the Point G in half; the draw AE and DB, which likewise intersect each other in half in H ; then draw CH and Dg, which shall intersect AB at I, making AI $\frac{1}{3}$ of AB, and AE at K, making AK $\frac{1}{3}$ of AE ; draw CK and DI, these shall intersect the lines AB and AE at L and m, making AL $\frac{1}{4}$ of AB and Am $\frac{1}{4}$ of AE, and so proceed in infinitum : This will also give you all the aliquot parts of AB or AE. Or a Series decreasing in reciprocal proportion to any Arithmetically increasing Series, as 1, 2, 3, 4, 5, 6, 7, &c. in infinitum. The Demonstration of which Problem is much the same with that in the preceding Problem, and therefore I shall not spend time in the repetition thereof.

Tab. 11. *Fig.* 5.

And thus far I have proceeded to shew how any line given may be divided into an infinite Series of Reciprocals to a Series in Arithmetical Progression, of which sort I have only instanced in that Reciprocal to 1, 2, 3, 4, 5, 6, &c. but the same method will serve to give the Reciprocal to the Series that expresses the differences between square numbers of the prime Arithmetical Series, as 1, 3, 5, 7, 9, or any other such Arithmetical Progression, whatsoever the common excess or difference be, as I could plainly demonstrate if it were material to my present design, and may hereafter more at large upon another Subject ; but I shall now rather proceed to shew how any line given may be divided into an infinite series of Parts in Geometrical Proportion continually decreasing or increasing, according to any proportion whatever assign'd, as 1, $\frac{1}{2}$, $\frac{1}{4}$, $\frac{1}{8}$, $\frac{1}{16}$, $\frac{1}{32}$, $\frac{1}{64}$, and so onward in infinitum : Or, 1, $\frac{1}{3}$, $\frac{1}{9}$, $\frac{1}{27}$, $\frac{1}{81}$, $\frac{1}{243}$, and so onward to any proportional less then can be assign'd, and how to find the sum of such an infinite decreasing Series or a line equal to them, all added together.

Tab. 11. Fig. 6.   To effect which, let AB be a Line given to be divided into an infinite series of Geometrical proportionals, according to any Ratio given ; as suppose of 1000 to 999, or any other Ratio whatever ; for instance, let it be of 8 to 7 cross the line AB at the point or end A with another straight line, as CAD, which may be drawn at Right Angles, or any other Angle pretty near it, for the same effect will follow ; then opening your Compasses to any distance, but as near as you can guess to an eighth part of the length of the Line CD, *viz.* according to the conveniences you may have of drawing or producing the said Line on the Plain or Table you are delineating upon and setting one Foot in A, set off the same eighth part from A to C on one side of the Point A : Then on the other side set off the said distance AC seven times, *viz.* to D. Then draw from the Point C the Line CE parallel to AB, and from the Point B to draw BE parallel to AC, so as to compleat the Parallellogram or Rhombus ABEC ; then through the Points D and E, draw the Line DE, cutting the Line AB in F ; through F draw FG parallel to AC or BE ; and through D and G draw DG cutting the Line AB in H ; through H draw HJ parallel to AC or BE, and draw DJ, cutting AB in K ; and through K draw KL parallel to AC, and so proceed to draw DL, Mn, Dn, op, &c. as far as you please. These Points F, H, K, M, o, &c. shall divide the Line AB into a series of Geometrical continued proportionals in the Ratio of 8 to 7, as was describ'd or requir'd to be done : For AB shall be to AF, as 8 to 7, and AF. AI, :: 8. 7, and AH. AK :: 8. 7, and so onward in infinitum, or as far as shall be requir'd ; and not only so, but the whole line AB shall be made up or compounded of an infinite series of continual proportionals, in proportion as 8 to 7, all which infinity of proportionals being joined or added together into one line will be equal to the line AB, and neither exceed it, nor be shorter than it.

Now that this division will be rightly done, will appear by the following Demonstration, AB and CE being parallells to each other, and equals as by the Construction is requir'd to be done ; DC also being a straight Line touching the Line AB in A ; and DE being a straight Line cutting the Line AB in F ; the two Triangles DCE and DAF will be similar ; and consequently as DC to DA, which, by the construction, is made, is as 8 to 7, as was requir'd ; so CE (which was put equal to AB) to AF. In the same manner FG being drawn parallel to AC, CG and AF are equal, and the Line DG being drawn cutting the remainder AF in H ; he two Triangles DCG and DAH are also similar, and consequently as DC to DA ; so is CG (which is equal to AF) to AH. Now DC to DA is put as 8 to 7, therefore also AF to AH is as 8 to 7, as was requir'd : By the same Ratiocination, may all the rest of the infinite proportionals be proved to be to one another, as 8 to 7, and consequently they will be all an infinite series of continued proportionals, decreasing infinitely in proportion as 8 to 7' which was the thing requir'd.

Now since the whole Line AB, and the Ablata AF, AH, AK, AM, are in continual proportion, as 8 to 7, as is prov'd, the Reliqua BF, FH, HK, KM, &c. will be also in the same Geometrical continu'd proportion one to another, as 8 to 7, as is evident by the 17th of the 5th of *Euclid*, &c.

To express these Proportionals in Numbers is very difficult, but if this Series be express'd Algebraical it will be easily perform'd ; for putting the first difference a, and the second b, it will be this, $a, b, \frac{bb}{a}, \frac{b3}{a2}, \frac{b4}{a3}, \frac{b5}{a4},$ &c.

This method of finding and easily describing a Rank or Series of continual proportionals, I have the rather chosen to explain and demonstrate by this Problem, because by means hereof the true Nature of Logarithms and the Logarithmick Line will the more plainly be understood and comprehended, which by reason of the reservedness and design'd obscurity of most of those who have written concerning the method of compounding and forming the Logarithmick Tables, are not so obvious to every Reader ; for in this present
                                                                    Problem

Problem, if the continual Proportionals BF, FH, HK, KM, MO, and all the reft be put for the abfolute Numbers: Then BE, BE ÷ FG, BE ÷ FG, ÷ HI. BE ÷ FG ÷ HI ÷ KL, will be the Logarithms to thofe Numbers, that is 1, 2, 3, 4, 5, 6, &c. for Logarithms are nothing elfe but the Numbers of the proportionals that are in the Series pitch'd upon, or made choice of between any two abfolute Numbers (or becaufe a unite is the firft and root of all other Numbers) between one and any other abfolute Number whatfoever. And to that end in the making of Logarithms, becaufe if the proportional difference between the antecedent and the confequent be very great, it will hardly fall out, that any of the proportional Sections will either fall in the equal Section of the abfolute Number exactly, or fo near the fame as will be fufficient to make the number of the proportional differences exact enough to ferve for the Logarithm; therefore the greater the number of thofe proportionals are between the unite and the other abfolute number, the nearer will the equal divifions of the interjacent fpace approach the proportional Sections of the fame; and by the increafing the numbers of the intermediate proportionals, if the equal divifions do not *coincidere* with the proportionate exactly, yet the approach may be made within any difference whatfoever required, which is all that the nature of the thing, in fome cafes, will bear, they being infinite and incommenfurate; for the making of which Logarithmick Numbers or Tables various ways have been made ufe of by feveral Authors, fome more eafy in the Invention than others, yet they are all to the fame effect, tho' fome of the Progreffions are more accommodated for ufe than others; as that of Mr. *Briggs*, where the Logarithm of one is, put a, 0, and the Logaritthm of 10, 1 of 100. 2 of 1000. 3 of 10000. 4 with a certain number of Cyphers after them, as Mr. *Briggs* puts 14. So that he fuppofeth One hundred Millions of Millions of proportional parts between one and ten, and between 10 and 100, and between 100 and 1000, and fo onward in the Decimal progreffion; or between 1 and $\frac{1}{10}$, and $\frac{1}{100}$, and $\frac{1}{1000}$, and $\frac{1}{10000}$, of which in 100 Millions of Millions, there are thirty Millions of Millions, One Hundred and Two Thoufands, 999 Millions, 566 Thoufands, 368 continual proportionals between one and two; and becaufe it would be impoffible ever to enumerate and calculate all thefe, therefore there have been various Expedients found to facilite this *tædium* of working proportionals by Multiplications and Divifions, and extractions of the Roots, and to perform the fame thing for finding the Logarithms or the number of proportionals in the feries pitch'd upon, anfwering to each abfolute number, by little more trouble than bare addition, which doth fave an infinite of trouble; and confidering the great Ufe and Benefit of them in folving many difficult and almoft infolvable Queftions of Geometry by any other way, is a part of Geometry extreamly defirable to be thoroughly known and underftood, neverthelefs it being not fo much to my prefent purpofe, and belonging more particularly to the bufinefs of Arithmetick, I fhall not further proceed in the explication thereof at prefent.

But rather proceed to the Explication of the Logarithmick Line, and fhew how it depends upon the Problem I have now explained, of dividing a Line given into any infinite feries of continual proportionals, becaufe, as I fhall after prove, the fame is the true Line of the Rumb in thofe projections which I defign to defcribe.

Let AB then in the fecond Figure reprefent the Radius, BC a line at right *Tab. 12.Fig. 1.* Angles with it, and equal to it the tangent of forty five Degrees, which is to be divided into an infinite feries of continual proportionals; fo that BC to BG fhall be as any one number to any other number affigned. For inftance, as 100000 to 99999, make B d equal to $\frac{1}{100000}$ part of AB, and draw d e parallel to BC; then make ds, st, tv, vx, &c. each equal to dB, and draw the Lines s, 1. t, 2. v, 3. x 4. &c. parallel to BC. Then proceed to divide the Line BC into the feries of proportionals cg, gi, jl, ln, np, &c. as I fhew'd in the preceeding Problem; and through the Points g, i, l, n, p, draw the Lines gf, i 1. l 2. N 3. P 4, &c. parallel to the Line AB meeting or cutting the fore-faid Parallels de s 1. f 2. V 3. X 4. in the Points f, 1, 2, 3, 4, &c. the Curve Line drawn through the Points C, f 1, 2, 3, 4, will reprefent

Sfffff   the

the Logarithmick broken Line being compoſed of the Diagonal Lines fC, hg, ki, ml, on, &c. in which BC, df, S i, f 2, v 3, x 4, the ordinates to the Line AB, ſhall repreſent the abſolute numbers which are here a rank of continual proportionals anſwering to the numbers 1, 2, 3, 4, 5, B or nought, and Bd, Bs, Bt, Bv, Bx. The reſpective Logarithms to them increaſing as the abſolute do decreaſe, according to *Neiper*'s method, or elſe BX, DX, SX, TX, VX, X, or o, will repreſent the Logarithms decreaſing as the abſolute decreaſe, according to Mr. *Briggs* and moſt others.

This Line which I have here deſcribed is not a true Curve Line, but a Line compos'd of fragments or ſhort pieces of ſtraight Lines, *viz.* of the ſtraight Lines of cf, gh, ik, lm, no, pq, &c. which are all Secants to the Radius db of the continual proportionals put as tangents, becauſe fg, hi, kl, &c. are all equal and parallel to it; and as AC the Secant of 45 is to AB; ſo fc to fg=dB as Radius; ſo fi=gh, 12=ik, &c. ſo cfi 2, 3, 4, 5, is equal to the ſeveral Secants Cf; gh, ik, lm, no, pq, &c. and ſuppoſing dB one infinite part of AB, theſe fractures will be infinitely ſmall, and ſo the Logarithmick Line or Rhumb-line will be a true Curve Line compos'd of infinite of theſe infinitely ſmall Secants.

From which Generation of this Curve Logarithmick or Rhumb-line, may be deduc'd, Firſt, That the Line AB being infinitely continu'd towards A, ſhall be the Aſymptot Line to the Logarithmick Curve cf, 1, 2, 3, 4, &c. nearer and nearer, to which it ſhall always approach, but never touch it.

Secondly, That if from any Point of this Line infinitely continued either way a perpendicular or ordinate to AB be drawn, and alſo a tangent, the diſtance between the ordinate and tangent interſection of the Aſymptot ſhall always be equal to the diſtance AB; from which propriety the mechanical Deſcription thereof, with great exactneſs and certainty, I ſhall prove to be eaſy.

But becauſe this Line may be various other ways deſcrib'd alſo, which will alſo give light to the Nature of it; it may be conceived to be generated by the compoſition of two differing kinds of motions croſſing each other at right Angles with differing tendency and velocities.

As ſuppoſing a Point or Atom at C, actuated by two equal tendencies or velocities, the other towards W. Suppoſing the velocity towards C to remain always the ſame, and uniform the motion or velocity towards W will continually increaſe ſo that when the Atom has paſt, for inſtance, $\frac{1}{10}$ of the diſtance between CW and AB, the velocity from BC towards AW will be as $\frac{10}{9}$, and at the end of the ſecond ſpace of time, as $\frac{10}{8}$, of the third, as $\frac{10}{7}$, of the fourth, as $\frac{10}{6}$, and ſo $\frac{10}{5}$, $\frac{10}{4}$, $\frac{10}{3}$, $\frac{10}{2}$, and 10, and ſo onwards in infinitum.

If on the other ſide we ſuppoſe the tendency, velocity or motion from BC towards AW, to be always equal and uniform, that is, in a certain ſpace of time, to move a ſpace equal to one tenth of the length CB, then the motion or velocity from CW towards AB, will decreaſe continually by an infinite ſeries of continual Proportionals, according to the differing velocities of the two tendencies. Theſe Proprieties I have not now time to demonſtrate fully as they ought, but I ſhall reſerve them to another opportunity.

Tab. 12.Fig.2. THere being mention made at Page 524. above, of an *Inſtrument for drawing Spirals or Rhumbs* but not *deſcribed I have here added a ſhort deſcription of an Inſtrument I remember he ſhewed the model of to the Royal Society with its performance. Let there be made a thin flat Ruler a b c, having a ſlit through the middle of it c d to ſlip freely upon a Center Pin fixt perpendicular in a plain, upon which the Line is to be drawn: At the end of this Ruler c there muſt be cut a round hole with a Ring of Braſs exactly fitted to it, and in this Ring a ſmall Truckle Wheel with its Axis well fixt at right Angles: Then by moving this Ring in its Socket in the Ruler, the plain of the Wheel may be ſet to any Angle with the ſlit in the Ruler; which done, by moving the Ruler upon the Plain round the Center, the edge of the ſaid Truckle-wheel will deſcribe, upon the Plain, the Spiral with the Angle required at every revolution proportionally approaching the fixt Center. E is the Truckle-wheel and Ring taken out of its Socket in the Ruler.*

The

THe Author having mentioned the great difficulty of drawing the Arches of very large Circles at Page 523 Supra, and finding a Lecture of his proposing several methods of performing it, I thought best to insert it here, the ways being, as I judge, new and ingenious.

R. W.

*M*Ay 8th 1685. It is a Postulatum in Geometry, that 'tis possible or practicable to draw or describe a Circle to any given Radius, and also from a Point given to any other Point to draw a straight Line; but tho' in Speculative Geometry it be only to be understood, that a Circle of any bigness may be conceived as drawn about a Center given, or a straight Line may be conceived to be drawn between any two Points given; yet in Practical Geometry where the *Postulata* are to be produc'd to effect and to be actually executed, if either of them are very large, the difficulties are greater than every one will easily imagine, and neither the one nor the other can, with any tolerable exactness, be perform'd. 'Tis true that a Line may be extended and streined between two Points at a considerable distance, and so that Line may be said to be a straight Line as to its swarving laterally; but as to its straightness in the Perpendicular Plain that passes through those two Points, 'tis not in the power of Art to make it; for that the power of gravity acting on it will bend it into a Curve (which has of late Years much excercised the Speculative Geometers to contemplate, and they have given it the name of the *catenaria*) but none have found any ways of describing it otherwise than by Points, which are very troublesome and tedious, and at best but imperfect (which yet I shall shew how to do some other time) but I at present only mention it by the by, to shew, that tho' a Line may be strained between two Points, yet gravity will bend it from its straightness; and tho' 'tis Possible in great part to take off that gravity by a fluid, in which the said Line shall be immers'd, yet that for a great length will not obviate the Objective. 'Tis true, if the Points be plac'd perpendicular one over another, a Line may be extended straight without any impediment from gravity, but then any motion of the Air, through which it passes, is apt to bend it some ways or other, so that even that way is not free from Objections. And I found in my Observation of the Parallax of the Earth, that there was very much trouble and difficulty to find the true Perpendicular Point under the Center of the Object-glass, which yet with perseverance, I conceive, I did at last attain. However some have propounded ways of performing that Observation which have ten times the difficulty to execute it to any tolerable satisfaction that was found in mine.

The difficulty of drawing a strait Line.

Now as this first *Postulatum* of actually drawing a straight Line between any two Points has its difficulties, so the next of drawing a Circle to a Center and Radius given, has many more, especially when the Radius is large. 'Tis almost impossible to make a Beam for the Compass that is to describe it that shall not bend and warp, and shrink and stretch in the using of it; and I remember when Mr. *Reeve* was to make a Gage for a Tool to grind an Object-glass for a Telescope of sixty Foot, after much Charge and Labour to perform it, tho' all possible care and caution was imploy'd to effect it, yet after all he was near a Month in Gaging his Tool before he could bring it to any tolerable perfection, and even then he found it not to be of a Sphere of its due length, but considerably less; which caus'd me to contrive a way how to do it true at once with a much less aparatus, and that of as great a Sphere as should be requir'd, as of six hundred as well as of sixty Foot, which I publish'd in my Micographia in the Year 1664; but one *Campani* an *Italian* above ten Years after publish'd the same thing as his own Invention, not taking any notice of what I had done. I know Mr. *Auzout* Objected, that there were some difficulties in adjusting the Machin, but I soon satisfy'd him that they were all insignificant.

Or the Arch of a large Circle.

So that we see, that tho' Science can easily suppose and conceive things as possible to be done, yet Art doth find many difficulties in the actual performance of them, and both ought to be call'd in for assistants in the prosecution of experimental Philosophy: Wherefore there ought to be as much care taken for the improving and perfecting of Art, as there is requir'd Sagacity and Perspicacity in observing the effects and methods of Nature.

Now Nature in its Operations, is, for the most part, Regular, Constant, Exact, Potent and Effective, and whatsoever is thereby design'd, it accommodates all things necessary to the performance thereof; it not only makes the Materials of a proper Substance, but it shapes the parts of their due Figure, and joins them in their due order, and actuates or moves them with proper motions. But Art, which at best does but mimick Nature, must search for materials where it can find them, and make use of such as can be procur'd. These it must shape and fit for its purposes as the Matter will indure, and as the Tools and Instruments, made use of, will perform, and they must be join'd and compos'd together as other circumstances will permit, and actuated by uncertain, irregular and insufficient Powers. So that at best the productions of Art in respect of those of Nature, are very much inferior in perfection.

The benefits of Art. And yet they are of great significancy for the accommodating the productions of Nature to the use of Mankind. Thus Art doth form a Ship to pass the Seas as big as the largest Fish, which it animates and directs with Men, and makes the Wind to move and convey from Port to Port. Art doth often also help and promote Natures Operations; as it improves the Sight by Spectacles, Microscopes and Telescopes. It divides and measures the parts and intervals of Time by Watches: It converts Corn into Bread by separating the Husks and Bran by the Sive and Searce, kneading the more nutritive part into Dough, and last of all baking it in the Oven. And the Fruit of the Vine it improves to a most pleasant Spirituous Liquour for drink. We owe almost all our Accommodations of our Life to the productions of Art. Nature puts us into the World more naked than most other of our fellow Creatures; but Art has abundantly supply'd that Defect, by accommodating the teguments of other Animals and Vegetables for that purpose. Nay, Minerals also and Metals have been made subservient. I might instance also in infinite other accommodations and conveniences of Life. So that tho' Art be far short of Nature in perfection of acting, yet since the power of it is placed in Man, it seems to be of as great a concern to him to be knowing and potent therein; for every new discovery therein gives him a new Power which he had not before. Thus the discovery of the Magnetical Needle inabl'd him to cross the Ocean and discover a New World; and to incompass the Earth and converse with the remotest Inhabitants. Thus the discovery of Telescopes inabled him to discover Cælestial Bodies never so much as dreamt of before; and the Miscroscope has discover'd a New World which was before wholly invisible. The discovery of the Pendulum has actually proved the inequality of the length of Days, and divided the intervals of Time more exactly than the Sun.

The discovery of Gun-powder and Guns has chang'd the whole method of offence, and defence both by Land and Sea. I might instance in many other effects of Art to shew how much the Power of Man is increased by them: but these are sufficient, and by these we may be inabled to judge of their significancy when they are made use of as they ought.

By these also we may be sufficiently inform'd how much a new Discovery or Observation may be considerable when duly apply'd, tho' in itself it seems never so obvious, slight and common, as to instance in the Pendulum, or in Printing, the grounds of which were sufficiently obvious to all, and therefore slighted, whereas the due application of them has perform'd almost miracles. And there are other things as obvious as them, which being duly apply'd, will be as effective tho' in another kind. An Experiment or Discovery is not therefore to be slighted, because, when it is shewn, it seems easy, and obvious, and trivial, and because the consequences or uses thereof are not presently detected.

What

What I some Weeks since propounded concerning the drawing of a Circle true to a large Radius, I do very much doubt whether the best Mechanick, it should be propounded to, would presently be able to effect it ; which I am the more inclin'd to believe from the Experimets I have seen try'd to that effect, by the most accomplish'd Persons both for Science and Art ; and yet when discover'd, I doubt not but almost every one will be apt to say, he knew as much ; and yet I do not find that any one has mention'd it in their Writings. *Guidus Ubaldus* and *Stoffler* have shewn a way of drawing a part of a Circle of a large Radius by the help of two Rulers fix'd at a proper Angle, and sliding against two Pinns at the extreamities of the Arch to be describ'd, which is founded on a proposition of *Euclid* ; but our Mathematical-Instrument-makers seldom or never make use thereof, because of the difficulty of its use, and imperfection of its performance ; and tho' Mr. *Reeve* had procur'd one made with great exactness, yet it did not perform its effects ; but he made a Beam compass of sixty Foot Radius, which did it not much better, by reason of the warping at so great a length, which I conceive also Sir *Chr. Wren* complain'd of in striking the Circle for the Dome at St. *Paul*'s, tho', for that effect, it were accurate enough. The Mathematical-Instrument-makers instead of the Angular Rule make use of a Steel Bow, which they can, by a Screw, bend more or less as they have occasion, and so can strike a small Arch of a Curve, which, tho' not exact, is yet near enough to the Arch of a Circle they have occasion to make upon their Instrument, and serves well enough for common use in small Instruments ; but where the Instruments are large and the Arches great, the irregularity may be discover'd ; and if a Planispherical projection of a Sphere of twenty or thirty Foot Diameter were to be drawn, both these Inventions would be insignificant.

The contrivance which I shall at present describe is such as will perform *The method for drawing large Circles.* what is necessary for the describing a Circle of two hundred or three hundred Foot of Diameter ; which for most uses in making Instruments or Mapps of the Planispherical Projection as large as any I have yet seen, or for striking Gages for Glass Tools or Dishes larger than any have been yet made ; tho' for such Tools indeed, the method I have describ'd in my Micrography is much better, because it doth at once, gage the Mould for casting, or the Tool for working of the true Spherical Surface requir'd, whereas this only making or describing a Line, the Mould and the Tool must be turn'd by that Gage to make the Surface thereof, of the Sphere requir'd. But there are other considerable uses of it as I shall shortly have occasion to shew.

Thursday, May 16. The Royal Society met, I discours'd of my Instrument to draw a great Circle, and produc'd an Instrument I had provided for that purpose, and therewith, by the direction of a Wire about a hundred Foot long, I shew'd how to draw a Circle of that Radius ; which gave satisfaction ; the way was by a small Truckle-wheel fix'd in a thin Ruler, so that the Axis of the Truckle kept parallel to the extended Wire Radius. Which Ruler had two small Staples fix'd in it, through which the Wire could easily slip to and fro. I explain'd also to them the other way of fixing the Truckle at the end of a small long Pipe of Brass that had a hole at the Center of each end, through which holes that Wire was to pass that was extended from the Center, and the same Truckle being always at right Angles with the Radiant Wire, and the Wire being free to slip to and fro in the holes, the edge of the Truckle would describe the Arch of the Circle exact.

Wednesday May 22. 1695. I have the last Meetings indeavour'd to explain the difficulties there are in making considerable discoveries either in Nature or Art ; and yet when they are discover'd they often seem so obvious and plain to be understood or to be discover'd, that it seems to be more difficult to give a satisfactory Reason why they were not sooner discover'd than how they came to be detected now. How easy it was (we now think) to find out a method of Printing of Letters, *&c.* and yet except what may have happen'd in *China*, there is no Specimen or History of any thing of that kind done in this part of the World. How obvious was the vibration of Pendulous Bodies ? And yet we do not find that it was made use of to divide the spaces of time, 'till *Galileo* discover'd the Isochroness of its motions, and

thought

thought of that proper ufe for it. What I fhew'd an Experiment of and explain'd the laft Meeting, may poffibly be thought obvious and eafy enough to have been fooner thought of, by fuch as may have had occafion for its ufe, and yet I never found the leaft mention made of it in any Author I have yet met with. That contrivance will ferve very well for defcribing a Circle of two, three or four hundred Foot Diameter, and will defcribe it as exactly and curioufly as any fmall Beam Compafs will do a Circle of two, three or four Foot. But when it doth exceed a certain length, even that alfo will begin to fail, and the difficulties will much increafe; for that a Wire will be too weak to bear a weight fufficient to ftrain it near enough to a ftraight; fo that there is in this way alfo a *a non plus ultra*, but *eft aliquid Prodire tenus*; this is much farther than could be done any other way; and by this way, if a true plain be given, any part, or even a whole Circle may be defcrib'd of as great a Diameter as I have already mention'd.

But if a greater be yet neceffary, Mechanicks do hitherto fail us and Nature alfo gives us none greater nor lefs than the Circumference of the Earth, and that in the Surface of the Water, when the Air is Stagnant, or without Wind, or in the Surface of fuch Water frozen into Ice. But this is fo great a Spherical Surface, that it can be of no Mechanical ufe that I yet know of, unlefs it be to afford us a Plain large enough to defcribe a large Circle upon, which is otherwife difficult enough to be procur'd. But when we have procur'd fuch a Plain by the help of Nature in this manner by freezing, yet to defcribe a Circle of a thoufand or two thoufand Foot Diameter, will be impoffible by any way I have yet met with; and yet I think it not beyond the power of Art, nay, tho' one of twice that magnitude were it neceffary.

And tho' it may be difficult enough to find a way before it be fhewn, yet when difcover'd, every one will be ready enough to fay, 'tis eafy to do, and that it was obvious to be thought of and invented; for that indeed every one fees the Experiment of it daily, and yet no one has thought of applying it to this purpofe, as in the inftance I juft now mention'd of the Pendulum: And that I may the more plainly evidence this, I have prepar'd an apparatus for the effecting thereof experimentally; which, tho' it be not a compleat Inftrument, fuch as I defign to have made (when I can procure a proper Workman at leifure) yet by this, and the demonftration of the truth of the Grounds and Reafons thereof, it will be put out of doubt. This Apparatus, and the demonftration, I will prefently produce.

THe *Author not having given any farther defcription of his way, and the Apparatus of performing it, I thought it might be acceptable to tranfcribe the account of it as I found it enter'd in the Journal of the Royal Society as follows. May 22. 1695. Dr.* Hook *produced and read an account of an Inftrument for defcribing a very great Circle, being, by the help of two rouling Circles or Truckles in the two ends of a Rule, made fo as to be turn'd in their Sockets to any affigned Angle, thereby to become the two Tangents of any great Circle to be defcribed; the inclination of the plains of the two little rouling Circles being always equal to the Angle, the length of the Ruler fubtends to the Radius of the Circle propofed.*

This is all I find concerning it; it were to be wifht there had been fome draught thereof preferved; but this way may be better apprehended by the next following.

R. W.

June 20. 1695. I have in my former Difcourfes or Lectures fhewn fome new methods of defcribing the Arches of very large Circles, fuch as are very hardly poffible to be defcrib'd by any other way, at leaft not to that exactnefs, nor without almoft infinitely more trouble and labour; and thefe by Inftruments eafy enough to be made and ufed, and as eafy to be underftood and demonftrated, and thofe founded on Experiments and Practices fo univerfally known, that one would wonder how fuch an application as this

fhould

should not be thought of by any one that had occasion for the use of it; and this the rather, because we know it to be the reason on which is founded the practice not ony of turning the Waggons, Coaches, and such other four Wheel'd Carriages, but also of Boats, Lighters, Ships, and other Vessels; as also Fishes for moving upon and through the Water, and of Hawks, Kites, and other Birds which move through the Air. But we need not much wonder neither, when we consider at the same time how obvious the grounds of the Art of Printing were by the use of Seales, and of rectifying Clocks by the use of Pendulums, and yet how long the World was without those Arts before they were thought of for those purposes and reduc'd to practice. The true cause of which is the unwillingness that Men generally have to be at the trouble of thinking and meditating, especially when they observe that those that are so, do generally reap nothing for all their Labour, but either Contempt, and the nicknames of Madmen and Projectors, or the Emulations of others, which creates them continual troubles. Nor is there less difficulty in procuring the Instruments or Apparatus necessary to put a new Invention into use and practice, than to invent and contrive the same; for Workmen are generally very unwilling to be put out of their common Road of working, and make a hundred Objections before they will undertake, and very often make as many mistakes in the performing, before they will rightly execute what is desir'd; and the inventer must be content not only to afford them his patience, but his Purse also, otherwise no further progress is to be expected, and often also, tho' both are supply'd, yet nothing will procure any further trials; and new hands must be sought, where possibly the inventor speeds little better; but supposing him at last to have executed his design and made his purchase, what has he got but some *Difficiles Nugæ*, some new *Swing Swangs*, which were the names that the Barometer for the Weather, and the Pendulums for Clocks did a long time bear; but when Truth at length doth prevail, and the usefulness of an Invention appears, then every one claims it for his own, tho' possibly he never had the thought of it, 'till all the World knew it. These may be some of the reasons why inventions have come so thin and seldom into the World: And why many parts of useful Knowledge do yet remain undiscover'd; nor can we well expect that they should be more frequent, 'till the allurements that should prompt the Inquiry have another appearance. However, whether from the Genius of these later Ages, or from the increase of Literature by the propagation and communication of Knowledge by Printing, or from some other happy influence from above; we have found that the present Age has been much more fruitful in that kind than many preceeding, and we may hope that the approaching may be yet more, if at least *invenire discamus invienendo, ut Scribendo discimus scribere; Nam Res dat lumina Rebus.* This was one cause why I contriv'd the following addition to what I have already explain'd concerning the methods of describing very large Circles. The first of which was how to describe such a Circle about a Center given, and the length of the Radius, and that of so great a length, that it is almost impossible for to make any Beam Compass long enough to perform it without warping and bending, or any string strong enough to do it without stretching and shrinking; all which inconveniences I have thereby shew'd how to obviate most easily by making use of one small Truckle put upon a Wire strain'd from such a Center to its Circumference. The second way was how to describe a Circle, or any part of it be the Radius almost never so great, and that without knowing or making any use of the Center, but only upon knowing the length of the Radius or the desir'd Magnitude of such a Circle, or the Magnitude of the Subtense of the Arch of a Degree, Minute or Second, &c. of such a Circle. Now because there may be yet another condition desirable for some occasions, which cannot be well perform'd by either of those methods, and yet may be of necessary use for the solving of some Problems, or the actual execution of some Designs; upon further contemplating this Subject I have contriv'd this present Addition; and that is to draw the Arch of a Circle to a Center at a considerable distance, where the Center cannot well be approach'd, or where, by reason of incumbrances interjacent, a Wire cannot be extended; as from

the

the top of a Pole set up in the midst of a Wood, or from the spindle of a Vane at the top of a Tower in a City, or from a point on the other side of a River, or in a Lake or Morass; in all which the Center cannot conveniently be approach'd or come at otherwise than by the Sight. This Requisite then I perform by the help of two Telescopes, so plac'd at the Truckles as thereby to see through both of them the same Point which is propos'd for the said Center, and, by thus directing of them to such a Center, to set the Truckles in their due posture, so as to describe by their motion any part of such a Circle as shall be desir'd, whose Center shall be the point of the Pole or Spindle mention'd. The qualifications of the Instrument necessary for this Effect are, First, That the Centers of the Truckles be exactly equi-distant from the Center of the Compass; that is, that the Arms of the Compass be of equal length. Secondly, That the plains of the edges of the Truckles do exactly intersect in the Center of the Compass. Thirdly, That the two Telescope Sights be exactly Perpendicular to those two Plains at two Points, as near as may be over the Centers of the Truckles.

Tab. 12. *Fig.* 3.   This will be more plain by a delineation, where ab, ab are the two Telescopes directed to the inaccessible Center E. c, c the two Truckles plac'd at right Angles to the Telescopes. c d, c d, two Rulers jointed at the Center d, b b a Ruler upon which the two Telescopes slide, so as to be fixt upon occasion after being directed to the distant Center.

An Extract out of the Parisian *Academies· Memoires relating to the alteration of the Axis of the Earths motion, Read to the R. S.* July *the third* 1695.

As there are some Inventions that are the Products of Design and Ratiocination, such as are acquir'd by the use of known Principles by the way of reasoning, Application or Contrivance; so there are others found out by meer chance upon Trials made for other purposes, as Gun-powder, the Magnetical Vertue, Telescopes, &c. But there is also a third sort of Inventions which may be ascrib'd partly to the one, partly to the other, partly to Design and Ratiocination, and partly also to Chance and Observation: Of this kind was that of the cause of the Cælestial motions and of the Spheroidical form of the Earth; of which I have long since discours'd, as also of the Parallax of the fixt Stars, and likewise of the alteration of the Poles of the Earths diurnal motion. Now tho' this Doctrine has hitherto met with great opposition on the one Hand and contempt on the other, because the later part of the invention has not been compleated by some lucky chance to prove it positively, by finding out some instances among the many Observations that are recorded that might put it beyond dispute, nor by hitting upon a *medium*, by which that might be verify'd in a short time; which, according to the known methods of Observations, require a very long one, yet I hope that a little time will produce some such proof as will put it out of doubt; and if that does not succeed according to my expectation, yet I hope I shall in some little time be able to shew a way how to effect it. I am not displeas'd that Monsieur *Cassini* thinks it worth his inquiry, and I am apt to believe is conscious of the truth of it, and that he begins to think of expedients how to solve the Phænomena when they shall be certainly found to concur with this Hypothesis, if he be not already convinc'd of it, and to be able to loose the inventer of it by finding a great number of old pretenders to it. 'Tis true that many have mention'd such a suspicion, and have indeavour'd to prove it, but they seem to have grounded their Conjectures only upon Experiments or Observations made at several times in the same place, but not upon the Theory of the causes of such a variation, whereas my Conjectures concerning it were deduc'd from a Theory, which I conceive may be consonant to the processes of Nature; I know, indeed, that 'tis a very difficult matter to find out such a Theory, and almost impossible to make it so evident as the Principles of Geometry; for that the Nature, Composition, and internal Operations and Powers of mixt Bodies are far beyond the reach of the Senses; nor will

the

the Analogy hold between the motion of grofs and fenfible Bodies and thofe of minute and infenfible, as can plainly enough be prov'd. And upon that account the *Data*, upon which the Ratiocination is founded, being uncertain and only conjectural, the Conclufions or Deductions therefrom can at beft be no other than probable ; but ftill they become more and more probable, as the Confequences deduc'd from them appear upon examinations by Trials and defign'd Obfervations to be confirm'd by Fact or Effect. So that the Effect is that which confummates the demonftration of the Invention itfelf ; and the Theory is only an affiftant to direct fuch an Inquifition, and by what means to procure the demonftration of the Exiftence or non-exiftence thereof. Thus by my Theory I was led to believe that the body of *Jupiter* had a motion upon its *Axis*, and thereupon I had a long time indeavour'd to difcover by my fight, whether it were really fo as I fuppos'd ; but I could not perceive it 'till I procur'd and made ufe of a very good Telefcope, and there was a Concurrence of a due pofition of the permanent Spot in *Jupiter*, and a clearnefs of the Air, and poffibly of my Eyes that affifted me in the Obfervation ; however therefore, tho' the Obfervation were the Demonftration, yet the Theory was the occafion of feeking after it : And the fame was that difcovery of the Parallax of the Earth, and of the Cæleftial Motions, which I have mention'd in my Difcourfe, Printed on that Subject. Now, tho' I do not find that any have given themfelves the trouble to repeat the Experiments and Obfervations neceffary for that purpofe ; and tho' I think there is no one that can find a real Objection againft the way and method of verifying it, which I made ufe of, yet there have not been wanting divers who have fo far taken notice of it as to fuggeft other ways of doing it, tho', I conceive, much more troublefome, and abundantly more liable to Objection than that which I contriv'd. But let every one take his own method (for there may be many, but I believe it will be hard to find a better or fo good) provided they do actually make the difcovery of the reality thereof ; and I am very apt to believe that the fame has been verify'd in *France* and elfewhere alfo by my way, tho' they feem unwilling to own it, and have not publifh'd the Fact ; and that poffibly may be, becaufe they (that have made it) are unwilling to be thought to learn from others ; and becaufe I fear they cannot find another way of their own that will be fo good as mine. And this I am inclin'd to think from a late Difcourfe Publifh'd in the *Memoires of the Parifian Academy* and elfewhere, by which they would have it be believ'd, that the Well in the Obfervatory of *Paris* was made for that purpofe before the publication of my attempt, tho' 'twas two Years after I had made thofe Obfervations, and read them to the Royal Society ; and that Monfieur *Caffini* has purpofely made Obfervations of the Latitudes of Places to find whether they do alter or not, and that thereupon he had detected fuch a variation of the height of the Polar Star, which might ferve to make him the difcoverer of the annual Parallax. The mode of the whole Difcourfe is fomewhat fingular, which I have therefore extracted, to fhew what methods are us'd by fome to raife Arguments againft a truth they are unwilling to have known ; and the rather, becaufe it is alfo fomewhat akin to Difcourfes for the fame purpofe of our own *Englifh* Manufacture.

" The irregularity of the Seafons of fome late Years, and the frequent
" *Earthquakes* which have happen'd in divers places has made fome fufpect a
" change in the *œconomy* of the World, and there have been fome Aftrono-
" mers who believ'd that there has been of late fome confiderable changes
" of the height of the Pole. Mon. *Caffini* having been confulted on this affair
" from divers places, has computed the prefent pofture of the Heavens,
" with the Obfervations he has made for above thirty Years, as alfo with
" thofe of the moft antient Aftronomers, to fee not only whether there has
" been any change of late, but even for many paft Ages.

" The Antients took great care to compare the parts of the Heaven with
" thofe of the Earth, obferving the Circles of the Heavens which corre-
" fponded with the Mountains, Promontorys, and other notable parts of
" the Earth ; and from time to time took notice whether thefe did alter :
" 'Twas not long before they found fome. *Eratofthenes* about two Thoufand

The ufe of Theories.

Alteration of the Latitude of places.

Years

" Years fince found by preceding Charts (as *Strabo* relates) that the Moun-
" tains plac'd on the Eaſt part of the Continent, had chang'd their Site,
" declining more to the North, as had alſo the *Indies.* He corrects thoſe,
" and by a new Chart draws a parallel paſſing between *Hercules's Pillers,* thro'
" the *Streights* of *Sicily,* over the South extreams of *Peloponeſus,* and con-
" tinu'd through *Cilicia* to the Gulph of *Iſſus,* and from thence to the *Indies,*
" over the Mountain *Taurus* parting *Aſia* into the North and South. Theſe
" in *Ptolomy's* time, four hundred Years after, had changed places, *Taurus*
" lying three Degrees more North than the *Streights* of *Hercules.* But if
" the heights of the Pole in *Ptolomy,* now 1550 Years fince, were exact,
" the Poles are gone back and are come to the places where *Eratoſthenes* found
" them, *Taurus* and the *Streights* being both plac'd at 36°, but this parallel
" runs two Degrees South of *Sicily* ; and indeed the moſt part of the heights
" the Pole, obſerv'd by the Antients, differ very much from thoſe found at
" preſent. If any could be rely'd on, thoſe ſhould be at *Marſeilles* and *Byzan-*
" *tium* ; the one made by *Pytheas,* and the other by *Hipparchus,* two of the
" moſt famous Obſervators of their times. Theſe were made by *Gnomons*
" of great height, and at the Summer *Solſtice,* well circumſtantiated, and
" with all the exactneſs Aſtronomy was then able to effect. Now if theſe
" were exact, 'tis certain great alterations have happen'd fince the times of
" *Hipparchus* ; for *Hipparchus* found *Byzantium* in the parallel *Pythias* had plac-
" ed *Marſeilles* ; yet *Strabo,* who liv'd 150 Years after *Hipparchus,* affirms
" *Byzantium* to be more North than *Marſeilles:* For the Parallel that paſt
" through the *Streights,* was only 3°, 34', South of *Marſeilles,* but from *Bi-*
" *zantium* it was remov'd ſeven whole Degrees. The Oriental Aſtronomers,
" who liv'd divers Ages after *Strabo,* make *Byzantium* two Degrees more
" North than it was in *Hipparchus's* times, as is plain by the Tables of *Naſſer*
" *Eddir.* and *Ulug Beg.*

" But in this Age on the clean contrary, *Marſeilles* is two whole Degrees
" more North than *Bizantium* ; for *Caſſini* going on purpoſe to *Marſeilles* in
" 1672, found the Latitude of it 43, 17. and *Deſchales* at *Byzantium* obſerv'd
" its Latitude only 41°. 6'. which agrees alſo with the Obſervations of Fa-
" ther *Beſnier,* from all which, if ſuppos'd true, there muſt have happen'd
" great changes.

" The difference alſo between the Latitudes of divers places recorded by
" *Ptolomy,* and thoſe obſerv'd in the ſame places by other Aſtronomers, fince
" may be argument enough for our Beleif, that the Pole has chang'd much
" fince the time of *Ptolomy.* This difference appear'd ſo convincing to *Do-*
" *minick Maria* of *Ferrara* (a Man of an excellent *Genius* as *Maginus* affirms,
" and who was Tutor to *Copernicus*) that he aſſerted that the height of the
" Pole did continually change, and that places now in the *Torrid Zone,* would,
" in proceſs of time, come into the Frigid and the contrary ; and that the
" Mountains of *Æthiopia,* now roaſted by the Sun, would in time be co-
" vered by Snow and Ice. *Maginus* alſo, and the Aſtronomers of his time,
" affirm the Poles alſo to have changed. And *Ticho* was ſo far mov'd by this
" Opinion, that he deſir'd the State of *Venice* to ſend an able Aſtronomer
" on purpoſe to ſee, if the preſent Latitude of *Alexandria* were the ſame that
" *Ptolomy* had found it ; but this without effect ; however 'tis expected from
" ſome, fince ſent for that purpoſe by the *French* King. 'Tis true, the ex-
" actneſs of antient Obſervations was not to be compar'd to the Modern,
" and therefore no more ſhall be ſaid on that head at preſent.

" But next to come to Obſervations leſs to be ſuſpected, as being made
" this laſt Age. *Rothman* aſſures *Ticho* by a Letter, that he had found a dif-
" ference of the height of the Pole of a Minute or two, between the Win-
" ter and Summer of the ſame Year. *Snellius* and *Ricciolus,* who are both a-
" gainſt this Opinion, do yet report Obſervations that confirm it, as that
" *Ticho* obſerv'd the Latitude once 50°. 6'. another time 50°. 4'. 30". ſuch are
" the Latitudes of *Paris* found by ſeveral Men, 48. 39'. [48. 45.] 48. 50. and
" ſome 48. 55. Great differences are alſo found of the Latitude of the ſame
" place taken at different times by *Riccioli* and *Grimaldi* with the greateſt ex-
" actneſs. *Grimaldi,* in 1645, finds the Tower of *Modena* in 44°. 37'. ex-

actly,

" actly, and the same *Grimaldi* with *Riccioli* in 1654, finds it 44. 38'. 50". the
" same found a place on the Mountain of *Bolonia* 44°. 27'. and the same
" place another time 44. 27'. 50". The same in 1646, found his Observatory
" in *Bolonia* 44°. 29'. 30". but in 1655, he, with *Cassini*, found it 44°. 30'. 20".
" the same says, *Ferrara* was once observ'd 44°. 50'. another time 44°. 51'.
" 7". and *Cassini* another time since, by repeated Observations, found it 44°.
" 52'. In the Year fifty six *Cassini* found the Palace of *Farnesi* in *Rome* 41°.
" 52'. but in sixty eight he found the Palace of *Cardinal d'Este* (which should
" have been more) only 41°. 51'. At *Paris* 1668. *Cassini* and *Picart* found the
" height of the Pole-star at the Kings Library 48. 53. and by that the height
" of the Observatory must have been 48°. 51'. 10". two Years after when
" the Observatory was finish'd, *i.e.* in *September* 71. *Cassini* finds it 51°. 19'.
" 40". and the twelfth of *October* following 51°. 19'. 50". and the eighth of
" *September* 51°. 19'. 10". *Picart* at *Uraniberg* 1671. on the eighth of *Octo-*
" *ber* finds the greatest height of the Pole-star 58°. 23'. 15". but in *November*
" he finds it 58°. 22'. 55". and in *December* 58°. 22'. 45". He adds other in-
" stances of his own and other Observations too long to repeat at this time,
" by which he seems to prove a change of the Latitude of Places, or the
" height of the Pole even at the Observatory of *Paris*. But after all he pro-
" ceeds thus————.

" Notwithstanding all these Observations of apparent variations, it may
" be said only, that in these later times there has happen'd no extraordi-
" nary change either in the height of the Pole or Meridian Altitudes of the
" Sun ; but also that the Heavens have at all times kept the same Position
" to the Earth that they have at this present Age ; since it may be believ'd
" that all those variations, of which I have spoken, may have proceeded from
" Defects in the Observations : As, First, From the defaults of Instru-
" ments, since it is certain that Instruments do suffer alterations from time
" to time, the causes of which are imperceptible, which is the cause why
" they are sometimes examin'd and corrected. Secondly, From the difficulty
" of distinguishing the parts of a Minute. Thirdly, From the differing
" Refraction of the Air, especially at the Observatory of *Paris*, being on the
" South side of so great a City. Fourthly, As there is a variation of the
" direction of the Magnetical Needle, so there may happen some change of
" the direction of the Perpendiculars of Instruments, and these changes may
" be more sensible in some places than in others. Lastly, As to the Observa-
" tions, of these the Antients were made with very course Instruments, they
" had no regard of Refraction or Parallax or other Circumstances that might
" cause Errors, and thence we need not wonder at such considerable differences
" among them, besides the mistakes of Numerical Figures by the Transcribers;
" so that making allowances for all these, there will remain little difference of
" Position of the Heavens to the Earth, or the motions of the Stars to be
" rely'd on, and it is more reasonable to ascribe those that are found to these
" accidents than to a change in the Heavens.

" And yet it is most probable that there is some small variation of the
" height of the Pole which happens from time to time, but that never ex-
" ceeds two Minutes, and it will be settled in time. This is very remark-
" able in the height of the Pole of *Alexandria.*; for *Ptolomy* with all his
" care found it sometimes 30°. 58'. at other times 31°; so tho' there be a
" little change, yet this must not pass as extraordinary, since it exceeds not
" two Minutes. The difference between those of *Ticho* and those of *Picart*,
" in 71 and 72. is but 50". in 88 Years ; and we must consider that this is
" not in proportion, since we have found a greater change in one and the
" same place in one Year. For twenty two Years now since the Observatory
" has been built, *Cassini* has found but two variations : This variation the
" said *Cassini* has attempted to reduce to some Rule; he fancies the Altitudes
" of the Poles diminish as the Sun approaches the Æquinoctials and Solstices,
" and increase as it departs from them.
" Mr. *Cassini* also believes there is some change in the Solstitial Altitudes,
" and has actually found them, but those not so great as those of the Pole;
" and these variations he conceives, will in time settle also. We have al-

" ready feen, that thofe of *Pythias* made at *Marfeilles* three hundred Years
" before Chrift, and *Caffini*'s in 1672. differ but fome Minutes, and we may
" fhortly expeɕt, whether thofe fent by the King on purpofe to *Alexandria*,
" will find any difference from *Ptolomy*'s Soliftitial Altitudes.

" It is of great importance in Aftronomy to know to what precifenefs the
" height of the Pole can be found ; for if we cannot with all our care, be fure
" of it within half a Minute, 'tis in vain to make ufe of it for finding the
" Parallax of Planets above the Moon, or for fetling the hour of the Sol-
" ftice, where fome few Seconds are confiderable ; but indeed for *Geogra-*
" *phy, Navigation,* or *Chorography,* this is curious enough".

What the defign of this long Difcourfe of Mr. *Caffini* may be I cannot gather, unlefs it be to feem to deny the variation of the Altitude of the Pole,
becaufe poffibly he is oblig'd fo to do, and yet at the fame time exaɕtly prove
it ; or by a new way to folve the annual Parallax of the fixt Stars; which he
feems to grant, but yet 'tis by a new fancy of his own, for which I can conceive no reafon. Me thought Monfieur *Comiers* was much more conceivable, tho' extravagant enough, that every Star mov'd in a little Epicicle of
a Minute in Diameter, once round in a Year. Next I cannot but wonder to
find him at the fame time relying on Obfervations of the Antients to prove
what he would have to be fo, and rejeɕting as far (and befpattering indeed all)
that are not for him ; an eafy way to prove or difpove any thing. Thirdly, I
obferve, that tho' what I had formerly fpoken of the alteration of the Center
of the Gravitation of the Earth, were look'd upon as a very extravagant and
improbable Opinion, yet I conceive it is not fo efteem'd by the *Parifian Aca-*
demians ; otherwife it would not have been Printed. I am alfo now apt to
fufpeɕt that *Ticho Brahe* did *doulein Hypothefei* ; fince, by *Rothman*'s, he was
advertis'd of fuch an annual Phænomenon or Change, and that he might
eafily have fatisfy'd himfelf by his own Obfervations, without fending to *Æ-*
gypt for information. To conclude, as Monfieur *Caffini* conceives thefe little variations or fwayings of the Poles and Solftices will, in fome fhort time,
fettle and fix in their true places ; fo I conceive that all thefe ftruglings to
make it this or that, fomewhat or nothing, more or lefs, will at laft terminate in that Explication thereof, which I have long fince propounded.

La Meridiana del Tempio di S. Petronio, &c. *i. e.* The Meridian Line of the
Church of St. *Petronio,* drawn and fitted for Aftronomical Obfervations in
the Year 1655, Revis'd and reftor'd in the Year 1695. by *Joh. Dominico Caf-*
fini primary Aftronomer. Pontificial, Mathematician, and one of the Royal
Accademy of Sciences ; Printed at *Bolognia* 1695, in twenty two Sheets in
Folio.

In this Book written by Mon. *Caffini,* but Publifh'd by *Dominico Guglielmini* ;
there is an account given of the occafion of making this Meridian Line in
the Year 1650, of the method of doing it, and of the exaɕtnefs with which
it was perform'd by Mr. *Caffini* at that time ; then of the ufes that have
been made of it, and of the alterations that have happen'd to this Church
fince that time, and of the Reftauration and Examination of it in the Year
1695, by Monfieur *Caffini* himfelf ; and laftly, of the ufes that may be made
of it for the future.

To this is adjoined a Difcourfe of Snr. Dominico Guglielmini, Mathematician and publick Leɕturer of *Bolognia,* giving an account of the Operations
made, and of the Inftruments us'd in this laft Reftauration of the faid Meridian Line. Monfieur *Caffini* in the firft Seɕtion, fays, this verifycation
was the more confiderable, Firft, Becaufe it fell out to be the Year before
the laft intercalation of the *Gregorian* Year, before the omitting of one Leap
Year (which is to be done in the Year 1700, in order to make the vernal Æ-
quinox to be on the twenty firft of *March*) and fo would give an opportunity to obferve exaɕtly the time of the Suns entrance into *Aries.* And, Secondly, For determining a Controverfy much agitated now among the Learned,
whether the Pofition of the Meridians and Parallels on the Earths Surface
do really alter ; for that not only the prefent pofture of them are found very different from thofe of the Antient Geographers ; but differences are found
alfo among the more modern Obfervations, as the prefent Meridian of *Ura-*

nibur

neburg has been lately found by Monfieur *Picart* and others, to vary 18'. towards the Eaft from that fixed by *Ticho Brahe* above a hundred Years fince; and the *Pyramid* of *Egypt* has been found newly to ftand in a pofture that two fides of it refpect the South. Now he having found that the Meridian and Parallel of *Bononia* have not alter'd at *Bononia* in fourty Years, conceives thofe other alterations, fuppos'd to be found, are to be afcrib'd to the defects of the Obfervations themfelves. In the next place he relates the firft occafion of making a Meridian Line in this Church of St. *Petronio*, to be for rectifying the time of *Eafter*, and the Feafts of the Church which depend on the true time of the Vernal Æquinox. Now the Prelates of *Alexandria* (who were deputed by the Council of *Nice* to ftate that time) found it then to be on the twenty firft of *March*; but Pope *Gregory* being inform'd, that it, in this time, fell on the eleventh of that Month; he alter'd the *Julian Account*, and made the eleventh to be the twenty firft. This was the occafion of *Ignatio Dante*'s firft making a Meridian Line in the Pavement of that Church in the Year 1575, before this alteration which was in 1683; but this Line being found to vary from the prefent Meridian, and to be ferviceable only for obferving the Solftices, and being fufpected to be fo mifplaced by reafon of the obftruction of the Pillars of that Church was the occafion of Monfieur *Caffini*'s finding a fitter place, and fixing there his new Meridian Line in the Year 1655. the place where, and manner how he more particularly and fully expreffes, becaufe it was of fo confiderable, and, as it were, of facred ufe to the Church: He names all the eminent Aftronomers who were his Concomitants in the Operations, as witneffes of the exactnefs of it. After this he relates feveral variations that have happen'd to that Fabrick fince he firft fixed this Line, and thereby fhews the neceffity and ufe of the Reftauration, and adjufting it for the time to come, by which any further alteration that may happen to that Building for the future, may be fo far remedied, and the effential parts of this Line fo far reftor'd and rectify'd, that they fhall be as effectual as if no alteration had happen'd. The ufes of which will be not only to fhew the true time of the Suns ingrefs into the Tropicks and Æquinoctial Points, but likewife into all the other Signs, and fo ferve for the verifying or rectifying the Calender. The fame being now fo plac'd as that the Perpendicular height of the hole by which the Light is admitted (which is an Inch in Diameter) is a thoufand Inches of the *Paris* Foot above the Pavement and the Meridian Line which is as a tangent to it, as the tangent of 45°. divided into 100000 parts upon one of the Marble Cheeks that border the Ruler of Iron that expreffes the Meridian Line, and upon the other Cheek of Marble are mark'd the Degrees of the diftance of the Sun from the *Zenith*, whereon are alfo mark'd the places of the Signs of the Ecliptick. From the Obfervations made by this Line Monfieur *Caffini* calculated his Tables of Refractions, which have been fince verify'd by other Obfervations.

These confiderations induc'd the Senators of *Bononia* who had the care of the faid Edifice committed to them to be at the charge to repair the faid Line, and to take care that it fhould be preferv'd for the future; to which intent they not only caus'd the Inftruments made ufe of in the fixing this Line to be fafely preferv'd, but they alfo defir'd *D. Guilelmini* to make fo good a defcription of them, that in cafe of decay it may be known how to fupply and make ufe of them for this purpofe for the future; which intention and defire the faid Learned Profeffor hath fully perfected and compleated in his Difcourfe fubjoined to that of Monfieur *Caffini*, and has likewife added fome ufeful Tables, as that of the parts of the Radius anfwering to the divifions of the Tangent into Degrees, Minutes and Seconds. Secondly, That of the Refractions and Parallaxes of the Sun at feveral Altitudes. And, Thirdly, A Table of the Declination of every Point of the Ecliptick, anfwering to the Minutes of Declination for the obliquity of the Ecliptick, which he makes to be 23°. 29'. 12". He fays alfo, that he by accurate Obfervations finds the height of the Pole at that Church to be 44°. 30'. 15". which is 1'. 15". greater than what Monfieur *Caffini* had found it in the Year

The Authors Remarks.

1655. All which Particulars, and many other remarkable will be found in the Treatise itself, to which the Reader is referr'd.

That the Meridian Line which was fix'd by *Dante*, was not plac'd in the true North and South Line, but did vary a little from it at first I can easily grant, by reason of the Position of the Church and the Pillars thereof which would not supply a fitting Room and Space for a more convenient Situation of it ; and for that I find the Author *Dante* to acknowledge as much in his *Anemographia*, Printed 1578. namely, that it did deflect a little towards the North-East ; for that he says, that the Sun, when it come to pass his Line, was a little fallen from its Meridian Altitude ; but whether the same did then respect the Meridian with the same Inclination as now it is found to do ; namely, with an inclination of 9°. 6'. 20". as *Riccioli* observ'd it, we have no Evidence ; and I do very much doubt whether we should have been acquainted with it if there had been found a real variation ; because the very imagination of such a variation was condemned in *Galileo*, who brought it as an Argument to prove the motion of the Earth ; who, as *Riccioli* words it, *ex nimio Pruritu annuum motum telluris undecumq; fulciendi, Statim ac audivit mutationem Liniæ Meridianæ a Marsilio assertam concepit animo Spem hinc argutum aliquid pro terræ motu annuo excudendi.* And such as are zealous to defend a Profession of their own, or receiv'd Doctrine of the Religion they profess, or of the Church of which they are a Member, are very unwilling to hear any Argument that shall be urged against it ; much less to produce or publish any new Argument or Evidence of their own finding ; however, 'tis very hard to suppose the noble *Ticho Brahe* to have been so negligent or ignorant as to place it eighteen Minutes wrong, and the variation observ'd by *Guilielmni* of the Latitude of *Bononia* to be different from that observ'd by Senr. *Cassini*, seem to argue somewhat for a variation. But let Time determine this Controversy to Posterity, and every one for the present satisfy himself as well as he can with what evidence he can meet with : That there are as great mutations as these in the Globe of the Earth, and of some of the other Globes I hope I shall be able some other time to prove.

Vide p. 530.

HAving met with the following Paper among the Authors loose Manuscripts, I judged it might not be unacceptable in regard the foregoing Discourses, concerning the Rumb-line, is left so imperfect.

R. W.

Sep. 25. 85. The projecting the Rumb-line from the Pole, maketh it a proportional Spiral upon a plain parallel to the Æquator, and consequently the Rays from the Center being Meridians, are the true tangent Lines of half the Angles from the Center, or of half the Degrees of the Complement of the Latitude, and consequently the intersection of the Rumb-line is easily found by the propriety of the proportional Spiral, equal differences of Longitude dividing the said Meridian or Tangent Lines into continual Proportionals ; which continual Proportionals are easily found by the Logarithms, and by the Logarithms of the half Tangent Lines the Degrees of the Complement of the Latitude are also found ; and in a plain projection upon a Cylinder, the division of the Meridians are made in proportion of the Logarithm of the half Tangents of the Complements of the Latitude ; but if it be made by the projection beyond the Æquinoctial, then the Logarithms of the half Tangent of the Latitude will give the divisions of Latitudes upon the Meridian.

The

THe Author not proceeding any further in the former Disquisition as to the other methods of finding the Longitude at Sea, except some fragments relating to the improvement of Time-keepers, which possibly I may some time or other give an Abstract of, if I can reduce them to any Order, they coming to my Hands very imperfect, many parts of the Discourses being lost : I say, the Author breaking off the former Discourse abruptly, I shall here present the Reader with a method by him propounded for finding the Latitude of Places.

R. W.

Read before the Royal Society, May 11th. 1687.

I mention'd, in some former Discourses, some ways of discovering the Latitudes of places at Sea without knowing the Meridian, and without taking an Altitude, which were perform'd by the help of some true Projections of the Cælestial Hemespheres, whereof the Polar Points were the Centers, by finding and observing some remarkable Stars in some one Azymuth or Perpendicular, and two other remarkable Stars in some other ; and this to be performed either when such Observations happened to be made both at the same instant, or the one of them some known or noted time after the other.

The former of these two ways, which supposeth both the said Observations to be made at the same instant, I shew'd by the Tangent Projection upon a Plain touching the Polar Point, or any other Point of the Sphere that comprehended all the four Stars ; the Zenith Point of the Place, and the Polar Point or Æquinoctial Circle, was very easily perform'd by the help of a Ruler and Compasses, by drawing a straight Line cross the Projection with black Lead, passing through two of them that were observ'd in one Azymuth, and then laying the Ruler over the other two that were observ'd in the other Azymuth, and noting the Point where the said Ruler shall cut the former Line drawn with black Lead upon the Projection ; for that That Point of Intersection will represent the true Point of the Heavens then in the Zenith of the place where such Observation shall be made. Now by finding the true distance of that Point of Intersection either from the Polar Point, if it be comprehended in the Projection, or from the Æquinoctial Circle, if that be comprehended, it will not be difficult to find the true Latitude of the place ; and, if it be desir'd, the Positions of those Azymuths and the hour of the Night, and the true Meridian Line, and the like, which would be too long to explain and exemplify at this time and place. *[marginal note: Ways of finding the Latitude. I do not remember to have seen the Lecture preceding this.]*

The former of these two kinds of Observations may also be perform'd by the planispherical Projections, or the half Tangent Projections, where the Polar Points are made the Center of the Projections more easily, or somewhat more difficultly where any other Point of the Sphere is made the Center of the Projection ; which is perform'd by drawing great Circles upon the said Projections with black Lead which shall pass through each of the two Stars observ'd in the one and the other Azymuth or Perpendicular ; for that the Point of Intersection of the two great Circles thus drawn, will shew, upon the said Projection, the true Zenith Point of the place, whose distance from the Polar Point of the said Projection (which is easily measurable) will give the Complement of the Latitude of the place. The greatest difficulty in this way, is the drawing of a great Circle upon the Projection, which shall pass though the two Stars observ'd in the same Azymuth or Perpendicular. But this, as it may be perform'd divers ways, some more easy, some a little more difficult, some of which are Printed, and others may if occasion require ; so I think none so difficult, but that an ordinary Capacity may, in a short space, be inform'd how to effect and perform the same with accurateness enough. But the explaining these ways would be too long for this present Meeting.

As

As for the second fort of Obfervations, wherein the two Azymuths are obferv'd at two differing times ; that is, the fecond Obfervation of any two noted Stars in fome Azymuth is taken, fome known or meafur'd fpace of time after the firft hath been taken notice of : Thefe may be made alfo ferviceable for the finding not only the Latitude of the place, but alfo of all the other *Poftulata* mention'd to be found by the former way, but with fomewhat more of Operation, and that not only by the Projections of the Sphere made according to the Tangents, but alfo by thofe of the fame made by the half Tangents of diftance from the Central Point thereof : And both thefe may be divers ways effected upon the faid Projections ; but the moft eafy, and that which is accommodated to both thefe kinds of Projections, is by fuppofing that part of the Heavens to ftand ftill, wherein the firft Obfervation was made, whilft the reft of the Heavens have pafs'd on their ufual progrefs proportion'd to the interval of Time between the firft and fecond Obfervation ; for by that means the two Azymuth-Circles both paffing through the Zenith of the place, both the ftraight Lines reprefenting them in the Tangent Projection crofs each other in the Zenith Point, or in a Point as far diftant from the Pole of the Projection, as the Zenith of the place is from the true Pole in the Heavens ; and alfo the Circles in the half Tangent Projection reprefenting thofe great Circles of Azymuths will crofs each other in the Zenith Point at the later Obfervation.

Tab.12. Fig.4.   To make this the more intelligible, let ℞ r, ♋ ♌ reprefent four notable Stars truly plac'd in a Tangent Projection of a large part of the Northern Hemifphere, whofe Polar or Central Point let P reprefent.

Let ℞ r, by Obfervation, be found to be in the fame Azymuth or Perpendicular one above the other at fome time of the Night ; lay a Rule over thofe two Stars in the Projection, and draw the Line FA r ℞ ; this Line therefore muft reprefent the faid Azymuth Line or great Circle in which is the Zenith-Point at the time of Obfervation ; which Zenith-Point we are yet to feek and find out, becaufe the great Circle that paffeth through the other two Stars ♌ ♋, doth not crofs the former now in the Zenith-point, but in fome other Point, as A at an unknown diftance from it ; but by watching them they are found by fome good Time-keeper, as a Pendulum-watch, or the like, to meafure the Time, and a convenient Inftrument to find when they are in fome one and the fame Perpendicular, at two Hours after the firft Obfervation, to be in one Azymuth Line. Now, tho' not before, a ftraight Line drawn through them, reprefenting a great Circle, will alfo be a true Azymuth Circle, and will pafs through the Zenith-point of the place at the time of the later Obfervation. Let a, n, g, reprefent the Angle made at the Pole by the Heavens moving Weftward in the fpace of two Hours, *viz.* thirty Degrees. Suppofe then the Azymuth Circle firft taken, *viz.* FA r ℞ to ftand ftill, and all the reft of the Heavens or the two Stars ♋ ♌ to be mov'd forwards or Weftwards thirty Degrees, and ♋ ♌ be now at S s, draw the ftraight Line through them, *viz.* b S s, cutting the other FA ℞ r, not in A as at the time of the firft Obfervation, but, at Z, I fay ; this Point of Interfection Z, fhall reprefent the true Zenith-Point of the place, both in the firft and laft Obfervation ; for APB is made equal to a n g, denoting the interpos'd time, and P b s S is made equal to the Angle PA ♌ ♋, which fhews their refpects to the Pole in the later and firft Obfervation. Now FA℞ and b s S both paffing through the Zenith, there can be no other Point in them to reprefent the fame, but where they crofs each other, *viz.* Z. Z therefore is the true Zenith Point, and its diftance from the Polar Point P being meafur'd upon the Projection, will give the Complement of the Latitude of the place.

The fame thing may be perform'd upon the half-Tangent Projection, and with more convenience, by reafon of its great Capacity, and the lefs inequality of divifions : It hath only one Operation fomewhat more difficult than the other, and that is the drawing great Circles through the faid Stars inftead of ftraight Lines in the preceding way ; but in all things elfe the Method and Demonftration is the fame with that, and the Point of Interfection section of the fixt Azymuth, and remov'd Azymuth is the Zenith-Point of the place.

Now the ways of drawing a projected great Circle which shall pass thro' two Points given of this kind of Projection, being many, and most of them easy enough ; I conceive this method of finding the Latitude of places may be of very good use for Navigation, especially at such times, as, by reason of Foggs or other Impediments (as the unknown declination of the place) Altitudes cannot be so well observ'd or made use of at Sea.

But for the finding the exact Latitude of places upon the Land where great Instruments may be us'd, I have other methods, not depending upon the suppos'd true placing of the Stars, whereby that inquiry may be answer'd to what accurateness shall be desir'd, which will be of very good use for that other question which I have propounded ; that is, whether the Latitude of places alter and vary upon the Earth in process of time; and since, if there should be any such, the variation is but small, and therefore very slow, and the unaccurateness possibly of former Observations cannot much be depended upon ; I conceive that by those ways it may be possible to resolve that in a very few Years, which, by the commonly known methods, cannot be expected in less than some Ages, which is the best way of redeeming Time by making the best use of what we have yet to come.

This Lecture, and the following, treat of the inequality of the Earths Motion, and of the methods of observing and examining it.

May 25. 1687. It has been no small discouragement to my progress in explicating some Phænomena of Nature by some new Hypotheses, to find that they have been misrepresented, or at least misunderstood or misconstru'd ; misrepresented I mean, when, First, I have been said to assert that absolutely and positively, which I only propounded as an Hypothesis, or as Queries to be further examin'd by Reason, Experiments and Observations. And, Secondly, When I have been represented, as affirming things which I never did nor could have done with coherency to the Hypothesis ; as that the Earth hath been many times, besides in *Noah*'s Flood, all cover'd with Water and dry'd again : Misunderstood I mean, when the Arguments I produc'd were not rightly consider'd and duly weighed, and that it seem'd indifferent to the Examiners to conceive of the matter as I had argued for it, or the quite contrary : As to conceive that the Figure of the Earth may be either a prolated Sphæroeid, or an oblong Sphæroeid, or neither of these. Misconstrued I mean, when that which I propounded for one end and use, is wrested to quite another; as because I had doubted of the sufficiency and certainty of the Astronomical Observations for this purpose, only for determining whether the true Latitude of places, or their true Meridian Lines, had varied, therefore I am represented as calling in question all History, both Divine and Humane. These kinds of proceeding might have been expected from a provoked Adversary ; but why they come, whence they they do, I know no reason. However, by the Sequel I doubt not but that even those who shew the most prejudice, will make it evident by the benefit and use they make of them, that there was no reason for such kind of treatment ; nor shall it deter me from proceding to propound some other Conjectures ; which, whether rightly propounded or not, I shall leave to further examinations by Experiments and Observations, as I did the former ; all I desire is a fair trial ; let the Testimonies of Nature itself be examin'd, and their Evidence not wrested nor bafled.

The thing I shall at present propound, is what I hinted in my attempt to prove the motion of the Earth. *Page* the 27, *Line* the 31, 32, &c. I did there hint, that I had then, in some of the foregoing Observations there mention'd, discover'd some new motions even in the Earth itself, which perhaps were not thought of before ; one of which was this which follows, which whether it were ascribable to this or any other cause, I will not contend ; let trials more accurate and curious than possibly those first were may determine it ; I propounded it only as a query for examination. It is eighteen

Of an inequality of the Earths diurnal motion.

Years

Years since I made the Observations, and they were made by a Clock which went three Years without winding up more than once, which was the first of that kind, where the weight of the Pendulum was very near as big as the weight that kept it going for so long a time ; whether the cause of the inequality were to be ascrib'd to the Clock, or the Earth, or some other unheeded Circumstance, I will not now contend ; yet I did, with what care I then could, consider of all I could think of, and upon the whole conceived them to be ascribable to some inequality in the motion of the Earth ; but let further trials determine it.

I conceiv'd then that there was some inequality in the diurnal Revolution of the Earth, not such a one as *Kepler* supposeth, only of the Earth turning quicker when nearer the Sun, and slower when further from it, but an inequality in every Revolution ; that is, that in one part of the Revolution it was slower, in another somewhat quicker ; which, whether to ascribe it to the power of the Sun, or that of the Moon, or both, let farther examination determine ; for there may possibly be causes, why both of them may effect it in its diurnal Revolution. I do therefore propound as Queries, whether there may not be in the Body of the Earth some parts which, tho' as to the gravitating powers of the Earth, may be duly situated and poised for its equal Revolution upon its Axis, yet with respect to the gravitating Power of the Sun or Moon may not be counterpois'd, but be over ballanc'd on one side of its Axis.

That there may be a difference in the kinds of gravitation in different Bodies.

I know that if the gravitating Power in the Sun and Moon be exactly the same with that of the Earth, the Query I propounded can have no ground ; but tho' they may in most particulars be consonant, as I shall prove in my Theory of Gravity, yet there may be a cause (and there seems to be some assignable) why there may be something Specifick in each of them, of that kind which I now propose, as may be possibly conceiv'd from the Moons Libration, or its turning or keeping pretty near the same side of its Body to the Surface of the Earth. For tho' the supposing it to turn upon its Axis in respect of the Sun, so as to make a Revolution Isocrone to its Synodick Revolution about the Earth, be an ingenious Hypothesis ; yet the Physical Reason of such an equality seems pretty difficult to be conceiv'd, unless we suppose some cause from the Constitution of the Body of the Moon itself, which makes one part of it gravitate more towards the Center of the Earth than another in such a Revolution. And if such there be (as I see yet no clear reason to the contrary) then must the unequal progresses of the Moon produce a kind of Vibrating, Librating, or Pendulous motion thereof ; so that the equal motion suppos'd will be blended or compounded with a Pendulous motion of that part towards the Center of the Earth. I will not presume to assign what this cause may be in the Body of the Moon ; whether one side of its Body next the Earth be more dense and solid, and the opposite more porous and spungy, or whether the one be constituted of Bodies more heavy in Specie than the other, as that those parts which respect the Earth, should be more of the Nature of Earth, Stone, Rocks or Minerals, and the opposite of Waters, Seas, Atmosphere, Air, or somewhat anologous to them ; which some appearances do seem to favour, and some others purposely and designedly contriv'd and perform'd, may give us further information of : But upon the whole it seems to me there is a necessity of some such supposition to solve the Phænomena hitherto taken notice of ; and there may be a necessity of some other suppositions to solve some other Phænomena which I shall on another occasion mention. As to suppose that the Body of the Moon, tho' it be Sphærical as to its Circumference which appears in the Full and New Moon, in Ecclipses of the Sun, when view'd from the Earth, yet that its Body may be in that Diameter of it which respects the Earth much longer than in any other Diameter ; that is, it may be of an oblong oval Figure whose longest Diameter respects the Earth ; whose Centers of Gravity, tho' they are in the Axis, are yet not in the middle thereof, but nearer towards the Earth. Now if there be such a diversity of the Body of the Moon with respect to the Earth, why may there not be some such in the Body of the Earth with respect to the Sun, nay, tho' it have a Revolution upon

Of the Moons Librating and Constitution of its Body.

its

its own Axis ? For supposing the Earth suspended on its Axis of motion, if any *of the cause of* one part of that with respect to the Gravitation towards the Sun do more than *the inequality* over-ballance the part opposite to it on the other side (tho' as to the Gravity *of the Earths* to the Earth they are ballanced) then must that part have a tendency to-*diurnal motions* wards the Center of the Sun, if at any time it be remov'd out of that Position ; and that tendency must be Analogous to that of a single Pendulum (here suspended) towards the Center of the Earth ; so that when the motion of Rotation is carrying it towards its lowest or direct Point, that power must accelerate that motion, and when it hath pass'd that Point, and is beyond it, that power must retard it according to the Degrees or Proportions by which a vibrating Pendulum is accelerated, when mov'd towards the Perpendicular, and retarded when mov'd from it ; and this Acceleration and Retardation must intermix and blend itself with the equal Circular motion, and Accelerate it in one part, and Retard it in another part of its Revolution ; as will be more conceivable by the Experiment I shall by and by shew with a Wheel whose Axis lies Horizontal, and one of whose sides is somewhat heavier than the other. Now, as I Conjecture or Query, whether there be not some such Principle acting with respect to the Sun ; so I do somewhat farther query whether there be not some such Anomaly with respect to the Moon, between which and the Earth there seems to be a much nearer kindred and affinity than between that of the Earth and of the Sun ; and possibly somewhat of the Phænomena of the change of the Sea by Tides and Currents, and of the Air by Winds or Motions thereof may be found to be influenc'd by such a Discovery.

What ever the event may be upon a strict examination by Experiments, I conceive it will not be unacceptable, since it will be a truth in Physick ascertain'd, which will influence many other ; and I know no other way of trying it, than by that which gave me the first hint of it, which was the observing the Velocities of several Stars at several times of the Night in their passing by the Zenith, by comparing the several Arches they make in a certain space of time with one another, and with the time exactly kept by a curious Pendulum Clock ; for if we find that several Stars plac'd in or very near the parallel of Declination which passeth over the Zenith in several parts thereof do all of them pass a certain Arch thereof when they transit the Zenith in the same space of time exactly, then we may conclude that the diurnal Rotation is equal and uniform in a whole Revolution ; but if it shall be found that some of them pass an equal Arch in a longer, some in a shorter time ; (which was the Phænomena I took notice of) then it will be further requisite to prosecute such other Observations as may determine the Reasons and Causes thereof, and farther Light will follow from it whatever way the Experiment shall determine it, provided they be carefully and accurately made with accurate Clocks, and with Instruments fitted with Telescope Sights.

Now because the things to be observ'd, which are necessary to compleat the Observation, are only two, namely, First, The length of an Arch mov'd by a Cælestial Body. And, Secondly, The time wherein that Body that moves such a determinate Arch ; therefore I have contriv'd two Instruments of sufficient accurateness in their respective kinds for performing these Observations ; and they are, First, A Telescope for the Sights of the first Instrument for determining the parts of the parallel Circle, or Circle of Declination in which the Cælestial Body moves. And, Secondly, A Pendulum to measure and divide the time, during which the Body doth actually move such an Arch.

As for the first, namely, the Telescope, I have already sufficiently de-*Instruments* scrib'd it in my Discourse of a way for accurately finding the Meridian Line *for the obser-* and the Axis of the Earth, and therefore I shall not here need to repeat it. *vation.* *Vide.* p. 358. *Supra.*

But for the second because of the curiosity of the Observation to be made by it, I shall be somewhat more particular in its description.

There are then three sorts of Pendulums, which may be so adapted, as *The Pendulum* that, by the help of them, the time between the transits of a Star over two *for this Obser-* Meridians, at ten, twelve or fifteen Degrees distance may be measur'd to the *vation.*

fifteenth

fifteenth part of a second of time, if by the use of the Telescope Sight there be occasion for so great exactness.

The contrivance of them all consists in these particulars; First, That they all move during the whole interpos'd space by the first impress'd force when they are first put into motion, without any addition of new force to continue their motion, and by that means all irregularity, caus'd by the Wheel-work, is avoided.

Secondly, That they are all made with very heavy Weights, and of the most proper Shapes for passing through the Air, so that they receive very little Impediment from it, and much less of Irregularity by reason all extraneous motion of the Air is kept off by the case in which they are included.

Thirdly, That their decrease of motion is regular and certain ; so that tho' their extream Excursions do approach nearer the Center or Perpendicular, yet that being always done in the same proportion, the same number of Vibrations will always be made in the same quantity of time ; that is, how many Vibrations, and what part over doth measure the time of an hour at one time, so many and such part will measure the time of an hour at any other time, whether of the same Day or Night, or at times distant more than a Day.

Fourthly, For that the motion of them is so adjusted, that be the Vibrations greater or less, they shall be all isocrone and of equal duration.

Fifthly, That the time of the motion through the whole length of one excursion, whether longer or shorter, shall be actually divided into equal parts by unequal divisions, but proportion'd so as to answer exactly to the given Proportions or Divisions of time.

Sixthly, That they are all so contriv'd, that the observer shall be able to mark the very moment of the last Transit himself, and the same of the first Transit by the help of an assistant ; and this to as small a time as a humane Moment, or as quick as Thought : So that he shall be able certainly to know in what point or part of the excursion, the weight of the Pendulum is in, when the Star is observ'd to be in the Zenith or Meridian of the place, or in any other Meridian where the Stars there appearing does terminate and finish the second Transit, or the end of the time to be observ'd.

This contrivance consists in two parts, First, To let go, or set in going, the Pendulum by a touch of the Finger at the very moment of the first Transit of the Star to be observ'd, which hath this also of convenience or perfection rather, that the Pendulum is always set in going, or beginning with the same Arch of Descent, and not at an uncertain heighth. Secondly, That with the like touch of the Finger at the moment of the second or last Transit, there is a part of the Instrument that marks the very point of the whole excursion, through which the Center of the moving Pendulum is at that moment passing.

It may be perform'd with three sorts of Pendulums, namely, the Circular, the Slope and the common Perpendicular Pendulum ; each have their advantages wherein they exceed the other two, and each their disadvantages wherein they are exceeded by them ; but upon ballancing the whole three I do most approve of the last before either of the other, for the simplicity of its make and thence its exactness and certainty of going ; its Regularity in not loosing its power and motion, but by Degrees very slow, which bear a proportion to the number of Vibrations, and the regularity of its motion as to the dividing the Excursions into parts answering to equal Moments or Spaces, and the easiness for letting go, and also for taking notice of the last moment ; all which particulars I shall more particularly explain in the Module I shall produce, which will much more intelligibly express it than a Draught or Scheme.

What this Module was I never knew, but the ingenuous will easily apprehend the contrivance and meaning of the Author without any Scheme, by considering the following Paragraph ; therefore I have not thought fit to trouble the Reader with a Conjectural Draught of my own. R. W.

As to the divisions of the parts of an Excursion, the whole length of the Excursion on each side of the Perpendicular Point is to be made as the Radius of a Circle of that length, and to be divided into a Line of Sines answering to such Divisions of an Arch of a Circle, answering thereto, as shall be convenient for the Division of the time of an Excursion; as if the whole Excursion be perform'd in a Second of Time; then for Thirds the Semicircle is to be suppos'd divided into sixty equal Parts, and accordingly the Radius into a Line of Sines answering to every three Degrees, which make thirty in the half, and sixty equal times in the whole Vibration; for the Velocities in the Diameter being in proportion to the ordinate Sines, the times will be as the Secants complement, and consequently as the parts of the Arch.

Wensday June 25. 1687. I shew'd here, at the last Meeting, one sort of Instrument for the measuring and dividing the parts of time to as great an accurateness, as I conceive, 'tis possible to be done by any kind of Mechanical Invention whatsoever; for that it is capable of dividing and measuring it, not only to the accurateness of the Thoughts of a Man, but, if need require, even to Moments that are shorter some hundred times than humane Moments. What I mean by humane Moments, I have formerly, in some of these my Cutlerian Lectures explain'd to this Honourable Auditory; and because I find that sometimes the repetition of former Experiments and Observations are not ungrateful to some, I shall now again shew that the Thoughts of a Man move or change in a limited space of Time; not so quick but that such moments are yet divisible into moments infinitely smaller or shorter of duration, and thence that each humane moment is capable of Division into any definite Number of Parts, how many soever shall be assign'd; as if the humane moments be as small as a third Minute of Time, which yet, I conceive, very few are able to distinguish by their Thoughts, yet that Third of Time containeth sixty Fourth Minutes, and each Fourth containeth sixty Fifths, and each fifth containeth sixty Sixth Minutes of Time, and so onwards, which we find Astronomers will take notice of, and account for in their Computations of equable Divisions, tho' they are in themselves but very small and altogether insensible parts of one humane moment: I say insensible, by reason that they are quicker than the Thought of a Man can distinguish a Prior from a Posterior moment: For who is there that can distinguish the 3600 part of the Time of a Second, which yet is but a fourth minute of Time? Much less will any one be able to distinguish the 216000 part, which is a fifth or a 12960000 part thereof, which is a sixth, and yet we must acknowledge that such parts there really are included in every Second minute of Time, tho' never so much smaller or shorter in duration than a humane moment, and that they really have their Power and Effect in natural motions and alterations proportionable to such their duration, and are measurable or conceivable there, tho' they are so much quicker than our Thoughts and Abilities to distinguish one from another: For if we take for a round Number that a Semidiameter of the Earth be four thousand Miles, and thence find that the Circumference under the Æquinoctial Line be 25132 Miles, and 7412287183459, 10000000000000, which is 01290888208650 of a Mile in a Second of Time; or to omit the accurateness of the Fractions and to keep to round Numbers, which, in this case, serve better where the Matter and Design aim'd at is but Illustration, and to help Conception, let us conceive that a part of the Earth, under the Æquinoctial, moving in a Second of Time an 86400 part of that Circumference of the Earth; which, to keep still to round Numbers, we may conceive to be near ¹⁄₃ of a Mile, of 6000 Foot to each Mile; then will each part of the Earth there move every Second of Time 1800 Foot, and in every Third of Time thirty Foot, and in every Fourth of Time six Inches, and in every Fifth of Time ¹⁄₁₀ of an Inch. Now, tho' the Conception of this part of Time be really impossible, otherwise than by Proportion and Analogy to the sensible parts, yet the motion of Nature doth really measure it, and its progresses are adæquate to such moments, and each fifth Minute of Time the part hath mov'd a tenth of an Inch forward into another place, in respect of its Position to the

At the end of the Lectures of Light.

Of the Minute divisions of Time.

Zzzzzz   Heavens,

Heavens, or to the parts of Space confider'd as immovable: And the progresses of progressive or local motion being suppos'd equal or commensurate to the moments of Time (how small soever) the Body must move in every sixth Minute of Time, a six hundred part of an Inch forward; which length our Senses can reach and distinguish, tho' it cannot the minim of Time, which is not so to be magnify'd.

This Speculation I have been the more large upon, to shew that there may be a use of this Instrument for distinguishing and numbering the parts of Time, which are abundantly much less than a humane Moment; which, tho' not distinguishable by our Thoughts, yet have their effects, in Nature, and, in many Experiments, are very considerable and pertinent to be taken notice of; as I shew'd by many Experiments try'd before this Society above twenty Years since, by an Instrument somewhat like this, for the measuring the times of falling Bodies, which possibly some here present may well remember.

Tho', I say, these small moments of Time are not distinguishable by a Man's Thought, yet by many Mechanical Contrivances they can be made distinguishable, and thereby they can be made useful in multitudes of Physical and Philosophical Inquiries, and even in this, which gave the occasion of the mentioning of it; namely, the measuring of the exact time that any Star that shall be observ'd, is moving from any one Position to any other; and that even to a shorter or lesser time than that of one third Minute of an Hour, which, if the motion of the Star be in, or near, a great Circle, is about a quarter of a Second of a Degree. The way of effecting which, is the making the Telescope to move along with the Star, and when the Star is come to a certain point, and consequently the Telescope that follows it, then doth that Telescope let go the Pendulum, and set it going with a certain degree of Velocity; and again, the same Telescope being kept moving along with the Star, at least, some small time before it arrive at the second station; then doth it, in its motion, let go the Stopper, or Stay of the Pendulum, or Index thereof, just at the very moment as the Star is passing the Point of the second Station; which denotes the precise moment of such Touch or Transit. Now, tho' this be abundantly more quick than Thought, and so cannot be perform'd so nicely by the motion of the Finger, yet by this means I speak of, where the Telescope is kept in motion with the Star, which is easily enough perform'd, as I have often had Experience, the moments, tho' exceeding small, will yet be numbred thereby. To this I could add the description of a second Instrument, which is made with a Pendulum also, but moving Circularly suspended by a round Steel Wire, and is to be let go, and to be stay'd in the same manner, by means of the motion of a Telescope, which follows the motion of the Star; in which Instrument the circulating motion of the Pendoulus Weight doth describe a Spiral Line, which, by equal Angles from the Center, is divided into equal Spaces of Time, and thereby the number of the Spaces in that Spiral, past by the Pendulum between the two Transits of the Star, being computed, do give the exact number of third Minutes of Time that have pass between the two Observations; but this Instrument being somewhat more complicated than the former, and that being sufficiently accurate for such trials, I shall omit the further description thereof at this time.

And because I understood that the Demonstration I read of the true way of dividing the Arch of its motion, into parts of equal duration, or of equal Time, was not so fully comprehended by some then present, which was this I now read;

These Schemes are lost. Therefore for a more full Demonstration, and particular Explication thereof, I have drawn some Schemes, by the explaining of which I doubt not to make it evident, in every particular thereof, to any one that shall doubt of any part thereof, whereby the truth and certainty thereof will more plainly appear.

June 29. 1687. I spent some time in my last Lecture upon the consideration of sensible Time, and of the equal Division and Mensuration thereof; for which purpose I explain'd two Instruments, the most exact that have been
thought

thought of, far exceeding, as I conceive, any that have been yet publickly known, and capable of performing, or of helping to perform, such Observations of Cælestial Bodies as no Istrument, yet made use of, has perform'd; at least, not the best that I had ever heard of; some Instances of which I shall shortly acquaint you with; for tho' our Methodists have made compleat Systems of Sciences, yet, when they come to be a little more nicely survey'd by a doubting Examinant, many of those Maxims, that are so Dogmatically and Positively asserted, will be found not altogether so Congrous to the truth of Nature as they have hitherto been believ'd; and those none of the least Considerable and Fundamental.

I could carry this Mechanism yet further, by shewing some Instruments by which to measure the parts of insensible moments; I mean such moments as a Man cannot distinguish by his Thoughts into a preceding and subsequent moment, or is able to number or distinguish one from another by his Eye or Ear, far less than that I call insensible; not but that the Sense doth really distinguish moments, yet prodigiously less above a thousand times, nay, ten thousand times, as I shall afterwards prove; but it is not under the Idea of Time and Number, but under that of sound, Tone, Harmony, and the like; wherein how curious the Sense of Hearing is, I appeal to such as are skilful in Musick, who can easily, by their Ear, tell you when the Vibrations of Musical Strings are one as quick again as the other, that is, when Diapasons, when their Proportions are as 3 to 2, or as 3 to 4, or as 8 to 9, that is, as a Diapente or Fifth, that is, a Diatesseron or Fourth, that is, a whole Note or Tone, and the like, and when they are of such or such a determinate Tone, as *Gam ut*, *A re*, *B mj*, and the like, which they distinguish, I say, by the Ear, or the Sense of Hearing, tho' not under the same Idea or Phantom as they do when the Vibrations are so slow as to be singly distinguish'd one from another, but under the Idea of Sound; which, when the Vibrations are Isocrone, as I have formerly here prov'd those of strained or extended Strings to be, which act upon the principle of Spring; as also Bells or sounding Metals, and the Vibrations of the Air, which depend also upon the Spring and Power of Recoile, they are Musical Sounds; but when they are not Isocrone they are not Musical. In these cases the Sense runs a step higher and brings us into another Region, where we find another prospect of Time, and the Partitions thereof far differing from that of the first and inferior Region, wherein we distinguish the parts of Time by Monades or Unites; for in this we distinguish them by Aggregates, Bodies, Bulks, Armies, Thousands, and the like great Numbers, not considering them singly, but together; for this purpose I shall hereafter produce some Mechanical Contrivances, by which these quick motions and minims of Time may be reduc'd to Number and Computation, which I conceive absolutely necessary in all Philosophical or Physical Experiments; but I shall not now digress into Experiments of that kind, but proceed in that method which I have begun, to shew the use of this Instrument I have already describ'd, and shewn the Module thereof, by explaining how the same may be of use for finding the Latitude of a Place without the incumbrance of Refraction, at least by such a way as is the least of any I have yet known discover'd by any, in Print, or any other ways.

This method I describe in order to the prosecution of that Inquiry which I lately propos'd of examining, whether the Axis of the diurnal Rotation of the Earth did, or doth change its Position in respect of the parts of the Earth; that is, whether the Latitudes of Places do, in process of time, vary as well as the Meridian Line; for if the said Axis doth vary, one of these two ways, or both, will be sufficient to discover it in any part of the Earth whatsoever; for if such motion of the Axis as I have propounded shall happen to move in the Meridian Line of the place where the Observation of the Meridian, for that purpose, shall be made; then, tho' no such variation of the Meridian Line can be, by that means, observ'd, there being none, yet this way for examining the Latitude of the Place will soon detect it. Again, if that motion should happen to be at right Angles to the Meridian of the Place, then this way would be ineffectual, and the former way of finding
the

the true Position of the Meridian Line, with respect to the known parts of the Horizon, would perform it ; and in case its motion be any other way inclin'd to the Meridian, then the comparing of both these two ways together will state and determine it, as it doth also in both the preceding Cases, because it determines which way and how much in all.

P. 358. *supra* & *alibi.*
It was necessary therefore that the way of finding the Latitude of a place should be as accurate and as little liable to Objections, as the way I have already shewn of finding the Meridian Line ; which I conceive is the most exact that has been hitherto discover'd, and may be as easily made, and is sufficient to perform what is requisite in the Inquiry propos'd.

The method then for finding the Latitude of a Place, is by finding out the true Zenith-Point of the Place where the Observation is to be made ; how to do this I have elsewhere shewn, and therefore shall not need here to repeat it : This may be done to what accurateness shall be desir'd ; for that longer and longer Telescopes may be made use of for the determination thereof; and it is not difficult to procure Object-glasses of any length desir'd, accurate enough for performing such Observations : Having determin'd that, I observe what Stars pass over the Zenith-Point, or pretty near it, whose distance from that Point, in the Meridian, I can accurately measure ; then the following Night I observe that Star, I pitch upon, an Hour, or an Hour and half, or some certain time before it come to the Zenith, marking exactly the Point where I so observe it at the time I let go my Pendulum or Time-keeper, and measuring exactly the Angle that Ray maketh with the Perpendicular, finding also, if I please, the position the Plain thro' those two Lines hath to the Plain of the Meridian ; tho' that may be omitted, when it is only us'd for finding the Latitude : Then I compute the Time exactly that passes between such and such Observations, and the time it passeth the Zenith or Meridian ; and at an equal time, after such Transit, I again observe it on the other side of the Meridian, and find the Point or the Angle that Ray also maketh. From the comparison of which two 'tis evident, that the Declination of that Star is certainly determin'd, and consequently that the Latitude of the place, where such Observation is made, is also given. Now the reason why I observe it on both sides of the Meridian is this, because I thereby almost wholly avoid the Refraction of the Air, and yet measure a large Arch ; for that the Refraction of the Air is hardly sensible even to Telescopes of so great a length, as may be made use of for this Observation, when the distance from the Zenith is not greater than what is requisite to determine this Inquiry, to what accurateness almost shall be requir'd, and the Observation on both sides doubling the Angle at the Zenith, or the Arch of the Parallel, when it is only made on one side, the Refraction, what it is, is still made more insensible when an equal subtense of an Arch of the said Parallel is obtain'd by Observation on both sides, that when on one side only. This way of finding the Latitude of a Place, I did, at the same time, formerly acquaint this Society with, tho' not so particular, when I told them also the way of making use of the Stars in the Perpendicular for finding the difference of Parallels for measuring a Degree upon the Earth ; but this part of the Contrivance I do not find that the *French* have made any use of in their Observation of a Degree, tho' they have of the other ; possibly it might be, that he that acquainted them with the one, did not so well comprehend the other, and the rather too, because the Invention of the measuring and determining the small parts of time was not at the same time describ'd, but some of them before, and some of them afterwards upon some other occasions ; as that of the direct *Pendulum* was upon the occasion of the Experiments of falling Bodies, and that of the Circular Pendulum æquated by its motion in a Parabolical Conoeidal Surface at another, tho' both these parts or inventions which were omitted by the *French*, have been Publish'd by Mr. *Huygens* as his own, in his Book *De Pendulo Oscillatioar* many Years since.

The

THe following *Lectures* contain the *Description* and *use* of *some Sea Instruments* · They were first read before the Royal Society on the third of December, 1690. and afterwards on the fifth and twelfth of December 1694. with some additions, as they are here Printed. The *Instruments* are the Portable Barometer, a *Quadrant*, and some hints relating to the improvement of *Telescopes*. As to the first there is some *Account* Publish'd in the *Philosophical Transactions* N.185.p. 241. and for the last I shall sometime present the *Ingenious* with what, I suppose, new, when I am a little at leisure to make some *Experiments* of a *Hint* given by Dr.Hook in a Paper about the improvement of *Optick-glasses*, wherein I will candidly relate the success, and what I know of the *Invention*.

R. W.

DEcember 3. 1690. As the Design of this *Lecture* was for the improve- *The increase of* ment of the History of Nature and of Art, so was the Institution of *Knowledge* this *Honourable Society* for the improvement of Natural Knowledge, which, *like the growth* in other words, amounts to the same sense. This as it was at first (upon ve- *of a Plant.* ry mature deliberation, and with great Sagacity and Judgment) settled in a suitable and proper method to attain the end; so, 'till better methods be prov'd, it ought not to be alter'd and laid aside. The Design was for promoting the Growth and Increase, and Vegetation, as I may so call it, of Natural Philosophy from the first Seed or Embrio through all the Ages and Increasings of it, 'till it attain to a State of Perfection of Flowering and Blooming, and of producing Seed, and become Fruitful; for Natural Knowledge may not unfitly be compar'd to a Vegetable, whether Plant or Tree, which springs from a Seed sow'd in a Soil, proper and adapted, by a skillful Gardener, for that Plant. For as the Seed, by small Fibrills or Roots it shoots out, receives, from the Soil or Earth, a nourishment proper and adapted for ascending into the Body or Stalk, to make it grow in bulk and strength to shoot upward, and from thence to shoot forth Branches, and from them Leaves, thereby to draw and receive out of the Air a more refin'd, spirituous and inlivening Juice, which descending back into the Body or Stock, increases its Stature, Bulk, Circumference and Strength by new incirclings, and thereby inables it to send forth more Fibrills and greater Roots, which afford greater and more plentiful Supplies to the Stock or Trunk, and inables that to exert and shoot forth more Branchings, and greater numbers of Leaves; which, repeating all the Effects and Operations by continu'd and constant Circulations, at length bring the Plant to its full Stature and Perfection : Nor will a skillful Gardener suffer it to be tapp'd to have the nutritive and vital Juice drawn off to be us'd for other purposes than the nutrition of its own Body; well knowing it would hinder its Growth, prolong the time of its coming to Maturity, weaken its Constitution at least, if not render it wholly barren.

So Natural Knowledge doth receive its first informations from the supplies afforded by Select and proper *Phænomena* of Nature convey'd by the Senses; these improve the Understanding and inable it to raise some Branchings out into Conclusions, Corollarys and Maxims; these afford a nutritive and strengthening Power to the Understanding, and inable it to put forth new Roots of Inquisitions, Trials, Observations and Experiments, and thereby to draw new supplies of Informations; which further strengthening the Understanding, inable it to exert and produce new Deductions and new Axioms : These circulate and descend downwards, increasing and strengthening the Judgment, and thereby inable it to make more striking out of Roots of Inquiries and Experiments, which cause the like Effects as before, but more powerfully, and so by consent and continu'd Circulations from *Phænomena* to make *Deductions*, and from *Deductions* to inquire *Phænomena*, it brings the Understanding to a compleat and perfect comprehension of the Matter at first propos'd to be consider d; nor must the Natural Course or Circulation be stopp'd or diverted, 'till the utmost Perfection be attain'd, if at least it be aim'd to compleat and make it prolifique.

Aaaaaaa

It

Of the difference of Gravitation.

It was a Conclusion by some such method as this produc'd by me, and made known to this Society near thirty Years since, that the *Gravity* of the Earth was differing in differing Latitudes, and that it was greater under the Poles than under the *Æquator*, and the nearer to the Poles the greater; and the nearer the *Æquator* the less. This I first propounded to this Society upon the occasion of the trials of the *Pendulum*-Clocks carry'd at Sea; and again, upon the occasion of the *Pendulum* apply'd for a Standard Measure of length, *&c.* But as things new and Heterodox to the Opinions in Vogue, it met with a check, and so the further prosecution of it could not proceed, I have many times since again repeated the Suggestion, sometimes upon one, sometimes upon other occasions, but, as Extravagancies, they have been pass'd over; the last time I repeated it Dr. *Wallis* wrote a long Epistle to confound it, but Mr. *Newton*, it seems, upon examining it, found some reason for it, and sends up (a Fortnight after Dr. *Wallis*) his considerations upon it, consonant to what I had demonstrated to the Society: This made it begin to be taken notice of, and to be thought worth examining; however many other Doctrines that were deduc'd from as evident premises have been suffer'd to lie by, in expectation of a better opportunity, which I hope Time may afford; which, when I meet with, I shall not be unmindful of laying hold of; and I much rejoice at this which I have now met with of Captain *Knox* his Voyage to *India*, who has promis'd to be very observant of it, and to keep an account thereof; and in pursuance of the Order of this Society, I have got a Pendulum Watch fitted for that purpose, which I now produce.

There is yet another Inquiry which will, if accurately tried with fit Instruments, afford great and useful Information, both for use at Land, and also for the Sea and Navigation; and that is to find the Posture and Gravitation of the Air. This I propounded to the Society as a thing very well worth *Description of a Sea Barometer.* Trial and Examination some twenty five Years since; but as the use of the *Barometer*, even at Land, was not then heeded, tho' I had then reduc'd it to as much of Theory for foretelling the Weather, as is is known at this Day; so the Inquiry, after the use of it at Sea, was the less regarded; and when afterwards the thing came to be taken notice of by means of King *Charles* his observing it to follow the Rules that were then set, which was about ten Years after, many had thoughts of having it carry'd to Sea, but attempting it only by the common way of the Barometer, not knowing, I suppose, the way I had propos'd; the use of it at Sea was indeed impracticable, and, as such, laid aside. I shall not trouble you with a new Description, but if you please to afford me your Patience, I shall read the Description which I then produc'd, and it hath ever since remain'd in your Registers.

The Contrivance of this Instrument is much the same with what I explain'd to this Society about thirty Years since.

This being thus prepar'd will fully be sufficient to exhibit all the varieties of Pressure in the Air; and 'tis capable of shewing all those Variations with as great nicety and exactness as shall be requir'd even upon the Sea, tho' stormy and turbulent: Nor is there any great difficulty of preparing or making use of it; save only that, if the Gradations be requir'd to be very large, it will require a very long Tube of Glass; and that Tube to be doubled or folded to and fro to lie in a little room, which I have my self been able to do with no great matter of trouble; but it would be yet much better if a very long Tube of Glass, of forty or fifty Foot in length, were coiled round a Cylinder, after the manner of Sir *Christopher Wren*'s Weather-glass; which, with some few trials, I do not question may be effected; for that thereby it would be easy to make the difference of Gravitation in the Air as large and sensible, as it need to be desir'd; besides it will be, *&c.*

But tho' it will not in those other Tubes, which I propose, be capable of so great an Augmentation of that difference, yet these, if well adjusted, will, I conceive, be found of great use for fore-shewing the approaches of Storms and Calms, which extreams of the motion of the Air are very unwelcome and troublesome Concomitants at Sea. It will also give an account of
the

the comparative Gravity of the Air in several Climates and Latitudes; and thereby afford Indications, by which the Figure, Form, or Constitution of the Shell of the Air, which incompasses the Earth, may be judg'd of. It will likewise shew the Nature and Qualities of several Winds as to Pressure, and also as to Heat and Cold ; that is, whether an Easterly Wind be every where the heaviest, and the Southern the lightest ; as they are generally observ'd to be in *England*. What Winds are hotter or Colder ; that is, whether Sea-Winds or Brizes, or Land-Winds or Brizes ; whether there be any certain difference between the Pressure in the Night and in the Day, as there is constantly in the Heat and Cold ; whether the Rains or the dry Seasons are the Hotter ; and many others. And to this end it will be well to note the state of this Instrument at Noon and Midnight, and in the Morning and Evening.

Decemb. 12. 1694. The Instrument I mention'd the last Day, which I had about thirty Years since invented and shew'd to this Society, is, I conceive, an Invention of so great use, that if the Knowledge and Practice of making, adjusting and manner of observing with it, be once attained, it may be a means of saving many thousands of Pounds in a Year to the Merchant, and which is more, many hundreds of Mens Lives ; and therefore I think it ought not to be any longer neglected, but rather to be made and try'd as soon as possible ; and tho' we cannot as yet procure the means to make it of the most perfect and most convenient form for transportation and use on Ship-board, yet since it is easy and practicable enough to make it to shew all the differing Pressures of the Air as exactly as the common single Barometer does at Land, nay, twice as exact ; I think it may be first try'd, of the perfectest form we can now make it, and possibly that form may be most fit for the first trial, since the other being more nice, may so much the more perplex the unexperienc'd Mariner, and may better be introduc'd after the practice thereof, for the use of the Sea, hath made the Theory thereof more intelligible, and the benefits thereof more sensible and evident.

The method and grounds of my Invention, I conceiv'd, were very plain and obvious, as many others are after they are once discover'd and explain'd, and some are then so obvious, that even that becomes the cause why they are slighted, neglected, and not taken notice of; and possibly that may have been one Reason why it has fared so with this, it being so easy to be conceiv'd; I did not therefore spend much time in the explication thereof ; but having the last Day apprehended, by some Discourses, that the Theory thereof was not so perfectly comprehended, but that there remain'd some hesitancy or doubts concerning it, I have now made a somewhat more particular Description of the Instrument itself, and of the Ground and Reason of the contrivance thereof.

It is now about sixty Years since the *Thermometer* was invented for the use of indicating the degrees of Heat and Cold in the Air, by certain and determin'd measures, which was done by means of a bolt Head, or long necked Glass, as they are now commonly call'd, the Ball or Head of which, and part of the Neck, was fill'd with Air, but the Mouth or lower end was fill'd with some colour'd Liquor, and immers'd in a small Cestern or Receptacle of a quantity of the said Liquor ; by which means the included Air, which is rarify'd and expanded by Heat, and condens'd with Cold, did either depress the said tinged Liquor into the Cestern, or draw it up higher into the Neck of the Glass ; which property of the rarification and condensation of the Air hath been known ever since the time of *Hero*, and probably long before ; yet the Application of that knowledge for this use, I do not find was put into practice or taken any notice of, 'till about the Year 1630 ; some short time after which I find *Robertus de Fluctibus* or *Flud* did write a particular Treatise to explain the said Instrument and some uses of it ; but *Blancanus* ascribes the Invention of it to *Sanctorius* much about the same time ; but I will not dispute which of them we ought to ascribe it to ; but whoever it were, it was an ingenious Thonght, and adæquate enough to the Theory of the Expansion of the Air then understood. But Experimental Philosophy hath since made a further discovery, and shew'd us that the Air

The History of the Thermometer.

may

may not only be more or less expanded by the Degrees of Heat and Cold in the Ambient Air, but also by the alteration of the pressure of the Atmosphere, which doth less or more depress the Surface of the stagnant tinged Liquor in the Cistern or Receptacle; so that That Instrument, commonly call'd a Weather-glass, is no longer a true Standard to measure the Degree of Heat and Cold, but serves only to give us the result of two Powers acting upon it promiscuously; sometimes with a Concurrency both tending one way, and sometimes with Contrariety and Opposition, the one promoting the Expansion, the other the Condensation thereof; if therefore we can by any means discover the effects of the one at all times upon it, we presently find the Power and Effects of the other. If therefore we can by other means discover the Effects of Heat and Cold, we shall thereby discover what is to be ascrib'd to the Gravity or Pressure of the Air.

Now to do this effectually I make use of the Sealed *Thermometer* which was first invented, as I have been inform'd, by the Grand Duke of *Tuscany*, and the first that I ever saw or heard of was a small one brought into *England* by our Honourable President; by which I improv'd it by making several very large, and tinged the Liquor to make it more sensible to the Eye. This Instrument being Hermetically seal'd, and so all the influence of the Pressure of the Air being excluded, the included Liquor can only be acted upon by the Heat and Cold of the Ambient Air; so that hereby at all times I am ascertain'd of the Degree of that quality; knowing then what the Power of that quality is upon the Weather-glass, I can easily see what part of the Indication is to be ascrib'd to the Pressure or Gravity of the Air or Atmosphere.

The method of making the Instrument.

For this purpose having produc'd two convenient Glasses, the one for the open Weather-glass, and the other for the seal'd *Thermometer*, by a Standard *Thermometer* made and adjusted, according to the method I have prescrib'd in my Micrography, I adjust the *Thermometer*, putting all the Degrees of Heat and Cold above and below the freezing Mark where I begin my Account, or o, and making them with +1, +2, +3, &c. above that mark; and with --1,--2,--3, &c. below the same, I wait 'till such time as the Barometer stands at twenty nine and half Inches high, which is here in *England*, at least the standard Altitude between Fowl and Fair Weather; then putting the Balls of both the Glasses into Water heated to a certain Degree, which may be hot enough to answer to the greatest Degree of heat that I conceive the Air will sustain in any part of the Torrid Zone, I suffer them both together to remain in that Degree of heat, 'till the Liquor in the *Thermometer*, and the Air in the Weather-glass, be reduc'd to the same Degree of heat; then I observe the mark'd Degree of the *Thermometer*, and mark the Weather-glass with the same; then I permit the Liquor, in which the two Balls are plac'd, to cool by degrees, and thereby observe how the Liquor in the *Thermometer*, and the Air in the Weather-glass, do contract by the motion of the Liquors in their Stems, and by the Degrees of the *Thermometer*, I mark the Degrees in the Weather-glass that answer thereunto; and when the Liquor is cold, I intend that Cold, with Niter, and Ice to procure the Divisions below the freezing mark; by which means I find all the marks of the Weather-glass that answer to all the marks of the *Thermometer*, when the Gravity of the Air is equiponderant to twenty nine and half: Whenever therefore the Gravity of the Air is more or less, I shall easily discover it by the difference there is between the two Glasses; for that a greater Pressure will more condense the included Air in the Weather-glass, and a lesser will suffer it to expand more than it would have otherwise done by the Degrees only of Cold and Heat. And by this method it will not be difficult to adjust two such Glasses as will receive no manner of alteration from the motion of the Ship, and may be safely and easily carry'd and made use of in all parts of the World, to the extreamest hot or extreamest cold, that can be indur'd by any one that is to observe with them. For as there is no doubt to be made of the Experiment of the Spirit of Wine seal'd in the *Thermometer*, so there is no fear of loosing or freezing of the Quicksilver in the Weather-glass, if it be made after the way that I have herein propos'd; the varying of which Instrument I have

many

many ways contriv'd, and some other methods, if I can procure Glasses made, I shall some other time acquaint the Society with.

As the Subject of my last Discourse was the Description of two several *Of a new Sea* Instruments that I conceiv'd would be of great benefit to Navigators and Na- *Quadrant.* vigation in general, so I design in this Discourse to add the Description of a third, which, I judge, will be much more advantageous, by reason of its frequent, nay constant, use and because so much of information concerning the true Latitude of the place, where the Ship is, depends upon the exactness and practicableness of it, I have propounded it by way of Query to divers very skilful both in the Theory and Practice of Navigation; but (like things of this Nature before they are known) they have all judg'd it to be impracticable, if not impossible, and yet I doubt not (when it comes to be known) some of them may say, they knew as much as this before : Others possibly may persist in the use of such Instruments, as they have been hitherto acquainted with, and others be offended at it because it is new ; and yet I doubt not but that, after some time, it may become of general use. The Instrument which I shew'd the Society, some Years before the Sickness, by making use of a Telescope-glass, instead of the small hole or slit of the Shadow-vane of a Back-staff, was not made use of 'till about ten Years after, and yet now it meets with general approbation, and is of continual use, and pretended to be the invention of another, tho' my shewing thereof was Printed in the History of the Royal Society. It cannot well be expected that I should spend my Time and Studies in inventing Instruments, and be at the expense of making and putting in practice those which I have contriv'd, without receiving any Benefit or Assistance from those to whom they may be of use, or any other. It may, I conceive, be judg'd sufficient, by reasonable Men, for the inventor to contrive and describe the Means and Ways how such as have occasion, or desire of experimenting the thing, may, with ease enough, put the same in practice ; at least, if his Reward be consider'd, which, as the Learned Author of the History of the Royal Society has observ'd, is commonly ill Treatment, and not only rough Usage from those that envy his acquists, but even from the Artificers themselves, for whose sake he has labour'd; whilst another that adds some small matter to it, is inrich'd thereby, but the first discoverer is dismist with Contempt and Impoverishment.

The Instrument which was for a long time us'd for taking the Altitude of *The Instru-* the Sun at Sea, was an *Astrolube,* which is yet in use among the *Spaniards,* as *ments now* I am inform'd; the Instrument is, by many Authors, very fully and sufficient- *us'd.* ly describ'd that it need not be here repeated, since that, the *English,* *Dutch,* and *French* have made use of a *Cross-staff,* *Back-staff,* or *Quadrant* for that purpose, as being found by Experience to be much more exact and certain, and the adding of a Telescope-glass to the Sights, hath, as I mention'd before, much improv'd both these qualifications; but they are yet liable to some Inconveniences and Defects.

As, First, They are of little use in a dark Night, by reason of the diffi- *Their Defects.* culty of exactly seeing the Horizon.

Secondly, They are useless also in the Day time, if Foggs or Mists do hinder the distinct discovery of the Horizontal Line.

Thirdly, They are uncertain when Refraction doth elevate or change the true Horizon, which a certain vaporous Air, near the Surface of the Sea, doth often cause.

Fourthly, They are useless when the Sun is in or pretty near the Zenith.

Fifthly, They are troublesome and require great Dexterity and much Practice to be us'd so as is necessary .

Sixthly, They can hardly be so well made or so well us'd, as to afford the Observer a nearer certainty than about half a Degree.

All which inconveniences I hope may be avoided by the Invention which I have here made a Module of, in order to make it the more intelligible. For,

First, It is as proper and as practicable to take the Altitudes of the Stars in a dark but clear Night as in the Day, and that to as great exactness; tho' neither the Horizontal Line, nor any Stars near the Horizon, by reason of Foggs or Clouds that darken them, can be discover'd.

Secondly, It is sufficient to take the Altitude of the Sun whenever it appears, tho' the Horizon be not discoverable by reason of Foggs or Vapours.

Thirdly, It will be sufficient for the same purposes, whenever the Horizontal Line may be displac'd by Refraction, and thereby misguide the diligent observer in the other way.

Fourthly, It will be sufficient to find the true height of the Sun, tho' never so near to the Zenith, and that with as much ease and certainty, as if it were near the Horizon.

Fifthly, The use and practice of making Observations with this Instrument, I conceive to be no more difficult, than the easiest way of observing with any of the Instruments now in use.

Sixthly, I conceive that Observations may be made with this Instrument, much more accurate than 'tis possible to make with those now commonly us'd; and as they may be made more exact, so the instrument itself doth afford a greater certainty, by reason that the Eye-glass doth make the Divisions as large and distinguishable, as if the Instrument, without that help, were four times as large at least, nay, I can safely say, as if the Instrument were ten times as large.

Tab.12.Fig.5. THe Author himself having given no Description or Draught of the above-mention'd Quadrant, I judg'd it would be acceptable to have some farther account of it; wherefore finding a Rude Model of such an Instrument, I have here attempted a Delineation and Description thereof, rather than it should be quite forgotten and lost, tho' I am sensible that I have omitted several Particularities, which if the Inventor had made the Description himself, would have render'd the Instrument more compleat and manageable; which Defect I hope some ingenious Mechanician will at some time supply.

ABC the Quadrant, C the Center, which is so contriv'd, that the Socket, with the Eye-glass, is fixt into it at right Angles to the Quadrant. DE a Telescope moving on the Center C upon the back of the Quadrant, on which also the Divisions of the Degrees are made with Diagonals, as usually. D the Object-glass. At the end C, of the Telescope, is placed a Reflecting-plate at an Angle of 45°. casting the Image to the Eye-glass. AF a Plumb-line passing over the Center of the Instrument between the Reflecting-plate and the Eye-glass, by which means the Object and Perpendicular are seen in the Center at the same time, and so the true Altitude of the Object taken, by fastning the Telescope on the divisions on the backside. GHIK an hollow Cover over the Plumb-line, which serves also for an Handle for the Quadrant. It may be likewise very convenient to have the Plumbet play in a small Vessel of Water fastened to the lower end of the Handle at F, by which means the Plumbet will be less subject to vibrate far, by the opposition of a thicker medium than the Air, which yet will not in the least hinder its Perpendicularity.

The preference of this Instrument consists in the taking the Angle from the Zenith, rather than from the Horizon, which many times is not distinguishable, and always subject to unnertainty from the difference of Refraction.

R W.

Of a Sea Telescope. There is another Instrument which will be of great use for discovering the Latitude of places both by Sea and Land, and that is a small Telescope; whereby a skilful Navigator, or any other ingenious Person, may easily discover the Eclipses that happen of the *Satellites* of *Jupiter* upon the Sea; the use of which Eclipses, as *Galileo* did first mention, so have they been by many Persons approv'd of for that purpose, and several have indeavour'd, by Observations, to perfect the Theory of them, as *Hodierna, Borelli,* Mr. *Rooke* of this Society and Colledge, and now lately the *French* King's Astronomer Monsieur *Cassini,* and a very curious discovery has been made by Monsieur *Romer* the *Dane,* which is generally now approv'd of by knowing Astronomers,

mers, tho' Monfieur *Caffini* (poffibly becaufe the Invention of a Tramontane) feems to hefitate concerning the certainty of it. Mr. *Hally* alfo has lately in-deavour'd to facilitate the ufe of Monfieur *Caffini*'s Tables for calculating the true times of them, which, I conceive, he may yet make more eafy for vul-gar Capacities, fuch as many of the Seamen are, who will have occafion for the ufe of them. But fuch difficulties, I confefs, will be eafily remov'd by Ephemerides, purpofely calculated by fome skillful Aftronomer, and Pub-lifh'd in a Sheet of Paper for feven or ten Years before hand, which Mr. *Hally* can eafily perform ; but yet they will be of no great ufe for the Sea, 'till fuch time as they are fupply'd alfo with convenient Inftruments for the Obfervation of them, which, I hope I may have the freedom and opportu-nity to communicate in fome fhort time, and fhould have done it long fince, if I had not been difcourag'd by undeferv'd Troubles. But I fee it to be the general Fate of all fuch as make any new difcoveries, and therefore bear it with more patience ; however I do not doubt but that the humour of Man-kind, in that particular, has ftifled the Productions of many ufeful Difco-veries.

Certain it is, that the invention of Telefcopes is not yet brought to its greateft Perfection, no nor of Microfcopes neither, tho' Mr. *Leuwenhook* feems to have fome of greater Perfection than ordinary ; but I doubt not but that I fhall be able to fhew, that both the Telefcope and the Microfcope may be eafily enough advanc'd to much higher degrees of Perfection than what have been hitherto produc'd. It is not very long fince the invention of Convex Eye-glaffes was found out for feeing a larger Area of the Object ; which, tho' it do not, I confefs, make the Object more diftinct, yet is it of great ufe in Cæleftial Obfervations, efpecially at Sea for the eafy finding and retaining of the Object in the Telefcope, which, in Telefcopes, with Concave Eye-glaffes, is extreamly troublefome, even in the fhorteft, and much more in long ones ; however this feems not to have been found out 'till about the time that *Reita* Publifh'd his Book call'd *Oculus Enochi & Eliæ,* i. e. about the Year 1645. for perufing that Author in Sir *Ch. Scarborough*'s *Auction* I accidentally met with two places, wherein he has, in a fecret Cha-racter, communicated fome Secrets about the making and ufe of Glaffes, which feem to have been unknown to the World at that time : Thefe, as finding little elfe confiderable in it, I tranfcrib'd, and having fince deciphred them, I find them to comprehend thefe words, *Chartam patinæ leniffimo pul-mento ingeniofe agglutina tripoli vitrum polito in ea.* This feems to be much *Reita's Secreta deciphered.* the fame way which Mr. *Marfhal* did here fhew this Honourable Society, tho' what he apply'd it unto for Polifhing many Glaffes at once, is an addi-tion of his own, of which he fays he took the hint from what I did Publifh in the Preface of my *Micrographia*, concerning the Polifhing of many Object-glaffes at once for Microfcopes. This Ænigma of *de Reita* is to be feen in Page 344 of his Book, now mention'd in thefe Characters.

Cphaatritnæ lpeunlimfefnitmoo jang ggelnuitoifnea
Turijtproulmi pionleiato, &c. *Pag.* 344.

The other Ænigma or Secretum, as he callsit, is in Page 356. in this Cypher.

Cqounauteuxoar---mdeitcituas---oebrijegcutnat
Maumlptluimf---qiuceat---ruietreo---tceorlt---
Lioucma icnopnufnucftiuomnis---Suuennto---vtirtiraa--
Occoun luaer xiaa---oobujaercttuimuum--.

That Deciphered I find to contain thefe words.

Convexa quatuor melius, dicta Objecta erigunt multumq; amplificant. Rite vero tertium Colloca in punctum confufionis. Sunt vero vitra tria ocularia convexa, Ob-jectivum quartum.

This

This it feems was then a fecret, tho' now generally known and made ufe of for Day Objects, and that even in fhort Lengths; but for the Cæleftial Obfervations where there is not great need of erecting the Object, one or two Eye-glaffes is much more convenient; for that they may be made to take in a much larger Area, and reprefent the Object much more bright and diftinct; howbeit they are both capable of much further improvement, and confequently be much more adapted for the ufe of the Sea, for which occafion I have at this time difcours'd of them.

And I will undertake to accommodate Navigators with Telefcopes of two Foot in length, with which they fhall be inabl'd, not only eafily to find the Object, but to difcover alfo the times of the Eclipfes of the *Satellites* of *Jupiter*, as exactly as fhall be needful.

Let therefore fuch Ephemerides be provided, and I fhall procure an ingenious Workman, who fhall provide fuch Telefcopes fit for that purpofe; fo that nothing will then be wanting to compleat the ufe of thofe Eclipfes for the difcovery of the Longitudes of fuch parts as they fhall be obfervable in, fave only an exact Time-keeper to obferve the precife times of fuch appearances, which I can alfo accommodate them withal; fo that if the precife time of the Setting of the Sun for that Night be known, they fhall be fure of the time of the Eclipfe to a very few Seconds.

By fuch Methods and Inftruments as I have now defcrib'd, if carefully us'd, I doubt not but that the Sea-Coafts of all frequented parts of the World might be truly plac'd as to their Longitudes and Trendings; and the method of taking Latitudes being a little amended, the exact Situation of all fuch places in fome few Years, might be obtain'd, which would be of great benefit for the perfecting that part of Geography which at this time is very imperfect.

In my laft Difcourfes I explained three feveral Inftruments for the Ufe and Benefit of Navigation, two of which have not been ever yet thought of by any (that I have heard of) which yet I conceive will (if well made and put in practice) be of very great advantage to Navigators; for that they are new affiftants to them in giving them information of what they have no other ways of Learning: For by means of the laft of the three they will be inabl'd to difcover the Latitude, when, by the commonly us'd Inftruments, they are neceffitated to depend only upon Conjecture; namely, at fuch times either of the Day or Night as the Horizon is not vifible, and when the Sun paffes near the Zenith; and 'tis fo much the more ufeful, for that Nocturnal Obfervations may be made at all times, when the parts of the Sky, near the Zenith, fhall be clear and free from Clouds. And Obfervations may be taken of fuch Stars as pafs over or very near the Zenith with more eafe and certainty than of the Sun itfelf in the Day time; for that the Star obferv'd doth more precifely fhew the very Points, when and where it paffeth the Zenith or the Meridian near it; and the Declination of the Star (which may be learned from Tables ready calculated for that purpofe, efpecially for the moft notable and confpicuous) will readily give the Latitude of the place.

As for the affiftances the other may afford, it is hard to afcertain, yet fince it hath been found to be of very good ufe at Land to prejudge the Conftitution of the Weather, efpecially of great ftore of Wind or Rain, 'tis very probable it may be of as much, if not more, benefit at Sea, where the Air feems to be of more general uniformity, efpecially in fuch parts of it as are far remov'd from any Lands; for that the Situation of Mountains or other diverfify'd parts of the Earth, which are oftentimes the Caufes of Storms and Rains on the Land, have little influence upon the parts of the Sea far remov'd from them: Tho' poffibly it may be found that the Gravity of the Air may be differing at Sea from what it is at Land; which, if fo, might be of no fmall benefit to the Navigator, if he could from that be inform'd of his approach to Land. 'Tis not impoffible neither, that it may afford him fome intimation of the depth of the Sea where he may be, and many other things very defirable to be known, which I will leave to the difcovery of the diligent Obferver. There are many things, that before they are difcover'd, are look'd upon as impoffible, which yet, when the are found,

are

are said to be known by every one, the inventor only excepted, who must pass for an Ignoramus.

I have many Years since shewn to this Society (as will, I suppose, appear *Of a way wiser* by their Journals) an Instrument to keep an exact account of the way of a *for a Ship at* Ship through the Water; whether it has been since try'd I know not, yet I *Sea.* have many Years since that, heard of one or two who were getting a Patent for a like Instrument; whether they succeeded or not, I have not inquir'd, for I freely imparted it for a general Good, and should be glad to here that it were put in practice, and perform'd what may, in all probability, be expected from it, which, I conceive, will be a very exact and certain information of the way of the Ship that useth it through the Water, it not only measuring the length of the Run, but the Rumb of the Leeward way; and the Angles made upon the several Tacks and Courses; but yet 'tis defective for finding the true way of the Ship over the parts of the Earth subjacent to to that Sea, because it distinguisheth not the current or setting of that part of the Sea without some other assistances, whence, 'till they are added, 'tis useless for the invention of the Longitude, which is to be found by other means: However, 'tis of great use to know the true Velocity of a Ship through the Water, in short Voyages, or in foggy or dark Weather; because it is a great help to judge of their present Position as to the true Course they design to hold, and in narrow places they can better judge when 'tis fit to tack about and stand another way.

There is another addition which I thought might also be of good use and *A Contrivance* information to a Navigator, and would afford him a means of exactly mea-*to know the* suring that which he now knows only at random and by guess, and that is an *strength and* Instrument, which being fixt at the top of the Antient or Flagg-staff, should, at *point of the* *Wind.* all times, give the true strength or velocity of the Wind; and the information thereof may easily be convey'd into the great Cabbin or the Steeradge of the Ship. By the help of this and the former way of measuring the way of a Ship, it would be easy to find with what Winds, whether large or scanty; with what Sails, whether more or fewer, or how plac'd; with what Trim, with what Burthen or Lading, with what Ballast, &c. the Ship makes the best way. This is a Proposition hitherto only prov'd by guess and strong Opinion, for the most part very prejudicate and precarious; but by this means it might be brought to a certain Standard of measure. By this means also the comparative goodness of Ships for sailing or making their way through the Water might be brought to a certainty of measurement, which cannot so well be done by any other way now used; for tho' two Ships may now sail not far asunder, and both intend the same course, yet which ever has the better of it in sailing fastest, it will be disputable whether that be the better Sailer; for tho' they are not far asunder, yet that which came first to the Port, might have great advantages of the Wind, which the other had not; and possibly it might be the contrary, there being yet no certain way of determining it, unless by multiplicity of such trials, it shall always be found that the same Vessel has the advantage, and yet even in this way the probability indeed is greater, but yet 'tis but a probability, since 'tis possible that such advantages may happen for five or ten times together, and yet may fail the eleventh time; whereas by this Instrument it will plainly appear which hath had the greatest quantity or strength of the Wind, and which the least; and by the same Instrument it may be certainly determin'd with what Sails, with what Trim, with what Burthen and with what Course, whether by or large, a Ship, comparatively, Sails best; as also it may be practically examin'd with what Trim or set of the Sails a Ship sails the best when it goes near a Wind, and the like to see how far Experience will agree to the Theory; as also whether flat and taught Sails do better than bellying or bunting Sails, which I conceive they do, tho' the most part of Seamen do believe and affirm the contrary with great confidence. I could enumerate many other useful informations these Instruments duly made would afford, but it is needless at present, since what I have mention'd are matters of so great concern in Naval Affairs to be truly inform'd of, that they alone are sufficient (one would think) to induce some Inquisitive Men concerned, to be

knowing

knowing in thefe Affairs, to caufe fome trials to be made thereof, fince no one can deny but that the Confequences that I have afferted muft neceffarily follow; that is, that all thofe Particulars which are hitherto only acquir'd by Conjecture and Guefling are by means hereof reduc'd to certainty of Number, Weight and Meafure ; and tho' fome very skillful in thefe Affairs may fay they can do all that is requir'd well enough, without any fuch Invention, by their own Judgments and long Experience ; yet, I conceive, that he that ufes a pair of Compaffes fhall be able to draw a truer Circle than ever *Apelles,* or the greateft Artift that ever drew Line with his Hand, would be able to do without them.

The Inftrument I defign for this purpofe, is but little differing from that which I long fince contriv'd for meafuring the velocity of the Wind, and caufed one of them to be made for the Weather-clock. It has been fufficiently feen and try'd, and therefore will not, for this time, need a more particular Defcription ; however, if any one defigns to make trial thereof, I fhall not be wanting to give the Workman, that makes it, fufficient Inftruction.

ALL that I can find of thefe Inftruments are only the two following Extracts out of the Regifters of the Royal Society, which I have here publifht, hoping they may give the Ingenious fome hints of improving them, which indeed has been my chief aim in Printing many of the foregoing Difcourfes.

R. W.

November 14. 1683. *Mr.* Hook *fhew'd an Inftrument to meafure the Velocity of the Air or Wind, and to find the ftrength thereof, which was by four Vanes put upon an Axis, and made very light and eafy for motion ; and the Vanes fo contriv'd, as that they could be fet to what flope fhould be defir'd : It was feveral times try'd and examin'd in the long Gallery in* Grefham College *; whereby it appear'd, that by walking from one end thereof to the other, and carrying the fame above ones Head, the Doors and Windows of the faid Gallery being fhut, and fo the Air within it being not in motion but ftagnant, the Inftrument made fo many turns as there were Circumferential lengths of the faid Vanes in the length of the Gallery ; and if by trial it were found to be more or lefs than the due meafure of the Circumferential lengths, then by fetting the faid Vanes either flatter or fharper in refpect of the way of its motion through and againft the Air, the fame was eafy to be adjufted ; the ufe of which may be of very great confequence in the bufinefs of Sailing and fteering a Ship upon the Sea, and for examining the power and ftrength of the Wind upon Land in order to the Theory of Shipping for which it was defign'd.*

A Way wifer for the Sea ; *November 28. 1683.*

I fhew'd an Inftrument I had contriv'd, and fhew'd fome of the Society above twenty Years fince, by which the way of a Ship through the Sea might be exactly meafur'd, as alfo the velocity of any running Water or River, and thereby the comparative velocity of it in it's feveral parts ; by this alfo the quantity of the Water vented by any River into the Sea, or any other River, might be found ; it was one part of a way wifer for the Sea. The whole Engine being defign'd to keep a true account not only of the length of the Run of the Ship thro' the Water, but the true Rumb or Leeward way, together with all the tackings and workings of the Ship. This part of the Engine now fhewn was the Vane, Fly, or firft mover of the whole, feeling, as it were, and diftinguifhing the feveral Qualifications of the Ships Courfe, but was to be regulated by feveral other Additions in the compleated Engine, which I defign fhortly to get executed.

A

A Lecture of the preference of strait to Bunting Sails, Read March 5. 16⁸⁰⁄₉₀.

I have in this place formerly read several Discourses, and shewn many Experiments concerning Light and Gravity, which are two great and universal powers in Nature ; by the later of which all Terrestial Bodies are powerfully, and (if their way be not impeded by the *Media,* through which they pass) most rapidly mov'd towards the middle parts of the Earth, with velocities always accelerated in sub-duplicate proposition of the aggregate of Powers moving ; of the effects of which Monsieur *Huggens* hath treated no further than thereby to find what is the comparative Gravitation here upon the Surface of the Earth, with respect to the Gravitation at the distance of the Moon; by which Examination of the proportion of Gravity he is much convinc'd of the truth of that Theory which I had the happiness first to invent, and of which I shall have occasion to discourse more at large on another Subject. The other effects of Gravity upon Bodies here upon the Earth, which he omits, have been fully discover'd by *Galileo, Torricellius,* and divers others since that time, who have all proceeded upon the equal power of Gravity, and consequently suppos'd an equal addition of Acceleration in equal spaces of time; which in short spaces of Descent near the Earth, is *quoad sensum* true, there being no sensible difference between the power of Gravity in so small a difference of height, as Nature has allow'd Mankind a Liberty or Power of arriving at, to make his trials in : As the top of some high Hill, or at the bottom of some deep Mine ; tho' yet possibly with curious Instruments and accurate Observations, somewhat of discovery might be made on such a Hill as *Tenariff,* or the *Alps :* For which Inquiry therefore one of the Experiments, which I formerly propos'd, to be try'd at *Tenariff* (and which I try'd many times my self, both at the top of St. *Pauls* and at *Westminster-Abby,* tho' without finding any sensible difference) was intended ; as will appear by the accounts of those trials, tho' they were unsuccessful as to what they were design'd for ; however several other Discoveries were made not unuseful. But I shall not further proceed upon that Contemplation at present, but, rather, in this following Discourse, consider a third Power of Nature arising from the motions of the Air and Water, two fluid Mediums which incompass the Body of the Earth. And among the various Effects they produce, I shall at this time, consider only one which is procur'd by means of Art, and that is for the moving or regulating of Ships or Vessels by means of Sails, Oares, Rudder, and the like artificial Methods of gaining and making use of their Powers : It being of great use for Merchant Ships in those times of danger, to know the best Methods and Means of making these Powers the most serviceable to them that may be for flying from and escaping the pursuit of their Enemies. There are therefore very many things that must be consider'd, in order to the perfecting of this effect to the greatest advantage that is possible. As the Shape and Bigness of the Vessel with consideration of its Use and Design, the manner of Rigging it and fitting it with Masts, Sails, and other Tackle, and with Rudder, Oares, Keel, Leeboards, *&c.* The Shapes and Magnitudes of each, and the ways of applying and using them to the best advantage. And herein will come the consideration of the Power of the Wind upon Sails, Masts, Rigging, and Hulk of the Vessel : The power also of the Water against the Rudder, Oares, Leeboards, Keel, Head and Sides of the Vessel will come under consideration ; for it must be determin'd what quantity of Sails this or that kind of Vessel will bear ; and what the form of the Sail is best to be, and how to be order'd or fitted to the Vessel ; how much Ballast such Vessels so built and rigged, will require, and what strength of Wind each kind of Vessel can indure; what the strength of the Wind is with relation to its swifter motion or higher blowing; what strength and length of Oares is necessary for induring the powers to be apply'd to them; and what Powers, whether of Men, or other, can be apply'd ; and what are the best and most advantageous

Traite de la Lumiere.

Several matters to be known in the Art of Sailing.

vantageous ways for such applications : These, and many other particulars, ought to be fully examin'd, both by the known Principles of Mechanicks, and by Experiments on the several Materials that must be introduc'd into the Propositions of such Ratiocinations ; for that abstracted Notions will not be so serviceable in these Inquiries as the knowledge of the concrete Qualities and Proprieties. And to be furnish'd with these many an pertinent Experiments must be invented, made, and diligently, as well as knowingly, observ'd ; for that the preponderancy of such Effects, may, and do often lie in unheeded Circumstances, and in almost insensible differences ; which, nevertheless, upon the result of greater trials, prove very notable ; and yet, by reason of the Difficulty, Charge, loss of Time, and many other Inconveniences, which are the necessary Concomitants of such greater Experiments, the smaller trials, tho' they require much more watchfulness and perspicatiousness are much to be perferr'd : For that more may be examin'd and verify'd in a Year by these, than by the other in an Age. And tho' the business of Shipping and Navigation hath been many Ages in a way of improvement, and somewhat very considerable has been done towards it, insomuch that the present state thereof is look'd upon as the highest Perfection it is capable of, yet a few small trials might easily make the groundlessness of that Opinion plainly appear, almost in every particular of the artificial Structure of Vessels fitted for that design. I am not insensible of the difficulties that attend any one that shall be an asserter of this Doctrine ; I have experimentally verify'd the effects of propounding new Inventions to improve such as are at the present in vogue ; witness the improvment of Astronomical Instruments, the Spring-watches, the universality of Gravity, and the motions of the Heavens, according to the Rules and Laws of Mechanical Motions. And yet after all the obloquy and reproaches, and unhandsome treatment I have met with for making those discoveries, I find the things themselves, in tract of Time, become to be approv'd, and come to be of general use. There are, I believe, but very few in the World now that will adhere to *Hevelius* his magnify'd Contrivances for Instruments with plain Sights, tho' at the same time they joyn with him in the Aspersions he hath cast upon me. But to let those Reflections pass at present, I know very well, that I shall find, opposite to this Doctrine about Ships, not only all the Architects or Ships Builders, but the Crue of Navigators also, who are very hard to be brought to the Use and Practise of a new Method, and are not otherwise to be prevail'd with but *gradatim* by length of Time, and dear bought Experience. But tho' the most are thus qualify'd, yet they are not all : There are some that are willing to be better inform'd in this or that Particular, and will make use and trial of things, tho' they carry with them but a probability ; for the sake therefore of such, 'tis if any discovery be made ; but for the rest *Si Populus Vult, decipiatur.*

Of flat Sails.   I have had many Discourses both with some of the ablest Ship-writes, and with as skilful Navigators, and both agree in their Opinions or Judgments, that a Bellying or Bunting Sail doth more promote or carry a Vessel to Windward, than a flat and smooth Sail that bellies not at all ; the contrary of which I have divers times indeavour'd to defend. In order to clear the reasonableness of this Assertion, I have, in the first place, consider'd the Nature and Power of the Wind upon the Area of a Sail, various ways expos'd to it ; by which, by degrees, I shall come to the evident Demonstration of what I have asserted : But because, possibly after all that can be said and manifested by such a Demonstration ; those that have asserted the contrary, will not grant the Conclusion, after the Demonstration ; I shall prepare an Apparatus for the trial of an Experiment where the effect itself shall speak the Conclusion, and that beyond the power of Contradiction.

To come then to the Reasons that induc'd me to make this Conclusion ; I say that fluid Bodies mov'd, do impress a motion to other Bodies, they are mov'd against proportionate to their Gravity and Velocity : This may be prov'd by thousands of Experiments. Next I find the Air to be a ponderous fluid Body, whose integrant parts have both bulk and weight in them as well as the integrant parts of other fluid Terrestial Bodies ; as Water, Oil,

Oil, Quickſilver, and the like; and tho' they have a leſs proportion of Gravity, if compar'd to their bulk, or the ſpace they ſeem to fill, and that ſo very ſmall, that they have, for a long time, been aſſerted to have a contrary quality of lightneſs, yet, by undeniable Arguments drawn from Experiments, they are demonſtrated to have their proportion of Gravity with relation to their bulk: Which proportion compar'd to the like proportion of Water, is, for the moſt part, near as 1 to 800 or 900. It follows therefore, that the motion of this fluid Body muſt, according to the quantity of its Gravity, impreſs upon another Body that it is mov'd againſt, ſuch a quantity of motion in the ſame manner as the like quantity of another fluid Body, as Water, and if the motion be the ſame, the motion communicated will be as 1 to 800. If the Motions be reciprocal to the Gravities of the ſtriking Bodies, the motions or powers communicated will be equal; for if there be by the Velocity 28, 3 times as much Air in bulk mov'd againſt the Recipient Body as there is of the bulk of Water in the ſame time, and that the Velocity be 28,3 ſwifter than that of the Water, then 28, 3 x 28, 3 will produce an equality of Motion with the eight hundred Gravitating parts in the Water mov'd with one degree of Velocity, as I ſhall more particularly prove afterwards. Thus, if on a Stilyard a weight of thirty Pound be hung at thirty times the diſtance from the Center that a weight of nine hundred Pounds is hung, the Stilyard ſhall remain in æquilibrio, and neither end prependerate; for the thirty Pound cannot be mov'd but it muſt have thirty times the Velocity that the nine hundred Pound muſt have, and therefore the Stilyard muſt remain without any motion at all, but ſtand in a æquilibrium. Since the product of the bulk and Velocity of the one is equal to the Product of the Bulk and Velocity of the other; this therefore holds where effects equiponderate.

The Wind then is nothing elſe but the Body of the Air mov'd as a fluid with a certain degree of Velocity towards a certain part of the Horizon upon the Surface of the Earth or Sea, and, as other fluid Mediums, it taketh the eaſieſt and ſhorteſt way it findeth to continue its direct motion; moving round the edges of the Body that ſtandeth in its way, after it hath beat againſt it, and been reflected from it, and the parts reflected are quickly again, by the ſucceeding Parts, recruited in their motion, and move along with the other parts which have received no Impediment. The power of the Wind therefore is to be computed according to the bigneſs of the Priſm of the Air which cometh to daſh or ſtrike againſt the Body that is expos'd to it; and according to the Velocity that this Priſm is mov'd forwards to ſtrike againſt it: For a fluid Medium, in motion, is to be conſider'd as made up of an indefinite number of ſmall Cylinders, Priſms, Wires or Strings lying cloſe together, and ſo making up the Solidity of the greater Priſm of the Body of the fluid that is mov'd towards the Obſtacle; and again each of theſe ſmall Priſms or Wires may be ſuppos'd as made up of an indefinite number of ſmall Beads or Dies lying one behind another, and ſo following each other immediately in the ſame Line, and with the ſame Velocity of motion, and every one of theſe compounding Beads or Dies coming to beat or ſtrike againſt the Body that lieth in its way, it ſo ſtrikes it and communicates a motion; what motion it doth not communicate to that Body it meets with, is reflected back from it, with, or by an Angle equal to the Angle of Incidence. So that upon this conſideration each of the ſmall Priſms may be computed as a ſingle Bullet or Die, ſo ſtriking the Surface of the expos'd Body with one degree of power all of bulk equal to the many ſingle ones ſeparate; and the larger Priſm made up of an indefinite number of theſe leſſer Wires or Priſms, may be conceiv'd and computed as a larger Bead or Die, relation being always had to the Gravity and Velocity of the impelling or ſtriking Body. Now a round Body being mov'd againſt another Body, impreſſeth on it ſome degree of motion, and what it doth not communicate, is reflected from it, according to the known Laws of Reflection; that is, the reflected Angle is equal to the Angle of Incidence upon the plain of the Body ſtruck, and the Body ſtruck receiveth a motion Perpendicular to the Surface of it that is ſo ſtruck.

To come then to the Application of the Power of the Wind upon the Sails of a Veſſel, we are to conſider the Expanſion of the Sail, as it is expos'd to the Impulſe of the Wind; whether the Surface of it do cut the Priſm of the Wind that beareth againſt it at right Angles or Oblique; if it cutteth the Priſm at Right Angles, then the whole power of a Priſm of Wind or Air that cometh to blow upon it for a certain time, whoſe Baſis is equal and at right Angles with the length of the Priſm, is to be computed as communicating all its motion: But if the Area of the Sail cut the Priſm at oblique Angles, then we muſt conceive the Scalene Priſm as cut at right Angles, and compare the Area thereof with the Area of the Sail; and this will give the magnitude or quantity of the impelling Priſm of Wind againſt the oblique Sail. Again, to know with what force this Scalene Priſm doth preſs or impel the Sail ſo obliquily poſited Perpendicularly to its Surface, we

The Calculati-on of the ſtrength and difference.

muſt compare the Degrees of Velocity, with which it is mov'd directly towards the Area of the oblique Sail, and ſee what proportion it holdeth with the direct and perpendicular motion upon the direct Sail; and by both theſe Examinations duly made, the comparative power of the Wind upon the Area of the ſloped Sail will appear. Let a b then repreſent the breadth of a Sail of a given height, and let a b c d repreſent a Priſmatical Body of the Air, which being mov'd from d c to a b in a given ſpace of Time, maketh a Wind of ſuch ſtrength bear or beat againſt the Surface of the Sail a b directly oppos'd to its courſe, and in the given time all the parts of the Priſm a b c d have ſtruck againſt the Surface of the Sail a b. Suppoſe then a b n o, to repreſent a Priſm of Water, of equal Baſe with the ſaid Sail a b, and that a n, or b o, the length of the ſaid Priſm be $\frac{1}{30}$. of the length a d or b c the Priſm of Air mov'd the contrary way with thirty times the Velocity, if the proportion of the Gravity of the Air be to the Gravity of the Water, as one to nine hundred: I ſay, the Sail ſhall not be mov'd either way, but remain in an æquilibrium: For as the Velocity of the motion of the Water a n, 1 is to the Velocity of the motion of the Air a d 30; ſo the Gravity of the Priſm of the Air a b c d 30, to the Gravity of the Priſm of Water a b o n 900. Now becauſe the ſame power is impreſt on the Sail, whether the Cylinder of Water be mov'd againſt the Sail from n o to a b, or the Sail be mov'd againſt the Water from a b to n o; if the ſaid Cylinder of Air be made one degree ſwifter, it muſt drive the ſame Sail from a b, to n o.

Next ſuppoſe E f to repreſent the ſame Sail, ſet obliquely to the Priſm or Current of the Wind, draw e h, and f g, parallel to a d. Firſt then it is plain, that a k h d and b c g i of the former Priſm do now not at all touch the ſaid Sail e f, but only the middle part of the ſame, namely, k i g h; now the quantity of this to the quantity of the former, being as k i to a b; that is, as p f, the ſine of the Angle of incidence p e f to the Radius e f, or a b; it follows that the quantity of Wind upon the direct Sail to the quantity ſtriking the oblique Sail is, as Radius to the ſign of the Angle of Incidence.

Again, the power of this Priſm upon the oblique Sail e f, is to the power of it upon the direct Sail, equal to k i, as e l to f l; that is, as f p to f e; that is, as the ſine of the Angle of Incidence p e f to the Radius; therefore the power of the Wind upon the Sail a b, directly oppos'd to its motion is to the power of it upon the ſame Sail ſet oblique to its motion, as the ſquare of Radius, to the ſquare of the Angle of Incidence, or of the obliquity to the Wind p e f.

Now that the motion of the oblique Sail is to the motion of the direct Sail by the ſame Priſm of Wind as p f to f e, will plainly appear: Suppoſe p f g h a ſolid Cylinder meeting with p f a direct Sail at p f, and f e the oblique Sail; then p f will be carry'd on to q l, at the ſame time that e f will be mov'd to l m; the motion therefore of p f is equal to f l, but the motion of e f is equal to e l: But as f l to e l, ſo f e to f p, ſo Radius to the ſine of Inclination or Obliquity.

Now that the ſtrength or power of the Wind upon the Oblique Sail is Perpendicular to the ſaid Sail, is evident from this Conſideration, that if the Sail be ſuppos'd perfectly flat and ſmall in its Surface, there is no part that the Wind can take hold of to drive it forward in its own way, and having no

patr

part opposite to the power thereof, but only the said smooth Surface that can only receive a Perpendicular pressure, and that pressure can only move or thrust it toward the Perpendicular of its Surface : If therefore a Sail be perfectly flat and smooth, all the force it receives is towards the Perpendicular of its Surface. Which Perpendicular force notwithstanding may cause it to move in any other direction which is inclin'd to the said Perpendicular, by some Angle less than a right, according as the said Sail may be so fix'd to a Body that shall have a more easy way for it to pass that way than towards the Perpendicular. This may be explain'd from the consideration of the power of Gravity : The power of Gravity then we know tends to move the heavy Body towards the Perpendicular of the Horizon, that is, towards the Center of the Earth ; but if the heavy Body be so posited on a Plain that has any inclination to the solid Perpendicular ; that is, maketh a less Angle with it than a right Angle ; we know that the power of Gravity, tho' it acts directly towards the Perpendicular, yet it moveth and impelleth it to descend obliquely in any other Plain dipping below the Horizon. Now the proportion of the power of the Wind upon the oblique Sail to drive it backwards towards the Perpendicular, is to the proportion of its power to drive it in any other Plain, is easy to be determin'd, but that I shall refer to another opportunity.

Now since by this afore recited Cause it is evident, that the power of the mov'd Air or Wind upon an oblique Sail, doth press or protrude it Perpendicularly to the Surface of the Sail, and thence, if there be as free a passage that way, as any other, the Sail will be mov'd, and move the Vessel to which it is fix'd in the said Perpendicular; it follows, that if there be any other part of the said Sail that has a differing inclination, it will have a differing Perpendicular, and consequently every part of the bent Sail will have a differing pressure and a differing tendency ; and because that part of the Sail which is next the Wind, is less belly'd than that which is from the Wind, more of the Perpendicular Tendencies will be to fall from the Wind than to go nigh or towards the Wind, and consequently, the composition of all the tendencies together, will have less power to press the bent Sail towards the Perpendicular of the set of the Yard of the Sail, than if the Sail were all smooth in the plain of the Yard ; for the fore part of the Sail next the Wind becometh, by the bellying, to stand too sharp and near the Wind, and so receiveth little power or force from the Wind, to promote it according to those Perpendiculars, and the Aft-parts of the Sail stand too full, and so receive most of its power, whose Perpendiculars tend too much from and before the Wind ; and the middle parts of the Sail which stand only true, are so small a part of the whole, that the most part of the effect of the Wind is lost or mistaken for the desir'd end.

This is one of the great Reasons why a Vessel, that is thus rigged, is not able to sail on any Rumb within four Points, and why even there so little way is made to the Windward, tho' there are several other Reasons also ; of which I shall Discourse on another opportunity.

A Lecture of the manner of Rowing the Antient Gallies, *Read* July *the* 2d. 1684.

THo' this Lecture was read several Years before some of the former, yet I thought it best to reserve it to the last ; the foregoing seeming to me more to depend upon each other, and by some sort of Connection join together. In this the Reader will find the Authors Sentiments very differing from all that have wrote upon this Subject ; I think his Reasons have a considerable weight in them ; but this is left to the Readers Judgment, as all other matters contain'd in this Volume, which I shall end with these Discourses, finding no more that properly belong to Navigation or Astronomy, and reserve some Miscellaneous Tracts, Fragments on several Subjects, some Inventions, accounts of Experiments, &c. for a Supplement or second Volume, which I purpose to publish in some short time, if this first find any acceptance, and not increase the bulk of this, which has prov'd longer than I at first expected.

R. W.

A

A Lecture of the manner of Rowing of the Antient Gallies, *read* July 2. 1684.

The greatest promoter of Mens Industry, Study and Invention for the discovery of Arts, has been the necessity of usefulness of them for humane Life. To which end next to *Agriculture* and *Architecture*, I conceive *Navigation* may be rank'd, by means whereof Men have pass'd to places of the Earth otherwise inaccessible, and the whole Surface of the Land has been inhabited and peopl'd. And as it has been very useful in itself, so it has been the occasion of inventing and perfecting many other Arts and Sciences, as *Geometry, Astronomy, Geography,* &c.

And tho' the devouring Teeth of Time hath scarce left us any scrap of History that should acquaint us with the knowledge and practice of Men in the first Ages of the World, yet such as we have do sufficiently inform us, that in the younger times of the World, Ships and Navigation were known, witness *Homer, Jason,* and the *Argonauts* not now to insist on, what we find in Holy Writ concerning the *Ark of Noah,* which, tho' the Shape, Dimensions and Manner of building that Vessel, which was for a very peculiar and extraordinary Use, were divinely reveal'd to *Noah,* yet it seems not unlikely but that there might be many other sorts of Vessels known and in use long before that time, as in probability there were many Arks or Chests for common use long before the Lord directed *Moses* in the Bigness, Form and Materials of the second *Ark,* which was the *Ark of the Testimony.* But this I shall not insist on; I know the Accounts are but very short, and so nothing positivively concluded from thence that there were Ships; much less can we find what they were, or to what perfection *Navigation* was practis'd : Nay, we are much to seek what was the true form of Ships in the more modern Times of the *Greeks* and *Romans*; of which times, notwithstanding, in respect of other particulars, we have much more full and compleat Relations. That there were Vessels of prodigious bulk and burthen, we are assur'd by *Pliny, Plutarch,* and others; that they carry'd prodigious numbers of Men, both of Soldiers and Seamen, that they had great numbers of Oars and Men to manage them; and that they had Ballast, Masts, Sails and Rudders, and could Sail both before and by the Wind, is also evident. But then what was the true shape of the Vessel both under and above the Water; what the form of their Oars and how they us'd them; what their greatest velocity either of Sailing or Rowing; what their strength for bearing Sail, or induring the Sea, and the like; of these Histories give so little an account, that the best Judgments of the greatest Criticks, are but uncertain Conjectures and short of giving satisfactory Answers and Solutions, And had not the antient Carvers help'd the Historians, we should have been much more to seek; for according to the Descriptions that Criticks have given us of the way of using their Oars, which is much after the Modern way of using them in Boats, Barges and Gallies; I see not how it could be possible to manage the uppermost Oar of forty or fifty; for so many, 'tis said by *Plutarch* and *Pliny* and others, have been us'd in each order. I have therefore omitted all the Criticisms concerning this matter; of which there is much to be found in *Budæus, Bayfius, Scaliger, Snellius, Pancirollus,* and more especially *Meibomius*; and apply'd my self to consider the thing as I find it express'd in the remaining *Basso Relievos* of the Antients. And upon the whole I conceive that the way of Rowing us'd by the Antients, was wholly differing from what we now use, and not at all like that which the Learned *Meibomius* has taken so much pains to explain.

I shall not trouble you with long *Ambages* either in confuting the Opinions of others or Criticising upon the Words or Phrases of Historians, but rather in short tell you the sum of what I judge of this matter.

First then, I conceive, that the Oars us'd by the Antients were very much like the Oars now us'd, but broader and flatter, shorter and lighter, and manag'd only by one or two.

Secondly, That they were mov'd not vibrating forward and backwards as ours now are, but inwards and outwards.

Thirdly,

Thirdly, That they did not lie Horizontal as ours do, but almoſt Perpendicular; and when they lay a ground, the Oares ſerv'd inſtead of Legs or Props to ſuſtain the Veſſel or Hull when its Belly was not broad enough to lie upright, and it was crank ſided.

Fourthly, That they were not lifted out of the Water, but always remain'd immers'd.

Fifthly, That they always promoted the Veſſel whether they were mov'd outwards or inwards.

Sixthly, That the Rowers did ſeldom ſit with their Faces to the Poop of the Veſſel, but ſometimes with their Faces toward the Prow, and, for the moſt part, with their Faces outward and forwards.

Seventhly, That in the ſmaller Veſſels as *Biremes, Triremes Quadriremes*, and *Penteres*, the Oares went through round holes made in the ſides.

Eighthly, That in the *Triremes* the *Thranites* ſat formoſt, and at the top the *Zygites* juſt behind him and below him; and 3*dly,* The *Thalamites* behind the *Zygites* and below him, and ſo the *Zygites* Oare was mov'd up and down behind the back of the *Thranites* and the *Thalamites* behind the *Zygites*.

Ninethly, That the Hull of the *Triremes*, &c. were built much bredthing or ſpreading upwards, and over hanging, ſo that the holes that were made for the Oares of the *Zygites* and *Thalamites* went out almoſt Perpendicular; and in ſome there was an overſailing or projecture of the Hull at the place, but eſpecially in greater Veſſels; the Oares of the *Thranites* were either put thro' a hole of the checquer'd Railings at the top, or elſe laid in a Notch on the edge of the Ships ſides, and bound down either with an Iron or Rope; ſo that when the *Thranites* thruſt the handle of his Oar from him, it would not riſe out of the Notch.

Tenthly, That the *Remiges* or Rowers in greater Veſſels, ſuch as the *Hepteres, Octoeres,* &c, were plac'd in Galleries which overſail'd the Hull of the Veſſel, which were made by Beams lying quite croſs the Hull of the Ship and made a very broad Deck, not like the Modern Gallies, but ſuch, as I conceive, was quite fluſh from end to end of the Beams; at the other ſide of which Galleries there was made a grating or ſide to defend the Rowers. In theſe kinds of Veſſels the *Remiges* or Rowers did ſtand ſide to ſide, and the Oar went Perpendicular into the Sea, in the out part of the overſailing Beams, and the Rowers, in the way of Skulling, mov'd their Oars altogether, either outward or inward; by which means they were able to employ ſuch a vaſt number of Rowers, wherein every one ſhould be able to exert his whole ſtrength in promoting the Ship, and ſo muſt needs be able to make it move with a prodigious ſwiftneſs, much beyond the ſwiftneſs of any Gally or Galliot.

By this means what *Plutarch* writes concerning the Veſſel built by *Ptolomæus Philopator* may be well conceiv'd, which would otherwiſe ſeem incredible and impoſſible; for 'twas 280 Cubits long, or, as *Snellius* computes, 420 Cubits and 38 in bredth, or 57 Foot; the height from bottom to top was 52 Cubits; it carry'd 400 Mariners beſides 4000 Rowers, and near 3000 Soldiers. How theſe Rowers ſhould be plac'd according to the forms they conceiv'd, both *Scaliger* and *Snellius* were at a great loſs; inſomuch that *Snellius* thinks it impoſſible to diſpoſe the Rowers, unleſs they were pack'd up like Salt Herrings. *Ut nefas ſit credere hæc tranſtra a Remigibus occupari potuiſſe, niſi forſan eos tanquam halices & ſalſamenta ſtipatos intelligas*, are his words. And, according to the manner of Rowing they conceiv'd, it would have been very difficult. Nor would *Meibomius* his Contrivance have help'd them; but in the way I propounded of the ſpreading of the Veſſel upward; it will not be difficult, where, tho' the higheſt Oars will be ſtill the longeſt, and ſo they will need a Counterpoiſe of Lead at the Handle to ballance the weight of the Shank, as *Athenæus* affirms they had in this Veſſel of *Ptolomæus Philopator*, yet going down into the Water nearer to a Perpendicular than a Horizontal Poſture, it may eaſily enough be conceiv'd; but theſe kind of monſtrous Veſſels were rather for ſhew than uſe, as *Snellius* well obſerves.

Eleventhly, That the flat of the Blade of the Oar did not go into the Water Perpendicular, and croſs the length of the Veſſel, as our Oars now, but rather parallel with the length of the Vessel, and so were canted with the foremost edge outwards, when they were strained outwards and the foremost edge inward, when they were strain'd towards the Vessel; by which means they always promoted and impell'd the Vessel forwards, and that in a very natural and efficacious way; in the same manner, as all Fishes do swim and force their way through the Water.

Twelfthly, To confirm this Opinion, I shall only instance in the Modern Practise, which is yet in use in the *East-Indies*, where this manner of Rowing is still in use, tho' somewhat mixed with the Northern or our modern way of Rowing; for in their Barges the Rowers all stand, and indifferently with their Face or Back to the Prow of the Vessel, and sometimes half one way half the other, and so indifferently can make the Vessel move forwards or backwards without altering their posture; as, without question, all the antient Vessels could likewise be mov'd; which gives a Reason why, in *Ptolomy*'s Vessel, there were four Rudders, namely, one on each side before, or in the Prow, and one on each side behind or in the Poop. And the *Indian* Rudder also which is still in use, is of the same fashion with that of the *Greeks* and *Romans*, save only, that instead of planting it on each end the Vessel, they place it in the middle abaft, and so it indifferently serves for Steering the Vessel, whether going forward or backwards, and is much more convenient and easy to manage than the way of Rudders now in use with us. The Curry Curries also are still mov'd or row'd in the same manner with those of the Antients, as I conceive, the Rowers sitting all on Bamboos at a distance from the Vessel and Sculling the Vessel by canting the Oars in the manner I have describ'd; and 'tis not unlikely but the Gallerys of Gallies might have been some Remainder of the Galleries of the Antients, tho' they are accommodated to the Modern way of Rowing.

I am not insensible how great the Difficulties are in the introducing a new Opinion: Or to persuade one, that has long believ'd a thing to be one way, that it is another, especially about such matters as are thought to be thoroughly understood, and most generally put in practice and approv'd. But then I know also, that how generally soever any thing be believ'd and asserted to be true, and the best that 'tis possible, yet that there may be, hath been, and always will be left room enough to find out farther Discoveries and Improvements of Mens Knowledge and Understanding, even in that particular, and that 'tis as hard to find and set Bounds and Limits to the power of the Mind; as to set what is the greatest or least Extension or Demension of Body in Nature: I expect the Criticks first, next the Skilful in the present Naval Architecture, And, Thirdly, Such as have not so much consider'd this part of Mechanicks, may be opponents to this particular Opinion and Explication of this piece of antient History, whose fate it hath been hitherto either not to be understood, or not to be believ'd; for what hath hitherto been the cause of these Effects may still remain so to have an influence upon Mens Minds, as not easily to admit the entrance of a new or contrary proposal. However, as far as I am able, I shall indeavour to satisfy each of these Opponents in the explication of those things which may seem the most difficult.

It cannot be expected, I suppose, that from some few collected Rafts and Fragments which have scap'd the devouring Sea of Time, in which the Arts and Knowledge of the Antients have been Shipwrack'd and lost, I should be able to give so true and positive an account of every particular part, as could not be contradicted: But taking for granted that the Histories are true that afford us that information we have; I conceive there is no difficulty to shew a way how the same might be effected which is affirm'd to have been done; and to begin with the smallest which was the μονόκωπος, or a Boat with one Oar: This was fastned to one side behind, in the same manner as the *Temo* or Rudder, by a Strap or Ring, or else was put through a hole; the handle of which, the Rower sitting with his Face towards the Prow, and holding in his two Hands, mov'd fromwards and towards the side of the Vessel, canting the *Tonsa* or Blade thereof with his Hands, by which the Vessel was both readily promoted and also guided; of this Oar the *Tonsa* or blade was very broad,

by

by which means the Rower could exert his whole strength the better. The Δίκωπος or δίσκαλμος had two of the flat Oars behind on each side one, which were either mov'd by two Men, or else sometimes by one who manag'd the two Oars, in each Hand one. So *Lucian* brings in *Charon* in his Dialogues thus speaking, *Ego quamvis senex duos remos concitans navigo Solus.* Not like our common Scullers which manage their Oars almost on a level, but after the same manner, as I before mention'd was done by the Μονόκωπ⊙: The manner of using these will appear plainly from the Basso-Relievos on the *Columna Trajana*, which is a most undeniable Record of History, and to be prefer'd before any Writings in Books of those times, since there may have been so many Transcripts or Coppies made one after another, of Historians, and every one of those might multiply the Errors and Mistakes of the first Transcriber, whence Criticks find and amend so many Errors and make more, whereas this has undoubtedly stood the same since it was first erected, which was in the time of *Trajan* when those Vessels were actually made and us'd. This gave me the first Hint or Conception of this way of using the Oars, and I cannot find any one passage either in the Carving or Writings of the Antients that doth any ways contradict it; and taking that for granted, it will be easy to explain all that is related in History concerning their greater, even their greatest Vessels which had the greatest numbers of Rowers and Oars, which I take to be almost impossible to be done any other way.

Now that this is not so preposterous a Conception as some may imagine, nor so fantastical, ridiculous, silly and insignificant a way of using Oars, as some have thought; give me leave to add one Argument, and that is this, that Nature is generally the best guide for Art to imitate. If this be doubted, I can produce Arguments enough to evince it; but if it be not, then, I say, that this way of Rowing (which I propose) comes the nearest to the method of Nature in the making animated Bodies pass through fluid Mediums, and therefore 'tis probably the best; for there is scarce a Fish in the Water, a Bird or Insect in the Air but moves itself through those fluid *Media* by the same method with this I propound; that both the Tails and Fins of Fishes are this way mov'd, is most evident to any one that shall strictly examine it; and *Borelli* in his Book *De motu Animalium*, has well explain'd it, that several of those Birds that dive under Water, such as *Didappers, Coots, Puffins,* &c. do under Water move their Wings in this manner, I have often times seen my self and observ'd: And that all Birds and Insects by the same kind of motion of their Wings, fly in the Air: Any that will examine will so find it. So that could there have been a better way, Nature would have taken it. Some motions indeed there are that seem a little to imitate this, and that is the motion of the Sea Fowl, *Swans, Geese, Coots,* &c. at the top of the Water, when they begin to rise and take the Wing; but then 'tis but by accident; for all these Fowl indeavouring to use their Wings by striking the Air, being near the Water, strike the Surface of it with the extreamity or blade of their Wings, after they have first struck the Air; and with the flat of their Feet help to push themselves forward to get a celerity of Progression, which is necessary for their rise, treading, as it were, the top of the Water, and for want of that help, some of the short Wing'd Fowl, as *Puffins,* &c. are not able to rise into the Air from plain ground, but from the Rocks they precipitate themselves on their Wings to acquire a necessary velocity; which all other long Winged Fowl are able to procure by the help of their Feet, swiftly treading the Ground, and with their long Wings beating the Air.

The greatest Objections I have yet met with are these, First, That 'twas absurd to conceive, that the Ships Row'd sometimes backwards as well as forwards, and had Rudders at both ends, but for this *Suidas* upon the word δίκερlος, says *sunt & quædam quæ binis gubernaculis a prora & a puppi instructæ sunt, ut ubiq; conversione in hostes navis feratur aut Recedat, eosq; tam progressu quam Recessu fallat.* And that some Ships had such Rudders. *viz.* two before and two behind, is evident from the Description of *Philopator*'s Ship also in the fifth Book of *Athenæus*, where he says it was δίπρωρ⊙ κ̣ δίπρυμν⊙, *biprora & bipuppis*, a double bottom'd Vessel, or two join'd together; for otherwise I cannot conceive how three thousand arm'd Men could be plac'd between the Rowers,

Rowers, on which there were two thousand on each side. Now by this way of Rowing, I suppose the Rowers could very easily, with the same motion of the Oar, Row the Ship either forward or backwards ; and tho' they had but one Rudder, yet they could easily Steer the Vessel by it, tho' it were mov'd backwards ; for the Blade *Tonsa*, or palm of the Rudder, was broad and e-qually extended on both sides the Stalk or middle, and so was always on a Counterpoise.

The manner how the *Tonsa* of the Oar cut the Water will be better un-derstood by the Figure than by the words alone. Let AB represent the Wa-ter Section of a Dicrotos ; E and N the canting Section of the Palm of the Oars in the Water ; these being mov'd outwards from the Boat, slide against the Water from E to F, and from N to O, and at the same time carry the Vessel from AB to CD ; then the Cants of the Oars being alter'd at G and P, and mov'd inward, they slide against the side of the Water by the Lines GH and PQ, and promote the Vessel from IK to LM, and so successively ; which is the same motion with the Tail of a Fish in the Water, by which its Body is most powerfully carry'd forwards ; which is easy to be conceiv'd, and will effectually perform what it ought to do.

This single motion then once understood, it will not be difficult to con-ceive all the rest in any of their other Vessels.

For the *Moneres* was nothing but several Couples of these Oars lying one before another, as thick as they could sit, leaving only room for the Perpen-dicular motion of the Handle of the Oar behind the back of the next Rower that sat before him, and not so much space as is requir'd in the modern way of Rowing, where the motion of the Handle or Blade of the Oar is Horizon-tal.

The *Dieres* or *Biremes* were double Orders of those Oars or Rowers ; the Rowers sometimes sitting side by side, upon the same Bench, the *Thranites* sitting next the side, and the *Zygites* next within ; the *Thranites* Oar usually lay at the top in a half round Notch, and in the inside was tied down with a Strap call'd *Strappum* by *Vitruvius*, or else it way thrust through some hole of the Rails at the sides of the Vessel, the Oar of the *Zygites* pass'd through a hole, a little below and nearer to the Poop, and cut the Water with the same inclination.

The *Trieres* or *Triremes* had three *Versus* or Files of these Rowers, there being three in each *Ordo* or Rank ; the *Thranites* and *Zygites*, for the most part, sat as in the *Biremes*, but the *Thalamites* sat upon the Foot-step of the *Thranites* ; the Oars of the *Zygites* and *Thalamites* went through round holes in the side of the Vessel.

The *Quadriremes* had four Rowers in a Rank, sitting upon the upper Bench, and two upon the Foot-step ; the *Thalamites* and *Thramites* sat next the side of the Vessel, and the *Zygites* next within them.

The *Hepteres* had all the Men sitting or standing in one Rank, and at one Height, but that Rank a little sloped, to let the Oars have free passage one by another.

Those of a greater number of Rowers in an order, had both several stati-ons of Seats and several Men upon each Seat; as the *Dekeres* might have three ascents of Seats, and have three Rowers on the lowest, three on the next, and four on the highest Bench : But these are but Conjectures, as are, for the most part, all the other above the *Triremes*, there being nothing that I have yet met with in the Writings of the Antient Historians, or in the *Basso Rilievos* now remaining that can clear that Doubt. But certain it is, that by this way of Rowing, as great a number of Men may conveniently enough be plac'd to manage each his Oar ; and thereupon exert his own strength for the promo-ting of the Ship, as are Recorded to have been made use of by the Antients, which I conceive cannot be done by any other way of Rowing yet known.

I shall not now insist upon the great use there may be made of this Princi-ple in Shipping, but only hint, that how slight soever it may at first appear, it may possibly be prov'd to be of as great concern to *England*, as any thing hitherto done in Shipping.

F I N I S.

Fig:1. p:356.

Fig:2. p:356.

Fig:3.
p:367.

Fig:4.
p:370.

Fig:5. p:497.

B   E F G H I K   D

Fig:6. p:498.

Fig:7.
p:499.

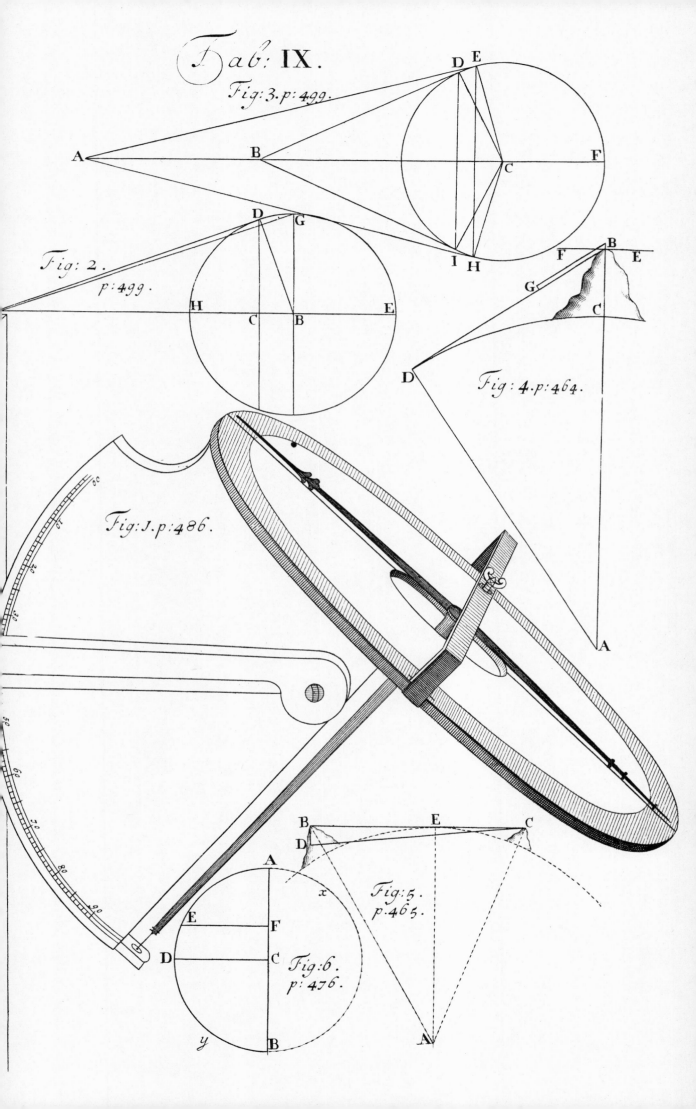

Tab: IX.

Fig: 3. p: 499.

Fig: 2.
p: 499.

Fig: 4. p: 464.

Fig: 1. p: 486.

Fig: 5.
p: 465.

Fig: 6.
p: 476.

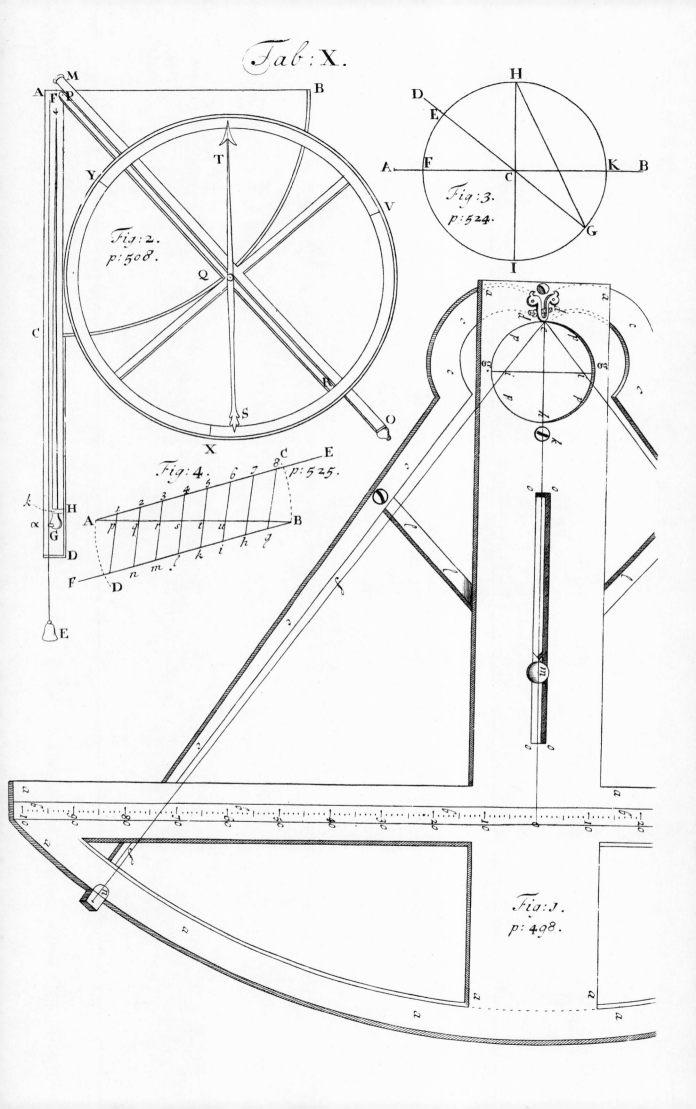

Tab: X.

Fig: 2.
p: 508.

Fig: 3.
p: 524.

Fig: 4. *p: 525.*

Fig: 1.
p: 498.

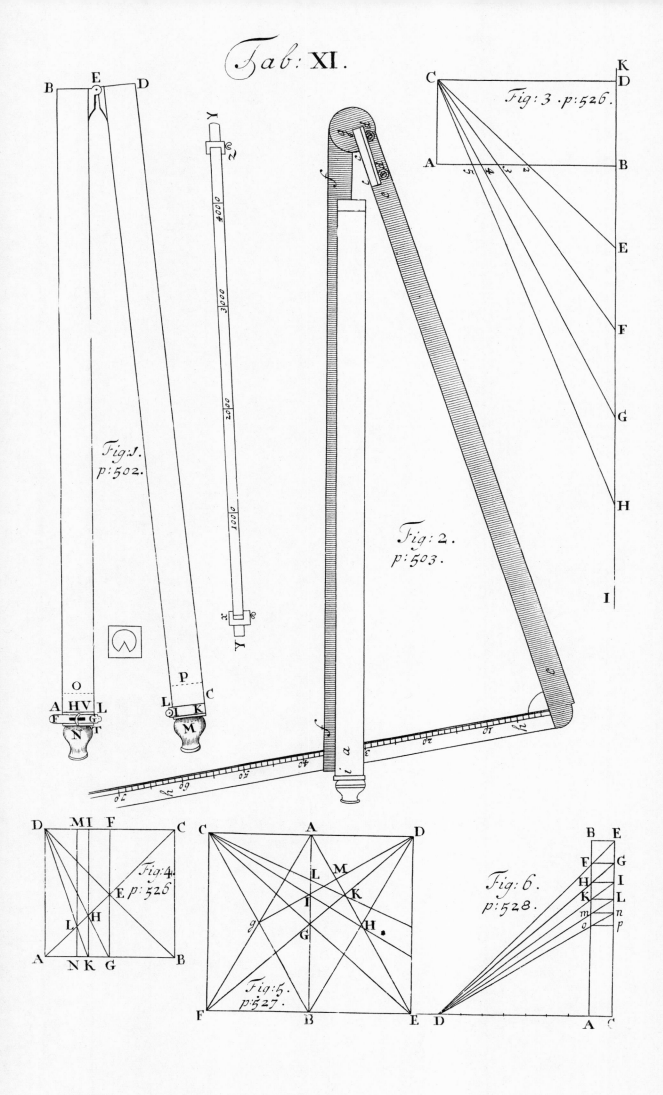

Tab: **XI**.

Fig:1.
p:502.

Fig:2.
p:503.

Fig:3 .p:526.

Fig:4.
E p:526

Fig:5.
p:527.

Fig:6.
p:528.

Tab: XII.

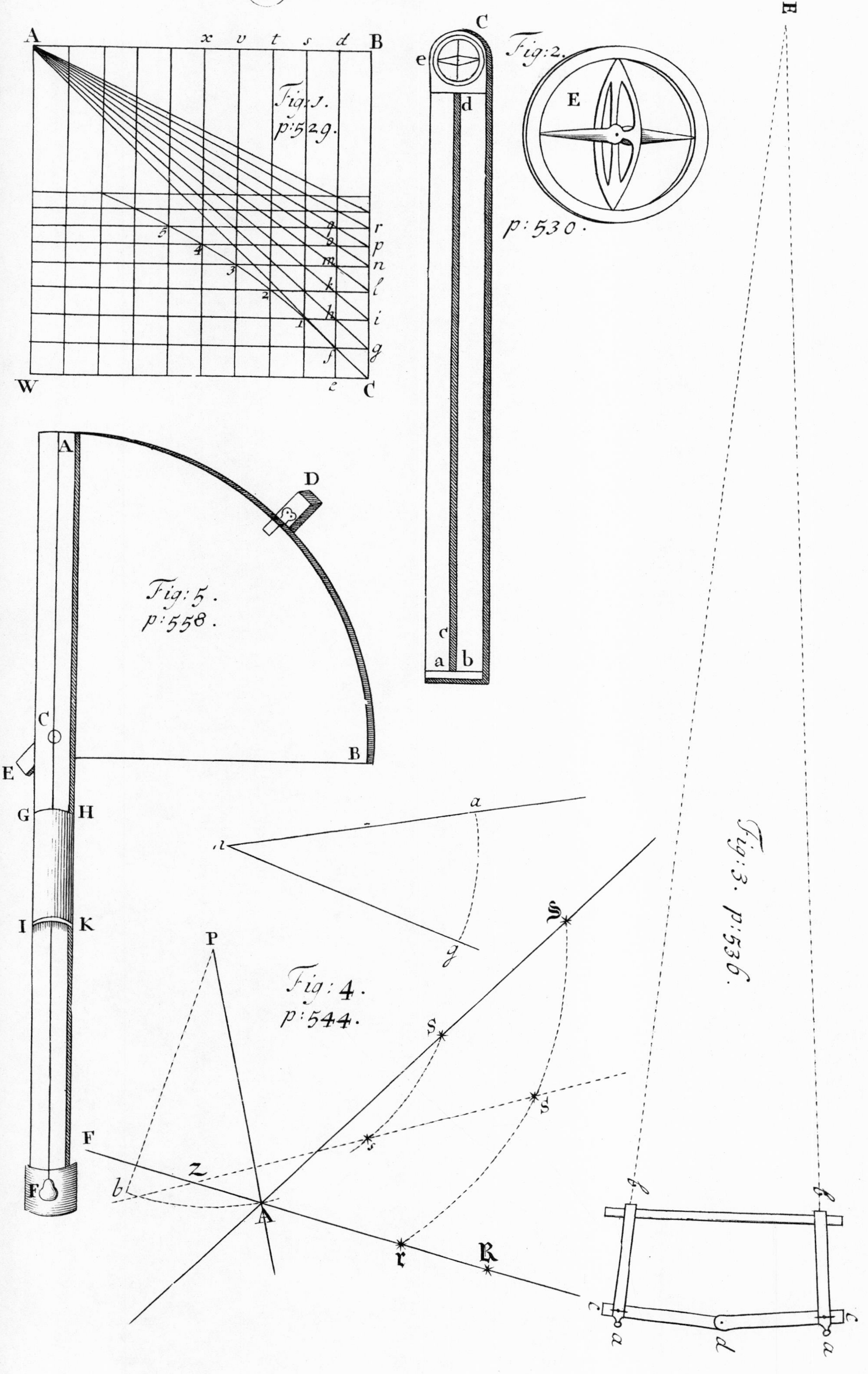

Fig: 1.
p: 529.

Fig: 2.
p: 530.

Fig: 5.
p: 558.

Fig: 4.
p: 544.

Fig: 3. p: 536.

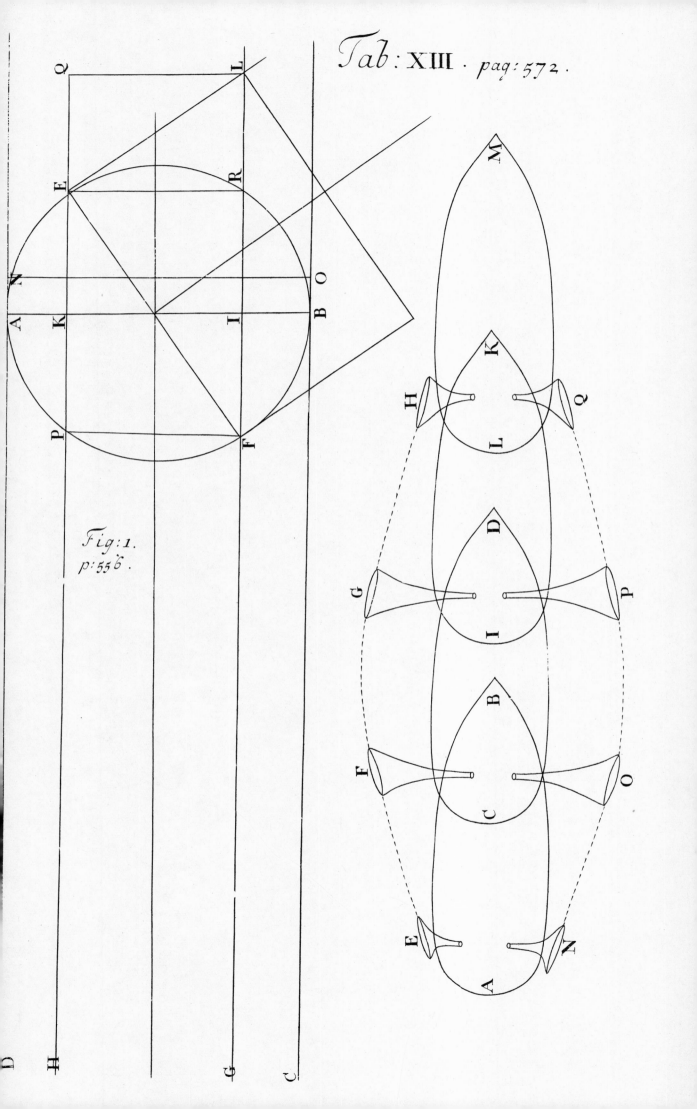

Tab: **XIII** . *pag:* 572 .

Fig: 1.
p: 556.

An ALPHABETICAL
INDEX.

Wherein thofe Matters that have an * *Prefix'd, refer to the Pages of the Author's Life.*

An Alphabetical INDEX.

Circle.

K k k k k k k   *Hypothefis*

Perfections

An Alphabetical INDEX.

Lllllll   *See*

How

An Alphabetical INDEX.

THE END.

ERRATA.